William T Henderson

THE

PRINTING

INDUSTRY

Illustrated by Edith P. Strauss

Typographic Design by Hans Schneider

THE
PRINTING
INDUSTRY

An Introduction to its Many Branches, Processes and Products

By VICTOR STRAUSS

Published by  Printing Industries of America Inc.

20 Chevy Chase Circle, N.W., Washington, D.C. 20015

In Association with R. R. BOWKER COMPANY New York and London

1180 Avenue of the Americas, New York, N.Y. 10036

Foreword

Our tradition of developing and publishing books needed by the industry but not available on the market dates back to the end of the nineteenth century. It began in 1895 when at the Ninth Annual Convention of our Association there was appointed a "Committee on the Preparation of a Manual for Printers." Since that time the national association has published many books that played a notable part in the advancement of the printing industry.

Changing conditions require continual re-evaluation and adaptation of all industry programs. Changing conditions were responsible for a fundamental change in trade association concepts. When Printing Industries of America was reorganized in the 1940's and embarked upon its extensive new educational program it had become clear that training of specialists—be they craftsmen, technicians, or management personnel—had to be accompanied by education to assist them in understanding that their work is not an end in itself but part of a greater coordinated effort. With this broadened view efficient increases in communication can be made more readily and duplication of effort and waste is avoided. Elimination of unnecessary waste and increase in efficiency not only have the potential of improving profits but aid morale, lessen tension, and result in an improved working atmosphere throughout the company.

Increased specialization was the obvious result of increased application of science to all stages of printing which brought about a higher level of graphic arts techniques. It was recognized that this tendency would accelerate and that industry complexity was bound to become more serious as time went on. It was decided by PIA that the industry needed a book which could serve as a common platform for all persons active in the industry. Ideally such a book would explain why correct decisions made at any particular point of production must consider all other stages as well. This concept meant, finally, that such a book should be of use not only to printers and the supply industries but also, and perhaps even more so, to our customers, whom it should assist in planning their printed materials with a minimum of waste and a maximum of efficiency.

Identifying an industry objective is a great step in the right direction but it is only the first step on the road that ends with its achievement. If this road must be built through uncharted territory, it can prove to be longer than assumed and beset with more obstacles than anticipated. Early hopes of obtaining our objective by part-time writing had to be abandoned. It took six and one-half years of full-time work to produce the final result.

When it was suggested that Victor Strauss should undertake the writing of this book he was well known in the industry as a participant in research activities and as a writer of unusual skill in describing complicated processes in non-technical, easily understandable language. We were further convinced that he had the necessary tenacity and dedication to accomplish this industry objective once he committed himself. Last but not least, we knew from past experience that he was suited by habit and temperament to work with other people and to gain the cooperation of the hundreds of industry specialists needed to provide information, comments, and suggestions.

Victor Strauss has produced the most comprehensive book ever written on the printing industry. His work points up the common denominators of all branches of the industry; it removes the mystery from printing and opens the gates of knowledge to everyone: to the young man or woman who enters the industry, to the seasoned craftsman or manager looking for related information, to those who market their products to it, and to its customers. All interested in basic information can now consult a single source to gain an understanding of the manufacturing techniques, procedures and relationships of the graphic arts industry. The PRINTING INDUSTRY provides a new opportunity for printing management to accomplish coordination through knowledge and understanding among those who are responsible for the design, planning, and production of printed products. A consistent and in some instances newly created terminology provides a common language for all concerned with graphic reproduction.

In the words of President John F. Kennedy printing is "a human achievement that has demonstrated far greater power to shape the world than all the forces of modern weaponry." At a time when the world of communications is undergoing tremendous changes, Victor Strauss' book is of great topical value because it demonstrates, often in great detail, that printing has continued to adapt itself to the needs of changing times. As long as this spirit prevails printing will retain its position of preeminence in the arts of communication.

Washington, D. C., June 1967

Bernard J. Taymans
President,
Printing Industries of America, Inc.

Preface

Everybody who consults a reference book has a right to know for what kind of reader it is intended, what the purpose of the book is, how the wanted information can be found, and what procedures were used to insure correctness of the contents. This preface answers these four questions.

For what kind of person was this book written? This book was planned for everybody who wants more information on the printing industry; it is a book for the intelligent layman. (And everybody is in this era of specialization a layman in everything but his own specialty.) It should be of help to everybody whose work or avocation makes him want to know more about one phase or the other of printing. The assumed reader may occupy a position in one of the three industry groups that are directly concerned with printing, or he may be an artist, a writer, a journalist, or collector of books and prints.

The three industry groups that are directly interested in printing are the industries that need printed products, the industries that produce printed products, and the industries that provide the equipment and materials whereby these products are made. These industries coalesce in the printing plant where the users of printing, the producers of printing, and the suppliers of equipment and materials meet. All three are equally indispensable: Without customers there would be nothing to print, without printers and without machines and materials printing could not be done. It is only logical to discuss printing from this common ground.

What precisely is the purpose of this book? The object is to guide you, the reader, to the point where you have sufficient control over the subject on which you seek information. This manual enables you to understand the language of the specialists whom you may meet in working situations; speaking their language and knowing of their working conditions will improve communication. Most generally used terms, and some of their variations, are explained; the terminology of the text is consistent.

This book is planned as an introduction and consequently assumes that the reader has no knowledge of the subject on which he wants information. The intention is to guide you into each of the many subjects by explaining basic facts and controlling conditions without which the many different processes cannot be understood. The aim is always to engender understanding and never to teach operational skills. The cutoff point is where general background information ends and where concrete instruction can begin.

Some readers may want to consult this book preliminary to research in a particular field. This purpose was kept in mind in the planning and writing of the book. The superior numbers in the text refer to the sources on which the writer drew. These are given in the back of the book under "Notes and References." The text should enable the qualified reader to follow the specialized technical literature. "The Printing Industry" does not presuppose knowledge of mathematics, physics, chemistry, and other sciences but the specialized literature usually does.

How can you find the wanted information fast? Read the Table of Contents, consult Table I "Printing Processes and Methods," pages 2 to 7; Table II "The Twelve Main Stages of Printing Production," pages 44 to 47, and the index. The typography of this book was planned to help you: Running heads indicate chapter and section, subheads major breaks, and bold-face paragraph lead-ins pinpoint the discussed subjects. The functioning of the most important kinds of typesetting, printing, and binding equipment is explained in many flow charts. Schematic illustrations and their captions are self-contained, forming as it were a book within the book. Cross references indicate chapters and sections related to the discussion in hand.

How was correctness of information obtained? The subject matter is so large that no individual can know everything to be covered. This is not an exceptional situation; modern technology poses the same problem in every field. Publishers have developed different methods to cope with this condition. The choice is between two kinds of books: One is the book written by a single writer whose manuscript is reviewed for correctness by different specialists; the other is the compendium where each chapter is written by a specialist and all chapters are tied together by an editor. Each of these methods has its advantages and its disadvantages. The present book is written by a single writer whose manuscript was reviewed by many specialists. The detail of procedure and the names of reviewers are printed under "Acknowledgments", beginning page 810.

At this point it is pertinent to mention that PIA (Printing Industries of America), the publisher, is a national trade association with many contacts and resources not available to others. Without PIA the writer would not have been able to secure the cooperation of the many specialists, organizations, and corporations without which this book could not have been written.

Finally it should be expressed that this book would not have been completed, nor would it be as well illustrated and printed, without the steadfast backing by one man. To him I owe a great debt of gratitude for his confidence in me not less than for upholding the project itself. This is the reason why the book is dedicated to Bernard J. Taymans, a true servant of the American printing industry.

V. S.

Philadelphia, June 1967

Contents

Process and Equipment Flow-Charts

THE

PRINTING

INDUSTRY

Chapter I

Printing Processes and Methods

The printing industry is a collective name for a wide variety of different industries, crafts, and trades which belong together because they all serve fundamentally similar and related purposes within our modern communications system. For the purpose of discussing printing in terms of a single industry, it is necessary to identify the essential tasks and functions to be performed in all kinds of printing. When these are understood it becomes possible to relate many branches of the industry to each other and to the totality of contemporary printing. This community of functions throughout the whole printing industry is the guiding thought of the present manual.[1]

The following chapters are devoted to functional discussions crossing most branches of the industry. These chapters explain such subjects as composition, full-color printing, graphic arts photography, platemaking, printing stocks and printing inks, not to forget presses and presswork. The present chapter was written to connect these functional discussions by descriptions of the main branches of the printing industry. These descriptions will provide the reader with a foundation for the functional chapters that follow.

It is customary to divide printing in four broad process groups according to different principles on which their printing-image carriers are based. (The term "printing-image carrier" is a collective name for a variety of intermediate products which all serve the same purpose in printing production but are usually called by their individual names such as electrotypes, gravure cylinders, offset plates, photoengravings, rubber plates, screens for screen process, stereotypes, types, and so forth.) Each of those four process families is divided further into printing methods which use image carriers based on the same principle but are otherwise so different that they need individual treatment.

The four process families are: (1) relief printing, (2) intaglio printing, (3) planographic printing, and (4) porous printing. But not everybody active in the printing industry is necessarily conversant with these collective names. For example, some who are familiar with lithography may not know that the group name by which this kind of printing is technically classified is planographic, and those who are used to the designation screen-process printing may not immediately recognize the term porous printing. Classifying expressions are not needed for practical activity in printing, but they are a necessity where this complex industry must be discussed systematically.

The present chapter consists of six sections. In the first section the common denominators of printing are explained; the second section is devoted to the process family of relief printing, the third to intaglio, the fourth to planographic, and the fifth to porous, or screen-process, printing. The sixth section summarizes the main stages of printing production for all processes and methods. Subjoined, on page 51, is a brief introduction to electrostatic printing.

In addition, this chapter contains two tables which should help the reader to find his bearings. At the beginning of this chapter is Table I, "Printing Processes and Methods." This table identifies the characteristic points of each printing method, and it correlates printing-image carriers, printing stocks, printing inks, as well as presses and image transfer with each method. Table II, "The Twelve Main Stages of Printing Production" is placed in Section 6.

Table I

PRINTING PROCESSES

Processes and Methods	Characteristic Points	Printing-Image Carriers
RELIEF PRINTING The printing areas of the image carrier are raised above the plane of the supporting material. *Letterpress*	The original method of printing with type; the only method capable of using type directly. Letterpress is a widely diversified method; it has equipment for short, medium, and extremely long runs; it is used for job-and-commercial printing, books, magazines, as well as for package printing; it has many applications in specialty printing. Revision of copy can be made in many production stages, thereby permitting great flexibility.	Different image carriers are needed for (1) type forms, (2) plate bases, (3) traditional rotary presses, and (4) wrap-around presses for direct, and (5) for indirect relief printing presses. In type forms, type-high materials are assembled, including foundry type, Monotypes, slugs of type, wood type; photoengravings, blocked electrotypes, stereotypes, plastic plates, hand-engraved plates, and Dycril photopolymer plates. On plate bases, materials of a much lower height such as flat duplicate plates, hand-engraved plates, and Dycril are needed. On traditional rotary presses, curved duplicate plates (electrotypes, stereotypes, rubber, and plastic plates) and Dycril plates are used. On direct printing wrap-around presses and on indirect relief presses, shallow-etched metal plates, Dycril, and Kodak Relief Plates can be the image carriers.
Newspaper Relief Printing	A printing method developed for the production of a single kind of product: newspapers; it is not generally used for other products. Newspaper relief printing obtains high efficiency within acceptable limitations.	Curved-cast stereotype plates, cast from mats taken mechanically from type forms that usually contain metallic composition, photoengravings, and flat duplicate plates.
Flexography	A relief printing method for package materials and for specialties. Can produce either rewound, or sheeted, or inline fabricated products.	Duplicate plates molded of natural or of synthetic rubber in mats taken from original relief material, type and photoengravings; for some jobs hand-engraved rubber plates can be used. Rubber plates are distinguished from other image carriers by their resilience.

AND METHODS

Printing Stocks	*Printing Inks*	*Presses and Image Transfer*
Letterpress can print on many different grades of paper and on paper boards; for fine halftones, coated papers are customary.	Letterpress needs a wide range of inks for the wide range of stocks and of presses used in this method. Inks for slower presses are more viscous than those for faster ones. Some letterpress inks dry by oxidation and polymerization. Heat-set inks, needed for high-speed web printing, are "set" or dried on their surface by evaporation. All letterpress inks ultimately form a dry ink film on the stock.	Letterpresses are (1) platen presses, (2) flatbed-cylinder presses, (3) sheet-fed rotaries, (4) roll-fed rotaries, and (5) direct printing wrap-around presses. (1) can be hand-fed or equipped with feeders, (2) are made as single-color, two-color, and perfecting presses, (3) are made as multicolor presses, (4) are usually multicolor perfecting presses, and (5) can have either multiroller inking systems or a single large inking drum. Wrap-around presses are sheet-fed and made in one, two, or more colors. Image transfer is direct; relatively high pressure is needed. Ink image should, ideally, be on top of stock and not forced into it.
Newsprint, an inexpensive uncoated paper, consisting primarily of groundwood fibers and having little filler.	News ink, an inexpensive material that has no film-forming ingredients, hence never clogs pipes and ink pumps. News ink does not form a dry ink film on the paper, but dries by absorption of the ink vehicle.	Newspaper-relief printing presses are complex installations usually spread over three floors. They consist of roll-feeding equipment on the lowest floor, series of perfecting units followed by folders on the second floor, and the mail room on the third floor. The folded papers are automatically transported from the second to the third floor by conveyors. Image transfer forces ink image into fibers of paper. Roll-fed flatbed-cylinder presses which print the web on both sides are used by smaller newspapers. Roll-stands are manually operated; flying pasters are semi-automatic or fully automatic machines. Similar equipment is used in other kinds of web printing.
A wide variety of papers, paper boards, metal foils, plastic films, and others.	Flexographic inks: low viscosity, solvent evaporating, either colored with dyes or with pigments, or combinations of dyes and pigments. Film-forming ingredients differ in different types of flexographic inks.	Web presses are equipped with roll-stands, several printing units, driers, rewinds, sheeting or fabricating machinery. Web is not usually perfected; printing is done on one side primarily which may also be provided with protective coating. Image transfer is direct and done under least possible pressure.

Table I-2

PRINTING PROCESSES

Processes and Methods	Characteristic Points	Printing-Image Carriers
Indirect *Relief Printing*	A method combining the features of relief printing with indirect image transfer and executed on existing sheet or roll-fed offset presses. Also known as "dry" offset and as "letterset."	Printing-image carriers for indirect relief are thin plates that assume the curvature of the plate cylinder without treatments. These are: (1) shallow-etched metal plates, (2) Dycril photopolymer plates, and (3) Kodak Relief Plates.
INTAGLIO PRINTING Printing areas are sunken in the image carrier, non-printing areas are on its surface. *Steel-Die Engraving* *and Banknote Printing*	These two methods are combined in this manual because of their similarity. Both use intaglio image carriers but not of the same construction. There is one significant difference between steel-die engraving and banknote printing. Steel-die engraving combines embossing with ink transfer thereby raising the printed areas in a characteristic way, whereas banknote printing does not emboss. Products of steel-die engraving are social announcements, calling cards, labels, and others; products of banknote printing are our currency, stock and bond certificates.	Printing-image carriers for steel-die engraving may be hand-engraved plates, plates made by pantograph engraving machines, or plates made by photoengraving. The traditional plates for banknote printing are hand-engraved or machine-engraved plates and duplicate plates made by siderography. The development of electrolytically made plates for rotary intaglio presses has outmoded traditional plates.
Sheet-Fed and Rotogravure	Sheet-fed and rotogravure are similar methods. Sheet-fed gravure, little used in the United States, is a high-quality picture printing method; rotogravure is done as web printing and produces long production runs of publications, package material, and many specialties. Package printing is often done on inline equipment which fabricates the printed stock in a single pass through the whole installation; publication printing uses equipment similar to newspaper relief printing for feeding of rolls and for folding.	The printing-image carriers for sheet-fed gravure are usually copper plates in the United States, those for rotogravure copper-plated cylinders; both plates and cylinders are etched and usually chromium plated for longer press wear.

AND METHODS

Printing Stocks	*Printing Inks*	*Presses and Image Transfer*
The same stocks as used in letterpress are also printed by indirect relief.	Printing inks for indirect relief are of the same general composition as other inks for letterpress, possibly formulated with stronger pigments to compensate for double splitting of ink films.	Presses for indirect relief are mainly offset lithographic presses whose plate cylinder may or may not need a deeper undercut. Many American press builders and some European ones make all offset presses suitable for both indirect lithography and indirect relief printing. Presses built exclusively for indirect relief have no dampening units; presses for both indirect lithography and indirect relief have dampening units which are either disconnected or removed for indirect relief since the plate does not require dampening. Image transfer is indirect; the ink image is transferred from the plate to the blanket and from the blanket to the stock. The ink film is thereby split two times.
Steel-die engraving uses a variety of papers. Banknote printing is done with papers of high quality, having such features as will make counterfeiting easily recognizable.	Printing inks for both methods are highly viscous; United States Bureau of Engraving and Printing, which prints United States currency, makes its own inks for security reasons; so do many private firms engaged in banknote printing for private business.	Presses for steel-die engraving are of the platen type and come in relatively small sizes; some are hand fed, others are equipped with automatic sheet feeders. Contemporary banknote printing uses rotary presses. For image transfer, plate surface is cleaned with doctor blade, then plate is wiped with crepe paper. Image transfer is direct.
Sheet-fed gravure is done on better grades of paper, including coated stocks; rotogravure for publication printing can be done on inexpensive papers; high-grade products are printed on coated papers. Paper boards, metallic foils, and a wide variety of plastic films are used as stocks in package printing by rotogravure.	Gravure inks are of low viscosity and dry by solvent evaporation. Various kinds of stocks and end uses of the printed product require differently formulated inks.	Presses for sheet-fed gravure have automatic sheet feeders and exist in varying numbers of printing units. Presses for publication printing by rotogravure resemble newspaper relief presses, particularly when the products are newspaper supplements; when the products are high-grade magazines, the folder is different. All rotogravure publication presses differ from those in some other methods because the web cannot be printed on both sides simultaneously in gravure.

Table I-3

PRINTING PROCESSES

Processes and Methods	Characteristic Points	Printing-Image Carriers
PLANOGRAPHIC PRINTING The printing and the non-printing areas are in the same plane of the image-carrier. *Offset Lithography*	Offset lithography, so called because it uses indirect image transfer, is a most widely used printing method. In scope and diversification it can only be compared with letterpress. Like letterpress, offset lithography has equipment for short, medium, and extremely long runs; it is used for job-and-commercial printing, magazines, package material, book production, and many specialties, possibly in combination with letterpress. Web offset is increasingly utilized for the printing of smaller newspapers.	Printing-image carriers, called plates in this industry, are available in a wide choice for offset lithography. Offset plates are made mainly by photomechanics, but direct-image plates and electrostatic plates also exist. Plates vary in their costs, in certain technical points, and in the number of impressions that can be produced with them. Presensitized plates are made of paper board, plastics, or of metal; wipe-on and deep-etch plates are shop coated; bi-metallic plates are the result of complex manufacturing processes and made by concerns specializing in them (these include lithographic trade shops and platemaking departments of large lithographic companies). Most plates are made photomechanically; direct-image plates can be made by proofing of relief material, typing with typewriter-like composing machines, by hand tusching or drawing.
Direct Lithography	Direct lithography is used mainly for labels, box wraps, posters, decalcomanias, and other items needing great color strength which can be obtained better by single transfer lithography than by offset.	For short printing runs, all kinds of lithographic plates can be used. For long and repeat runs, bimetallic plates are necessary.
Collotype	Collotype is the oldest photomechanical printing method, distinguished by the ability to reproduce continuous-tone images without converting them into halftones. In this country collotype is mainly used for high-grade reproductions and commercial work.	Collotype plates are made photomechanically; each collotype concern makes its own plates; presensitized, factory-made plates do not exist for collotype.
POROUS PRINTING *Screen-Process Printing* The printing areas consist of open pores of the image carrier; the blocked pores become the non-printing areas.	A printing method widely used for reproducing artwork consisting of pictures alone or in conjunction with some reading matter; it uses exceptionally low pressure during image transfer, can be executed by hand printing and by means of presses, deposits a thicker ink film than other methods. Screen process is often selected for printing of metal signs, short-run billboard posters, and for decoration of thermoplastic sheets for subsequent vacuum forming.	Screen-process printing can be done with many different kinds of image carriers. The carrier material can be natural silk, artificial fibers, and metal cloth woven of copper, stainless steel, and other metal threads. Most frequently used contemporary stencil-making techniques are (1) knife-cut stencils, made by manual skills, and (2) photographic stencils made by photomechanics.

AND METHODS

Printing Stocks	*Printing Inks*	*Presses and Image Transfer*
Offset lithography can print on an exceptionally wide range of papers, cloth, plastic, and foils; indirect image transfer makes it possible to print fine halftone images on rough or purposely structured papers which are often desired for aesthetic reasons. Direct printing methods, letterpress and sheet-fed gravure, for example, need smooth papers for reproduction of fine halftones. Indirect methods do not have this limitation.	Printing inks for offset lithography are available in a range corresponding with the range of printing requirements. Some inks for offset lithography dry by oxidation and polymerization. The viscosity of inks decreases as the press speed mounts; web offset printing is done with heat-set inks which "set" or dry on their surface by evaporation of solvents under the influence of heat and air currents.	Presses for offset lithography are all based on the rotary principle. The two main kinds are sheet-fed and roll-fed, or web, presses. Sheet-fed presses are made in many sizes, up to six-color presses, and also as multi-color perfecting presses. Web presses are made in several basic kinds, but blanket-to-blanket presses predominate. Web presses for offset lithography can have a varying number of perfecting units, say, between one or two and eight, are provided with roll-feeding machinery, various kinds of folders, drying units, and electronic controls for color printing. Web presses for job-and-commercial work differ in their construction from web offset presses for newspaper printing; those for specialties have again distinctive features, depending on their purpose.
Papers for direct lithography are smooth; in general, coated papers are preferred.	Inks for direct lithography are of the same basic formulation as other lithographic inks.	Presses for direct lithography are not standard equipment but custom made.
As a direct printing method, collotype needs smooth papers for high-quality reproductions. Coarse papers abrade the collotype plate and are hence not considered practical.	Collotype inks are highly viscous and dry by oxidation and polymerization.	American collotype presses are either specially built or rebuilt old direct lithographic presses. They run at a low speed, are hand fed, and handle sheets up to a size of 44 by 64 inches.
Screen-process printing can use practically any stock. In addition to paper and paper boards, metal foils, plastic materials, sheet metal, glass, and wood are among the stocks printed in this method.	Inks for screen-process printing must be suitable for the stock to be printed and for the end use of the final printed product. As these vary considerably, a corresponding variety of screen-process inks is available.	Most printing equipment for screen-process printing is for sheet feeding. Sheet-fed printing equipment for screen process can be (1) hand printing presses, (2) mechanically operated flatbed presses, and (3) mechanically operated cylinder presses. Since the ink film in screen process is too thick for stacking printed sheets without individual drying, a number of driers, from racks to completely automatic machines, operating as adjuncts to screen-process presses, are in use.

Section 1: Printing and Its Common Denominators

From the middle of the fifteenth century until approximately twenty-five or thirty years ago, the word "printing" had a clear and generally accepted meaning; it referred to the reproduction of reading matter by means of metallic types—either alone or in combination with pictures. Other graphic reproduction processes such as etching, lithography, or engraving were known by their own names. The reason for this distinction was perfectly sound: no other graphic reproduction process was capable of using metallic types, no other reproduction process could reproduce reading matter in bulk. For more than four hundred years—from 1450 to the last third of the nineteenth century—printing and other reproduction processes were not competitive but complementary. Printing had a monopoly on the reproduction of reading matter in bulk, but it was rather limited—to lines and areas—in the reproduction of pictures. Other graphic arts processes were incapable of reproducing reading matter in bulk but excelled in picture printing. Illustrated books expressed this condition by the fact that they were often printed in two processes: either plate printing or lithography supplied the illustrations and letterpress the printed text. For this reason pictures are listed as plates in older books, and some publishers still follow this habit.

The effects of photography and photomechanics on printing technology. These conditions prevailed until graphic arts photography and photomechanics became workable. The result was a complete change in all branches of the graphic arts. Letterpress found in photoengraving the long-wanted means for the making of pictorial printing-image carriers and became therewith equally capable of reproducing pictures and reading matter; the application of photography and photomechanics to classic picture reproduction methods such as etching, engraving, and lithography made it possible to reproduce reading matter not only by letterpress but also by gravure and lithography. The traditional division between the reproduction of pictures and that of reading matter was thereby overcome, and most graphic processes became in time capable of both the reproduction of pictures as well as that of reading matter in bulk, though, of course, with certain differences. As a result, all industrial graphic arts processes became functionally printing.

The Contemporary Meaning of Printing

Let us approach the question: What is printing? by looking at various printed products. In spite of all possible differences, all printed products have nevertheless one thing in common. This common denominator is so much taken for granted that it is rarely even mentioned. It is the fact that *all printing can be seen*, can be perceived with our eyes. This fact holds true for all printing, disregarding its particular purpose or manner of production. *The result of printing is always a visible image.* (In printing for the blind the word "printing" has a different meaning. There the final product is not so much visible as it is tactile, and it is not usually produced by printing, but rather by stamping or similar methods.)

Image conversion and image transfer. Printing production can perhaps best be characterized as an image conversion and transfer process. *Original images*—meaning art-and-copy—must first be converted into *printing-image* carriers. This conversion requires different steps which depend partly on the kind of printing selected and partly on the nature of the original images. Many times, though not always, it is necessary to convert original images into *printable images* prior to making of printing-image carriers. After the printing-image carrier is made, its printing image is inked. The printing ink conforms to the detail of the *printing image* and thereby forms the *ink image* on the image carrier. This ink image is finally transferred—directly or indirectly—to the paper or to other printing stock where it appears as the *printed image* which is the main aim of graphic reproduction.

On the basis of this description we can divide reproduction by printing into an image-conversion phase and into an image-transfer phase. The image-conversion phase ends with the production of the printing-image carrier; it includes a wide variety of operations such as photography, color separation, retouching, and platemaking, to mention some. The image transfer phase is generally called *presswork*. Presswork entails the combination of four different elements: a printing-image carrier, a printing ink, a printing stock, and a printing press. Image transfer is accomplished in the press; presswork is normally a completely mechanized production step. If we add that presswork is usually followed by one or the other of

Diagrams showing four stages of printing production. The first picture symbolizes original images, the subject matter of printing. The second picture shows how original images appear on a printing-image carrier for relief printing, letterpress for example. The third picture shows the ink image on the image carrier, and on the fourth picture you see the final printed image on a sheet of paper.

various binding or finishing operations which are needed for making the final printed product, we have identified the most important common denominators of printing production. Each of these is the subject matter of one or several chapters in this manual.

Before we go further, we must discuss two points because their understanding is basic for all that follows. One point is the difference in the treatment of reading matter and of pictures; the other point is the reason for converting original images into printable images.

Reproduction of Reading Matter and of Pictures

You may have wondered why we insist on distinguishing between reading matter and pictures when we discuss printing. This distinction is necessary because reading matter and pictures pose very different reproduction problems which can best be understood if we consider art-and-copy, as the subject matter of printing is usually called, in terms of images.

Considered as images, reading matter and pictures are prepared quite differently. Reading matter, usually called manuscript or copy, is a typescript, or, very rarely, though, in our time, handwritten. This typescript must be converted into the desired images by composition. The image presented by the manuscript, as distinguished from its content, is usually not reproduced as the final printed image but replaced by type images which are the products of composition of one kind or another. Reading matter is thereby completely changed in its appearance for the purpose of printing.

Exactly the opposite is true in the reproduction of pictures. If we assume that they were carefully prepared for printing production, something as desirable as it is rare, their appearance should be changed as little as possible during the process of reproduction. In high quality picture reproduction the aim is, as you undoubtedly know, highest fidelity. Ideally, the images presented in the artwork and the final printed images should be identical, even though this result is either not possible or not practical in all but very rare cases.

The dual function of metallic composition. This difference in the treatment of reading matter and of pictures must now be explained; it has its roots in the dual nature of typesetting. Typesetting, or composition with metallic types, can combine two different functions in a single operation. One function consists in converting the images presented by handwriting or typing into standardized letter forms of a certain style. The other function of typesetting is the assembly of the physical printing-image carrier which can be used in presswork for producing the final printed image. But these two functions are not inseparable. In the present time we are witnessing the growth of a new kind of composition which does not use metallic types and is therefore classified as non-metallic in this manual. (Other terms often used in the trade are "cold type" and "photographic composition.") Non-metallic composition does not result in printing-image carriers but solely in images showing the result of converting reading matter into standardized letter forms of a selected design. The same result is achieved if metallic composition is used for the pulling of reproduction proofs rather than for printing in the press.

This dual function of composition can cause a certain amount of confusion if not properly understood. Whenever composition has only the purpose of image conversion it can be considered as a part of art-and-copy preparation. In these cases, and they are not infrequent, the product of composition, a reproduction proof or a photographic print, is combined with the rest of the material to be reproduced and becomes part of art-and-copy which is turned over to the printer for reproduction. But when metallic types are to be used as printing-image carriers, composition represents a quite different stage in printing production. (Various functions of metallic composition and different methods for metallic as well as non-metallic composition are described in Chapter II.) We turn next to image conversion of pictures.

Some reasons for conversion of pictures into printable images. Conversion of pictures into printable images is not a generally used expression. Printers usually speak of halftone and color-separation photography, the two methods most commonly used for this purpose. But a discussion of the reasons for converting pictures into printable images is nevertheless necessary to help the uninformed reader in gaining a true understanding of the reasons for halftone and color-separation photography which are not the only steps preceding the making of actual printing-image carriers.

Image detail and image control are essential in all printing methods, particularly in high-fidelity reproductions of photographs in black-and-white and in color, in wash-drawings, and in paintings. To understand the problems to be met in printing, a brief description of the manner in which rendered and photographic original image detail is constituted and the manner in which printing can reproduce such detail is presented in the following. This discussion will explain why some original images must be converted into printable ones.

The rendering of continuous-tone images. If we compare the manner in which a picture is drawn or painted with the manner in which it must be reproduced in printing, we notice several striking differences. Take a simple wash-drawing, for example. The artist painted this picture with a brush and liquid india ink. In the very dark tones of the picture, called the shadows, he applied his ink very concentrated and in heavy strokes. Where he wanted to paint an area lighter, he diluted the ink and softened his strokes, or he washed over already applied ink with plain water, thereby lightening the respective areas. By changing the pig-

ment concentration or the deposit of his painting media and by washing, the artist can modulate, without interruptions, the color values throughout the whole picture—from the faintest gray to he deepest jet black. But wash-drawings are not the only kind of pictures that show a constant change in value; the same holds true for black-and-white photographs. Both wash-drawings and

The artist achieves differences in tones, or values, by his rendering techniques. Letterpress, offset lithography, and other printing methods obtain tonal effects by means of halftones consisting of tiny dots of varying size.

black-and-white photographs are technically classified as continuous-tone pictures. In black-and-white photographs, changes in value are due to varying amounts of metallic silver; the stronger the concentration of silver is in an area of a photographic picture, the blacker this area appears. Smaller deposits of metallic silver on film or on white paper produce correspondingly lighter or darker grays. That silver deposits are black seems to conflict with our everyday experience, according to which objects made of silver, such as coins and others, have a characteristic light color. But in photographic prints, silver is present in extremely small particles, and in particles of such size the color of the metal is black rather than silvery.

The next point to be clarified is that artists and photographers on the one hand, and printers on the other, achieve different tones (or values) quite differently. No printing process is capable of changing the pigment concentration of its ink within the same press run; and with the exception of collotype, a rather rarely used method, no printing method is either capable of changing or of modulating the thickness of its ink deposit without interrupting the continuity of the deposited ink film.

The reproduction of continuous-tone images. Printing cannot approach the reproduction of continuous-tone images along the lines of ink control alone. In printing, the image carrier must be endowed with such characteristics as are needed to produce printed images of the desired quality. In all relief methods, in lithography and in porous printing the reproductions of continuous-tone images consist of discontinuous ink films of more or less uniform thickness. (In some methods, letterpress and lithography among them, it is possible to vary the thickness of the ink film in one direction of the sheet or web, but this possibility is of no consequence for the present discussion.) Collotype and the most frequently used gravure method apply ink films of graduated thickness, but there are also gravure methods that can apply ink films of uniform thickness. Original continuous-tone images are converted into printable images for relief, planographic, and porous printing, as well as for certain gravure methods by halftone photography, a subject explained in Chapter IV, "Graphic Arts Photography."

Not all image carriers used in relief printing for reproduction of continuous-tone images must pass through the stage of halftone photography. Black-and-white photographs, for example, can be converted directly into relief printing-image carriers by electromechanics. Electromechanical equipment is capable of producing image carriers for letterpress and newspaper relief printing having detail of correct size and shape without need for halftone photography.

Color separation for full-color printing. The wash-drawing and the black-and-white photograph are two examples of single color, or black-and-white, continuous-tone images; a Kodachrome, or a painting done freely by the artist without any restriction in the number of colors he wishes to use, are two examples of another type of originals requiring a different kind of image conversion. The reproduction of such subjects has several considerations of its own. It is, of course, not practical to reproduce such original images by attempting to match each of their innumerable colors. But this is fortunately not necessary. Modern printing has developed procedures which make it possible to obtain a relatively wide gamut of colors by printing with a small and carefully selected number of color inks. This kind of reproducing colorful pictures is des-

ignated as *full-color* printing; it is usually done in three or four printings. Here, too, just like in the printing of continuous-tone single-color images, the printing-image carrier must be very carefully planned to be adequate for this difficult task. For this purpose the colorful originals must be divided first into a corresponding number of printable images, an operation known as *color-separation photography*. (The subject of full-color printing, including color-separation photography, is discussed in Chapters III and IV.) To avoid misconceptions, it should be added that full-color printing may or may not require halftone photography, depending on the specific printing method selected for the reproduction of a job.

Electromechanical engraving and electronic scanners for color separation and color correction. As already mentioned, continuous-tone images can be converted into relief printing-image carriers without intermediate conversion into printable images. One line of domestic electromechanical equipment handles continuous-tone images in a single color, including photographs. Such equipment is more useful in the newspaper industry than in job-and-commercial printing. There are also electromechanical engraving machines that can convert full-color subjects into sets of relief printing-image carriers without photographic color separation and halftone photography. (Electromechanical engraving machines are described in Chapter V, Section 3.)

Electromechanical engraving is mentioned at this point of our discussion to make clear that it has become possible to go directly from original images to relief image carriers without the intermediate steps of photographic color-separation and halftone photography. But at the time of writing, electromechanical engraving machines are not generally used in this country. Continuous-tone pictures are still converted for printing mainly by halftone photography. Color separation and color correction is either made by photography or by electronic scanners. (Scanners are discussed in Chapter III.)

The controlling position of printing-image carriers. The end product of image conversion is an image carrier of one kind or the other. Image carriers are one of the component elements of presswork. The nature of its printing-image carrier is a most characteristic element of every printing process. It accounts for many capabilities of a printing process or method and also for ap-

The four printing processes are relief, intaglio, planographic, and porous printing. In relief printing, the printing areas are raised above the supporting carrier material; in intaglio the printing areas are embedded in the carrier; in planographic printing both printing and non-printing areas are practically in the same plane; in porous printing the pores of the image carrier are open in the printing areas and sealed in the non-printing ones.

pearance differences in printed images. (These points are explained in detail in Chapter V, "Printing-Image Carriers.") It is therefore customary to divide contemporary printing into four broad process groups according to the four different principles on which printing-image carriers are based.

The four printing processes and their image carriers. In the introduction to this chapter, the four printing processes were identified as: (1) relief printing, (2) intaglio printing, (3) planographic, and (4) porous printing. Now the different principles that distinguish the image carriers of each process from those used in other processes will be explained. *Relief printing* (letterpress, for example) uses image carriers where the printing image is in relief, or raised, over the body of the carrier. *Intaglio printing* (gravure, for example) uses image carriers where the printing image is in intaglio, or embedded, in the body of the image carrier. *Planographic printing* (offset lithography, for example) uses image carriers where the printing and the non-printing areas are in the same plane of the carrier material. *Porous printing* (screen process, for example), finally, uses image carriers of a porous nature where the image is determined by controlling the image carrier as to its porosity in different areas.

Some Appearance Characteristics of Printed Images

All printing production entails a combination of four elements: (1) a printing-image carrier, (2) paper or another printing stock, (3) printing ink, and (4) a printing press. Each of these four elements contributes in some measure to the appearance of printed images.

Classification of printed images. Differences in the appearance of printed images can perhaps be best discussed systematically by relating them to the five most common printing tasks. These are: (1) the reproduction of reading matter in bulk, (2) the printing of pictures consisting of lines and areas, (3) the reproduction of continuous-tone pictures, (4) multicolor printing, also called printing in flat colors, and finally (5) reproductions of colorful pictures such as paintings or color photographs by means of full-color printing. Individual printing jobs may entail any combination of these five reproduction tasks. A more detailed treatment of various kinds of art-and-copy can be found in Chapter XI. We turn next to a brief discussion of the relations between printing-image carriers and printed images.

The effects of different printing-image carriers on printed images. Image carriers can affect the appearance of the printed image in several respects. It is practical to divide these into direct and indirect ones. The direct effects are related to the very nature of a printing-image carrier, to the principle on which an image carrier is based. This nature expresses itself most significantly during presswork, the image transfer phase of printing. The construction of a press, the inking system, the formation of the ink image, and the manner in which image transfer is accomplished are all influenced by the dominant characteristics of image carriers. The indirect effects depend upon the printing paper, or other stock, and the printing ink both of which may differ very considerably in several respects for various kinds of printing-image carriers.

The combined effect of all these factors expresses itself in the appearance of printed images, particularly in their detail. A sensible discussion of the manner in which image carriers affect appearance, directly and indirectly, requires a discussion of image carriers, stocks, inks, and presses, which is not possible at this point. This introduction has the purpose of making you aware that these relations exist, but it cannot go into detail. In the following sections, which are devoted to individual printing processes and methods, you find more on the subject. (A full discussion of printing-image carriers is offered in Chapter V.)

Some effects of paper on the appearance of printed images. Even though paper is by no means the only printing stock, it is still the one most frequently used. Paper can affect appearance in at least four respects: (1) smoothness, (2) brightness, (3) whiteness, and (4) gloss. In this introduction we are limited to brief explanations; these subjects are more fully treated in Chapter VIII, "Paper and Other Printing Stocks." Paper is manufactured in various degrees of smoothness; newsprint, the paper for newspapers, is rather coarse; machine-finished paper used for utility printing in letterpress is less coarse; coated paper, on which many magazines and other products containing full-color images are printed, has a surface which is quite smooth.

The *smoothness* of paper has a direct bearing on the size of halftone dots that can be printed on it, and the size of dots, or the fineness of halftones is, in turn, a highly important appearance factor. But smooth paper is not always desired. For certain jobs, such as some greeting cards, a structured paper may be preferred to a smooth paper. As various printing methods differ in their ability to print on structured papers, the surface characteristics of the paper are not only important for the appearance of a specific printing job but at times also in deciding what printing method is to be selected for its production. You can see that various points are interrelated in printing. Often a change in a single factor means a complete reconsideration of a job and its production.

Our next characteristic is *brightness*. The term "brightness" is used in the paper industry to indicate the extent to which a paper reflects blue light. Brighter papers are often preferred to less bright ones for appearance reasons. *Whiteness* of paper counts in many cases but especially in full-color printing. The whiter the paper the better the quality of reproduction, other conditions

assumed equal. *Gloss*, our final characteristic, also affects appearance strongly. In some cases a glossy paper enhances the finished product; in others, mat paper is an aesthetic asset.[2]

The influence of printing inks on the appearance of printed images. The most obvious contribution of printing ink to the appearance of printed images is so much taken for granted that it is usually not even mentioned. But we want to give ink its due and we must remember that all printing is predicated on printing ink, because the printed image consists normally of ink and nothing else. Printing inks influence the appearance of printed images in at least three ways: (1) by color, (2) by gloss, and (3) by the thickness of printed ink films.

The effect of *ink color* on appearance is crucial in full-color printing, since full-color printing depends on the correctness of the three or four ink colors by which the whole color gamut must be obtained. (See Chapter III, "The Theory and Practice of Full-Color Printing.") But color must never be neglected, particularly not in a simple black-and-white job. Even the simplest and least expensive job can be immeasurably enhanced by printing a jet-black ink on a truly white paper. *Gloss and matness* of printing inks influence appearance very noticeably. A glossy ink confers luster and distinction upon the printed page, a mat ink contributes by its inconspicuousness and modesty. An invitation to a formal reception will gain in prestige if dressed up with a high-gloss ink; an informal sketch will keep its casual look if printed in a mat ink.[3]

Finally, we must not neglect the *thickness* of the deposited ink film. For some purposes a thin and quite transparent ink film is essential; for others the ink should be very opaque and have a strong hiding power. Full-color printing and the overprinting of various inks with a view to obtaining additional colors need highly transparent inks. Jobs requiring the printing of light colors on dark papers—as is often done in the printing of catalog covers—must be printed with very opaque inks. As various printing methods deposit ink films of differing thicknesses, these requirements can control the selection of the printing method in certain cases.[3]

Printing Processes and the Appearance of Printed Images

If we want to compare different printing processes and methods as to their ability to produce various aesthetic effects, we can do so best by establishing three different zones for every printing process or method. These zones can be designated as (1) the zone of uniqueness, (2) the zone of interchangeability, and (3) the zone of inability.

The three appearance zones. In the *zone of uniqueness* we put effects and results which are peculiar to a printing method, which depend on its intrinsic nature or, to be practical, on existing equipment, and cannot be duplicated by any other process or method. In the *zone of interchangeability* we can place such effects and results as can be produced more or less equally well by two or more printing methods. In the *zone of disability* belong effects and tasks for which a given method is not suitable at all.

It should be clear that these zones are only suggested as aids for the analysis of a complex and rather controversial subject. For this reason they will not be here established, nor will examples of uniqueness, interchangeability, and disability be presented. Every example could be taken as representing a hard and unalterable rule, which would be misleading, since every printing job must be evaluated on its own merits. These three imaginary zones serve a useful purpose nevertheless. They are an analytical tool making it possible to see the long range trends of printing development. At present the trend seems to be toward a uniformization of all printing methods, toward a leveling of their traditional differences.

The long range trend of printing development. The most outstanding and auspicious example of the leveling process in the printing industry is already known to you: it is the fact that practically all printing methods can be used for the printing of reading matter and of pictures. A second and more recent example lies in the development of modern lithographic methods on the one hand, and letterpress methods on the other, which has more or less leveled appearance differences in printed images produced by either method. This statement may not be acceptable to the die-hards of letterpress and of offset lithography, but it is considered correct by many open-minded, unprejudiced people in both industries. Those who disbelieve in process competition, such as letterpress *versus* offset lithography, are strongly relying on their experience with buyers of printing who usually let such practical considerations as price and delivery decide which method will be selected for a job in hand. Another clue can be seen in the use of sheet-fed and web-offset presses for indirect relief as well as for indirect lithog-

raphy. The great number of combination plants, practicing both letterpress and lithographic printing confirms this general trend.

Photography and photomechanics broadened the zone of interchangeability. In the past, before the development of graphic arts photography and photomechanics, almost every printing method fell mainly in the zone of uniqueness; the zone of interchangeability did hardly exist and was, where it existed, so small as to be practically negligible. Modern printing technology has constantly broadened the zone of interchangeability. The more recent achievements and improvements in single-unit, shallow-etched relief plates, which are available as etched metal plates, as duPont Dycril plates and as Kodak Relief Plates, lend new impetus to the process of reducing the differences between letterpress and lithography. But the zones of uniqueness and of inability still exist and will probably continue to exist. It is likely that some jobs will always be done best in a certain printing method. For this reason students of printing are interested in appearance differences of printed products due to differences in printing processes and methods.

Fine-Art Printing and Industrial Printing

In our time, the expression "graphic arts" is used indiscriminately and collectively for all kinds of industrial printing, but this was not always so. Originally the graphic arts meant only such fine arts as painting and drawing. In time the meaning of graphic arts expanded and shifted to various picture reproduction methods including engraving, etching, lithographing, and, as the latest addition, serigraphing. Finally, the graphic arts industry has become simply a different name for the printing industry.

The scope of fine-art printing. Fine-art printing is used by artists for self-expression as distinguished from creative artwork serving for expression of purposes and ideas in the interest of other people, for industry and commerce. In fine-art printing, the artist makes the printing-image carrier more or less completely with his own hands, and he may also do his own presswork. Printing-image carriers for fine-art printing are, hence, traditionally made by hand without use of photography and photomechanics. Presses for fine-art printing are simple in comparison with those for industrial printing, and since they are hand powered they are also limited in their size and the sheet size which they can print. The artist-printmaker may

An artist printmaker at work. Artist printmakers work with simple hand tools and use hand presses for production of their own prints in small quantities. Industrial printers produce reproductions of customers' art-and-copy in quantity with highly mechanized equipment.

or may not do his own presswork, though presswork done on hand presses can change the appearance of etchings and lithographs considerably. Most artists either do their own presswork or turn it over to expert craftsmen who specialize in this kind of press work and have great experience in it.

The products of fine-art printing are usually numbered and signed prints. Their edition varies depending on the method of printmaking and its purpose; it is often smaller than, say, fifty prints and rarely larger than a few hundred. Fine-art printmaking is to be distinguished from *fine-art reproductions*. These are prints produced by industrial printing; the original images can be paintings, watercolors, drawings, and also fine-art prints. If such reproductions are made with great care and high fidelity to the original works of art, they are often called *facsimiles*, or facsimile reproductions.

Fine-art printing played a decisive part in the growth of picture printing. Private presses greatly helped in developing a taste for well-printed books with publishers and printers alike.[4]

Private presses. Private presses differ from fine-art printing in several respects, but not in all. Private presses, too, are operated for the purpose of expressing the artistic convictions of their owners. The best known private press in the English-speaking world is the Kelmscott Press which was set up by William Morris in 1891 in England. It had the purpose of showing that books can be beautiful and was established as a reaction to the low level of book design and production in the nineteenth century. The Kelmscott Press had a great influence on book design in Europe but also in this country.[5]

Private presses have become a hobby in the United States. People who operate such presses have various purposes and produce a variety of products. At its best, a private press publishes books that are most carefully designed, illustrated, printed, and bound. Some, who follow the ideals of William Morris, want the whole book printed and bound as it was made by the great masters of printing in the fifteenth and early sixteenth century. Such private presses are most concerned with the design of their books and the quality of materials and workmanship. Ideally, they do their presswork on hand presses, hand fold and hand sew the book, and they may even attach its covers by lacing, as it was done before the invention of casemaking. But it is extremely time consuming and expensive to produce substantial books in this manner, and compromises must often be made. Hobby presses rarely print books; their output consists in single sheets or booklets primarily. Foundry type is used for hand composition, presswork is done on paper manufactured by paper mills; the presses used are often hand-fed platen presses, and if the product is bound between hard covers, these are binder's cases which are standard in contemporary industrial binding but can also be made by hand in small quantities.

This picture shows a defaced engraving printed in an expensive limited edition as evidence that the engraving could not be used again. Strongly reduced from William Savage, Practical Hints on Decorative Printing, *London, 1822.*

Limited editions. Customarily, private press books and others printed in limited editions contain a statement as to the total number of copies printed, and each book is usually hand numbered. If this statement is on the last printed page, the book is said to have a "colophon." The contents of colophons varies; if printer and publisher are not the same, the colophon may mention the name of the printer; other items are the type face and the paper used for that book. If the same information is printed in front of the book, the word colophon is not usually applied to it by bibliophiles.[6]

In the more recent past the meaning of "limited edition" has been watered down by some publishers. This is not desirable. Books called "limited editions" should state the total number printed, and each copy should be individually numbered. The meaning of limited edition is that not more than the specified number of copies will ever be printed. In some old limited editions, the plates are defaced and printed in the defaced state as proof that they cannot be used again. Calling an unspecified small edition a limited one may add prestige to the publisher but deprives the term of its true meaning.

The discussion beginning with fine-art prints has taken us to private presses and landed at commercially published limited editions, thereby leading us back to industrial printing, the main theme of this manual. In the following four sections the four process families are explained in their essentials.

Section 2: Relief Printing

You know already that in relief printing the printing image is raised over the body of the image carrier. If you look at our illustrations of two typical relief image carriers, and particularly at their cross sections, you can see this very clearly. The type face, which is the printing image of metallic types, and the dots, which are the printing images of photoengravings, are

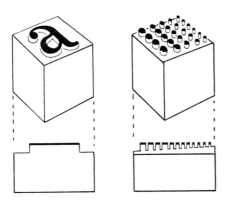

Diagram of printing-image carriers for letterpress. The type face on the left and the dots of a halftone on the right are raised above the supporting material.

both raised over the bulk of the supporting material.

In technical language such raised images are very well described by the word *relief;* hence this word has been in use for quite some time as a generic term for all methods of printing which are based on raised printing-image carriers. Terminology is here as in many other instances far from uniform in the printing industry. The designation letterpress is used by many people in two senses: generically, for all printing methods using relief image carriers, and more specifically for one relief method, the oldest kind of printing in its present form. This usage does not contribute to clarity; the term *relief printing* is therefore selected in this manual as the generic one, reserving the word "letterpress" for its generally accepted and more restricted meaning. In all relief-printing methods image transfer is accomplished by applying printing ink to the raised areas of the image carrier and by transferring the resulting ink image, directly or indirectly, to the printing stock in the press under pressure.

This description summarizes the essential features of relief printing. But you may be surprised to learn how many different relief image carriers exist and how widely the various methods of relief printing differ from each other. These differences are so strong that it is sometimes difficult to realize that different methods belong to the same process family. Different methods of relief printing produce different kinds of products; they use different printing inks and printing stocks, as well as different equipment for presswork. Based on these differences, relief printing is divided in this manual into four printing methods: (1) letterpress printing, (2) newspaper relief printing, (3) flexographic printing, and (4) indirect relief printing. Each of these four methods will be here described considering its purposes and products, image carriers, printing stocks, inks, and presses.

Letterpress Printing

Letterpress is the oldest form of printing; it is the method we have in mind when we speak of the invention of printing by Johannes Gutenberg more than 500 years ago. Printing and letterpress were, as already explained, synonymous until a relatively short time ago because letterpress was, and still is, the only reproduction method capable of using metallic types in the press. Metallic types on their part were historically the exclusive means for printing of reading matter. This condition remained unchanged for more than 200 years. It was first modified in the eighteenth century by the invention of stereotyping. Stereotyping made it possible to replace individual types for presswork with cast metal plates made from the original composition. The invention of electrotyping, made in the nineteenth century, added a second kind of duplicate plates and made it possible to free letterpress further from the limitations imposed on press construction and presswork by composition consisting of metallic types. But in spite of duplicate plates and composing machines, which were developed in the last third of the nineteenth century, metallic type remained the only means for converting reading matter into standardized letter forms. The next big step ahead was made after World War II when non-metallic composition became possible with the Fotosetter which was followed by many other non-metallic composition systems. How stereotyping, electrotyping, and non-metallic composition influenced letterpress technology will be discussed later. At this point the significance of using metallic type directly in the press must occupy our attention.[7]

The significance of being able to print directly from metallic types. The exclusive ability of letterpress to print directly from metallic types distinguished letterpress for hundreds of years from other printing methods. Even at present this ability can make letterpress a most economical printing method for jobs consisting mainly of reading matter, particularly when it is possible to print the whole job directly from type. These two conditions do not always obtain, but the number of jobs which can be printed directly from type is still legion. Letterpress is for this reason, and for others

to be explained in the course of this unit, a most widely diffused printing method.

Job-and-commercial printing. Letterpress is particularly well represented in *job-and-commercial printing*. This is the name for printing as a service business to distinguish it from other more specialized types of businesses within the printing industry. Job-and-commercial printing serves the public at large; it has the functions of providing society with custom-made printing as needed from day to day. It should be understood that job printing is done in all printing methods, in letterpress as well as in lithography, gravure, and screen process.

At this point it must be mentioned that many printed products can be produced by several printing methods. It should therefore not be assumed that a product, mentioned in this manual as an example for the application of a particular method, must necessarily be printed by this method and cannot be printed by any other method. As explained in Section 1, the zone of interchangeability of printing processes and methods is growing; consequently, you may find the same products listed as examples for the use of more than a single printing process or method.

Range of products printed in letterpress. Letterpress is the traditional method for the printing of books; it serves for the production of most magazines, many in relatively small editions, but some of an enormous circulation. Other products coming from our letterpresses include advertising and sales promotional material; letterheads, envelopes and calling cards; catalogs of various kinds;

A type form locked up in a chase for letterpress printing. Type forms can be used as printing-image carriers on platen and on flatbed-cylinder presses.

labels, business forms, tickets, and many other items. As mentioned before, most of these products are not necessarily printed in letterpress but can also be produced by other printing methods. Nor is it unusual that several printing methods are combined for the making of certain printed products.

One of the reasons for the great popularity of the letterpress method lies in its ability to produce printing in almost any required quantity with economy and dispatch. A few dozen calling cards, printed by a neighborhood printer, are an example for very short runs; millions of national magazines, produced by huge printing plants, indicate the other end of this scale. Every kind of business organization can be found in the letterpress industry, from the one-man shop to giant industrial combines.

This wide diversification of services and products and the equally wide range of quantities in which the printed products must be supplied, would not be possible without a corresponding diversification and specialization within the letterpress industry itself.

The Letterpress Industry

The letterpress industry is, generally speaking, not an integrated industry. In the printing industry the term *integrated* means that a particular printing company does usually make all or most of the image carriers needed for the jobs printed by it. Letterpress can and must use many different image carriers. These are traditionally divided into the three major groups of type, photoengravings, and duplicate plates. In the recent past several new image carriers were added. They are wrap-around plates consisting either of thin etched metal sheets, photopolymers, or etched plastics. All these many kinds of image carriers serve particular purposes and are produced by complex manufacturing processes requiring specialized skills and expensive equipment.

The printing-service trades. Some letterpress shops are too small to support their own composing rooms, and only big organizations, such as those specializing in large-scale publication printing or in the manufacturing of books, may have a sufficient volume of business to warrant their own photoengraving or duplicate platemaking departments. Many letterpress printers rely for their image carriers on the *printing-service trades*. These consist of *trade composition* businesses that set

type; *photoengravers*, who produce pictorial relief printing-image carriers and wrap-around plates; *electrotypers* and *stereotypers*, who manufacture duplicate plates; and *trade binderies*, where the printed sheets are bound. The printing-service trades are an important segment of the printing industry. They are, so to speak, the composition, photoengraving, duplicate platemaking, and binding departments of the whole industry.

The result of this condition may be surprising to you, but there is really only a single phase of printing production which is handled by all letterpress printers. This phase is presswork. A letterpress printer may buy his composition, photoengravings, wrap-around, or duplicate plates from the service trades, and he may not do his own binding or other finishing, relying on trade binderies, die-cutters, and finishers for the com-

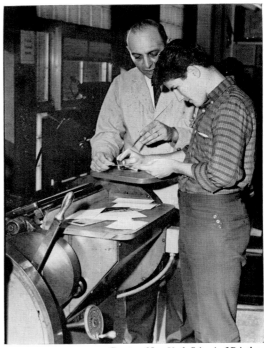

Courtesy New York School of Printing

An instructor explains press preparation on an open, hand-fed platen press to a high-school student.

pletion of the job. But all letterpress printers have one point in common: they do their own presswork.

In the following you find brief characterizations of the four elements which are needed for presswork, or printing in its narrowest operational meaning. These are printing-image carriers, printing presses, paper and other printing stocks, and printing inks. A detailed discussion of these subjects is provided, in the same order, in Chapters V, VI, VIII and IX. Presswork itself is the subject matter of Chapter VII.

Printing-Image Carriers for Letterpress

Letterpress uses an exceptionally wide range of printing-image carriers. These can be divided into metallic composition, which provides image carriers for reading matter; various kinds of pictorial image carriers, usually photoengravings; image carriers capable of combining type images with pictures; and a number of different duplicate plates. We begin our introduction with metallic composition, historically the most important kind of printing image carriers for the printing of reading matter.

Metallic composition. From the invention of Western printing at about 1450 until the invention and perfection of line-casting machines during the last decade of the nineteenth century, all reading matter was converted for printing by hand composition, an assembly method of individual type characters. These are cast from type metal and have their printing areas in relief. Such characters are called *foundry type* at present and not used any more for composition of reading matter in bulk. The invention of the Linotype and the similar Intertype which cast solid lines of type mechanically, and the invention of the Monotype, which mechanically casts lines consisting of individual characters, made hand composition of reading matter in bulk obsolete. But hand composition attained a new importance in the field of advertising typography where it is done either with foundry type, or by hand assembling of type matrices for casting of lines in the Ludlow, a machine developed after the Linotype and Monotype, at the beginning of the twentieth century. At the present time, most composition is done by metallic type, but non-metallic composition is increasingly used, particularly when physical type is not suitable for presswork.

Non-metallic composition. Non-metallic composition attained maturity after World War II. It comprises a vast number of utensils and machines. Some non-metallic composing machines serve for composition of display types. Non-metallic composition of reading matter in bulk can be done by a number of relatively simple, typewriter-like machines, but also by complex electronically operated ones. Full-range composition systems are capable of producing display composition and that of body types. In addition to these three kinds of non-metallic composition systems there are also various machines for composition of lists consisting of changing items. Non-metallic composition is not suitable for use in the press, since it does not result in physical type but in type images exclusively. Many systems of non-metallic composition are based on photography. When the printing-image carrier is made by means of photomechanics, as are shallow-etched metal plates, Dycril plates, and Kodak Relief Plates, the product of photographic composition serves as an intermediate in platemaking. Most recently, computerized composition has entered the lists. Computerized composition can be combined with line-casting machines, the Monotype, and also with photographic composing machines. (Composition of all kinds is discussed in Chapter II.)

Some printers have their own composing rooms and do all their composition, others buy all composition from trade composition houses, and some combine operating of their own composing room with purchasing certain kinds of composition from trade shops.

Pictorial image carriers. For more than 50 years photoengraving provided practically all pictorial image carriers for letterpress. Wood and metal engravings, which were used before the development of photomechanics, are not suitable for the reproduction of photographs and other continuous-tone images. Handmade pictorial image carriers, which include besides woodcuts and wood engravings also linoleum cuts and rubber engravings are but rarely used for industrial printing at present. Not long ago photoengravings were practically the only existing kind of pictorial image carriers for letterpress. In the fifties and sixties of our own century several new kinds were developed. These are shallow-etched metal plates, photopolymers, and others.

Photoengravings. Photoengravings were the first kind of pictorial image carriers that made the reproduction of photographs and other continuous-tone images a reality for letterpress. They are the end products of complex manufacturing processes in which photography, photomechanics, etching—and possibly some hand tooling—are combined. Photoengravings are not limited to pictures but can also be made of type images, alone or in combination with pictures.

The products of photoengraving are metal plates—copper, zinc, or magnesium—that can be mounted on wooden or metal bases. Photoengravings can be used in two different ways: one kind of use is as printing-image carriers, either in type forms or on plate bases; the other kind of use is as original materials, alone or together with metallic type, for the making of duplicate plates.

Electromechanical engravings and wrap-around plates. Both electromechanical engravings and wrap-around plates were mentioned before. Electromechanical engravings are functionally similar to photoengravings inasmuch as both are relief image carriers of individual pictures which must be assembled with other image carriers for common presswork. Wrap-around plates differ functionally from them as they are completely assembled single-unit, or integral, image carriers combining all images to be printed in the same press run.

At present we have three kinds of wrap-around plates; (1) shallow-etched metal plates, (2) Dycril plates, and (3) Kodak Relief Plates. Wrap-around plates are so designated because they can be put on the plate cylinder of a rotary press without separate curving. This is possible because wrap-around plates are much thinner and much lighter than other relief plates suitable for high quality letterpress. (All image carriers other than physical type are discussed in Chapter V.)

We cannot end our brief characterization of image carriers for relief printing without discussing duplicate plates. Not all kinds of duplicate plates are equally suitable for each letterpress job, but all of them have a place in the letterpress industry.

The main reason for the existence of duplicate plates. Type forms cannot be curved and are not usable as image carriers on the fastest kind of letterpresses, called rotaries, which are described under the next side heading. Duplicate plates are made from *original material*, a term not to be confused with *original images*. (Original material comprises metallic composition and pictorial image carriers, prepared for duplicate platemaking, whereas original images are pictures and other artwork supplied to the printer for image conversion.)

Letterpress uses various kinds of duplicate plates. Each of them is the result of a specialized manufacturing process. But all duplicate plates have certain points in common. The first is that they all are relief printing-image carriers; the second point is that they all are made from al-ready existing relief image carriers, such as metallic composition and photoengravings, and therefore require the making of an intaglio intermediate known as *matrix* or *mat;* and the third point is that duplicate plates can be either flat or curved.

Courtesy Electrotypers and Stereotypers Handbook

A cold-rolled stereotyping mat is lifted from the type form after molding. This mat is then used for casting of a stereotype plate.

Assemblies of metallic type and photoengravings are called *type forms;* they are approximately one inch high and consist either of individual characters or solid lines of type, often in combination with photoengravings mounted to the height of type.

The four kinds of duplicate plates and their main uses. Duplicate plates differ in their ability to render detail, in their wearing qualities, and in the materials of which they are made. Four kinds of duplicate plates can be used in letterpress; all of them can be either curved in the course of their production or they are curvable by their nature and therefore suitable for rotary presses. The four kinds of duplicate plates are: (1) stereotypes, (2) electrotypes, (3) rubber plates, and (4) plastic plates. *Stereotypes* are the oldest of all duplicate plates; they are at present much less important for letterpress than for newspaper printing, but they still have a limited use in the printing of books and trade magazines. *Electrotypes* are the elite of the duplicate plates; they are capable of highest quality and greatest precision and are equally suitable for the printing of long press runs. Both stereotypes and electrotypes can be curved and are therewith usable as image carriers on rotary presses. *Rubber plates* serve in letterpress mainly for the printing of inexpensive, paper-bound books which are produced in huge quantities. They are widely used in specialty printing—of business forms, for example—and in flexography, another method of relief printing. *Plastic plates*, finally, are used in letterpress for many purposes that do not warrant the making of electrotypes. (A detailed discussion of duplicate plates is provided in Chapter V, Section 3.)[8]

Presses and Presswork for Letterpress

Presses for letterpress printing are customarily divided into the three broad groups of platen presses, flatbed-cylinder presses, and rotary presses. These divisions are based on the nature of the printing unit which is a most characteristic element in all printing presses. The printing unit of letterpress presses consists of two main members; one serves for placement of the image carrier, the other for positioning of the paper (or other stock) and for exerting the required printing pressure.

Evolution of printing units. If we compare the printing units of these kinds of presses, we notice a simple evolution. In *platen presses* the member bearing the image carrier, known as the press *bed*, has a flat surface; the impression member, called the *platen*, is also flat. In *flatbed-cylinder presses* the bed is still flat but the impression member is a cylinder; and in *rotary presses* both members are cylinders.

Relations between kinds of presses and image carriers. When we relate these differences in press constructions to the kinds of printing-image carriers that can be used on each of these three kinds of presses, we see immediately that platen and flatbed-cylinder presses need flat image carriers, whereas rotary presses must have curved ones. Concluding, we may say that platen and flatbed-cylinder presses will be used for jobs that can be printed directly from type forms which are assemblies of metallic types, alone or in combination with photoengravings and other flat relief printing-image carriers. The third kind, rotary presses, requires either precurved image carriers or image carriers that can follow the curvature of the plate cylinder without precurving. Precurved image carriers for high-quality letterpress are mainly electrotypes. Some wrap-around plates do not need precurving, though they may also be made curved when this procedure is preferable to making them flat.

Relations between kinds of press and length of press run. Type is not suitable for long-run printing, and is usually not considered capable of producing more than, say, 50,000 impressions. Platen and flatbed-cylinder presses, which can print from type forms, serve for the production of much shorter runs than rotary presses. Rotary presses can print much faster than platen and flatbed-cylinder presses and are therefore needed for long production runs. Even though platen and flatbed-cylinder presses can be either sheet-fed or fed from a roll of paper, roll-fed platen and flatbed-cylinder presses are not used in letterpress as generally practiced in job-and-commercial printing. Rotary letterpresses can be either sheet-fed or roll-fed. Roll-fed letterpresses are mass production equipment on which many magazines, printed in hundreds of thousands and even millions of copies, are produced. Sheet-fed rotary presses occupy a position between the much slower flatbed-cylinder presses and the much faster roll-fed rotaries; they are used for letterpress printing of many jobs in runs of many tens of thousands and possibly hundreds of thousands impressions. The variety of available letterpress printing equipment is prodigious; it cannot be discussed at this point but is detailed in Chapter VI, Section 1, "A Survey of Printing Presses."

Presswork for letterpress printing. Presswork is the image-transfer phase of printing. In the press the properly positioned image carrier is inked and the resulting ink image is transferred to the paper under pressure. Letterpress printing uses traditionally multiple-unit image carriers which must be assembled for common presswork. Wrap-around plates, on the other hand, are single-unit or integral printing-image carriers for relief printing. Type forms are assemblies consisting primarily though not exclusively of type and photoengravings. Image carriers for rotary printing are, generally speaking, electrotypes for high-quality letterpress; other kinds of duplicate plates and, most recently, wrap-around plates are also used, depending on the nature of a job and the kind of presses available in a plant.

Assembling of image carriers for common letterpress printing. The page is the unit of assembly for all products having individual pages, notably books, magazines, and booklets frequently used for advertising. It would obviously be impractical to print a book or a magazine page by page, one page at a time. Therefore, a number of assembled units, each representing a page, must be further combined for common presswork. How many pages are actually assembled depends upon the nature of the work, the size of the press, and other factors. The number of assembled pages may be as small as four or eight, and it can be as large as one hundred and twenty-eight, and possibly even larger.

The assembly of pages for common presswork is done according to a carefully developed plan which is known as *imposition*. The kind of imposition selected for a specific job depends largely on available bindery equipment. (Impositions are discussed in Chapter X.) Type forms are assembled in a sturdy metal frame, called "chase"; if flat duplicates are to be used, the press bed must be built up by means of metal blocks to the required heights. (Duplicate plates are much less high than type, for which the press bed is dimensioned in its height.) These blocks are known as patent bases if they are of proprietary design, if not they are called plate bases. *Patent bases* provide various means for attaching and adjusting of plates as to their position, usually hooks which run in the grooves of patent bases and are simply tightened when the plates are in their correct location. Similar arrangements are used for the attaching of curved plates to the plate cylinders of rotary presses. Flat or curved plates are beveled on their edges and the hooks catch them at some point along their bevel. For this reason plate hooks are often called *catches* by pressmen.

Wrap-around plates are already completely assembled when they arrive at the pressroom. Assembly of pages is done by *stripping*, prior to the exposure of such plates to strong lights as needed in photomechanical platemaking.

Press preparation and makeready. Preparing a press for a new job comprises a number of operations, usually summarized as *makeready*. In job printing, particularly, where every new job can differ in many ways from the last job, makeready may require a considerable effort and many adjustments. The subject is complex and, therefore,

not further pursued at this point. A detailed discussion of press preparation and makeready for letterpress is provided in Chapter VII.

Running. The last step is running. Running is the payoff for the long and tedious effort of image conversion and press preparation. It is by no means an automatic process that can be simply left to the press without care or supervision on the part of the pressman. If a job is well prepared, it should require few adjustments during running; but even a well-prepared job can need plenty of supervision when it is on the press. The printed paper must be removed, and new paper must be added; ink must be replenished; spoilage must be held down to a minimum; and, last but not least, the quality of the job must be maintained at its predetermined, approved, level. If you consider that all of these operations may take place under intense time pressure, you will agree that presswork is a complex and responsible phase of printing production, requiring intelligent, alert, and conscientious craftsmanship.

Our brief description of presses and presswork for letterpress has come to an end. The next two subjects are papers and inks for letterpress printing.

Papers and Inks for Letterpress

The range of papers and inks used in letterpress is not any smaller than that of letterpress image carriers and presses. Not every kind of the many available papers is suitable for letterpress printing, and not every letterpress paper can be used indiscriminately with every image carrier. The same holds true for inks, but with the additional restriction that not every letterpress ink is fit for every

Courtesy Cottrell Company

The center and delivery end of a five-color Cottrell magazine press.

kind of press. Remember that each of the four elements combined in presswork (press, image carrier, paper, and ink) must be carefully attuned to all others.

Relation between image detail and paper surface in letterpress. The interrelatedness of all elements combined in presswork can be very well illustrated by discussing the relations between image detail and paper surface. Letterpress cannot print halftones on coarse or textured papers; the finer the halftone the smoother the paper must be. Appearance of the paper can be deceptive; unfortunately it is not always possible to evaluate the paper surface without magnification. For this reason, paper mills indicate in their sales literature the kind of halftone that can be used with a specific kind of paper. Papers are made in many different finishes; smooth papers are passed between stacks of calenders which consist of metal rolls at the end of the paper machine. Calendering may or may not be followed by coating. In coated papers, various kinds of coatings are applied to the paper surface. (Calendering and coating of papers are discussed in Chapter VIII.)

Inks for letterpress printing. Much as letterpress inks may differ according to paper, press, and image carriers with which they are to be used, they must nevertheless all be capable of forming an ink image that preserves the detail present in the printing areas of the image carrier. This necessity implies that they must be rather viscous or stiff, and not too fluid, if compared with the rather liquid gravure inks. Very fluid inks could not form a correct image on the plateau of the relief image carrier because they would tend to run down its sides. But various kinds of letterpress inks differ among other points also in their fluidity. As a general rule, fluidity increases as press speeds mount. Inks for platen and flatbed cylinder presses are less fluid than inks for high-speed magazine letterpresses.

Letterpress inks are strongly pigmented, and their final layer is thick enough to convey the impression of great color strength whenever this effect is desired. Modern ink technology has been instrumental in making increases in the speed of presswork possible by developing fast drying heat-set inks, a subject further explained in Chapter IX, "Printing Inks."

Newspaper Relief Printing

Like many other printed products, newspapers can be produced by several printing methods.

Relief printing is most prominent in the newspaper industry; other widely used methods are rotogravure and web offset. Rotogravure serves for the printing of millions of supplements to Sunday newspapers, and web offset is gaining in popularity for the printing of weeklies and of smaller daily papers, meaning those of a low circulation if compared with that of metropolitan newspapers. To avoid the impression that all newspapers are printed by relief methods, the more correct albeit somewhat cumbersome designation "newspaper relief printing" is often used in this manual.

Before we begin an explanation of newspaper relief printing it seems indicated to explain why we distinguish this method of relief printing from letterpress. The reasons for considering newspaper relief printing a method different from letterpress can be grouped under two heads: structural differences between the letterpress industry and the newspaper industry, and differences in printing technology.

Structural differences between the letterpress and the newspaper industry. The letterpress industry as a whole is overwhelmingly a service industry, equipped and organized for production of a great variety of custom-made products. There is, following the trend of the times, growing specialization in the letterpress industry. Some publication printing plants, which may be owned and operated by corporations publishing general-interest magazines, use the letterpress method for single-product manufacturing. But by and large the letterpress industry is a service industry, equipped for the printing of such items as are needed by the whole community.

If we compare the letterpress industry with that segment of the newspaper industry which uses relief printing, we can notice striking differences. Practically all large metropolitan newspapers are printed by relief printing. Newspaper relief printing has been the exclusive manufacturing method of large metropolitan papers in the past, and there are no indications that this method will be superseded by a different one in the foreseeable future. (It should be understood that this comment applies to large metropolitan newspapers only; as already mentioned, smaller dailies and weeklies are turning increasingly to web offset.) Large metropolitan newspapers are single-product industries: their plant is designed for the most efficient manufacturing of one product, and one product exclusively: the newspaper. A newspaper publishing company may have a single newspaper or two of them, and possibly more, but the products are always newspapers, either full-size morning and evening papers or tabloids published as morning and as evening papers. The equipment for newspaper production is essentially single-product machinery. It is true that newspaper relief printing can produce other products besides newspapers, but these products look like newspapers and they are of no economic significance in comparison with newspapers.

There is also a vast difference in the size and structure of the kind of organization which is—to use a statistical term—the mode in either industry. The kind of organization most frequently found in the letterpress business is much smaller, much less capitalized, and much less complex than that prevalent in the newspaper industry publishing metropolitan morning or evening papers. Nor are the attitudes of management and craftsmen the same. In newspaper production all efforts are bent to make possible the most efficient manufacturing of the same product, day in and day out. But the success of a newspaper does not depend primarily on manufacturing: editorial skill and the ability to sell advertising space are at least equally important to manufacturing know-how, and, as a rule these two points are much more decisive than manufacturing for the success of a newspaper.

In the letterpress industry conditions are radically different. In printing as a service business, management and craftsmen alike must be willing to tackle almost any kind of job. The skills of management and craftsmen in devising solutions that do justice to the purpose of unusual jobs, paired with the know-how whereby the production of difficult jobs is made possible within budgetary limits, is probably more decisive for the success of printers engaged in job-and-commercial printing than any other factor except sales-mindedness. Sales-mindedness and great versatility in production usually go hand-in-hand.

Technological differences between letterpress and newspaper relief printing The technological differences between letterpress and newspaper relief printing are, even at a casual inspection, quite noticeable. They can be found in all four elements combined in all printing, and particularly in presswork. Beginning with paper, letterpress uses quality papers more than others, but even in strict utility printing, papers for letterpress are smoother, more durable, and much less absorbent than the paper on which newspapers are printed.

Next, there is an essential difference between inks for letterpress and those for newspaper relief. Letterpress inks dry by several kinds of drying action, but with the same result: the printed image consists of a dry ink film in letterpress. This is not so in newspaper relief printing. The vehicle of the ink for newspaper printing is absorbed by the porosity of the paper, but news ink is not capable of forming dry films, and some of the black pigment sitting on the surface of the paper has a tendency to rub off during the handling of a newspaper. A look at the hands of newspaper vendors will confirm this observation.

The third element needed for printing, in addition to paper and ink, is an image carrier. Image carriers of relief-printed metropolitan newspapers are curved stereotypes exclusively. (Many smaller newspapers are printed on roll-fed flatbed-cylinder presses from type forms.) And it might be mentioned at this point that fine halftone images are not used in newspaper relief printing. This method is limited to halftones that are rather coarse in comparison with those used in letterpress. Newspaper presses, our fourth element, are highly specialized machines not built for sheet-feeding but exclusively for web printing. They are provided with folding equipment, which is also designed for single-product manufacturing. Last but not least, image transfer in newspaper printing differs essentially from image transfer in letterpress. In newspaper printing, the impression is made by forcing the inked image carrier into the fiber of the paper. Such a technique of printing is contrary to the rules for presswork in letterpress.

To sum up, the differences in printing technology, in products, in craftsman and management attitudes, not to forget differences in the structure of organizations, are sufficiently pronounced to divide newspaper relief printing from letterpress and to justify its separate treatment. We turn next to a brief discussion of newspaper printing in single color, multicolor, and full color.

Various kinds of color printing for newspapers. The editorial parts of newspapers, and most of their advertisements, are printed in a black ink. Multicolor printing is often used to enliven advertisements; a second color is never used in the editorial parts of some newspapers, whereas others do add emphasis to headlines by printing them not in black but in a second color. More

Courtesy The Bulletin, Philadelphia

A modern newspaper pressroom. The picture shows the aisle between two rows of presses; curved stereotype plates ride with both ends on conveyor built into pressroom floor. The printed and folded newspapers move up in streams to the mailroom floor.

recently, full-color printing has attained growing importance in the newspaper industry. Full-color printing, known as ROP in the newspaper industry, is used primarily for advertisements but also editorially. ROP stands for run-of-paper, indicating that the whole edition is so printed. ROP is based on standardized ink colors specified by the Research Department of the American Newspaper Publishers Association.

Image conversion for newspaper printing. Reading matter is converted into type; pictures are either converted into photoengravings or into electromechanical engravings for newspaper relief printing. Many newspapers use metallic type without exception, but some prefer photographic

composition for display advertisements. Metallic composition of body type is done on line-casting machines, such as Linotypes and Intertypes. These can be operated in three ways: (1) by keyboarding, (2) by the TTS (Teletypesetting System), and (3) most recently, by punched paper ribbons resulting from computerized composition. Metallic composition of headlines and display advertising is usually done by the Ludlow System in which type matrices are hand assembled for the casting of lines. Since all reading matter and all pictures must be finally converted into curved stereotype plates—which are made from flat relief image carriers—photographic composition and pictures must be converted first into original relief plates by photoengraving. Therefore, many metropolitan newspapers have their own photoengraving departments; some papers have working arrangements with independent photoengravers which are usually located in the newspaper building. These engravers take care of the needs of the paper and may or may not handle other business as well. All metropolitan papers have, of course, their own composing rooms.

Curved stereotypes. It was mentioned before that curved stereotypes are the image carriers for relief newspaper printing. Each full-size newspaper page is individually made up. The material combined in such a page may include, besides cast lines of type and photoengravings, electromechanical engravings, electrotypes, flat stereotypes, and other items. The made-up page is first used for the making of an intaglio matrix, usually called mat, in which the curved stereotype is cast. Curved stereotypes are made by more or less automatic equipment and can be cast very fast. The process is faster and less costly than the making of any other kind of curved plates. (The curved casting of stereotypes is described in Chapter V.)

Newspaper presses, newsprint and news ink. Newspaper presses, newsprint, and news ink were already briefly characterized in the discussion of technological differences between letterpress and newspaper relief printing. Newspaper presses for metropolitan newspapers are highly specialized equipment. Usually, three floors are needed for such installations: on one floor are the *spiders* which are needed for placing rolls of paper in position for web feeding; on the floor above are the actual printing units and folders; on the third floor, the folded papers, carried up from the second floor by vertical conveyors, are bundled and dispatched. Presses for newspaper relief printing are not only manufactured for large metropolitan papers but also for papers having much shorter runs. The variety of this equipment is discussed in Chapter VI, "Printing Presses," the actual printing operation in Chapter VII, "Presswork."

Newsprint is the least expensive printing paper; it is made from mechanical, or ground wood pulp, with varying amounts of chemical pulp added. The meaning of these points as well as other details relating to newsprint are explained in Chapter VIII, "Paper and Other Printing Stocks." Here it is sufficient to add that newsprint is not a lasting paper, that it must be very absorbent and that it is therefore not or only slightly sized. The absorptive qualities of newsprint are indispensable for the drying of news ink, as already explained. (News ink is discussed in Chapter IX, "Printing Inks.")

Equipment and materials for newspaper relief printing are well balanced and enable the American newspaper industry to produce technically outstanding products at an exceptionally low sales price. Newspaper printing is an example of the high technological level at which contemporary printing can be done: it demonstrates how mass production methods are successfully used in the printing industry.

Flexography

Like some other printing methods, flexography passed through an initial development period during which its results were rather crude. Then it was known as *aniline printing*, a name derived from aniline dyes which were in this period used exclusively as colorants of flexographic inks. Aniline dyes produce very intense and brilliant colors but they are fugitive and have other limitations which disqualify them for many purposes.

As flexographic printing matured, its methods, equipment, and inks became more refined. It was learned that fugitive dyes can be replaced with less fugitive ones and also with pigments, which are available in a wide range of lightfastness. Now the name aniline printing, which was considered no asset by the industry, became also incorrect. It was therefore decided by leading firms in this industry to abandon the name aniline printing in favor of a new, untarnished name. In 1952 this industry, guided by the Packaging Institute, adopted the newly coined word "flexography" as the official process and industry name, thereby re-

A molded rubber plate and its matrix The printing areas are in intaglio in the matrix and in relief on the molded plate.

placing the undesirable aniline printing. After more than a decade has passed, this name change can be considered an excellent move, greatly contributing to the growth of the flexographic industry.

The main uses of flexography. Flexography is primarily a package printing method; it is based on a combination of rubber plates, solvent evaporating inks, and web printing. Rubber plates can be original engravings, but in actual practice they are mainly duplicate plates, made by molding and remolding of relief material consisting of type and original photoengravings. Unlike traditional metallic relief printing-image carriers, rubber plates are flexible and have a somewhat porous structure. The flexibility of rubber plates makes it possible to use them on rotary presses without the need for precurving; rubber plates will conform to the curvature of the plate cylinder by their inherent flexibility. (The importance attributed to this characteristic can be seen from the fact that the chosen name of this printing method is flexography.) The porous surface structure of rubber plates permits the use of very fluid inks. Such inks have several advantages, of which only two will be mentioned at this point: one advantage of very fluid inks is that the inking system of flexographic presses is much simpler than that needed for highly viscous inks as used in letterpress or offset lithography; the other advantage of such inks is their suitability for the printing of plastic films which have become so widely used in the packaging field.

Flexographic presses and inline installations. Flexographic presses are usually rotary web presses equipped for the printing of one or several colors. If they are used for package printing on paper or paperboard, they print only one side of the web; but they can also be made to print both sides of the web. Flexographic presses are very often *inline* equipment. Inline is a term which indicates that a press is part of a whole production line of machinery as required for the more or less complete manufacturing of a given product. Printing is an important phase in package production, but it is only one phase among several.

The paper or plastic to be printed and converted into package material is normally supplied in rolls; it is first printed and may thereafter be sheeted, slitted, die-cut, stripped, re-wound or otherwise processed in one pass through the whole production line. Paper bags, for example, are completely produced by flexographic inline equipment. At one end of the line, rolls of paper are fed; at the other end of the line the printed bags are delivered, ready for shipment.

Like all other package printing, flexography has grown rapidly in the last decade. The flexographic industry is not an integrated industry; it relies on the printing-service trades for its original material: on trade composition houses for type and on photoengravers for pictorial image carriers. The final image carrier, consisting of natural or synthetic rubber plates, is normally supplied by concerns specializing in this field. But there are also flexographic printers who maintain their own molding departments for the making of rubber plates.

Indirect Relief Printing

Letterpress, newspaper relief printing, and flexography are direct printing methods. In direct printing methods, image transfer is made directly from the image carrier to the paper or other printing stock. Indirect printing, on the other hand, uses an intermediate element between image carrier and paper. This intermediate element is known as the *blanket.* The ink image is first transferred to the blanket and then from the blanket to the stock. In this method of printing the image carrier is never brought directly in contact with the stock.

Indirect image transfer. Indirect printing is the dominant method in contemporary lithography; it is known as *offset printing* and is practically synonymous in colloquial speaking and writing with lithography. Indirect relief printing is often designated as *dry offset* to distinguish it from lithographic offset printing which requires a dampening of the image carrier at every printing cycle, whereas indirect relief printing does not need dampening.

Dycril and Kodak Relief Plates as image carriers for indirect relief. Indirect relief printing was for a long time more or less limited to specialty print-

ing. The invention of photopolymer relief plates such as Dycril, and the development of the Kodak Relief Plate, which is based on silver halide emulsions in combination with controlled etching of a plastic base, tend to change this situation. At the time of writing, indirect relief printing has again captured the interest and imagination of printers. Many believe that this method holds great promise for high speed, sheet-fed letterpress printing, and that single-unit image carriers which are used for indirect relief printing, are time-saving alternatives in comparison with traditional multiple-unit letterpress assemblies.

A duPont Dycril wrap-around plate is being mounted on a precision curved metal saddle for attachment to the plate cylinder of a rotary letterpress.

Presses for indirect relief printing. Presses suitable for indirect relief printing are available in a vast variety of sizes and colors, for sheet-feeding and for web printing: they are offset lithographic presses which may or may not need adjustments of their plate cylinders for indirect relief. In recent years many American press builders have designed plate cylinders to be usable either with offset lithographic plates or with wrap-around plates. In certain sizes, older models of lithographic offset presses do not provide sufficient space on their plate cylinders for the thickness in which wrap-around plates for indirect relief printing are commonly made. Such presses can be made usable for indirect relief by increasing the undercut of their plate cylinders. In 1964 duPont announced that Dycril wrap-around plates were made in thicknesses not exceeding those of usual offset lithographic plates. These thin Dycril plates have the purpose of making indirect relief printing possible on presses which were not usable for thicker Dycril relief printing without changing the undercut of plate cylinders.

The advantages of indirect image transfer are explained in Chapter VI, Section 2, at the discussion of printing units on offset lithographic presses; the points made there are also valid for indirect relief. In Chapter VII, Section 2, you find an operational discussion of indirect relief printing on web presses.

Section 3:   Intaglio Printing

Intaglio printing is the name of a process family comprising a variety of printing methods which all use printing-image carriers with the printing areas sunken, or embedded, in the depth of the carrier material. Such images are technically known as intaglio (pronounced "intalyo") as opposed to relief images. (In relief image carriers the printing areas are, as explained in the preceding section, raised above the bulk of the supporting material.) This difference is by no means a mere formality but has some interesting consequences, as you will see immediately.

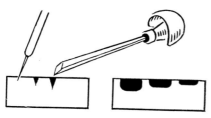

Comparative diagram of hand-engraved and etched intaglio image carriers. Picture at left shows engraved image carrier, the hand tools used and the incisions made by them. At the right is an etched image carrier with cells of identical areas but varying depth.

The formation of ink images in intaglio printing. Let us begin by comparing the formation of ink images and image transfer in relief and intaglio printing. In relief printing, the ink image comes about in a single operation which consists in applying printing ink to the top surface of the relief image carrier. This surface is identical with the printing image. But in intaglio printing things are quite different. Here the non-printing areas are on top of the image carrier whereas the printing image is sunken in the depth of the carrier material.

The reasons for wiping, or doctoring of intaglio image carriers. Unfortunately we cannot put printing ink into the depth of intaglio image carriers without applying it at the same time to its top surface. But the top surface of the image carrier represents the *non-printing areas*, and inking must therefore be followed in intaglio printing by a second operation whereby the printing ink which was *involuntarily* applied to the non-printing surface of the carrier is removed. The step of removing the unwanted ink is known as *wiping* or as *doctoring*. After inking and wiping, the paper or other stock is pressed against the image carrier and the ink image, which lies in the depth of the carrier, is transferred to the printing stock where it forms the printed image.

Various kinds of intaglio printing. Intaglio printing is one of the oldest graphic reproduction processes. It was the classic method of picture printing from the sixteenth to the beginning of the nineteenth century. Then its position was challenged by the newly invented planographic process of lithography, and also by wood engraving. In our time, many of the various intaglio methods developed in the course of history have disappeared from industrial printing and are now exclusively used for fine-art printmaking. Fortunately, the intaglio principle has not been lost for industrial printing. It has been revived, and its scope has been greatly broadened during the twentieth century which has witnessed a remarkable growth of several modern intaglio printing methods.

In this manual, intaglio printing is divided into three kinds: (1) fine-art intaglio methods, (2) steel-die engraving and banknote printing, and (3) sheet-fed and roll-fed gravure. Each of these three divisions is now briefly explained.

Fine-Art Intaglio Methods

The history of intaglio printing and its several methods teaches us the evolution of picture printing and how the graphic arts learned to cope with problems which remain important.

Engraving and etching. Printing-image carriers for intaglio can be made by engraving, by etching, and by a combination of etching and engraving. The image carrier for intaglio is always a metal plate, usually copper, but possibly also zinc or steel. The engraver works with hand tools that are much harder than the plate. He cuts a furrow into the plate or he scratches it, depending on the technique elected. Engraving of metal plates results automatically in intaglio images of varying depth; varying depth of intaglio printing-images is a most characteristic feature of all intaglio methods, including contemporary gravure which uses image carriers made by entirely different methods than hand engraving.

For etching, the plate surface is first protected by an acid-proof resist in the non-printing areas and left bare in the future printing areas. Then the plate is treated with an etchant, often called mordant in the older literature, which attacks the base metal, dissolves it and therewith produces an intaglio image. The depth of this image depends, other conditions being equal, on the length of time for which a particular area is treated by the etchant. The longer the etchant can act on the metal, the deeper the image becomes.

Consequences of varying the depth of intaglio printing areas. The variation of depth in the printing, or image areas, of intaglio image carriers has far reaching and beneficial consequences for the appearance of the printed image. Intaglio printing can vary the amount of ink to be deposited in different areas of the stock within the same press run; thereby is added a new feature, *variation of color value*, to the final printed image.[9]

This unique ability accounts for the remarkable progress made by intaglio printing in the art and technique of picture reproduction. Intaglio was so flexible, so versatile, that it developed method after method until it became possible to reproduce—more or less faithfully—by etching and engraving, the images which were created by an artist with his pencil, quill, or brush. What human hands originated, human hands were also able to duplicate. Step by step, intaglio methods expanded the art of picture printing from line, to tone, approaching continuous tone and even achieving a kind of full-color printing. All this was accomplished, as you want to remember, long before the invention of photography and photomechanics revolutionized the reproduction of pictures. (Various fine-art intaglio methods and the kind of pictures made by them are charac-

terized in Chapter V, "Printing-Image Carriers.") We turn next to a brief description of image transfer in fine-art intaglio printmaking.[10]

Presswork in fine-art intaglio printmaking. Intaglio plates for printmaking are printed on hand presses. As the ink must be very stiff, the plate is usually warmed prior to inking; the ink is applied by hand, either with a roller or a dabber. Then the plate is wiped clean on its surface with a rag. Inking an intaglio plate is far from being a mechanical operation. The appearance of the final print can be greatly changed by the manner in which the plate is inked. The paper must be dampened for printing; thereby it becomes limp and able to pull the ink out of the minute and shallow intaglio recesses of the image carrier.

Printmaking is a slow and tedious business, and the number of prints that can be taken from a handmade intaglio plate is relatively small. But printmaking affords a satisfaction of its own to the practicing artist. For the printer, fine-art printmaking connects the industrial present with the handicraft past and with a great tradition of picture reproduction. Such famous artists as Duerer, Rembrandt, Goya, and Whistler all made their own etchings, and so did many others.

Steel-Die Engraving and Banknote Printing

Steel-die engraving is an intaglio printing method executed in combination with embossing. At the same step at which the paper is printed, it is also embossed in the image areas. The result is a product on which the printed images stand out in relief above the paper surface. This method is mainly used for the printing of formal items, including stationery for business and private use, as well as calling cards, announcements, and invitations to formal affairs. Steel-die engraving is also used in the production of greeting cards; for high prestige labels, and other decorative printing. Steel-die engraving is done by many companies throughout the United States. The industry is integrated in the sense that steel-die engravers usually also make the necessary image carriers in their own plants.

Banknote printing, finally, is in a class by itself; it serves for the production of the most generally desired printed product, a product of which the vast majority of people never get enough nor tire: our dollar bills. These are not printed in the United States by privately owned concerns but exclusively by the United States Bureau of Engraving and Printing which also prints, among many other items, government bonds and our postage stamps. Private companies engaged in banknote printing may print currency, bonds, and postage stamps for foreign governments; for the domestic market, they are producers of stock and bond certificates for private enterprise. Stock and bond certificates for private business are also printed by lithography.

Differences between steel-die engraving and banknote printing. At first glance there seems to be such a difference between steel-die engraving and banknote printing that their common discussion appears to be far-fetched. It must be conceded that there are differences between the products for which these two methods are used and between the manner in which image transfer is accomplished during presswork. Steel-die engraving is done from flat image carriers on presses equipped with two parallel planes, a flatbed and a platen. Banknote printing is done from curved image carriers on rotary presses. But both methods use line images primarily; the inks for both methods are of a high viscosity, and the non-printing areas of image carriers for steel-die engraving and banknote printing are wiped in a similar way.

Reasons for grouping together of steel-die engraving and banknote printing. The best explanation of the reason for discussing steel-die engraving and banknote printing together is their difference from the next and final group of intaglio printing methods, sheet-fed gravure and rotogravure. If you compare either steel-die engraving or banknote printing with rotogravure, which is the dominant contemporary mass production

intaglio method you will, so the writer hopes, share his opinion that these two methods have more in common than in difference.

Sheet-Fed Gravure and Rotogravure

Sheet-fed gravure and rotogravure are based on photography and photomechanics; both printing methods are capable of reproducing continuous tone pictures, and also line drawings, together with type images. Sheet-fed gravure is often designated as photogravure in distinction from rotogravure. Unfortunately these two names do not indicate the true differences between the two intaglio methods to which they are applied. These differences lie neither in the use of photography— on which both methods are based—nor in the rotary principle of printing, because this principle, too, is common to both. Technically speaking, the main differences between the methods are two: first, that photogravure is done on sheet-fed presses, whereas rotogravure uses exclusively roll-fed equipment; and second, that the image carriers of photogravure are flat metal plates, whereas those for rotogravure are etched metal cylinders. (In Europe, sheet-fed gravure is often done with etched cylinders rather than flat plates as image carriers.)

The original meaning of photogravure is different from its present one; originally the term indicated a method in which the intaglio cells were formed by a random grain pattern. This method is not used anymore, and the term "photogravure" is applied by some to sheet-fed gravure

Courtesy The Beck Engraving Company

View of a press for sheet-fed gravure. The feeder is in the middle, the delivery in the rear, and the printing unit on the left. The printed sheet travels overhead from the printing unit to the delivery.

in the United States. In the service of clarity "photogravure" is confined in this manual to its original meaning; the two contemporary gravure methods are discussed under the heads of sheet-fed gravure and of rotogravure.[11]

Products of sheet-fed and of rotogravure printing. In the United States, sheet-fed gravure is not a widely used printing method. It produces printing of high quality in quantities which may not be small by themselves but pale in comparison with those of rotogravure. Among the products printed by photogravure are fine-art reproductions, art books, advertising materials, greeting cards, annual reports, and short-run package materials. Among those manufactured by rotogravure are newspaper supplements, magazines, catalogs, and mass production package items, disregarding many specialties which are outside the scope of this manual.

Three distinctive characteristics of gravure. All contemporary gravure printing is distinguished in three points from all other printing processes. These are (1) that all gravure copy—reading matter as well as pictures—must be screened; (2) the use of the doctor blade; and (3) that gravure is capable of reproducing tonal values in three ways: either by changing the proportions between printed and non-printed areas, or by changing the amount of ink deposited in the printed areas, or by a combination of both. These different possibilities of tonal reproduction are characteristic for gravure and find their concrete expression in a number of proprietary gravure conversion methods. The subject is discussed in Chapter V and need not be further pursued in the present context. At this point, a brief description of the most frequently employed gravure method is required because without this description other essential features of gravure could not be understood. We turn therefore to conventional, or straight, gravure as our next subject.

Conventional, or straight, gravure. Like many other terms in the printing industry, *conventional* or *straight gravure*, is not descriptive but a make-shift, devised in the wake of technical development. As long as all gravure printing was based on a single image conversion method this method obviously needed no name of its own; it was simply an integral part of gravure production. Later, when different image conversion methods began to appear, these were considered new or unconventional, and the names of conventional gravure or of straight gravure became in time established throughout the gravure industry for the originally nameless method.

In conventional gravure, the intaglio image carrier is divided into a vast number of tiny individual cells. The nature of the work determines the number of cells per linear inch. The higher this number is, the smaller are the individual cells. The cell number per linear inch is rarely less than 120; in extreme cases is may be as high as 220. As numbers go in our time, these seem rather small. But if you consider that 120 cells per linear inch are almost 15,000 cells per square inch and that the corresponding figure for 220 linear cells is close to 50,000 per square inch, you may be a little more impressed. Each of these cells has the same area, but the depth of the cells is not the same throughout. Darker tones have deeper cells, lighter tones have less deep ones. In conventional gravure, the tonal values of the printing image are brought about by varying the depth of individual cells.

Image transfer in gravure. For printing, all cells are filled with ink; deeper cells hold, naturally, more ink than less deep ones. The quantity of ink transferred to the paper varies according to the depth of various cells. The ink image corresponds to these differences in cell depth and ink quantity, and so does the final printed image. The thicker the ink deposit is, the more intense will the final color appear, other conditions, of course, assumed equal, and the thinner this deposit is, the lighter will a printed area look. Conventional gravure is consequently capable of varying the amount of ink deposited on the paper in relation to the values in the image to be so reproduced.

The manner in which gravure can reproduce continuous-tone images is unique. It differs radically from the manner in which tonal values are expressed in most other printing processes and methods, particularly in relief and planographic printing. There, continuous-tone images are reproduced as halftones, and the area of the printed dots varies in accordance with tonal values, but the ink film is of constant thickness throughout.

Cells and lands. Every cell is separated from every other cell by its walls or lands. The *lands* form the non-printing surface of the gravure image carrier which is usually a plate in sheet-fed gravure and always a cylinder in rotogravure. The width of the walls, or lands, is the same throughout an image carrier but it is possible to make image carriers which have different ratios of cell width to land width. This point is explained in some detail at the discussion of gravure image carriers in Chapter V.

Relation between cells and ink viscosity. Gravure cells are quite shallow; they are not deeper than approximately 0.002 inch in the shadow areas, where they are deepest and much less deep in all other areas. The depth of gravure cells is therefore measured with special microscopes. The printing ink used for gravure is quite liquid, much more so than inks for other intaglio methods. Ink must remain in the cells for printing, but it must be removed from the surface of the image carrier which represents in gravure the non-printing areas.

It is, of course, not possible to remove the excess ink from the plate or cylinder surface by wiping with a rag and polishing, as it is done in fine-art intaglio printmaking. Such a procedure would not only disturb the ink in the cells, which must not happen, but also reduce the printing speed of gravure to a ridiculously slow one. Gravure would simply cease to be an industrial printing method under such conditions. Fortunately, gravure has in the *doctor blade* a most efficient implement for the wiping of the non-printing areas.

The function of the doctor blade and of the lands. To understand the problem of wiping, you want to keep in mind that the gravure image carrier is either a cylinder or a plate mounted on a cylinder. This cylinder rotates during inking as well as during wiping. Wiping is done by a steel strip running across the length of the cylinder, known as the *doctor blade*. This strip of metal touches the rotating image carrier with its edge and wipes the surface free of ink without disturbing the ink in the cells.

It is impossible to control the position of the doctor blade without supporting it on the surface of the gravure image carrier. Without this support the blade could not be perfectly straight as required, but would sag or lift and therewith not be able to do its job. The lands, which are spaced in close intervals on the cylinder, provide the necessary support for the doctor blade; they are its riding surface.

The reason for screening of all gravure copy, including type images. The procedure by which conventional gravure image carriers receive the required cellular pattern is known as *screening*. Many people who are not informed of the true function of screening in conventional gravure confuse this operation with the screening whereby continuous-tone images are converted into halftones. But these two operations serve not only entirely different purposes, they are in addition executed in a very different manner, even though they both can use a similar implement, namely, a ruled glass screen. (Until the advent of vignetted screens, cross-line or glass screens were a necessity for halftone photography. This condition has changed, and vignetted screens are widely used for halftone photography, as explained in Chapter IV.) The kind of ruled glass screen which is needed for halftone photography is different from the kind of screen needed for screening of gravure copy. If you understand that screening is done in gravure to provide the lands which are indispensable for supporting the doctor blade, you will need no further explanation why type, too, must be screened. The screening of type images does not improve their quality on the printed sheet. But gravure has learned to handle type images satisfactorily and to identify type faces that are not suitable for gravure and should, therefore, be avoided. Generally speaking, gravure has reached a high level of technology and is capable of combining type images and pictures for common presswork, resulting in products of high quality.

The Three Branches of Rotogravure

Different from sheet-fed gravure which is used for the printing of relatively short runs, rotogravure is a method for the mass production of certain printed products. These are customarily divided into publications, package materials, and specialties. Since specialty printing is not discussed in our manual, the following introduction to rotogravure is limited to publication printing and to package printing.

Before we begin discussing different branches of rotogravure, it is mentioned that gravure, sheet-fed as well as roto, is done in single color, multicolor, and full color. Single color does not need an explanation, the terms multicolor and full color are clarified in Section 1, and more fully discussed in Chapter III, "Theory and Practice of Full-Color Printing." At this point it must be mentioned that single color is in gravure generally called *monotone*. Monotone is an awkward term which does not do justice to the capabilities of single-color gravure since this method excels in the wide gamut of tones that it can produce by single-color printing. If another designation than single color is preferred, the word *monochrome*, which means the same as single color, appears to be the wanted term. Since monotone is generally used, this term cannot be excluded from the present manual.

Publication printing by rotogravure. Publications printed by rotogravure include various kinds of magazines and mail order catalogs which are either completely or partly printed in rotogravure. Other products of gravure publication printing are mass-produced booklets and folders for advertising, sales promotion, and related purposes. Most recently, rotogravure is used for full-color printed advertising material which is re-wound and combined on the press with relief printed newspapers prior to their folding. The production of a high-quality magazine, printed on coated paper in monotone, multicolor, and full-color rotogravure, is described in Chapter VII.

Rotogravure in the newspaper industry. In the newspaper business rotogravure plays a steadily increasing role. One large newspaper, the *Philadelphia Inquirer*, prints its comic color sections in gravure. The *New York Times*, which was a pioneer in the use of rotogravure and began publishing a rotogravure supplement in 1914, uses this method for two magazines which are part of the Sunday paper. One is the "New York Times Book Review," printed in monotone, and the other is the "New York Times Magazine" which is printed partly in monotone and partly in color. Many other magazine-like additions to the *Sunday Times*, mostly advertisements, are also manufactured by rotogravure.

Rotogravure supplements. Few newspapers are large enough for the publishing and printing of their own gravure magazines, and most of them rely on *syndicated newspaper supplements*. These are magazines supplied by publishers specializing in this branch of the newspaper business. The publishers of syndicated rotogravure supplements handle the editing and the sale of advertising space. For obvious reasons it would be much too expensive and much too time consuming to print newspaper supplements at a single point from which they would then be shipped all over the United States; nationally distributed newspaper supplements are therefore produced simultaneously in several geographical regions.

Package printing by rotogravure. The constantly growing role of gravure in the rapidly expanding packaging industry is related to several congenital features of rotogravure. The success of gravure in package printing can be attributed to five points:

Courtesy Gravure Magazine

Delivery end of a six-color gravure press with inline cutter-creaser. The roll feed and the six printing stations are hidden by the cutter-creaser. Two technicians inspect die-cut carton blank. The cut and stripped blanks move in two overlapped streams to the foreground where they are removed by a workman.

(1) Rotogravure is an exceptionally fast printing method; running speeds are usually several hundred feet per minute and may be much higher. (2) Gravure cylinders yield very large numbers of impressions, under proper handling several millions, without need for make-overs. (3) Rotogravure is based on fluid inks, and these can be formulated for printing on an astounding variety of printing stocks which are wanted in package printing; plastic films, metal foils, papers, and paper boards can all be printed in rotogravure. (4) The final printed images are of excellent visual quality. (5) The rotogravure industry has very efficient fabricating machinery at its command which can be operated *inline*, fabricating the end product at the same speed at which presswork progresses.

The main phases of rotogravure production. In rotogravure, like in all other branches of the printing industry, production can be divided into two broad phases: one is image conversion, the other is image transfer. Image conversion includes all steps leading to printing-image carriers; image transfer is as usual the task of presswork.

Conversion practices in the gravure industry. At the discussion of the letterpress industry it was mentioned that printing companies which produce the image carriers needed by them for presswork are considered integrated plants and that those who buy their image carriers are non-integrated. The gravure industry can neither be classified as integrated nor as non-integrated. Some rotogravure printers handle the production of cylinders in all its phases in their own plants. Others buy copper-plated cylinders and color-separation positives but do their own etching; a third group buys completely prepared cylinders. All depends on the size and policy of specific plants. The gravure industry includes trade engravers who make color separations, etch plates, or cylinders, and proof them. For some purposes sets of gravure color separations are supplied to the printer, in other cases trade engravers furnish sets of etched rotogravure cylinders.

In the newspaper supplement industry, national advertisers or their advertising agencies usually rely on the services of trade engravers for their own full-color advertisements. Trade engravers make color separations of such advertisements, etch plates for proofing, print proofs in full color, make all corrections wanted by their customers, and finally provide sets of corrected photographic intermediates, continuous-tone positives, to each of the several plants where supplements are printed for a geographical area. Sets of proofs accompany the continuous-tone positives, serving as a guide for local cylinder etching and presswork. This procedure was developed in order to attain a high degree of uniformity of printed images produced in different plants. (Proofing for gravure is discussed in Chapter VI, Section 8.)

The main steps of image conversion for gravure. Image conversion for gravure includes the making of continuous-tone intermediates for photographs and wash-drawings in a single color. Paintings, water colors, color transparencies, and similar colorful images must pass through color separation and color correction, subjects discussed in Chapters III and IV. Reading matter must also be photographed if it is supplied as reproduction proofs. The products of photographing reading matter are line positives, different from the already mentioned continuous-tone positives. Depending on the kind of gravure process selected, halftone photography may or may not be needed in the image conversion of pictures. Retouching

and layout for cylinder making are two additional steps of great importance in preparation for rotogravure.

As already mentioned, rotogravure uses etched cylinders as image carriers. The making of cylinders comprises several operations. First, the base cylinder must be made. Base cylinders are usually cylinders of the required construction but without a copper-plated surface. Plating of cylinders with copper is the next step. After plating the cylinder is provided with a photomechanical resist for etching. This resist contains the images which will finally appear in intaglio on the cylinder and serve as printing images. Etching converts the copper surface of cylinders into image carriers. The etched cylinder is proofed, corrected, reproofed, and chromium plated for long production runs. All these points, including various gravure conversion methods, retouching, and gravure layout, are discussed in Chapter V, Section 4. We turn immediately to our next subject, presses for gravure.

Presses for gravure. As you know, we distinguish four branches of gravure: (1) sheet-fed, (2) rotogravure publication printing, (3) rotogravure package printing, and (4) gravure for specialty printing. Each of these branches is based on equipment differing in some respects from that used in other branches of gravure. In Chapter VI, Section 1, you find a discussion of available gravure presses with the exception of those needed in specialty printing. (Specialty printing is, as you may remember, outside the frame of this manual.) The main difference between rotogravure presses for publication printing and those for package printing is the fact that publication presses are not built to permit inserting of cylinders varying in their diameters, whereas presses for package printing can handle cylinders varying in their diameters within a given range. (A detailed description of presswork in sheet-fed, publication, and package gravure is contained in Chapter VIII, Section 3.)

Printing stocks and inks for gravure. As explained, gravure can print a wide variety of stocks, an ability that is at the root of its popularity for long-run package and newspaper supplement printing. For the printing of newspaper supplements, a stock known as rotogravure paper is available. The same or a similar paper may also be used for utility printing of publications and catalogs in rotogravure. This paper is inexpensive, and it is made with a smooth surface which contributes to the appearance of gravure-printed images. The quality of printed images is superior in rotogravure to the quality of printed images obtainable in newspaper relief printing, even though rotogravure paper is rather inexpensive. More expensive, coated papers are used for the gravure printing of high-quality magazines, cata-

logs, and many other items. As to the gravure inks, it was explained that they are quite liquid and can be formulated for successful printing of all stocks to be processed by rotogravure, including a great variety of plastic films. (Printing stocks are the subject matter of Chapter VIII, and printing inks are discussed in Chapter IX.)

Section 4:   Planographic Printing

In this manual the term "planographic printing" is used for a group of several printing methods (lithography, for example) which are all based on printing-image carriers on which the printing areas and the non-printing areas are practically in the same plane. As both kinds of areas are on the same plane, "planographic" has become established as a generic term for all methods using such image carriers.

Distinction between printing and non-printing areas in planographic printing. That printing and non-printing areas are on the same plane in planographic printing poses the problem of distinguishing between them in the formation of the ink image. Immediately the question comes to mind, how it is possible to apply printing ink to the image areas without at the same time applying it also to the non-image areas if both are on the same level. The answer to this question is based on the long-known fact that grease and water do not mix readily. Printing inks for planographic printing are quite greasy, and the printing-image carrier is especially treated to make the printing areas ink receptive and the non-printing areas ink repellent, under the same conditions. In all kinds of lithographic printing the ink repellence of the non-printing areas must be refreshed by *dampening*, whereby a chemical solution containing either water alone as a solvent, or a mixture of water and an alcohol, is applied to the plate. In lithography, every printing cycle requires dampening of the plate before it can be inked. Without wanting to go into details which are discussed in several other chapters, it is merely mentioned that the non-printing areas must remain receptive for the dampening solution and repellent to the printing ink, whereas the printing areas must be ink receptive and repellent to the dampening solution under the same conditions. Not all planographic methods use dampening as part of every printing cycle. In collotype, the only exception, the plate retains its proper ink receptivity for

many hundreds of cycles, as will be found described in Chapter VII, Section 4. But all lithographic methods require dampening and inking during each printing cycle.

Four planographic methods. At present, offset lithography is the only planographic method of general importance. For the sake of completeness we present three other methods in addition, which are either not at all commercially important or of very limited importance. This section is, therefore, divided into four units presenting brief discussion of four planographic methods which are: (1) stone lithography, (2) direct lithography, (3) offset lithography, and (4) collotype. But the emphasis of the following discussion is on offset lithography because this method dominates the field of planographic printing.

Stone Lithography

Stone lithography is the original form of lithography. In our own time and in the United States it is completely obsolete as an industrial printing method. In this country, stone lithography has become a fine-art printing method used exclusively for artists' printmaking in limited quantities. But in Europe and on other continents, stone lithography is still used to some degree for commercial purposes.

If you are aware that the original meaning of lithography was *stone writing* or reproduction by means of graphically treated stones, you may object to "stone lithography" as a redundant expression. But words change their meaning. In our time, stones are not used any more as image carriers in lithography, nor are people generally aware that the word stone is part of the word "lithography." For this reason, the term "stone lithography" is a sensible and practical designation for the only existing planographic method that still uses stones as image carriers.

As stone lithography has ceased to exist for industrial printing and has become a fine-art printing method in the United States, our discussion of stone lithography can be very sketchy. But it should not be forgotten that stone lithography was for longer than a hundred years more or less identical with lithographic printing, and that this method is of great historical interest.[12]

Fine-art lithography is based on manually made image carriers. The artist prepares the printing image either directly on the stone or on a lithographic transfer paper by drawing, painting, spattering, or engraving. The lithographic artist works with fatty lithographic crayons and with lithographic tusche which form ink-receptive images. The stone is chemically treated to make it ink repellent in the non-printing areas and to improve its printing qualities. Printing for fine-art purposes is always done on hand presses. The stone is dampened and inked by hand and the ink image is transferred to the paper in a hand press. Fine-art lithography is capable of producing very beautiful results. Lithography owes many of its advances to several great artists—Goya, Daumier, Menzel, Whistler, and Toulouse-Lautrec among them—who worked in this method either for self-expression or in the course of earning a living as illustrators, caricaturists, commercial and poster artists. In the flowering of stone lithography during the nineteenth century, the division between commercial and non-commercial artists was either non-existent, or where it existed it was much less rigid than in the middle of the twentieth century. A great painter would not consider it beneath his dignity to make a poster, nor would advertisers expect the kind of specialization which is characteristic for commercial art in the present time.

Direct Lithography

Direct lithography was an outgrowth of stone lithography. It was intended for faster and more efficient job-and-commercial lithography but was not successful and was superseded by offset, or indirect, lithography. In contemporary America direct lithography is rarely used, and then mainly for specialties such as labels, for example.

The name *direct lithography* was selected to distinguish this method clearly from indirect lithography, or offset lithography. In direct lithography, the ink image is directly transferred from the image carrier to the printing stock, whereas in indirect lithography the image is transferred first to the blanket and then from the blanket to the

printing stock. Direct lithography can deposit thicker ink films than indirect lithography and it may therefore be preferred for work where heavy ink films are essential. Together with direct lithography, rotary presses and metal plates were introduced into the lithographic industry which was then still tied to the heavy stones and flat-bed-cylinder presses. The reasons why direct lithography failed to become generally accepted also explain the immediate success of indirect, or offset, lithography; they are therefore briefly discussed.

Plates for direct lithography can be made by many different methods. When direct lithography was introduced plates were made mainly by hand tusching and crayoning and also by photomechanics. Albumin plates, later called surface plates, were then the only kind of plates that could be made photomechanically. In such plates the printing areas, which consist of albumin compounds, are on the surface of the plate. These areas are inked, and the ink image is directly transferred to the stock under pressure. The image-forming photomechanical coating is evidently much less robust than the image areas of relief plates on which the printing areas are of metal. The relatively frail photomechanical image is easily injured by abrasion during image transfer. Paper, apparently a rather soft material, can abrade the image areas of lithographic plates if it is strongly forced against the plate during the impression. The life expectancy of albumin plates was consequently rather short in direct lithography. In offset lithography, where image transfer is done indirectly, plate and paper do not meet, and the soft rubber blanket has no abrading effects on photomechanical, or for that matter, tusched and crayoned plates.

These limitations of direct lithography, combined with others in comparison with indirect image transfer, arrested its growth. At present it is possible to obtain long production runs in direct lithography by means of bimetallic plates on which the printing areas consist of one metal, usually copper, and the non-printing areas are formed by another metal, steel for example. But bimetallic plates did not exist at the time when direct lithography was tried and found wanting.

A detailed description of direct lithography is unnecessary for our purposes. Most of the procedures followed in offset lithography are applicable to this method as well. It might be added that direct lithographic presses are so rarely used that they are not available as standard equipment, but must be made to order.

Offset Lithography

Offset lithography is a major printing method measured by any yardstick. A large number of printers practice offset lithography and a correspondingly large number of craftsmen are employed in doing offset printing. Like letterpress, offset lithography can be classified a universal printing method because it too can produce an extremely wide range of products. These include practically all kinds of printed items; among them are advertising and sales promotion material, forms for business and government, stationery, premium stamps, labels, decalcomanias, maps, greeting cards, posters, displays, books, magazines, newspapers, package materials, and many specialties. This breadth of scope is based on great diversification of printing procedures and techniques, not to forget that of available equipment.

Lithography was originally, as you know, a picture reproduction process not suitable for the printing of reading matter in bulk. It remained in this condition for nearly a hundred years, up to the invention of photomechanical methods and the development of graphic arts photography. But direct lithographic printing put too much of a strain on printing-image carriers made by photomechanics and thereby deprived lithography of benefiting fully from these advances. When indirect, or offset, printing was introduced, this situation changed radically. Now lithography grew by leaps and bounds until it became a universal printing method, equally suited for the reproduction of reading matter and pictures.

In the past, lithographers operated integrated plants throughout, but at present conditions are somewhat different. Many offset printers do their own camera work and platemaking; but there are also those who neither maintain their own camera departments nor have platemaking facilities of their own. Such printers buy either the products of graphic arts photography (negatives or positives) or the final plates for presswork from lithographic trade shops which fulfill the same functions in the lithographic industry as do photoengravers in the letterpress industry. The importance of trade shops in the lithographic industry has been growing consistently in the more recent past. Some lithographers use the services of lithographic trade engravers for preparatory work that requires highly specialized craftsmen, particularly for color separation and color correction. Other lithographers which maintain their own color departments turn to trade shops when these departments become overloaded.

In the past, much less was known about the preparatory phases of lithography and about photomechanical platemaking. It happened quite frequently that plates needed make-over, and a lithographic shop wanted to handle such situations with a minimum of delay in its own platemaking department. At present our knowledge of platemaking is much improved, thanks to the work of the Graphic Arts Technical Foundation and to the application of science to platemaking. Even though plate troubles still occur, they are much less frequent than 20 or 30 years ago. Under these improved conditions many plants, particularly those who expand into the field of offset, find it advantageous to buy their plates from lithographic platemaking shops; frequently, the same trade shop can supply both photoengravings and lithographic plates.

Unlike letterpress, offset lithography is based on single-unit printing-image carriers and on rotary presses. Platen presses were never suitable for lithographic printing; stone lithography for job-and-commercial printing was done primarily on flatbed-cylinder presses; direct lithography introduced rotary presses, and all production presses for offset lithography are rotaries. Offset lithography can also be done with presses on which a flatbed replaces the plate cylinder and the impression cylinder. Such presses are used for proofing as well as for the production of certain specialty products. (Proof presses for offset lithography are described in Chapter VI, Section 8.)

After this general introduction to offset lithography some of the more important phases of image conversion and image transfer as practiced in this method will be briefly explained.

Image conversion for offset lithography. The standard conversion method of original images for offset lithography is based on graphic arts photography. Art-and-copy is usually prepared ready for the camera. Reading matter in bulk must be converted into standardized letterforms by composition. Often reproduction proofs of metallic composition are incorporated in the assembly of original images.

Photography, or camera work, provides intermediate transparencies, either positives or nega-

Craftsmen assemble photographic negatives for common exposure to a photopolymer or lithographic plate. The light tables are equipped with precision measuring apparatus. The assembly operation is commonly known as "stripping a flat."

tives, as needed for photomechanical platemaking. Continuous-tone originals such as wash-drawings and black-and-white photographs must be converted by means of halftone photography into printable images. Color photos or paintings to be reproduced by full-color printing need color separation and color correction as well as halftone photography. (In some methods color separation and halftone photography are done at the same time.) Besides photography, image conversion may entail a variety of manual adapting and adjusting operations such as retouching, dot-etching or color-etching, generically known as *litho-art.* The final result of this phase of image conversion is a series of photographic transparencies.

Assembling of transparencies for photomechanical platemaking. These transparencies are next assembled into a single unit which is the equivalent of the future lithographic image carrier as regards the quantity, content, and the position of the material to be printed together. The operation of assembling the material is known as *stripping;* the product of stripping is called a *flat.* As already mentioned, lithographic plates are *single-unit* or *integral* image carriers. They are in this respect similar to gravure plates and cylinders, but different from such letterpress image carriers as type, photoengravings, and duplicate plates which are multiple-unit image carriers. Wrap-around plates, on the other hand, which comprise shallow-etched metal relief plates, Dycril plates, and Kodak

Photo Relief plates, are single-unit plates for letterpress.

At this point it is worth emphasizing that all image carriers combining a number of units for common presswork require assembling at some point; in certain printing methods of relief printing this assembly is done on the press causing expensive press down-time. In lithography, the assembly is done away from the press whereby press down-time caused by assembling is eliminated. (A description of stripping for offset lithographic platemaking is provided in Chapter V, Section 5.)

Seven kinds of lithographic plates. The assembled material is converted by photomechanics and subsidiary processes into a lithographic press plate. Lithography has a variety of plates at its disposal. These can be divided into the following seven types: (1) albumin plates, (2) presensitized plates, (3) wipe-on plates, (4) deep-etch plates, (5) bimetallic plates, (6) direct-image plates, and (7) electrostatic plates. The first five kinds are used in commercial lithography; the sixth, direct-image plates, and the seventh, electrostatic plates, are mainly used for office duplicating. But these divisions are not exclusive; presensitized surface plates are also used for office duplicating and direct-image plates can have a place in the lithographic business. (Descriptions of different plates, and the method by which they are made, will be found in Chapter V, Section 5, "Planographic Printing-Image Carriers." In that section you find a much more detailed discussion of offset plates and a more technical classification.) The costs of plates vary and so do their life expectancies. It is merely mentioned that direct-image plates are not used for longer runs than several thousands; some presensitized plates are good for medium-length runs in the high ten thousands; other presensitized plates, wipe-on plates, and deep-etch plates can be used for longer runs, say, in the hundred thousands; bimetallic plates, finally, are capable of yielding several millions of impressions.

These figures are included for the sole purpose of conveying to you approximate differences in the range of plate wearing qualities; but these figures must not be mistaken for standard data and uncritically applied to individual jobs. In actual practice everything depends on the nature of a job and on its detail, and every job must be individually evaluated on its own merits.

Lithographic presses and presswork. The lithographic industry has a wide choice of standard-size presses. Offset presses are made for the printing of sheets and for the printing of webs. Sheet-fed presses come in many different sizes and for the printing of a varying number of colors in one trip through the press. Some presses can print both sides of the sheet in one operation either in a single color, or in two and more colors per side.

Web offset presses are widely used for job-and-commercial printing and for many other purposes. These presses run much faster than sheet-fed ones and offer many advantages in long-run printing. One of the advantages is that web offset presses can deliver a variety of folded signatures thereby saving time and labor which are needed when folding is done off the press as a separate operation.

The discussion of available equipment for offset lithography can be rather brief because the subject is treated extensively in Chapter VI, "Printing Presses." In Section 1 of that chapter you find a survey of sheet-fed and web-offset presses, indicating available standard sizes, number of colors, and operating speeds. Offset lithographic presswork is the subject matter of Chapter VII, Section 4. In that section the main considerations applying to lithographic presswork are analyzed; presswork on sheet-fed and web-offset presses is there explained and described.

Ink and paper for offset lithography. Offset lithography is capable of using a wide variety of printing papers and other stocks including paper boards, metal foils, binder's cloth, and many other materials. Coarse or purposely structured papers can be remarkably well printed in offset lithography, thanks to the resilient nature of the blanket; coated papers and paper boards are

Courtesy American Type Founders Company, Inc.

An ATF web offset publication press. In the foreground is the roll-feeding equipment including a flying paster, then come five blanket-to-blanket perfecting units which print both sides of the paper web simultaneously. The drier, the chill rolls, and the folder of this press are out of sight.

widely used for full-color jobs. When speaking of paper, you do well to remember that lithography is a chemical printing method and that the paper must be endowed with several characteristics, just as it must be free of certain others, to be usable for lithographing. The moisture content and the acidity of printing papers, coated ones especially, are only two examples of the many points that must be checked for trouble-free lithographic printing. (Further information on paper and other printing stocks is provided in Chapter VIII.)

The demands put upon lithographic inks are rather unusual. As the plate is dampened at every printing cycle, lithographic inks must be formulated for permanent coexistence with moisture. Pigments that are partly soluble in the fountain solution must be avoided because such pigments would leave traces of their colors in the non-printing areas which are supposed to remain un-inked. This is of course only one of many points of importance for the performance of lithographic inks on the press. (More information about lithographic inks can be found in Chapter IX, "Printing Inks.")

Offset lithographic printing deposits a relatively thin film of ink on the printing stock. This is understandable if we remember that there are two ink transfers in offset printing—one from the plate to the blanket, the other from the blanket to the stock—and that the ink film is split at every transfer. Lithographic inks must make up in pigment concentration for the thinness of the printed ink film wherever opacity is wanted. When a very high degree of transparency is essential, the lithographic offset method is also capable of excellent results, as is proved by innumerable lithographic full-color reproductions.

Collotype

Collotype, also known as *photogelatin*, is the oldest planographic printing method completely based on photomechanics. Collotype is not very widely used in the United States—here much less than in Europe—but it is a most interesting printing method that should be known to every student of the graphic arts.

The most distinctive technical feature of collotype is that it is capable of reproducing continuous-tone images without halftone photography. Collotype has two separate fields of application which are, surprisingly, at opposite ends of the quality scale. On one end, collotype is used for the reproduction of paintings and other fine-art subjects which require highest quality and utmost fidelity. On the other, it serves for the printing of large-size posters, particularly those used in the lobbies of motion picture theaters, where the quality requirements are not too high.

Collotype is done by direct printing. The image carrier is a metal or glass sheet coated with a formula of bichromated gelatin suitable for photomechanical image formation. In the United States, there are no presses manufactured for collotype printing; the market is so small that the development of specific collotype presses would not pay. Most of our now existing collotype presses are adaptations of either flatbed-cylinder or rotary direct lithographic presses. Rotary collotype was introduced in this country, whereas European collotype printers used flatbed-cylinder presses, not capable of the same production as is possible on rotary presses. (Readers interested in collotype plates will find the subject discussed in Chapter V, Section 5; presswork on rotary collotype presses is described in Chapter VII, Section 4.)

Section 5:   Porous Printing

The dominant method of porous printing is screen-process printing which is also known as "silk screen" in the trade. Screen-process printing, at least in its contemporary form, is the youngest of all printing arts. It poses several terminological difficulties which are best explained immediately.

Two meanings of the term "screen." Many people are confused by the word *screen* which they know as halftone-screen but not in the sense in which the word is employed in screen process.

The screen in screen-process printing is a cloth tautly stretched and attached to a frame; a thus prepared frame serves as the printing-image carrier of this printing method. Cloth for making screen-process screens has a large number of very small orifices, or pores. The printing image is brought about by blocking some of these pores and by leaving others unobstructed, all this in accordance with the design to be reproduced. For printing, the stock is placed under the printing-image carrier, and the ink is pressed through the unblocked orifices of the image carrier onto the printing stock where it forms the printed image.

The reason for selecting "porous" as generic term. Up to now we have no generally accepted technical designation for the principle on which screen-process printing is based. Suggested were *mitography, trans-printing, foraminous* printing (a term used in the patent literature for describing a cloth having many very small orifices) and also *porous printing.* As the word porous seems to indicate the basic feature of the image carrier of this process family more simply and less confusingly than other terms, this word was selected for generic characterization; porous printing is consequently the name of the fourth printing process in this manual. Porous printing can be executed in several ways. One of them, *mimeographing,* is outside our discussion because mimeographing is not used for printing but for office duplicating; *screen-process* printing and *serigraphy* are the two methods of porous printing which are here briefly characterized.

Screen-Process Printing

Screen process is as much a decorating process as it is a printing method. It is primarily a picture printing method, used for displays, greeting cards, decalcomanias, banners; metal, glass, and plastic signs; printed circuits, fabrics, and other textiles; wall paper and many other items. The screen is the printing-image carrier of screen process. In the past, screens used in job-and-commercial screen-process shops were made almost exclusively of silk, hence the name silk screen. During the last decade stencil cloths woven of synthetic fibers and of various metals have found increasing uses instead of cloth woven of natural silk.

The difference between stenciling and screen process. The name "stencil printing" is not as descriptive of screen process as is sometimes assumed. Most people think of stenciling in terms of the crude markings which can be seen on shipping containers. These markings are stigmatized by the fact that such letters as the "O" and the "B" are partly disfigured because their centers must be connected by "bridges" or "ties" to the body of the stencil. Disregarding the method by which stencils are made, they—and the images stenciled with them—remain always hampered by these ubiquitous connectors that restrict the scope of stenciling severely. So uninviting is the term "stenciling" that some people in the stenciling

Courtesy M & M Displays, Philadelphia

Operator feeding a large sheet of paper on a flatbed screen-process press. To the left is the infeed of a custom built drying oven with conveyor belt.

business prefer to call their work *pochoir* printing; pochoir being the French word for stencil and carrying, like many other French words, a high degree of prestige, particularly with those who do not know its meaning.

Screen process overcomes the limitations of stenciling by an ingenious, entirely different technique. In screen process a porous printing-image carrier is combined with stencils made by various methods. The porous screen provides the necessary support for all unconnected stencil areas, thereby eliminating all connectors and design restriction due to them. For this reason it is not correct, or if you prefer advisable, to name screen process "stenciling" and thereby to associate this printing method with the crude images which are in the mind of the public the results of stenciling.

Some characteristic points of screen process. Screen process is distinguished by several technical characteristics. Of these the following six are mentioned: (1) Screen process is the only printing method in which hand printing is still found practical and where hand printing is used side-by-side with printing on mechanical presses. (2) Screen process achieves image transfer with exceptionally low printing pressure. (3) Inking is done in screen process as part of image transfer whereas in other printing methods inking precedes the act of image transfer. (4) The inking apparatus is not only of the simplest, it is also part of the image carrier, whereas other printing methods require more or less complex independent inking systems. (5) The printed ink film can be extremely thick; it is normally much thicker than ink films in letterpress and offset lithography. (6) In consequence of the heavy ink films, screen-process printing requires individual drying of printed sheets before they can be piled.

The thickness of the ink film can be a most important appearance characteristic of screen process; screen-process prints show exceptionally strong colors. It is even possible to print enamels and to evoke the effects of embossed images by screen process.

Image conversion for screen-process printing. Screen process is primarily a picture printing and decorating method. It is not a method for reproduction of reading matter in bulk, as needed in the printing of books and newspapers; but screen process can reproduce lettering, and even small type, surprisingly well. Though it is limited in its ability to print very fine halftone images, full-color reproductions are at present successfully done by the better practitioners of screen process in many cities. Traditionally, screen-process printing is a most effective reproduction medium for artwork using line designs in conjunction with bold color areas, particularly in multicolor jobs.

It is not surprising, under these conditions, that photography is not the exclusive method of image conversion for screen process. Very often multicolor artwork, if prepared final size, can be best separated by manual techniques into the required color separations. A widely used manual method for making screen-process image carriers is the knife-cut film method. Photomechanical methods, of which there are many to choose from, are known by the names of their materials or their manufacturers, for example, as the carbon-tissue method, the Eastman Kodak Ektagraph Process, or the Dupont Rotofilm Process, to mention some of the more widely known ones. (Various stencil-making methods for screen process are described in Chapter V, Section 6.)

Screen-process image carriers are of the single-unit, or integral kind; the material to be present in the final image carrier must be either assembled

prior to its application to the screen or as part of the operation whereby the screen is made. But once the material is *adhered to the screen*—as the trade calls this operation—individual images cannot be moved any more. A completed screen resembles in this respect other single-unit, or integral, image carriers.

Printing equipment and presswork for screen-process printing. Screen process uses an exceptional variety of printing equipment. The great diversification of screen-process applications is paralleled by an equal diversification of equipment. A few examples will illustrate this point. Shower curtains and large loaves of Swiss cheese can both be decorated in screen process, but obviously not with the same equipment; nor is it possible to imprint medical ampules and thirty-gallon oil drums in the same way. These examples are only a few of the many possible ones. As a discussion of such highly specialized equipment is outside the design of our manual, its description must be omitted.

Screen-process printing can be done as sheet-fed and as web printing. Web printing is used for screen printing of fabrics, shower curtains, and wallpapers, which are all classified as specialty printing and hence outside the frame of this manual. Sheet-fed printing is done on hand presses, flatbed presses, and cylinder presses. Flatbed presses and cylinder presses are power-driven machines, manufactured in different sizes by several press builders. A survey of screen-process presses is included in Chapter VI, Section 1; drying equipment for all printing methods, including screen process, is the subject matter of Chapter VI, Section 7; and presswork for screen process is described in Section 5 of Chapter VII.

Printing inks and stocks for screen process. Since screen process is used for the printing of a wide range of materials, and since these materials differ in the kind of inks needed to meet specifications, the supplier of inks for screen process must be prepared to develop new inks to keep up with the new products to be screen printed. It must be added that not every kind of ink is usable with every kind of image carrier. Some inks must contain certain solvents or other ingredients in order to be fit for the printing on certain plastics, such as vinyls, to mention one kind. But these inks may not be compatible with the material used in the making of an image carrier, for example with knife-cut films made of cellulose esters. Inks of varying composition are, in addition, a necessity for appearance reasons. Screen process can vary the thickness of the printed ink film within rather wide limits. In some cases, very heavy layers of ink are desired, for example, in the printing of daylight fluorescent materials; but where overprinting of transparent inks is used for the obtaining of additional color effects or for strong, luminous colors by printing on cast-coated stock (explained in Chapter VIII) relatively thin ink layers are a necessity. Thinner ink films are also desirable because they dry faster. As to printing stocks, screen process is almost without limitation in its ability to handle flat material. Among stocks for screen process are papers and paper boards, sheets of plastic, metal foils, sheet metal, glass, fiberboard, and wood. (Printing stocks are the subject matter of Chapter VIII, printing inks are discussed in Chapter IX.)

Serigraphy

Serigraphy is the fine-art printing variant of porous printing. In our listing it follows screen process because it followed it historically, thereby differing from other fine-art picture printing methods which preceded industrial applications based on the same principle. Serigraphy serves for artistic self-expression, like all other fine-art

printing methods, and has become widely used for printmaking by artists. In many ways commercial screen process and its fine-art relative, serigraphy, operate on the same technical basis, as both may use handmade image carriers and hand printing. The differences between the two are not so much in their methods and in their equipment as in their finished products.

Some artists use the knife-cut film method for the making of serigraphic screens, but many prefer a different technique which can be executed with the familiar artists' brushes rather than with the strange film-cutting knives. This technique is known as the *tusche* method. But the tusche method is not exclusive with serigraphy; in some cases it is also used for commercial work.

Serigraphy is not only an American term, coined in 1944 by Mr. Carl Zigrosser, Curator of Print at the Philadelphia Museum of Art, but also a distinctly American contribution to fine-art printing. It may be interesting that the first books printed completely by serigraphy were limited editions in the true sense of the word, created by the French artist, André Girard, who printed them himself in the United States. Serigraphy has spread to Europe and to Asia from this country and enjoys a steady growth all over the world.[13]

Section 6:   The Main Stages of Printing Production

In the preceding sections you were introduced to more than a dozen different printing methods. In this section we will try to connect them and to show how the various functions common to all printing can be related, process by process and method by method, to one another. This is particularly important since the following chapters of the manual are not organized according to different processes but according to functions common to all kinds of printing.

The four major divisions of printing production. All printing production can be divided into four major divisions: the first is art-and-copy preparation, the second is the conversion of art-and-copy into printing-image carriers, the third consists in presswork, and the fourth in binding and other finishing.

Art-and-copy preparation provides the subject matter of printing or, to say it in other words, the original images to be reproduced. The conversion of original images results in printing-image car-

riers of various kinds, specifically in such image carriers as are needed for the production of the job in hand. Presswork is the image-transfer stage of printing. During presswork the image carrier is inked and an ink image is formed on, in, or through the printing areas of image carriers. The preposition "on" refers to relief and planographic, the preposition "in" to intaglio, and the preposition "through" to porous image carriers. Presswork provides the printed image which is the final object of all printing production. Binding and other finishing operations turn the printed sheet or web into such physical shapes as are needed for the end use of the final product.

Each of these four main divisions can be the field of activity for an independent business or for a department within a printing organization. Some of them are best subdivided into a number of different major production stages for a comparative study of various printing processes and methods.

Table II

THE TWELVE MAIN STAGES

Stage	*Specialists Concerned*	*Purpose of Stage*
STAGE 1 *Art-and-Copy Preparation*	Advertising, marketing, sales, and public relations executives; airbrush artists, art directors, book designers, commercial artists, copy writers, display designers, paste-up men, photographers, printing buyers, typographers. For consultation: binders, mounters, and finishers, paper salesmen, photoengravers, printing salesmen, printing production men.	Determining the purpose, contents, and appearance of item to be printed.
STAGE 2 *Composition*	Hand compositors, layout men, lockup men, makeup men; operators of Linotypes, Intertypes, Ludlows, Monotype keyboards, Monotype casters, photographic composing machines; programmers for computerized composition, proofers, TTS perforators, typists for typewriter-like composition, typists for preparing copy for computerized composition, typographers.	Conversion of reading matter into standardized letter forms and assembling of composed matter as required.
STAGE 3 *Graphic Arts Photography*	Camera men, color-correction specialists; color-separation, halftone, and line photographers; operators of electronic color-separation and color-correction equipment; photographic chemists, engineers, and technicians.	Conversion of continuous-tone and full-color original images into printable images providing transparencies of all kinds of original images including type and line drawings for photomechanical making of image carriers.
STAGE 4 *Dot-Etching, Opaquing and Retouching*	Camera men, color-etchers (or dot-etchers) opaquers, photographic technicians, retouchers, air-brush artists.	Adapting of photographic transparencies for printing method to be used and for job in hand. Correcting values of color-separation transparencies and of halftone images for single or multicolor; elimination of blemishes, flaws, and defects of transparencies.
STAGE 5 *Planning of Printing-Image Carriers*	Bindery production men, estimators, foremen of stripping departments, lay-out men, lockup men, planners, printing production men.	Most economical arrangement of pages or other units for common presswork, considering available presses and bindery equipment. This stage is not to be confused with general production planning, an administrative function.

OF PRINTING PRODUCTION

Product of Stage	Following Stage	For Explanation See
Art-and-copy as needed for reproduction; layouts and dummies.	Image conversion of original images, depending on its detail and on method selected for reproduction.	Chapter XI: *Art-and-Copy Preparation*
Product of composition can be: (1) metallic type to be used in type forms; (2) metallic type for foundry lockup; (3) reproduction proofs taken of metallic type; (4) direct-image litho plates made by proofing of type forms; (5) film negatives or positives of photographic composition; (6) paper positives or negatives of photographic composition; (7) typewriter-like composition on paper; (8) typewriter-like composition on direct-image litho plates; (9) bands of paper positives or negatives from photolettering machines.	If product is (1) presswork on platen or flatbed-cylinder presses; if product is (2) duplicate platemaking; if product is (3) art-and-copy preparation; if product is (4) presswork on offset lithographic presses; if product is (5) assembling of positives or negatives for lithographic platemaking, platemaking or cylinder making in gravure, and for making of photographic screen-process screens; if product is (6) art-and-copy preparation; if product is (7) graphic arts photography; if product is (8) lithographic presswork; if product is (9) art-and-copy preparation.	Chapter II: *Composition for Printing* Chapter V: *Printing-Image Carriers* Chapter XI: *Art-and-Copy Preparation*
Products are photographic transparencies, positives or negatives on film; type and line drawings become line transparencies, continuous-tone images and color separations become halftone images for relief, lithographic, porous printing, and some gravure methods. Conventional gravure needs continuous-tone positives; collotype, continuous-tone negatives.	Transparencies may or may not need stage No. 4. If they do not need stage No. 4; the next stage depends on their purpose; those for photoengravings pass to stage No. 8; those for wrap-around plates, lithographic plates, gravure, and porous image carriers pass next through stage No. 6.	Chapter III: *The Theory and Practice of Full-Color Printing* Chapter IV: *Graphic Arts Photography* Chapter V: *Printing-Image Carriers*
Photographic transparencies usually contact printed on film for further use.	If transparencies are needed for photoengraving the next stage is No. 8; if for single-unit printing-image carriers, next stage is No. 6.	Chapter IV: *Graphic Arts Photography* Chapter V: *Printing-Image Carriers*
Product of stage is a layout or an imposition diagram for job in hand.	If single-unit image carriers are wanted the next stage is No. 6. If assembled image carriers are wanted the next stage is No. 8.	Chapter X: *Binding and Finishing*

Table II-2

THE TWELVE MAIN STAGES

Stage	Specialists Concerned	Purpose of Stage
STAGE 6 *Stripping and Gravure Layout*	Foremen of layout or stripping departments; layout men, strippers.	Assembling of photographic intermediates (negatives or positives, halftone or continuous-tone) according to layout or to imposition for photomechanical exposure of single-unit image carriers.
STAGE 7 *The Making of Single-Unit, or Integral, Image Carriers*	Electrochemists, electroplaters, operators of mechanical engraving machines, operators of step-and-repeat machines, platemakers, setup men.	Production of single-unit printing-image carriers as needed for the actually selected printing method.
STAGE 8 *Producing Original Materials for Multiple-Unit Image Carriers*	Compositors; engravers of linoleum, wood, or rubber; operators of electromechanical engraving machines; photoengravers.	Converting of reading matter and pictures into relief image carriers.
STAGE 9 *The Making of Duplicate Plates*	Electrochemists, electrotypers, molders of rubber and plastic plates, stereotypers.	Making one or more replicas of original relief materials, as needed for a particular printing method or technique in relief printing.
STAGE 10 *Assembling of Multiple-Unit Image Carriers*	Assistant pressmen, lockup men, pressmen, stone-men or stone-hands.	Assembling of original relief material for presswork or for duplicate platemaking; assembling of duplicate plates for common presswork.
STAGE 11 *Presswork*	Assistant pressmen, feeders, helpers, off-bearers, pressmen, production supervisors, quality control supervisors, roll tenders, squeegee men, takeoff men.	Image transfer of the ink image from the image carrier to the printing stock.
STAGE 12 *Binding and Other Methods of Finishing*	Layout men, library binders; makers of high-dies, of steel-rule dies; operators of adhesive binding equipment, bronzing machines, building-in machines; case-making, casing-in machines, collators, folding machines, gatherers, guillotine cutters, inserting, jacketing equipment, laminating machines, McCain sewing machines; mounting, oversewing, pebbling, perforating machines; operators of saddle and side stitchers, Singer and Smyth sewing machines. Also, planners, pressmen, and production men.	Making the printed sheet or web suitable for its end use.

OF PRINTING PRODUCTION

Product of Stage	Following Stage	For Explanation See
Completely assembled intermediates, known in offset lithography and the making of wrap-around relief plates as a "flat," in gravure as "layout," in screen process as "setup."	Next stage is making of single-unit image carriers, stage No. 7.	Chapter V: *Printing-Image Carriers*
Products are: in relief printing, shallow-etched metal plates, Dycril, and Kodak Relief Plates; in intaglio: gravure plates and cylinders, plates for banknote printing; in planographic printing: surface, deep-etch, bimetallic, and collotype plates; in porous printing: knife-cut film and photographic screens for screen process.	Next stage is presswork, stage No. 11.	Chapter V: *Printing-Image Carriers*
Individual types, slugs of types, photoengravings, electromechanical engravings; handmade woodcuts, wood engravings, linoleum cuts, and rubber engravings.	Assembling of original materials either for presswork, stage No. 10, or for duplicate platemaking, stage No. 9.	Chapter II: *Composition for Printing* Chapter V: *Printing-Image Carriers*
Flat, flat-curved, or curved-cast electrotypes and stereotypes. Flat rubber and plastic plates which may or may not need mechanical curving.	Next stage is assembling of multiple-unit image carriers, stage No. 10.	Chapter V: *Printing-Image Carriers*
Foundry lockup; duplicate plates attached to plate bases or to plate cylinders; type forms.	Next stage is presswork, stage No. 11, if assembly is done away from the press, if assembly is done on the press, assembling is part of presswork.	Chapter II: *Composition for Printing* Chapter V: *Printing-Image Carriers* Chapter VII: *Presswork*
The completely printed sheet, signature, web, or inline fabricated product.	Next stage is usually, though not necessarily, binding and other finishing, stage No. 12.	Chapter VI: *Printing Presses* Chapter VII: *Presswork* Chapter VIII: *Paper* Chapter IX: *Printing Inks*
The products of this stage comprise the whole gamut of printed items. These cannot be enumerated as they were never catalogued. Among generally used printed products are advertising materials, banknotes, books, business forms, greeting cards, newspapers, magazines, maps, stationery, package materials, and many others.	This is the final stage of printing production. It is usually followed by delivery of the printed product to the customer or distributor.	Chapter X: *Binding and Other Methods of Finishing*

To help you in finding your bearings, this section contains a table that identifies various stages of printing production and indicates the occupational classifications, purpose, and product of each stage and the chapter, or chapters, in which it is explained in this manual. For the purpose of a comparative study, printing production is here divided into the following twelve main stages: (1) art-and-copy preparation, (2) composition for printing, (3) graphic arts photography, (4) dot-etching, opaquing, and retouching, (5) planning of printing-image carriers, (6) stripping and gravure layout, (7) the making of single-unit, or integral, image carriers, (8) producing of original materials for multiple-unit image carriers, (9) making of duplicate plates, (10) assembling of multiple-unit image carriers, (11) presswork, and (12) binding and other methods of finishing. It must be understood that not each printing job passes through every one of these twelve stages, but you will certainly find it useful, and possibly indispensable, to know each of them. To make the consulting of this table more easy for you, each stage is numbered and in the following briefly identified.

Stage 1: Art-and-copy preparation. Art-and-copy preparation provides the subject matter of graphic reproduction and is therefore a required stage in all kinds of printing. The preparation of art-and-copy must be undertaken with a view to the method in which a specific job will be produced. Wherever possible, art-and-copy should be prepared considering equipment and procedures of the printing plant where the job will actually be produced. Even though we speak of art-and-copy as a unit, it must not be forgotten that reading matter on the one hand, and pictures on the other, are converted into printable form by very different procedures.

Art-and-copy preparation stands at the inception of a printing job. But the subject cannot be understood without some knowledge of printing methods and materials, as well as of binding and finishing. Therefore it is not presented at the beginning of our manual but is the last chapter, following explanations of all other stages of printing production. Art-and-copy preparation is the theme of Chapter XI.

Stage 2: Composition for printing. Composition converts reading matter into standardized letter forms; it may be used for one of the following three purposes: (1) to provide physical type that can be used directly in the press; (2) to provide

type images that can be combined with original pictures or with pictures converted into transparencies, for further conversion; and (3) to provide physical type for the making of duplicate plates which are used as image carriers in such relief printing methods as letterpress, newspaper relief printing, and flexography. If composition is used for the conversion of reading matter into type images, it can be considered as a step of art-and-copy preparation; otherwise it is a stage in the conversion of original images into printing-image carriers. Composition is explained in Chapter II.

Stage 3: Graphic arts photography. Graphic arts photography is needed to provide the necessary transparencies for photomechanical image-carrier production. It is also needed for converting continuous-tone and full-color originals into halftones and color separations. Line pictures and type images are not changed in their detail by graphic arts photography; for such images, photography has the purpose of providing trans-

Courtesy The Beck Engraving Company

The copy board of a color separation camera. The artwork to be subjected to color separation photography is attached to this board when it is in a horizontal position. Then the board is swung up to make the copy face the camera lens. The camera is built into the darkroom, its optics can be seen in the rear.

parencies, negatives or positives on film, as needed for photomechanics.

Transparencies for photomechanical processing can be made on glass plates, plastic films, and possibly on transparent or translucent papers. If they have the same distribution of light and dark as the original images, photographic transparencies are known as *positives;* if these relations are reversed they are called *negatives.* Almost all industrial picture printing methods need these operations which are the subject matter of Chapter III and Chapter IV.

Stage 4: Dot-etching, opaquing, and retouching. Each printing method has its own image conversion problems. Some of these must be considered in the preparation of photographic intermediates. Transparencies may, consequently, need a smaller or larger amount of work, consisting in various treatments, before they are properly adapted to the needs of a specific image conversion method and can be used for successive steps.

The operations by which transparencies can be adapted for further processing are known as retouching, dot-etching, and opaquing if they are done by graphic arts photographers. In actual shop practice, manual and photographic methods are usually combined. Dot-etching, opaquing, and retouching as well as photographic masking are explained in Chapters III, IV, and V.

Stage 5: Planning of printing-image carriers. The planning of printing-image carriers should not be confused with general planning. General planning is an administrative function that manifests itself in all stages of printing production and is therefore not specifically listed. (You find several examples of general planning in Chapter VII at the discussions of presswork in various printing methods.) The planning of printing-image carriers is a highly technical stage of printing production in which it is decided how many units are combined in the running of a given job.

Most printing jobs are done by combining several, and often many, units for a common press run. For the purpose of effective combination, the printing-image carrier must be properly planned as to the number of units and as to their exact position. The individual units are pages in the printing of booklets, magazines, newspapers, and books. But individual units can also be displays, folding paper boxes, labels, posters, and stock certificates, to mention just a few examples.

The arrangement of units for common presswork is either known as the imposition or as the

A high-skilled craftsman at work in changing and combining parts of electrotypes. Electrotypes can be cut apart, cropped, changed and interchanged as the job may require. This flexibility is a great advantage of single-unit plates in letterpress.

layout of a given job. Letterpress printers, lithographers, and binders traditionally use the term "imposition"; in gravure and screen process both layout and imposition are current. As the available folding equipment controls the imposition of pages just as finishing equipment may control the arrangement of units other than pages, the planning of image carriers is set forth in Chapter X.

Stage 6: Stripping. Stripping is the operation whereby photographic transparencies, negatives or positives, are assembled for photomechanical exposure in the making of single-unit image carriers. The image carrier may be a flat plate or a cylinder. Even though photomechanics is the most frequently used method, some single-unit, or integral, image carriers can also be made manually, by the knife-cut film method for screen process and by hand tusching of lithographic plates. But hand tusching has become an extremely rare technique, and practically all lithographic plates as well as shallow-etched relief plates, Dycril photopolymer plates, and Kodak Relief Plates are made by stripping. In lithography stripped assemblies of transparencies are called *flats.* Thin relief plates are based on similar manufacturing techniques and have expanded the use of this term. (The word "flat" is also used in photoengraving but with a different meaning.) Stripping techniques are discussed in Chapter V.

Stage 7: The making of single-unit printing-image carriers. The product of the preceding stage, a stripped flat, is used in the making of single-unit image carriers which are produced by means of photomechanics. (Image carriers made with knife-cut film and used in screen process exclusively are the main exception. Practically all other single-unit image carriers are made photomechanically.) Photomechanics may or may not be followed by other closely related steps such as etching, depending on the kind of image carrier in question. Some single-unit carriers, especially plates and cylinders for intaglio methods, may be chromium plated to extend their life expectancy.

At the time of writing, single-unit image carriers are less widely used in relief printing than in the other three process families. But things are in a state of flux in the letterpress industry, and single-unit image carriers may achieve much greater importance in the foreseeable future. Either kind of image carriers, single-unit as well as multiple-unit ones, has certain congenital advantages and disadvantages. The main advantage of single-unit image carriers is that they can be put on the press without much delay and that the press can be started running more or less immediately thereafter, avoiding the long press down-times incurred with multiple-unit image carriers. This relative immediacy in change-overs from one job to another is called in the trade "fast get-away."

A disadvantage of single-unit image carriers is that they do not permit exchange of individual parts, pages for example, and that they must be made more perfect than assembled image carriers where individual units can be adjusted. At present the trend is clearly toward integral image carriers in the American printing industry. The making of image carriers is the subject matter of Chapter V.

Stage 8: Producing original materials for multiple-unit image carriers. Assembled image carriers consisting of many different units (classified in this manual as multiple-unit image carriers) are mainly found in relief printing. The original material can be of a great variety, including individual type characters, slugs of type, and possibly even type made of wood (which is used in larger sizes only), photoengravings, electronic engravings, image carriers made by hand engraving of linoleum, metal, rubber, and wood. Some original materials can be used in the press only; others, and these include type, photoengravings, and electronic engravings, are assembled especially for the making of duplicate plates. Original materials are discussed in Chapters II and V.

Stage 9: The making of duplicate plates. Duplicate plates are of four kinds: stereotypes, electrotypes, rubber plates, and plastic plates. All duplicate plates are made from original relief printing-image carriers; the four different kinds are all needed in relief printing though for different purposes. The making of duplicate plates is described in Chapter V.

Stage 10: Assembling of multiple-unit image carriers. This production step is primarily needed in relief printing. Multiple-unit image carriers may consist of original materials or of duplicate plates. Under certain conditions it is found practical to combine original materials with duplicate plates for common presswork. Assemblies of original material are known as type forms and cannot be used on rotary presses because type forms cannot be curved. Duplicate plates may be either flat or curved. Flat duplicate plates can be used on presses with a flatbed whereas rotary presses require curved image carriers.

Various branches of relief printing use different duplicate plates. Newspaper relief-printing is predominantly done with curved-cast stereotypes; flexographic printing is based on flat molded plates of synthetic or natural rubber; rotary letterpress printing is done with curved electrotypes, possibly also with rubber or plastic plates. Type forms may contain duplicate plates in combination with original materials, and forms on plate bases may contain various kinds of duplicate plates in combination. The only relief-printing method that is based on single-unit image carriers exclusively is indirect relief, or letterset printing, which uses wrap-around plates. The assembling of type forms is discussed in Chapter II, that of image carriers for rotary letterpress, newspaper relief, and flexographic printing in Chapter VII.

Stage 11: Presswork. Presswork produces the printed image which is the real object of all graphic arts production; presswork is therefore a most important stage in every printing method. Presswork for all printing processes and methods is extensively discussed in Chapter VII; every discussion of presswork must be related to printing inks, which form ink images and printed images, and to paper or other stocks on which these images are deposited. Chapter VIII is devoted to a discussion of paper and other stocks, Chapter IX to printing inks.[14]

The Smyth casing-in machine at the left combines books with their cases. The cased-in books slide down a chute, are inspected by an operator, put back on the conveyor, and moved into the building-in machine at the right. There they are pressed and dried between heated clamps. The built-in books are discharged to another conveyor and travel to the inspection table in the rear. After inspection, books are ready for packing and shipping.

Stage 12: Binding and other methods of finishing. The printed material may need a long series of production steps before it becomes suitable for its end use. These steps consist often in the binding of paper-covered or of hard-covered books; they may include surface treatments such as varnishing or laminating with plastics, and a variety of finishing procedures known as die-cutting, embossing, mounting, stringing, pebbling, deckling, and so on. The most important binding and finishing operations are presented in Chapter X.[15]

Electrostatic Printing

The outstanding success of xerography in photocopying and the great strides made in electrophotography have inspired many graphic arts scientists to explore the possibilities of electrostatics in the printing industry. For this reason an introduction to the subject is offered here. It is pointed out that electrostatics is a highly active field, that a great deal of work is in process, and that this introduction is elementary by necessity. Space limitations required the placing of supporting material in the notes which should be consulted by interested readers.[16]

Electrostatic printing is based on the long known fact that particles of the same electrical charge repel each other whereas particles of different charges attract each other. This fact was at the root of the earliest patent by Huebner, in 1931, who wanted to transfer conventional ink from any image carrier to the paper by moving it out-of-contact with the image carrier through an electrostatic field. This approach was not industrially successful.[17] At present the Gravure Research Institute has revived electrostatic ink transfer as an auxiliary to ink transfer under pressure.[18] Image transfer without pressure (in contact or out-of-contact with the image carrier) is a unique feature of electrostatic printing accounting for the printing of many objects that cannot withstand pressure by electrostatic stencil printing.[19]

The decisive turn in electrostatic printing was made by Carlson's invention, patented in 1944, expanded and refined by Battelle Memorial Institute, which made dry photocopying and printing practical and created a whole new industry.[20]

Carlson and Battelle created electrophotography and therewith changed electrostatics fundamentally. What appeared merely as a possibility of image transfer without pressure before this work became now a method for image creation as well. *Electrophotography* or *xerography* is based on the photoelectric properties of certain materials. (Photoelectric materials change their electric conductivity under the influence of light.) If a xerographic surface is charged and then exposed to light the areas hit by the light lose their charge whereas the non-illuminated areas retain it. The result of exposure is an invisible latent photoelectric image. This image is made visible by treating the exposed surface with a medium containing colorants whose particles have the opposite electric charge. Generally speaking, photoelectric receptors are negatively charged, colorant particles have a positive charge.[21] Even though several materials can be used as photo receptors only two will be discussed here, as this discussion is limited to Xerox photocopying and to electrophotography on paper.

In *Xerox photocopying equipment* the photoelectric material is a thin layer of selenium on a conductive plate or drum. This plate is first electrically charged, then exposed, and the resulting invisible, latent, image is made visible by development with a dry powder containing a silica base coated with plastic combined with a colorant, carbon black, for example. The developer has a positive charge and adheres to the latent image which has a negative charge. Since the selenium plate or drum is part of the equipment, the developed image is transferred to paper, and because the dry particles can be easily displaced, the plastic coated powder is fused to the paper by heat or solvent vapor treatment.[22]

The substrate material for *electrophotography on paper*, as practiced in the RCA Electrofax Process and others, is coated with a formula containing dye-sensitized zinc oxide in a resin binder. (Zinc oxide coating can also be applied to other material than paper.) Electrofax or other zinc oxide paper must also be charged prior to exposure, exposed, and developed. But as the visible image remains on the material, no transfer is required. Development was originally done with a magnetic brush, as described in Chapter V, Section 3; a more modern method is liquid development. Liquid electrostatic developers

The electrostatic five-color map printing machine, engineered and built for the Army Engineer Geodesy, Mapping Research and Development Agency by Harris-Intertype.

are dispersions of toners in organic solvents of the required characteristics; "control and fixing agents are part of such developers; the first regulate the electric charge of the toner particles, the second bond the toner image to the support."[23] Development is done by dipping or spraying. The negatively charged unexposed areas attract the positively charged pigment particles.[24] Liquid development is used in the five-color map printing press and in the Remak Electrograph Process[25] for color proofing, as described in Chapter VI, Section 1. (To avoid confusion, it is emphasized that such terms as developer, developing, fixer, and fixing have entirely different meanings in electrophotography than in silver halide photography.)

To sum up, electrostatic printing has not yet become an all around printing process, comparable to letterpress or offset. Existing installations of electrostatic printing fall in the class of specialty printing and are discussed in Chapter VI, Section 1 under the head "Specialty Printing." In 1946 Schaffert invented a process for quantity reproduction using an image carrier and dry powder ink in combination with xerographic image transfer. This process, *Xeroprinting*, has not been introduced in the printing industry.[26] The dividing lines between printing and photocopying get blurred by advancing photocopying technology: The Xerox 2400 can produce 2,400 copies per hour even though a single copy and a large number of copies are made by the same procedure without use of a printing-image carrier.

Chapter *II*

Composition for Printing

Composition or typesetting is the first step on the long road from the written to the printed word; composition is therefore basic for the whole graphic arts industry. Every printing process that reproduces reading matter needs composition; and as practically every process must print reading matter to some extent, the whole printing industry rests more or less completely on the foundation of composition.

The primary function of composition. Composition converts writing into printable form. It is essentially an image-conversion method. If we compare the products of handwriting with the product of composition we notice a striking difference in the images presented by these two. In handwriting, where we shape the letters as we go, every letter is a compromise between its established form, as taught to us in school, and our individual manner of rendering it. So personal is the character of our own writing that our signature is considered unique and that some people have even devised graphological systems for telling our character and predicting our acts by studying our handwriting. By composition this personal nature of our handwriting is entirely eliminated; it is now replaced with standardized letter forms which are completely impersonal. These are known as *printing types*, or simply as *types*.

Composition and typewriting. Our handwriting can be converted into types not only by composition but also by typing. But image conversion by typing is merely a cruder kind of image conversion by a simplified kind of composition. The typewriter is based on printing types; its very name is a combination of type and writing. The develop-

ment of the typewriter took place in the second half of the nineteenth century and runs almost parallel with that of composing machines. In our time, evolution is about to make a full circle; now the typewriter is becoming an important factor in non-metallic composition, as you will see later in this chapter.

Types are images first and physical objects second. Types were for many centuries physical objects for the printer, and people who still adhere to this tradition may object to seeing types considered in terms of images rather than things. Yet general usage did not restrict, even in the past, the meaning of type to physical objects, but applied this word equally to type images. In the present time when metal types have lost their exclusive position, and where the conversion of reading matter into printable images can be achieved in many different ways, it is indicated to think of types in terms of images first, and secondly of their physical properties.

Diversification of contemporary types. Another important change is worth noting at this point. It is the growth of the trade composition business. This business is an economic necessity caused by the enormous diversification of types in our time. In past centuries the number of available type faces and sizes was quite small compared with that now existing and offered for choice. But even then the average printer could not afford more than a few faces each in a few sizes.

In our times, no single printing plant, not to speak of a small print shop, can afford a full stock of all available types. Nor would any printer or individual plant have sufficient demands for each of

*Some Stages in the
making of Foundry Type at*
AMERICAN
TYPE FOUNDERS

1 *Letterforms for a new type face are drawn by the designer. Here an ATF staff designer inks final version of an open face alphabet.*

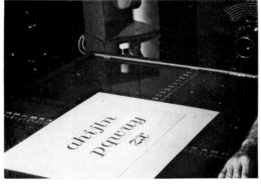

2 *Original designs are photographed and negatives used to make pattern plates.*

3 *Complete set of pattern plates for ATF Century Nova.*

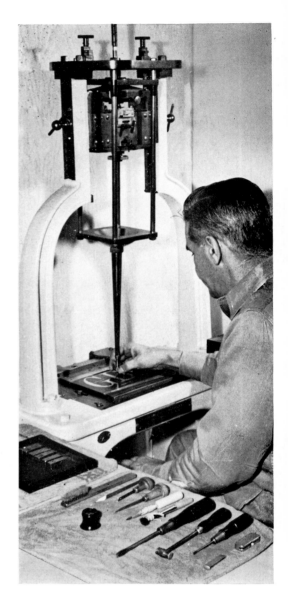

4 *Matrix for each letterform in every size required is engraved by skilled craftsmen on the Benton engraving machine. Blank matrix in holder is mounted in head of machine, and proper cutting tool inserted (some finishing tools used by ATF have cutting faces as small as .0015"). The pattern plate is mounted at the base of the engraving machine. Each movement of the follower within the pattern produces a corresponding— but greatly reduced—movement of the cutting tool on the matrix. The unique head on the Benton machine is adjustable to provide the necessary slight variations for the optical and mechanical requirements of each type face size.*

names are sometimes confusing because rather similar type faces are differently named by different manufacturers, and also because different manufacturers make under the same names their own versions of several basic designs which are in general demand. *Bodoni* and *Baskerville*, for example, are two type faces made by several companies. If a specific version of these faces is meant it is, therefore, always specified which manufacturer's Bodoni or Baskerville is wanted.[3]

If you look closer at certain type faces you will find a considerable similarity between type designs which are offered by several manufacturers under different names. For this and other practical reasons, type experts like to classify type faces into a small number of groups. As there are no objective standards for the grouping of type designs, and as the experts differ on what is essential and what not, this subject is rather controversial. We have no reason to participate in this discussion, and simply follow the PIA *Composition Manual* because it is recognized as authoritative in the printing industry of the United States.[4]

Type families. Types differ not only from design to design; they are also made in many variations within the same basic design. These variations comprise a *type family*. Variations within type families can be in the proportions of the type size or character width as well as in the relative weight, or blackness, of the letters. Variations in character width are indicated by adding such descriptive adjectives as *extra-condensed*, *condensed*, and *expanded* to the name of the type face; variations in weight are indicated by adding *light*, *medium*, *heavy*, *bold*, or *black*. Various width groups often are available in various weights. All this is not restricted to roman type but also carried through, more or less completely, in the corresponding italic versions. Type families can indeed be rather large ones and might, perhaps, better be called "clans."

Type series. Most types are made in series, or a more or less wide range of different sizes. Type series often begin with a 6-point size and go up to 36 point. (The meaning of the term "point" is explained in the following section under the head of the "American Point System.") But many types are also available in smaller and in much larger sizes, such as 48, 72, or even 96 point. Type can be bought still larger, up to 2 inches high, but these exceptionally large sizes are usually made of wood rather than metal. It should be understood that not all type faces are available in all sizes. The

Record Gothic
Record Gothic Extended
Record Gothic Extended Italic
Record Gothic Condensed
Record Gothic Condensed Italic
Record Gothic Extra Condensed
Record Gothic Medium-Extended
Record Gothic Bold
Record Gothic Bold Italic
Record Gothic Bold Extended
Record Gothic Bold Extended Italic
Record Gothic Bold Medium-Extended
Record Gothic Thinline Condensed

Courtesy Ludlow Typograph Company

A large type family.

sizes in which a type face is cut depend on the purpose for which a particular face is intended.

The preceding introduction, limited as it is, has tried to convey that type exists in an inexhaustible variety of styles, designs, weights, and sizes. There is, nevertheless, one common denominator in this seemingly completely arbitrary variety of designs. This is the relative width of various characters. Related to relative character width is the tradition of uniform line length, or *right-hand justification*. These two features of type and composition are of crucial importance in all typesetting methods, in hand composition, hot-metal

6   There are hundreds of typefaces with which
8   There are hundreds of typefaces wit
10 There are hundreds of typefac
12 There are hundreds of typ
14 There are hundreds of
18 There are hundred
24 There are hun
30 There are h
36 There are

Courtesy Ludlow Typograph Company

Typical point-size range of a type series.

machine composition, and also in non-metallic composition. For this reason they are here briefly discussed and explained.

Differences in character width. Whatever the reasons may be—and they are possibly traditional more than anything else—the average person somehow feels that the different letters must have a certain proportional relation. These differences in the width of letters have their root in the way we write and in our alphabet. The "i" and the "m" illustrate this point quite clearly. Type design recognizes this condition. Two type faces can be very different in their design, but the proportions of character width are still more or less the same. Nobody can expect to design an acceptable type face if he severely infringes on these relations.

If you look at our next illustration you can decide for yourself whether you recognize the reading matter on the top as typed on a standard typewriter, but not as "printed" or produced by composition. If you ask why a typed line is so different from a composed line, you can find the answer by studying the width of individual characters in the typed lines shown on the top: everything—letters,

```
Alexander Anderson, the
father of wood engraving
in America, was born in
```

Alexander Anderson, the father of wood engraving in America, was born

Courtesy Ludlow Typograph Company

Difference between typed and composed characters.

signs, and figures—has the same width. But in the reading matter shown on the bottom, every letter has its correct proportionate width, and the impression is, therefore, immediately that of "printed" and not typed.

Right-hand justification. The requirements of varying character width posed a very serious problem in the development of all composing machines; it is closely linked to the second and final point of our discussion, namely, to right-hand justification. Right-hand justification means that type lines are arranged in equal length throughout a paragraph, or a column, or a page—whatever the unit happens to be.

Joell Munsell, a publisher and printer of eminence was born in Northfield, Massachusetts, in 1808, and began

Joell Munsell, a publisher and printer of eminence was born in Northfield, Massachusetts, in 1808, and began as

Courtesy Ludlow Typograph Company

Difference between unjustified and justified composition. The upper three lines are unjustified, the lower three justified.

As you will see in the following section, right-hand justification is a technical necessity in hand composition as well as in hot-metal machine composition. But in non-metallic composition no such need exists. There, right-hand justification is strictly an appearance requirement. As right-hand justification is rather difficult to achieve, and as it adds considerably to the cost of non-metallic composing machines, some people have questioned the wisdom of maintaining a practice that contributes no other than a traditional appearance value to the printed page.

Taking sides in this debate is outside the purpose of this manual. But it might be mentioned that at present composition systems neglecting either proportionate letter width or right-hand justification have not been found generally acceptable. On the other hand, there can be no doubt that where the content of the printed page is decisive; where appearance is a minor but cost a major consideration, systems compromising in proportionate character width have proved successful, particularly if they provide right-hand justification.

Section 2:   Type Fundamentals and Hand Composition

Composition looks back at more than five hundred years of continuous history. Type fundamentals were developed during the first four-hundred-fifty years when hand composition of metallic types was the only existing kind of composition. The

next fifty or sixty years changed this condition, but type fundamentals remained the same. For this reason we must begin our discussion of type fundamentals with hand composition.

Composition as an assembly process. In modern

terms, hand composition can best be characterized as an assembly process. Metallic types are the physical implements by which writing is converted into printable form. The assembly operation takes place mainly but not exclusively in the *stick*, or composing stick, a simple hand tool. The work is done by a skilled craftsman, a *compositor* or *comp*, who assembles individual types into lines, these into paragraphs, then into columns, and finally into pages. He uses four simple tools: (1) the composing stick, (2) tweezers, (3) a bodkin, and (4) a line gauge. As the composing stick holds only a few lines, the assembly of the composed lines into larger units is done outside the composing stick.

The individual type characters, known generically as *sorts*, used to be stored in two *type cases*. The *upper case* housed the *capitals*, and the *lower case* the small letters. In contemporary practice, only a single case accommodating all sorts is preferred to two separate cases, but the terms "upper case" and "lower case" are so firmly established that they are generally used in type specification and even for designation of the corresponding kinds of letters on typewriters.

Typesetting. Setting type, or typesetting, as the assembly of type is called, is a meticulous business. Each word must be assembled character by character; word follows word until the line is filled. The whole work must be done according to a well-thought-out plan or layout.

As the composing stick holds but a few lines, these must be transferred by the compositor to an assembly tray known as a *galley*. Transferring the set lines from the stick to the galley is a tricky job, requiring skill and experience. The trade calls this operation ironically *dumping the stick*, but if you tried to really dump it, the composition would of course be spoiled, or *pied*, to say it in the printer's language. If the set type is to be used directly for printing in the press, the matter accumulated on galleys is further assembled into *type pages* and these into the final image carrier, or *type form*. After printing (and possibly reprinting) the form is broken up and the type is *distributed*, meaning that it is put back into its cases for storage and further use. The cycle of composition can then begin anew.

Three essential requirements of physical type. Type must be precision-made to be usable for composition. Of the many requirements that must be met by composition, we mention here only three; first, all lines must be parallel and uniform; second, all lines must be of the prescribed length

which is in *body type* composition—as composition of reading matter in bulk is often called—the same throughout; and third, the faces of the assembled types must present a level plane within close tolerance. If these three requirements are not met, composition and printing from type are impossible.

The basic element of composition is the individual type character. If we want to know how metallic type composition obtains the required essential characteristics, we must begin with a description of individual characters. For this purpose it is best to take a look at a schematic drawing of a type character and to study its features in relation to the foregoing three requirements.

Dimensions of foundry type. Our diagram does not show all items used in a complete description of type characters but is a simplified version, concentrating on those which are pertinent to our discussion. Foundry type, as type made exclusively for hand composition is usually called, is a bar-like object that consists of a body (which serves the hand compositor as a handle) bearing a raised image, namely, the *type face*. This raised image, which is the printing image, is inked for printing, and the ink image is transferred to the paper where it forms the printed image. You also see that the three dimensions of the type unit are designated by different terms. One dimension is called *height-to-paper*, another *body size*, and the third *set-size* or *set-width*. The body size and the set-size or set-width of types vary according to their size and design, but the height-to-paper is the same for all

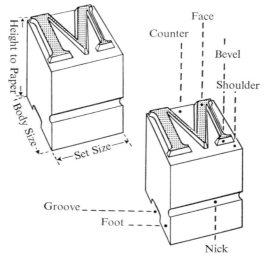

A type character and its parts. The type face is in relief above the supporting material.

types. Uniform height-to-paper is an indispensable type feature without which a level surface of the composed types is absolutely impossible.

The body size varies according to the size of the type; small type has a smaller body size than larger type. Uniformity of body size is a prerequisite for producing parallel lines of composition. The set-size of type, finally, varies not only for different type sizes but also for different characters within every body size. This difference is rooted in the nature of our alphabet as you may remember from the discussion in the preceding section.

The American Point System. If we want to express differences in type sizes we do this by saying that a type measures or has a certain number of *points*. The following illustration shows you a few lines in 8- and in 12-point type. The term "point" is part of a measuring system peculiar to typesetting and printing. Printers all over the world use such systems, though not the same throughout.

William Bradford, the first printer in New York, was born in Leicester, England, in 1658, and began business as a master printer in Philadelphia in 1682. Many disagreements with the ruling authorities compelled him to go to New York, where, in 1693, he published his first print. He printed in New York

William Bradford, the first printer in New York, was born in Leicester, England, in 1658, and began business as a master printer in Philadelphia in 1682. Many disagreements with the ruling authorities compelled him to go to

Courtesy Ludlow Typograph Company

Different type sizes occupy different areas on the printed page. The upper five lines are in 8-point, the lower in 12-point type.

In the United States we use the *American Point System* which is also used in other English-speaking countries. "The American Point System was initiated in 1886, at Niagara by a meeting of the United States Typefounders Association when a committee was appointed to examine into and report upon the new system. Eighty-three picas were set as equal to 35 centimeters. The American Point System follows the Methods of Fournier and Didot, differing from them only in its selection of another body of pica as its basis."[5]

The American Point System has two units: the *point* and the *pica*. Body sizes are specified in points; the length of lines and the depth of composition are measured in picas. One typographic

point is, carried to six decimals, 0.013832 inch. (For most practical purposes four decimals are sufficient, and one point is usually known as 0.0138 inch. In the Monotype System one point is expressed as 0.01383 inch.) Twelve points are equivalent to 1 pica and measure (in three decimals) 0.166 inch. Six picas are close to an inch; they measure (in three decimals) 0.996 inch.

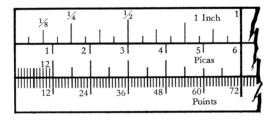

Enlarged diagram of inches and picas. For explanation one inch may be considered equivalent to six picas. Actually six picas are somewhat less than an inch and this difference adds up as the number of picas increases.

For the sake of completeness it should be added that we use actually two different typographic points. One is the point measuring 0.01383 inch, which is used for foundry type, in the Ludlow and in the Monotype systems. The manufacturers of Linotypes and Intertypes, on the other hand, use a point measuring 0.014 inch. When foundry type or Monotype composition must be combined with slugs of type these can be cast to the correct dimensions by adapting the line-casting machine for this purpose. The height of type to paper is not expressed in typographic points or picas but in thousandths of inches; it is standardized at 0.918 inch and called *type-high*.[6]

It should be added that several other typographic systems exist. Outside the English-speaking world, the French *Didot System* is the most widely used one. It is called in Germany the *Didot-Berthold System* and is based on the Didot point which is considerably larger than the American point. Twelve Didot points are known as a *Cicero* in German, and as *cicéro* or *le douze*, meaning the twelve, in French. This body is larger than our pica which is roughly equivalent to 11 Didot points. The height-to-paper of the Didot System, finally, is also somewhat more than ours.[7]

Typographic area measuring unit. In addition to their measuring units for height and length, printers have also their own unit for the measuring of composition areas. This unit is called the *em*. It is the square of the body size. (In the Monotype

System the em is differently defined and may or may not be the square of the body size, as is explained in a later unit. But Monotype composition, which is often supplied to printers by trade composition firms is nevertheless specified in terms of ems which are the square of the body size and the completed composition is also measured in the same units. From the point-of-view of the non-Monotype printer the Monotype em is a strictly internal unit, used solely by those who produce Monotype composition.) The actual area of an em, expressed in points, changes with the type size. But the proportion remains always the same. A 12-point em is a square having a side length of 12 points, a 14-point em has a side length of 14 points, and so forth. The unit em has no precise meaning without indication of its body size. If printers speak of ems without adding a specific body size, they usually mean the pica, or 12-point, em. Traditionally printers express the extent of body-type composition, either the work to be done or the work already performed, in ems rather than in lines of a given length. These calculations are rather technical and need no further development in this manual. We turn now to spacing of types where we will meet the em again.

Quads and spaces. The spacing of type lines consisting of individual characters is achieved by means of *quads* and *spaces*. All of them are metal units of the same body size as the type to be spaced, but as the spaces must not leave an impression on the printed sheet they are less high than type. Type-high is, as you know, 0.918 inch whereas quads and spaces are less than 0.800 high.

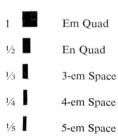

1		Em Quad
½		En Quad
⅓		3-em Space
¼		4-em Space
⅕		5-em Space

Quads and spaces.

(In the Monotype System higher spaces can be used if the composition serves as original material for duplicate platemaking.) Depending on the kind of spacing to be done, spaces of different width must be used.

The wider spaces are known as quads, the narrower as spaces. The *em quad* is the square of the

body size; the en quad (also called *nut quad*) is half as wide as the em quad. Quads are used for the filling of big spaces such as paragraph indentions at the beginning of a line, the centering of lines, and the filling of lines at the end of a paragraph.

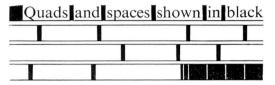

The quad at the beginning indents the paragraph, spaces separate words, and the last line of the paragraph is filled with spaces and quads.

Word spacing and letterspacing. Spaces of different width are used for the spacing of words and, where this is wanted, for the spacing of letters within a word. Good spacing is a most essential aspect of typography. In book composition, tight spacing, meaning small spaces between words, is widely practiced. Uneven spacing of words is considered objectionable and so is word spacing resulting in rivers of white spaces running down the page. Letterspacing is, as a rule, avoided in lowercase roman and particularly in italic composition. But in display composition using capital letters, it is often necessary to use letterspacing especially in larger sizes. Both word and letterspacing are of great importance in the composing of lines of uniform length, our next subject.

Handling composition consisting of individual characters. In the preceding section it was mentioned that equal line length is a physical necessity in metallic composition, particularly if the composition consists of individual types. Why this is so you will immediately understand when you consider the several operations necessary in typesetting. Take, for example, the composition of a page in book work. A typical page may have approximately 40 lines, and each line may have from 50 to 75 characters on the average. Our typical book page consists, therefore, of 2,000 to 3,000 individual units, types and spaces. These must be carefully assembled into a single page of proper size, and these 2,000 to 3,000 characters must be kept together by simple means, formerly a piece of string, for printing and possibly also for storing. If the lines are not of the same length throughout, it is almost impossible to do this. The 2,000 or more characters would simply fall apart when you tried

A hand compositor at work, setting individual type characters in the composing stick above a type case.

to handle them. But it is unlikely that you could ever get to the assembly of type pages. Your hand composition would probably be pied when you wanted to transfer a few unjustified lines from the composing stick to the galley. Even justification is also required in the lockup of a typeform for presswork or duplicate platemaking.

Spacing-in and spacing-out. Uniformity of line length can be achieved in hand composition by two different spacing techniques. These are called *spacing-in* and *spacing-out*. If the compositor needs a little more space to get a few letters into the same line, he will space it in, meaning that he exchanges the spaces between words for thinner ones, thereby gaining room for the additional letters. Spacing-out is used where a syllable or a word is best moved into the next line. Now the compositor fills his line again by exchanging spaces, but this time he replaces narrow word spaces with wider ones.

Leading. Spacing within a line is not the only kind of spacing needed in composition. Spacing between lines and also between paragraphs, as well as the filling of open spaces within a composed unit, an advertisement for example, are other essential spacing tasks. For these the compositor uses strips of spacing material which are known as *leads* if they are less than 6 points and as *slugs* from 6 points up to 18 points. Still thicker spacing material is available in wood and metal under the name of *furniture*. It might be mentioned that type slugs (which are produced by line-casting machines) and Monotype composition can be cast on a larger body which saves the operation of leading.

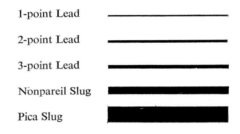

Leads and slugs.

All composition, be it metallic or non-metallic, be it done by hand or by machine, must be proofed, corrected, and assembled according to its final purpose. These operations will be presented in Section 5 of this chapter. But first we must become familiar with hot-metal machine and non-metallic composition. This is the subject matter of the following two sections.

Section 3:   Hot-Metal Machine Composition

For hundreds of years all composition was done by hand. Hand composition is obviously much too slow and much too expensive for our fast living mass production century. The needs of contemporary society for composition of body type, or text composition, which represents the bulk of book work and of the editorial content of our newspapers and magazines (at least of that part which is not occupied by pictures) has taken on almost fantastic dimensions if compared with similar needs in the past. Contemporary mass production printing is unthinkable on the basis of hand composition. Without machine typesetting neither our newspapers nor our books, catalogs, and magazines could be produced.

But slowness is only one drawback of hand composition. We must not forget another and most serious attending disadvantage. This is the high cost of, and investment in, foundry type, without which hand composition is impossible.

In contemporary printing practice the main value of a printing plant is represented by the investment in the pressroom whereas the investment in the composing room is usually less substantial. As mentioned earlier in this chapter, there exist many printing plants which do not operate their own composing rooms but rely on trade composition firms for their type. In the past, until the end of the nineteenth century when hot-metal composing machines became generally used, but particularly in Colonial America as well as in the young United States, things were quite different. Prior to the invention of printing machines as distinguished from the traditional hand presses, the printer's investment in his pressroom was negligible in comparison with the capital needed for type. In 1796 Isaiah Thomas, the well-known American printer, evaluated his presses at $732.66 and his types at $12,437.78.[8] Type was then used for direct printing in the inefficient hand press and not as today, primarily for reproduction proofs and for duplicate platemaking; and as presswork was based on crude application of brute force rather than on precision equipment, type wore heavily and soon needed replacement where printing of better quality was wanted.

The enormous capital needed in past centuries for keeping type "standing," or ready for reprinting, was a severe handicap for the reprinting of books. It was most strongly felt in the production of the Bible, the most printed book of all. Bible printing stimulated the development of flat stereotypes, particularly in England. Other disadvantages of the storage of made-up type pages included the need for space and for expensive storage facilities, the handling of substantial weights, and the danger of pieing composition which was then kept together merely by a piece of string. Some of these disadvantages continued when hand composition was superseded by machine composition. Most of the problems of type storage are still with us, and it is more or less generally accepted in the industries concerned that only nonmetallic composition will finally eliminate these problems.

The slowness of hand composition was particularly objectionable to the printers and publishers of newspapers. To them hand composition was a real handicap. Not only was its cost rather high, but hand composition also added to the interval of time that elapsed between the receipt of the news by a paper and the offering of this news in printed form for sale to the public. As the nineteenth century was one of highly personal journalism and of rather fierce newspaper competition, the publishers of some newspapers were among the most aggressive promoters of machine composition just as they were, generally speaking, the most persistent advocates of improvements in all other phases of printing related to the production of their papers.

Courtesy New York School of Printing

Class working in the composing room. In the foreground, an instructor teaches hand composition to a student.

This is not the point to sketch the historical events that resulted in hot-metal machine composition. Here we want to make clear that hot-metal machine composition of various kinds made it possible for the whole printing industry to overcome the time and cost limitations imposed by hand composition. Hot-metal machine composition is not limited to newspaper printing but pervades all branches of the graphic arts. Books, advertisements, business and other forms, and all kinds of promotional printing employ hot-metal composition, often in conjunction with hand composition of some kind or other.

Hot-metal machine composition is a broad subject. It is here divided into six units: (1) the main problems of hot-metal machines; (2) the Monotype System; (3) manually operated line-casting machines such as Linotypes and Intertypes; (4) tape-operated line-casting machines; (5) the Ludlow System; and finally (6) subsidiary composing-room equipment. The discussions aim at explanation of essentials and not of operational detail. Points related to the final product are explained because they are of more general interest than the detail of mechanical performance.

The Main Problems of Hot-Metal Machines

Composing machines are complex mechanisms. They pose many different and sometimes unexpected problems to those who design and construct them. But when we speak of the main problems with which hot-metal composing machines must cope, we do not refer to the many problems of design and engineering which must be solved in the construction of every complex machine. At this point we want to direct your attention to two specific problems that occupy a key position in the mechanization of composition. One problem is posed by the necessity of producing lines of composition which are of a predetermined equal, but of course easily changeable, length. This problem can be simply labeled as the problem of justification. The other problem is the elimination of distribution of the printed type. The first problem, that of justification, is not limited to the construction of hot-metal machines but is equally present in the design of non-metallic composing machines and, hence, remains of contemporary importance. The second problem does not exist in non-metallic composition and is, therefore, typical for hot-metal typesetting equipment. Our discussion begins with justification in the sense of producing uniformly spaced lines of composition.

The problem of line justification. At the outset it must be mentioned that the word justification has several meanings related to composition and printing. One meaning of justification refers to mechanical and structural considerations related to the firmness of composed lines consisting of foundry types or Monotype as needed for assembly and presswork. In the following discussion justification is not used in this sense but in its other meaning which solely refers to appearance, namely to the composition of lines of equal length.

Justification is related to four items: (1) the length of a given line, or group of lines; (2) differences in the set-width, or relative width, of various type faces; (3) differences in word length; and, finally, (4) the division of words into syllables at the end of a line. A hyphen is placed at the end of the division which may be either a syllable or a word in compound nouns. For this reason division of words or compound nouns is called *hyphenation* in the trade. Division of words from line to line is, generally speaking, not considered desirable because it retards the progress of reading. But word division can rarely be completely avoided. Assuming the same text, word division will occur more frequently in lines of shorter measure than in lines of longer measure. The compositor or the machine operator must follow the rules of spelling in the dividing of words. He must decide whether a word must be divided and where to place the dividing hyphen. Hyphenation is particularly important in newspaper composition which uses exceptionally short lines of type.

"Spacing in"

Diagram of a line before and after spacing-in. *The lower line has two characters more. These were spaced-in by reducing the width of spaces between words in the lower line.*

Two approaches to automatic justification. Before we discuss automatic justification of composed lines a brief reminder of manual justification methods is indicated. Hand composition employs, as explained in the preceding section, the two techniques of spacing-in and spacing-out for justification. Both consist in changing the width of spaces between words and, if necessary, also between letters. The method of spacing-in reduces the spaces between words, that of spacing-out increases these spaces. In certain instances, spacing-

"Spacing out"

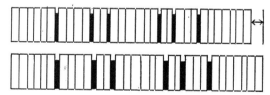

Diagram of a line before and after spacing-out. *Both lines have the same number of characters and spaces. The spaces in the lower line are wider and thereby fill the line.*

out may be combined with letterspacing. But letterspacing is, as already mentioned, considered permissible only in the composition of display types but not in that of body types, or reading matter in bulk.

Automatic justification of lines can use either

one or the other of these techniques. But spacing-out is much more common than spacing-in. Actually, slug-casting machines use spacing-out exclusively whereas the Monotype can use both, spacing-in and spacing-out, though spacing-out is much more usual than spacing-in.

If we apply the techniques of justification by spacing to automatic typesetting, we come to the following conclusion: *Automatic justification of composed lines requires automatically controlled width of word spaces and possibly also of letter-spaces.* This is indeed done in all existing automatic systems, either those for composition of metallic or of non-metallic type. Our next question is how this result, namely automatic control of space width, can be provided. History has simplified the answer to this question by eliminating many solutions which were hopefully and ingeniously developed but, alas, found wanting.[9] There are only two basic solutions that have stood the test of time: These are either the mechanical or the numerical control of space widths. *But it should be remembered that in both of these techniques word division, or hyphenation, remains the task of the compositor or machine operator.* This holds true for all typesetting systems but computerized composition.

Differences between mechanical and numerical control of spacing. All automatic line-casting machines are based on mechanical space control. The implements whereby changes in space width come about are known as *expandable spacebands.* These are described under the heading of line-casting machines. For the present discussion, it is sufficient to state that their expansion takes place strictly mechanically without any calculation whatever.

Numerical control of space width was originally developed for the Monotype System. It is essentially a method whereby the set-width of all characters and spaces that form a line of a given length is measured and added. All measurements, including that of the line length, must be expressed in

numbers within the same system. The width of spaces is automatically determined before the final line of justified types or type images is produced. The Monotype is the only hot-metal machine based on numerical control of space width. The Monotype System is described under its own heading and need not occupy our attention at this point. But two consequences of numerical space control have attained general importance and are therefore briefly explained.

Numerical space control has been used in many methods of non-metallic composition. The importance of this principle has therefore generally increased. This development must not surprise us as numerical space control can be rapidly performed by electromechanical and by electronic techniques which may include application of methods developed for high-speed computers.

The second but not less significant consequence of numerical space control is the division of typesetting into two related but independently executed operations. In the Monotype System, which introduced this division approximately 70 years ago, these are *keyboarding* and *casting.* In other, non-metallic systems, keyboarding is still one phase, but casting is replaced either by photographing or by percussion typing of type images. How unpredictable the development of techniques is can be seen from the fact that numerical *and* mechanical space control have been effectively combined in the design of tape-operated line-casting machines. There keyboarding is predicated upon a version of numerical control whereas the actual casting operation employs mechanical space control by means of expandable spacebands.

After this introduction to justification, the main problem of composing machines in general, we turn to distribution which has great importance in hot-metal machine composition but has completely disappeared in non-metallic typesetting.

The problem of distribution. Foundry type was the only existing type prior to the invention of hot-metal composing machines. As foundry type was very expensive, it was distributed, or put back in its storage place, as soon as the nature of the work permitted this step. Distribution of type was, as can be readily understood, an expensive and also a time-consuming, non-productive operation. The history of composing machines teaches us that many machines were developed for the mechanical assembly and for the mechanical distribution of foundry types. But the same history teaches us also that all of these machines disappeared

1 em = 18 "units"

5   9   18

Three type characters showing the relative value of units. The "M" has 18 units, the "A" is half as wide and has 9 units, and the "I" has only 5 units.

when hot-metal composing machines which solve the problem of distribution in a radical manner became at last practical. The solution to the problem of distribution was simply to eliminate it completely or, as it is often said facetiously, to introduce *distribution through the melting pot.* Hot-metal composing machines are not just machines for the mechanization of hand composition. *They are machines for the manufacturing of custom-made iustified lines of types.*

Two common features of hot-metal machine composition. Each of the existing hot-metal systems differs in many points from all others. But all systems have two crucial points in common: (1) all hot-metal machines manufacture lines of especially cast types and (2) the product is not distributed after use but melted down. As practically all but a small fraction of the type metal can be used again, the melting-down of used type is most economical.

Hot-metal machines are type-casting equipment. The difference between hand composition and hot-metal machine composition should be firmly grasped. Hand composition is an assembly process whereby already existing individual type characters are arranged into words and lines. Hot-metal machine composition does not use already existing types. It is a manufacturing process for correctly assembled lines of type. You can, perhaps, get the best idea of hot-metal machines if you think that they are highly specialized type foundries.

Hand composition presupposes the existence of type. Hot-metal machines begin with matrices which are either correctly assembled or correctly positioned for the casting of type. The matrices remain with the equipment until all work to be done with them is completed. Then they are removed and exchanged for assortments, or fonts, of different matrices. The cast type is the final product of machine composition; it is removed from the machine in smaller or larger batches for further assembly.

The handling of matrices in hot-metal composing machines. Hot-metal machines provide two different kinds of products: either correctly justified solid lines, or slugs of type, or correctly justified lines which consist of individual type characters and spaces. Slugs of type are produced by line-casting machines whereas lines of individual characters and spaces are the product of the Monotype. All hot-metal composing machines use matrices for the casting of type. But matrices are of different construction and are handled differently

in essentially differing systems. In line-casting machines such as the Linotype or Intertype, matrices are assembled into lines and automatically distributed after casting as part of the machine cycle. In the Ludlow and similar systems, matrices are manually assembled and manually distributed after the line is cast. In the Monotype, matrices never leave their storage case during casting and are consequently not distributed at all. How these systems function is explained under their respective headings.

A line composed of foundry type.

Slugs of type made by line-casting machines.

A group of lines consisting of individually cast Monotypes.

A Ludlow slug cast from hand-composed matrices.

You can see that casting is an essential function of hot-metal machine composition. For this reason we turn now to a discussion of type founding, or type casting, which will include an explanation of the matrix and its function. We begin with a brief description of hand casting with the adjustable type mold which is the historical method of type production.

Type casting with the adjustable mold. Foundry type, as individual type characters for hand composition are called generically, was cast for approximately 400 years in the adjustable mold, an ingeniously thought-out precision mechanism for the casting of individual letters of differing width. "Type casting ends with the finished type but it begins with designing the type face. The next step is punch cutting wherein the design is engraved on the end of a small bar of soft steel that is then hardened until it is strong enough for matrix punching. The matrix is a flat bar of copper into which the punch is driven forming an intaglio image of the punch design on the surface. In this stage the copper bar is called a *drive*. It is next made perfect for use in the mold and then considered a finished matrix."[10]

Casting takes place in the adjustable mold which consists essentially of two matching metal parts protected on their outsides by wood. In their center a channel is formed for casting the metal character. The height of this channel corresponds to the height-to-paper, the depth to the body size, and the width to the set-width of the cast character. The height is fixed, the depth usually adjustable for different bodies and the width is determined by the width of the matrix to be cast. Each matrix serves as the bottom of the mold where it is put with its intaglio cavity up, toward the channel, for casting. The top of the mold is shaped like a funnel to facilitate casting. The type caster pours the hot molten type metal with a ladle into the funnel, makes a characteristic jerking motion with his hand and removes the still hot cast type from the mold before he repeats casting. "The type metal is an alloy consisting of lead, antimony, and tin. Lead constitutes the bulk of the type metal. Antimony counteracts shrinkage upon solidification and adds to the fluidity of the alloy; tin improves fluidity too and also reduces the melting point of the metal; both make the finished type harder."[11] Type cast in the adjustable mold must be finished by hand before it is fit for composition.

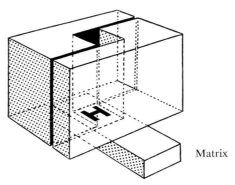

Matrix

Schematic of the adjustable type mold. The two halves of the mold can be adjusted for different set widths without affecting the point size and height-to-paper of cast characters. (Adapted from Gustav Bohadti, Die Buchdruck Letter.)

The adjustable type mold is no longer used in our time for production casting. It has been superseded by completely automatic equipment. Data as to the production obtainable by means of the adjustable type mold vary. Joseph Moxon, the earliest English writer on the subject, says in his famous work on printing, published in London, 1683–84, that "a workman will *cast* about four thousand letters ordinarily in one day."[12] Simon Pierre Fournier, the great French type founder, writes in 1764–66 that casting "is repeated two and three thousand times per day."[13] A contemporary automatic casting and finishing machine can produce approximately 15,000 characters of 6-point or 8,000 characters of 12-point type per hour.[14] Assuming a 14-hour day for Moxon's and Fournier's time, the comparative figures are 2,000 to 4,000 hand-cast characters and 112,000 to 210,000 characters cast with contemporary automatic equipment in 14 hours. Roughly speaking, a single automatic machine can deliver as many characters as 60 men can cast with the adjustable type mold. The difference becomes considerably greater if we consider that the product of hand casting still needs finishing, whereas that of con-

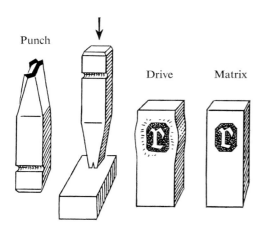

Punch

Drive   Matrix

Some stages of matrix making with punches. The steel punch at the left has the character in relief; next this punch is shown on the metal bar to be made into a matrix; then comes the unfinished and finally the finished matrix.

temporary type-casting machinery is automatically finished as part of the machine cycle. The development of type casting from the hand mold to the present automatic equipment progressed in many steps and took more than one hundred years.[15]

Automatic type-casting equipment for foundry type and that for custom-made justified lines of type differ, of course, in many respects. But all type-casting machines use matrices and molds. The word *matrix* is related to the Latin word for "mother"; it is generally used to designate "that which gives form, origin, or foundation to something enclosed or embedded in it."[16] It should not be too difficult to remember that matrices are used to cast the type faces, or the printing images, of machine-composed types. It might be worth mentioning that the original of a type is not the matrix but the punch, sometimes also called analogously the *patrix*, or father, of the face.

In conclusion of this introduction, it is repeated as a summary that (1) all hot-metal composing machines use matrices, that (2) they must provide a means for justification of correctly dimensioned lines, that (3) they must be equipped for the casting of the actual type, and that (4) they must have effective control over matrices and spaces during all phases of operations. How various systems achieve these results will be seen in the following discussions of hot-metal machine composition systems.

The Monotype System

We begin our discussion of hot-metal machine composition systems with the Monotype for two reasons. One is that the Monotype is based, as the name implies, on the individual type character and therefore more closely related to hand composition than line-casting machines. Another reason lies in the general approach taken by the Monotype System to the problem of justification. This approach is the basis for both tape-operated, more or less automatic line-casting machines and for many non-metallic composition systems. The Monotype System of hot-metal composition is, of course, itself widely used in actual printing practice.

Summary description of the Monotype System. The Monotype System comprises two main units: the keyboard and the caster. The product of the keyboard is a punched paper ribbon which contains all information needed for directing the operation of the caster where the actual type lines are manufactured. For casting, the paper ribbon is placed in the caster; the punched holes direct the caster mechanism in the casting of characters and of such spaces as are needed to produce justified lines of individual types. As Monotype equipment is pneumatically operated, the punched holes of the steering ribbon (also called "controller ribbon") act simultaneously as valves for the air power system.

The Monotype System uses a single matrix for each character. These matrices are stored in the *cellular matrix case* and are not removed from it for casting. Justification is done by casting individual word spaces of such width as will perfectly fill a given line measure. The dimension of these spaces is arrived at by the Monotype Unit System, our next subject.

The purpose of the Monotype Unit System. The Unit System is the keystone of the Monotype. The system requires a number of calculations which are usually bewildering to the uninitiated. But if you keep firmly in mind that the purpose of this system is the proper dimensioning of word spaces whereby lines of individual type are justified, you should not find it difficult to understand its principles. The detail of calculations which must be known to operating personnel is, of course, not of concern to the reader of this manual.

Spacing-out on the Monotype. As explained in Section 2 of this chapter, the justification of hand-composed lines can be achieved either by spacing-in or by spacing-out. The second technique is more widely used and consists in composing a line to the point where it is almost filled. The remaining space which is too small for the next word or syllable is filled by adding to the spaces between words, thereby increasing their width.

The principle of spacing-out is generally used on the Monotype. The difference in comparison with spacing-out in hand composition is that the correct width of word spaces is numerically established on the Monotype prior to casting. As a problem of arithmetic the calculation of the proper width of each word space is not a difficult thing, provided we have the following four items of information in the form of numbers when we want to do spacing-out. Again we assume that the line is almost completely composed and ready for spacing-out like in hand composition. At this point we want to determine the correct width of each word space. The four items we must know for this purpose are: (1) the prescribed final length of the line to be justified; (2) the length of the already composed line; next we deduct the composed line lengths from the prescribed final line length and thereby establish in numbers the space that remained unfilled; (3) we must know the number of word spaces placed in the composed line; and (4) their actual width. The whole problem is solved by a division of the unfilled line length by the number of spaces and by adding the quotient to the original width of each word space for the casting of the final space. All these calculations are made mechanically on the Monotype keyboard. Some of the mechanics by which this result is obtained are explained in the description of the Monotype equipment and its operation. Here we continue with the explanation of the unit system.

The whole Monotype approach to justification is straightforward and simplicity itself. The Monotype was a development of great consequence because it introduced exact numerical measurements of character widths into typography. Picas and points were, of course, much too crude for the needs of the new system. This is not surprising; both units were intended for entirely different purposes, namely, the measuring of body size, length of line, and depth of composition.

The Monotype Unit System. The Monotype Unit System provides measuring units which make it possible to express the width of each character numerically. This is done in two ways. One is the assignment of a comparative value to each character of each body size and of each type face. These comparative figures can be expressed in decimals of inches and become thereby measurable.

Unit Value	Row	A	B	C	D	E	F	G	H	I	J	K	L	M	N	O	Row
5	1	|	|	l	t	'	'	.	,	▮	l	i	j	[	'	|	1
6	2	j	f	i	!	:	;	-	j	f	l	l	/	:	;	▮	2
7	3	c	r	s	e	)	(	'	'	r	s	t	J	v	°	z	3
8	4	‡	q	*	b	g	o	?	I	z	c	e	z	s	†	?	4
9	5	I	▮	9	7	5	3	1	0	.	9	7	5	3	1	0	5
9	6	C	▮	8	6	4	2	$	-	$	8	6	4	2	▮		6
9	7	x	k	y	d	h	a	x	J	g	o	a	P	F	L	T	7
10	8	A	fi	u	n	.	S	v	y	p	u	n	Q	B	O	E	8
10	9	D	▮	fl	p	fl	fi	q	k	b	h·	d	v	y	G	R	9
11	10	H	&	J	S	œ	æ	ff	▮	Z	▮	ff	X	U	K	N	10
12	11	O	L	C	F	w	£	æ	L	P	F	¶	M	Z	Q	G	11
13	12	E	&	Q	V	C	B	T	O	E	A	w	P	T	R	B	12
14	13	D	A	Y	ffl	ffi	m	œ	Y	U	G	R	œ	æ	w	V	13
15	14	K	N	H	ffl	ffi	X	D	N	K	H	m	&	lb	X	U	14
18	15	Œ	Æ	¾	¼	½	W	M	—	..	M	W	%	Œ	Æ	▮	15
Unit Value	Row	A	B	C	D	E	F	G	H	I	J	K	L	M	N	O	Row

One arrangement of a Monotype matrix case. This case has 15 rows of 15 characters, or a total of 225 matrices. All characters in the same row have the same unit value. Matrix cases can be arranged to suit the job in hand.

For our purposes an understanding of unit values and their comparative functions is more important than the mastering of the exact numerical data.

The Monotype uses (with rare exceptions which do not concern us) a maximum value of 18 units. This figure is usually allotted to the "W" as the widest character of our alphabet. Less wide characters have a proportionally smaller number of units. The "i" and the "l" of *Times New Roman*, the type in which this book is composed, have 5 units; the "c," "e," and "J" have 8 units; "h," "p," and "S" have 10 units; "w," "B," "E," and "F" are characters measuring 12 units; and "D," "N," "K," and "H" are examples of 15-unit letters; finally, "W," "M," as well as "¾" and "½," belong in the 18-unit group. The relative unit figure is more or less the same for all body sizes of a type face. A 6-point "W" and a 12-point "W" of the same design have both the same unit values, namely 18; and a 6-point "i" has usually 5 units as does a 12-point "i" of the same face. This does not mean that the same letter has the same width in each type design, or type face. "For example, a normally designed lower case 'a' may be designed to 9 units width or altered to 8 units or 10 units, according to the designer's fancy."[17]

Body size and set. The set of any Monotype font expresses in points the width of the 18-unit characters in that font. The Monotype Company publishes the equivalent of 18 units for every type face and size in terms of typographic points and their fractions under the designation of *set*. Monotype is therefore internally specified by listing the point size, which indicates the body size of a type, and by adding the set figure which indicates the equivalent of 18 units, or maximum character width, again in points. The present face "Times New Roman" is 9 point and 9 set. Other faces of 9 point body may or may not have the same set. The following two examples illustrate this point. *Perpetua* 9-point has an 8½-point set, whereas *Bell* 9-point has a 9½-point set. Perhaps it is a help for the beginner to think of *the Monotype set in terms of the specific maximum character width of a given face and size expressed in typographic points.* The higher the set of a given body size the more space this face occupies; the lower the set, the less space a face will need. Some typographers say that faces of the first kind *spread* whereas those of the second *pack*.

It is to be added that the line length is not measured in terms of picas by those who do Monotype composition but expressed in terms of Monotype ems, meaning set-width units. (The other printing trades are, as already mentioned, not concerned with these internal measurements.) The Monotype Company publishes conversion tables for points and picas into ems of different sets.[18] The whole system presupposes that all matrices and characters are manufactured to the specifications of the system, otherwise the best equipment could not insure proper performance. For this reason precision in matrix manufacturing and also in type design is essential. We turn next to a discussion of Monotype equipment, beginning with the keyboard.

The Monotype keyboard. Monotype composition begins with *keyboarding*. The Monotype keyboard is arranged like that of a typewriter. The number of keys varies depending on the model and its purpose; not all keys represent characters; some are needed for machine functions. All Monotype machines have at least 225 different characters available; some have a capacity of 255 or 272 characters; the latest addition to Monotype machinery, called the *Monomatic*, provides 324 characters.

The operator sits in front of the keyboard with the marked copy before him and does his work by striking the corresponding keys. Thereby he transmits the content of the copy to the keyboard and through it to the paper ribbon on which the position of each character and space is indicated by the position of automatically punched holes. The Monotype keyboard provides at the same time automatic addition of the units of width occupied by each character and space belonging to a line. This addition is done mechanically by the Unit Wheel "which has 162 teeth representing 9 ems of 18 units in one complete revolution."[19] You will see later in the discussion of other tape-operated composing machines that mechanical counting

Punched Justification Signals   are put in first to guide Spacing

In the Monotype system a paper tape, called the controller ribbon *is punched on the keyboard and inserted, end first, into the caster.*

can be replaced by a number of electric and electronic methods. The principle, though, remains the same.

The equipment, further, counts the number of word spaces per line, warns the operator when the end of the line is approaching, and finally indicates to him on a characteristic part, the *justifying scale* mounted on a rotating drum, which keys he must strike in order to obtain the casting of spaces of the required width. After these keys are struck by the operator, the counting mechanism is reset for the next line. After composition is completed, the punched ribbon is removed from the keyboard and then *inserted into the caster with its end first, thereby transmitting the signals for the casting of spaces before the line itself is cast.* This principle, too, is used on several contemporary tape-operated machines for non-metallic composition.

Tape operation has several noteworthy advantages which are not peculiar to the Monotype but exist in all tape-operated typesetting machines. A Monotype punched ribbon, or another kind of punched tape, can be easily transferred from one place to another for casting or typesetting. This transfer may take place within the same building or require shipment over long distances. Punched tapes or ribbons can be stored for months or years before they are further used, and they can be used repeatedly for casting of Monotypes and Linotype slugs or for production of non-metallic types.

The Monotype caster. The caster is the machine that manufactures justified lines consisting of individual type characters and spaces. Whereas line-casting machines produce a single slug of type per line, the Monotype casts the required characters and spaces individually. Just as the circulating matrix system is characteristic for line-casting machines, so is the cellular matrix case characteristic for the Monotype. Depending on the model, this matrix case may hold either 225, 255, 272, or 324 matrices. Monotype equipment sold at present has either 255, or 272, or 324 matrices. Each matrix is used for a different character. All are stored in the matrix case where they remain during casting. The matrix case is continually moved to put the proper matrices into casting position. During casting the matrix case remains stationary for a brief interval. In this interval, the matrix is pushed down into contact with the mold and a carefully regulated squirt of hot molten metal is injected into the mold for casting. Then the matrix is returned to its non-casting position, and the matrix case is moved again for the next casting cycle.

The MONOTYPE *System of Composition, its Keyboard and Caster*

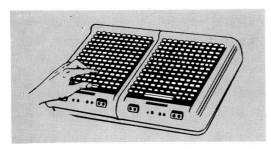

1 *When the operator touches a key, holes are punched in the ribbon. Each line of holes represents a character, and the copy is thereby transferred to the ribbon. Air pressure supplies the motive power for the different keyboard mechanisms.*

2 *As keyboarding progresses a counting mechanism adds width units; within justification area close to the end of the line the machine gives a warning.*

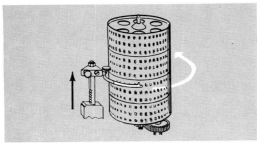

3 *The justifying scale moves and a mechanism indicates to the operator what keys he must touch for justification.*

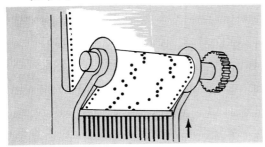

4 *The proper width of word spaces is punched into the controller ribbon, completing keyboarding of a line.*

The Keystone of the Monotype is the unit system. The width of each character is expressed in a number varying generally between 4 for the narrowest and 18 for the widest. During keyboarding these numbers serve for automatic determination of the width of characters. The keyboard produces a punched ribbon containing all information for casting of characters and spaces. This ribbon controls the work of the caster. The products of the Monotype caster are lines of uniform length consisting of individual characters and spaces.

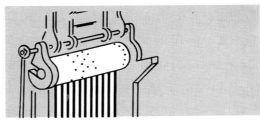

5 *The completed ribbon is put in the air tower of the caster for controlling the flow of air power signals.*

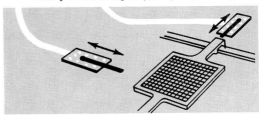

6 *Each character is a matrix resting in the matrix case; this is moved into casting position as determined by two air pin blocks.*

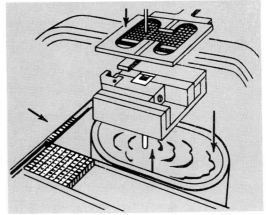

7 *For casting, the proper matrix is pinned to the mold, a squirt of hot metal is injected into mold and matrix, and the final character is thereby cast.*

Justification is achieved by casting word spaces of a predetermined width. As you remember, the exact adjustment for this dimension is made on the keyboard at the end of each line. The paper ribbon that controls the operation of the caster is inserted with its end first into the caster as already explained. The line itself is, of course, cast from right to left. After all characters and spaces forming a line are cast, the line is deposited on a galley where a number of lines is assembled. Monotype machines can produce composition of a body size ranging from 4½ point to 24 point. The length of lines can be up to 60 picas.

The preceding description is for obvious reasons limited to the barest essentials. Readers interested more deeply in the subject will find a few selected books listed in the notes to this chapter.[20]

Uses of the Monotype composition. Before we end the unit on the Monotype, it might be mentioned that the "Monotype is used in printing and publishing plants throughout the world to cover general typographic needs. While Monotype and slug-casting equipment are directly competitive, larger plants frequently operate both kinds of machines."[21] The unit system of the Monotype and many other of its features make the Monotype particularly suitable for tabular, scientific, and mathematical composition.[22]

Line-Casting Machines

The invention of line-casting, or slug-casting, machines established hot-metal machine composition in the United States. Two makes of machines are available for this purpose: one is the Linotype and the other is the Intertype. Both are sufficiently similar not to need separate treatment for our purposes. As the product of either machine is a solid line, or slug, of type both kinds of machines are here discussed under the heading of line-casting machines.

Scope of line-casting machines. Line-casting machines produce in the United States more reading matter than any other kind of composing machines because they dominate the composition of newspapers. Newspaper text matter, or body type, is practically always set on line-casting machines; much of newspaper advertising composition is also produced on line-casting equipment though other machines are often supplementing the Linotype and the Intertype. But line-casting machines are not restricted to newspaper composition. Many books, trade, and general-interest magazines are composed on them and so is a sub-

stantial portion of commercial or job printing. Nor should the vast field of line-cast composition for advertising be forgotten. Line-casting machines can be equipped for the setting of body types, as well as for that of display types. In certain instances Linotype or Intertype composition is supplemented by display type composed on the Ludlow or similar systems. Where reproduction is based on type images, the products of line-casting machines are often combined with non-metallic composition and also at times with hand lettering.

In mid-twentieth-century America much of the public interest in the field of composition has been absorbed by the many developments of non-metallic, photographic typesetting. The great strides made in line casting were more or less unnoticed by the public at large until they were called to its attention by the long strike of machine operators at the *New York Times* and all other New

Line-cast slugs of different point sizes. Large sizes are cast in recessed molds with metal-saving hollows.

York newspapers in the winter of 1962–63. At this time tape-operated line-casting machines and their possible automation became a subject of discussion in many newspapers and general-interest magazines.

The relative economic and technical importance of line-casting equipment and that of photographic typesetting needs to be pointed out. Even though we have no precise statistical data on the number of composing machines in existence, it is conservatively estimated by people in a position to do so that there are between 75,000 and 100,000 line-casting machines operating in the whole world. At the time of writing, informed sources estimate that there are between 550 and 650 full-range photographic composing machines (meaning machines capable of producing more or less the same range of text and display composition as are line-casting machines) in existence. These figures speak for themselves; line-casting machines are beyond any doubt at present our most generally used typesetting equipment and will remain in this position for quite some time to come, certainly for the near future. The introduction of high-speed tape-operated models and the latest addition of computerized composition retain the advantages of line-casting machines and add substantial improvements in the efficiency of composition done with them. A good familiarity with line-casting machines is, therefore, a necessity for everybody interested in composition.

One of the reasons for the strong and abiding position of line-casting machines in the newspaper field is relief printing from stereotypes. Non-metallic composition does not result in relief images and is hence not usable for stereotyping. Non-metallic composition may require an intermediate production step for relief printing, particularly if the final printing-image carriers must be curved stereotypes. This intermediate etched plate is used for the making of mats for stereotyping. But some newspapers make standard page-size photoengravings by use of transparencies obtained by photographic composition. The metal used for these photoengravings is thin and flexible enough to be wrapped around the plate cylinder of a newspaper press. Printing is done directly from the engraving, saving thereby the additional expenses connected with the making of stereotypes. On the other hand, it must be mentioned that newspapers printed by offset lithography do not need type in relief and can utilize non-metallic composition. But at the time of writing practically all metropolitan daily newspapers are printed by relief printing.[23]

General description of line-casting machines. It was already explained that hot-metal composing machines do not assemble types but matrices from which the final lines of type are automatically cast. The *circulating matrix* principle is as characteristic of line-casting machines as the cellular matrix case is characteristic of the Monotype System. All manually operated line-casting machines have "four

major divisions: (1) the magazines which contain the matrices; (2) the keyboard and its related parts; (3) the casting mechanism; (4) the distributing mechanism."[24]

Line-casting machines differ in several points from Monotype machines. The circulating matrix principle and stepless justification of line-casting machines as compared with the cellular matrix case and numerical justification of the Monotype are already known to you. Another essential difference between the Monotype and manually operated line-casting machines is discussed next. In the Monotype System, keyboarding is done on one kind of equipment and casting on another. Line-casting machines were originally designed as single-unit machines; keyboarding and casting are both performed by the same machine. Later, during the 1930's, the Teletypesetter System (TTS) was introduced which permits a division between keyboarding and casting similar to the Monotype. Our discussion will at this point concentrate on manually operated Linotype and Intertype machines. Tape-operated line-casting machines will follow in the next unit. The first point in our explanation of line-casting machines is, as in the Monotype, justification.

Line justification on slug-casting equipment. The justification of lines is here completely mechanical. All calculations and preparations on which the Monotype Unit System is based are avoided in line-casting machines *as long as they are manually operated*. The key to justification is the adjustable spaceband, a truly ingenious invention. Spacebands consist of two wedge-shaped metal parts which are slideably attached to each other. All word spaces are replaced by spacebands. At their maximum extension the width of the spacebands is smallest. As the two wedges are pushed together the width increases until it reaches its maximum of approximately three times the smallest width at the most compressed position. Justification is done by spacing-out, or increasing the width of spaces between words, until the line is brought to its full measure. Close to the end of the composed line the operator must determine whether the unfilled space of the line can take an additional word or syllable. The remaining *slack*, or unfilled space, should be much less than the expansion capacity of all spacebands used for the line in question. Experienced operators can appraise this condition with a glance. The extent to which the spacebands will be expanded is not calculated. Expansion of spacebands is a stepless and strictly mechanical

Flow Diagram of the INTERTYPE

The Intertype casts lines of type or slugs instead of individual types such as are used for hand composition. The slugs are cast from matrices punched with the letters and characters needed for typesetting. The matrices are returned automatically to magazine channels for reuse after each slug is cast.

Matrices for each type line are assembled by manual or tape operation of a keyboard. Tapered spacebands are also assembled between matrix word groups in an assembly elevator. The nearly-full line is delivered to casting position in front of the mold. Spacebands are driven upward, spreading the matrix line tightly between pre-set vise jaws. The slug is cast and ejected onto galley. Meanwhile, spacebands are returned to their storage box, and matrices are raised into distributor for conveyance back to magazine channels.

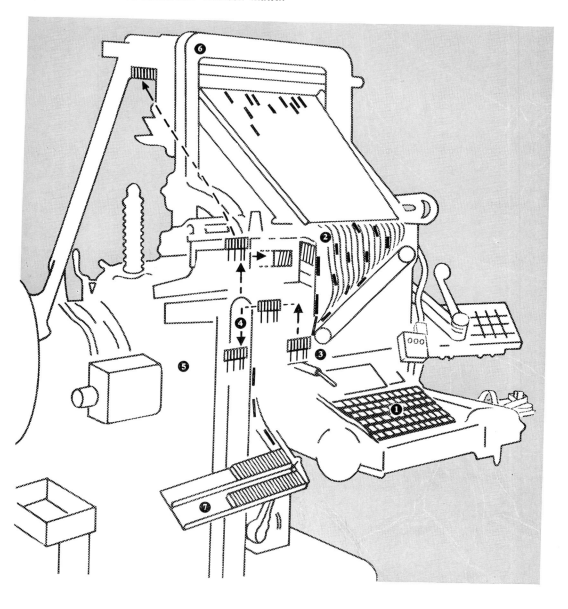

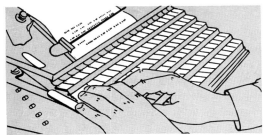

❶ Assembly of matrices and spacebands is controlled by manual or tape operation of keyboard.

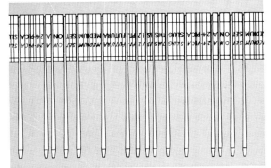

Sleeve

MATRIX

Wedge

SPACEBAND

❷ Matrices carry punched letters and characters. The spaceband thickness increases as wedge is driven up.

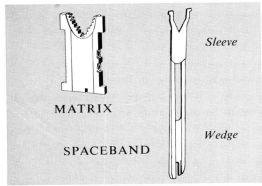

❸ The matrix line shown from metal pot side, illustrating female punched letters and spacebands between words.

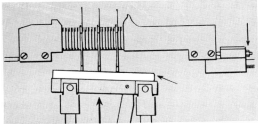

❹ Tapered spacebands, driven upward, spread out or "justify" matrix line to pre-set line width.

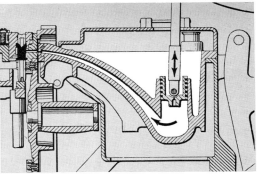

❺ Pot plunger forces molten type metal into mold and against justified line of matrices to cast slug.

❻ Matrices moved by distributor screws drop off combination bar as they reach channels in magazine.

❼ Slugs or lines of type have type characters in relief on top surface for printing or molding.

Thus, the Intertype is operable on a continuous basis, since matrices and spacebands are circulating simultaneously in different sections of the machine. While a line of matrices is being assembled, another may be in transit to casting, another actually at the casting point, another in intermediate transfer, and another in process of distribution to the magazine.

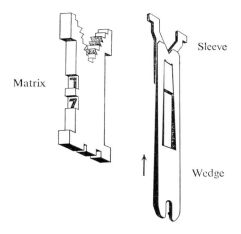

Matrix

Sleeve

Wedge

A duplexed matrix and an adjustable spaceband. You see the casting side of the matrix bearing the letter "L" in italic below the same letter in roman. (Both characters are upside down.) The adjustable spaceband consists of two tapered parts, the sleeve and the wedge, which can slide freely against each other. As the wedge moves up, the width of the space is increased; the outsides of spacebands always remain parallel.

operation that widens all spaces equally throughout the line.

Manually operated line-casting machines. Such machines are equipped with a *keyboard* which is similar to that of a typewriter but arranged in a different pattern. The machine compositor, known as *machine operator*, has the copy to be set in front and actuates the mechanism of the machine by fingering individual keys. This type of work is commonly known as *keyboarding*.

The striking of keys puts a series of connected operations into motion. Matrices and spacebands are released from their respective storage places and collected in their proper order in the *assembly elevator* where the line is formed. The operator sets the assembly elevator to the required line length and, as the assembly takes place in full view from his position, he watches the progress of assembling matrices and spacebands for a line. Linotype and Intertype matrices are punched with the intaglio type-casting cavity on their edges. This casting edge is assembled toward the machine and is not visible to the operator. But the opposite edge of matrices, which faces the operator is stamped with identifying *reference characters*, often either whitened or blackened for better readability. The reference characters make it possible for the operator to read the assembled ma-

trices and therewith to check his own keyboarding. Since assembly goes from left to right, and as the reference characters are stamped in their normal reading position, checking the assembled matrices is not too difficult. When the line is ready for justification, which means, as already explained, that it is almost completely filled, the operator depresses a handle, a step known as *sending-in a line*. From this point on the equipment performs completely automatically. The assembled line of matrices and spacebands is justified, a slug of type is cast from the justified line, this slug is trimmed and delivered on a galley, and the matrices and spacebands are automatically distributed, or returned to their respective storage compartments. The operator continues to keyboard during the automatic machine cycle. "Thus three lines of matrices, in the three functions of composition, of *assembling*, of *casting*, and of *distribution*, are in the various parts of the machine at one time."[25]

The circulating matrix system provides "three simultaneous actions: (1) the matrices are assembled by the operator's touch on the keyboard to form a full line; (2) this first line is moved automatically into the casting position while a second line is being assembled; (3) the first line, after the slug is cast, proceeds automatically to the distribution of its component matrices; meantime, the second line has moved to the casting position, and a third line is being assembled."[26] Next we want to take a good look at several important parts used in line-casting machines.

Matrices for line casting. If a matrix is handed to an outsider, particularly a matrix for body type between 8 and 12 point, such a person is usually puzzled, especially if he has some familiarity with foundry type for hand setting. It has been repeatedly observed that the novice does not find without aid the intaglio cavity of the matrix in which the type will be cast. He wonders about the large size of the matrix and is perplexed by the whole design of the object. The first point to be made is, therefore, that the matrix provides not only the intaglio image of the type but that its design and construction must consider justification, casting, and distribution as well. A typical line-casting matrix "is made of brass, alloyed to a special formula, and has gone through some fifty or more manufacturing operations to reach its finished form. It is rectangular in general shape, 1¼ inches high, ¾ inch wide across the upper and lower lugs, or ears, and ⁹⁄₁₆ inch wide across the body. Its thickness varies with the type character it carries."[27]

Matrices have the same height and width for all body sizes; they vary only in their thickness.

A few words on some of the features of matrices may be interesting. The *ears* or *lugs* play important parts in all phases of the operation, in the release of matrices, in their assembly, justification, and casting, as well as in the distribution and storing of matrices in the magazine. The vee-shaped top of matrices "corresponds to the shape of the distributor bar and has seven teeth on each side. Cutaway combinations of these teeth control dropping of matrices from the distributor bar during distribution."[28] Each matrix has its reference characters on the edge opposite to that bearing the intaglio cavity for casting; each font has an identifying slot.[29]

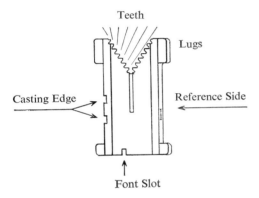

Teeth

Lugs

Casting Edge

Reference Side

Font Slot

Diagram showing the parts of matrices for line casting. The lugs serve for alignment, the teeth for returning matrices to their proper place after casting. Matrices ride with their teeth on the distributor bar above the magazine. When a matrix arrives over its own channel it is automatically released due to the arrangement of its teeth.

Matrices for text composition usually have the same character in two different versions. These are placed one above the other on the matrix. Thereby a single font of matrices carries two fonts of type. Combinations of roman and italics, or roman and bold of the same type face are among the most generally used arrangements, but it is also possible to combine two entirely different faces on matrices for line casting. Matrices bearing two fonts of type are either called *two-letter* or *duplexed*. The term "two-letter" can be misleading to the uninformed as both characters are always identical in their meaning though, of course, different in their design. And as these matrices include figures and marks of punctuation in addition to letters, the

term "duplexed" seems preferable. If a word, or several words, are to appear in the second design of a duplexed matrix, say in italics to distinguish it from a text in roman, this can be simply accomplished. The matrices which are supposed to be cast as italics are placed by the operator in the upper rail of the assembly elevator. Both roman and italic characters will line up perfectly on the cast slug of type as the equipment and the matrices are made with this purpose in mind.

Two other terms often used in conjunction with matrices as well as types are "logotypes" and "ligatures." *Logotypes* have two or more independent characters side by side on the same matrix, "or consist of two or more matrices riveted together."[30] *Ligatures* also combine two letters but these are "tied together and cast on the same body like fi, ff, and others."[31]

Types of a body size up to and including 14 point are usually considered text types, whereas those of a larger body are classified as display types. Matrices of text types and those of display types up to and including 24 point are duplexed. Matrices for larger display types are made in various sizes up to and including 60 point, but matrices for larger body sizes than 24 point are not duplexed but bear only a single casting cavity. Finally, it is mentioned that the matrices manufactured by the Linotype and those manufactured by the Intertype can be used on either machine.

Magazines for matrices. The matrices of a given type face in a given size for line-casting machines are housed together in flat, channeled receptacles made either of brass, or of aluminum, or of plastic, or of a combination of these materials. These receptacles are known as *magazines*, and are interchangeable. Magazines for line-casting machines are open at both ends. At the top the magazine receives the matrices from the distributor bar. At the bottom of the magazine, an escapement mechanism releases the matrices during keyboarding for assembly. "While the machine is in operation there is a virtually continuous flow of matrices in and out of the magazine."[32]

Magazines have 90 channels corresponding to the 90 keys provided by the keyboard, but there are also 72 channel magazines in existence. Some machine models are equipped with a supplementary keyboard and need supplementary magazines which are either known as *side magazines* or *auxiliary magazines*. These supplementary magazines have 34 channels. Ninety channel magazines are available as "*full-length*, three-quarter split, or half-split, capable of storing 20, 16, and 10, or 11 matrices of each character, respectively. Supplementary magazines are supplied by various companies in varying capacities, ranging between 8 and 20 matrices per character."[33] Finally, a word on the weight of magazines: "A full-length magazine, made of brass and carrying an average full font of matrices, weighs over 70 lb.; a lightweight aluminum magazine 50 lb., and a plastic magazine 22 lb."[34] It should be understood that these figures are mentioned solely for the purpose of giving the reader an idea of the weights involved in the handling and changing of magazines for line-casting machines. The exact weight of a specific magazine depends on the make of machine, material from which the magazine is made, and the number of matrices carried by it.

Spacebands. Spacebands, which are the equivalent of spaces in line casting, consist "merely of two wedge-shaped pieces of metal. They taper in opposite directions so that the outside faces are always parallel."[35] The two elements have different operational functions and differ in size and design. The shorter element, often called the *sleeve*, has two lugs and is of approximately the same length as matrices. The longer element, called the *wedge*, is approximately three and one-half times as long as the sleeve, and has no lugs. During justification the sleeve is stationary whereas the wedge is pushed upward, thereby increasing the effective width of the spaceband. Spacebands are

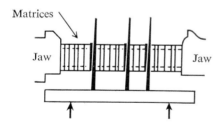

Diagram showing that the wedges of spacebands are driven up to fill the line. The sleeves of spacebands remain stationary.

available in a number of different width ranges. These go from extra thin ones, which are used in tight composition of text types, to extra thick ones for composition of larger display types. The expansive power of spacebands is approximately three times.[36] Spacebands manufactured by either of the two companies can be used in both Linotype and Intertype machines.

Justification takes place immediately before casting and is part of the automatic machine cycle. The part which actually does the job is known as the *justification block*. It presses, or pushes, the wedges of all spacebands up until the line is evenly spaced.

Line length and body sizes cast by line-casting machines. All line-casting machines can cast lines up to 30 picas wide; some models are built to permit the casting of 42 pica lines. Line-casting machines are used for both body and display composition. The assortment of type sizes in which matrices are made is not uniform. Some faces begin with 4 points, or with *agate*, which is 5½ points, others with larger bodies. They may range from these sizes up to 14, 24, or 48, or 60 point depending on the purpose of a type face. Agate is an important size for the composition of classified newspaper advertisements. Body sizes of 8 to 14 point are used for text composition; the larger sizes from 18 point on are needed for display advertising composition.

Models of line-casting machines. Line-casting machines are manufactured in a number of different models. At its simplest, a line-casting machine using duplexed matrices offers composition in two fonts, usually but not necessarily the roman and italic of the same face, comprising a maximum of 180 different characters. Models equipped with supplementary keyboards and magazines provide 34 additional channels. Their duplexed matrices contain a total of 248 characters. This number can be substantially increased on *mixers* which permit the assembly of mats from more than one magazine in the same line. Mixers are equipped with multiple distributors. They should not be confused with machines that can hold several magazines but have only a single distributor. These machines neither permit the assembly of matrices from several magazines in the same line nor their automatic distribution to several magazines. Last, but not least, it is worth mentioning that special matrices which are not available in the regular fonts can be hand inserted by the operator. These are known as *pi matrices* and are often used in highly technical or scientific composition.

Each model of a line-casting machine is designed to serve a specific purpose. It is outside the frame of the present manual to list and describe existing Linotype and Intertype models. But it should be of interest to the reader to know that ten different factors account, singly and in combination, for differences in machine models. The major differences may be grouped as follows: "(1) single distributor machines; (2) multiple distributor machines; (3) machines limited to a single magazine; (4) machines with multiple magazines; (5) machines carrying main magazines only; (6) machines carrying main plus supplementary magazines; (7) text matter or line machines; (8) display machines; (9) text and display machines; and (10) multiple magazine machines with power shift."[37] These ten different factors refer to manually operated machines and omit additional differences in tape-operated equipment which is the subject of the following unit. Those interested in further information find a selected list of books in the notes to this unit.[38]

Tape-Operated Line-Casting Machines

Tape-operated composing machines have become relatively common in the last few years, much more so than they were five to ten years ago. The cost of composition has been rising constantly, and tape operation is one of the methods whereby this process can be counteracted. Punched paper tapes have become firmly established in the composition industry, for operation of line-casting and photographic composition equipment, not to forget computerized composition.

Tape-operated line-casting machines preceded high-speed photographic typesetting and computerized composition by about 20 years. There are several makes of high-speed photographic composing machines which can produce faster than hot-metal machines, but line-casting equipment is nevertheless more widely used than photographic composition machines. The newspaper industry in particular still relies on line-casting machines because it takes less time to convert the written word into stereotype plates by hot-metal composition than by any other method.

Line-casting machines were conceived as single-unit equipment. The operator fingers the keyboard and thereby causes matrices to assemble. The act of determining the contents of a line and that of physically assembling the line is coincident on single-unit machines. The Monotype System proceeds in a different way. It is a two-stage system in which the stage of determining the contents of composition and the stage of assembling the cast types are the tasks of two different machines, the keyboard and the caster. Tape operation of line-casting machines requires two equivalent stages: one is tape punching, the other is casting of slugs of type. If the tape is computerized on independent equipment, computerizing is a third stage, interposed between tape punching and casting.

Tape for line casting can be punched by various machines and systems. There is first the original Teletypesetter System, abbreviated TTS, which does not produce a typed record of the punched tape. For this reason TTS tape-punching equipment is called *blind* in the trade. Tape punching can also be done on machines equipped with electric typewriters. Such machines have two products: one is the punched tape, the other is a concurrently established typed record of the tape contents. This typed record is known in the trade as *hard-copy*. Blind tape punching and hard-copy tape punching differ in several operational points.

Until the advent of computerized composition all tape punched for operation of line-casting machines was justified. This means that the tape contains all instructions needed for the casting of lines of uniform length. If a word must be divided at the end of a line, the operator who does the tape punching must take care of word division. Computerized composition changed this condition and diversified the field of tape preparation in several respects.

Computerized composition can be divided into two major groups with respect to operation of line casters. One group comprises systems that use general-purpose computers which justify unjustified tape and also take care of word division at the end of lines. Such systems are not discussed here but in Section 6. The other group of systems uses special-purpose computers which are designed solely for one purpose: the efficient preparation of tape for line-casting machines. Systems of this kind, in use at the time of writing, differ in many points but have one common characteristic: word division at the end of the line remains an operator function. Special-purpose computer systems reduce the instances of word division to a minimum, and they provide valuable aids to the operator, thereby increasing speed and quality of tape preparation and casting.

Diversification in consequence of computerized typesetting is often a puzzle to non-specialists. Therefore some of the most common methods of tape preparation will be identified. Tape can be prepared either justified or unjustified. Justified tape poses no problems of understanding—it is the kind of tape that is used to operate line-casting machines. Unjustified tape must be prepared in conformity with the system whereby it will be justified. A first dividing line can be drawn be-

The Intertype MONARCH
Line Casting Machine

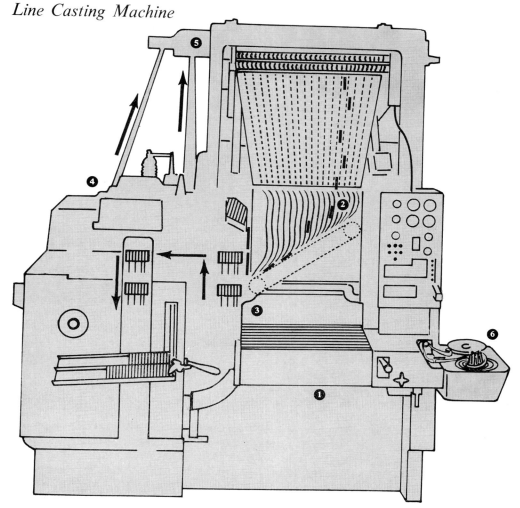

The Intertype Monarch is the fastest line casting model in the company's current equipment line. It was developed initially as a keyboardless machine to obtain maximum output under continuously automatic operation. High-speed features are now available on a keyboard-equipped Monarch as well (see photo).

A centralized control panel on right side permits instant changes in cyclical rate up to and including 15 lines per minute. Pushbuttons and signal lights simplify monitoring functions for the attendant. In regular routine, the machine is operated by wire service or locally perforated tape passing through a reader on the operating unit. Matrices are assembled at speeds up to 750 impulses per minute as escapements in the magazine are released. Lines of matrices and spacebands move from the assembly area to casting under hydraulic control. After slugs are cast and delivered to the galley at the front of the machine, the matrices and spacebands are returned to their storage magazines. Up to four 90-channel magazines can be accommodated at the same time on the Monarch. Pushbutton control moves them instantly to position for operation or removal. All design features of the machine assure stability and smooth operation, from the unique base to the rugged side brackets and the two-point support distributor bracket supporting the magazine frames.

1 *Monarch takes output of operating units rated at speeds up to 750 impulses per minute.*

2 *Vacuum manifold under matrix delivery belt holds matrices firmly on moving belt for continuous assembly.*

3 *Delta design assembler and unique spaceband chute combination assure smooth, steady inflow of matrices.*

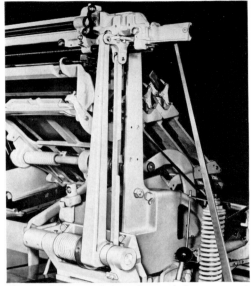

4 *Parallelogram design of second elevator speeds pickup of matrices and smooth delivery to distributor.*

5 *Elbow-action linkage for first-elevator slide permits rapid vertical movement with maximum smoothness.*

6 *Tape feed and rewind unit permits fast loading, steady feed into reader, and continuous rewind on back reel.*

tween tapes to be justified by special-purpose computers, such as the Linasec, and that to be justified by general-purpose computers. The Linasec is briefly described in this unit; general-purpose computers are the subject matter of Section 6. At this point it is merely mentioned that the preparation of unjustified tape for general-purpose computers is not the same for all systems of fully computerized composition.

Things are further complicated by the fact that some equipment for tape preparation can be used for punching either justified or unjustified tape; that there are also machines that are suitable for unjustified tape preparation only, and that there are systems that are never used for preparation of unjustified tape. (And it may even become possible to prepare magnetic tapes together with hard-copy for use in general-purpose computers. The first specimens of such machines are making their appearance at the time of writing.)

It is not possible in the available space to describe each of the existing machines for tape preparation, nor would such descriptions be of interest to readers who want to become acquainted with the subject rather than to specialize in it. In the following you find discussions of four systems: (1) the Teletypesetter, (2) the Friden LCC line, (3) the Linasec, and (4) the Di-An Computer Keyboard. The Teletypesetter is the original method of blind tape punching for line casting; the Friden LCC line permits tape punching in combination with hard-copy, the Linasec is a special-purpose computer system for converting unjustified tape, punched on blind or on hard-copy equipment, into justified tape; the Di-An Computer Keyboard, finally, uses special-purpose computers for producing justified tape and hard-copy.

The original Teletypesetter System. The first system for tape-operated line-casting machines was the Teletypesetter System, abbreviated as TTS in the literature. Several sources contributed to the development of TTS. One of them was the existence of the Teletype (not to be confused with the Teletypesetter System) which made the wire transmission of typed messages possible. A second factor was the growth of newspaper chains and the desire of publishers to use the same editorial material in several papers of their chains. There was also the well-established example of the Monotype where keyboarding and casting are separate functions and where the caster is tape operated. The "original inventor of the Teletypesetter System was Walter Morey, a former printer, com-

posing room superintendent and Monotype salesman. His early experiments in the 1920's were carried on in Newark, N. J. He later secured the backing of Frank Gannett, newspaper publisher, Rochester, N. Y."[39]

Morey's invention was more or less perfected by 1932. "The original concept of Teletypesetter operation included tape produced at a central point and transmitted to various receiving points by telegraphic means." It is worth mentioning that "perhaps the first important transmitted tape operation in the United States prior to World War II was used by *Time* magazine. Transmission of tape using reperforations was done from New York to Chicago and from New York to Philadelphia. These installations enabled *Time* publishers to gain a day in production."[40]

It was already explained that tape operation divorces the keyboarding function from the casting function. Keyboarding is now done on a separate machine which has the layout of a typewriter. Matrix and spaceband assembly, line casting, and all other related operations are performed by a Linotype or Intertype machine, operated by the product of keyboarding, a punched paper tape.

The next point that must be firmly grasped is that keyboarding for tape perforation is essentially different from keyboarding on line-casting machines. On the machine the operator watches the assembly of matrices and spacebands and decides visually when the line is ready for sending-in. As there is no assembly of matrices and spacebands in keyboarding for tape operation, the method of numerical width control of characters and spaces must be employed. This control is based on a unit system patterned after the Monotype Unit System though with certain differences. Tape-operated line casting combines the two methods by which hot-metal composition can be justified. Keyboarding is based on numerical width control; in the actual assembly and justification of line casting the different principle of mechanical spacing-out is applied. The punched tape informs the line-casting machine on the amount of matrices and spacebands that will fill a line; the expansion of the spaceband whereby the line is actually justified is done mechanically exactly as it is done on manually operated line-casting machines. Tape operation merely replaces manual keyboarding. The other functions of line-casting machines are not influenced by it.

The original Teletypesetter System (TTS) provides means for keyboarding and tape perforating.

This system was designed for wire transmission and, consequently, it includes a *Reperforator* at the receiving station. In order to make it possible to use already existing line-casting machines with the new system, an *Operating Unit* for the tape and a *Keyboard Adaptor* were developed as attachments to line-casting machines, and a *Page Printer*, providing a typed copy of the content of the tape is optional, both at the transmitting and at the receiving station. In the course of time, additional equipment was developed by several companies. In the following the most important component parts of tape operation are briefly discussed.

The Standard Perforator. The original Teletypesetter System was based on the *Standard Perforator* as the keyboarding machine. "Features of the Standard Perforator are its basic typewriter keyboard layout, its punch mechanism, and its counting device. The Perforator is driven by electric motor which provides power for perforating the tape and for actuating the counting mechanism. The touch on the keyboard is about the same as that of a standard typewriter."[41] The Standard Perforator requires the use of especially made matrices which are known as *unit matrices*. "Unit matrices are made in widths directly proportional to the 'em' quad of the type face, each unit being 1/18 of the brass width of the quad matrix (sometimes the capital M is referred to as the basis, the M being equal to the em quad in width). With the unit system, eleven groups of various unit widths are used for the entire font of type characters. The narrowest is 6 units wide; others are 7, 8, 9, 10, 11, 12, 13, 14, 15, and 18."[42] *It must be remembered that the Standard Perforator cannot be used with other matrices than those specially made to the unit system.*

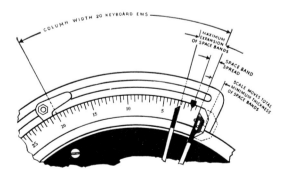

The Indicator Scale *on a Multiface Teletypesetter Perforator. This scale indicates the extent to which the line is filled and also the maximum expansion of spacebands. The scale guides the operator in his end-of-line decisions.*

Both the Linotype and the Intertype supply such matrices in a selection of type faces and in the sizes needed for text composition of newspapers, say in a range between 5½ and 11 points.

Keyboarding on the Standard Perforator. The Standard Perforator has, as mentioned, the usual typewriter layout, several additional keys to control machine functions, provisions for tape punching, a counting mechanism, and the indicator scale. The Standard Perforator differs from a typewriter in one additional point: it does not produce the typed images of percussion typing. In other words, the Standard Perforator of the TTS does not provide what the trade has come to call *hardcopy*, namely, a typescript. The operator controls justification visually, though not in the same manner as on a line-casting machine. There he can observe the actual assembly of matrices in the assembly elevator. In the TTS Perforator this is, of course, not possible. Here visual control of the progress of composition is provided by the indicator scale which also indicates the justification area of the line. The operator must decide whether he can put a syllable, or a word, or neither in the remaining slack. Proper word division is, hence, one of the operator's duties in the TTS.

Transmitting and Reperforating equipment. The original TTS was, as you already know, intended for wire transmission of perforated tape. The perforated tape "is immediately fed into the *Transmitter Distributor* which sends electrical impulses over the wire in accordance with the code holes in the tape. These may be carried to any distance, by telegraph or telephone wire (or by radio)."[43] In the receiving composing room a *Reperforator* is needed for converting the electrical signals coming over the wire into a duplicate of the original punched tape. Reperforators can be located in many different places and connected to the same transmission equipment. Where a typed record of the received tape is desired, a Page Printer is connected to the wire.

The Operation Unit and the Adaptor Keyboard. Most line-casting machines used for tape operation are equipped with keyboards and were built for manual rather than tape operation. To make such a line-casting machine suitable for tape operation it must be equipped with an *Adaptor Keyboard* and an *Operating Unit* for the tape. Both units work together. The Adaptor Keyboard is mounted under the manually operated keyboard which remains usable for manual keyboarding. The operator can change from manual to tape op-

The MERGENTHALER
Elektron Linotype

Fastest Linotype for both tape
and manual operation,
with continuous assembly,
straight-line delivery,
hydraulic justification,
and push-button control.

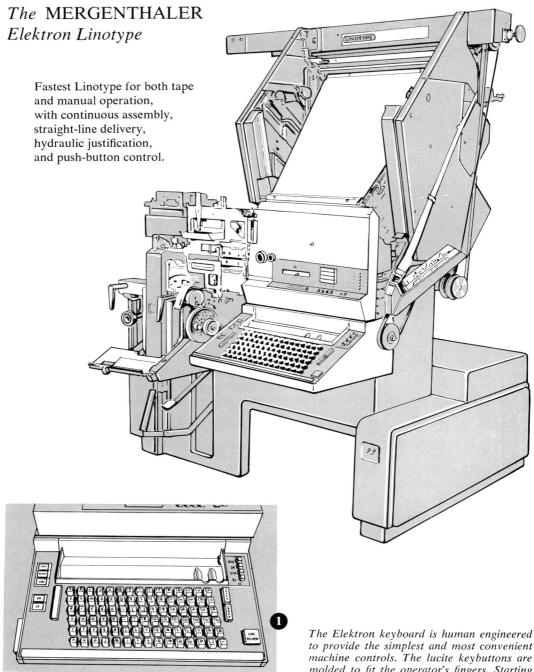

1

(A) *Sending a line to casting position is easy. The operator uses his left hand to lift a trip lever; power delivers the line.*

(B) *To use his right hand, the operator just presses a button on the right side of the keyboard. Again, powered delivery takes over.*

The Elektron keyboard is human engineered to provide the simplest and most convenient machine controls. The lucite keybuttons are molded to fit the operator's fingers. Starting and stopping, Upper or Lower Rail selection, and Line Delivery buttons are within easy reach. The control panel above the keyboard contains the Line Length Indicator, magazine selection, elevate and fan buttons, and six safety indicator lights.

The Linotype Elektron is the fastest and most productive linecasting machine ever built by Mergenthaler. Strikingly new in design, the tape-operated Elektron delivers slugs to the galley at the rate of 15 standard newspaper lines a minute.

From its sturdy H-shaped base up, Elektron incorporates many engineering innovations: continuous, uninterrupted assembly of matrices; straight-line matrix travel that *eliminates* the assembling elevator; push-button control of basic machine functions; hydraulic justification and a full complement of machine safeties.

Also available are the Elektron II for manual operation and the Elektron Mixer which permits mixing from adjacent magazines, for either manual or tape operation.

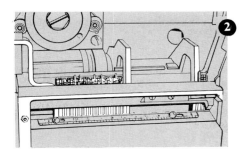

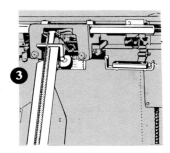

While one line is on its way into the elevator jaws, the operator can start to assemble the next line. There is no stop and go on the Elektron Linotype.

The parallelogram action of the second elevator provides for smooth control of matrices at all times.

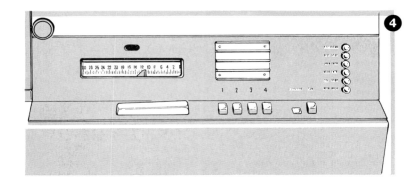

On Elektron's centralized control panel are the new eye-level Line Length Indicator, magazine selector buttons, and the elevate and fan controls. The six indicator lights on the right are easily visible to an operator or monitor.

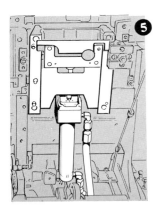

The hydraulic cylinder and justification bar drive the spaceband wedges upward to justify a line. Hydraulic justification means that forces are constant regardless of operating speed.

The Elektron can accommodate up to four standard 90-channel Linotype magazines, and elevate or fan them hydraulically by push-button control. The angle of the magazines is 52½ degrees.

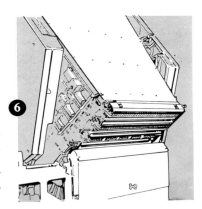

eration and vice versa "with the turn of a control lever."[44] The operating unit "mechanically *senses* the tape transforming the code combination into mechanical actions which set the matrix lines and govern the associated line delivery functions. Auxiliary key levers act as the connecting links between the operating unit and the line-casting machine."[45]

Not all line-casting machines need an Adaptor Keyboard and an Operating Unit for tape operation. The most recent models are designed for tape operation and do not require these two equipment items. One is the Intertype *Monarch*, the other is the Linotype *Elektron;* both are designed for high-speed tape operation. The Monarch as well as the Elektron come in models equipped with keyboards. Such models can be operated either manually or by punched tape, whichever method may be preferred in a given situation. The Intertype Monarch is also available in a model without keyboard, and this model is designed for tape operation exclusively.

The restriction of the original Teletypesetter System to unit mats which had to be specially made to conform to the counting mechanism of the Standard Perforator limited the system to newspaper composition. Job and commercial printers, as well as book manufacturers, have substantial investments in matrices for line casting and needed a tape-operation method which was not limited to unit matrices but could utilize their existing stock of matrix fonts. The same need exists also in newspapers for locally punched tape. For this reason a different keyboarding unit was developed which is known as the *Multiface Perforator*.

The Multiface Perforator. "Its general principles are similar to the Standard Perforator, the essential difference being in the counting mechanism. To count an accumulating line of normal (not unit-manufactured) matrices, it was found that the full font of these matrices could be divided into 28 groups by set-width. For the basis of counting the em quad (or capital M) is divided into 32 units. The narrowest character is 5 units wide or 5/32 of the em quad."[46]

The counting-magazine and its purpose. As each type face differs from all others, and as the same holds true for each body size of matrices, rapid changeover requires certain provisions. The desired result is obtained by an item known as *counting-magazine* which is needed for the use of Multiface and of Universal Perforators. Perhaps a brief explanation of the reasons for counting-magazines

will aid in the understanding of the subject. You might recall that the number of units is fixed for each matrix character that can be used with tape punched on the Standard Perforator. This limitation is a handicap in book, job, and commercial printing, as already explained. The Multiface and the Universal Perforator have the function of eliminating this undesirable condition. But it must be kept in mind that the width of matrices varies from one type face to another for the same characters. These variations are particularly strong between condensed and extended designs. The counting-magazine, which is supplied to the users of Multiface Perforators, is especially made for each type face and enables the counting mechanism of Multiface and Universal Perforators to count the correct number of units for each character of the type face for which the counting-mechanism was prepared. Counting-magazines can be easily exchanged by the operator of the perforating equipment.

The Universal Perforator. A single font of matrices is often insufficient for composition with line-casting machines. For this reason the already mentioned *mixers* were developed which have several different magazines ready for combination. The Multiface Perforator is still limited to a single font of duplexed matrices. In certain kinds of book composition this limitation is overcome by the manual inserting of pi matrices. The following report shows how serious these limitations can be: "We have examined 983 pages of manuscript. A total of 123 special characters were located and tabulated. This involves 4,575 pi stops. If we project these figures over the entire pages of manuscript of this project we would expect 166,430 pi stops. We find from timing tape-operated casting machines that the production loss from hand insertion of pi characters on this job would be 1,387 hours of continuous caster production. The operator marking-in the pi mats would lose approximately 2,400 hours of operator production."[47] The *Universal Perforator* has the purpose of eliminating such bottlenecks. This kind of equipment is still quite new. Some Universal Perforators can handle two counting-magazines for two different fonts of duplexed matrices; others are equipped for four counting-magazines, thereby making it possible that four-magazine mixers can be tape operated.

Summary of different TTS Perforators. The Standard Perforator must be used with especially made unit matrices. Its main application is in wire transmission by newspaper services. The Multiface Perforator can be used for a single font of every kind of matrix used for text composition. Each font and body size needs a counting-magazine which is inserted into the Multiface Perforator. The Universal Perforator is capable of producing tape suitable for the operation of *mixer* models; some Universal Perforators can operate four different counting-magazines and produce tape for four-magazine mixers.

The Friden LCC line of tape perforators. Friden tape perforators for operating composition machines were evolved from the Friden Justowriter composition system which produces justified composition of body types with typewriter-like machines. (The Justowriter is described in Section 4 under the side head "Non-metallic Composition of Text Types.") Friden offers a number of models and can also supply machines that combine the features of some models for greater flexibility. A typical Friden tape perforator consists of six major operating components. These are: (1) the tape reader, (2) the code translator, (3) an electric typewriter, (4) the code selector, (5) the tape punch, and (6) the computer. The operator fingers the keyboard of the typewriter and produces two products simultaneously: the main product is the perforated tape, the by-product is a typed record of the tape codes, the often mentioned hard-copy.

The keyboard of LCC models has a number of buttons related to machine function in addition to those needed for letters, numerals, and marks of punctuation. When the operator strikes a key

A Friden LCC-S *tape perforator. This typewriter-like machine provides both punched paper tape for operating of composition equipment and hard-copy for proofreading.*

button the *code selector* converts this mechanical action into a series of electrical impulses which are transmitted to the punching mechanism, and the punch perforates the tape with the code assigned to the struck key button. The *computer* calculates the width of spaces between words and the progress of composition can be read by the operator on a numbered scale. If a Friden perforator is used to punch justified tape this scale guides the operator in deciding whether he should end a line without dividing the last word or by word division. In punching unjustified tape the operator continues without concern for the correct length of lines.

The punched tape can be used for producing a typed record. This possibility is of value if the punched tape needs additions or corrections. Now the *tape reader* comes into play. It mechanically senses codes punched in tape and converts each code into a series of electrical impulses which are transmitted to the code translator. The *code translator* converts electrical impulses into a mechanical action whereby a key lever is operated to produce the typescript.[48]

All Friden LCC tape perforator models are equipped for punching six-level tapes. Upon request the number of punched tape levels can be either six or seven or eight. The Model LCC-C is designed for punching of unjustified tape to be computerized. The Model LCC-S can produce tape for TTS unit matrices and corresponds to the TTS Standard Perforator.

Then there is the Model LCC-VF which corresponds to the TTS Multiface Perforator. As different type faces and type sizes have characters of differing set widths a plugboard is used in conjunction with the LCC-VF for each face and size. This plugboard controls the computer that informs the operator through the numbered scale on the line-wise progress of composition. The LCC-VF can be equipped for punching both justified and unjustified tape. Unjustified tape is punched for computerizing, justified tape can be used directly on line-casting machines. Two plugboards can be connected to a typewriter, though only if both are wired for type faces of the same point size. The resulting tape can operate a mixer model with two duplexed magazines.

The Linasec. The Linasec System is designed to convert unjustified paper tape into justified tape suitable for automatic operation of line-casting machines. The system comprises four connected units: (1) a Linasec II Computer Console, (2) a Monitor Display, (3) an input reader for unjusti-

A typical Linasec II *installation. The monitor is seated before the video screen on which end-of-line words are displayed if a monitor decision is required. Hyphenation buttons are so arranged that the monitor can put the hyphen between the letters where it belongs. High-speed reperforator is to the left of monitor, input tape reader to his right.*

fied tape, and (4) an output punch to produce the final, justified tape. The Linasec Computer is a special-purpose computer, programmed by actual wired circuitry as contrasted with stored programs needed for general-purpose computers.

During operation the monitor is seated in front of the Monitor Display, a cathode ray, or video tube. When a word needs division "the Linasec stops and displays this word on the cathode display tube. This display is presented so that the characters which are outside the measure are clearly indicated and in such a way that a marker terminating at a white button appears at each character interstice. The monitor operator then depresses a button beneath the acceptable hyphenation position and the Linasec will proceed automatically, inserting the hyphen code and the end-of-line code in the output tape, carrying over to the next line those characters after the hyphen."[49] The preceding description refers to the Linasec II; the Linasec I, which is much less widely used and not now being manufactured, has a somewhat different arrangement.[50]

The Linasec II can produce justified tape at the rate of 6,000 to 7,500 newspaper lines per hour. In large installations up to 12 input stations and the requisite number of line-casting machines can be controlled by a central monitor station. The Linasec system provides a number of special programs for editing of stock market report tapes, for editing of telephone directories and for tabular composition. Then there is *Keyboard Shorthand*, another feature of the Linasec which can save 14 per cent of operator keyboard strokes by automatically capitalizing the first letter at a new paragraph, by providing a single code for five of the most frequently used words (the, and, of, to,

in), and by other features too technical for discussion. The *Linasec JusTape*, finally, is a basic building block computer of the wired program type which in its simplest form converts unjustified tape into justified tape without any hyphenation at line endings.

It is of interest to notice that the Linasec System was preceded by the *Directory Tape Processor*, or DTP, a special-purpose computer designed to simplify the keyboarding of telephone directory listings and to improve casting of the resulting slugs. Compared with the high specialization of the DTP the Linasec System is of much wider scope. Its application to filmsetting extends this scope still further.

The Di-An Computer Keyboard. The Computer Keyboard is designed for efficient production of six-level tape as needed for tape-operated linecasting machines. The equipment comprises an electric typewriter, supplemented with a number of keys for punching machine function codes. Since the Computer Keyboard is designed for a single purpose, especially trained operators are not needed. There are no character codes to be typed, nor are programmers required.

The operator must be a good typist and he must know where to hyphenate words. He fingers the keyboard looking at the copy which is on the copyholder facing him. This copyholder has a number of signal lights at its bottom that guide the operator in error correction, justification, and hyphenation. Typing produces the usual hardcopy, a typed record suitable for proofreading. As the line is typed it is simultaneously assembled in the magnetic core memory of the computer; all corrections made during typing are automatically also made in the computer memory. When the carriage of the typewriter returns for typing the next line, the tape is punched.

If the composed line does not need word division, which is the case when the composed material falls within the expansion zone of the space-bands, the next depression of the typewriter space bar will automatically return the carriage and release the justified line to the tape punch. If word division is required at the end of the line, the operator is guided by seven en-lights which show how many ens are still left to be composed in the line. (The en is a typographic measure amounting to one half of the em which is the square of the body size. In many type faces an en is more or less equivalent to average character width.) When the line comes within seven ens of the line length the first white en-light goes on, when only six ens are left, the first light goes out and the second flashes, and so on. As these lights are on the copyholder the operator can observe progress of composition at a glance. If the line is overset, the yellow light and all white lights go out and the red error light goes on; now the keyboard locks except for keys needed for correction.

The buttons provided for punching of function codes are used for including typographic requirements such as insertion of different spaces and selecting of upper or lower characters on duplexed matrices. Computer Keyboard permits a choice of nine type fonts; five of them are unit size, the other four can be of any design.[51]

The effects of tape operation on the line-casting industry. It took almost a quarter of a century from its first appearance in the field until the Teletypesetter System was widely accepted. The main success of tape operation was greatly stepped up after the end of World War II. "There were only a few newspapers using it before the War, but since the War there have been 800 to 1,000 installations up to 1959. And there are only 1,400 to 1,500 daily newspapers. The Teletypesetter equipment was a wonderful device for selling wire service. Wire service, such as that offered by Associated Press, United Press and International News Service, in turn was a great answer to the problem of the small daily newspaper because they could obtain well-edited material over the wire and receive it fast and efficiently. This solved the problem of writing and editing as well as the problem of labor costs in the composing room, and the composing room cost for a small newspaper comes as high as 60 per cent of the total manufacturing cost."[52]

Tape operation has left indelible marks in the newspaper industry. In other branches of the graphic arts its impact has been considerable though not nearly as strong. Composition for book work and composition of reading matter for magazines is a natural field for tape operation. Multiface Perforators have extended the use of tape operation to these areas. The introduction of universal perforators, which permit the application of tape operation to more complex composition tasks, will most likely secure a still bigger share for tape operation in many composing rooms, particularly for complex composition tasks in book work of a technical nature.

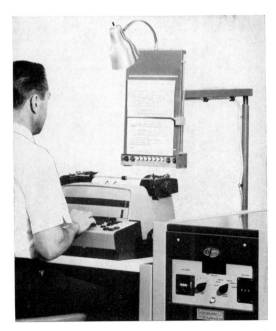

Keyboarding for tape-operated linecasters on a Di-An Computer Keyboard, Model LC-III. Operator is guided in word division by the light signals on the copy holder. Control panel at his right permits selection of line length, font, and other typographic features,

The Ludlow System

The Ludlow System combines the hand composition of matrices with the casting of single lines of type as slugs. Just as the Linotype and Monotype succeeded to mechanize the composition of body types, so the Ludlow System achieved the mechanization of the casting of display types. Furthermore, in the development of smaller type sizes, lining type faces, italics, scripts, ruleform, and other matrix equipment, the Ludlow has extended

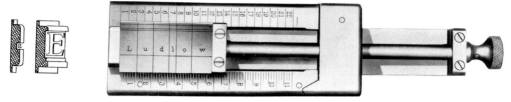

Two Ludlow matrices *and a* Ludlow self-quadding matrix stick. *Note that the matrices are of the same height even though the type cast from them differs strongly in its point size. Ludlow sticks are available up to 112¹/₂ picas line length; matrices have right-reading reference characters.*

its range to include job and miscellaneous composition of the average commercial or specialty plant. When the first Ludlow machine appeared in 1911, it represented another major advance in hot-metal composition.

Hand composition of type matrices in a Ludlow composing stick.

While the Ludlow was originally developed particularly for display type composition, and is capable of producing letters up to 144 point and figures up to 240 point, its matrix equipment has been expanded so that most type faces have a size range from 6 point to 48 point, or larger. Accordingly, the Ludlow System is also used extensively for the composition of commercial printing, business forms, rubber stamps, and paper specialties, to mention the more important fields of application. The system comprises specially designed matrices, matrix cabinets, composing sticks, and accessories, as well as a casting machine. The compositor gathers and assembles the matrices and spaces in the Ludlow composing stick, locks and inserts the stick full of matrices in the Ludlow Typograph Casting Machine, where the type slug is automatically cast and ejected.

The growth of machine composition has not obliterated the need for hand composition which has actually increased rather than diminished. Hand composition has many tasks of its own and supplements machine composition in many cases. The Ludlow System is a substantial contribution to our composition technology because it improves the quality and the handling of hand-composed matter and because it is a great space saver and, therefore, a time saver.

The quality of hand composition is improved because Ludlow type is always new and does not have defects associated with the use of worn type. The handling of hand composition is much simpler in the Ludlow System on two counts. For one, the matrices of all type sizes are of the same size which makes it much easier to compose lines of small body sizes than by using foundry type which changes in its size for every different body size. The second point is that the product of Ludlow composition is a slug of type as opposed to the product of hand composition which consists of individual characters. The used slug of Ludlow

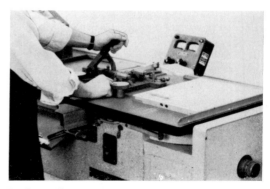

In the Ludlow System *slugs of type are cast from individually assembled matrices. You see an operator locking a Ludlow composing stick with a line of type matrices in a Ludlow caster.*

composition is melted down and not distributed; however, Ludlow matrices are distributed. This is done promptly while the slug is being trimmed and delivered.

The saving of space, finally, is a considerable advantage of the Ludlow System in actual plant operation. In hand composition with foundry type, each type case must contain a much larger quantity of individual characters, or sorts, than are necessary in the Ludlow System. The Ludlow type library, consisting of matrices, can be stored in a much smaller space which reduces the non-productive time and efforts of the hand compositor.

Like all other hot-metal composing systems, the Ludlow System has many distinctive features of its own. Some of these are too technical for our discussion, but it is worth mentioning that italic and script types can be cast in a slanted position, which enhances the beauty of their composition. *The Ludlow Ruleform System* permits the casting of intersecting horizontal and vertical rules. This system, together with lining type faces, makes the slug composition of business forms, invoices, and similar items possible. More recently a competitive machine is being imported in this country from Italy. It is sold here under the name of *Nebitype* and differs in certain points from the Ludlow.

Subsidiary Composing-Room Equipment

Our discussion of hot-metal machine composition should not be closed without mentioning some other equipment items which have been found to be necessary in many composing rooms. These are grouped into (1) material makers; (2) machines that cast individual types and spaces; and (3) accessories for line-casting machines.

Material makers. A composing room needs not only type but also spacing material. The *Elrod* "machine forms molten type metal into leads, slugs, rules, and base materials in continuous strips which it automatically cuts off and stacks in any desired length from 5 to 140 picas."[53] Other machines that make strip material include the *Monotype Material Maker* which produces strip material such as leads, slugs, rules, and ornamental borders, and the *Universal Strip Caster* which is also used for the making of leads, slugs, and rules. Each of these machines is distinguished by certain capabilities and has been developed with certain specific purposes in mind.[54]

Machines to cast individual types and spaces. Some machines can produce both strip material

and individual characters. One of them is the *Monotype Type and Rule Caster* which can cast types with a body size within a range from 4 points up to and including 36 points. The leads, slugs, and rules cast by this machine range from 1½ points up to and including 12 points. The *Monotype-Thompson Type-Caster* is a machine that is sometimes called a complete type foundry. It uses all kinds of matrices, not only those made by the Monotype but also Ludlow, Linotype, and Intertype matrices. The range of body sizes is from 6 point up to and including 48 point. "The Monotype Company features a Matrix Library comprising many of their series through which matrices may be rented."[55] The *Monotype Giant Caster* can cast types from 14 point up to and including 72 point, as well as metal furniture and base for the mounting of photoengravings and duplicate plates. Furniture and bases can be cast in the same point range as types and in length not exceeding 24 inches.

All Monotype casting and material-making machines mentioned up to here are domestically manufactured. The *Monotype Super Caster*, which is used to some extent in the United States, is a product of the English Monotype Corporation. This machine combines many features of the

A Margach Automatic Metal Feeder installed on a line-casting machine. This feeder provides constant, controlled feeding of type metal.

Monotype Giant Caster and the Monotype Material Maker.

Accessories for line-casting machines. In this group of equipment belong several machines that

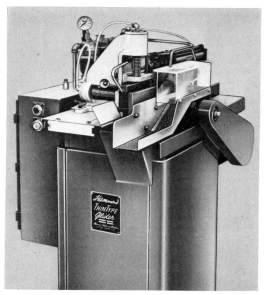

The Hammond Thintype Glider *is a saw for stripping the type face of slugs of type as needed for hot metal pasteup of display advertisements.*

are either used in conjunction with the casting operation or for the processing of the cast product. The Margach Automatic Metal Feeder and the Monomelt have the first-mentioned purpose whereas the Mohr Saw, the Ludlow Shell-Hi Slug Shear, the Margach Lino Slug Router, the Morrison Slug Stripper, the ThinType Glider, the Rouse Band Saw, the Hammond TrimOsaw, and the Ludlow Supersurfacer are used for the second. Most of these machines are briefly identified in the following.[56] The *Margach Automatic Metal Feeder* can be used with any hot-metal composing machine. It can carry one or two pigs of metal, each weighing 30 pounds, and lower them into the melting pot at the same rate at which molten metal is consumed by the progress of casting. The Monomelt "is fundamentally an electric or gas-heated *crucible* which melts and cleans metal, then feeds it automatically into the regular melting pot of the type-casting machine."[57] The Monomelt is made for use on all hot-metal machines.

Now to machines that are used for adapting or improving the cast line. There is first the *Mohr Saw* which is an automatic slug saw that can be

incorporated in both Linotype and Intertype machines. "It saws each odd measure slug to its predetermined length when the slug is ejected and delivers it to the galley as a finished product, ready for use; it is most useful on machines that require many changes of measure."[58] The *Ludlow Shell-Hi Slug Shear* makes it possible to use composed lines on plate bases rather than on the bed of a platen or flatbed-cylinder press. Flat duplicate plates are usually made in a thickness of 0.152 inch and the bed of the press is built up to 0.765 inch in order to bring the material to its proper printing height. It may happen that changing information or other circumstances demand the combination of cast lines with duplicate plates. Since such lines come type-high from the machine, they measure 0.918 inch and therefore cannot be put on plate bases which occupy 0.765 inch, or almost three-quarters of the standard height-to-paper. The slugs of type must therefore be diminished in their height to the dimension of duplicate plates, namely 0.152 inch, before they can be used on plate bases. This result is produced by means of the Ludlow Shell-Hi Slug Shear and other machines. The *Morrison Slug Stripper* fulfils the same task though in a different manner. The *ThinType Glider*, finally, produces somewhat similar results as the Ludlow Shell-Hi Slug Shear and the Morrison Slug Stripper. The main difference is that the ThinType Glider can strip all types of machine-cast slugs either singly or in multiples.

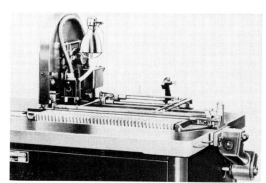

The Rouse Band Saw *is an independently operated machine for cutting slugs of type in correct alignment.*

The *Rouse Band Saw* cuts slugs produced on line-casting machines to varying measures in one operation without resetting, using a guide which has been cast on each slug. But whereas the Mohr Saw is part of line-casting equipment, the Rouse Band Saw is used independently. *Hammond Trim-*

Osaws are used in composing rooms to saw and trim slugs, rule, border, base materials, and flat letterpress printing plates. The last item to be mentioned in this brief review is the Ludlow *Super-surfacer*. This machine improves the printing surface of cast slugs, especially those of larger body sizes that are used for the pulling of reproduction proofs, which are printed on coated paper for photographic reproduction. The improvement is achieved by passing the slugs under a cutting head which removes a tiny fraction of the type surface from the slug.

Our discussion of hot-metal machine composition is at its end. The reader can see the great variety and specialization of methods and machinery. In the following section on non-metallic composition the diversification and specialization of our contemporary composition methods is augmented by more than two scores of machines used in different systems.

Section 4:   Non-metallic Composition

Since the end of World War II, non-metallic composition has occupied a prominent place in graphic arts research and development. The exceptionally strong interest in non-metallic composition can be attributed to a number of different reasons. Among them is the growth of offset lithography and gravure which cannot use metal types directly, but need only type images for reproduction. A second reason can be seen in the opinions of many modern machine designers who believe that hot-metal machines are outmoded in their basic designs in terms of contemporary engineering practice. When hot-metal composing machines were developed they were considered marvels of mechanical engineering. In our own time electrical and electronic engineering permit great advances in equipment construction. The advocates of the application of electrical and electronic engineering to composing-machine construction are convinced that much greater speed and wider scope of such equipment will be thereby achieved. Last, but not least, there is the perennial complaint about the cost of composition which is considered much too high for short-run utility printing where the quality of the printed message or information has much less importance than its content. As the need for such composition has vastly increased in our specialized society, this problem is a serious one.

The diversity of motivation expresses itself in the variety of the now existing non-metallic composing methods and machines. If one wants to develop a low-cost composition system for short-run work one must obviously approach the subject in a different way than in a project aiming at highest speed and efficiency in the production of quality composition. At the time of writing, things are still in the state of flux. Some non-metallic composing machines have already become well established; others are in various stages of development. The whole field is far from settled and will probably remain unsettled for some time to come.

Graphic arts history informs us that the development of metal composing machines was time-consuming and rather expensive. We must not be surprised if history repeats itself in these respects at the development of non-metallic composing machines. Electronic equipment in particular requires relatively high investments in money and time during the development period.

The terminology of non-metallic composition. Like in any other new field, the terminology of non-metallic composition tends to proliferate and to become troublesome. The reader may have noticed that terminology is discussed in many places of this manual as one of the stumbling blocks in the printing industry to proper communication. Many writers on non-metallic composition complain about the existing medley of terms as "misleading and confusing. Some of the most popular of these have been 'typewriter type,' 'phototypesetting,' 'photocomposition,' 'filmsetting,' and what is apparently the most ambiguous and popular one of all, 'cold' type. The term 'cold type' is almost meaningless and useless, however, since it neither explains nor clarifies."[59] The heading of the present section as non-metallic composition is open to criticism on similar grounds as it merely draws a dividing line but does not offer help in explaining the subject. Recently the word *flat* type appeared in the literature; this new generic name certainly deserves consideration as it focuses on an essential aspect of all non-metallic type. Metallic type bears relief printing images and is almost an inch high. Non-metallic composition is mainly done on photographic papers or films. It does not have relief images and is much less bulky than metallic type.

Functional differences between metallic and non-metallic composition. Metallic composition can be used for three different kinds of purposes. These are: (1) direct printing in a platen or flatbed-cylinder press; (2) duplicate platemaking; and (3) use of type images, either in the form of reproduction proofs, or by means of image conversion. These products are primarily used for photomechanical platemaking. In direct printing of metallic type the relief image is inked and the ink image is transferred to the paper or other stock under pressure. Duplicate platemaking, which is extensively discussed in Chapter V, produces relief printing-image carriers of four kinds: stereotypes, electrotypes, rubber plates, and plastic plates. Each of these products is the result of a lengthy manufacturing process. But all have one common phase, namely, the making of matrices by impressing the relief material into a malleable intermediate which results in an intaglio replica of the relief material. Matrices can be made either by pressure alone, or by heat and pressure combined, depending on the process employed. The final product, the duplicate plate, is again a relief image carrier that is used in one of the several methods of relief printing. The first two uses of composition for direct printing and duplicate platemaking are predicated upon the relief character of metallic type.

The third use of type as a reproduction proof does not depend on the physical or relief construction of type but is based solely on the resulting type images. Type images can also be obtained by non-metallic composition. The manner in which type images are recorded in non-metallic composition differs according to their production method. But all non-metallic composition is based on the principle of visual *contrast*, whereas metallic composition relies on the relief principle. Relief composition separates the image and the non-image areas by differences in metal height. Non-metallic composition separates these two kinds of areas by contrast. In positive composition the image areas are black and the non-image areas are either white or transparent; in negative composition the image areas are white or transparent whereas the non-image areas are black. The black areas may consist of printer's ink, as in reproduction proofs, or in particles of pigment deposited by a typewriter ribbon, or in photographic composition by colloidal deposits of metallic silver which looks black to the eye as explained in Chapter IV, "Photography for the Graphic Arts." The base on which these images are deposited is either

paper or film. Photographic methods can use papers and plastic films; reproduction proofs are mainly made on paper but can also be pulled on plastic films.

Diagrammatic comparison of metallic type and a filmset character.

Low weight and bulk of non-metallic composition. The nature of non-metallic composition accounts for its low weight and low bulk in comparison with the weight and bulk of metallic composition. As you may remember from Section 2 the height of metallic type is standardized at 0.918 inch. Non-metallic type occupies usually less than one-tenth of the cubic space of metallic type. The weight of non-metallic type is much less than that of metallic type, not only because it has a much smaller cubic area but also because the substratum on which the type images are here deposited, paper or plastic, has a much lower specific gravity than type metal which consists mainly of lead. This feature of small bulk and low weight seems to be the only generally valid characteristic difference between all kinds of metallic and non-metallic composition. All other generalizations that the present writer has seen in the literature or tried to establish himself must be qualified with one exception or the other. Each of the many existing non-metallic composition systems has certain distinguishing characteristics. At the time of writing not less than 48 different non-metallic composing machines were listed in a survey of this field, not counting various models of the same kind of equipment.[60] How many of these products will stand the test of time remains to be seen.

The four kinds of non-metallic composition. For the purpose of organization it seems to be best to divide non-metallic composition into four groups. These are: (1) non-metallic composition of display types; (2) composition systems for text or body types; (3) full-range composition systems capable of producing text types as well as display types; and (4) composition of lists. At this point it should be mentioned that techniques for the use of type images produced by metallic composition are discussed in Section 5 under the head "Image Conversion of Metallic Composition."

It is only natural that the many developments in the field of non-metallic composition made it necessary to devise correlative equipment and techniques for the efficient handling of non-metallic composition. Layout, correcting, and proofing are different from the same operations in metallic composition, to mention some obvious points. All these many items add, unfortunately, to the complexity of the subject.

Non-metallic Composition of Display Types

Non-metallic composition of display types preceded all other kinds of such composition. Originally it was used to prepare advertising material for offset lithography and screen process, less for gravure. It is possible to do this kind of composition with relatively inexpensive equipment in comparison with the cost of equipment used for non-metallic text composition, not to speak of the cost of full-range machines. Our discussion is divided into four points: (1) hand composition of type images, (2) hand composition with photographic matrices, (3) photolettering machines, and (4) keyboarding of display types.

Hand composition of type images. This kind of composition requires the least expensive equipment. It is done with a tool which is equivalent to a composing stick and resembles the hand composition of display types. The *Fototype* System, for example, provides fonts of type consisting of individual characters printed either on lightweight index card stock or on a translucent acetate. The system includes a composing stick where the precut letters are assembled and spaced to the required measure. After the composition of a line is completed, the line is held together with double-coated pressure-sensitive tape and pasted into the layout or the finished art of a job. The individual characters are not normally used again. This kind of composition is more practiced by commercial artists and in reproduction departments of larger concerns than by compositors.

Hand composition with photographic matrices. This method of photographic composition has the trade name of *Hadego* and was developed in Holland where the equipment is manufactured. The Hadego is often, and to the point, compared with the Ludlow System of metallic composition. Photographic matrices are assembled in the Hadego composing stick where lines can be justified by spacing. The assembled line is placed in the photoprinting unit which has an optical system whereby the final type images can range from 4 to 82 point by use of two sizes of matrices, which are either 20 or 48 points. The product of the machine is usually a sheet of film with a maximum type area of 11¾ by 15¾ inches. Lines are individually exposed according to a layout. The developed product, either a positive or a negative, can be used for photomechanical platemaking without requiring additional work.

Photolettering machines. The term "photolettering" is inaccurate as most of the machines so classified produce images of display type. But the term is generally accepted and therefore not easily avoidable. Equipment belonging in this classification has been mushrooming during the last ten years. Most machines are of domestic manufacture but there are also imported photolettering machines sold in this country. Some come from England or from Germany, and one machine is imported from Japan. Each of the dozen or so existing models has its own distinctive features; these are not easily classified, nor do they need to be for our purposes.

The Filmotype *is one of many different photolettering machines.*

Some machines operate by contact printing; others have optical systems for enlargement and reduction of the final type images. The manufacturers of all machines offer a large choice of different type fonts. Type fonts come in a number of physical forms. Several machines, the *Filmotype* and the *Typro*, to mention some, have bands of films not exceeding two inches in height. A large number of such filmband fonts can be connected for common storage on the machine, giving the operator a choice of 15 to 20 fonts. Among font arrangements we find disks in the *Monotype Photo-Lettering Machine* and in the *VariTyper Headliner*, font plates in the *Morisawa*, and individual slides for each character in the *Fotorex*. The range of body sizes varies from machine to machine. Some go from 12 to 144 point; others, from 6 to 72 point or to 90, 96, and 144 point. Type fonts can be present as negatives, resulting in final positive type images, or as positives when reverse lines are wanted.

Nor are the products of all photolettering machines the same. Machines having fonts on filmbands produce bands of photographic paper or film in a corresponding width. Other machines may also produce such bands of composition, but several machines, or systems, can assemble a whole layout of type on a single sheet of photographic material. The *Morisawa*, for example, has a type area of 59 × 71 picas, and the *Protype* can handle rolls of photographic material 17 inches wide and 50 feet long. Photolettering machines can be operated in daylight and most machines are available either with or without automatic photographic processing units.[61]

Most photolettering machines are used for the composition of unjustified lines. The operator selects each character by hand and places it by eye using the spacing indications provided by the equipment as a guide. In some machines he can observe the placement of characters with a magnifying glass, in others magnification is not required. Complex composition problems may require a so-called dry test run where the matrices are not actually exposed, or a second run after the first has been made and revised to fit the job in hand. Composition of display types, which comes often in long paperbands from the photolettering machine, can also be adjusted by slicing the product prior to its use for paste-up. Each of the existing machines has its own distinctive features, and experienced operators usually develop their own working techniques.

Keyboarding of display types. One machine is built exclusively for the keyboarding of display types. This is the *ATF KD-84 Keyboard Display Unit*. It can produce unjustified composition from 18 to 84 point in lines up to 11½ inches long. Each different type face requires a separate type disk; the different type sizes are made possi-

ble by the optical system of this machine. The operator keyboards the copy on a keyboard resembling that of a typewriter. He can vary the space between lines in 3-point increments up to and including 96 points. The product of this machine is either photographic paper or film which can be automatically processed in the *ATF Fotorite Processor*. Composition of display type can, of course, also be done on full-range photographic composition machines.

Non-metallic Composition of Text Types

The non-metallic composition of text, or body, types has spread to a remarkable extent in the more recent past. Much of this work is done by a clerical staff, mainly typists, employed in the offices of companies using office duplicating equipment, but there are also many graphic arts firms active in this field. The equipment used for this kind of composition varies considerably in scope, complexity, and of course, cost. We divide the subject into the two broad groups of non-metallic composition produced by percussion typing and that produced by keyboarding. The word typing is in this context used for the operation whereby the final type images are produced directly with a typewriter. Keyboarding, on the other hand, may or may not be done on specially equipped typewriters, but it does not produce the final type images by typing. The product of keyboarding is a punched tape which is used to assemble lines of justified type images on composing machines equipped for tape operation. A second simultaneously produced result of keyboarding may be a typed sheet of the keyboarded material, the already mentioned hard-copy. Hard-copy has unjustified lines and does not show the final type images as they will appear after composition.

Most non-metallic composition systems can use keyboarding on typewriters equipped for the punching of tape. But generalizations are hazardous in this field which is far from settled. The Monophoto, for example, does not use a typewriter for keyboarding, and some photographic composition machines may be operated by tape produced on Teletypesetter perforating or reperforating equipment. Most systems for non-metallic composition use photographic assembly of the final type images, but the Justowriter does not, as will be seen in the following description.

Composition by typing. Composition of text matter by typing can be done on three different kinds of machines: (1) office typewriters with uniform character width; (2) office typewriters having a number of different character widths, known as *proportional spacing* typewriters; and (3) typewriters designed for office composition. All these equipment groups achieve justification by a second typing. A number of adjuncts to typewriters is available to the typist for making justification an easier and faster operation. Finally, unjustified type lines can be justified by a French machine which combines optical and photographic features, the *Optype*. Each of the more generally important kinds of this equipment is now briefly characterized.

Office typewriters with uniform character width. Our common office typewriters have usually either *pica* or *elite* type of various designs. Pica types have ten characters to the inch, elite types twelve. Each character and space has the same width on these machines. Single character width is not only contrary to the aesthetics of typography, but makes it more or less impossible to produce justified lines of composition having a pleasing, natural appearance. This kind of composition, if such it may be called, can be justified either by a second typing, or by photographic equipment that optically changes the width of lines. But all these techniques distort the final product in some way or other. It should be added that typing occupies much more space than composition and therefore becomes less economical as production runs increase. At a certain point the higher cost of paper and printing more than balances the saving in composition.

Office typewriters with proportional letter width. Typewriters with proportional spacing divide all characters in one of four width groups and move to some extent in the direction of typography. But as printing types are made in twelve or more different width groups, proportional spacing is, typographically speaking, far from adequate.

Several manufacturers offer proportional spacing in their lines of office typewriters. Composition with these machines produces much better results than can be obtained from single-character width typewriters. For the purpose of right-hand justification double typing is usual.

Typewriters designed for non-metallic composition. In this group we have mainly the *VariTyper Composing Machine*, perhaps the first successful typewriter-like machine for office composition. A distinguishing feature of the VariTyper is the exchangeability of different fonts of type. "Two fonts fit into the operating anvil at one time and changes are made from one type style to another

A VariTyper Composing Machine. *This machine can produce utility grade composition in different type faces.*

by merely turning the control knob. This permits the use of matching italics, bold face, etc., of the same family without actually removing the fonts."[62] The VariTyper has many other features that are not to be found on office typewriters. Here we mention merely one, namely, line spacing in the American Type System ranging in steps of half-points from 0 up to 18 points.

The VariTyper exists in a number of different models. Older models have single character width; the newer models have four width groups, or proportional spacing. Justified copy is obtained by double typing. The appearance of composition made on proportional spacing machines is, of course, nearer to typographic standards than that produced on single character-width typewriters.

Auxiliary devices for justification of typewriter composition. The adjuncts to typewriters mainly count the number of spaces that must be filled in the second typing for justification. Among them are the *Justi-Gage* and the *Marginator*. The *Optype* justifies unjustified composition line for line by optical means. The justified line is exposed to photographic material, film or paper, which has a maximum type area of 6½ × 10¾ inches. This machine can reduce, extend, condense, and italicize the original typing.

Non-metallic composition of text types by keyboarding. Composition by means of keyboarding can be characterized as composition requiring two equipment units. The final type images are not produced on the keyboarding machine but on a different unit. Most keyboarding equipment results in punched tape of one kind or another, but one composition system uses magnetic tape. The type images are in most systems a result of photo-

The MONOPHOTO *Filmsetter, using the Monotype Keyboard*

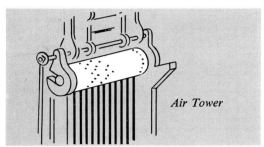

1 *A tape perforated on the keyboard, passes over the air tower and controls the filmsetter.*

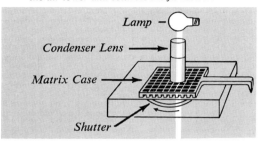

2 *One character at a time is projected through the optical system to the film.*

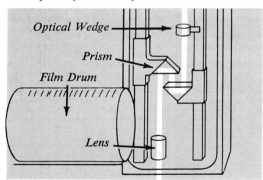

3 *Using a lens with two prisms, type sizes of 6 to 24 point can be obtained.*

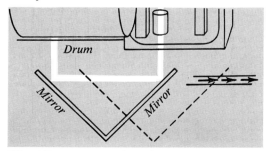

4 *Mirrors connected to the "set" sizing system traverse the line while the film is held stationary.*

A separate Keyboard unit with a choice of seven alphabets and specially equipped for filmsetting prepares the punched tape from which the film-setter is automatically controlled. Each unit working on a compressed air supply is fundamentally mechanical in operation. Since the photographic film is mounted in a removable cassette, processing can be done within an established darkroom.

To ensure typographic perfection, two sizes of matrices are specified for most type faces, and a single lens system which is adjustable, permits precise sizing of the type up to 24 point with a maximum line width of 60 pica ems. This unique system allows the make up of fractions, superior and inferior characters on the Keyboard, from which line spacing can also be controlled. Utilizing 272 individual character matrices in a 16 x 17 row arrangement, the MONOPHOTO Filmsetter adds considerably to the scope of the MONOTYPE hot metal Composition Casting machine.

The product may be either right or wrong reading on the emulsion side, depending on the final printing process involved, and a readable paper proof is quickly obtained by using diazo dry proofing materials. For correcting and make-up, no special equipment is required as paste-up is done on a plasticized sheet superimposed over a grid layout.

5 *After exposure, the film cassette is unloaded in the darkroom and developed under safelights.*

6 *Corrections and make-up simplified considerably with the use of plastic transfer sheet material provided by Lanston.*

graphic methods, but one very widely used system produces justified lines of type by percussion typing. As explained in the preceding section on the Monotype and on tape-operated line casting machines, the tape contains all information needed for the directing and controlling of the image producing unit.

Paper tapes for all non-metallic composition systems with the exception of the Monophoto are the result of typing on electric typewriters equipped for tape punching. Typing produces besides the punched tape also a typescript, the already mentioned hard-copy, which can be used for proofing and editing.

In the following you find brief descriptions of seven systems for non-metallic composition of straight matter: (1) the Friden Justowriter, (2) the Monophoto, (3) the ATF Typesetter, (4) the Alphatype, (5) the Photon 713 Textmaster, (6) the Photon Zip 900 Series, and (7) the Linofilm Quick. With the exception of the Friden Justowriter, all here-described composition methods are based on optics and photography. (The IBM Selectric Composing Systems were announced when this chapter had already been made up in pages. Their description is subjoined on page 148.)

All of the six photographic composition systems for text matter use projection of photographic matrices. Some systems have their matrix assemblies on glass, others on film. Some can produce a variety of point sizes from the same matrix grid by use of different lenses, in others the final composition is of the same point size as the type images on the matrix grid. The number of type faces available at the same time varies from system to system and so do other features including speed. Speed of composition can be expressed as the number of characters exposed per second or minute, and as the number of lines composed per minute. The speed at which a given system can project a character is not the only factor that influences productivity. Another and often neglected point is the time taken for end-of-line functions. This time differs for various systems and has a great influence on total production. When the suppliers of photographic composition systems speak of newspaper lines, they mean an 11 pica 8 point line. Some systems require more time for composition in larger point sizes than in smaller ones; in other systems point size does not influence speed of output.

The Justowriter composition system. This system produces lines of justified type by means of specially equipped typewriter-like machines. The Justowriter System comprises two units: the *Recorder* and the *Reproducer*. The Recorder is basically an electric typewriter, equipped for the punching of tape. The typist produces at the same time a typescript, showing the input of the tape in readable form. The punched tape is removed from the Recorder and put in the Reproducer, which is also an electric typewriter. Here justified lines of type are automatically composed according to the instructions incorporated in the tape. The justified

The Friden Justowriter System *produces justified typewriter-like composition. Typing of copy on the* Recorder (*at the left*) *results in unjustified hard-copy and punched tape. The punched tape operates the* Reproducer (*at the right*) *which composes justified lines, either on paper for photographing, or on a paper plate for offset duplicating.*

composition can be either on paper and later photographed, or it can be directly typed on so-called
masters, meaning paper plates for offset-lithographic printing on office duplicating machines.
Recently it has become possible to produce justified copy on the Recorder, too. This makes it possible to have two type faces in the final copy, one
face from the Recorder and another from the
Reproducer.

The Justowriter system is a most economical
system for utility composition. Characters are
made in four different widths, whereas those of
traditional composition require between 12 and 15
widths groups. Every Reproducer is limited to a
single body size and type face, namely, that provided by its keys. As the typewriter keys are not
exchangeable, different Reproducers are needed
for different type faces or for different body sizes
of the same face. The Reproducer can be equipped
with one of the 13 typefaces which are available
at the time of writing. Body sizes are made from
8 to 14 point.

The Monophoto. The Monophoto is the photographic counterpart of the Monotype as the Fotosetter is that of the Intertype. This system was not
developed in the United States, but is a product of
the English Monotype Corporation. The Monophoto is less popular in the United States than
overseas. The Monophoto System comprises, like
the Monotype, two units. These are the Keyboard
and the Filmsetter which takes the place of the
Monotype caster. The Keyboard is similar for
cast and for photographed composition. This fact
has considerable advantages as existing Monotype Keyboards can be adapted for photographic
composition. The similarity of the Monophoto
and the Monotype facilitates the training of operating personnel who can learn to operate either
machine.

Like the Monotype caster, the Monophoto has
a matrix case which holds 255 individual character matrices. The matrices for the Monophoto are,
of course, not of metal but negative images of
characters suitable for projection photography.
The Monophoto "can produce any point size or
fractional point size from 6 to 24 point.[63]" This
machine uses only a single lens for all sizes. Usually two sizes of matrices are sufficient for all body
sizes; in some cases three fonts of matrices may be
needed. Reduction or enlargement of character
images is achieved by changing the focus of the
lens and the lens stop. Focus is adjusted by means
of focusing bars; lens stops "are selected accord-

ing to type size and speed of film being used."[64]
The maximum line length is 60 picas; leading, or
the spacing of lines, can be done in half-point increments. The photographic material, paper or
film, is loaded under darkroom conditions into the
drum unit which holds a maximum sheet of 11⅛
× 26 inches having a maximum composition area
of 10 × 24 inches. Smaller sizes can, of course,
also be used.

The operation of the Monophoto is controlled
by the punched ribbon which is the product of
keyboarding. Like the Monotype Caster, the
Monophoto is operated with air power. Justification is automatic once the proper machine elements for this purpose are inserted. The completed
composition is on the exposed photographic material. The drum unit, in which the light-sensitive
material is housed, is removed to the darkroom
and there unloaded. A second drum unit is kept
ready for an uninterrupted flow of production.
The Monophoto provides matrices for a grayscale
which acts as a guide for processing. Thereby uniform density of composition can be attained.[65]
After completion of development, the set copy is
proofread; the Monophoto provides a device for
making of corrections by removing wrong composition and replacing it with corrected images.

The ATF Typesetter. The ATF Typesetter has
been on the market for several years and has established its place in the composition of text and
tabular matter. It is available in various models.
The equipment consists of a *Keyboarding Unit*

ATF Typesetter, Model B-8, *photographic unit.*
*Punched tape, prepared on the keyboard unit, controls
the operation of the machine. The changeable type disks
have two fonts, usually a roman face with its companion
bold or italic.*

and a *Photographic Unit*. The Keyboarding Unit is an electric typewriter equipped for the punching of tape. During keyboarding a typescript serving as a proof sheet is simultaneously produced. The Photographic Unit is operated by the tape punched during keyboarding.

The ATF Typesetter uses a unit system for the measuring of different character widths. Type fonts are available in many styles and can also be assembled for a special purpose. Type fonts are supplied as disks and have a total of 168 characters. A usual font is equivalent to a font of duplexed matrices for line casting. It may comprise the roman and italic version of a type face or its bold face, or any other desired combination of two fonts. The body sizes for the ATF Typesetter range from 5 point up to and including 14 point. Each different body size requires a different font disk. The ATF Typesetter can produce lines of maximum length of 7⅜ inches. The type images are exposed to photographic paper or film; as the images on the font disk are negative, the final product is positive. In the darkroom the photographic material is loaded in a receptacle and then placed in the Photographic Unit which is operated in daylight. After the loaded material is exposed it is removed from the Photographic Unit for processing in the darkroom.

Another quite recent development is the *ATF Press Wire Tape Convertor*. This unit converts TTS tape as emitted by the press wire services to tape suitable for operating the photographic unit of the ATF Typesetter. Conversion can be done at speeds up to 30 lines per minute. "From the tape a 'hard-copy' can be produced for editing insertions, or deletions in only a few minutes, or, it can be fed directly to the ATF Typesetter Photo Unit where the unedited 'story' is produced at high speed on photographic paper."[66] This adjunct is of importance for newspapers which are printed on web-offset presses and are equipped for the reperforating of tape as required in the TTS.

The Alphatype. The Alphatype comprises three units: (1) an electric typewriter for keyboarding and for the simultaneous typing of hard-copy; (2) the Alphatype Recorder to which the keyboarding machine is electrically connected; and (3) the Exposure Unit. By typing, the operator transmits the proper signals for each character to the Recorder where it is received as a signal on magnetic tape. Justification is done by spacing-out; the slack of the line is automatically transmitted to a computer when the carriage of

the keyboarding machine returns for the next line. The computer determines the proper width of word spaces automatically. The magnetic tape is fed into the Exposure Unit where the type images are projected through lenses onto photographic paper or film. The Exposure Unit is placed in a darkroom; the other two units are operated without restriction in illumination.

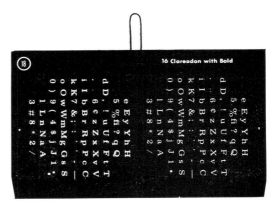

An Alphatype *font plate of two alphabets, comprising a total of 168 character images.*

Alphatype uses a unit system for calculation of character width. Units go from 4 to 18, with a total of 15 different widths. The type images are on a font plate as negatives. Each font plate is mounted in an aluminum holder and has two fonts comprising 168 characters corresponding to the two fonts present on duplexed line-casting matrices. At the present time Alphatype can compose type of a body size ranging from 6 to 18 point. The maximum line measure is 60 picas. The maximum depth of composition that can be projected onto a sheet of photographic paper or film, the equivalent of a galley in hot-metal composition, is 11½ inches. The electronic system is transistorized and does not use vacuum tubes and electromechanical parts.

Alphatype was developed for text composition such as book work and composition for magazines. The system is also suitable for composition of tabular matter.

The Photon Textmaster 713. The Photon Textmaster is a tape-operated composition machine designed for composing of body type, or straight matter, as distinguished from display or advertising composition. Straight matter composition is needed in book work and in composing the editorial contents of newspapers and magazines. The

Diagram of character projection in the Photon 713 Textmaster. *Revolving drum has two matrix strips. Each strip has four type faces of 90 characters. Type images are flashed by a lamp inside the rotating drum. The eight lenses of the lens turret can produce eight different point sizes. The prism moves intermittently, stopping for projection of four or five characters. Mixing of type faces is done by optical merging. At the end of line, the prism returns to its starting position; the film is advanced for leading and exposure of the next line.*

Textmaster 713 is rated for production of 30 newspaper lines of 11 pica length per minute or for composing 70,000 characters per hour in book work. The Textmaster consists of a tape control unit and a photographic unit. Any tape-punching equipment that produces a justified tape during punching or unjustified tape that will be later justified by electronic computers, can provide the input tape for this equipment. The Textmaster itself is not designed to hyphenate but it computes the line deficit and distributes this deficit among the word spaces. The input tape must provide end-of-line information and hyphenation. The speed of the Textmaster is such that it can handle the output of seven tape-punching units.

The tape-control unit has a photoelectric reader for punched paper tape. A complete line is stored in the magnetic core of the tape-control unit. The magnetic core transmits the necessary signals to the photographic unit which produces the actual composition, either on photographic film or on photographic paper. The Textmaster is a solid state transistorized machine; it can have eight type faces, each consisting of 90 characters. The type images are on two matrix strips; both matrix strips are supported by the matrix drum which revolves 30 times per second. There is also a lens turret with eight lenses for producing eight different point sizes, ranging between 5 and 18 points, from the same matrix strip.

The Textmaster can be operated by six, seven, or eight level tape; it can compose lines up to 45 picas in length, and justification takes place by varying of spaces between words.[67]

The Photon Zip Series 900. In May, 1964, the first production model of the Photon Zip was installed at the National Library of Medicine, Bethesda, Md., as part of MEDLARS (the Medical Literature Analysis and Retrieval System) developed by the *National Library*. There the Photon Zip was designated GRACE (Graphic Arts Composing System), and production with this equipment has been continuous since the composition of the August, 1964, *Index Medicus*. The results accomplished with GRACE at the *National Library* are briefly described in Section 6 under the head "The Cumulated Index Medicus." More detailed descriptions can be found in articles published by officials of the National Library of Medicine.[68] The Photon Zip was redesigned by its manufacturers and in the present unit you find some features of this complex, high-speed composition system identified.

It is perhaps best to concentrate on the method whereby type images are assembled by projection on the photographic material, film or paper. The Photon Zip uses glass matrices having eleven vertically arranged rows of 24 characters each, amounting to a total of 264 characters on the matrix. Whereas the type disk of the original Photon spins during composition, and the plastic matrix strips of the 713 Textmaster revolve together with the supporting drum, the glass matrix of the Zip is stationary. The photographic material onto which

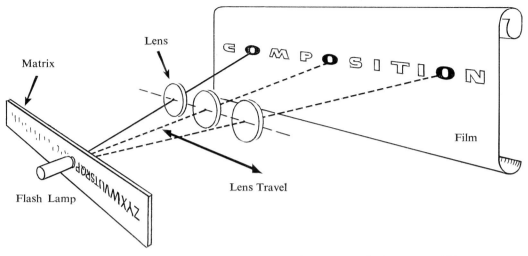

Diagram of character selection *in the* Photon Zip. *Matrix with eleven rows of 24 characters is stationary. Lens sweeps linewise back and forth, exposing a line at every sweep. Each type image on matrix is exposed by its own flash lamp assembly. Illustration shows various positions of lens at exposure of* O *in* COMPOSITION. *A computer and electronic circuits coordinate lens positions with flashing of type images. (For simplicity, only a single flash lamp, behind the "O" is shown.)*

characters are projected is also stationary during the composition of the line. (After the line is composed, the film is of course advanced to provide space for the next line.) The moving element during composition is the lens that sweeps with controlled speed between the matrix and the photographic material. The assembly of images is done first mathematically by the computer. After the computer has established the precise location of each type character of the line and has stored the relevant data in its memory section, the actual exposure of type images to photographic film or paper takes place. Each character of the matrix has its own stationary flash-lamp assembly. Since there are 264 characters in the machine this means that

there are also 264 flash-lamp assemblies. When the lamp behind a character flashes, the character is exposed. The accompanying diagram of optical geometry explains how a stationary type image can be exposed to different places within the same line by means of a sweeping lens.

Geometrical optics explains the linewise location of a character, but does not suffice to explain how characters from different lines of the eleven row matrix are mixed. The problem here is one of placing characters which are above or below one another in the same composed line. This problem is solved by interposition of a pair of reflecting mirrors between the moving lens and the film. The type images from the eleven rows of characters

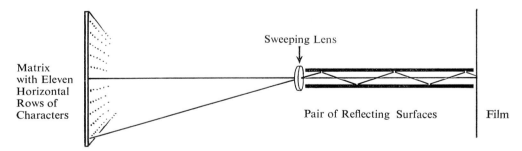

Side-elevation diagram of character mixing *in the* Photon Zip. *Matrix has eleven rows of characters which are composed in the same line with the help of two reflecting mirrors. Characters in the extreme top or bottom row need five reflections.*

borne by the stationary matrix are merged on the same line by use of reflecting surfaces. The second diagram, drawn in side elevation, shows the eleven levels of character rows on the matrix, the lens, a pair of reflecting mirrors, and the resulting location of characters from different rows within the same line.

The Photon Zip uses magnetic tape for input; it can vary line length between 4 and 11 inches and point size between 6 and 14 points. Lines are composed during both directions of the lens sweep. The Photon Zip can expose approximately 652 characters per second or 39,000 characters per minute.[69]

The Linofilm Quick. The Linofilm Quick is a filmsetting machine for straight-matter composition. It differs in concept and detail of operation from the Linofilm System which is designed for full-range composition and described in the next unit. The Quick can be operated from six-channel tape which may be produced by TTS equipment or by typewriter-like systems such as manufactured by Friden. (The Friden LCC line is described in Section 3 under the head "Tape-Punching Methods Providing Hard-Copy.")

The Quick is the photographic equivalent of a mixer model for line casting. Characters are on matrix grids, each grid has 184 characters, and the Quick can be equipped with two or with four such grids; mixing of characters can be readily accomplished. Like matrices for line casting those for the Quick are made individually for each point size. The Quick does not use optics for enlargement or reduction of point sizes. Quick matrices are made in a range beginning with 5 points and ending with 18 points. Each grid must be used together with a

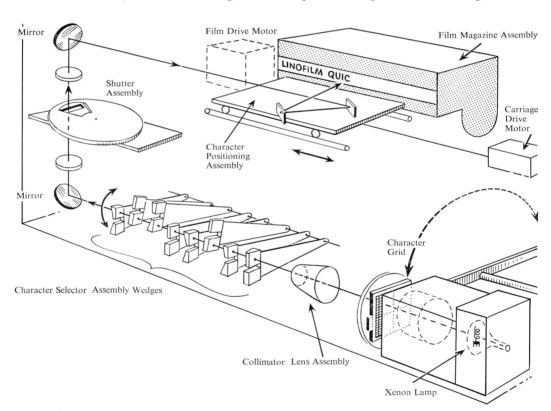

Diagram of character selection in the Linofilm Quick System. *Punched tape controls selection of matrix grid and characters. Xenon lamp illuminates the whole grid; collimator assembly produces bundles of parallel rays. These enter the character selection assembly and emerge as individual type images. Type images arrive on the character position assembly before they land on the film. Characters are selected by optical wedges borne by oscillating arms. There is a specific wedge combination for each of the 184 positions of the matrix grid.*

width plug which assigns the proper width values to each character during operation. Character assembly and linewise projection are illustrated in a diagram and here not further discussed.

The Quick is based on solid-state circuitry and uses its own unit system. Spacing is done between words. The tape reader operates in two directions. First it scans each line for justification, then it reverses the tape to the start of the line for actual filmsetting. The Quick uses different matrix grids for each point size; all Quick matrices are designed as counterparts of corresponding Linotype matrices, and the punched tape can be used either for line casting or filmsetting depending on actual plant conditions.

The Quick can set lines up to 45 picas in one-point steps; it can be equipped for automatic quadding, permits use of pi characters, can do letterspacing and leading in increments of one-quarter points. The product of the Quick can be right or wrong reading film or photographic paper; the speed is rated at 20 newspaper lines of 11 picas per minute.[70]

Full-Range Photographic Composition Systems

Full-range non-metallic composing equipment is capable of producing both text and display composition. All full-range machines are based on photography and optical enlargement or reduction of type images to the required body size, and many machines are tape operated. The Fotosetter is manually operated but a recent model of this equipment, called the Fotomatic, can be either manually or tape operated. Some models of the Photon are keyboard operated and many are tape-controlled. Like all other tape-operated composing machines, full-range systems are based on numerical determination of character and space widths which is achieved by various unit systems.

Various full-range systems operate on different concepts of design and construction. Among them we find the circulating matrix system and mechanical justification, the use of electromechanics, of electronics and, most recently, even high-speed computers. Another point worth mentioning is that some full-range machines have a considerable number of type fonts ready for immediate mixing. The exact number of matrix fonts depends, of course, on the design and purpose of a specific kind of equipment. Full-range machines are used for composition of body types and, particularly by newspapers, for that of display advertisements. Photographic composition is not only used for

newspapers which are printed by offset lithography but also by many papers that use stereotype plates as their image carriers. The photographically composed advertising page is in this application photographed on a transparent or translucent material and converted into a relief printing-image carrier by powderless etching in an etching machine. Then a mat is made from this relief plate, and this mat serves as usual for casting of stereotype plates. Newspapers using this procedure have established that the advantages of photographic display composition more than compensate for the added steps which are needed in etching a relief plate.

In the following the most important systems of full-range photographic composition are described. These are: (1) the Fotosetter, and Fotomatic, (2) several models of the basic Photon, (3) the Linofilm, (4) the Fototronic, and (5) the Linotron.

The Fotosetter. The Fotosetter is the oldest existing universal non-metallic composing equipment. The Fotosetter, developed by the Intertype Corporation, was field tested in the U.S. Government Printing Office in Washington, D.C., in 1946. It was introduced to the printing industry at the Second Graphic Arts Education Show in Chicago, 1950, and is at the time of writing a widely used full-range non-metallic machine.

Essentially, the Fotosetter is built like an Intertype line-casting machine with the casting equipment replaced by a photographic mechanism. But this summary description does not do justice to the many new features that are incorporated in this pioneer development of photographic typesetting.

The Fotosetter retains the keyboard and the circulating matrix system used in line-casting machines. The matrices for the Fotosetter are called *Fotomats* and are in many points identical with matrices for line casting. But whereas matrices for hot-metal composition have their intaglio casting cavities punched on one of their edges, Fotomats have photographically made negative images of their characters in the body of the matrix, under the teeth needed for distribution. These type images are protected by two plastic covers between which they were embedded. These images go through the body of matrices which have holes punched for this purpose. Another difference is in the justification of the Fotosetter and a line-casting machine. The expandable spaceband on which justification of line casting is based is not used in

The INTERTYPE *Fotosetter*

The Intertype Fotosetter is a photographic line composing machine. It produces justified composition on film or photographic paper. The machine sets type from 3 through 72 points in size and in lines up to 51 picas wide in one operation. Provision is also made for setting quadded, tabular, connecting script, full kerning characters, advertising and other types of composition. The Fotosetter is a machine based on familiar typesetting principles. It fits into the work flow of any composing room without extensive re-training of personnel. Hundreds of these machines are used by newspapers, commercial printers, typographers, thermographers and specialty printers to produce top quality engravings and plates.

Fotosetter methods are flexible. Angles, boxes, circles, make-up around illustrations, and other operations can be done. Fotofonts are stored in Visilite transparent magazines similar to those used on the Intertype linecasting machine. The Fotosetter magazine contains 117-channels, making it possible to place all the basic characters of a font in a single magazine—lower case, caps, small caps, figures, spaces, points, etc. Up to four magazines may be carried on the machine and Fotomats from any two adjacent magazines can be mixed in the same line.

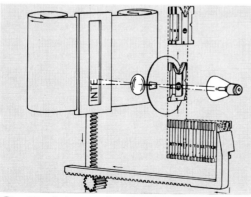

1 *Fotosetter produces mixed and other complex composition at finger-flip speed.*

2 *The simple Intertype single distributor box system automatically separates mixed matrices after use and returns them to their proper magazines.*

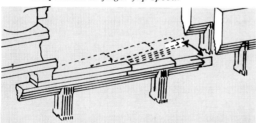

3 *Circulating matrix principle and individual exposure of characters produce high-quality composition.*

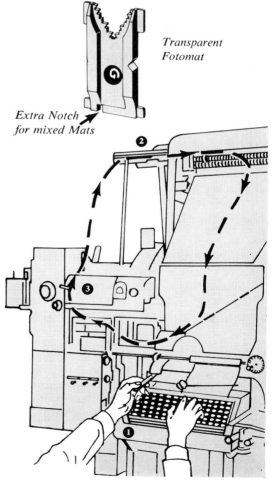

Transparent Fotomat

Extra Notch for mixed Mats

The INTERTYPE *Fotomatic*

The Intertype Fotomatic sets type on photographic film or paper. A circulating matrix photographic typesetting machine, it sets directly from conventional 6-level tape or manual keyboarding.

The Fotomatic uses a standard 90-channel keyboard. Fotomatics can use the new two-letter Fotomats or one-letter Fotosetter matrices. In phototypesetting the two-letter Fotomat permits the Fotomatic to operate from tape in the same, direct manner as a hot metal machine.

An 8-lens turret provides 8 type sizes, ranging from ½-size reduction to 3-times enlargement for each font of Fotomats.

Justification of lines is interword. The machine has quadding capabilities, and uses a single 90-channel magazine.

Using single-letter Fotomats the machine can be utilized for headline and advertising composition.

Fotomatic composition offers all the flexibilities that can be derived from photocomposition during the make-up operation.

Where photographic paper is utilized, Fotomatic composition can be processed instantly, using modern auxiliary equipment.

Two-Letter Fotomat

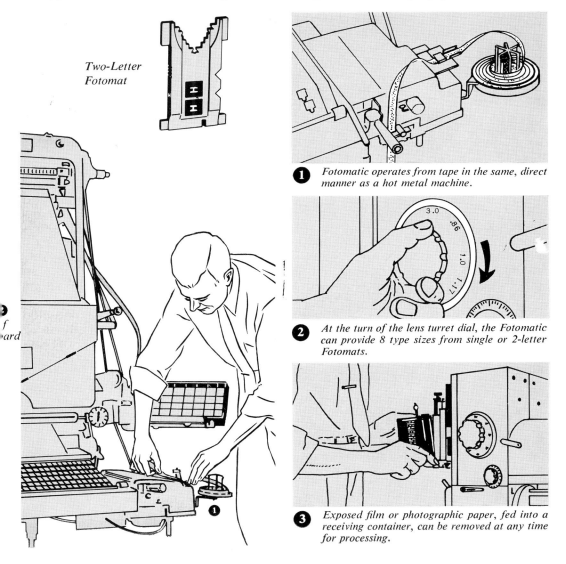

1 *Fotomatic operates from tape in the same, direct manner as a hot metal machine.*

2 *At the turn of the lens turret dial, the Fotomatic can provide 8 type sizes from single or 2-letter Fotomats.*

3 *Exposed film or photographic paper, fed into a receiving container, can be removed at any time for processing.*

the Fotosetter. Here spaces between words are of a fixed width. Justification takes place as matrices and spaces are released, after assembly for automatic photographing. The slack of the line was originally spaced out by dividing it evenly not only between spaces but also between all characters forming a line. This method of spacing-out amounts to a minute letterspacing in addition to word spacing. Later models of the Fotosetter permit elimination of letterspacing and achieve justification by word spacing exclusively. By means of special Fotomats pi material can be added to supplement type fonts.

Each character is individually projected onto the photographic material, paper or film, by an optical system. The Fotosetter has a number of different lenses which can be instantly brought into operation. "Fourteen pre-focused lenses can be mounted in the Fotosetter lens-turrets and all are available for selective use. The operator merely turns the indexed turret dial to the body size which he wants to produce. Three fonts of basic type design cover the usual range of body sizes from four to thirty points. With fourteen lenses the Fotosetter camera will produce many different body sizes from each basic font. A Fotosetter machine, equipped with four magazines and fourteen lenses, can produce thirty-two different type faces or type sizes. Since each magazine may contain 114 different characters, the Fotosetter, equipped with fourteen lenses, places directly at the disposal of the operator a maximum of 6,384 keyboard characters which may be composed up to 51 inches wide. This number of characters can be increased by use of pi characters."[71] The number of needed matrix fonts is consequently substantially less on the Fotosetter than on line-casting machines.

The photographic material, either film or paper, is used as a roll up to 30 feet long and in the proper width (up to 51 picas) for a job. This roll is placed in the darkroom into a light-proof container removably attached to the machine. The Fotosetter is operated in daylight. The exposed material is wound up in a second light-proof container, which may be removed from the machine for processing the exposed sensitized material. Film must be processed in the darkroom, but photographic paper can be fed directly into the Fotorite Rapid Processor in daylight.

Fotomats are stored in magazines like mats for line casting. The Fotosetter carries four 117-channel magazines, and matrices from any two adjacent magazines can be intermixed from the keyboard, thus providing direct access to 234 characters without a change or shift of magazines.

The original Fotosetter cannot be tape operated, but the *Fotomatic* is a version of the Fotosetter that can be either manually or tape operated. This machine can use tape supplied by the press wire services; it has a 90-button keyboard and can handle 2-letter Fotomats. The Fotosetter is used for many purposes. Among them are composition of body types for newspapers and periodicals, display composition for newspaper advertisements, and book composition, especially of a scientific and out-of-the-ordinary nature and for the solution of exceptional, not generally met, composition problems.

All systems of full-range composition provide a number of adjuncts, for correction, layout, and other purposes. The Fotosetter has a special line punch for the correcting of lines. There the incorrect line is punched out and replaced with a corrected one. For display composition, various layout boards can be used. Finally, the *Wash-A-Mat* is mentioned, a machine that cleanses and dries Fotomats in order to remove dust, dirt, and fingerprints from them without injury to the type images.

The Photon. The Photon is a photographic type composition machine differing radically in construction from line-casting machines. It originated in France and is known in Europe as the *Lumitype*. The basic Photon has gone through several design and engineering stages, and models belonging to several of these stages are operating in the field. Rather than describing these details we concentrate on the performance of the Photon Composition System.

The Photon comprises the following three main units: (1) a Keyboarding Unit; (2) the Relay Rack; and (3) the Photographic Unit. The Keyboarding Unit uses a specially equipped electric typewriter and a considerable number of control elements. The typewriter produces hard-copy during keyboarding. In display composition for newspapers, a field for which many of the existing Photon installations are used, a "Photon Makeup Panel gives the operator visual control of both horizontal and vertical dimensions and positions of any work being composed."[72] The Keyboarding Unit can be equipped for the punching of perforated tape or it can operate the equipment directly.

The Photon Relay Rack is an intermediate element, often called the *memory-unit* of the system.

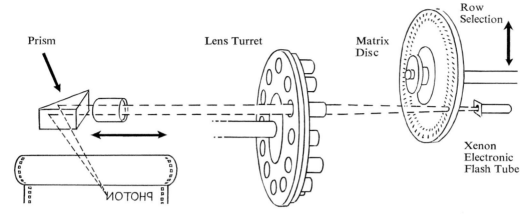

Prism   Lens Turret   Matrix Disc   Row Selection

Xenon Electronic Flash Tube

PHOTON

Diagram of character projection in the basic Photon. *The matrix disk has 16 type faces, two on each of the eight concentric matrix circles. Type faces are selected by moving the matrix disk up or down and by choosing the corresponding perimeter of the matrix circle. Each of the 12 lenses can produce a different point size. Exposure is done by a timed flash during rotation of matrix disk. Linewise motion of prism-and-lens assembly projects characters in proper places on photographic material. After line is composed, the prism assembly returns and the film is advanced for leading and exposure of next line.*

It is the unit where a line is justified, where tabular composition is properly arranged, and where several other requirements of composition are met. It is also the unit which controls the actual photographic composition. The detail of operation is highly technical and, therefore, is not further discussed.

Justification is based on a system using 24 units in the Photon. The fonts of type for photographic composition are on a matrix disk having 16 different fonts of 90 characters each, amounting to a total of 1,440 characters. The matrix disk rotates continuously at the speed of 10 revolutions per second. At each revolution a single character is selected for photographing. The exposure light is a stroboscopic flash, thereby optically stopping the character image for photographing. The maximum line length is 54 picas; body sizes range from 4 to 72 point. Various point sizes can be produced from the same matrix disk by selecting the proper lens for projection. The Photon is equipped with several lenses which are housed in the lens turret of the Photon Photographic Unit. Photon composition can also be done from punched tapes, including Monotype paper ribbons, and from punched cards as used in the Flexowriter or IBM systems.

At the time of writing Photon, Inc., manufactures six different models for photographic composition. According to the three different principles on which they are based, these can be divided into three groups: The Photon models 200, 513, 540, and 560 all use the spinning matrix disk principles; the Photon 713, also called Textmaster, is a drum machine, and the Photon Zip Series 900 a high-speed computer. The 713 Textmaster and the Zip are designed for composition of text types and therefore discussed in the preceding unit together with other equipment serving the same purpose.

The currently manufactured basic Photon is the *Model 200.* This model can be operated from an integrated keyboard as a single-unit machine. Composition of the line takes place immediately after the operator has completed the keyboarding of the line. Another version of Model 200 is equipped for integral, single-unit operation and for operation with six-level paper tape. All other Photon models are two-stage machines in which the stage of keyboarding and the stage of image projection are performed by independent equipment.

The *Photon 513 Displaymaster* comprises three parts: (1) is a six-channel Friden Teletypesetter Reader, (2) is a chassis rack, and (3) is a modified Model 200 Photo Unit. These items must be supplemented by equipment for punching of justified six-channel paper tape. The machine functions by reading the TTS tape back and operates as instructed by punched codes. The 513 Reader performs a number of functions automatically, among them the selection of the intended type face, the selection of the intended lens whereby point size is determined, multiple justification, leading, quadding, and others too technical for a discussion in this manual. The *Photon 540* is another version of the basic Photon spinning matrix disk machine, though now in combination with a Photon keyboard for perforation of eight-level paper tape. This model has the essential features of the Model 200, offers the same choice of type faces and type sizes, and is rated at an output speed of ten characters per second.

Then there is the *Photon 560*, an inexpensive version of the standard Photon Model 200. The Model 560 can process eight-level tape that may be produced by a suitable tape-punching machine and justified by a computer. (The Photon 560 is not designed to justify unjustified tape.) The equipment includes a standard photographic unit with 12 lenses, a transcription rack for reading of punched tape, and a control panel. The typographic quality and performance of the Photon 560 are the same as that of the 200 or the 540

Photon; its output speed is also ten characters per second.[73]

The Linofilm System. The Linofilm System comprises four basic and several subsidiary, or accessory, units. The four basic units are: (1) the Keyboard Unit; (2) the Photographic Unit; (3) the Tape Editor; and (4) the Composer. *The Keyboard Unit* has an electric typewriter and a number of controls. Here the copy is keyboarded; tape for operating the Photographic Unit is automatically punched, and a typed record of keyboarding is simultaneously established. A new accessory for the Linofilm Keyboard has been made available, permitting users to set up three different line lengths, sets of point sizes, and leading information. Any one of these can be selected by simply flipping a three-position switch. This accessory has the effect of making possible complex composition at materially reduced keyboarding time. For example, food store composition involving three different sizes can be handled most efficiently with this device.

The *Photographic Unit* of the Linofilm does the

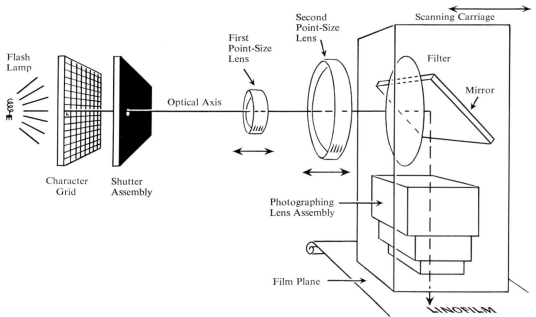

Simplified diagram of character selection, enlargement, and projection in the Linofilm System. Punched tape controls operation. When different point size is wanted, lenses are automatically shifted before composition of line begins. During assembly of line, only the scanning carriage moves; everything else is stationary. Carriage moves linewise at constant speed, controlling timing of illumination. Shutter assembly selects each character prior to firing of stroboscopic flash lamp. Eighty-eight lenslets, one for every matrix character, and other optical features serve for correct positioning of characters on film. (Lenslet assembly is not shown in this diagram.)

actual composition of justified lines. Fonts of negative matrices have 88 characters and are loaded in a Font-Turret which holds up to 18 font plates. The total number of available characters without exchange of font plates is, consequently, 1,584. "The output of the Linofilm Photographic unit is positive, right reading type on film or photographic paper. The range of the system is 3 to 108 point in width through 96 picas."[74]

The Linofilm *Tape Editor* is used to cut and splice tape in order to correct it. The Linofilm *Tape Combiner* is another major accessory whereby an error-free tape can be produced by combining tape resulting from original keyboarding with tape containing the corrections made in proofreading. The Tape Combiner consists essentially of two Linofilm *Tape Readers*, which are selectively actuated by the operator; a slave typewriter, and a Linofilm perforator. The output of the Tape Combiner contains the originally correctly composed material as well as all corrections inserted where they belong. The slave typewriter produces a typescript of the final, or output, tape as an additional product of the tape-combining operation.

The *Linofilm Composer* is one of the basic units of the system. This unit is primarily intended for newspaper display composition. The Linofilm "Composer performs two basic functions, makeup and enlarging, producing full made up pages with all type properly sized and positioned. It is only necessary to add illustrations or artwork before proceeding with the platemaking process."[75]

An interesting additional special purpose unit is the *Linofilm Converter*. This machine tapes the output of digital high-speed computers and converts the magnetic tape which is produced by the computer into tape whereby the Linofilm Photographic Unit can be operated. Through the Linofilm Converter "digital information computed, selected or arranged by computers or other data processors can be put in the form of Linofilm paper tape. Through a Linofilm Photographic Unit this tape in turn results in printout of the computer output. Accepting magnetic tape after its generation in a computer or related piece of data processing equipment, the Linofilm Converter reads the magnetic signals, rearranges the information content into standard Linofilm Format and punches a 15-level paper tape ready for use as control input to a Linofilm Photographic Unit."[76]

The Intertype Fototronic system. The Intertype Fototronic is a full-range composition system which can be operated either by manual keyboarding or by computerizing. For manual keyboarding the Fototronic consists of two kinds of machines. One is a specially designed keyboard console, the other is the photographic unit. Keyboarding results in two products. One is an eight-level paper tape for operating the photographic unit. The other is the customary hard-copy, a typed record of keyboarding that permits the operator to control the progress of keyboarding and can also be used as an internal or intermediate proof. (The use of hard-copy for proofing is discussed in Section 6, "Computerized Composition.") The speed of the photographic unit is much greater than the speed of keyboarding, and two or more keyboards may be needed to keep a photographic unit operating at full capacity. If the photographic unit is to be operated by computerized tape, unjustified tape is punched first and is then justified either by the Intertype computer or by a general-purpose computer capable of producing eight-level tape. The following description covers the Fototronic keyboard and photographic unit.

The Fototronic can be compared in its capacity with a mixer model of a line-casting machine that has two duplexed fonts of matrices ready for operation. Each of these duplexed fonts is now one type disk bearing 240 character images. The photographic unit can handle two such disks, thereby providing a choice of 480 characters. The *Fototronic keyboard console* comprises a standard electric typewriter with three shift positions and seventeen auxiliary keys located in front of the typewriter whereby the keyboard operator controls a number of typographic functions. The Fototronic uses a unit system of 32 units. Each type disk has its corresponding space-code disk. Two such disks can be used at the same time during keyboarding. "The disks signal the computing unit how much width is used by each character in a given style of type as the operator strikes each key." This information enables the computing unit to control the punching of the tape. Electronic mechanisms also actuate the dials that indicate to the operator when he is in the justification zone of a line. In fully computerized composition this function is taken over by a separate computer.

The operator of a Fototronic keyboard can reject or "kill" a whole line or part of a line; he can insert pi characters to supplement those of the type disks; he can signal to the photographic unit that the film should be cut at a certain point; he

Operation of
The MERGENTHALER
Linofilm System
of photocomposition.

The Linofilm System consists of a Keyboard Unit, Photographic Unit and Composer, providing the necessary tools for every step in setting and making-up photocomposition.

At the Keyboard Unit, the operator controls all the typographic functions of the Linofilm. Eighteen fonts are instantly available, each font grid covering one of the following point size ranges: 6 to 12, 12 to 24, 18 to 36, 36 to 48 and

Separate keyboard and photographic functions allow maximum utilization of operator skills and time, and the System is economical in the use of floor space in composing rooms. The Keyboard Unit's function is to provide the complete command information to the Photo Unit. The Keyboard itself is an electric typewriter—one of the fastest and simplest ever devised

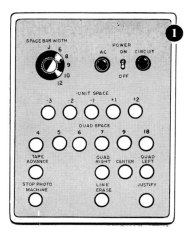

From his seat at the keyboard console, the operator controls all the typographic functions of the system. Centering, quadding and justification are controlled by push buttons on the left-hand console.

On the right of the keyboard console are the font selection controls. Eighteen buttons give the operator instant access to 18 different fonts, each of which provides up to six sizes of type.

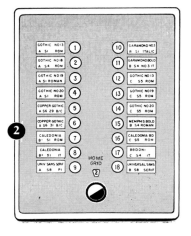

48 to 54 point. Leading is provided in 1 point increments by easy dial setting. Centering and quadding left or right, as well as justification are merely push-button operations. Display sizes of type can be keyboarded at the same speed as text matter. "Hard copy" in the form of a typescript is produced in addition to paper tape.

The Photo Unit, entirely automatic, receives its instructions from the coded tape and changes font, point size, leading and line length on signal. The Photo Unit product is positive type on photographic film or paper. Tape from several keyboards can be sent to one Photo Unit.

The Composer is a complete makeup department housed in a single unit. In seconds it enlarges or reduces type, or "angles" it, and fits it accurately to a layout—up to full newspaper page size—all through simple knob control.

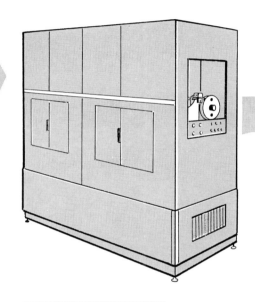

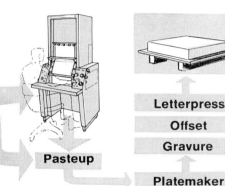

Letterpress

Offset

Gravure

Pasteup

Platemaker

The Photo Unit is completely automatic in operation, handling the changing of character fonts, point size, leading and line length in response to signals received from the paper tape produced by the Keyboard Unit.

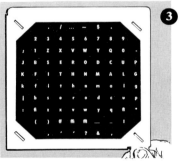

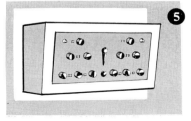

3 *A Linofilm grid is a complete font of type, equal to several magazines of hot-metal matrices.*

The Linofilm grid turret holds 18 grid fonts. This makes 108 faces and sizes available. At a moment's notice, any font may be removed and replaced. **4**

5 *With the Linomix attachment, intricate mixing is produced at high speed.*

At the end of a job, the operator removes the cassette containing exposed film or paper from the Photo Unit for processing. **6**

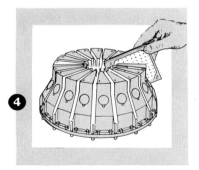

Operation of the Intertype
FOTOTRONIC *System*

The Intertype Fototronic System will produce photocomposition on film or paper at high speeds. It is a tape operated system. A typical system will consist of several keyboard consoles producing refined 8-level tapes which will automatically operate a photographic unit. Another systems approach is to have the 8-level refined tape produced by a Computer.

Fototronic offers a wide range of point sizes from 5 through 72 point. The system is based on a whirling disc concept. At the keyboard console there will normally be 2 space code discs feeding character width information into built-in computing facilities to accomplish proper justification and quadding. On the photographic unit, whirling type discs carry the characters to be photographed as well as selection and spacing information.

Line length, line spacing, and a variety of auxiliary features are controlled by pushbuttons. Line lengths can be selected in ¼ pica increments from 0 through 51 picas, and type can be composed on film or paper widths of 18, 30, 42, or 51 picas. Material comes in 100 foot rolls. Different type styles and point sizes can be composed in the same line; built-in facilities make the necessary calculations automatically.

A standard 44 keybutton electric typewriter, using 3 shift positions, gives the operator control of 120 different character positions. Type Positioning Control (buttons below typewriter) permits programming the horizontal position of characters, lines or blocks of composition.

Copyholder is illuminated and power operated.

Keyboard Consoles produce an 8-level perforated tape programmed with all necessary function codes to automatically operate the photographic print-out unit.

The Keyboard Console

The Photographic Unit

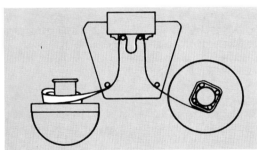

④ Perforated 8-level tape, which may be keyboard or Computer output, directs all operations of the photographic print-out unit.

Type Disc on the right is in exposure position

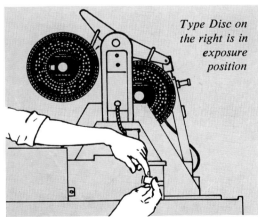

⑤ The two type discs from which characters are exposed, and a pi character being placed into position.

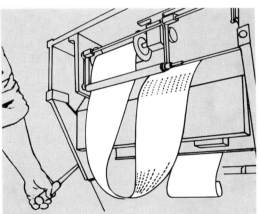

⑥ View inside dark booth shows photographic material in position on carriage. Film is automatically cut-off when the unit is so directed by tape signal. Dark booth permits removal of completed composition without interruption of operation.

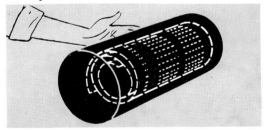

⑦ Light-proof cassette permits handling of photographic material in normal room light.

can insert leaders, and he can quad left and quad right, can underline characters or put accents over them, and he can even kern letters, typographically a very desirable feature. The Fototronic can also be used for tabular composition; other more technical features of this unit must be left unmentioned for reasons of space.

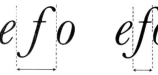

Courtesy Intertype Corporation

Illustration of kerning in filmsetting. The descender of the letter "f" is partly under the letter "e," the ascender of the "f" is partly above the letter "o" in the kerned version on the right.

The *photographic unit* of the Fototronic exposes the type images that are borne by the type disk to photographic paper or film. As mentioned before, this unit is operated by eight-level tape which may be the product of manual keyboarding or of computerizing. Type disks are supplied in three different point sizes. The optical system of the photographic unit can produce a wide range of point sizes in the final composition from each of these disks. The 10-point disk is capable of producing type images varying from 5 to 36 points; the 15-point disk has a product range from 7.5 to 54 points, and the 20-point disk can span a gamut from 10 to 72 points.

The photographic unit is capable of exposing up to 20 characters per second. This speed is equivalent to 22 newspaper lines of 11 picas per minute. "The light source is a confined spark of very high intensity which permits character exposures of one millionth of a second." The intensity of exposure is automatically controlled and so are many other operational features including the selection and adjustment of all of the 19 lens positions. The film carriage can hold 100-foot rolls of photographic film or paper in widths of 18, 30, 42, and 51 picas. The number of composed lines can be read on an indicator, and material consumption is recorded in 10 increments per foot.[77]

The Mergenthaler Linotron. At the time of writing the Linotron is still in the process of development. The following description is therefore not based on facts that can be verified by inspecting the equipment but on information published by the developers. The evolutionary process that resulted in the development of the Linotron took more than a decade. In this evolution the U.S. Government played an important role. In 1961, to mention one turning point, the Rome Air Development Center requested a system "that would automatically make up the pages as well as set quality type, and would provide illustrative material automatically as well. Mergenthaler was awarded this study by the Air Force after competitive bidding."[78] In the middle of 1962 Mergenthaler entered into an agreement with CBS to build a phototypesetting machine, and in 1964 the U.S. Government Printing Office awarded Mergenthaler a contract for two machines.

The Linotron combines photographic matrices with electronic character generation in an especially developed electronic generation tube. The matrices represent the shape of characters, electrons flowing in this tube produce character images and these are formed on a cathode ray, or video, tube which exposes them in proper position onto the photographic material. The matrix grid contains 256 characters; the total grid size is 3 $\times$ 3 inches. Four matrix grids can be used in the same page.

The Linotron is conceived as a page composition system according to the original request that reading matter and pictures must be produced together. The composed area will be 8 $\times$ 10½ inches. Magnetic tape will be used as input. "Each grid can produce types ranging from 5 to 18 points in size. The speed of the machine will range from 1,100 characters per second at 5-point to 250 characters per second at 18-point." The designers of the Linotron "are also providing a 10,000 character per second output rate for small point sizes, and perhaps more significantly, a 5,000 character per second rate for all sizes. (Character quality at these high rates will be that of the standard-speed output, but character alignment will not be as good.) This will be useful for proofing purposes." The quality of standard-speed composition is intended to be better than the quality of reproduction proofs taken from line-cast matter.

The fact that the Linotron is a page composing machine can be of great consequences for many composition tasks, the composition of newspaper display advertising pages among them. The electronic switching and servo mechanism is such that every distance in either page direction can be determined in increments of 0.001 inch. Composi-

For the makeup of advertising composition and that of magazines the customer usually provides a more or less detailed layout, or dummy, as a guide for the makeup man. In book work consisting mainly of body type, an experienced makeup man may merely require a general layout according to which he will arrange the pages following his own judgment and the rules established for page makeup in a particular plant.

Page makeup is not merely concerned with the appearance of the assembled page but also with the suitability of the material for use in the following production steps. As made-up pages can be intended for direct work on the press, or for duplicate platemaking, or for image conversion, and as different uses put different demands on the detail of the makeup operation, the makeup man is always advised whether the made-up material will be used directly on the press, or for duplicate platemaking, or for image conversion. Makeup for electrotyping, for example, is designated as *foundry lockup*. In most cases the made-up pages are proofed, in others not, depending on the nature of the work and the instructions given by the customer.

Imposition and Lockup

Before the made-up pages can be used as image carriers they must be *imposed* and *locked-up;* pages to be used for duplicate platemaking do not usually need to be imposed but must be locked-up nevertheless. The first-mentioned operation refers to the arrangement of pages for common presswork. The order in which the pages are assembled for this purpose is known as their *imposition*. As this order depends mainly on the following folding and binding of the printed sheets, imposition is in this manual discussed in Chapter X, "Binding and Other Finishing Processes."

Foundry lockup of a type form. This kind of lockup is needed for electrotyping.

Lockup follows the imposing of pages and has the purpose of securing the imposed pages in their proper place for further handling in presswork or in duplicate platemaking. Lockup is customarily done by a hand compositor, who usually also takes care of imposing, known either as *stoneman* or as *lockup-man*. (In some large plants the stoneman is not a compositor but independently classified.) It is a very responsible operation that consists in placing one or several pages—often as many as thirty-two or even more—within a sturdy metal frame, the *chase*, and in fastening these pages within that frame in exact position.

Lockup for duplicate platemaking has its own requirements and is called *foundry lockup;* it is thereby distinguished from lockup for presswork. During lockup the pages are surrounded with the already mentioned *furniture*, a spacing material much wider than slugs. Furniture may be made of type metal, iron, steel, or wood. Then, this whole assembly of pages and furniture is fastened within the chase by means of *quoins* (pronounced "coins") which can be mechanically adjusted in their width and in the pressure exerted by them on the assembled material. The locked-up assembly is known as a *form* or as a *type form* (in old American literature and in the United Kingdom this word is spelled *forme*); it is the final image carrier for relief printing done from type-high material.

Proofing and Correcting of Non-metallic Composition

The first difference between metallic and non-metallic composition as regards proofing is that proofing with ink on a proof press is of course only possible in metallic but not in non-metallic composition. Proofs of photographic and other non-metallic composition can be produced by typing, by photomechanical methods, and by a combination of both.

Most photographic composition systems provide a typed record, the often mentioned hardcopy. Hard-copy can be used for internal proofreading and for correction of tape prior to its use for operating the photographic unit of photocomposition systems and the reproducing unit of the Justowriter. (The use of hard-copy as submission proof to the printer's customer is discussed in Section 6.) Hard-copy may also be used for correcting unjustified tape intended as input for computerizing of composition.

The Fotosetter and the Monophoto do not provide hard-copy. In these systems proofs are made photomechanically by making diazo prints from the composition on film. The same procedure may be followed in systems that provide hard-copy. After all internal corrections are made diazo contact prints of the composition on film are prepared for the customer. Another possibility is the use of input tape first for a proofing run on photographic paper, which is less expensive than film. The photo-proof is submitted to the printer's customer and used like any other proof. Then the indicated changes are made in the tape and the final composition is set on film. If corrections must be made in film, this can be done too. Many ingenious procedures were developed for this purpose.[81] Without wanting to go into detail the writer must mention that it is much easier to set a line of type over on a line-casting machine and to exchange type slugs than to correct photographic paper or filmset composition.

As explained in Section 6, computerized composition has posed new problems of proofing and correcting and also introduced new equipment for intermediate proofing. It is possible that proofing techniques of photographic composition will be greatly changed by the advent of systems that can expose several hundred to several thousand characters per second. The only existing machine of this kind is the Photon Zip which can expose approximately 650 characters of 6-point type per second. The Linotron, still under development, is said to be capable of exposing 5,000 characters per second for proofing, and other systems of extremely high speeds will probably appear in the future.

Page Makeup of Non-metallic Composition

Many techniques are used for page makeup of non-metallic composition; these are not standardized and vary somewhat from plant to plant. For the purpose of discussion, we will divide them into three: page makeup by pasting, by stripping, and by photocomposing. In the first technique photographic prints of the composition are assembled on a paper board which may or may not have photographically non-recording light blue guide lines. This kind of work is often done by artists or paste-up men in art studios as part of art-and-copy preparation. The completed assembly may include besides non-metallic type images reproduction proofs of metal type and line art. This assembly is next photographed and the product of the camera serves as a transparency in photomechanical image-carrier production.

Filmset type images can be used for exposure without photographing. They are differently assembled if the composition consists of body types or straight matter, as needed in book work, and if the filmset images are for display composition. Makeup of pages in book work is done by skilled graphic arts craftsmen. Organizations specializing in this kind of work use techniques best suited for their needs which may include peg boards, punching systems, transparent grids, and others.

Display types can be assembled either manually or with equipment especially designed for this purpose. In manual assembly of display pages the photographic makeup man uses the layout and often a grid that permits him to place the composed matter precisely on a sheet of transparent plastic material. This plastic sheet may have a coating of adhesive, or the filmset material may be coated with a suitable adhesive before it is attached to the base.

Equipment for photocomposing of display pages is mainly used in the newspaper industry. Two such machines, the Linofilm Composer and the Perry Photo-Composer, are briefly characterized. The *Linofilm Composer* permits the enlargement and positioning, as well as slanting, of individual characters or composed lines over a width of 180 picas and in any wanted depth up to 24 inches. The equipment has a range of enlargement up to six times and of reduction down to one-third of the composed material. The *Perry Photo-Composer* produces precisely positioned advertising copy on photographic paper. It is used at the *Palm Beach Post-Times* in West Palm Beach, Fla., in conjunction with computerized composition. Six-channel tape operates a Photon and the Perry Photo-Composer. This machine automatically projects filmset type images to the proper position as called for on the layout in any size starting at 6 point. The composer will create angles up to 90 degrees and it will add borders.

Image Conversion of Metallic Composition

All printing-image carriers that are made by means of photomechanics require type images rather than physical type. Originally such image carriers were primarily used in offset lithography and gravure but within the past few years wraparound and photopolymer plates have found increasing use in relief printing. As a consequence of changing printing technology, many jobs that were originally printed from relief image carriers, either type forms or duplicate plates, are reprinted

The Perry Photo-Composer *produces precisely positioned advertising copy on photographic paper. Six-channel tape from an RCA computer automatically operates the Photon and the Perry Photo-Composer. The composer automatically projects the content of the film produced by the Photon to the position called for by the layout. The composer can create angles up to 90° and add borders.*

with photomechanical image carriers. In all such cases, image conversion of the relief material (which may comprise photoengravings or duplicate plates, such as electrotypes, in addition to metallic composition) is required. Much metallic composition is, of course, never intended for relief printing but planned and produced for printing by offset lithography, gravure, and other methods which cannot use physical type but type images only.

The conversion of relief matter into images can be done in a number of different ways. For our purpose, the subject is divided into four points: (1) reproduction proofs; (2) direct image transfer methods; (3) photographic image conversion of type forms; and (4) image conversion by combining mechanical with chemical methods. Each of these is briefly identified in the following.

Reproduction proofs. Reproduction proofs, also known as *repros* for short, are made by inking the composed matter and by transferring the ink image to a sheet of opaque, translucent, or transparent material, such as coated paper which is opaque, glassine paper which is translucent, and plastic film which can be either transparent or translucent. Reproduction proofs are made on proof presses. The quality of both composition

and proofing, not to forget the material on which the proofs are pulled, and the ink must be carefully controlled.

Reproduction proofs can be either photographed or used directly for exposure in photomechanical platemaking. If they are photographed, the product of the camera, which may be either a negative or a positive depending on the photomechanical method selected, serves for exposure of type images. Where photographing is omitted, the reproduction proof itself becomes part of the assembled intermediates for photomechanical plate- or cylinder-making. Reproduction proofs for photographing are usually pulled on white coated paper, whereas those for direct exposure are printed on translucent or transparent materials. Which procedure is selected depends on the detail of the job in hand and on the practice followed by different plants. As the opacity of type images is more critical in proofs used for direct exposure than in proofs to be photographed, repros on transparent or translucent stock are sometimes subjected to dusting with opaque pigments when the ink is still wet. (Aluminum powder is frequently used to dust reproduction proofs.)

Another method for the making of transparent proofs with improved image opacity was made public by the U.S. Government Printing Office. This method uses proof presses equipped with a rubber blanket and capable of printing both sides of a plastic sheet at the same time. First the type images are printed on the blanket, usually three times, and then a sheet of ethyl cellulose (a transparent plastic) is printed at the same time from the blanket on one side and from the type form on the other. Specially formulated inks must be used in this process.[82] The last method of making reproduction proofs to be mentioned in this brief discussion was developed by the Printing Products Division of the Minnesota Mining and Manufacturing Company. This company supplies, under the trade name of *Scotchprint*, a plastic material especially developed for the making of reproduction proofs. Scotchprint is a translucent plastic sheet which has a mat surface of "excellent ink receptivity, is resistant to temperature and humidity changes, has no curl or grain, and is tear resistant."[83] Scotchprint reproduction proofs are pulled on proof presses. The product of image transfer can then be used either for photographing or for contact printing. The photographic images made from Scotchprint can be either positive or negative intermediates for photomechanical platemaking.

Direct image transfer methods. Several methods are used for the transferring of relief images to off-set-lithographic plates by means of printing ink. The simplest method consists in pulling an impression from the relief material on offset direct-image paper plates which are available in a number of different sizes. Another method, known as *Double-Offset Transfer*, was developed by the Graphic Arts Research Department of Rochester Institute of Technology. "Double-offset transfer is an indirect method of proofing onto an offset plate. Conversion is made by proofing directly onto the surface of a rubber blanket-covered proof press cylinder; substituting the form with another rubber-covered type-high impression base and transferring the cylinder image onto this second blanket. Next the offset plate is positioned to the guides and this second (laterally reversed) image is offset-printed onto the plate."[84]

Finally, we mention the *d-i Offset Process* developed by Standard Rate & Data Service, Inc., and marketed by Direct-Image Offset Corp. The Process is based on a specially constructed offset plate of grained aluminum foil laminated to a heavy paper backing. The plate receives its image directly from type on any transfer or proof press. Using standard letterpress procedures, the image is embossed into the aluminum foil by means of a heat-set transfer ink. The plate is then baked to insure a permanent image, thereafter desensitized to protect the non-image area, and finally debossed on a specially developed machine which restores the embossed image of the plate surface.

Photographic image conversion of type forms. The *Brightype* Method of the Ludlow Typograph Company, Chicago, is designed for the photographic image conversion of type forms containing both metallic composition and photoengravings. The form is prepared by spraying it with a special non-reflecting black lacquer which dries immediately. After spraying, the relief image is cleaned with a soft rubber eraser to remove the lacquer from the printing face. This prepared type form is then photographed with specially designed equipment. The image areas reflect the incident light whereas it is absorbed by the non-image areas which are sprayed with black lacquer. A competitive equipment, the *Lanston Verticon Camera*, uses essentially the same approach but has different design and operational features.

Image conversion by combining mechanical with chemical methods. Under this heading we discuss the duPont *Cronapress Conversion System*, the latest development in this area. This system produces negative images from type and type forms containing type and pictorial image carriers. It requires the following equipment and materials: (1) a clarifying machine; (2) "Cronapress" conversion film; and (3) "Cronapress" densifying and stabilizing solutions. In addition to these three items, photographic litho or direct positive films are sometimes used for contact printing.

The following description is limited to the most essential features of this ingenious system. In principle the duPont Clarifier produces a clarified (transparentized) image by applying pressure to the surface of a relief image carrier which is covered by a sheet of "Cronapress" conversion film. This new film is composed of a very thin, translucent white, cellular, pressure-sensitive coating on one side of a 0.002 inch polyester base.

Next we turn to a description of the clarifying action. In the "Cronapress" No. 1 Clarifier, when a single ball bounces and applies momentary pressure to the conversion film against the metal printing surface, it exerts enough pressure in the tiny spot where it hits to collapse the minute cellular (tiny bubble) structure of the conversion film coating. Where this collapse (clarification) takes place, the film becomes essentially transparent. On the other hand, when the vibrating balls bounce off

Courtesy The Beck Engraving Company

Positioning of Cronapress conversion film on an engraving in the duPont Clarifier.

the taut polyester base where it covers non-printing areas, no pressure is exerted and the conversion film remains white.

The "Cronapress" No. 2 Clarifier, which is in limited production use, applies clarifying pressure by stroking or mechanically scanning the relief surface with flexible metal fingers adjusted to apply clarifying pressure only to the printing areas.

After clarification, the conversion film is dyed with "Cronapress" densifier solution. The uncollapsed non-image areas accept the densifier; the collapsed image areas remain unstained. Finally, the densified film is treated to insolubilize the dye; then it is rinsed and swabbed to remove residual dye, and finally dried. When dried, the dyed "Cronapress" negative is no longer pressure sensitive and can be handled like a litho film.

Completed "Cronapress" negatives can be used for the making of relief plates by exposing them directly to one-bite zinc or magnesium photoengraving metal. They can also serve as intermediates for lithographic platemaking by exposing the completed "Cronapress" negatives through the base of 0.002 inch Cronar polyester film to surface offset plates to produce text and fine screen (133 lines) halftones of good fidelity. The "Cronapress" negative can also be contact printed to direct positive or litho films to provide positive or negative images and proper image orientation for the various printing processes.[85]

Section 6: Computerized Composition

Had this book been published before 1963, computerized composition would not have appeared in it. Early in 1963 the American trade press reported that some newspapers were successfully using digital computers for typesetting. These announcements had an electrifying effect, and the great possibilities of computers for composition entered the minds of many graphic arts people. (The practical utilization of computers for composition had, of course, become possible by the efforts of a relatively small number of pioneering specialists who had been working on this new application of computers for a number of years.) Computers became immediately a most topical subject in the whole industry, and computerized composition must therefore be discussed in this manual.

The purposes of different composition methods and machines are explained in preceding sections of this chapter. In these sections the emphasis is on the kinds of solutions different systems provide for composition problems. This approach is not suitable for the subject in hand. Computerized composition is much too young, much too complex, and too far from being settled, to permit descriptions of various systems and their equipment. At the time of writing computerized composition is in its earliest stage. The equipment used is in most cases not designed for this purpose but adapted to it. This holds true not only for the machines which do the actual composition but also for various kinds of intermediary machines which are used in conjunction with computers and in a sense for computers themselves.

Descriptions of systems for computerized composition will become possible when things will be stabilized, or at least more stabilized than they are at the time of writing. For the purpose of this manual, which is to provide the assumedly uninformed reader with such information and explanations as will enable him to follow the literature on his own, it is best to point up some of the problems faced by computerized composition and to discuss some of the approaches whereby these problems are solved.[86]

Opinions appear to be divided on the extent to which the reader must have a concept of how computers function to follow intelligently a discussion of computerized composition. Some point out that many American business executives use computers steadily and quite successfully without finding it necessary to burden themselves with technical detail. Executives of larger businesses rely on competent staff technicians for specialized knowledge in this field as they do in many others.

But there are other people, occupying leading positions in the printing industry, who hold that conditions are different in the use of computers for data processing on the one hand and in their use for computerized composition on the other. Data processing is an administrative function whereas computerized composition is a complex manufacturing process. Apparently then, there is a need for an elementary explanation of computers among graphic arts people, particularly those in organizations without staff specializing in computers.

*Some Essential Features of Computers
for Composition*

This section begins with an elementary explanation of some computer functions. The explanations should not be taken as a general introduction to computers. Those who want to study this subject can find a considerable number of texts in every large library. The discussion offered in the following is written with a single purpose in mind: to put some of the problems and procedures of computerized composition in the proper graphic arts perspective. The writer confines himself to a selection of such points as are relevant to this purpose; many other points which would need extensive treatment in a general discussion of computers are either not mentioned at all or swiftly glossed over. To avoid misunderstandings it should be made clear that in this discussion the word "computer" always means *digital electronic computer*, the only kind usable for computerized composition.

Computers and other calculating machines. Computers are calculating machines. They differ from other, non-electronic, calculating machines in many points. One is that they can process not only numbers but also letters, signs, and symbols, or, speaking with composition in mind, all kinds of characters. Another most characteristic point is the fabulous operating speed of computers. Computers have the ability to compare data with other data which may either be developed during operation or stored within the reach of the system; they can collect intermediate results, and they can process and manipulate data according to a plan which must be precisely formulated and expressed in a manner usable by the system. Finally computers can have facilities for conveying the result of processing in alphabetic and numeric characters on paper, suitable for reading. How these capabilities of computers can be used for setting type will be explained later.

Speed, a key to computer applications. Speed of operation is at first glance the most impressive feature of computers. (On further acquaintance speed may become less intriguing than the data manipulating abilities of computers.) Computers use electrons for computation and they operate by shifting electrons as needed. It could be asked: "Why should a machine using moving electrons be so much faster than one using mechanical wheels? The answer to this question is very simple. The speed with which anything can be made to move depends on its weight, and the weight of an electron is practically non-existent when compared to any mechanical gadget."[87] To simplify, it may be said that the operative units of computers are pulses. "A pulse is defined as an electrical disturbance whose duration is short in relation to the time scale of interest, and whose initial and final values are the same."[88] Computers can use pulses and their different patterns effectively. The speed at which pulses can be utilized is not the same on all computers. Some have a speed of 100 pulses per second, the speed of others is measured in *milliseconds* (one thousand milliseconds amount to one second), and the most recent models have speeds expressed in *nanoseconds* equivalent to the billionth part of a second. (The word *nano* is derived from the Latin word *nanus*, meaning dwarf.)

Pulses are represented in computer diagrams either as the presence or as the absence of voltage in computer elements. Simplifying things further it can be said that computers operate on the basis of the on-or-off principle. Each change in voltage means a pulse; pulses take place at several locations, simultaneously and in sequence. Computers are based on the intrinsic simplicity of the on-or-off principle combined with the incredible speed at which these basic pulses can be made to happen and at which they can be manipulated according to plan. *All material to be computerized must consequently be arranged in a form that can be expressed in pulses.* This necessity is the dominant consideration of the whole system. All computer procedures are designed to suit this necessity, a point that should be firmly kept in mind.

The main components of computers. Computers do their work by means of five main components: (1) The *input* which receives the data in a form usable for processing. (2) *Storage*, or in computer language, the *memory*, where a varying number of coded data necessary for operation are kept. (3) The arithmetic or *logic section*, where the operations on data are carried out. These include the arithmetic operations of addition, subtraction, multiplication, and division as well as operations like comparing data, shifting data to the left and right; other logical operations, not usually thought of as arithmetic, are also executed in this section. (4) The *switching* and *control* section, which directs the operation of the rest of the computers. (5) The *output* unit, finally, presents the product of processing. Most computers also have *buffers*, or buffer units, which compensate for a difference of the rate of flow of information when transmitting information from one device to another.

A buffer can accept information at one speed and transmit it at another speed. For this purpose, the buffer must be capable of temporarily storing data; in many cases, buffers are equipped for performing also other functions.

The storage, logic, and control sections are often combined in a single piece of equipment, called the central processing unit, abbreviated CPU, whereas the machinery needed for converting the material into a form suitable for input and that for reconverting the result of processing from coded signals to letters and numerals for output are independent units. In some systems all needed data can be stored in the CPU; others may need auxiliary equipment which is said to be *on-line* if it is under control of the computer.

How computers calculate. Computers reduce all mathematical operations to a single one: the addition of pulses. By accumulating pulses, computers can perform addition. As multiplication is nothing but a more sophisticated form of adding, computers can also multiply. Accumulation of pulses can also be organized to result in subtraction; as division is nothing but a more sophisticated form of subtracting, computers can also divide. (The technique whereby addition results in subtraction is as ingenious as it is simple; it is explained in every textbook of computer arithmetics.) The essential simplicity on which computers are based has resulted in some rather uncomplimentary comparisons, such as the following: "The digital computer is extremely fast but it has the brains of a moron. Basically all the machine can do is add."[89]

Semantics and computers. The first difficulty (first in time, that is) every person must overcome when trying to understand computers is semantic. "As a result of the publicity given to electronics in recent years, many people seem to believe that computers are actually electronic brains."[90] Computers are neither geniuses nor morons. They are the culmination of a long evolutionary process in the pure and applied sciences including mathematics—and a relatively new branch of mathematics, mathematical logic—physics, and electrical engineering. They are "indeed marvelous inventions, but they cannot replace the judgment of the human brain. A computer can do only what it is ordered to do."[91]

Things are complicated by the growth of a computer jargon in which technical terms are mixed with words belonging to the stock of everyday language but used with a meaning that cannot be made out by applying the standard rules of grammar. *Idiot tape* and *hard-copy* are examples of this rather undesirable tendency. Tape can be neither idiot nor brilliant and the adjective hard cannot modify the noun copy any more than soft copy would make sense as its opposite. There seems to be a general tendency among computer people, who often show signs of fervent emotions akin to those of believers in causes, to endow the products of their creation with faculties that traditionally are considered exclusive attributes of human beings. Now, in the computer field, inanimate objects are said to read, to think, to use language, to have a memory, and so forth. The reasons for reversion to anthropomorphic language (the kind of language whereby primitives endowed certain objects with human and superhuman powers) cannot be analyzed here, though the fact may be worth pointing out.

Computer terminology. Like every other highly specialized field, that of computers needs its own terminology. Those who want to learn about computers must realize that they must learn new words and expressions without which they simply cannot follow the literature nor converse intelligently with specialists in computerized composition. Some simple terms were already mentioned and explained; more are to come.[92] The two most frequently used computer terms, *binary notation* and *bit* will be immediately introduced in the discussion of the conversion of copy for processing by computers.

Conversion of letters and numbers for computer processing. The material to be computerized must be prepared in a form that makes it possible to process it by means of pulses. The preparation can be in the form of punched cards, punched paper tapes, and magnetic tapes. The system most widely used for this purpose is technically known as "binary notation with the radix 2, for which two digits are used, namely 0 and 1. The reason for the prevalence of binary representation in computers is that there are many physical devices which can exist in either one of two states. For example, a switch may be on or off, an electrical charge may be positive or negative, a magnetic pole may be north or south, a hole in a paper tape may be present or absent, a vacuum tube may be conducting current or quiescent [and so may be solid state electronic elements which did not exist when the quoted work was published] and in each of these cases a correspondence may be set up with the binary digits 0 and 1."[93]

Some familiar non-decimal systems. People not conversant with binary notations are first confused because a number like 111 means *one hundred eleven* in the customary decimal system whereas it means *seven* if written in binary notation. But this confusion is not worse than that inflicted on an American traveler in the United Kingdom with its peculiar monetary system constituted of pennies, shillings, and pounds. In this system a notation in terms of 12 is combined with one in terms of 20 and with the usual decimal notation: 12 pennies are 1 shilling, 20 shillings are 1 pound, and pounds are counted in the customary decimal system. A traveler from continental Europe where the metric system is standard has an equally difficult time until he gets used to our own units of measuring weight, distance, and cubic content. Ounces can be either fluid or avoirdupois, meaning those in which weight is reckoned. In calculations of volume we use a mixed system of ounces, pints, quarts, and gallons, shifting from one kind of notational basis to another: 32 fluid ounces are 1 quart, 4 quarts a gallon. Things are not any more easy in measuring distances: the smallest we measure in fractions of inches; and we switch from inches first to feet, then to yards, and, when needed, to miles, every time changing the notational basis. In printing, too, we use a system of counting in points and we convert 12 points into a pica.

Psychologically, the difference between binary notations and those mentioned above is that we are so familiar with ounces, inches, gallons, and the like that we take them simply for granted. Binary notations are new to us and must be learned, and learning is considered troublesome by many. The "new math" now taught at grade school, will equip a new generation better for understanding a computer-dependent civilization.

Computers are calculating machines, and the material must be prepared in a numerical form. Composition comprises not only the ten digits of our decimal system but also letters and other characters which may be signs or symbols. All these must be put into a code, or technically speaking, *encoded* in such a manner that each character and number is distinguished from all others and that no confusion between them is possible. Encoding must permit not only correct processing by the computer but also assure that

the product, computerized composition, will be suitable for its purpose.

The meaning of "alphanumeric." Computer people call the totality of all elements, letters, numerals, signs, and symbols which must be encoded for processing "alphameric" or "alphanumeric," a term resulting from combining *alpha*betic and *numeric*al. The material to be encoded in the binary system contains (in nonmathematical composition) primarily alphabetic elements. Encoding consists in assigning to each character a distinguishing numerical expression. After completion of processing the binary data by the computer the reverse process takes place. Now the binary items are reconverted into their original, mostly alphabetic, state. The binary system can be applied to punched cards, paper tape, and magnetic tape. Since the eye cannot notice a difference in coded and uncoded magnetic tape but can see a difference between punched and unpunched paper tape, the following discussion is based on paper tape as the material for encoding.

The two working dimensions of paper tape. Paper tapes for encoding have two working dimensions. One is its webwise, or long dimension, the other is across the tape width. Tapes are made with different capacities for the number of holes that can be punched across their width. If a tape can take five holes next to one another across the width it is said to be a *five-level tape;* if it can take six holes in a row it is called a *six-level tape,* and so forth. The number of available tape levels is of course not arbitrary but depends on the nature of the system in which a tape is used.

Different functions of punched patterns in mechanical, electrical, and electronic systems. The earliest industrial use of punched cardboard patterns is in Jacquard looming which was widely practiced early in the nineteenth century. In Jacquard looming a chain of punched cardboard patterns, "the Jacquard, controls each warp thread separately which it raises or lowers to make the pattern."[94] In the Monotype, the paper controller ribbon is produced during keyboarding and directs the casting mechanism in selecting the proper matrix. In both systems, punched holes have a mechanical function. In the Jacquard they act as selectors for the hooks which lift the longitudinal threads of the fabric thereby forming the shed for passage of the shuttle which places the transverse threads, or *wefts,* across the *warp;* in the Monotype, the punched holes act as valves permitting the passage of compressed air which is part of the mechanism whereby the matrix case is moved to put different matrices into their casting position.

Even though counting is needed in Jacquard looming and calculating in the Monotype system, the punched holes of the Jacquard and those of the controller ribbon have no part in counting or calculating. In the Teletype System, punched paper tape is used on a higher technological level. There a coded pattern of holes is used to transmit electrical signals which in conjunction with electrical and mechanical devices on the receiving typewriter produce the desired typed message. A tape for the Teletypewriter System looks very similar to punched tapes used in computerized composition, but counting and calculating is not part of the system. In the Teletypesetter System a paper tape is punched to operate line-casting machines by combination of electrical and mechanical equipment. In this system counting is a major function, but the punched holes of the tape, and the whole tape itself is again not part of the counting mechanism. In electronic systems this situation changes entirely. There punched tape is a major part, or perhaps better said, an indispensable element in all counting and calculating operations, though it is of course not the only element needed for calculating in computerized composition.

Character codes and their purpose. In electrical systems using coded tapes, the number of tape levels in conjunction with machine characteristics controls the number of possible combinations. In electronic systems the number of possible combinations can be considerably increased by use of special codes which are here called *character codes* because they consist in combinations of various type characters. Some systems of computerized composition use mathematical signs and symbols and have different names for different codes. These codes mainly serve for directing the equipment needed for metallic or photographic composition. In present systems of computerized composition which combine, as mentioned before, existing equipment designed for other purposes, character codes may appear in both hard-copy and printout. Different people evaluate character codes differently as to the degree to which these codes affect the readability of hard-copy and printout. It may be assumed that the developing computer technology will find ways to eliminate these codes in the records needed for proofing of composition.

Relations between code levels and character assortment. The Teletype System uses five-level tape permitting 32 different combinations. The number of characters produced by the *teleprinter*, a term which distinguishes typewriters for teletype from other typewriters, is not 32 but 52. (This is shown in the illustration of tape for teletype.) The teleprinter has 26 character-bearing keys, and each key has two characters one above the other, like any office typewriter. But there is a difference between teleprinters and office typewriters as regards capitals and lowercase letters. The teleprinter has no lowercase letters but caps only, whereas our usual typewriters have both kinds of letters.

On the teleprinter all letters are in the unshift position whereas figures and marks of punctuation are in the shift position. The term *shift* refers to depressing the selector button on typewriters and similar machines for typing of a character that is above another character on a typewriter key. *Unshift* means letting go of this selector button. In office typewriters all lowercase letters are in the unshift position, capitals or uppercase letters are in the shift position. On the teleprinter there are no lowercase letters as you can see on the illustration of the teleprinter code. If you look at the letter "E" you see that it is in the unshift column; next to it in the shift column is "3" which is above the "E" on the same key. The selection between letters and figures is accomplished by a *precedence code* which precedes every change from letters to figures and vice versa. The last code in our illustration is the *letter code*, it has five holes in a row; the code before the last is the *number code* which has four holes. (Some prefer *function* code to *precedence* code. Either word refers to a different aspect of such codes: *precedence* to their relative position, *function* to their purpose.)

In the Teletypesetter System six-level tape, permitting 64 combinations or codes, is needed. These 64 codes can select at least 172 different type characters of duplexed matrices. The standard code used for tape-operated line-casting machines is illustrated and there briefly explained. This system, too, is based on precedence codes, though on more codes and somewhat more complex ones than teletype. The principle of precedence coding is also widely used for computerized composition.

Precedence codes can substantially expand the scope of composition systems based on six-level

Five-Level Tape

TAPE LEVELS (1 2 FEED 3 4 5)	Unshift	Shift
	A	—
	B	?
	C	:
	D	$
	E	3
	F	!
	G	&
	H	
	I	8
	J	'
	K	(
	L	)
	M	.
	N	,
	O	9
	P	0
	Q	1
	R	4
	S	BELL
	T	5
	U	7
	V	;
	W	2
	X	/
	Y	6
	Z	"
	SPACE	
	CARR. RET.	
	LINE FEED	
	FIGURES	
	LETTERS	

Six-Level Tape for TTS

TAPE LEVELS (6 5 4 FEED 3 2 1)	Unshift	Shift
	a	A
	b	B
	c	C
	d	D
	e	E
	f	F
	g	G
	h	H
	i	I
	j	J
	k	K
	l	L
	m	M
	n	N
	o	O
	p	P
	q	Q
	r	R
	s	S
	t	T
	u	U
	v	V
	w	W
	x	X
	y	Y
	z	Z
	1	1/8
	2	1/4
	3	3/8
	4	1/2
	5	5/8
	6	3/4
	7	7/8
	8	—
	9	&
	0	?
	.	.
	,	,
	;	:
	$	!
	)	(
	'	'
	-	+
	Tape Feed	
	En Space	En Leader
	Em Space	Em Leader
	Vertical Rule	
	Thin Space	
	Space Bar	
	Carriage Return	
	Elevate	
	Paper Feed	
	Shift	
	Unshift	
	Upper Rail	
	Lower Rail	
	Stop Code	
	Code Delete	
	Space Bar	
	Thin Space	
	Quad Left	
	Quad Center	
	Quad Right	
0 1 2 3 4 5	TTS EQUIV.	

Five-level tape adapted from Bell Telephone literature.

Six-level tape for TTS adapted from Friden LCC-FV literature.

Five-Level Tape

Five-level tape has 32 combinations which result by use of *shift* and *unshift* precedence codes in 52 typed characters. (The shift code is identical with the four-hole code for figures, the unshift code with the five-hole code for letters.) All letters are caps.

Six-Level Tape

Six-level tape has twice as many combinations as five-level tape. In the Teletypesetting System six-level tape can select a varying number of characters depending upon the actual composing system and upon the number of function codes. The TTS code at the left permits selection of 172 characters of duplexed matrices. In some systems of photo composition six-level tape can select four type faces in 8 point sizes amounting to more than 2,800 characters. In the TTS System the *shift* and the *unshift* codes select uppercase and lowercase letters respectively, and other characters, as shown in the two columns. There are two more precedence codes to select the lower or the upper image of duplexed matrices. These are the *upper rail* code which is often used for italics and the *lower rail* code, which is usually the code for roman.

tape. Linotype Auto-Controlled Elektrons use six-level tape and can automatically choose matrices from two adjacent magazines, thereby increasing the number of available characters to more than 330. This figure can be multiplied in photographic systems equipped with multiple-lens systems for changing the point size of characters present on a given matrix assembly.

The common operational feature in punched tapes and pulses. There are good reasons for encoding material to be computerized by punching holes in tapes or cards. Punched tape embodies the same on-or-off principle that is also present in electronic pulses. In a pulse the voltage is either present or absent, in punched tape holes are either present or absent in a certain place. (Many computers cannot use punched tape to generate pulses but convert paper tapes first into magnetic tapes for processing.) All holes punched in a paper tape are the same as to their size and shape; the only point in which holes differ is their relative position in a row across the tape. The decisive difference between holes is strictly one of position across the tape.

Binary position and decimal value. The binary system has, as mentioned before, only two figures, 0 and 1, whereas the decimal system, which we use in everyday practice, has ten different figures or digits, from 0 to 9. *In the binary system the value of a hole is doubled in terms of the decimal system from position to position or from level to level within a row of the tape.* The term "level" will cause no trouble if you look at a ribbon of tape as

Schematic diagram of tape levels and decimal values of holes punched on different tape levels. (Black circles indicate punched holes.)

illustrated. There you can see why a tape can be conceived as having as many levels as it has longitudinal divisions; levels are sometimes also called channels. The figure 1 and the figure 0 are called *bits* in binary notation; the word "bit" is a fusion of the letters "bi" in *bi*nary and the letter "t" in digi*t*. Tapes are also characterized as

five-bit tape, *six-bit* tape, and so forth, expressions equivalent to *five-level* or *five-channel* and *six-level* or *six-channel* tape.

On the first or lowest binary level a hole has the decimal value "1," on the second level a hole has the decimal value of "2" on the third level, a hole has the decimal value "4," on the fourth level it has the decimal value "8," on the fifth level its decimal value is "16," on the sixth level it is "32," on the seventh level it is "64," on the eighth

Schematic diagram showing number of combinations possible on six-level tape without character coding. If you add the figures in the decimal value column you arrive at 63. (Black circles indicate punched holes.)

it is "128," on the ninth it is "256," and on the tenth level its decimal value is "512."

Six-level paper tape is most common; eight-level tape less. Most systems operated by eight-level tape use one tape level for checking and seven levels for encoding, but there are also systems using all eight tape levels for encoding. The Photon Zip Series 900 uses nine-bit codes for its internal calculations because "it is necessary to use nine bits in order to have a unique character code for each of the 264 characters and for all the function codes which are required to operate the Photon 900."[95]

Adding of bits in terms of the decimal system. If you want to add holes punched in the binary system you do so row for row, across the tape. Each row across the tape normally represents a single letter, number, sign, or symbol. (In some

Four tape levels suffice for expressing any number. Each row across the tape is a single figure. The coded holes of this illustration represent 9,760,245. (Black circles indicate punched holes.)

Tape Level	Decimal Value of Hole	Codes for Numerals, Letters, Symbols
Sixth Level	32	
Fifth Level	16	
Fourth Level	8	
Third Level	4	
Second Level	2	
First Level	1	

0 1 2 3 4 5 6 7 8 9 A B C D E F G   *etc.*

Tape Direction

Schematic diagram showing that all numerals and letters can be encoded on six-level tape. The numeric value of "A" is 49, that of "B" is 50, and so forth. This diagram also shows that it is not possible to encode uppercase and lowercase letters in addition to numerals and marks of punctuation on six-level tape. For this reason precedence codes are needed on six-level tape. (Black circles indicate punched holes.)

computer systems more than a single letter or character can be placed in a single row.) But you cannot simply add the number of holes present in a given row if you want to arrive at the total decimal expression for which these binary holes stand. To arrive at the correct decimal number represented by binary holes you must add each hole with its decimal value to the decimal value of each other hole *across* the tape. If a six-level tape has six holes in a row across the tape the decimal value of these six holes is not six but 63. It comes about by adding 1 plus 2 plus 4 plus 8 plus 16 plus 32 = 63. Consequently, a six-level paper tape permits 63 different combinations.

If you have at first a little difficulty with adding holes at different decimal values according to their relative position you might remind yourself of the fact that in everyday life similar looking objects can have different values too. Our dollar bills have the same size and general layout: they look almost alike; and yet we know their different values by the figures printed in their corners. Poker chips, too, look all alike but we distinguish their different values according to their color. *What printed figures are for banknotes and different colors are for poker chips, relative position is for binary holes.*

Requirements for computerized typesetting of justified lines. It is perhaps best to begin not with the copy but with the typesetting equipment that will be operated by the output tape of the computer. This equipment can be either a type-casting machine or a machine producing non-metallic composition. Type-casting machines can be either Monotype casters or tape-operated line-casting machines, Linotypes or Intertypes. Different models of line-casting machines differ consider-

ably in their scope and operation. The same observation holds true concerning full-range, non-metallic composing equipment. Each of these machines has its own operational features, and the tape produced by the computer must fit them. Most photographic composing machines are at the time of writing operated by punched paper tape rather than by magnetic tape. The high-speed, several-hundred-characters-per-second composing machines which exist already, are operated for various technical reasons with magnetic tape.

The computer must be provided with such codes as are necessary to operate the actually selected metallic or photographic typesetting equipment. In addition the computer must have data on the set-width of each character used in the selected type face and size; it must have data on the permissible and preferred width of spaces, as well as specification of the line length. What data must be known for numerical justification is explained in Section 3, under the head "The Monotype System." Summarized, the length of the line and the set-width of each character and space must be expressed in a common numerical system. The Monotype System uses its own kind of units; these are mechanically added as keyboarding progresses. When the line is almost completely filled and after the operator has made the decision either to divide or not to divide the last word in the line, the mechanism indicates to the operator what signals he must punch in the Monotype ribbon in order to cast spaces of the proper width.

The computer, too, must add corresponding figures, compare their total with the total numerical length of the line, establish the difference between the filled and the total line, divide this difference by the number of spaces and indicate the actual set-width of the spaces needed for spacing-out. Up to this point it is assumed that the computer does nothing other than the Monotype mechanism, even though the computer can do its work much faster. But in most computerized composition systems the computer has another task to perform: it must decide whether a word must be divided from one line to the other, and if word division is necessary, at which point this division or split will be made.

The computer has assumed the last operator function that was not performed by machinery before, word division. This function presents a formidable machine task as you will see later on. We continue with a brief description of the equipment needed for computerized composition.

Equipment for Computerized Composition

Equipment for computerized composition varies depending on the nature of the work, the system selected, and the composition equipment that will be used for metallic or non-metallic composition. Physical equipment, or machinery, including the computer, is called *hardware* by the trade; the parallel term *software* is used for computer programs and procedures. Hardware can be divided into five kinds: (1) machines needed for converting the copy to be processed into coded form, (2) machines that adapt the product of conversion for use by specific computers, (3) the computer itself, also called the CPU, (4) printout equipment, whereby the tape bearing the product of computer processing in coded form is reconverted into readable characters, and (5) equipment for conversion of this tape to such kinds of tape as are needed to operate the typesetting machine which was selected for a specific job.

Equipment for converting copy into coded form. Four basically different kinds of machines are capable of converting copy into coded form as needed for computer input: (1) tape perforators as originally designed for the Teletypesetter System, (2) electric typewriters equipped for punching of paper tape. (3) card punching equipment, and (4) machines based on the principle of optical character recognition.

Tape perforators as originally designed for the Teletypesetter System have keyboards similar to those found on typewriters. They differ from the second mentioned kind, electric typewriters equipped for tape punching, primarily by the fact

that TTS perforators do not produce hard-copy, or a typed record, concurrently established with tape punching. TTS perforators and electric typewriters equipped for tape punching are used for encoding reading matter in bulk, as needed in newspaper and book composition.

If TTS perforators are used for computerized composition, the operator punches an unjustified tape which is often called idiot tape. The computer will justify the composition and the computer output tape will be suitable for producing justified slugs of type on tape-operated line-casting machines. In systems based on TTS perforators for input, there is no hard-copy available. Such systems do not usually include computer printout. Since computer printout is essential for verification of the correctness of the tape, systems without printout cannot catch mistakes in the tape before the actual composition. Correcting of composition must wait for proofing of the composed matter in proof presses.

In systems of computerized composition providing hard-copy, the typescript turned over to the printer (or for that matter to a trade-composition firm or a computer service) is first marked to indicate the codes necessary for a particular job and a given system. Especially trained computer typists, who are familiar with these systems and their commonly needed character codes, retype the copy including the codes. Computer typing results in two related products: the main product is unjustified coded tape, the by-product is a concurrently established typed record of the tape contents, the already mentioned hard-copy.

The use of punched cards is practical as computer input whenever the subject of printing consists of relatively short units that need continual updating and revision, such as mailing lists and parts catalogs, to mention two examples. Punching of cards is done with specialized equipment; usually card punching produces also a typed record of the punched information on the card itself but not a continuous record indicating the contents of groups of punched cards. After the cards are processed by the computer, printout equipment can be used to provide a continuous record of their contents.

The last method, optical character recognition, is at the time of writing not in general use but in the stage of pilot operation. The purpose of this method is to avoid retyping of manuscript and to convert typed sheets into coded tape as needed by computers for processing.[96]

Courtesy Perry Publications, Inc.

Electronic Retina Character Reader *equipment in operation at the* Palm Beach Post-Times, *West Palm Beach, Fla. This equipment has the capacity of "reading" printed or typed copy into predetermined electrical impulses which are stored on magnetic tape. Magnetic tape is converted into paper tape as needed for operating line-casting or photographic composition machines. The Retina Character Reader System uses optical character recognition.*

Equipment for adapting punched cards and tapes for computer input. The circular holes of tapes and the rectangular holes of punched cards must be converted into electrical signals for electronic processing. Some computers are equipped to handle magnetic tapes, punched paper tapes and punched cards as part of the operations performed by the central processing unit. On others it is more economical to do this conversion separately by intermediate equipment known as *tape readers* or as *card readers*. The product of these intermediate machines is magnetic tape, often called *mag tape*, encoded for computer input.

The computer and on-line storage facilities. The computer is the heart of an installation for computerized composition. Its main sections and functions are already described. A detailed explanation is much too technical for the purposes of this manual nor is it necessary. "The graphic arts industries have continually used processes, equipment, and materials that were not fully understood by graphic arts people. Electronic engravers and scanners, adhesive binding, four-color process wet-printing, ink transfer systems, Dycril, and even Xerography will illustrate the point. The printing industry has learned to control the conditions of operation for the processes and materials being used to obtain a desired

result."[97] The printing and publishing industry is following this same approach in the handling of computerized composition. The initial evaluation of a given system of computerized composition may or may not be possible without the assistance of a specialized engineering staff, depending on the kind of decision to be made.

The cost of computers is significantly influenced by the capacity of the storage unit. Merely as an example it is mentioned that some computers used at the time of writing for composition have rental charges ranging between, say, $1,000 and $7,500 per month. In installations requiring large data storage as needed for coded dictionaries or for tables of set-widths and matrix widths, "it is usually more practical to use a random access storage device."[98] *Random access* is a term whereby storage devices on which information can be retrieved very quickly are distinguished from devices which require considerably more time for retrieval. In the latter class are magnetic tapes, in the former are magnetic cores and others. "In random access devices a search of the entire memory is not required to find a particular fact. The disk storage used in some systems of word division is an example of random access."[99]

Computer programs and their diversification. Computers cannot be used without the proper program. Since the actual composition can be done by several existing machines, and as each of these machines has its own distinctive features, computerizing requires especially developed programs for each of them. Among those are tape-operated line-casting machines of different capabilities: the Monotype, and several non-metallic composing systems, various models of the ATF Typesetter, the Intertype Fotomatic and Fototronic, the Linofilm, various models of the Photon and the Monophoto. (The Monotype and tape-operated line-casting machines are described in Section 3; photographic composition systems are explained in Section 4.) The development of computer programs is a time-consuming and highly expensive process.

In addition to programs for particular machines, firms specializing in computerized composition as a service business may need special-purpose programs. Among special-purpose programs developed by them, "Rocappi, Inc." list "a whole series of programs to handle industrial directories and product guides; a series of programs to accept fielded material from punched cards or magnetic tape where the output is destined to be typesetting; an elaborate series of programs for encyclopedia application, including the ability to code input material for indexing, to extract text and marginal reference clues, sort them alphabetically and generate an index, and many others not mentioned because of their uniqueness."[100]

Printout equipment. Computers can provide a record of the processed product in alphabetic characters and decimal figures. The equipment whereby this record is produced is called a printing device or, more specifically, a rack-type, or a type-wheel (cylinder or drum), or a spinning-disk, or a chain printer, depending on the main feature of construction.[101] In this manual the word printer is reserved for people active in the graphic arts industry and the word printing for quantity reproductions of original images as printed images. The word *printout*, which is part of computer terminology, will be used as an adjective to characterize machinery and as a noun to identify the product of machinery used to reconvert the encoded result of computer processing into readable, alphabetic, and numeric characters. This usage will avoid confusion in the minds of graphic arts people and be easily understandable to computer technicians.

Printout equipment must fit into the general plan of operation followed by computer systems. The style in which final data appear as printout is much less important than speed and efficiency. Most general-purpose computers are designed for the processing of administrative data, such as payrolls. For such purposes typographic niceties are not required. Printout equipment is generally specified in its speed by the number of lines it can produce per minute; line speeds of a few hundred are considered relatively slow; the latest high-speed equipment is rated at 1,000 lines per minute and even higher. The number of characters per line depends on the make and model of printout equipment; for computerized composition, printout contains often as many as 132 characters per line.

Printout machines are much closer to typewriters than to printing equipment. Like typewriters printout devices have a single permanent assortment of characters; these are impressed on the paper with a carbon ribbon, similar to carbon ribbons of typewriters. The product of printout machines can be a single copy or a number of carbon copies, 4 or 5, to mention a figure. If more copies are needed these must be made by

replicating (a term preferred in contemporary literature to the more customary *duplicating*) or by printing. For printing, computer printout may serve as copy for composition or it may replace composition and be used directly for camera

```
ADRENAL ENZYMES          13645C
ADRENAL HYPERPLASIA  13452F
ADRENAL INSUFFICIENCY
  13660B
ADRENAL PROTEIN BIOSYNTHE-
  SIS              13459C
ADRENAL STEROIDS BIOSYNTHE-
  SIS              13455H
  13456G
ADRENAL VIRILISM        13645G
ADRENALECTOMY EFFECT  13487C
ADRENALIN COMPLEXES  12424G
ADRENALINE              13459D
  13466A 13474H
ADRENALINE ANALOGS      13089H
ADRENALINE ANTAGONISTS
  13469E
```

Courtesy Mack Printing Company

Computer printout used for indexing of Chemical Abstracts; *printout is reduced to 46 per cent for printing by offset. Illustration is same size as print in* Chemical Abstracts.

work, for offset printing in the main. On most existing printout devices all letters are capitals, though some recently developed machines have upper and lowercase letters. Our illustration shows a sample of computer printout used instead of composition for the index of a scientific magazine, prepared directly by the computer.

Not all systems of computerized composition include computer printout. Printout can be used in various stages of computerizing. If it is used for correcting of mistakes, it may be made from unjustified tape, particularly if this tape was punched on a "blind" machine. (Perforators without facilities for hard-copy are sometimes called blind perforators to distinguish them from tape perforators that prepare hard-copy as a by-product of tape punching.)

The product of computerizing may or may not be suitable for operating the actual typesetting equipment. If computer output tape does not meet the requirements of the equipment, computer tape must be converted into the kind of tape whereby the selected typesetting equipment can be operated. The Monotype and the Monophoto need 31-level tape into which 6-level tape coming off the computer must be converted. The Linofilm is operated with 15-level tape. Six-level tape can be used if a Linofilm Computer-Option Photo Unit is part of the installation, otherwise 6-level tape must be converted for the Linofilm. The Computer-Option unit can be added to Linofilm machines already in operation, and both 6-level computerized as well as 15-level not computerized Linofilm tape can be fed to machines equipped with the adapter.[102]

Comparison between computer printout and proofs of composition. Computer printout serves for a number of purposes for which composition proofs were needed before. Comparing these two will be found useful by the reader. In such a comparison the following points can be made: (1) Proofs of metallic as well as non-metallic composition present both the intellectual contents of composition and its typographic appearance. (2) Printout presents the intellectual contents of lines of type to be composed; each future line of type is represented by a single line in the printout; but printout does not show the appearance of the final composition. At the present time, in most printouts, all type faces, all type sizes, all variations in design such as bold face, italics, and roman, appear alike. (3) Printout contains codes indicating these and other typographic characteristics. Such codes can be within a line, below a line or above a line. Those who have learned the codes used by a particular system of computerized composition can interpret printout for typographic qualities as well as they can read the intellectual contents of lines. The codes needed in printout are of course absent in the proofs of the final composition.

Composition Tasks and Their Solutions

Composition is the process whereby printers' copy, usually a typescript, is converted into standardized letter forms, called types, in accordance with a predetermined plan and format. The elemental units of composition are of three kinds: (1) type characters, or type matrices, or photographic assemblies, called grids; (2) spaces for word spacing, indentions, and other purposes; word spaces are usually adjustable spacebands on line-casting machines; (3) spaces between lines of composed types including type images. In metallic composition these spaces are called leads and slugs. (The word "lead" is pronounced like the metal which is the main ingredient of type alloys.) In non-metallic composition physical leads are not used but the verb "to lead," meaning to add space between lines, is still current.

All composition is an assembly process; computerized composition has not changed this fact as long as it still uses existing metallic or photographic typesetting machinery. Conditions may change radically when *digital character storage* systems will be perfected. In such systems type characters are not produced by use of metallic or photographic matrices but directly generated by the computer. A number of companies are working on such systems, and "according to Dr. N. I. Korman, Radio Corporation of America, a great many of these systems will be in operation by 1970. Photocopy generation will produce full pages of text, line drawings and halftones on film, automatically processed and handled. At a later stage of development, the film will probably be by-passed and the plate will be produced by an electron beam, an electronically controlled laser beam, by triggering of a chemical action or in some other way not yet established."[103] Not all industry people share the optimism of Dr. Korman; some believe that it will take a great deal of time and money to arrive at computer generated composition of an acceptable quality.[104]

In the fall of 1965 Bell Telephone Laboratories, Inc., Murray Hill, N.J., disclosed that a system of computer editing and typesetting was being developed. Type characters are generated electronically by adding elemental areas of standardized shapes that can be numerically described and identified. These elemental areas are designated by Bell Laboratories as PATCHs. (PATCH stands for Parameterized Area to Construct Holograph.) An average of ten PATCHs is needed to form the characters of a given type face.[105]

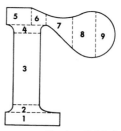

Courtesy Bell Laboratories, Inc.

Electronic character generation in the Bell System. Characters are formed by adding standardized units called PATCHs *by Bell.*

How metal types, metal or photo matrices, and other type images are assembled in various composition systems need not be repeated here. (Hand composition is explained in Section 2, hot-metal machine composition in Section 3, and non-metallic, mainly photographic composition, in Section 4.) In all composition systems words are separated by spaces; and lines, too, may need additional spacing. It is not always possible, particularly not when lines are short, to compose a line without dividing the last word, and composition of lines of equal, or justified length, requires several decisions related to word division. First, it must be decided whether a line should or should not be ended by dividing the last word. If it is not necessary to divide the last word, the word spaces within the line may or may not need changing to justify the line. If a word must be divided, the point of division must be established and again the word spaces may or may not need changing for line justification.

Composed lines of even length are a technical necessity in all composition consisting of individual type characters, as explained under the head "Handling of composition consisting of individual characters," in Section 2. In composition consisting of slugs of type, uniform slug length is still a technical necessity but the end of the slug can have no type characters without impairing its usability. In photographic composition lines of even length are without any technical foundation and merely a requirement based on traditional appearance of reading matter. Some newspapers have turned away from right-hand justification under the pressure of rising costs and encouraged by the re-evaluation of composition practice caused by computer application. The *Denver Post* changed to unjustified composition in mid-August 1963. "Reader reaction to unjustified lines was almost non-existent. A total of approximately 250 comments were received by telephone and mail—the majority critical—but none have been received since mid-September."[106]

> The recovery program was started in 1960, and was expanded later to include dispersal of military aircraft to civilian airports in a national crisis that held a danger of attack on the United States.
> Such a dispersal, designed to make the regular Air Force less vulnerable to knock-out on

Courtesy Denver Post

A sample of unjustified composition in use at the Denver Post *since August, 1963.*

At the same time when the decision was made to switch to unjustified lines, makeup men were told that "widow" lines were permissible. Inasmuch as the *Denver Post* uses a generally horizontal makeup, many columns needed leading to avoid "widow" lines.

Like every other assembly process composition needs inspection and verification of its correctness. These operations are needed in several production stages of composition. In all systems providing hard-copy or printout, verification is possible prior to proofing the composed type images. In systems that have neither hard-copy nor printout, verification must be delayed until final composition exists and can be proofed. If inspection, which is called proofreading in the composition industry, shows mistakes, these and their corrections must be marked on the proof. Marking of proofs is part of proofreading. The actual composition must be next corrected in accordance with the markings on the proof. After composition is corrected it can be passed on to its next stage which is usually page makeup. (Correction, proofing, and page makeup are discussed in Section 5; proofing of metallic composition is extensively treated together with other proofing methods in Chapter VI, Section 8.)

Proofing and correcting are first done to assure conformity between the composition and the typescript to be composed. Often correcting does not end at this point but just has its merry beginning. The printer submits the corrected "clean" proofs to his customer, usually a publisher. Present practice is that this proof is turned over to the author for two purposes: (1) to check the proof for correctness, (2) to improve the text, if he so desires, by changes. Such changes may be revisions of diction, additions and deletions, corrections of errors or mistakes made by the writer, and in some instances changes to fit space requirements. These changes are known as author's alterations, or a.a.'s, and are chargeable to the publisher. After the required corrections and changes are made, new proofs are pulled and again submitted to the publisher. These corrected proofs may or may not be transmitted to the author, depending on the rules adopted by a publisher. If the proofs are not submitted to the writer, an editor employed by the publisher does the checking. After final approval of galley proofs, the composed material is passed on for page makeup. Page proofs are taken after makeup, and corrections or changes are still possible at this stage. (Computerized composition has correction techniques of its own. These are described in the following unit where problems and practices of computerized composition are discussed.)

Word division in different composition systems. The decision about word division and the splitting of words to be divided is an operator task in all composition systems other than computerized composition. Even though computerized composition is the only method whereby word division can be done by the equipment, there are some systems of computerized composition that still require interference of the operator when word division is inevitable. The subject of word division is complex and discussed at some length in the following unit. There you also find an identification of a computer system in which the operator must act to divide words at the end of a line.

Different systems of line justification. Line justification can be accomplished in four ways: (1) manually, (2) mechanically, (3) numerically, and (4) by combining mechanical and numerical features. Hand composition of type characters (and of type matrices in the Ludlow System) is based on manual justification using the techniques of spacing-in or spacing-out. Hand keyboarded line-casting machines use mechanical justification with expandable spacebands; keyboard operated Fotosetters use a different but still mechanical kind of justification; the Monotype and the Monophoto and other tape-operated full-range photographic composition systems use numerical justification. Tape-operated line-casting machines, finally, combine numerical justification with mechanical justification.

Systems with hard-copy and systems without it. Hand composition, keyboard operated line-casting machines, the Monotype, the Monophoto, and keyboard operated Fotosetter models do not establish a concurrent typed record of composition as a by-product. The operator controls the progress of keyboarding by memory and visual inspection, differing in kind for different systems. The hand compositor assembling metallic types can read composed matter almost as fluently as print in spite of its abnormal reading position in the composing stick and on the galley. Operators of keyboarded line-casting machines and of the Fotosetter can read the line as it is being assembled due to the reference character borne by matrices. These reference characters are in proper reading direction and in the normal position of printed reading matter. Operators of Monotype and Monophoto keyboards have no visual record but they soon learn to read the Monotype paper ribbon. Operators of tape perforators for Teletypesetting are in a similar position, as the original TTS perforating machines do not produce a typed

record of composition. Other models of perforators, such as the Friden LCC line, are equipped for this purpose, and hard-copy is available on these machines for computerizing, for the Teletypesetter System as well as for the Intertype Fotomatic. Non-metallic systems for composition of body types, such as the ATF Typesetter line, and full-range systems such as the Linofilm, the Fototronic, and the Photon produce hard-copy, whereas manually keyboarded Fotosetters do not.

Page makeup. Techniques for page makeup differ in metallic and in non-metallic composition. Makeup of pages including display composition is an important cost element in the newspaper and trade magazine business. Standard techniques for page makeup are described in Section 5. Page makeup in computerized composition will be discussed in the following unit which is devoted to problems and practices of computerized composition.

Trends in the development of composing systems. Looking backward it becomes evident that the trend of development is away from keyboarding and toward typing in composition systems. The term keyboarding indicates in this context the fingering of keyboards on blind machines as opposed to typing which is applied for fingering keyboards of typewriters or typewriter-like machines which produce a readable typed record either as the main product or as a by-product of composition. The original TTS perforator is a compromise between the keyboard of line-casting machines and a typewriter: this perforator has the layout of a typewriter keyboard but does not provide a typed record of tape perforating. Nor has the Fotosetter, the first successful photographic composing machine, facilities for hard-copy. This is not surprising as the Fotosetter is designed following the pattern of keyboarded line-casting machines.

Another trend is away from one-unit composing systems toward systems that have at least two basic units and often many more. In one-unit systems the physical assembly of type characters, matrices, or photographic elements and the determination of the contents of the assembled line are coincident. In two-unit systems determination of line contents and assembling are two different tasks performed by different people with different equipment. The Monotype was the first generally accepted two-unit system. The increasing cost and speed of photographic composition systems make a division between the function of determining line contents and actual composition of the line a necessity. A high-speed photocomposition machine such as the Photon Textmaster not to speak of the Zip, can handle the output of a number of operators who punch tape which is functionally nothing but determining line contents. The computer is a third element, and the printout equipment used together with it a fourth. It takes the output of many tape punching machines to keep a computer or high-speed photocomposition machines busy. This should not be read to mean that single-unit systems are useless or doomed. For many purposes nothing is more efficient than to finger the keyboard of a line-casting machine. Tape-operated high-speed Linotypes and Intertypes have keyboards because keyboarding is most efficient for fast changes and corrections.

Problems and Practices of Computerized Composition

Computerized composition introduces new approaches and therewith new problems in at least three different stages of composition: (1) word division from line to line, (2) the use of hard-copy instead of galley proofs for proofreading and making of changes by editors and writers, and (3) correcting of computerized composition. After an explanation of these three points some examples of successful computerized composition will be described.

Word Division at the End of Lines

The first difference between computerized composition and all older composition methods is that computerized composition can decide on word division. Apart from its speed, computerized composition is distinguished from all other composing systems by its ability to perform word divisions at the end of lines which is an operator task in all other systems.

Some considerations in the division of words. Division of words does not look like an important point until the problem is faced in detail. American English is divided phonetically, or by the syllables of words. "Syllables are the sound units that make up a word."[107] Some words cannot be divided at all even though they have six or seven letters, "crazed" and "through," for example. One-letter divisions are never permissible and such words as amen, among, or enough are indivisible according to this rule. The rule does not only apply to one-letter divisions at the end of a line but also to the beginning of the next. A solitary "y" as in bind-er-y is to be avoided in print even though it is grammatically correct. Webster lists approximately 1,200 words which are differently pronounced by seven representative dictionaries; and such differences often mean differences in the formation of syllables.[108] Several printing and publishing organizations, among them the *New York Times*, the *U.S. Government Printing Office*, and the *University of Chicago Press*, have their own style books and their own rules for word division. Machine operators and proofreaders are familiar with these rules and are constantly reminded of them by the process of proofreading, marking, and correcting.

An ambiguous usage of "hyphenation." In the composition industry "hyphenation" indicates the division of a word, probably because a hyphen is placed after the last syllable at the end of the line. But hyphens are also used for other purposes, between certain compound words for example. Such words are called "hyphenated" by most grammarians who prefer a different term for word division. Using "hyphenated" for both purposes can become rather confusing. According to the *Dictionary of American Usage* hyphenated words must not be divided between syllables but only at the hyphen. (In secretary-treasurer, for example, neither the word sec-re-tar-y nor the word treas-ur-er must be divided by those who want to obey this rule.) Expressed in the terms of the trade the preceding rule would read: hyphenated words must not be hyphenated, which is senseless.

The reason for the popularity of "hyphenating" could be that neither a verb nor a noun indicating word division is generally accepted. In the latest edition of *Fowler* four verbs (syllabate, syllabicate, syllabify, and syllabize) and four nouns (syllabation, syllabication, syllabification, and syllabization) are listed, followed by this suggestion: "The best thing would be to accept the most recognized verb *syllabize*, give it the now non-existent noun *syllabization*, and relegate all the rest to superfluous words."[109] More recently the term "split" has appeared in composition trade literature. It is used both as a noun and a verb, avoids the ambiguity and length of "hyphenating" and is more familiar than the suggestions made in *Fowler*.

Various approaches to word division by computer systems. The problem of word division can be approached in a number of ways. One is the logic system of word division, another the dictionary system; then there is the method of monitoring, and "one proposed way of tackling the problem is that one might type the copy and tap a special 'hyphen' key at each and every position where a word could be split."[110]

The logic system is based on grammatical rules that can be found in many books. Webster, for example, lists ten "rules for the syllabic division of words in writing or print."[111] These rules are rather complex, have several subdivisions and many exceptions. A logic system may incorporate a varying number of these rules and their exceptions in encoded form, based on the frequency with which words falling under a rule or its exceptions are used. Word frequency has been studied by philologists and lexicographers for decades. Lexicographers, meaning makers of dictionaries, are particularly interested in relative word frequency since they want to explain the meaning of rarer words by defining them with more commonly used ones. A high-school dictionary used by the present writer has this introduction to word frequency: "If a word is one of the twenty thousand most used in a representative sample of about ten million running words from such books, magazines, etc., as high-school students read, a number is printed at the very end in italic type showing whether it is in the commonest thousand (1), the next common thousand (2), and so on, if it is in the 20,000."[112] In this dictionary, published in 1941, paper has the frequency number 1, ink 3, lexicographer 20, and computer is not even listed. Things have certainly changed in the last 25 years.[113]

The dictionary method of word division is based on smaller or larger word lists indicating syllables and correct divisions in coded form. Such word lists can be part of the computer memory or they can be stored outside on-line. There appears to be a tendency to combine the logic and the dictionary method, with the trend moving in the direction of logic systems. One competent observer of computerized composition methods suggests that experts in linguistics, logic, typesetting, and proofreading should establish a consistent set of rules for word division compatible with computer processing. "A computer program could be written from these rules to produce a word list, showing the new and logical

hyphenation for every word in the English language."[114]

How successful are computers in word division? "At the *Los Angeles Times*, a logic system based on grammatical rules of word division is used to guide an RCA 301 computer. It achieves about 85 per cent accuracy in hyphenation—that is 85 per cent of the lines ending with a word split are correctly broken according to Webster's first choice."[115] Other advantages of computerized composition of lines are that computers can compose tighter lines, avoid many word divisions which are made on manually operated composing machines and can save space by utilizing the available line length better. "In one newspaper operation, the computer has, on an average reduced a conventionally set 21½ newspaper column of type to 20 inches."[116]

Hard-Copy for Proofreading and Author's Alterations

Computerized composition can be corrected in several production stages: (1) after tape punching either by proofreading and marking the concurrently typed hard-copy or, if tape punching is done on blind machines, by making a printout and by marking it for corrections. In both techniques new tape is punched for the necessary corrections and both tapes are merged prior to computerizing; (2) after computerizing by proofreading and marking of printout, followed by punching of corrections and tape merging; (3) after typesetting, from galley proofs taken in proof presses or from galley proofs made by photocopying, and (4) after page makeup, either from printed or from photo-copied proofs. The first two stages are new, the second two are traditional and described in Section 5.

Hard-copy can be used for proofing and correcting in computerized composition but also in composition made by tape-operated line-casting machines and in composition by several photographic systems which may or may not be tape operated. In computerized composition systems either hard-copy or a preliminary printout may be used for verification of the punched tape. Final printout is read for verification of the computerized tape. The differences between hard-copy and final printout are the following: (1) hard-copy has usually capitals and lowercase characters whereas printout is usually completely in capitals, (2) in hard-copy the text runs on disregarding the contents of individual lines, whereas in the final printout each line represents the contents of the line to be typeset, (3) hard-copy does not permit verification of word division whereas printout of computerized tape does, and (4) depending on (*a*) the kind of tape-punching machine, (*b*) the kind of final composing machine, and (*c*) the kind of printout machine, printout and hard-copy may differ in the character codes appearing in either record. There will be more character codes shown in printout, especially if an all-cap printout machine is used.

Computer operator mounting punched paper tape on tape reader for processing.

Hard-copy is being introduced to replace galley proofs for proofreading by writers and editors. Since the middle of the nineteenth century metallic type composition is proofed in long galleys and these galleys are used by writers and editors for proofreading. At this point writers also make changes in the text, the controversial author's alterations. Technically, there is no difference in the correcting of mistakes in the composed matter and in making changes in the contents of a manuscript. Both are handled the same way. But there is a great financial difference: the publisher is charged for author's alterations whereas correction of mistakes is borne by the printer.

Author's alterations have been a problem in printing for centuries. Increasing production costs and advanced production methods have

given added importance to this problem, especially in computerized composition methods. Computer specialists apply the modern concept of system analysis to printing, and they want to improve efficiency by eliminating all unnecessary delays and changes.

Opinions are divided on the necessity of author's alterations and on the point when they should be made, if at all. In the words of Prof. C. J. Duncan, who has become one of the best known advocates of computerized composition and efficient printing systems, "one reason why authors or editors expect to be able to make alterations as well as corrections in proof is because printers and publishers have encouraged them to do so."[117]

Some publishers are trying to get all changes and corrections done on hard-copy. In one such instance "the author worked with typed hard-copy proofs rather than proofs of type. Proofs were read and corrected before a single line of type was set. Pages were 'made-up' in the publisher's office by the production man and the author before any type was set."[118] The present appearance of printout and hard-copy is not entirely satisfactory in the opinion of a competent observer and writer, Mr. Daniel Melcher, President of R. R. Bowker Company. If we want to use printout or hard-copy instead of galley proofs for proofreading "we must at least give the author, in this case, a typescript copy which is not all interlarded with incomprehensible symbols intended only to instruct the computer."[119]

Whether hard-copy and printout will in time become more or less generally accepted replacements of galley proofs depends on their improvements and also on the change in attitudes of computer people, editors, publishers, and writers. The better all concerned understand both the problems of writing and those of efficient composition and the greater actual cost savings will be, the sooner will traditional attitudes yield. Explanatory literature for authors and editors will be of great help to all interested in improvements.[120]

Correcting of Computerized Composition

Different methods of computerized composition differ in their correction procedures. For a grouping of correction procedures it must be remembered that a variety of equipment can be combined in computerizing of composition. These are: (1) blind tape perforators like those used in the TTS; (2) tape perforators that produce hard-copy. Either kind can be used for tape-operated line-casting machines and for some photographic composition systems; (3) computer printout equipment which can produce a readable record, either of unjustified or of computerized tape; (4) hot-metal composing machines whose product—the composed matter—is proofed in proof presses; and (5) photographic composing machines whose product is composition on photographic film or paper.

Unjustified tapes resulting from keyboarding of blind tape perforators can be proofed by putting these tapes through printout machines. The resulting printout serves as a proof that can be read and marked like other proofs. The unjustified tape is corrected by punching new tape where required, followed by elimination of the wrong taped material and by merging of the original tape with the correction tape. The corrected, merged tape, which is still unjustified can be again used for printout, and the second corrected printout can serve as second proof for reading and marking where necessary. At the time of writing newspaper composition uses mostly tapes punched on blind perforators for computerizing. In this industry it is not customary to use printout; corrections are made after the composed matter is proofed.

Unjustified tapes resulting from typing on typewriter-like tape punching machines producing hard-copy can be corrected either by using hard-copy as a proof or by making computer printout, or by both. The hard-copy or the printout is marked, correction tape is punched, and the two tapes are merged. The merging of tapes is highly technical business. For our purposes it is sufficient to mention that instructions concerning additions or deletions, or both, must be made in the form of codes by those in charge of correcting. As already made clear, computers do not act on their own initiative but only according to instructions.

In systems providing printout, the corrected tape can be used for computerizing, and a printout of the computerized tape can be made for correcting of oversights as well as for verification of word divisions. Word divisions cannot be seen on hard-copy or on printout of unjustified tape but only on printout of computerized tape which shows what the contents of each composed line will be. Mistakes are corrected by tape punching and tape merging, as described before. The printout of computerized tape, either before or after

correcting, can be submitted to the publisher in replacement of galley proofs. Some systems, still in the development stage, follow galley proof printout with printout representing made-up pages if composition is to be done on photographic typesetting equipment suitable for this purpose.

All correction methods discussed up to this point are previous to actual composition. After composition is done, the usual correction procedures are still available, even though it is hoped that additional correction will not be required on jobs that went through thorough correcting of hard-copy or printout.

Correction methods are in a state of flux and may change greatly in the foreseeable future. The Photon Zip, which is the first of the several-hundred-characters-per-second composing machines and already in operation in some plants makes an entirely different approach to correction, eliminating printout completely. This machine can set 650 characters per second in lines up to 11 inches long. This speed is said to make it practical to compose the text on photographic paper which serves as galley proof, showing not only contents but also appearance of composition. The photographic galley proofs are proofread and marked; thereafter the necessary corrections are made; instructions for page makeup and blank space needed for illustrations are provided, and the Photon produces the final com-

Courtesy Photon, Inc.

Operator with Photon Zip which is actuated by computer tape and was used to supply photocomposition for the Index Medicus.

INDEX MEDICUS

CARCINOMA, MUCINOUS (C2)

Peutz-Jeghers syndrome with metastasizing duodenal carcinoma. Williams JP, et al. **Gut** 6:179-84, Apr 65

CARCINOMA, PAPILLARY (C2)

Primary ureteric neoplasms: with a report of forty cases. McIntyre D, et al. **Brit J Urol** 37:160-91, Apr 65 [Contribution to the problem of radical surgery in tumors of the upper urinary tract] Marton I.

Courtesy National Library of Medicine

Sample of Index Medicus, *composed on a Photon Zip. Illustration is same size as print in* Index Medicus.

position.[121] Another approach to editing and formating is studied by the University of Pittsburgh, Computation and Data Processing Center under the name UPGRADE (University of Pittsburgh Generalized Recording and Dissemination Experiment). In this system the text is "displayed on a cathode ray tube screen, and the operator is able to make the changes he desires by use of a light pen and a typewriter keyboard."[122]

Some Examples of Successful
Computerized Composition

The field of application for computerized composition is constantly widening and many new examples will become available in the near future. These new experiences may supersede existing practices, but some examples are, nevertheless, given in the following.

The Cumulated Index Medicus. The most stunning application of computers and high-speed photographic typesetting equipment is so far the production of the *Cumulated Index Medicus* which was produced at the National Library of Medicine at Bethesda, Maryland. In May, 1964, the first Photon Zip Model 900 was installed there. The capacity of this machine is approximately 110 lines of 11 inches (not picas) per minute. "The lines of composition are fully justified; all lines are flush left and flush right. A choice of up to 264 different characters is available during continuous operation, and any combination of these characters can be mixed in the same line."[123] Formerly the *Index Medicus* was reproduced from all-cap computer printout. The 1964 *Cumulated Index Medicus* has four volumes totaling 5,700 pages of 6-point type. This work was set in 120 hours on the Photon Zip; the total elapsed time was two weeks. The composition required "over sixty million characters which would have taken over

four machine years to produce on the fastest hot metal line-casting equipment. Setting the book on Zip has several other economic and appearance advantages, compared with the readability of all-cap computer printout."[124]

Even though many graphic arts people may be most interested in the performance of high-speed composing machines, a few words on the conditions that make such machines a necessity are in order. The proliferation of scientific literature defies all imagination. We are so much used to huge numbers that they do not impress our minds, unless we must cope with the problems caused by them. Indexers of medical literature are facing such a situation. "The magnitude and significance of the indexers' task may be seen from the fact that 152,030 articles were indexed in 1964 and that the Indexing Section of the National Library of Medicine plans to index 300,000 articles annually by 1970."[125] The preparation and organization of this material, as well as its printing, is part of MEDLARS which stands for Medical Literature Analysis and Retrieval System, "a computer-based information storage and retrieval system currently in operation at the National Library of Medicine (United States Public Health Service) in Bethesda, Md."[126] Other fields of knowledge face similar problems and are all concerned with finding workable solutions to them. Wherever masses of information must be handled, computers are a necessity, and wherever such masses of information handled by computers must be printed, computerized composition with high-speed machines is a logical procedure.

The CIA system of computerized photocomposition. The Printing Services Division of the Central Intelligence Agency has the responsibility of printing "the classified material required for the operation of the Agency."[127] This material consists of confidential books and manuals which are usually prepared by the staff of CIA. The CIA departments that prepare or order printed products are the "customers" of the Printing Services Division. Even though the system developed by this Division is designed to meet the needs of CIA, it contains nevertheless some features of general interest. One of them is the utilization of "source" or "customer" tape. Such tape is produced by the customers of the Printing Services Division, which are as we want to remember, primarily other departments of CIA, as a part of developing the manuscripts for publications to be printed. "We found that our customers type and retype manuscripts from three to six times and we plan to have them use tape-producing typewriters so that most retyping will be automatic. We will get their final tape along with the manuscript, and this will eliminate keyboarding as we plan to use this tape for the first pass through the computer."[128] It will be interesting to see whether the use of customer tape will spread to commercial printing and publishing.

The second new approach in the CIA system is elimination of word division. To CIA printing engineers and computer specialists "it was apparent that the end-of-line hyphenating problem would require considerable programming time and computer capacity. Further, it was found that hyphenating inaccuracies, computer capacity, loss of speed, dictionary cost, etc., were still problems."[129] Hyphenless justified composition is accomplished by changing the set-width of characters to suit the needs of justification. Each character of physical type can be considered as consisting of the relief image and some additional width of the bare type shank which provides the necessary distance from character to character.

In composition with foundry type and on line-casting machines individual characters cannot be closer to one another than type or matrices permit, though they can be moved apart by letterspacing. In the Monotype system which casts justified lines of individual type characters, it is possible to vary the set-width and to cast type either in a narrower or in a wider set-width than that for which a particular type face was designed.

This illustration shows the distances between type characters as intended by the designer of type. In the CIA system of unhyphenated composition these distances are increased or diminished to form a justified line without word division.

The change in set-width does not influence the type face, though it influences the juxtaposition of set characters. If a type face which was made to be cast in 9 point set-width is cast in 8¾ or 8½ point set-width the type characters are pushed closer together and more of them can be put in a line of the same length. But casting type with a lower set-width than the originally intended one

fast becoming settled. They abound in Ohio, Michigan, Illinois,. and
8½ Indiana. They labor under the disadvantages of a scarcity of wood
7½ and water—evils of a serious character, until art has had time to supply the deficiencies of nature. As coal is said to abound in all that region, and wells are generally successful, the enterprise
7½ of the emigrants is gradually prevailing against these difficulties.

The second description of these natural meadows lies west of the
Courtesy Printing Services Division, CIA

Sample of CIA hyphenless composition. Lines without bold-face numbers have set-width as intended by type designs. Line marked 8½ has increased spaces between characters, and the two lines marked 7½ have decreased spaces between type characters.

has strong limitations: unintended overhanging of serifs may be the consequence of removing too much of the supporting shank of the type. Serifs that are not supported tend to get damaged or may break off completely.

In photocomposition these dangers do not exist, of course; the photographic film or paper supports type images throughout. Certain systems of photocomposition were well suited for increasing the distance between letters, or to say it in the typographer's language, for letterspacing. But it was not known that photocomposition could decrease the provided space between letters. In the words of Mr. Kunkel, who reported on the CIA system, "our investigation of photocomposing machines disclosed that the Photon 513 could vary set sizes from line to line by codes inserted in the control tape by the computer."[130] The result is that letters can be either "packed" or "spread" as required. The Photon 513 uses 6-level paper tape, carries up to 1,440 characters on a disk, composes lines of a maximum length of 7 inches, and has a maximum speed of 10 characters per second.

In the opinion of CIA computer technicians "the variable set-size system provides two important new typographic advantages. It allows for decreasing as well as increasing the space between letters (interletter space) and at the same time preserves the proportional relationship of the letters to each other and the areas (including shank) which they occupy. The resulting lines are aesthetically acceptable to CIA printers, as well as computer technicians, because they are proportionately letterspaced."[131]

CIA computer technicians emphasize the difference between their variable set size system and letterspacing done by putting spaces of the same width between each letter, disregarding letter width itself. "Fixed letterspacing destroys the proportional relationship of the letters and therefore the beauty of the composed line."[132]

Computers in the newspaper industry. The newspaper industry uses computers more extensively than other branches of the printing industry, at least at the time of writing. According to a survey made by the Research Institute of the American Newspaper Publishers Association in March, 1965, 38 newspapers having computers reported that all of them used computers for line justification and hyphenation, 10 newspapers used computers for composition of display advertising and only one paper planned to use a computer for page makeup.[133] These figures give a fair idea of the development stage in which computerized composition is in actual practice. Most common is the composition of body type including word division. This is the lowest technological level of the new art. Display composition is on a somewhat higher level of technology and practiced by one-quarter only (to be exact 10 newspapers of 38). Page makeup, a much more complex operation, is not even included in the table indicating different kinds of present computer applications—obviously because it is still in the pioneering stage.

Computerized composition on line-casting machines without spacebands. In high-speed line-casting machines spacebands cause several operational problems. Until computerized composition became a reality, operating personnel simply had to accept these. "But now by using a computer to calculate the amount of space needed between each word to justify each line, it is possible to insert brass matrices of various thicknesses between the words assembled in the line and to cast a justified line."[134]

Fully automated line-casting machines. A new development in tape-operated line-casting machines is mentioned at this point even though it does not depend on computerizing. This is the Auto-Controlled Elektron in which tape control is extended beyond the usual range of keyboarding alone. Elektron Mixer models can be supplemented by a basic automated package, supplied by Mergenthaler, which "consists of servo mechanisms and associated control circuitry to select, from tape control, magazine position, mold

position, auto-ejector selection, and knife block setting. These four machine conditions are obtained from one tape signal, with the mold, ejector, and knife block automatically positioned from the magazine elevate selection code to which they have been geared."[135]

The Perry system of computerized composition, the Perry organization in West Palm Beach, Florida, publishes magazines, operates three different publishing houses, and produces 14 daily and 12 weekly newspapers. This concern is one of the pioneers in computerized composition including display advertising and page makeup. The working methods of this organization are tailored to the needs of computerized composition and differ considerably from traditional newspaper composing room procedures.

"Mark up, as generally practiced in the trade is no longer used at Perry Publications. Instead, they now combine all the work of layout, artistry, typing, mark up, and inspection within a new department, called quality control and layout department."[136] The Perry Photo-Composer, developed at the Perry plant, "puts together all typographic parts of ads as large as a full page using the Photon and the instruction tape."[137] Methods and equipment selected for the Perry organization are, of course, tailored to the needs of this organization. Some highly experienced newspaper manufacturing executives doubt that these methods can suit the needs of large metropolitan papers.[138] Display composition and page makeup are expensive operations. Many newspaper and trade magazine publishers look forward to generally applicable computer equipment for these purposes.

Even though computerized page makeup is not yet practically used in newspaper composition, it has entered the fields of book production and that of directories. For instance, the Rocappi system of computerized composition includes pagination, running heads, dimensioning of the type page, combination of illustrations with text, as well as of captions and legends accompanying illustrations.

Computer printout on direct-image offset paper plates. An example for using computer printout equipment directly for the making of plates is afforded by the printing system used by the New York Telephone Company. The Data Processing Center of this company produces daily 1,000 directory pages with 5,000 changes in telephone numbers. These changes include addition of new and deletion of discontinued numbers. The computer takes care of all changes, and printout equipment produces direct-image paper plates ready for running on office duplicators.[139]

Directory preparation by computers. Industrial directories are important to many trades and trade publications. Often publishers of trade magazines also publish annual directories for the same industry. The proliferation of products and the consequent multiplication of trade names is such that specialized directories have become a necessity. Directories must contain alphabetic listings of products and of manufacturers who produce them. In addition a directory usually identifies advertisers by some typographical distinction, bold-faced type, for example, and there must be good cross referencing as an aid to the reader.

The basic information for an industry directory consists of the name and address of each manufacturer, the names of his products, and trade names of products or product lines. These items are usually recorded by the administrative staff of a magazine or directory publisher. Records may be kept at various levels of efficiency: from simple, typed file cards, possibly amended with handwriting of varying legibility, to punched cards on which each product and trade name is numerically classified, ready to be used as computer input.

The computer has many applications in the assembling of directories and can substantially shorten the transition from an informal system to a completely developed numerical one. Besides co-ordinating the required data and making a subject guide out of a name file, the computer can also be used for composition, and printout can be employed as a means for updating the material in preparation of next year's edition. Several publishers use computer techniques for their directories. Our illustration shows part of an entry in the "Merchandise Directory Number" of *Hardware Age*, July, 1965. This magazine is published by Chilton Company, Philadelphia; the computerized directory was prepared by Rocappi, Inc., and the composition was done on a tape-operated Photon. This directory is printed on a page size 8½ inches by 11 inches in three columns, and has 632 pages and a paper cover.

The development of a computer program for directories can run into tens of thousands of dollars. As most directories have requirements peculiar to themselves, each different directory may need an individual program.[140]

CANS, Ash and Garbage
(See also Receivers Garbage)
Adams Co Cypress St Dubuque Iowa
Boyco—See Boyle Mfg
Boyle Mfg Div US Steel Products Co 5100 Sante Fe Av Los
   Angeles
Cincinnati Galvanizing Co 4879 Spring Grove Av Cincinnati 32
★ Columbus Plastic Products Inc 1625 W Mound St Columbus
   23 O
DeLuxe—See Schlueter Mfg Co
Dover Stamping Co 427 Plymouth Av Fall River Mass
Eastern Can Co 306 Bremen St East Boston Mass

Courtesy Chilton Company

Sample of computerized directory, taken from Hardware Age, Merchandise Directory Number. *Note product cross references, stars and bold-face type which identify products described in advertisements and names of advertisers. Directory was prepared with computer; typesetting was done by Photon 513, activated by tape from an RCA 301 Computer.*

Computers, Computerized Composition, and Design

Some computer technicians, who may have felt stifled by lack of understanding for their problems on the part of graphic arts designers, have questioned existing design practices and values and challenged the attitude of bookmen in general. That bookmen sense a rift between themselves and computer engineers is clearly expressed by the headline, Bookmen vs. Computer Men, under which *Publishers' Weekly*, the trade journal of the publishing industry, reported the March, 1965, R & E Council Conference on computerized composition. *Publishers' Weekly* notes particularly that "a distinguished speaker from Britain thought the way to make art directors toe the line would be to 'take the schools of design out of the art schools and put them into the schools of engineering.' As for authors they should be taught not to 'fiddle about' with their text."[141]

This offhand remark misses the point entirely. The question is not in what kind of schools design for printing should be taught but what the student should learn and, more important, what the designer should know. (Some famous schools of engineering include design and art in their curricula, Carnegie Institute of Technology, to mention one.) It is elementary that a designer must know the materials, processes, and methods whereby the design will be executed. As computerized composition gains ground, designers of books, magazines, and other printed objects must familiarize themselves as a matter of course with this new kind of composition, its requirements, and economics. But it takes more to make a designer than such rudiments of the craft. A designer must have artistic ability, a sensitivity to changes in styles and fashions and, last but not least, he must have taste. Unfortunately (for some computer technicians that is), taste cannot be specified in numbers and as long as it is not so expressible it cannot be included in computer calculations. (For some computer-happy technicians tact, like taste not expressible in numbers, can also be ignored; tact seems to appear to them as "fiddling" with people, a sheer waste of time and energy.)

Reasonable people can be of different opinions as to the most desirable proportion of technical knowledge and artistic ability of graphic arts designers. They can debate whether it is more promising to develop the artistic abilities of technicians or the technical abilities of artists. Reasonable people will keep open minds on these points and decide on the basis of the best available facts and evidence. But the subject is too serious and too complex to be dismissed by anybody's fiat.

Computer people sense the trends of the times when they emphasize the constantly mounting role of computers. But they misread the signs of the times completely if they conclude that design does not matter. The last two decades are not only decades of scientific growth, they are also characterized by an equally unprecedented appreciation of art and design. The growth of the American middle classes, better education, and more leisure time all combine to this effect. And it could well be that standardization and uniformization, which are among the results of science applied to industry, could not be borne by the human race without some relief by works of fantasy and imagination. Fiction, music, and the visual arts are playing a growing part in the lives of many millions. In the wake of this new art consciousness changes in attitude to commercial and industrial art and design were inevitable. Everybody who has observed the scene of printing during this past quarter century knows that design has become a powerful force in contemporary printing. The vast majority of printed products are commercial and not artistic in the sense that art is their main purpose. All commercial design must recognize economic realities and the best design is that which is most adequate to its purpose and achieves the desired result with the least possible effort or—which is just another way of expressing the same idea—at the lowest expense compatible with its purpose. Different purposes need different designs: a menu of a luncheonette must be differently designed than a menu for a full-

dress dinner. All this is so elementary that the only justification for mentioning it is the fear of some concerned with efficiency that the word design means implicitly waste of money. In truth the opposite can be proved: good design saves money, and printed products must be adequately designed to be saleable or to serve as effective means of persuasion.

Computers hold considerable promise for design of illustrations as well as text, and some examples may be interesting to the reader even

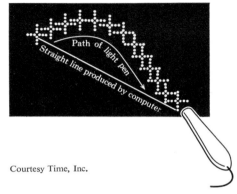

Courtesy Time, Inc.

The light sensitive pen or electronic stylus can be used to draw on the face of a TV-type display tube as if it were a piece of paper. Freehand informality is automatically changed to precise lines by electronic arrangements. Light pen can also be used to correct composition.

though the subject does not belong under the head of computerized composition. The cover of the July, 1965, issue of *Fortune* was printed in color and designed by aid of a computer. "This cover is the first in *Fortune*'s 35 years to have been

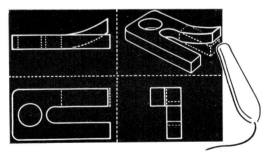

Courtesy Time, Inc.

The Animated Blueprint *is a feature of* Sketchpad. *The electronic draftsman can obtain modifications in design by indicating wanted changes with a light pen. A properly programmed computer makes drawings in four projections automatically.*

executed wholly by machine—a PDP-1 computer manufactured by Digital Equipment Corp."[142] *Fortune*'s art director, Walter Allner, specified what he wanted; a "program was written to Allner's specifications and punched into an eight-channel paper tape by Sanford Libman and John Price whose interest in art and electronics developed at MIT. Generating the design on an oscilloscope and photographing it required about three hours of computer time and occupied Price, Allner, and Libman until four one morning. Multiple exposure through two filters added color to the electron tube's glow."[143]

Then there is "Sketchpad," a design computer developed by Ivan Sutherland at the Lincoln Laboratory of MIT. This computer is also called "Robot Draftsman." On this computer "it is possible to use the face of a TV-type display tube like a sheet of paper, on which sketches can be drawn with a light sensitive pen or an electronic stylus. The 'Animated Blueprint' is one Sketchpad feature. Ordinarily, when human draftsmen want to modify a drawing they must redraw the whole thing. In the Sketchpad system it is sufficient merely to point at part of the drawing with the light pen and indicate how it should be changed."[144] The properly programmed computer does the rest.

Tentative Summary of the State of Computerized Composition

At the time of writing a summary of the role played by computers in composition is a questionable undertaking. Things are too much in flux to permit a well-balanced appraisal. With this limitation in mind a few comments appear, nevertheless, worth making.

First, computerized composition will probably not become important in the near future for printing businesses that need small amounts of greatly varying composition. Even though service centers for computerizing may be in existence all over the map before long, the small and even the larger neighborhood print shop will continue to provide composition for stationery and similar items in the traditional manner. Nor is it likely that display composition for national and regional advertisers and their agencies will be prepared by computers. Such advertisements contain in their vast majority a small amount of reading matter and consist mainly of pictures. (In the more recent past letter forms, too, have been used by designers of national advertisements as attention-getting pictures rather than to convey text.) Composition for persuasion printing, a class that includes advertising and promotional material in many different forms, must be skilfully blended with artwork and photographs. This kind of composition often needs repeated proofings and much too individual handling to be *prima facie* suitable for computerizing.

In the newspaper industry, which at present employs more computers than any other branch of the graphic arts, the advantages and limitations of computers are not uniformly assessed. Cost is, as always, a most important consideration.

Among advocates of computerized composition some believe that computers can pay for themselves if used for composition of body type *and also* for administrative purposes. Others do not share this opinion and intend to wait until computers can efficiently handle classified advertising and composition of display pages.

The preceding paragraph referred to the application of general-purpose computers to composition. But there are also those who believe that efficiency of hot-metal machine composition, which is most widely used for text matter, can be best improved by introduction of special-purpose computerized composition systems. Such systems are especially designed for producing six-level tape as needed by tape-operated slug machines. Two systems, the Linasec and the Di-An Computer Keyboard, are described in Section 3. At this point it is merely repeated that both systems leave word division an operator task whereas systems using general-purpose computers provide hyphenation automatically. Special-purpose computer systems do not have the flexibility of general-purpose computers but, as their advocates point out, this flexibility is not needed in many cases. The superiority of one special-purpose tape preparation system in comparison with tape preparation on blind keyboarding equipment, including line casting with either kind of tape, was documented by a painstaking study made by the research department of a large metropolitan newspaper.[145]

The most extensive saving in newspaper composition is expected in large display advertising which combines pictures with reading matter. At present the art of computerized page makeup is not sufficiently advanced to suit the needs of many metropolitan papers. Speed and cost of display composition are still on the side of traditional methods. Full pages can be assembled and proofed in the required quantity, often several hundred copies, at a lesser expense and in a shorter time than photographically made-up pages, which must be first converted into relief printing-image carriers for proofing and for stereotyping.

Different individuals evaluate the same facts and conditions differently. Some executives feel that a certain amount of risk is a worth-while premium for the opportunity to develop computer know-how within their organizations, other executives believe that waiting until things will be more settled is a better policy. The same attitudes also can be found in the field of book composition.

Here again opinions are divided on savings possible by using computerized composition for straight matter as needed in novels, biographies, and other trade books. Some feel that the possible savings are not large enough in this kind of composition to disturb existing working methods and relations with writers, others feel that savings are less decisive than making a beginning in revising outdated methods and practices.

The capabilities of computers are so great and so little explored for the graphic arts industry that those who claim a savings potential in computerizing even straight-matter composition deserve to be heard. In the composition of novels and other books which are intended to sell in both the hard-cover and the paperback market, a single computerized tape can be used for the different typesetting that is needed for products to be sold in either market. In biographies and other non-fiction works, computers can save time and money in indexing. In the composition of works of reference, computers can be used for bringing texts up-to-date by addition of new material and deletion of the superseded information.

It must be remembered that composition with general-purpose computers is at the time of writing seldom done by a system especially designed for this purpose, but by interposing the computer between machines which were originally conceived for different tasks. This condition is responsible for many intermediate steps whereby the products of other machines are adapted for the computer and whereby the product of the computer is rearranged to suit the needs of available photographic or metallic typesetting systems. The future will tell whether general-purpose computers which can be used for computerizing composition and also for the processing of administrative data will be preferable to specialized systems of computerized composition, designed exclusively for computerized composition.[146]

Computerized composition will have a great effect on the spread of high-speed photographic composition systems. One of the drawbacks of composition on film is the difficulty of making corrections. In this respect hot-metal composition is much more efficient. Computerized composition with its two additional facilities for proofing, hard-copy and printout, holds the promise that the final composition will not need correcting at all. If these techniques will be fully developed the much higher speed potential of photographic composition in comparison with that of hot-metal machines will be translatable into faster production and savings in cost.

Perhaps the greatest impact of computers is that made on the minds of graphic arts people. For the first time in the more than 550-year-old history of printing outsiders are in a position to examine printing procedures. Composing rooms are now the subject of study and analysis by systems engineers who are conversant with the most modern methods of analyzing manufacturing procedures. Such typographic esoterics as runarounds and widows are now investigated because each little item that was easily controllable in mechanical composition systems can cause most undesirable complications in computerized typesetting.

Printing history has seen many great advances in the past. But all of them were within the scope of judgment of printing artisans. Technical advances were enbodied in equipment and material; yet the use to which equipment and materials were put remained more or less in the discretion of craftsmen. Systems analysis is in its beginning in the printing industry, and the composing room has become the first testing ground. If systems analysis will show results, and there is no doubt in the mind of the present writer that it will, the camera department, the platemaking department, and the pressroom will be subjected to the same searching methods. Computerized composition is but the first step in a thorough transformation of the whole printing industry.

The IBM Selectric Composer and the IBM Magnetic Tape Selectric Composer

Both IBM Selectric composer systems are for composition of text by typing. The product of composition consists of type images on paper. This product is converted into the requisite printing-image carrier by means of photography and photomechanics. The difference between the two systems is not in the final product but in the extent to which certain functions are performed by the operator and by the equipment. Since the typographic features of the Selectric composer and of the magnetic tape Selectric composer are identical, this machine is described first.

The IBM Selectric composer. The IBM Selectric composer is based on the stationary carriage and moving type font principle which is used in the IBM Selectric typewriter. The type fonts are sphere-shaped units, approximately the size of a golf ball, which replace the type bars of conventional typewriters. Each type font has 88 characters. Selectric fonts are made in 6-, 7-, 8-, 9-, 10-, 11-, and 12-point sizes and in a variety of type faces including fonts for composition of scientific material. The exchange of fonts is simple and fast. The Selectric composer uses its own unit system; the maximum character width is nine units, the minimum character width is three units, and the total number of different character widths is seven. Pica is in this system one sixth of an inch exactly. Leading, or the vertical spacing of lines, can be done in one point increments. Among other features of the Selectric composer are facilities for tabulating, for speedy error correction, for centering of composition, and for pre-measuring of lines prior to composition.

Word division and right-hand justification. Word division and right-hand justification are differently achieved on the Selectric composer and on the magnetic tape Selectric composer. The Selectric composer requires double typing of each line for right-hand justification. The composer takes 15½-inch wide paper; this width makes it possible to type the unjustified and the justified line in one row. The line is first typed at the left. When the typing reaches the justification zone, the controls indicate to the typist which settings will result in a retyped line of uniform length. The typist sees, of course, whether the line can end with an undivided word or whether the last word must be divided, and acts accordingly when retyping the line.

In the magnetic tape (MT) Selectric composer many functions performed in the other system by the operator are taken over by the equipment. The MT Selectric composer consists of four basic units: (1) the MT Selectric recorder, (2) the Record-Only tape unit, (3) MT reader unit, and (4) the MT Selectric composer and its control console. Keyboarding is done on the MT Selectric recorder, a Selectric typewriter connected to the Record-Only tape unit. Keyboarding results in two products: the typed hard-copy for proofreading and the encoded magnetic tape for operating the composer. The encoded tape is transferred to the MT reader unit which has two tape stations, one for the original tape and one for correction tape. The MT Selectric composer receives its instructions through the control console. Composition takes place automatically in this system. The maximum speed is 14 characters per second.

Depending on personal preference the composer can be instructed to operate either without word division or to divide words at the end of a line. If word division is wanted, the actual division is made by the operator who monitors the system. The MT Selectric composer displays the word to be divided at the end of the next line automatically one line before by composing it outside the actual type area. The displayed word indicates up to which point letters can be placed in the line itself. On the basis of this display the operator decides where to divide the word. He pushes a button for each letter that will appear in the line and another button for the hyphen. The rest of the word is automatically transferred to the next line.

abcdefghijklmnopqrstuvwxyz &
ABCDEFGHIJKLMNOPQRSTUVWXYZ
1234567890 $.,:;!?¼½¾—†/+[ ] ( )=*-''@

Courtesy IBM Company

A font of Univers 11 point Medium type as used in the IBM Selectric Composer

Chapter III

The Theory and Practice of Full-Color Printing

Modern man is constantly surrounded by color. Everything is colorful, from the smallest household item to the largest building. Our cars, our clothes, our furniture, our homes all abound with color. Color photography, color movies, and color television add color to our leisure hours. Color, strong color, dominates the appearance of the contemporary American scene. Printing is no exception to this general trend. Color printing has, consequently, experienced a steady growth throughout the recent past.

Various kinds of color printing. When we classify printing jobs as to their color, we distinguish several kinds. One of them is *single color* or *black-and-white*, another is *multicolor*, or *flat color*, and a third is *full-color*. Here, too, as so often in the graphic arts, terminology is neither clear, nor precise, nor generally accepted. Some people use the term "black-and-white" for all jobs which are printed in a single color ink, be this color black or any other, others restrict it to jobs printed with black ink and prefer the designation single color for all other cases. Multicolor indicates printing in several color inks and so does full-color. But all kinds of multicolor printing differ in one decisive point from all kinds of full-color printing. This difference does not lie in the number of color inks used for the printing of a specific job, but in its final appearance. In multicolor printing, the final product shows a limited number of colors whereas in full-color printing the result presents a wide gamut of colors comprising a large portion of the color spectrum.

One can often hear such names as "process color" or "process printing," or "three-color process" and "four-color process" for full-color printing. These names are not very fortunate. As all products are the results of one process or the other, calling something merely a process without specifying the nature of this process does not contribute information. In this manual we always speak of full-color printing when the aim is the reproduction of a full-color gamut. All other kinds of color work are called multicolor printing in this manual.

Original images for full-color printing. Full-color printing is used for the reproduction of original images which contain an unrestricted play of colors. Examples of such colorful original images are fine-art paintings, color photographs, and commercial artwork made without restrictions as to the number of colors. These original images cannot be reproduced in any other way than by full-color printing.

Scientifically, full-color printing is the most advanced branch of printing and it is also the most efficient and therewith the most economical kind of color printing. These two facts are closely related. It may surprise you to read that full-color printing is the most economical kind of color printing. You may have heard that full-color printing is expensive, and you may wonder why it is here described as economical. As the economy of full-color printing is a decisive point, this statement must be clarified. This can best be done by comparing full-color and multicolor printing.

The difference between full-color and multicolor printing. In the reproduction of a multicolor job the printer matches each of the colors of the original artwork with a specific color ink. In full-color printing the printer does not match any individual color of the original subject with a specific color ink but he reproduces the whole color gamut with three different color inks which are apparently completely unrelated to any individual color present in the original image.

Consider for a moment how many dozens of different colors can be found in an oil painting or in a color photograph, and you will see the crux of full-color printing. Consider what it would mean to match each of these colors individually, consider what it would cost to proceed in the same way in which we reproduce multicolor work, and you will agree that it would be frightfully expensive to reproduce colorful originals in this manner, even if it could be done at all. For every different color we would need a separate image carrier and a separate press run. Twenty-five, fifty, and more of them would be required for a reproduction which in full-color printing is done in three or four printings with three or four different printing-image carriers and three or four printing inks of the correct colors.

To avoid misunderstandings, it is added that full-color printing is not inexpensive. If we compare the cost of a full-color job requiring four impressions with that of a multicolor job printed in the same number of impressions, the full-color job is usually more expensive. But if we compare the wide gamut of colors produced by one with the much more restricted gamut of the other, we cannot avoid the conclusion that full-color printing is most efficient and therefore also economical. The question how it is possible to achieve a wide gamut of printed colors by using not more than three or four different color inks can, unfortunately, not be answered without recourse to some theory.

This chapter is an elementary introduction to both the theory and practice of full-color printing. It is divided into four sections: (1) light and color theory, (2) color language and color systems, (3) application of theory to full-color printing, and (4) review of full-color printing methods.

Section 1:   Light and Color Theory

What is color? A short and seemingly simple question, but a question that unfortunately cannot be answered simply. The unabridged Webster dictionary uses almost a whole page, equivalent to perhaps eight or ten pages in books of a smaller format, for the definition of color. Even a high-school dictionary has eleven entries for the same subject. Three of these interest us particularly. Color is there defined as "a sensation produced by the effect of waves of light striking the retina of the eye"; but also as "red, green, yellow, blue, or any combination of these"; and lastly, as "paint, dye, pigment."[1]

Let us think about each of these three points for a moment. In the first-quoted definition, color is a sensation or something intangible. In the second definition we have a listing of several colors; but this listing omits two items which many people would include in such a listing, namely black and white. The last-quoted definition expands the meaning of color still further; now the word "color" signifies in addition to intangible sensations also tangible objects such as dyes, pigments, and painting media.

This diversity of meaning is one of the greatest stumbling blocks in the understanding of color. You are therefore invited to disregard your habitual color vocabulary in exchange for a more precise one. Such a color vocabulary was developed by color scientists. These define color as a "collective name of *the distinctive characteristics of light*."[2] Light is therefore the first point in our discussion of color.

Light and Seeing

If anything is elusive it is light. It changes constantly from day to day and from morning to night. But one thing is undisputed: without light we cannot see. Seeing and light are inseparable.

Seeing is a complex process in which many different things are combined. These include light, our eyes and brain, various objects, and, not least, our past experience, bodily disposition, and memory. When we speak of seeing we discuss what we see and, possibly, how well we see but not how we see at all. Usually, our mind is not concerned with light but exclusively with the objects which we see.

Light is radiant energy. In this discussion we must do the unusual and try to explore the role of light. Physicists, who know more about light than other people, think of light in terms of energy. Light is radiant energy. As you undoubtedly know, the sun is our natural and greatest source of light. But modern man is not solely dependent on the sun for his light; he can also use artificial light sources, such as candles, gaslight, kerosene lamps, electric bulbs, and fluorescent tubes. Electric lights depend on electrical energy for their operation. As you might remember from your school days, energy is defined as the capacity for doing work. Electric bulbs are an example for the conversion of one form of energy into another, namely, of electrical energy into radiant energy.

After this brief introduction it seems expedient to give a scientific definition of light. This definition states that "light is the aspect of radiant energy of which a human observer is aware through the visual sensations which arise from the stimulation of the retina of the eye."[3] This definition emphasizes the relatedness of radiant energy and the human body; of phenomena belonging with the physical sciences and phenomena belonging with physiology and psychology.

The human seeing apparatus. Stated in the most general terms, his eyes are man's intermediaries between the outer and the inner world. Rays of light enter our eyes through the lens and impinge on the *retina*, as the light-sensitive layer at the rear of our eyeballs is called. The effect of these outside forces is transmitted from the retina to the brain by our nervous system. The result of this process is the inner formation and interpretation by the human being of the seen outer world as its personal image.

It is important to keep in mind that not only these many elements, outer world and light, the eye and its retina in particular, but also nerves and brain including the human mind, co-operate in the formation of visual images. Our past experiences, our habits, and patterns of thinking participate very actively in this process. Few subjects are as fascinating as is a study of seeing. Various branches of the sciences have amassed an enormous amount of knowledge, much too much to give even the barest indication in the frame of

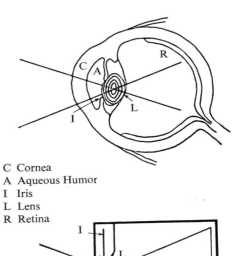

C Cornea
A Aqueous Humor
I Iris
L Lens
R Retina

S Shutter
L Lens
I Iris Diaphragm
F Film

Diagram comparing the human eye and a photographic camera.

this manual. Even though it is true that the exact workings of seeing are not yet known, a great deal of knowledge exists on many aspects related to the problem of seeing.

The retina. Everybody interested in seeing and color vision will want to know at least the most elementary facts about the retina. "The retina is the thin innermost lining of the eye and is the structure responsible for the detection of the light stimulus and the initiation of nerve impulses which will convey information about the stimulus to the brain."[4] Ten different layers have been distinguished in the retina which "has an average thickness of about 300 microns"[5] (300 microns are the equivalent of approximately .012 inch). Two of the structural elements in the retina are of particular interest to us. They are known as *rods* and as *cones*. "There is little doubt that the absorption of light takes place in the rod and cone layer and is converted into nerve impulses by a process not yet understood."[6] Rods and cones have different functions. The rods enable our eyes to adapt themselves to the dark, and the cones make our color vision possible.

Theories of color vision. It can be read in many books that man's color vision comes from three different kinds of cones, each of which is sensitive to a different color light. This opinion was held by two important men of science, Young and Helmholtz. (Thomas Young, who lived from 1773 to 1829, was an English scientist who stated his theory of color vision in 1807; Hermann Ludwig Ferdinand von Helmholtz, who lived from 1821 to 1894, was a German physicist; he published his *Treatise on Physiological Optics* in 1867.) In our times, science does not share this belief as "no histological or other evidence has ever been found which could distinguish such cones in the human retina."[7] Even though science has not yet been able to find out how we see color, other explanations are preferred over those suggested by Young and Helmholtz. "Fortunately, it is not necessary that one of the types of theory be accepted in order to understand the empirical facts."[8]

The tri-stimulus system. The empirical facts prove "that almost all colors can be produced by combination of three different colored lights."[9] Each of these lights must stimulate the retina in its own way. The system whereby colors are defined in amounts of three different components is known as the *tri-stimulus system*. Tri-stimulus values are the units of an international system of color description which will be noted later in this chapter. But at this point we must leave the human seeing apparatus and turn back to light and its behavior in relation to physical objects.

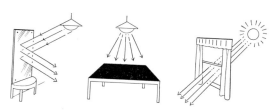

Examples from everyday experience for reflection, absorption, and transmission of light.

Reflection, absorption, and transmission. When light hits an object it is either reflected, or absorbed, or transmitted; in many cases all three things happen simultaneously but at differing degrees. Take, for example, a black-and-white photograph, placed on the copy board in front of a lens of a camera. This photograph is illuminated by strong lights as needed for photography. At the white areas of the copy, most of the *incident*

light (the light arriving on the copy) is reflected. The solid black areas of the copy absorb most of the light, and the gray tones between white and black reflect and absorb light to a varying degree.

The lens, through which the reflected light must pass before it can reach the photographic material behind it in the rear of the camera, transmits most of the light but it also absorbs and reflects some. Copy prepared on illustration board or other opaque material is therefore generically known as reflection copy, whereas color transparencies are classed as transmission copy because they are photographed by transmitted light.

Light as Waves

Light moves in the form of waves. Light waves are very small, much too small for measuring in such standard units of length as inches or centimeters. Light waves are therefore measured in units of their own. One is the *Angstrom*, abbreviated as Å or AU; the other is the *millimicron*, written as mμ and pronounced "em-mew" (the sign μ is a lower case "m" in Greek). One millimicron is the billionth part of a meter; ten Angstroms are equivalent to one millimicron. In the United States the millimicron is more used than the Angstrom.

Light waves vary in wave length from 380 to 760 millimicrons. This range of wave length leads us to a most important and not always appreciated point, namely, that light is composed of different parts. Our white light, as ordinary daylight is often called, is a mixture. The elements, if we may so call them, of which this mixture consists, are waves of different length. It is possible to separate light into its component parts, or, to isolate wave groups of different length.

Taking light apart. The technique of taking light apart utilizes a peculiarity of light called *refraction*. You remember that three things can happen to light if it strikes an object; it can be absorbed, reflected, or transmitted. *Refraction* is a phenomenon encountered in transmission. Light travels at different speeds through different media or materials. (Space, that is to say, a vacuum, of course, is in this context always counted as a medium too.) When a beam of light passes obliquely from one medium to another the change of speed expresses itself in a change of direction: the light is bent or refracted. The laws of refraction are very important; optical instruments, our lenses in particular, are based on them. Refraction is particularly noticeable in a prism, where light is refracted as it enters it and again very strongly as it leaves it.

All of us have learned at school of Newton's famous experiment whereby he dispersed light into various colors by the use of a glass prism. All of us have seen how such a prism works, how it divides a beam of ordinary white light into the rainbow colors which can be seen on a screen. This is possible because "the velocity of the light in a material medium varies with the wave length of the light, and it is found experimentally that the refractive index decreases as the wave length increases. When white light passes through a prism, therefore, light of different wave lengths will be refracted to varying degrees."[10]

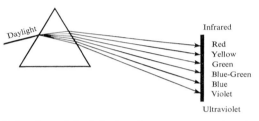

Refraction of daylight into its component colors by passing it through a prism.

The human eye is capable of noticing waves within the range of 380 and 760 millimicrons. This range of waves is distinguished from other forms of radiant energy by calling it the visible spectrum. The visible spectrum can be presented as an unbroken band of colors, and these can be correlated with waves of several length groups. Various authorities divide the visible spectrum in different ways for technical reasons.[11]

In a simplified manner, which will be used in the following, it is often said that the visible spectrum reaches from 400 to 700 millimicrons, and that it is divided into a blue zone from 400 to 500, a green zone from 500 to 600, and a red zone from 600 to 700 millimicrons.

The prism experiment is not the only one by which white light can be dispersed, but it is the most commonly known. Unfortunately, the prism experiment is sometimes misunderstood by people who merely follow the demonstration without absorbing its purpose and the thought behind it. Such people are inclined to assume that the prism is the cause of the colors they see on the screen. But the prism is no more the cause of colors than is the microscope the cause of bacteria in a drop of water, or the telescope the cause of the stars. Microscope, telescope, and prism are only instruments which make it possible for us to overcome the limitations of our eyes.

In any case, you should plant firmly in your mind that our daylight, so-called white light, consists of a balanced mixture of colors. This fact is of greatest importance for the understanding of our subject.

Putting light together. If it was possible to divide white light into its component colors, it must also be possible to combine these colors into white light. This is indeed the case; all that is required to prove it is a simple extension of the prism experiment. Instead of directly projecting the colors leaving the prism on a screen, they are now passed first through another prism. The law of refraction permits us to collect the dispersed waves and the result is white light.

But white light can also be produced in several other ways. One of them is by mixing equal amounts of properly chosen red light, green light, and blue light. Mixing lights of these colors produces other interesting results; red and green lights add up to yellow, red and blue to *magenta*, and green and blue to a color known as *cyan*. The only way of convincing one's self of these facts is the experiment.

The three colored lights used for this purpose are carefully selected; they are known as *primary colors* or *primaries*. In the definition of the Optical Society of America a primary "is any one of three components used for production of extensive gamut of colors by additive mixtures."[12] These, the *additive* primaries, must not be confused with the subtractive primaries, yellow, magenta, and cyan, which are the colors of our inks for full-color printing.

Objects and their colors. At this point of our discussion it is established that our so-called white light consists of a mixture of several colors and that these colors can be isolated, for example, by

Table III   THE VISIBLE SPECTRUM AND ITS COLORS

Wave Length in Millimicrons	*Color Name*	*Zone of Spectrum*
400 to 450	violet	blue
450 to 500	blue	
500 to 550	green	green
550 to 600	yellow	
600 to 650	orange	red
650 to 700	red	

refracting white light through a prism. But the prism experiment seems to be of no help if we want to know how the objects in our environment give us the sensation of color.

This point will now be taken up. The explanation is, as you will see, rather simple, but it is diametrically opposed to our customary notion that objects have their own colors, and that these colors are always the same independent of the light in which they are viewed. If you can free yourself of this notion and accept the fact that the color of objects changes as lighting conditions change, then you will not have much trouble with the following material.

If white light, which is a mixture of several colors, strikes an object, only three things can happen as you already know. Light can be transmitted, absorbed, or reflected. Assume that you direct white light on an opaque object such as a wall which appears red in daylight and is hence commonly called a red wall. In this case you can exclude transmission, and you have only absorption and reflection left. These two must explain how white light can lead to a sensation of red when we look at our wall.

Let us assume that our wall has the ability of absorbing the blue and the green zone of the spectrum and that this wall reflects only the red zone of the incident light. If this is so, we have obviously a simple explanation for the problem of how our wall gives us a red color sensation when viewed in white light.

Our assumptions are correct and this is exactly what generally happens when an opaque object gives us the sensation of color. Nor do things

change essentially if we replace the opaque object with a transparent one. In the case of a transparent object, say a red color filter, we may assume that no light is reflected and we must again explain our red color sensation with the two remaining phenomena which are now transmission and absorption. Just like our red wall, the filter, too, absorbs all other color components of the white incident light and transmits only its red components. Both opaque and transparent objects have *selective absorption;* but opaque objects reflect the unabsorbed portion of the light, whereas transparent objects transmit it.

We hope that you agree that this explanation of how objects convey color sensation is quite simple. But you might still feel that the request to relinquish your habitual color thinking, according to which colors are physical attributes of objects, was unjustified. You might feel that our explanation in reality changed nothing. *Instead of assuming that color is a fixed attribute of objects, we now assume that objects have a peculiar ability of selective absorption, transmission, and reflection.* Where, you may ask, is the real difference? The red wall has remained red and so has the red filter! Does it really make such a difference to say that objects have selective absorption and transmission or reflection characteristics rather than that they have their own colors? Is this whole distinction not just a play on words?

Your questions are well taken. If all light had the same composition, the preceding discussion would indeed be unnecessary, at least for our purposes. But the composition of light varies greatly, as you will see in the following section.

Section 2:   Color Language and Color Systems

From the Newton color experiment you know that light consists of mixtures of different wave lengths, or colors, and you also know that the so-called white light, our normal daylight, contains approximately equal quantities of these color waves. But all light is not the same; you know that some is more yellow and that other is more blue, for example. You may also know that if you buy electric light bulbs or fluorescent tubes you can choose between various types that will produce different lights.

Unfortunately our common language is not equipped for an exact specification of light. Such

expressions as *warm* or *cold, yellowish* or *bluish* light are not nearly precise enough to be technically useful. Imagine for a moment that you had to specify temperature or weight in the same manner, that you were limited to such expressions as cold, lukewarm, and hot instead of using degrees of Fahrenheit, or that you had to describe weight with such adjectives as light and heavy instead of numbers of ounces or pounds, and you will understand how limited our common light language is.

The concept of color temperature. Color temperature is a concept that makes it possible to identify and measure the color of light. Color temperature is expressed in degrees Kelvin, abbreviated K, after Lord Kelvin (1824–1907) who was a great mathematician and physicist and introduced a scientifically very important temperature scale. This scale is similar to the Centigrade scale. Its zero, though, is −273°C.; the zero of the Centigrade scale is the temperature of melting ice.

If you are surprised that the color of light can be expressed by a scale of temperature measurements, you should consider that light is radiant energy and that many materials glow when they are highly heated. As glowing is a form of radiation which can be used for illumination—in incandescent bulbs, for example—heat and light can be related to each other. Various kinds of radiation differ in their energy distribution and can thereby be specified as to their color.

The black-body radiator. If a black object is heated until it is red hot or white hot, there is a definite relationship between the temperature of the object and the color of the light which is emitted. The color can therefore be expressed in terms of the temperature. For example, if a light source is said to have a color temperature of 3800°K, this means that its color is the same as that of a black body heated to this temperature.

This point needs additional explanation. Light is composed, as you may remember, of waves ranging between 380 and 760 millimicrons. The shortest waves are violet and blue, the longest red. It takes more energy to produce waves of shorter length than long waves; the short waves can consequently discharge more energy than the long ones, a point good to remember in our later discussion of photomechanics. A change in energy input not only affects the quantity of radiated light, but also its energy distribution or color. The Kelvin scale makes it possible for us to specify the

Table IV   COLOR TEMPERATURE (in degrees Kelvin) OF VARIOUS LIGHTS[13]

White light from a standard black body	6,000
15 watt tungsten-filament lamp	2,483
100 watt tungsten-filament lamp	2,796
500 watt tungsten-filament lamp	2,925
1,000 watt tungsten-filament lamp	3,012
Photoflood filament lamp	3,490
150 watt daylight filament lamp	3,570
300 watt daylight filament lamp	4,035
Carbon arc lamp	6,400
Direct sunlight 9 a.m. to 3 p.m.	5,400 to 5,800
Light from clear blue sky 9 a.m. to 3 p.m.	12,000 to 26,000

color of light numerically. In Table IV you find a list of different lights and their degrees Kelvin.

With the growth of full-color printing, color temperature has become quite important for the printing industry. The nature of the light counts very heavily in the comparative viewing of original images and their full-color reproductions. All such comparisons must obviously be made in the same light. It seems that describing the viewing light in terms of its Kelvin number would insure this uniformity. This would indeed be so if the lights for which the same Kelvin number is given always had the same energy distribution. Unfortunately this does not always happen as color temperature—and Kelvin degrees with it—is sometimes used in a rather ambiguous manner.

Metameric color matches. Lights of the same energy distribution, which means the same as saying of the same composition of various color wave lengths, always match visually as well. But the converse is not true. Lights of the same visual qualities can have different energy distribution. Such lights are technically described as having a *metameric* match. (You must learn this term as we have no equivalent word in non-technical language for it.) It is not possible to conclude from the visual quality of a light what its wave composition is. For this purpose we must consult a graph showing its energy distribution.

Unfortunately light sources such as fluorescent tubes, which produce light of an entirely different energy distribution than we find in incandescent lights of a given Kelvin degree, are nevertheless designated as having the same color temperature if the visual qualities of these lights are the same. The practice of using degrees Kelvin for metamerically matching lights often leads to confusion.

An experiment in which the same object is viewed in two strongly different lights will prove why it makes a great difference whether we assume that color is an attribute of objects instead of understanding that objects have the property of selective absorption, transmission, and reflection of light. Light containing a small percentage of violet and blue color waves and a high percentage of yellow and red color waves will lead to a different color impression of the same object than lights containing a high percentage of blue and a low percentage of red color waves.

It might be helpful to think of the relation between viewing light, object, and color sensation experienced by the viewer along the following lines: The object can eliminate by absorption some or all of the color waves contained in the viewing light. But the object can never add color to those already present in the viewing light. If the viewing light contains, for example, a small percentage of blue color waves you will see the object differently than if a larger percentage of such waves is present in the light.

Two viewing systems. The viewing of printed products is an important problem for the printing industry. This problem was studied for several years by a joint committee of the Research and Engineering Council of the Graphic Arts Industry (R and E Council) and of the Illuminating Engineering Society (IES). In 1957 the R and E Council published a report on this subject where several standard light sources are described. The *Primary Standard Light Source* is to be used for comparing color quality of original artwork and printed sheets. This light source has a color temperature of 7400°K.[14] The use of this light is not satisfactory for the viewing of color transparencies as these are not balanced for viewing in a light as cold as this. Mainly for this reason a different viewing system is used by Time, Inc. This system was developed by the Springdale Laboratories Division of Time, Inc.[15]

Speaking of Colors

If we want to discuss our sensation of color we do this by referring to three different points: (1) what color, for example, green or red, do we have in mind, (2) how strong this color is, and (3) whether the color is dark or light. In this conjunction we use such terms as *hue*, *chromatic* and *achromatic*, *saturation* and *brightness*. Each of these is now briefly explained.

Let us discuss hue first. Hue refers to that property of a color which makes us designate it as red, blue, or green, for example. A red color has a red hue, a blue color a blue hue, and so on. Sometimes we speak of a reddish or a bluish color, or we use a combination of several hues such as blue-green for describing the hue of a color. It is assumed that the human eye can distinguish at best up to 200 different hues.[16]

But not all colors have a hue; some colors are *hueless*. Hueless colors are various grays, black, and white. Colors having a hue are also called chromatic colors; hueless colors are, conversely, designated as achromatic colors. Now a few words on black and on white. When we say that an object is white, we mean that it reflects more or less

all incident white light without selective absorption of color waves. When we call an object black, we mean that it absorbs more or less all of the incident light without reflecting any part of it. Black and white are, therefore, achromatic colors.

If we want to discuss the strength of a color sensation we speak of its saturation. Saturation is by one authority defined as the percentage of hue in a color.[17] Another authority defines saturation as the absence of white and says that "A saturated color is zero per cent white."[18] However, because of the confusion caused by this word, scientists prefer to speak of luminance.

If we want to explain the darkness or lightness of a color sensation we used to do this in terms of brightness. Now, if an object reflects a greater percentage of the incident light we say that its color has a higher luminance than that of an object reflecting a smaller percentage of the light that hits its surface.

Color Systems and Color Dictionaries

A considerable number of color systems and color dictionaries have been developed over the years. These enable us to identify, measure, and specify colors. We have selected five color systems and two color dictionaries for discussion in this manual because these are either of general interest or are particularly important for printing. In the following you find a presentation of the CIE, the Munsell, the Ostwald-Container Corporation, and the GATF-Preucil color systems. Then the Ridgway, and the Maerz and Paul color dictionaries are briefly discussed.[19]

The CIE System. The letters CIE stand for *Commission Internationale de l'Eclairage*, the official title of the International Commission on Illumination, which was also often abbreviated as ICI.[20] The CIE System is an international color system which combines physics, psychophysics, and psychology for the measuring and specifying of colored lights. Our discussion of color sensation followed this system and its terminology. The great advantage of this system lies in its comprehensiveness and in the simplicity with which colored lights can be matched.

The system uses three different color standards, known as the tri-stimulus standards, with which every color can be matched. The gamut of color is presented in a very ingenious *chromaticity diagram* which is a map of all possible colors where the position of a specific color can be easily plotted from a spectrophotometric curve.

The detail of this system is much too technical for further discussion. It is here merely mentioned that the three terms in which colored light is measured are: *dominant wave length* which corresponds approximately in terms of visual sensation to hue; *purity* which corresponds approximately to saturation; and *luminous flux* which corresponds to brightness.

The Munsell System. A serious objection to the CIE System and the chromaticity diagram is that equal color differences between various colors are not uniformly represented. This objection is overcome by the Munsell System, which is more closely related to the actual appearance of various colors.[21] The Munsell System is most widely used in the United States for the identification of colors as they appear on objects in the form of coatings, for example. Colors are classified in the Munsell System by three characteristics: hue, value, and chroma. These correspond more or less to hue, brightness, and saturation as used in the description of color sensation. These are Munsell's definitions: "*Hue is the name of a color.* It is that quality by which we distinguish one color family from another, as red from yellow or green from purple. *Value is the lightness of a color.* It is that quality by which we distinguish a light color from a dark one. *Chroma is the strength of a color.* It is that quality of color by which we distinguish a strong color from a weak one; the degree of departure of a color sensation from that of white or gray."[22]

The Munsell System is presented in the form of a tree; the trunk bears the value scale, the branches are one for each hue at each value, graduated from the trunk outward in their

chroma; "the branch ends represent the most powerful red, yellow, green, blue, and purple pigments which we now possess and could be lengthened should stronger chromas be discovered."[23] This open-end feature is notable.

Specific colors are identified by their hue and chroma. Hues are indicated by the capital letters, R, Y, G, B, P, standing for red, yellow, green, blue, and purple; intermediate hues are indicated by such combinations as YR, BG, and PB for example. The Munsell scale of hues comprises 100 steps, each of which is indicated by a figure from 1 to 10 and one or two letters. Value and chroma are also numerically designated: value from 1 to 10 and chroma from zero to the maximum available saturation. Combining the figures and symbols for hue, value, and chroma permits identification of a color in its essentials. The Munsell Foundation publishes various color cards and a color atlas for different practical purposes.

The Ostwald-Container Corporation System.[24] This system serves the same practical purposes as does the Munsell System. In the Ostwald System colors are described in three terms: hue, black content, and white content. The notation expresses these relations in percentage figures, for example, Color 5, White 4, Black 91.

This system, too, provides a color atlas where various colors can be identified for matching. In this country, the Ostwald System was not in use until the Container Corporation of America sponsored its practical application.[25]

The GATF-Preucil Color System.[26] This color system was developed by Frank Preucil at the Research Laboratories of the Graphic Arts Technical Foundation (GATF). It is designed for the efficient handling of full-color printing jobs. It integrates all phases of full-color printing, ink selection and evaluation, photographic color correcting, and finally controlling the actual production of a job on the press. The GATF-Preucil Color System is generally recognized as a major contribution in the application of science to printing technology.

The GATF-Preucil Color System evaluates the inks to be used for full-color reproduction by densitometric reading and simple calculations as to their strength, hue error, grayness, and efficiency. The necessary measurements can be made very simply, although they are not as accurate as some of the other methods of color measurement. These data serve not only as a guide for color correcting but can also be plotted

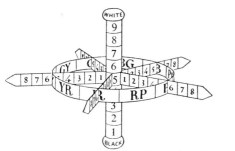

Courtesy Munsell Color Company

Hue, value, and chroma in their relation to each other. The circular band represents the hues in sequence. The upright central axis represents the scale of value. The paths pointing outward from the center represent the steps of chroma as they increase in strength from the center outward.

on the GATF Ink Hue and Purity Chart where they show at a glance how much the actual inks deviate from the ideal ones. The GATF-Preucil Color System provides in addition a color chart having 1,760 different color combinations which can be made with the three full-color inks and black. The printer is therefore guided as to the color gamut obtainable with his inks and the possible fidelity of reproduction.

The Ridgway Color Dictionary.[27] This color dictionary is the work of Robert Ridgway who was curator of birds at the United States Museum. His color dictionary is out of print but it "is still widely used for the description of the colors of birds, flowers, and insects. Fifty-three pages contain a total of 1,110 different painted samples. Each of these is named and also identified according to a notation corresponding to the systematic groupings of the standards on the charts."[28]

The Maerz and Paul Color Dictionary.[29] The Maerz and Paul Dictionary "contains 7,056 different color samples printed on semi-glossy paper. The sampling of the strongest colors is excellent, and the systematic arrangement makes it easy to find the color wanted. An alphabetical list of about 4,000 color names is given together with a key by means of which each corresponding sample may be found in the charts. The Maerz and Paul Dictionary of Color may be used as a collection of practical color standards in nearly every field. Furthermore, the scholarship and thoroughness of color-name treatment have given this work a wide reputation as the foremost authority on color names."[30]

Section 3:   The Application of Color Theory to Full-Color Printing

As you remember from our introduction to this chapter, color printing is divided into the two kinds of multicolor and full-color printing. In multicolor printing we match the different colors of the original image with different color inks. In full-color printing we do not match any particular color of a color original with any individual color ink but reproduce all colors of the original by means of three specific full-color inks—yellow, magenta, and cyan.

Color theory is a practical necessity. Multicolor printing may require considerable skill but its principle does not pose any problem. It is easy to understand that you match the colors of the original with the colors of the printing inks. But nothing in our past experience has prepared us for understanding that a whole gamut of colors can be reproduced with three different color inks. The only way in which we can learn to understand full-color printing is by studying the theory of light and color. This is the only reason we are interested as printers in color theory.

Stripped to its essentials the main problem of full-color printing is: How can we produce with but three color inks the same or at least rather similar color sensations that the artist produces without being limited in his colorants? If we want to achieve this result we must obviously find three different color inks which can be combined in the variety needed for our color gamut.

Finding the three full-color inks does not solve our problem completely. We must also have the corresponding printing-image carriers for these inks. This means that we must analyze every perceptible area of the original image into three color components, one for each of our full-color inks. Then we must incorporate the result of this process into the three different image carriers to which our three inks will be applied. Finally, we must transfer the three different ink-images in their correct relative location to the paper and thereby produce the finished reproduction.

Full-color printing is essentially a task of economizing and controlling. These enable the printer to duplicate with three different color inks what the painter created without any limitation in his colorants. The economy of full-color printing is by now clear to you. This economy is impossible without theoretical knowledge, minute planning, high skills, and constant controlling in all phases of full-color printing.

Inks for Full-Color Printing

We begin our discussion of full-color printing with the inks because they play a decisive role in this branch of printing. The three full-color inks are—as you know—yellow, magenta, and cyan. Each of them should ideally absorb one-third of the visible spectrum and reflect two-thirds of it. The absorption and reflection characteristics of yellow, magenta, and cyan are listed in Table V.

Table V   REFLECTION AND ABSORPTION CHARACTERISTICS OF "IDEAL" FULL-COLOR PRINTING INKS

Name of Ink	Absorbed Wave Lengths in Millimicrons	Names of Absorbed Colors	Reflected Wave Lengths in Millimicrons	Names of Reflected Colors
Yellow	400 to 500	violet and blue	500 to 700	green, yellow, orange, and red
Magenta	500 to 600	green and yellow	400 to 500 and 600 to 700	violet, blue, orange, and red
Cyan	600 to 700	orange and red	400 to 600	violet, blue, green, and yellow

Unfortunately it has not been possible up to now to manufacture full-color printing inks having ideal absorption and reflection characteristics. Two of the three color inks, the magenta and the cyan, are far from perfect. But it is possible to compensate more or less for their deficiencies by various color-correcting techniques.

The color gamut which can be produced with the three full-color inks is very extensive as you may remember from the preceding discussion of the LTF Color Chart. We owe this wide color gamut to the effect of *overprinting* of one color ink film over one or two others. By overprinting we change the absorption and reflection characteristics of individual color ink films and therewith the color sensations of the viewer.

Overprinting of three full-color inks results in seven different absorption and reflection areas. One of them absorbs nearly all incident light and consequently appears black, whereas the unprinted areas of the paper reflect all incident light and therefore appear white. For this reason full-color printing is considered sometimes as eight-color printing.[31]

Subtractive and Additive Color Mixing

At this point a brief explanation of existing terminology is indicated. Many of the difficulties commonly encountered in discussing full-color printing are due to muddy terminology. You may remember that many people speak of full-color printing as of *process* work; these often call inks for full-color printing *process colors*, or, specifically *process blue* and *process red* instead of cyan and magenta. *All serious workers in the field of color printing are agreed that these two inks must not be designated as blue and red but should always be called cyan and magenta.* Blue is, as you know,

the color obtained by overprinting of cyan and magenta inks, and red the color resulting from overprinting of magenta and yellow.

The creation of a wide color gamut by overprinting of full-color inks is usually known as *subtractive* color mixing. This term has a parallel expression in *additive* color mixing which refers to the mixing of color lights. We avoid both terms, not because they are wrong, which they are not, but because they complicate the subject without contributing anything. But you will meet them in many other books, and they are, therefore, here briefly explained.

Subtractive color mixing takes place in overprinting and also whenever physical colorants such as inks, artists' coloring materials, and dyes are mixed. Each of these materials has its own selective absorption range; the final mixture has the combined absorptive quality of all component elements. A mixture of colorants will, consequently, always reflect less color light than each of its components. This can also be expressed by saying that such a mixture is subtractive as it always subtracts or takes away some of the light which is reflected, or, in the case of dyes, transmitted, by its components. Additive color mixing refers to the mixing of colored lights. The final mixture contains all waves present in its components. As you remember, white light is a balanced mixture of the whole visible spectrum.

Full-color printing combines additive and subtractive color mixing. When we look at a printed picture we experience the results of both additive and subtractive color mixing. Often we find both kinds side by side. If you examine a letterpress or lithographic full-color print with a strong magnifying glass you will notice that large-dot areas overprint whereas small dots of different colors are often standing by themselves.

This concludes our discussion of additive and subtractive color mixing. You will not meet them again in this manual. Our next subject is the conversion of original colorful images such as color transparencies, for full-color printing.

Image Conversion for Full-Color Reproduction

As already mentioned, we distinguish two kinds of originals for full-color reproduction; these are classified as *reflection copy* and as *transmission copy*. In reflection copy the incident light is reflected by the surface of the original; in transmission copy the incident light is transmitted or passed through the copy for viewing. Reflection copy consists of paintings on paper or canvas, color photographs on paper, and other colorful images on opaque surfaces. Transparent color photographs, Kodachrome and Ektachrome transparencies, for example, provide the bulk of transmission copy; but it is also possible to use other colorful originals such as paintings on glass or on plastics as transmission copy.

Image conversion for full-color printing can be divided into four different phases. These are: (1) color separation, (2) color correction, (3) halftone photography, and (4) the making of printing-image carriers. Color separation produces the basic records for the making of the required image carriers; color correcting modifies and adapts these records for the condition of actual production; halftone photography converts them into the kind of printable images which are required in many printing methods for the reproduction of tonal values.

In this chapter we are more concerned with basic information on full-color printing than with the operative detail of each production phase. For this reason we limit ourselves in this section to a general exposition of color separation and color correction. The photographic aspects of image conversion for full-color printing as well as manual color correcting are presented in Chapter IV, "Graphic Arts Photography." Printing-image carriers for full-color printing, finally, are best treated together with other image carriers for each particular printing method. These are the subject matter of Chapter V, "Printing-Image Carriers."

The recent past has witnessed the application of electronics to image conversion for full-color printing. It has become possible to make color-corrected separations by means of electronics; to do color correction of photographic separations electronically; and even to bypass all intermediate conversion phases and to go directly from original color images to color-corrected electronically engraved relief image carriers. Even though electronic image conversion is merely in its beginning and many developments have not yet reached the production stage, we present a brief introduction to this subject in the last unit of this section.

Color Separation for Full-Color Printing

The great power of full-color printing lies in its economy, namely, in its ability to reproduce a wide gamut of colors with but three different color inks. (In many cases it is practical to use black ink in addition to the three color inks; but at this point of our presentation we do not want to complicate matters and, therefore, leave the discussion of black ink for the following unit.) As we need a different image carrier for every color ink, color separation has the purpose of providing us with three different records, one each for all image areas that will be present in the final image carrier for printing with the same color ink. This result is achieved by photographing the original image three times, but every time through a different color filter.

A color filter is in principle not different from

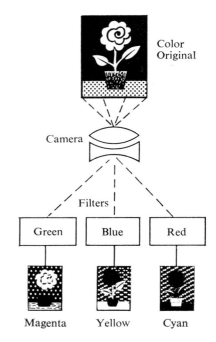

Schematic diagram of color separation photography.

Color as It Is Seen and Reproduced by Full-Color Printing

Full-color printing is a generic term for a number of methods and processes whereby color photos and other colorful originals are reproduced in print. The great selling power and attractiveness of color photos account for the steady rise of full-color reproductions in advertising, magazine, package, and catalog printing. Color printing is also used in educational and cultural publications, from medical text books to fine art reproductions. This persistent growth of full-color printing is due to the great advances in color photography and the big strides made in the reproduction of color originals. The detail of full-color methods is highly technical and the province of specialists, but the fundamentals of the subject can be understood by everybody and should be known to all who deal in some way or other with full-color printing. This four-page insert, printed in four colors, is designed for this purpose.

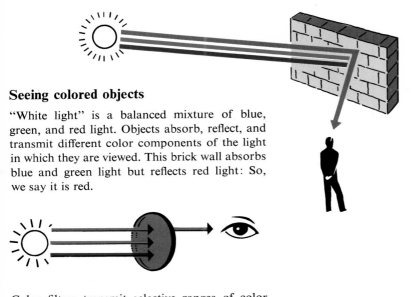

Seeing colored objects

"White light" is a balanced mixture of blue, green, and red light. Objects absorb, reflect, and transmit different color components of the light in which they are viewed. This brick wall absorbs blue and green light but reflects red light: So, we say it is red.

Color filters transmit selective ranges of color lights; this red filter absorbs blue and green light and passes red light only. Therefore, we say it is a red filter.

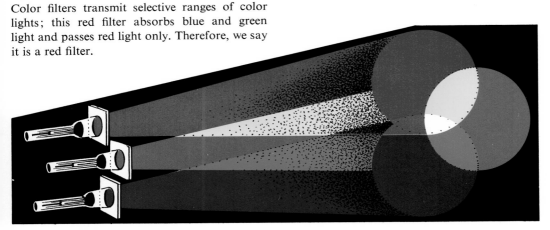

Blue, green and red light add up to so-called white light; a mixture of red and green light is yellow; a mixture of green and blue light is called cyan; and a mixture of red and blue light is called magenta. Mixtures of colored lights are said to be additive; mixtures of pigments, dyes, and inks are said to be subtractive. Yellow, magenta, and cyan are the three ink colors for full-color printing.

Photographic Color Separation for Full-Color Reproduction

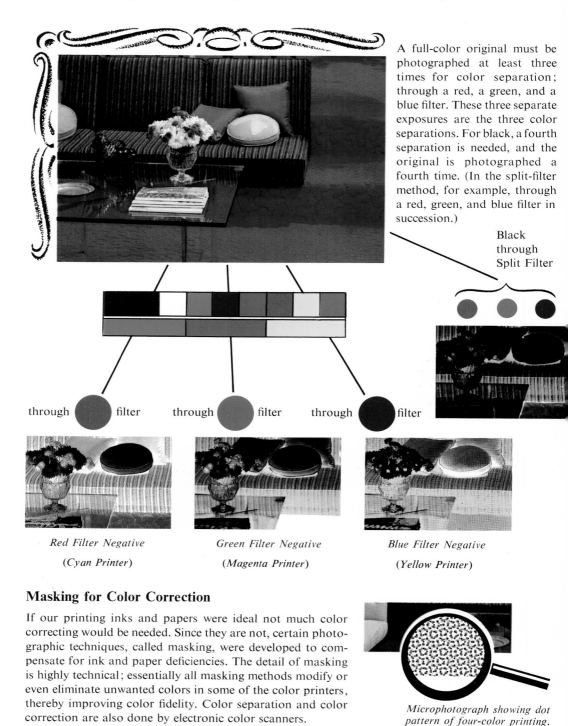

A full-color original must be photographed at least three times for color separation; through a red, a green, and a blue filter. These three separate exposures are the three color separations. For black, a fourth separation is needed, and the original is photographed a fourth time. (In the split-filter method, for example, through a red, green, and blue filter in succession.)

Black through Split Filter

through ◯ filter   through ◯ filter   through ◯ filter

Red Filter Negative
(Cyan Printer)

Green Filter Negative
(Magenta Printer)

Blue Filter Negative
(Yellow Printer)

Masking for Color Correction

If our printing inks and papers were ideal not much color correcting would be needed. Since they are not, certain photographic techniques, called masking, were developed to compensate for ink and paper deficiencies. The detail of masking is highly technical; essentially all masking methods modify or even eliminate unwanted colors in some of the color printers, thereby improving color fidelity. Color separation and color correction are also done by electronic color scanners.

Microphotograph showing dot pattern of four-color printing.

This four-color insert is presented to *Th*

Progressive Ink Proofs in Full-Color Printing

Yellow Impression

Magenta Impression

Magenta over Yellow

Cyan Impression

Cyan over Magenta over Yellow

Black Impression

A multicolor version of the full-color picture at the left. In the multicolor version the most important three colors of the art were matched by color inks, and black was added. The difference is self-evident.

Complete Full-Color Print

ry by the Du Pont Photo Products Department.

Color charts are valuable aids for matching critical colors

Printers use color charts on which the composition of each color area is indicated as numbered or per cent dot value of the different inks. The different color squares usually have punched holes which make it easy to compare a color of the original with colors on the chart. Comparing a critical color area with a chart of known composition guides dot etchers in local color correction.

Both additive and subtractive color mixing play a role in full-color printing. The diagram of additive color mixing shows individual small dots on white paper; the diagram of subtractive color mixing shows large overprinted dots. In actual printing both kinds of color mixing occur.

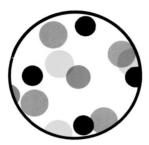

Additive Combination
enlarged

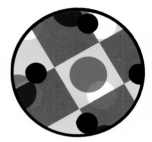

Subtractive Combination
enlarged

Table Showing the Overprinting of Three Full-Color Inks

Color Area	Color of Ink	Overprint	Absorbed Colors	Reflected Colors	Color Sensation
1	(bare paper)	none	none	white light	white
2	yellow	none	blue	mixture of green & red	yellow
3	magenta	none	green	mixture of blue & red	bluish red
4		magenta on yellow	blue & green	red	red
5	cyan	none	red	mixture of green & blue	greenish blue
6		cyan over yellow	blue & red	green	green
7		cyan over magenta	green & red	blue	blue
8		cyan over magenta over yellow	blue, green & red	none	black

any other transparent colored object. It absorbs a certain part of the spectrum and transmits the rest of the incident light. A blue filter will absorb everything but blue light, a green filter will absorb everything but green light, and a red filter will absorb everything but red light.

When we photograph our original image through each of these three filters we obtain three photographic records known as color-separation negatives. One records the blue light, the second the green light, and the third the red light which is either reflected or transmitted by the copy, depending on its nature. If we compare these records with the absorption characteristics of our three color inks we notice an interesting relationship. Each color-separation negative records exactly that part of the spectrum which is absorbed by one of the three color inks which we intend to use for printing. The blue filter color separation records the blue third of the spectrum, which is absorbed by our yellow ink, the green filter color separation records the green third of the spectrum which is absorbed by our magenta ink, and the red filter color separation records the red third of the spectrum which is absorbed by our cyan ink.

Interesting as this relation may be, it leaves us somewhat perplexed. As we will print with yellow, magenta, and cyan inks we must obviously have printing-image carriers where the color areas are identified for these ink colors and not for blue, green, and red. The question is now how we can use these three separation records for the making of our three image carriers.

The answer to this question is not difficult if you think of each color separation negative in terms of printing and non-printing areas. The black image on the transparent separation record represents the non-printing areas of the final image carrier whereas the clear areas of the same negatives identify the printing areas of our future image carrier. Depending on the type of image carrier to be made, it may or may not be necessary to reverse the clear and black areas in the following operations. But such reversals do not change the distribution of image and non-image areas in the final image carrier.

You will find it practical to add three new terms to your full-color printing vocabulary. These are *yellow-printer*, *magenta-printer*, and *cyan-printer*. These terms identify the three separation negatives not by the filter colors but by the ink colors with which the image carriers made from these negatives will be printed. The blue filter negative

is the yellow printer, the green filter negative is the magenta printer, and the red filter negative is the cyan printer. This shift in emphasis will help in keeping things clear.

This ends our introduction to color-separation photography. In the next chapter you find information on the equipment materials and procedures used in doing this kind of work. We turn now to our next topic, which is color correction.

Color Correcting

There are many reasons for color correcting. Among them we find the imperfections of our materials, primarily of our color inks, but also the limitations of our photographic materials, of printing papers, and, last but not least, of press-work. Depending on the job in hand and its purpose, these imperfections and limitations may need more or less correcting.

Many color jobs need adaptations and interpretations. Nor should it be forgotten that customers like to make changes in the original art-and-copy. Only in the rarest of cases is the printer asked to reproduce the original artwork exactly as it is. Whatever the artwork may be, and even if it is a painting by a great master, many customers like to improve on it, and they want to make the printer the instrument of their creative urges.

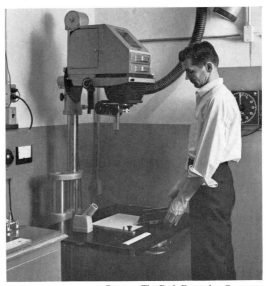

This precision Durst enlarger is used to enlarge transparencies for color-separation photography.

Often people must change their complexion, nature its moods, objects their appearance, all by customers' instructions as to color changes. In commercial printing for advertising and selling, fidelity of reproduction is less desired than sales appeal, and the customer is the final judge of this point. But changes of colors can make repeated color correcting necessary.

The technical reasons for color correcting lie in the nature of printing production. As there are no objective quality standards for color reproduction, the well-known term *facsimile* reproduction has no precise meaning and stands merely for high quality, every printing plant develops its own standards. Color correcting has the purpose of bringing a full-color job to the quality level at which a job is supposed to be produced.

The three main kinds of color correcting. Color correcting can be done in many production stages from the original artwork to the finished image carrier. But the most important color-correcting steps are usually taken in the phases of image conversion and prior to the making of the image carrier itself. These color-correcting procedures can be divided into three kinds: (1) photographic masking, (2) manual color correcting, and (3) electronic color correcting. In the following you find brief discussions of the first-mentioned two methods which are at the time of writing the most widely used ones. Electronic color correcting is presented together with electronic color separation in the next unit.

Color correcting by photographic masking. Photographic masking comprises a variety of techniques all of which have the purpose of obtaining the best possible color fidelity under the conditions under which a job will be produced. Items to be considered are, for example, the actual absorption and reflection qualities of the color inks, whether the job will be printed in three colors or with an additional black ink, whether the printing will be done dry or wet (meaning that each ink will be dry before the next is printed or still wet), and several others. All color correcting aims at improving the color fidelity of the final printing-image carrier. This means that the presence and absence as well as the relative size of halftone dots must be controlled. As these items depend on the nature of the photographic intermediates these must be changed accordingly.

Photographic masking attains this objective by combining various photographic images for this purpose. The subject is highly technical and re-

quires exact measurements and precise workmanship. Photographic masking is often supplemented by manual color correcting; masking is a great time saver in most cases and not only reduces the expense of manual color correcting very substantially but also improves the quality of the final result considerably.

Manual color correcting. Before photographic masking was as well developed as it has become in the last few years, manual color correcting dominated the field. Now, manual color correcting has become completely unnecessary in some cases and is, in general, much less important. The purpose of manual color correcting is the same as already explained, namely, the redistribution of detail in the several image carriers. This purpose is achieved by changing the relative values, or printing strength, of various areas on photographic intermediates before they are used for the making of image carriers. The craftsman works with hand tools, chemicals, and retouching dyes; he lightens or darkens the different areas on the different color printers according to his experience and judgment. As he must interpret various degrees of density in terms of the colors which will finally appear in these areas, he needs long experience and a highly specialized ability of visualizing. He can also use a densitometer to guide him in the interpretation of various color areas.

Color Separation by Electronics

Color scientists analyzed the problem of color printing not only in terms of optics but also mathematically. Seen as a problem of mathematics, the task of color separating and color correcting consists in determining the correct distribution and size of each color dot in every area.

This task is enormous if you consider that an average reproduction in letterpress or offset lithography usually consists of not less than 12,500 and up to more than 30,000 individual dots per square inch, or of not less than 50,000 and up to 120,000 dots in the four different ink colors which are normally used for industrial full-color printing. Color correcting means that the various imperfections of paper and inks as well as the adjustments for the black ink must also be considered in establishing, first, which color ink should print in every one of the 12,500 to 30,000 dot areas per square inch and second, how large each of the four ink dots must be.

A mathematical solution of this task is beyond

human ability but not beyond the scope of electronic equipment which can do in seconds what it would take people years to do. It was therefore only natural that several research organizations began to study the possibilities of applying electronics to color separation and color correction. Electronic color separation and color correction is being successfully used; it may be supplemented, in certain applications, by masking or by other color-correction techniques.

In 1955 electronic color separation and correction became industrially available with the perfection of the Time-Life color scanner which is now called the PDI Electronic Color Scanner. A number of these machines have been in constant operation, not only in the United States but also overseas. In the recent past, several additional electronic color separation and color correction systems have also become commercially available.

Equipment of this kind can be divided into three different groups: (1) electronic color-separation and correction machines, (2) electronic equipment for color correcting already existing color separations, and (3) electronic machines for the making of printing-image carriers. This last group is discussed in Chapter V, "Printing-Image Carriers." The first two are the subject matter of the following paragraphs.

General description of electronic color separation and correction. All electronic color separation systems include color correcting. Color separation is based on the usual color filters; some color scanners, as these machines are often called, can use both reflection and transmission copy, others are limited either to transmission or to reflection copy. The color copy is placed in the machine where it is scanned by a light beam. "Each minute area is evaluated electronically in terms of the proportions of each of the printing colors that will be used. These color values are translated into electrical currents by photocells. The computer evaluates these currents which represent the influence of ink, paper, tonal range, etc., and adds or subtracts from them. These modified currents are then fed into an exposing light source. The light varies in intensity in proportion to the corrected values of each element in the area scanned, and so exposes the corrected color separations on film."[32] The product of color scanners is a balanced set of continuous tone separations. These are converted into the requisite halftone images by the usual photographic methods.

In the following you find brief descriptions of

the PDI Electronic Color Scanner, the Fairchild Scan-A-Color, the Colorgraph, the Crosfield Scanatron, and the HPK-Autoscan.

The PDI Electronic Color Scanner. This system was originally known as the Time-Life scanner and has the longest continuous history of all electronic scanners, dating back to 1955. The PDI scanner scans transmission copy exclusively and is not suitable for reflection copy. The products of this equipment can be either continuous tone negatives or positives. Four different kinds of under-color removal are used depending on the process by which actual printing will be done. The material can be scanned either at 500 or at 1000 lines per inch; the higher figure is used where the scanned separations are to be enlarged more than three times.

In the course of time many valuable techniques were developed which pertain to masking, emphasis of detail and adjustments for transparencies of various ranges. The products of the scanner are widely used for the making of letterpress and lithographic plates as well as for the etching of gravure cylinders. In the United States, PDI Scanners are neither sold nor leased but are operated by Printing Developments, Inc., a subsidiary of Time, Inc. PDI maintains several service studios in the United States. These studios scan the color transparencies and supply their customers with the color separations.

Enlarging unit of a PDI scanner. The demonstrator holds the case in which the color transparency is placed for scanning. Enlargement ratio is from 2 to 30 times within the maximum scanning area.

The Fairchild Scan-A-Color. This machine can be used for scanning of both reflection and transmission copy. The product is a set of three or four fully corrected continuous tone separation negatives. "In the number of lines scanned, the Scan-A-Color offers its operator the choice of four rates of advance. Standard in the equipment is 340 lines per inch, 500 and 1,000. The fourth choice is either 250 or 1,250 lines per inch to be selected at time of installation. At 500 lines, the length of scanning time for a full 8 × 10 is 48 minutes; at 250, this time will be 24 minutes; 350 lines, 32 minutes; and 1,000 and 1,250 lines is 96 and 120 minutes respectively. The purpose in offering variable line scan is to get maximum speed of production when subsequent enlargement is not a problem, yet providing fine definition when great enlargements are to be made."[33]

The Colorgraph Scanner. The Colorgraph Scanner was developed by Dr. Rudolf Hell of Kiel, Germany, where this equipment is also manufactured. The system comprises two separate components. One is a scanning and scribing unit, the other an electronic computing and amplifying unit. At the time of writing there are four different models of Colorgraph scanners available: the oldest model which serves for color correcting only but is not suitable for color separation; a second model, which does color separation and color correcting of color transparencies; a third which does the same for reflection copy; and the fourth model which can handle both transmission and reflection copy.

The original color correcting model is briefly described. The scanning and scribing unit contains all optical and mechanical parts required for scanning the separation negatives and for exposing simultaneously three or four unexposed films which will become the corrected positives or negatives. It is built in the form of an easily accessible light-tight roll desk. The electronic computing and amplifying unit forms the second part of the machine. This is built into a separate control cabinet.[34] The separation negatives and the plate carriers are put in a common scanning frame. Another frame carries the scanning and scribing

system. The scanning frame moves across the machine, the optical frame moves at right angles to the scanning frame. Both frames alternate; when one moves the other remains stationary.

Another interesting development by the same company is the *Vario Klischograph*. This machine can convert reflection copy either into a set of color separations or into a set of relief image carriers for full-color printing. This machine is described in Chapter V.

The Crosfield Scanatron. This system for color correcting was developed by the J. F. Crosfield Ltd. of London. It uses continuous tone separation negatives which are successively combined emulsion to emulsion with unexposed films or plates for scanning. The product is a set of either three or four corrected continuous tone positives. Scanning is done "by means of a cathode ray scanner, and the density readings of two of the negatives are used to modulate the scanning beam which simultaneously exposes a contact positive through one of the three negatives. The Crosfield Scanatron has no moving parts and there are no scanning lines in the corrected positive. Time required is only ten minutes for each 12¾ × 17 inch positive."[35] Further development of the original model of the Crosfield Scanatron resulted in reduction of the scanning time to two minutes per positive, and the ability to produce screened positives as well as continuous tone positives.

The HPK-Autoscan. The Hunter Penrose Autoscan is manufactured in the United Kingdom. "The present available model is a combination of process camera and modulated, scanning light source. The device produces color-corrected separation negatives directly from reflection copy. The camera section permits enlargement or reduction within the limits of 150 to 33 per cent. Maximum copy size is 24 × 24 inches—maximum image 16 × 20 inches. The final images may be on glass or film according to the camera back selected."[36]

In conclusion it is added that the field of electronic color separation and color correction is still in flux. Existing equipment is improved and new systems are under development.

Section 4: Review of Full-Color Printing Methods

Full-color printing is, as you have seen, far from mysterious, but you have also seen that it cannot be understood without some knowledge of light and color theory. Unfortunately wide segments of the graphic arts industry are not too eager to acquire this knowledge. This is particularly true of designers, buyers, and sellers of printing. Their lack of exact information often leads to confusion, disagreement, and disappointment in the reproduction of various jobs by full-color printing.

This confusion feeds on many different sources. One is the excellence of contemporary full-color reproduction methods, another the technical nature of the subject, a third that many buyers want to believe that their jobs can be more simply and less expensively produced than is actually possible, a fourth that many salesmen can wax a trifle too enthusiastic in their presentation, and last but not least, that many people have in general somewhat naive attitudes to scientific methods which they tend to confuse with unlimited powers.

In everyday reality this means differences of opinion on the quality of a reproduction, on the matching of certain colors, on the number of color inks and press runs needed for a specific job, and on similar points. For this reason we will first discuss the limitations of full-color reproduction and then review the different full-color reproduction methods.

The Limitations of Full-Color Printing

The problems of full-color reproduction have been the subject of many highly technical studies and investigation. For our purposes it is best to concentrate on a few easily understandable points which will make the reader aware of some basic differences between original colorful images and their reproduction in full-color printing. As the two kinds of originals, reflection copy on the one hand and transmission copy on the other, pose somewhat different problems reflection copy and transmission copy are separately discussed.

Reflection copy designates, as already mentioned, colorful originals which are viewed in reflected light. These can be paper prints of color photographs, fine-art subjects such as oil paintings or water colors, and, not the least, originals painted for commercial purposes. At the risk of being repetitious it must be pointed out again that the conditions under which a colorful original is created and the conditions under which it is reproduced by full-color printing are quite different.

The creative artist selects his materials and techniques solely with a view to their aesthetic effects, and he can usually buy the best materials as their cost is insignificant in comparison with his time. Technically speaking, the artist enjoys utmost freedom in his creation.

The printer who must reproduce the work is in a much less favorable situation. While the artist has greatest freedom, the printer must work within the strictest of limitations. First, cost is a decisive consideration. Full-color printing is, as already explained, so exceptionally important because it is the most economical color reproduction method. It is widely used for mass-production work such as the printing of national magazines and mail order catalogs. The runs can be very long; they may amount to hundreds of thousands and even millions of copies. Every penny more spent per pound on ink or on paper adds up to very high sums in this kind of work. The artist can disregard cost of materials and use only the best, but the printer, who must control his cost very closely, simply cannot afford the best. This is particularly important in paper and inks. Then there is the functional difference between artists' paints—or other colorants—and printing inks. The artist selects his color media almost exclusively for their reflection qualities. If, for example, cobalt blue will give him the desired effect in one spot, ultramarine blue in another, and prussian blue in a third, the artist will naturally use all three in the same painting. The printer is in an entirely different position. He must find three different color inks, usually supplemented with black, with which he must reproduce all colors of the original.

The printer must evaluate his inks for their combined color gamut and not for their ability to match this or that area of the original. The evaluation of full-color inks cannot be limited to their reflection characteristics but must include their absorption range as well. You will realize this enormous difference if you look at an enlarged illustration of a full-color print and at its natural size. There you see that practically every area consists of dots of all ink colors.

The color gamut accessible to the artist is wider than the gamut which can be reproduced in full-color printing, precisely because the artist can use a large number of colorants whose combined gamut may be far in excess of the three full-color inks to which the printer is restricted.

This discussion has touched only one of the many inherent differences between color originals and their full-color reproduction. Remember that the painter can vary the thickness of his painting medium, which is impossible for most printing methods, that he has white pigments at his command, which are denied to the printer, that he can selectively control gloss and matness, which is either beyond the printer's power or only possible to a limited extent by additional operations.

Under these conditions it is obviously asking for the impossible if anybody expects an *exact* reproduction of painted originals by full-color printing. Some compromises must, unfortunately, always be made.

Now to the full-color reproduction of transmission copy such as Ektachrome and Kodachrome transparencies. The color gamut of color transparencies is much wider than that of average full-color inks. As you can see from our graphs, the yellow, magenta, and cyan dyes which are responsible for the colors in these originals come closer to the ideal requirements than do typical three-color printing inks.

But this is not the only difference. Color photographs are viewed in transmitted light, their printed reproduction in reflected light. "In the highlights a transparency can transmit virtually 100 per cent of the incident light while absorbing almost completely the light in the shadow regions. In practice this range is often up to a thousand to one."[37] The contrast range of a printed reproduction is unfortunately much smaller than the contrast range of the original color transparency. This point leads us into a discussion of the role played by paper and by presswork in full-color printing.

The role of paper in full-color printing. Contrast and color-reflection characteristics are two of several ways in which paper affects the quality of full-color printing. Ideally white paper should reflect 100 per cent of the incident light, which implies that it should reflect 100 per cent of each color. In reality average papers reflect 80 per cent of the incident light or less, and average papers do not reflect different colors to the same extent. Ideally the printed image should reflect no light at all in the deep shadows. In reality most printed images reflect not less than approximately 4 per cent in the shadow areas. As the light reflection is 80 per cent in the highlights and 4 per cent in the shadows the contrast range of average full-color

prints is not better than approximately 20 to 1. This contrast range must be compared with that of color transparencies which is, as explained in the preceding paragraph, up to 1,000 to 1.

The reflection characteristics of the paper control the amount of reflected light; they also influence the extent to which different colors are reflected. As most papers reflect least light in the blue, more in the green, and most in the red zone of the spectrum, the colors of the printed image are shifted toward the red. This is particularly undesirable as most cyan inks do not reflect enough blue light and do reflect some red light which they should completely absorb. The imperfections of the paper do not balance the imperfections of the inks but add to them.

The extent to which different papers for offset printing reflect different ink colors has been extensively studied by Mr. Frank Preucil of the Graphic Arts Technical Foundation, Pittsburgh, Pa. The latest color survey, based on actual specimens submitted by offset printers, contains data on the average reflection of the yellow, magenta, and cyan by uncoated offset paper, coated offset paper, and cast-coated offset paper. The range is in the yellow from 94.4 per cent of uncoated paper to 95.3 per cent of cast coated; in the magenta from 63.5 per cent of uncoated paper to 71.8 per cent of cast coated, and in the cyan from 70.7 per cent to 78.7. Coated paper has a pronouncedly better range than uncoated paper but is less good in its reflection range than cast-coated paper.[38]

The role of presswork in full-color printing. Presswork, finally, contributes also to imperfections of reproduction. The thickness of the printed ink film, the character of the halftone dots, and the time elapsed between the several runs, all influence the color fidelity of the printed image.

It is not necessary to continue this discussion of the many handicaps and limitations imposed on full-color printing. By now you will have become convinced that full-color printing is not at all simple and indeed very far from automation. Full-color printing is, true enough, the scientifically most advanced branch of the graphic arts, but it is nevertheless also an art. Science has not replaced craftsmanship, not eliminated the skills of hand and eye, but guides craftsmanship and enables it to attain better and more economical results.

Nor is color fidelity the only and exclusive consideration in full-color printing as you will realize. Price and speed of production rank in many instances higher than color fidelity. The printing industry must meet many different kinds of requests; in response to these it has developed a number of full-color printing systems or methods which are briefly described in the following.

Three-color printing. Three-color printing is done in three press runs with yellow, magenta, and cyan ink. Black results from the overprinting of the three full-color inks. The use of three-color printing was greatly stimulated by the Kodak Three-Color System which was developed by the Kodak Graphic Arts Research Laboratory. This system has the purpose of making it economically possible to produce full-color reproductions in small quantities up to 5,000 copies. In the Kodak Three-Color System every step is closely controlled and manual color correcting is completely superseded by photographic masking.

The Kodak System was specifically designed for the reproduction of color transparencies rather than for reflection copy. Reproductions made by this system are often designated as *pleasing color* prints to distinguish them from full-color jobs produced by more conventional methods.[39]

Four-color printing. Four-color printing is done in four impressions; one each with yellow, magenta, cyan, and black ink. Four-color printing is the most widely used full-color printing method, particularly for long-run work, such as the printing of national magazines and catalogs in letterpress and lithography.

The main difference between three-color and four-color printing is the addition of black ink to the three full-color inks. In four-color printing some of the gray and of course all black areas are printed with black ink; this is different from three-color printing where black is the result of printing all three inks over each other. Three-color printing must deposit three ink films or has an ink coverage of 300 per cent in the black, whereas in four-color printing black can be produced with a less heavy ink coverage where this is desired.

Most if not all mass production printing is done *wet-on-wet;* the sheet or web of paper is printed with all inks in one pass through the press. Ink films are here deposited on preceding ink films which are still wet. As the maximum permissible ink coverage in wet-on-wet letterpress printing is 240 per cent, black cannot here be the result of overprinting alone, but must be obtained by adding black ink.[40] As most mass-production work must be printed with black ink for the bulk of its reading matter, black is available for printing in any case.

But if the printing of black ink does not cause much additional expense in the presswork stage it may entail considerable additional costs in the stages of image conversion and of image-carrier production. The making of the black plate is often the most expensive part of color correction. Black signifies the total absorption of light and can therefore not be recorded by using a complementary filter. In principle, the black separation identifies tones rather than colors. Several methods are used for making the black printer separations. Most of them combine photographic color separation and color correction techniques with retouching and dot-etching.

Courtesy The Beck Engraving Company

A color retoucher at work. A highly skilled reproduction artist improves the quality of color separations. In this picture he works on a negative and is guided by the original color photograph at his right.

Five- and six-color printing. Two of our full-color printing inks, the magenta and the cyan, can sometimes prove to be unsatisfactory for certain reproduction problems, especially where great fidelity is wanted in the colors of human skin and flesh or in green foliage. In a not so distant past when the inks for full-color printing were not as good as now, and when there was much less known about color-correcting, it was common to run extra colors such as pink, light blue, buff, or light green. Even now pastel colors may be run separately if exceptional quality demands are made in these colors. Color separation and color-correction techniques are modified to meet these necessities. It might be added that the spectral qualities of the hemoglobin in our blood and the chlorophyl in plants are quite different from those of our full-color inks. This shows that we do not make spectral matches of flesh, skin, and foliage in full-color printing.

The use of mandatory colors. In full-color printing for advertising or sales promotion it is often demanded that certain colors be matched as closely as possible. The colors in question are often part of a trade-mark or package design and are in a sense as much the exclusive property of advertisers as are their trade-marks and other designs. The public can sometimes recognize a highly advertised brand from a distance by its well-known colors; this recognition may mean a valuable sales advantage, particularly for merchandise in stores and supermarkets.

It is only natural that national advertisers insist on a most accurate match of such colors, which are sometimes known as *mandatory* colors. Full-color printing is not always capable of producing the required color match. It is more often preferable to use special matching inks and to print mandatory colors as separate runs.

Chapter IV

Graphic Arts Photography

From the printer's point of view, photography can be divided into two very different kinds: creative photography and graphic arts photography. Both are related to printing, though in very different ways. Creative photography provides original images for printing and is an area of activity for commercial or industrial photographers, art studios, and for some printing businesses which offer their clients art-and-copy preparation services in addition to printing. Graphic arts photography, on the other hand, is photography in its application to the reproduction of art-and-copy, and, consequently, of more direct interest to most graphic arts people. This latter kind of photography is the subject matter of the present chapter.

More specifically, graphic arts photography is needed for the conversion of original images into printing-image carriers. Even though some image carriers are made without the use of photography, it can be said without exaggeration that the overwhelming majority of all pictorial image carriers are based on graphic arts photography. But this does not mean that all printing businesses have their own photographic departments. Some branches of the printing industry are operated as integrated plants, others are not, as you may remember from our discussion in Chapter I. Photographic departments can therefore be found in printing plants as well as in the service trades, at photoengravers, lithographic plate-makers, and gravure service companies.

Graphic arts photography has many different functions, some of them rather technical as you will see in the course of this chapter. But the subject can be conveniently divided into four major groups. This chapter is accordingly divided into four sections: first you find an introduction to graphic arts photography; line and halftone photography follow next; photography for full-color printing is presented in the third section; retouching, dot-etching, and opaquing are the subject matter of the fourth and final section of this chapter.

Section 1: Introduction to Graphic Arts Photography

In a time when almost everybody is an amateur photographer it seems rather unnecessary to explain what photography is and does. Most likely you know that you need four items when you want to make photographic pictures: a camera, some photographic film, an object, and light. And most likely you also know that the exposed film must be developed before the final print can be made. Essentially, the same is true for graphic arts photography.

Amateur photography and graphic arts photography. But if the principles are the same for both kinds of photography, the purposes and the execution of amateur photography and graphic arts photography are quite different. Amateur photography is a hobby, an avocation, which has

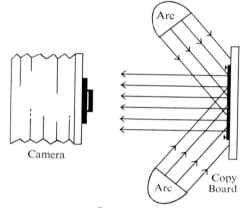

Courtesy Eastman Kodak Company

Different camera setup and illumination are needed to make separations from color transparencies or from color prints on paper, and artwork. The first kind is classified transmission copy, the second reflection copy.

the great attraction of the casual and improvised. Graphic arts photography is an industrial manufacturing process where every step must be well planned, highly controlled, and precisely executed. The *camera man*, as the graphic arts photographer is usually called, is far from being an amateur. He is a highly skilled craftsman who needs both theoretical knowledge and manual dexterity for his work.

If you take a closer look at graphic arts photography you will not be surprised that this is so. The graphic arts photographer works with light, cameras, and photographic materials. Physics, and optics in particular, explain the lens, the setting of the camera, and the nature of light. Chemistry provides an understanding of photographic materials and of their processing. As

graphic arts photography is far from automation and as the work must be done fast and very exactly, manual skills are certainly a great asset for a good camera man.

Operationally graphic arts photography can be divided into three broad groups: camera work, processing, and contact printing. Camera work consists in making a photographic record of the original image. This record is known as the *latent image;* it is not suitable for viewing in daylight and it does not present the final image until the material is chemically processed. Contact printing, finally, has the purpose of making additional photographic records from already existing photographic images without the use of a camera. The department for graphic arts photography is usually called the camera department in a graphic arts plant.

The camera department consists of the *camera area* and the *darkroom*. The camera area used to be called the gallery and is still so known in some photoengraving plants. The division into these two areas is necessary because camera work needs strong light whereas processing must be done in the dark. We will first discuss graphic arts cameras and then the darkroom.

Graphic Arts Cameras

Traditionally, graphic arts cameras are called *process cameras* to distinguish them from cameras made for portrait photography. This distinction was useful when both were *gallery* cameras and very similar to each other. But conditions have changed drastically since the early times of graphic arts photography. Graphic arts cameras have constantly increased in size and also changed vastly in appearance whereas gallery cameras have all but completely disappeared; for picture taking the contemporary portrait photographer prefers smaller and more versatile cameras.

But, as words change much more slowly than things, the process camera is still with us and confuses uninformed people who believe that process cameras are especially designed for full-color photography which they are not. In this manual we do not use the term process color, nor will we speak of process cameras. These misleading terms have earned a long rest and should be put out of circulation.

The six main units of graphic arts cameras. Graphic arts cameras consist of six main units: (1) the copy board, (2) the lens board, (3) the bellows,

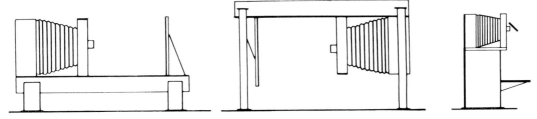

Diagram of floor type, overhead, and vertical camera construction.

(4) the rear assembly, (5) the lens, and (6) the camera bed. The copy board serves for positioning of the copy. Many copy boards are designed for both reflection and transmission copy. (Reflection copy is on an opaque background whereas transmission copy is usually on transparent film.) Copy boards suitable for both kinds of copy have a transparency section. When the copy board is used for reflection copy this section is covered with a felt pad. The lens board carries the lens and is movably connected to the rear assembly by the bellows which are light-tight. The rear assembly has provisions for holding photographic material—film or plates—halftone screens, and a ground glass for viewing. As the manufacturers of cameras do not make lenses, the lens is not considered part of the camera itself but an independent, though indispensable, element.

Gallery cameras and darkroom cameras. Graphic arts cameras are traditionally divided into two types, *gallery cameras* and *darkroom cameras.* Gallery cameras are independent of the darkroom and are completely located in the camera area. The light-sensitive material, usually film and more rarely photographic glass plates, must be transported to and from gallery cameras in light-proof holders. This condition is not conducive to efficient operation, and gallery cameras are in our times not much used. Now, darkroom cameras are generally preferred, particularly where a heavy work load must be handled.

Darkroom cameras are partly in the darkroom and partly in the camera area. Their front end is in the camera area, their rear end is built into a wall of the darkroom. Darkroom cameras are loaded and unloaded in the darkroom and can therefore be much more efficiently operated. Their copy board, lights, and lens are in the camera area. The camera man must therefore do some operational steps in the camera area and others in the darkroom.

The division of cameras into gallery and dark-

room cameras needs revision not only because gallery cameras are dying out, but also because recent developments have added a considerable number of new camera types. Some of these are now briefly identified.

Floor-type and overhead cameras. Darkroom cameras can be structurally divided into floor-type and overhead cameras. In the floor-type camera, the camera bed is the main supporting member which in turn is directly supported by the floor. In overhead cameras the different units are suspended from a single beam (or several beams) which on its part is supported by tall upright members from the floor. The overhead design makes the copy board, the lens board, and the camera lamps more accessible. Floor-type cameras are made in all sizes, but overhead cameras are usually not made in a smaller size than, say, 24 × 24 inches. (The size of a camera indicates the largest size of photographic material which can be put into a camera.)

Vertical cameras. Vertical cameras have become rather popular in the recent past. They are small and compact machines which save space. We can distinguish two types of vertical cameras. In one type all elements are arranged in a straight vertical line with the copy board closest to the floor. In another type the rear assembly and lens board are in one plane but the copy board is in another plane at a 90 degree angle to the first. This type of camera must be used with a reversing mirror or prism, whereas the first-mentioned type does not require image reversal. Both types of vertical cameras are limited in their sizes, the straight vertical camera usually more so than the two-plane type. The two-plane type is usually built into the darkroom with the copy board in the camera area, whereas the straight vertical camera is simply placed in the darkroom.

Roll film cameras. Roll film cameras can be loaded with two, three, or more rolls of photographic films which may be of different widths.

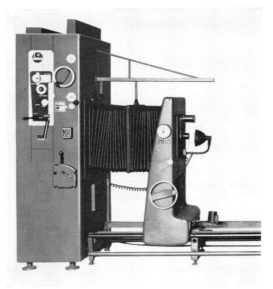

Courtesy Chemco Photoproducts, Inc.

A Marathon Roll Film Camera with flash lamp in working position. (Part of camera bed and the copyboard are not shown.) Camera is equipped for 3 rolls of film, has two halftone screens, and is operated completely outside the darkroom. Exposed film is automatically cut off and either collected in a drawer or conveyed into an automatic film processing machine.

The desired film is mechanically positioned for exposure and the exposed film is automatically severed from the roll. Roll film cameras were originally designed for mass production as needed in photoengraving for newspaper printing. They are highly efficient production machines, particularly if they are used in conjunction with automatic film processing equipment.

Enlargers. Enlargers play an increasing role in modern camera departments. They are built by several companies and are available in various sizes; some can handle 8 × 10 inch transparencies, others are especially designed for 35 millimeter film. Enlargers are often the preferred equipment for color separation of transmission copy, such as Ektachrome or Kodachrome transparencies, because they are more efficient than cameras. As you will read in the next section, color separations must be subjected to halftone photography for many printing methods. Some plants have adopted enlargers as standard equipment for screening of positives from small contact-exposed color separations. Exposure time of big enlargements can be much shorter with high-quality enlargers than with other equipment.

In addition to these camera types there are others of a more specialized nature which are not of interest for our purposes. Graphic arts cameras differ, of course, in many details and in the degree to which their operation is mechanized. All this is again much too technical for our purposes.[1] But we cannot leave the subject of cameras without a few words on the camera lens.

The lens. The lens is a crucial part of every camera; it has been often called its eye. The lens has a decisive influence on the size of the image, on the quality, and even on the speed at which the image can be recorded. Lenses are complex

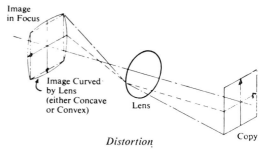

Distortion

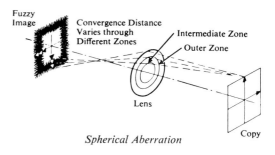

Spherical Aberration

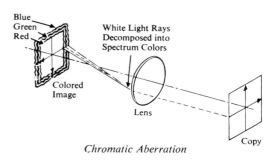

Chromatic Aberration

Schematic diagrams of lens distortion, spherical, and chromatic aberration. The consequences of these possible lens defects are shown at the left.

optical systems manufactured to extremely high tolerances. They can have several constitutional defects which are called *aberrations*. A few of these are now briefly described. If a lens has *distortion*, straight lines of the original will appear curved in the lens image. If the lens has *spherical aberration*, the image may be fuzzy at full-lens aperture, but can be acceptably sharp when the lens aperture is made smaller. If the lens has *chromatic aberration* the white light which consists as you remember of different colors will be refracted into these and focused to different sizes. Such a lens cannot be used for full-color photography. A lens free from chromatic and spherical aberrations is technically known as an apochromatic lens. The above-mentioned lens defects are only some of many possible ones. It should be added that lenses designed and produced by reputable manufacturers are of a high degree of perfection and well suited for the kind of work for which they are designed.

Cameras are equipped with many operational items. Among these are devices which save time in the setting of the camera, such as scale, counter, or automatic focusing systems, lamp carriers, integrating timers, prisms and mirrors for image reversal, flash lamps, halftone screens and many other accessories.[2]

The Darkroom

The darkroom is the place where the graphic arts photographer does most of his work. If his camera is a darkroom camera, he loads it here and he operates it more or less completely from here. The processing of the exposed photographic material and contact printing are also done in the darkroom. Several other tasks, including evaluating the copy, setting of camera size ratio, and selecting the lens stop, are usually performed outside the darkroom.

A modern darkroom must not only be well planned and equipped, it must also provide for convenience and speed of work. The first requirement is, of course, light control. All outside light must be completely excluded, and safelights of the proper kind must provide the correct illumination.

In the darkroom we find developing sinks, film and plate holders, driers, as well as contact printing facilities. Among the tools and instruments used in the darkroom are trays, scales, thermometers, timers, film trimmers, graduates, magnifying glasses, and possibly a densitometer.

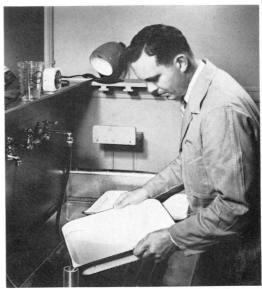

Courtesy Eastman Kodak Company

A photographic technician working in the darkroom.

Most modern darkrooms are air-conditioned. During the summer, control of temperature and humidity is equally necessary for the comfort of the photographer and for the quality of the photographic material. Changes in temperature and humidity can cause trouble by changing the dimensions and properties of photographic materials. Next, a few words on photographic fundamentals are in order.

Photographic Fundamentals

Light-sensitive photographic material consists of two main elements: a carrier and a light-sensitive coating known as *photographic emulsion*. The carrier can be either paper, or one of several kinds of plastics, or glass. If the carrier is paper we speak of photographic paper; if it is plastic, of photographic *film;* and if it is glass, of photographic *plates*. The photographic emulsion consists of varying chemical compounds and gelatin. If silver bromide or a similar compound is used in an emulsion, photographic chemists speak of a *silver halide* emulsion.

Exposure and the latent image. For photography, the light-sensitive material is exposed in a camera under carefully controlled conditions to the light which is either reflected by, or transmitted through, the copy. The exposure produces the *latent image* which must be chemically treated

Schematic of unexposed emulsion; irregular areas symbolize grains of silver-halide, for example silver-bromide, embedded in gelatin.

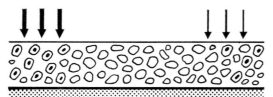

Silver nuclei formed by the action of light, which are important for initiation of development, are indicated by dots in irregular areas.

Results of development for high, low, and no exposure areas. Development reduces grains sufficiently affected by light and causes complete conversion to silver; halide ions pass out of emulsion into developer.

Schematic drawing of fixing. Undeveloped grains, such as those in nonexposed areas in center of drawing, are converted to soluble silver thiosulfate complex.

Schematic of final result. The soluble complex of silver thiosulfate was removed during washing.

Courtesy Dr. T. H. James, Eastman Kodak

Schematics of exposure, development, and fixing of silver-halide photo materials. All diagrams are sections through emulsion and support; thickness of emulsion is greatly exaggerated.

before it becomes a visible record suitable for further handling.

The chemistry and physics of photographic image formation are rather complex. By way of simplification the effect of exposure can be pictured as a change in molecular structure of the silver compound through the absorption of light energy. This change results in silver atoms whose presence greatly accelerates the rate at which the rest of the grain can be converted by chemical action into metallic silver. The required chemical action is known as *development* and *fixing*.[3]

Development. For development, the exposed material is treated with a developing solution which either can be bought ready for use or compounded by the photographer. A developer contains a number of different chemicals, in particular such as will be able to change the exposed emulsion grains into metallic silver. (Metallic silver appears black in its fine photographic dispersion and does not look at all like silver.) Several chemicals can act as developers. One of the most popular developing solutions contains a mixture of metol and hydroquinone as developers together with other chemicals which must be present to stabilize and preserve a developer.

Fixing. Development is followed by fixing. Fixing has the object of removing the silver halide in the unexposed areas, which have remained light-sensitive in spite of development. As they are insoluble in water or developers, the silver halides of the undeveloped areas must be dissolved in a different solution in order to be removed. This solution is known as the *fixing bath;* its principal ingredient is either sodium or ammonium thiosulfate, commonly called *hypo.* After fixing, the material is washed, then dried, and can thereafter be safely handled during the following operations.

The above-described development procedure is known as chemical development. It is also possible to develop certain photographic materials physically by heat treatments, for example; but as thermal development is at the time of writing unimportant in graphic arts photography, and as its explanation requires a rather technical discussion, it is here merely mentioned.

All photographic operations must be exactly executed. Time and temperature as well as the composition of various solutions must be closely controlled. The more precisely the work is done the more reliable and consistent are the results.[4]

Negatives and positives. At this point of our presentation a few terminological comments seem to be needed. You know already that a photographic image can be either a negative or a positive, and you remember that a negative shows the black areas of the original bare and the white areas black, a positive shows the black areas of the original black and white areas bare. The term *bare* means the absence of metallic silver on the base material. If the base material is transparent (in glass plates and films) the bare areas are transparent; if the base material is white (in photographic papers) the bare areas are, of course, also white.

The difference between image and non-image areas is more clearly pronounced in line and half-tone photography than in continuous-tone photography. On continuous-tone films we see various shades of gray rather than areas that are either completely black or completely bare.

Photographic images can be either in color or in black-and-white, and they can be either on transparent or on opaque material. If they are on transparent material they can be called *transparencies*, if on opaque paper they are known as paper *prints*. When we look at a photographic image we may want to describe it in five points: (1) whether it is a transparency or a paper print, (2) whether it is a positive or a negative, (3) whether the emulsion is up or down, (4) whether it reads right or wrong, and (5) whether it is head or foot up or down. These five distinctions are not always made and not always necessary; but at some time or other you will find it useful to make most of them.

Photographic Plates, Films, and Papers

The many different purposes to which photography is applied in the graphic arts industry are reflected in the variety of available photographic materials. Their differences are very technical, much too much so for a detailed discussion in this manual. Here we are limited to brief explanations of some very important properties.[5]

First a few words on photographic plates, films, and papers. These are available in many different emulsions and on different types of support. The limitations of glass in comparison with plastic films and paper are obvious. Glass is heavier and breakable; it is also not suitable for the fast mass production roll-film cameras or for use with contact screens. Glass has been almost completely replaced with stable base films which are generally employed where dimensional stability is decisive, for example, in color separation photography. Plastic materials are of many different kinds, and plastic films vary accordingly in their

dimensional stability. Polystyrene and polyester films are excellent in this respect, good enough for almost all graphic arts requirements. Cellulose acetate films change their size noticeably during storage and processing; cellulose nitrate films are no longer used on account of their inflammability. Paper is less dimensionally stable than film.

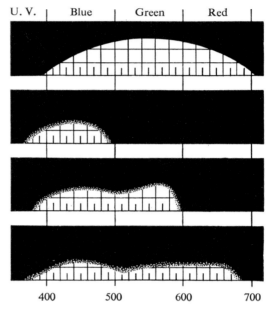

Comparison of the color sensitivity of the human eye and different photographic materials. The first illustration shows the sensitivity of the human eye; the next that of ordinary blue-sensitive film; in the third diagram you see the sensitivity of orthochromatic, and in the last that of panchromatic film.

Color sensitivity of photographic materials. The sensitivity to color is one of the most important characteristics of different photographic materials. As you remember, we divided the visible spectrum into three zones, the blue which goes from 400 to 500, the green which goes from 500 to 600, and the red zone which goes from 600 to 700 millimicrons. Photographic materials vary in their light sensitivity as follows: One kind which has the smallest range of light sensitivity can produce a record of blue light but is insensitive to the other two zones; it is therefore often known as *ordinary blue sensitive;* a second kind, called *orthochromatic*, is sensitive to blue and green light but not to red, and a third kind, known as *panchromatic*, is sensitive to light over the whole spectrum. But no photographic material matches the human eye

Manufacturing Chart of DU PONT "CRONAR"®Polyester Graphic Arts Film

One of the most significant achievements of the Du Pont Company in its more than 50 years of research and manufacturing in the photographic field has been the development of tough, durable "Cronar" polyester photographic film base.

Technically known as polyethylene terephthalate, "Cronar" is chemically a condensation polymer. As a support for graphic arts film products, it approaches the ideal flexible film because it has outstanding strength and durability as well as extraordinary dimensional stability and resistance to moisture (see below).

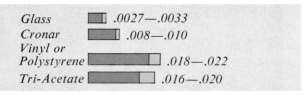

Glass	.0027—.0033
Cronar	.008—.010
Vinyl or Polystyrene	.018—.022
Tri-Acetate	.016—.020

EFFECT OF TEMPERATURE *Graph shows average size changes in a 30" length of film base with a temperature increase of 20°F.*

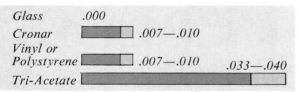

Glass	.000
Cronar	.007—.010
Vinyl or Polystyrene	.007—.010
Tri-Acetate	.033—.040

EFFECT OF HUMIDITY. *Graph shows average size changes in a 30" length of film base with a 20% increase in relative humidity.*

Manufacturer of CRONAR® Polyester Photographic Film Base

Ethylene glycol and dimethyl terephthalate react in an ester exchange to yield a monomer. Further treatment produces polyethylene terephthalate polymer, which after filtration is extruded at a high temperature onto a smooth casting wheel. Chilling on the wheel permits the web that has been formed to be stripped off for further treatments: **(A)** the application of a sub-strata which anchors the photographic emulsion, **(B)** orientation by stretching which confers the desired strength, and **(C)** stabilization which insures maximum resistance to size changes in use. The finished roll of CRONAR polyester film base **(D)** is now ready for application of the photographic emulsion, which, of course, must be carried out separately in the dark,

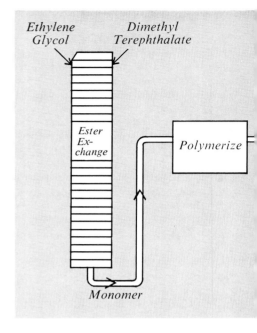

Ethylene Glycol   Dimethyl Terephthalate

Ester Exchange   Polymerize

Monomer

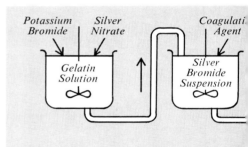

Potassium Bromide   Silver Nitrate   Coagulati Agent

Gelatin Solution   Silver Bromide Suspension

1 *After original precipitation, the silver ha emulsion is coagulated and washed to rem*

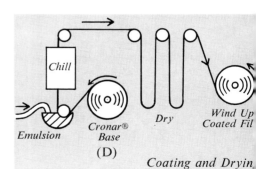

Chill

Emulsion   Cronar® Base   Dry   Wind Up Coated Fil

(D)

Coating and Dryin

3 *The fluid emulsion is applied to the CRONA base, (D) gelled in a chill chamber, dried un carefully controlled conditions, and wound large spools.*

Manufacture of CRONAR® Polyester Photographic Film Base

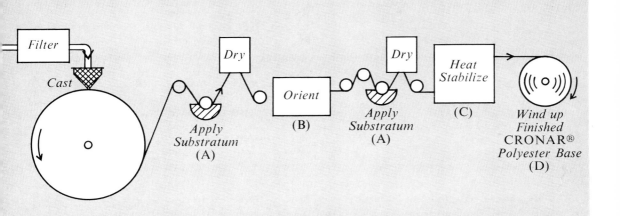

Filter

Cast

Dry

Apply Substratum (A)

Orient (B)

Dry

Apply Substratum (A)

Heat Stabilize (C)

Wind up Finished CRONAR® Polyester Base (D)

Sensitization of CRONAR® Polyester Film Base

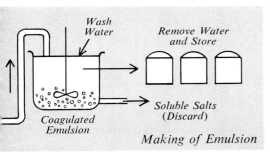

Wash Water

Remove Water and Store

Soluble Salts (Discard)

Coagulated Emulsion

Making of Emulsion

unwanted soluble by-products. It is then stored until needed for coating.

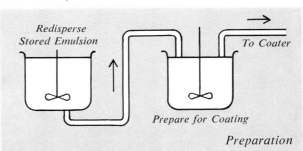

Redisperse Stored Emulsion

To Coater

Prepare for Coating

Preparation

2 The emulsion is redispersed and prepared for coating by heat treatment and addition of sensitizers, stabilizers, etc.

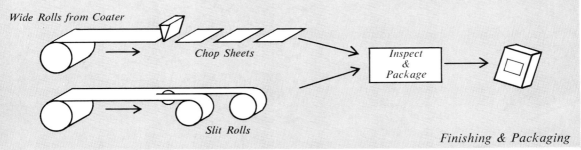

Wide Rolls from Coater

Chop Sheets

Inspect & Package

Slit Rolls

Finishing & Packaging

4 The wide rolls from the coater are cut to desired sizes, inspected and packaged ready for use.

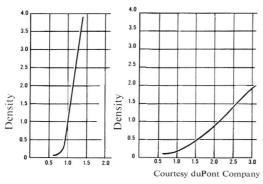

Courtesy duPont Company

Two characteristic curves of photographic films. The curve at the left is of high-contrast material, used in line and halftone photography; that at the right is of low-contrast film, used in continuous tone photography.

in its relative color sensitivity, as you can see from our illustration.

The characteristic curve of photographic materials. One of the most significant features of various photographic materials is their ability of recording a larger or smaller number of different *tones*. The term "tone," is here used as equivalent to the term "value" which is explained in the preceding chapter. *Tone refers to gradations within a color hue but not to differences between various hues.* The tonal range of photographic material can best be demonstrated by showing how it records a so-called gray scale which has several steps of grays from black to white.

Some materials record almost all 10 or 15 such steps. Others are much more limited. Materials which can photograph a wide range of tones are said to have a long scale and are typically developed to *low contrast*, whereas those which reproduce only a few tones are said to have a *short scale* and are developed to *high contrast*. This feature can be expressed in the form of a graph and is known as the *characteristic curve* of a photographic material. Our illustration shows the characteristic curve of a high and of a low contrast film.

Densitometry

Densitometry makes it possible to measure different tones with precision instruments and to express these measurements in numbers. The

densitometer, which measures the density of tones, has become the most widely used instrument for controlling many phases of tonal reproduction.

If you wonder why density is used as a criterion for measuring of tones you should remember that the photographic image consists of minute silver particles which are deposited on a transparent or on an opaque carrier. The denseness of these particles, their number for a given area, accounts for the difference in tone.

Density—meaning in this context always *optical* density as distinguished from *physical density* which relates mass and volume—expresses the relative light absorption by a photographic image in a given area. *The darker the area the higher is its density.* In the case of transparent photographs we speak of *transmission density*, and in the case of opaque pictures of *reflection density*. Densitometers are accordingly classified either as transmission, or as reflection, or as transmission *and* reflection densitometers. The scale in which density is indicated was developed with a view to express density measurements in the same proportions in which the human eye sees differences in tones. Even though this scale does not achieve the desired result with complete exactness, it approximates exactness sufficiently to be of singular usefulness for many different purposes in graphic arts photography.[6]

The great practical value of densitometry lies in its ability to replace vague personal judgments of color values by objective measurements which can be verified by others provided they have the required training. As "densitometric readings are expressed in numbers, they can be recorded. They have the same meaning for all craftsmen. They can be incorporated in tables or plotted on graphs to show their relationships to exposure time and development of negatives and positives, and to ink density and dot size in proofs and press prints. Mere word descriptions obviously could not be used in this way."[7]

Densitometry is not limited to photographic images and photography; its reach has been extended—primarily by the work of the Graphic Arts Technical Foundation—into platemaking, presswork, and most recently also into the evaluation of various color inks and of the paper for full-color printing.

Section 2:   Line and Halftone Photography

Line and halftone photography differ functionally in one important point and have another equally important point in common. They differ because halftone photography has the object of converting continuous tone images into printable form whereas line photography is used for the recording of images (usually black-and-white) containing no such intermediate tones. This means that the detail of the original images is in the first case changed during the process of halftone photography whereas it remains the same in line photography. The point that is common to both of these kinds of graphic arts photography is that original images are now recorded in a manner which makes it possible to convert them into printing-image carriers. Line and halftone photography have the object of providing intermediates, such as photographic negatives or positives, as they are needed for photomechanics whereby original images are most often converted into printing-image carriers.

Original images for line photography. Originals for line photography may be black-and-white, for single color or for multicolor reproductions. They may even be in colors, as in the Bourges System which is presented in the "Art-and-Copy Preparation" chapter, and they may be pictures or reading matter, singly and in combination. Line photography can of course also be part of reproduction jobs which require halftone photography, or photography for full-color reproduction. Headlines, line drawings, and reading matter are very often used together with continuous tone or colorful originals, as can be confirmed by a look at any national magazine.

The product of line photography is usually a photographic negative on film. Plates are only rarely used for line work, but the much cheaper photographic paper which is available in a translucent quality may be preferred to film for simple single color jobs. If positives are required they are commonly made by contact printing through negatives. If the needed size differs from that of the negatives, positives may be made in the camera by enlargement or reduction.

Before we turn to halftone photography it might be interesting for you to read a description of the most important steps taken in line photography. Operationally, line photography can be considered under eight headings: (1) inspecting and scaling of the copy, (2) placing the copy on the copy board of the camera, (3) setting the camera, (4) loading the camera with the photographic film, (5) exposing the film, (6) removing the exposed film, (7) processing the exposed film, and finally (8) inspecting and passing of the processed material for further use. All of these eight steps are individually discussed and illustrated in the following. For the sake of simplicity the phrase "light-sensitive material" is replaced by the short word "film," but you should be aware that glass plates or photographic paper can take the place of the film when required.

Inspecting and scaling of copy. All copy should be in perfect shape when it is turned over to the camera department. Various common flaws in copy for photographic processing are discussed in Chapter XI, "Art-and-Copy Preparation," and do not concern us here, but the meaning of the term *scaling* needs explanation. Copy for photographic image conversion is very often available in a size which is not identical with the size of the final job. Sometimes the copy is purposely prepared for reduction, at other times the size is different for other reasons, for example, because copy that was originally prepared for another purpose is now used for a different job. If the available copy is larger than the final job it must be reduced, and if it is smaller it must be enlarged by the camera. Scaling indicates the correct relation between the size of the available copy and the final size of the job.[8]

Placing the copy on the copy board. The inspected copy is placed for photographing on the copy board of the camera. The photographer selects the proper position, attaches the copy on the board, and adjusts, if this be necessary, the illumination for the job in hand.

Setting the camera. Like most other processes, photography requires a minute co-ordination of several items. These include the adjustment of the camera for the correct size of the job, the selection of the lens, which may or may not remain the same for a number of consecutive jobs, and the selection of the lens opening. The photographer may also inspect the photographic image on the ground glass, which is at the rear end of the camera, and he must select the kind of film he wishes to use and determine the proper exposure time.

Loading the camera. After the camera man has inspected and approved the photographic image on the ground glass, he removes the ground glass

Camera man operating a built-in darkroom camera for color-separation photography. The operator faces the ground glass. The circular screen holder is at the left; the camera back, which supports the film, is at the right.

and replaces it with photographic film. Modern cameras have vacuum backs that keep the photographic film perfectly flat during exposure. The film is placed in its correct position; then the back of the camera is closed, and everything is ready for exposure. The change from ground glass to vacuum back and vice versa can be made rather fast as the ground-glass frame and the vacuum back are independently hinged on modern darkroom cameras.

Exposure. During exposure, the photographic film is subjected to the light reflected from the copy; the result of exposure is the latent image of the copy on the film. It is not only important that the exposure time be correct, it is equally important that the calculated light be also truly delivered. The photographer makes sure that all these conditions prevail, and he has various instruments at his disposal for this purpose. Some camera departments are equipped with electronic devices, known as *integrating timers*, which automatically make the adjustments necessary for controlling the complete delivery of the determined light quantity.

Removing the exposed film. After exposure, the film is removed from the camera for further proc-

essing. In modern darkroom cameras this step is rather simple, as the camera back, where the film is placed for exposure, is within the darkroom itself. For gallery cameras the film or plate must be carried in a light-tight holder.

Processing the exposed film. During processing, the latent image is converted into a permanently visible image. The film is first developed, then put in a stop bath, thereafter immersed in the fixing solution, washed, examined on a light table, and finally dried. In plants with a large volume, automatic processing equipment can be found.

Inspecting and transmitting the processed material for further use. As the product of line photography represents the future printing image, the camera department must make sure that the transparency or paper print is in the proper condition for this purpose. If it needs improvements that can be done in the darkroom, these may be performed here. If it needs improving by manual operations, the departments where this work will be done are advised accordingly.

Now we turn to a discussion of the much more complex subject of halftone photography, and we begin with the problems faced by printing in the reproduction of tonal images.

The Reproduction of Tonal Images by Printing

Halftone photography has, as you know, the object of converting continuous tone images or images consisting of several discontinuous tones of the same hue into printable form. Continuous tone images contain a wide range of tones which flow without any boundaries in and out of each

A 133-line halftone and its appearance viewed with a strong magnifying glass.

other throughout the whole picture. Wash drawings and black-and-white photographs often have been mentioned as the two most common representatives of this kind of originals. Discontinuous tonal images are much less frequently met, but a gray scale or a uniform tint can serve as an example for their appearance.

You know already that printing cannot reproduce tonal images along the same lines as are followed in the preparation of original images. In principle, printing has three ways at its command for this purpose: (1) the halftone method whereby the tonal image is converted into a large number of small dots having different sizes which are then printed with ink of uniform film thickness within a given press run; (2) varying the ink deposit from area to area within a given press run; and (3) combinations of the first and the second technique. Unfortunately, not each of these can be used in every process. Intaglio is the only process group which can take advantage of all three possibilities. Collotype, an old established printing method, and screenless printing with presensitized positive-working lithographic plates, a method still in its inception, can reproduce continuous tone images without converting them first into halftones.

All other printing methods such as letterpress, newspaper printing, offset lithography, flexography, and screen process rely on halftone photography for the reproduction of tonal images. As rotogravure, the commercially most important intaglio method, is increasingly using the halftone process in one form or another it can be said without exaggeration that halftone photography is responsible for at least 90 per cent of all tonal picture printing.

All halftone processes aim at the conversion of continuous tone images into a pattern of exceedingly small and clearly defined particles of a controlled size. These small particles are known as *halftone dots* or simply as *dots*. Halftone photography produces the required intermediate records which are needed for photomechanical production of printing-image carriers. The printed halftone images, if viewed at the correct distance, convey the appearance of continuous tone images to the beholder because the human eye cannot recognize individual dots below a certain size at a certain distance, but perceives the printed image in terms of varying brightness throughout the whole picture. The dot size and the viewing distance vary, depending on the purpose of the printed material.

Fifteen inches is the usual distance for reading, several feet for display material, and twenty or more feet for highway posters. Halftone dots should be smallest for close viewing and may, of course, be larger for viewing at greater distances.[9]

Various Halftone Processes

As halftones can be made in several ways, we present in the following four different halftone processes. These are: (1) the crossline screen halftone process, (2) the contact screen halftone process, (3) the prescreened halftone process, and (4) bendays and other patterned images. The first three are photographic processes which are capable of converting continuous tone images into halftones. The fourth group cannot achieve this result and is rather limited in its effects. It is, nevertheless, presented in this context because these effects are often associated with halftone reproductions.

Construction of the cross-line screen. A and B show the opaque rules on each of the two glass plates before cementing. C shows the cross-line pattern after the two plates are cemented.

The crossline or glass screen halftone process. In the crossline screen halftone process a continuous tone image is photographed through a crossline screen in a camera. Thereby this image is converted into a halftone pattern. Crossline screens consist of two panes of glass, each ruled by precision equipment with a given number of lines per linear inch. The lines are made black and opaque, whereas the spaces between the lines remain transparent. The two ruled glass panes are then put at right angles to each other, and cemented into a single unit with the ruled lines inside and the unruled glass outside.

Crossline screens, often also known as glass screens, come in various sizes and are usually available in rectangular and circular mounts. They are specified, in addition to size, by two characteristics. One is the ratio between opaque and transparent line width, the other is the number of lines per linear inch. Screens for halftone photography have lines and clear spaces of equal width,

Seen in
Reading Distance

Seen from
a Distance
of Several Feet

Seen from a Moving Car

The distance from which a halftone picture is viewed influences the selection of the halftone screen. Halftone images that will be closely viewed are made with screens of higher line numbers than are used for halftones that will be seen from further away or in passing at a great distance.

but screens used for other purposes, mainly in gravure printing, often have a different ratio.[10]

Screens differ according to their ruling number. The lower the ruling number, the larger will be the individual dot and the coarser the printed image. And, conversely, the higher the ruling number, the smaller will be the individual dot and the finer the printed image. Screens with a low ruling number are used for newspaper printing, screens with high ruling numbers are required for high quality work. A 55-line screen is generally considered a rather coarse screen, an 85- to 110-line screen about medium, and screens with a ruling of 133 or more lines are usually considered fine. The main difference between coarse and fine screens is in the detail of the resulting image. The higher the screen ruling number is, the more detail will be present in the printed image.

It must, though, always be remembered that the quality of a printed product never depends on a single element alone, but that it is the combined result of many factors. In order to obtain a high-quality reproduction, all elements which are present in a specific printing task must be attuned to each other.

The halftone dot pattern. For photographing, the crossline screen is placed in the camera between the lens and the photographic material at a carefully calculated distance near the latter. The light reflected from the copy is absorbed by the black rules of the screen but transmitted through the transparent spaces. It produces a tone or dot pattern on the photographic material.

The halftone dot pattern is rather interesting; it is neither left to chance nor arbitrarily determined, but corresponds in a definite manner to the tonal values of the copy. The principle is quite simple and easy to remember: differences of tones in the copy are expressed as differences in the areas of halftone dots. Light tones are represented by the small ink dots of the printed images, darker tones by the larger ink dots. But if you look at our illustration of halftone dot patterns you will notice that the shape of dots changes together with their area or relative size.

Halftone dots are not all circles of different diameters, they have peculiar shapes of their own which make it possible for those familiar with these peculiarities to recognize the tonal values represented by various dots. The shape of dots is not the same in all halftone methods. Middle tones made with the crossline screen are approximately square, occupying about 50 per cent of the maximum dot area. There are also certain contact screens available which produce diamond-shaped middle tones. Their chaining conveys a smoother appearance to these tones. Most halftone dots are too small for the unaided eye and it is customary to inspect them with a good magnifier.

Contact screens. Contact screens, or vignetted screens, are of two main types, the magenta screen and the gray screen. These names are here mentioned because they refer to several essential features of this type of halftone screen. *Contact* indicates that this screen is not used at a distance from the photographic film but in direct contact with it. *Magenta* and *gray* refer to several kinds of contact screens manufactured for different purposes.

The crossline screen was practically the only kind of screen generally used for halftone photography until 1942 when the Eastman Kodak Company introduced its contact screen. Contact screens had been repeatedly tried in the past,

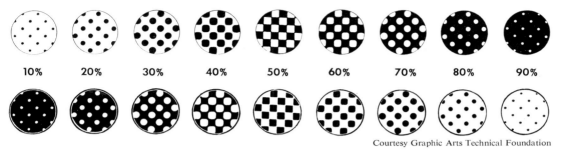

10%   20%   30%   40%   50%   60%   70%   80%   90%

Courtesy Graphic Arts Technical Foundation

Diagram of halftone dots. The dots in the upper row are positive, those in the lower row are negative.

though without any lasting success. The Kodak development made contact screens practical and added thereby a most valuable tool to graphic arts photography.

Vignetted dot patterns. The contact screen consists of a pattern of vignetted dots. The number of dots per linear inch varies and is indicated by a figure which corresponds to the ruling number of crossline screens. Vignetted dots are dots which have their greatest density in their centers and decrease in density from the center to their perimeter. These density variations are, of course, carefully planned and controlled. At its center where the dot has its maximum density, most of the incident light is stopped, but as the density decreases, correspondingly larger amounts of light can be transmitted through the dots of the contact screen. The photographic material, which is exposed in the camera to the light reflected or transmitted by the original image, records these light variations as larger or smaller dots. Originally the

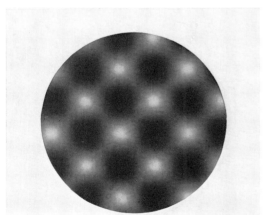

Courtesy Eastman Kodak Company

Part of a vignetted dot contact screen, greatly enlarged.

same contact screens were used for the making of both halftone negatives and halftone positives. As the use of contact screens spread it became established that the characteristics of screen dots should be different for making halftone positives and for making halftone negatives. When either kind was made with the same contact screen, cameramen used different exposure techniques for positives and for negatives. This need disappeared when the Eastman Kodak Company introduced negative as well as positive contact screens.

During exposure, the contact screen is, as its name indicates, placed in direct contact with the photographic material. This feature eliminates the necessity for adjusting the distance between screen and film and therewith a source of error. The screen distance is, as you will see in our following theoretical discussion, a very important factor in the use of the crossline screen. The magenta screen uses color filters for control of contrast. The gray screen takes the place of the magenta screen in direct color-separation photography where the magenta screen cannot be used. Operationally, halftone photography with the contact screen differs considerably from halftone photography with the crossline screen. But it should not be assumed that the contact screen has simply superseded the crossline screen. Both have their place in graphic arts photography.

Prescreened films. Prescreened films were announced in 1953 by Eastman Kodak Research Laboratories where this material was developed. Prescreened films do not need exposure through a halftone screen in order to convert a continuous tone image into a halftone image. In prescreened films the dot structure is already present in the light-sensitive emulsion.

If we want to understand the basic construction of this material we must think of each individual

The Manufacturing of EASTMAN-KODAK *Photographic Films*

The pictures on these pages show some manufacturing stages of photographic film at Eastman Kodak Company. Extensive research and development accounts for continuing improvement in the films produced by Kodak.

② *Here, prototype extrusion equipment is used t test a new compound for possible use in th manufacturing of polyester film base.*

① *Control panels for five-story high roll-coating machines on which acetate film base is made.*

③ *Technician at work on roll-coating machines these are operated 24 hours a day every day*

4 Kodak uses large quantities of silver, the heart of light-sensitive emulsions for photographic films and papers. Shown here is a little over a week's supply. Each bar is worth $1,000.

5 A technician combines the basic ingredients for a photographic emulsion—potassium halide, silver nitrate, and gelatine. Because the emulsion is light-sensitive, this and the next two operations actually take place in darkened rooms.

6 The emulsion is coated on the film base by large equipment in scrupulously clean rooms.

7 Packing Kodalith Ortho Type 3 Film in cartons at Kodak Park for shipping to roll film users.

8 Samples of finished film must pass a variety of physical and photographic tests before the film will be packaged.

9 Finally, the film is packaged in the familiar Kodak yellow box.

dot area as having a wide range of sensitivity. Depending on the relative brightness of the photographed image, each of these areas becomes a smaller or larger dot, just as in halftone photography with the crossline or contact screen.

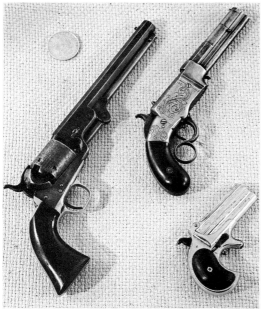

Courtesy Eastman Kodak Company

Reproduction of a picture taken with Kodalith Autoscreen Orthofilm. The photoengraving for this picture was made without separate halftone photography, by use of the Autoscreen negative.

The trade name of prescreened films is Kodalith Autoscreen Orthofilm. Its dot pattern corresponds to a 133-line screen. The Autoscreen film can be used not only for halftone photography of copy prepared for reproduction by printing, but also for the direct photography of various objects such as merchandise, machinery, or houses or buildings. In this case it combines the preparation of original images with the step of halftone photography. Autoscreen film is recommended for simple lithographic or screen-process jobs and is widely used for short-run work where simplicity of procedure and also higher sharpness of detail is a decisive consideration.

Bendays and tint sheets. Strictly speaking, bendays and tint sheets do not belong under the heading of halftones. The reason why these materials and their use are nevertheless discussed together with halftone methods, lies in the fact that bendays and tint sheets are very often confused with halftones.

The original benday process, named after its inventor, Benjamin Day of New York City, consists in applying inked patterns of different designs to an image carrier, such as a lithographic plate or photoengraving metal. Bendaying in its original sense was therefore always a shop operation, and it was always executed by a skilled tradesman. In our time the original benday process is but rarely used. Its name, though, has not only survived but has even become a generic term for a variety of tint laying techniques.

In many cases tint laying is still a shop operation, but very often it has become part of art-and-copy preparation. Shading or tinting patterns are manufactured by several companies for this purpose. They can be used by commercial artists to provide certain tonal effects of a limited range. But these techniques cannot convert continuous tone images into halftones; thereby they can be easily distinguished from halftone methods.

This discussion concludes our presentation of halftone processes. Our next subject is a brief exposition of halftone theory.

Two Theories of the Halftone Process

Several theories were developed to explain the formation of halftone images. Here we will briefly present two of them: the penumbra theory and the diffraction theory.

The penumbra theory. The penumbra theory takes its name from an astronomical phenomenon, a partial eclipse. When the moon comes directly between the sun and the earth, it interferes to a varying degree with our sunlight. At a total eclipse the areas which are behind the center of the moon are in its so-called *umbra*, or shadow, and do not receive any light. In a partial eclipse

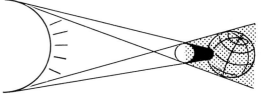

Courtesy Graphic Arts Technical Foundation

Umbra and penumbra on the earth. When the moon comes between the sun and the earth, the earth can be in the umbra, *or complete shadow, of the moon in some places and in the* penumbra, *where it is partially illuminated, in others.*

where the moon does not completely hide the sun, some areas of the earth are in a partial shadow zone, called the penumbra, where they receive different amounts of light as you can see in our illustration.

Applied to our problem, the penumbra effect can explain that light of differing intensity passing through a crossline screen will be recorded on a photographic material of certain characteristics in small units or dots of different sizes. If you study the accompanying illustrations you will understand what happens. Our first illustration shows you a diagram where you see the variations in light intensity behind a crossline screen. The following exploded view shows a cluster of halftones together with photographic negative, crossline screen, and photographic lens.

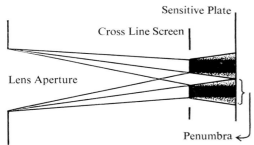

Sensitive Plate

Cross Line Screen

Lens Aperture

Penumbra

Courtesy Graphic Arts Technical Foundation

The relationship of lens aperture and dot structure with the glass halftone screen.

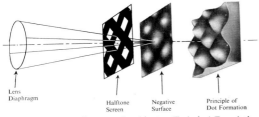

Lens
Diaphragm

Halftone
Screen

Negative
Surface

Principle of
Dot Formation

Courtesy Graphic Arts Technical Foundation

Diagram of halftone dot formation according to the penumbral halftone theory.

Halftone formation according to the penumbra theory was studied in detail on the basis of geometric optics. Such studies were of great practical importance because their results guided graphic arts photography in the practice of halftone reproduction. But the penumbra theory is not capable of explaining various observations made in the practical use of the crossline screen; particularly not those made in the setting of the screen dis-

tance for screens with high line-ruling numbers. These deviations from the penumbra theory observations can be much better explained by the diffraction theory of halftone formation.

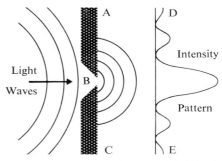

Light
Waves

A

D

Intensity

B

Pattern

C

E

Courtesy Graphic Arts Technical Foundation

Diagram of halftone dot formation according to the diffraction theory. A–C is a ruled glass screen, B is an opening in the screen, D–E is a photographic film. The new series of light waves formed at B produces an intensity pattern on the photographic emulsion as shown behind the film.

The diffraction theory. Broadly stated, each transparent area or opening of the crossline screen acts like a minute lens, and each opening forms a minute image of the camera lens aperture on the film surface. These images are not sharp, and as they also somewhat overlap, the result is a halftone dot pattern. According to the diffraction theory, each different screen ruling should be placed at a specific distance from the photographic material in order to obtain the best possible halftone image. These screen distances were calculated for various screens and found to be much more correct in actual application than the distances established by the penumbra theory.[11]

The key role of the photographic material. This brief theoretical discussion should not be ended without a remark on the important role played by the photographic material in halftone photography. The dot patterns are, as you can see in our illustrations, far from sharp if we consider light distribution by itself. But when the right kind of photographic material is used, the halftone images on it are much more clearly defined than you would assume on the basis of our illustrations. The film must be a high contrast material which records light intensities from a certain point up, but not below this point. Thereby it forms dots of the correct size and shape. You can study this aspect in the following illustration.

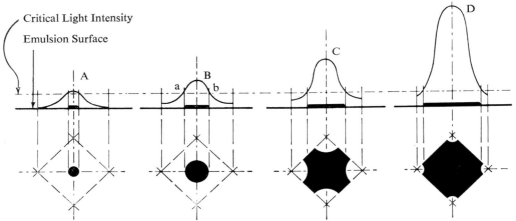

Diagram explaining the formation of halftone dots of different sizes with the cross-line screen. Curves A, B, C, and D represent different light intensities falling on the photographic emulsion. Note that light below the critical light intensity does not contribute to the size of dots and that only light above this line affects dot size. Critical light intensity is often called the threshold speed of a photographic film.

The language of halftone photography. The readers of this manual may not be interested in the operational detail of halftone photography, which is a highly specialized field in itself. But it seems desirable to explain some of the related terms, as these are much more often used than they are really understood.

We begin with *lens stops*, or *stops* for short. Lens stops are technically designated as *diaphragms*. Their function is control of the lens area

and the shape of dots. The *iris* diaphragm can be found on most cameras; it produces circular lens openings of adjustable diameters. You see it and several other stops which are used for special effects in our illustration of various diaphragms.[12]

Our next subject is *highlight, detail,* and *flash exposure.* It is customary to divide the tonal values into the three groups of highlights, middle tones, and shadows. In order to reproduce each of these groups as well as possible, the photographic material may be exposed several times, sometimes two or three times, under carefully established conditions. Flash exposures are made either by flashing light directly through the lens or by reflecting the light flash from a white sheet of paper mounted on the copy board. Flash exposures improve the quality of shadow dots.

Finally we must mention *highlight* or *drop-out negatives.* If a picture with a white background is photographed through a halftone screen, the screen leaves a record of so-called *pinpoint* dots in the white areas. These dots are often unacceptable and must be removed or, in the language of the photographer, *dropped out* by one of several techniques. The final product is called a highlight or drop-out negative.

This terminates our presentation of line and halftone photography. In the following section we will study photography for reproduction of full-color images.

An iris diaphragm and four lens stops together with the patterns made by them.

Section 3:   Photography for Full-Color Reproduction

Photography for full-color reproduction has the function of preparing such basic records of colorful originals as are needed for the production of the printing-image carriers to be used in full-color printing. As you know, we must have three different image carriers for three-color printing, and four of them for four-color printing. Each of these image carriers must present all areas that will be printed with the same color ink. And as you may remember, these inks are yellow, magenta, and cyan; they are supplemented with black ink in four-color jobs.

The original colorful image presents all kinds of different colors. The first task of photography for full-color printing is to make intermediate records suitable for the making of the requisite image carriers. These records are obtained by *color-separation photography* during which the original colorful image is successively photographed three or more times, each time through a different color filter onto a new piece of film.

But color-separation photography is only the first of several important tasks to be performed by photography for full-color reproduction. The second task consists in color-correcting and the third in halftone photography. Even though not every job in every printing method may pose all three tasks, the vast majority does. Color correcting and halftone photography are, therefore, essential phases of full-color photography.

Photography for full-color printing begins with planning. Planning is, of course, important in all printing production, but it is especially so in our subject. Not every job will be printed with the same number of color inks, not every job will be equally treated during color correcting. Standards must be set before the work begins, and it should always be considered by which department various phases of the work will be done, and what kind of intermediate transparencies will be needed for the making of the image carriers. Most of these points differ not only for various branches of the graphic arts—letterpress, gravure, and lithography, for example—or for various plants within a certain branch, but also for various jobs within a given plant, particularly in the service business.

Our presentation is divided into several units. First we will briefly consider the equipment and material for color-separation photography; then we will discuss this operation itself. Thereafter you find an exposition of photographic color-correcting, and a few remarks on halftone photography for full-color printing. (Readers interested in full-color printing should consult Chapter III, Sections 3 and 4.)

*Equipment and Materials for
Color-Separation Photography*

The equipment and the materials for color-separation photography are not basically different from equipment and materials used in other branches of graphic arts photography. The main difference is not so much one of kind as of degree. Everything must be of highest quality, and precision is essential. This holds true for the lens, the camera, the illumination, the equipment for processing, and the light-sensitive material. The same precision is demanded in the actual performance of the work.

To begin with the lens, its quality is of crucial importance. Without a completely corrected lens it is impossible to do color-separation photography. There are several types of cameras on the market that are especially designed for color work. They often have, besides the copy board, special holders for transparencies and many other technical features of great value for speed and efficiency in color-separation photography.

Rigidity of construction and precision of operation are here of particular importance because the several separation records must be used in conjunction with each other. If a black-and-white image is not of the exact size, for example, this defect may not be too serious. But if the three or four photographic intermediates which are part of a single set and will be used together for a set of image carriers, are defective in some way or other, the consequences can be most undesirable.

Illumination is a most important aspect of color-separation photography. Each individual separation is a record of certain wave lengths which are provided by the illuminating light and transmitted or reflected by the copy. Unless the illumination contains the required wave lengths in the correct distribution, the color-separation record may be inaccurate. White flame carbon arc lamps, which approximate the wide range of sunlight, were in the past a most widely used light source for graphic arts photography. More recently they have been replaced with quartz iodine or pulsed xenon lamps. Pulsed xenon lamps appear to be most popular for all around color work. (Carbon arc lamps are still widely used for exposure of photomechanical coatings, in the platemaking department.)

The camera light must be properly positioned and it must be made sure that the calculated light energy is actually delivered during exposure. This result is obtained by integrating light meters.

Chemical processing of color-separation plates and films requires high accuracy. Time and temperature of all operations must be closely controlled. This can be done in several ways; automatic mixing valves will deliver water of correct temperature, or the wanted temperature stability can be obtained by installing sinks which control temperature automatically; various timers help observe the prescribed time limits.

Finally, a few words on various photographic materials and their properties. All materials must be of highest dimensional stability in all phases of photography for full-color reproduction. The reasons for this requirement have already been discussed. As glass plates excel in dimensional stability, they are still used in some plants for large-size work. But the advent of stable film bases such as the duPont Cronar and the Kodak Estar made it possible to replace the fragile and hard-to-handle glass plates. At the time of writing the majority of color work in all sizes is done with films. For color-separation photography, panchromatic films are needed. These are sensitive to the whole color spectrum.[13]

Our last item is color filters. We need a blue, a green, and a red filter for color-separation photography. Each filter should absorb two zones of the color spectrum and only transmit light in its own color zone. The properties of color filters are expressed by their manufacturers in the form of graphs showing the wave length curves of the filters. Color filters come as colored glasses or as colored gelatin films which are sometimes cemented between two cover glasses but are most often used by themselves.

Color-Separation Procedures

As you are well acquainted with the purpose and theoretical basis of color separation from Chapter III we can go straight to a discussion of various operational procedures.

Color-separation techniques are numerous. Color separation can be done either in the camera, or with enlargers, or by contact printing. Reflection copy such as paintings, for example, must be handled in the camera, but transmission copy can be separated in each of the three mentioned ways. Which procedure is selected for a specific job depends, of course, not only on the nature of the job but also on the available equipment.

To complicate matters further, it must be mentioned that color separation can be done either by itself, or in combination with halftone photography, or in combination with halftone photography and photographic color correcting. In this unit we will assume the simplest and also most widely practiced procedure of color separation as an independent step. The other two cases will be

Courtesy Eastman Kodak Company

A reproduction technician comparing an original color transparency with a set of color separations. The original is on a viewer at the right, the four color separations are on the light table.

later considered. If color separation is not combined with halftone photography, the product of this operation is a set of continuous tone records usually, but not necessarily, negatives.

The original is photographed at least three times in succession, through a blue filter, a green filter, and a red filter. The corresponding separation negatives are known as the *yellow-printer*, the *magenta-printer*, and the *cyan-printer* because the yellow, magenta, and cyan image carrier will be made from these records. All this is, of course, already known to you from Chapter III.

Colored lights are recorded as photographic densities. The varying amounts of blue, green, and red light which are passed through each of the color filters are recorded on the three separation negatives as varying photographic densities. These densities are, of course, not in different colors but appear as blacks and grays on the transparent base of the photographic emulsion. At a first glance it must seem that this condition makes it very difficult to judge and control the quality of separation negatives.

It must seem, indeed, almost impossible to interpret different densities on three different negatives in terms of a full-color gamut. Who can be sure to *visualize*, in the literal sense of the word, all these disjointed grays as they will finally appear in color? These difficulties should not be denied or minimized. If the human eye is the only means for evaluating separation negatives, even experienced craftsmen can be easily deceived.

The densitometer is an important tool for color work. But things change very much for the better once we learn to use optical instruments for the purpose of control and evaluation. Then the lack of color on the different records changes from a liability to an asset. It is much simpler to measure photographic densities exactly than to do the same with the whole color gamut of the visible spectrum. All we need is a system for minute correlation of various densities with their corresponding colors. Then we can use the densitometer instead of the human eye and thereby replace subjective personal opinions with objective facts.

Color-control patches. The graphic arts photographer has two simple and most effective aids for tone and color control at his disposal. These are the photographic gray scale and the color-control patches. The gray scale consists, as you may remember, of a series of varying reflection densities. It can be either shop made or purchased from photographic material suppliers. The color-control patches are strips or squares of the three color inks and black in various significant combinations. Ideally, these patches should be printed with the same kind of inks and on the same kind of paper that will be actually used in the production of the job in hand, but they can also be purchased on the market.

The gray scale and the control patches are combined with the copy prior to photographing and recorded together with it on each separation negative. They guide the photographer in evaluating each of the many production steps and particularly in masking for color correcting. The full-color insert in Chapter III shows how color control patches are used in color separation photography.

A further discussion of color-separation photography is unnecessary for our purposes. The execution of each step is in principle the same as already described. We now turn our attention to the fourth intermediate element needed in four-color printing, which is the black-printer negative.

The Black-Printer Negative

Black is not one of the spectrum colors but signifies the more or less complete absorption of the incident light, as you may remember. The black-printer must therefore be made in a fundamentally different way than the three color-separation negatives. A number of techniques are known for the making of the black-printer; three are here briefly identified.

Three techniques for making the black-printer. In the *single-filter* method, the copy is photographed under controlled conditions through a yellow filter; in the *split-filter* method, all three color filters are used in succession for exposing the same photographic material for a predetermined time, and in the *no filter* method a straight exposure is used without a filter. Essentially all of these methods produce photographic records of tones rather than colors. The black-printer is often color-corrected by photographic masking and may or may not need manual color correcting.

Strictly speaking, the black-printer belongs more to color-correcting than to color-separation. It is, of course, not possible to use the black-printer simply in addition to the three color printers. The grays and blacks are more or less already present on these three printers. If they are left as they are, all shadow colors would be too much darkened by the additional black ink. One increasingly preferred four-color technique uses only a so-called light *skeleton* black-printer. When a fuller black-printer is wanted the other three printers are relieved by lightening in the shadow color areas. This operation is technically known as under-color removal, or UCR. It forms part of color-correcting, the topic of our next unit.

Photographic Masking for Color-Correcting

At the outset of this unit it should be mentioned that neither photographic masking is used exclusively for color-correcting, nor that color-correcting is done exclusively by photographic masking. But at the time of writing, and probably for quite some time to come, color-correcting is the most important application of photographic masking, and photographic masking is the most important color-correcting procedure.

Some reasons for color-correcting. You know already that many elements of graphic arts production contribute to some extent to the lack of color fidelity in the printed reproduction. And you also know that our full-color inks in particular are far from ideal. Each color ink should ideally reflect light in two-thirds of the spectrum and absorb light in the remaining third. Unfortunately our actual color inks absorb light in the spectrum regions which they should fully reflect, and they also fail to absorb as much light as they should in their absorption zones. The result of these shortcomings is very undesirable because it can amount to a noticeable decrease of color fidelity in the final reproduction.

The fidelity of printed full-color images can be considerably improved by color correcting. The usual way to think of color correcting for ink deficiencies is that the yellow-printer is corrected for the deficiency of the magenta ink and that the magenta-printer is corrected for the deficiencies of the cyan ink. All magenta inks absorb some blue light which should be absorbed by the yellow ink only. This condition is counteracted by correcting the yellow-printer. The yellow-printer is made lighter in the areas which are critically affected by the magenta ink. The result is that purples and blues, including sky colors, appear now in a truer and cleaner blueness. All cyan inks absorb some green light which should be absorbed by the magenta ink only. This condition is counteracted by correcting the magenta-printer. The magenta-printer is made lighter in the areas which are critically affected by the cyan ink. The result is that all greens become purer and brighter

and that the blues, including sky colors, appear now cleaner and less reddish. Pure lemon yellow inks do not create a need for color correction but golden yellow inks, which reflect less green light than they should, do. If such inks are used, the magenta-printer needs added corrections in orange colors.

The cyan-printer and the black-printer must also be color corrected by photographic masks. Magenta inks not only absorb some blue light, which they should completely reflect, but they are also deficient in not completely reflecting the red light. This second deficiency is counteracted by correcting the cyan-printer. The result of correcting the cyan-printer is that cyan ink is cleaned out of the pure reds and that the flesh tints are lightened. The black-printer, finally, is improved by a photographic mask which removes excess black ink from pure colors.

In some cases it is necessary to add densities, in others to diminish them, in still others to do both on various separation negatives. Different quality standards, inks, papers, image carriers, and presswork may all contribute to differences in masking techniques. Various methods were worked out for determining the correct photographic masks. The GATF-Preucil System stands out among these because it is an integrated system that can be worked according to simple basic formulas and by means of the densitometer. But other systems produce equally good results in the hands of capable and experienced people.

Progress in photographic masking. Color correction by photographic masking has gone through an evolutionary process in which many masking systems were devised, tried, and abandoned because they were too complicated or not effective enough. For many decades color correcting of separation negatives was done by high-skilled lithographic tradesmen by retouching and dot-etching. This kind of color correcting required long experience, was very time consuming and limited in its effectiveness because different variables influencing color fidelity were not sufficiently considered. Even though earlier multiple-stage masking systems failed to find acceptance, they established nevertheless that handwork could be greatly reduced by photographic masking.

In the course of time the role of various factors played in full-color printing became better understood and photographic masking methods were, consequently, simplified and made better controllable. This result is due to work done by color experts of manufacturers of photographic materials and to the efforts of the Graphic Arts Technical Foundation which disseminates color knowledge in the industry by color seminars and lectures. As a result of all these efforts masking has become generally recognized as a most important phase of full-color printing. At present much, though not all, manual color correcting is replaced by photographic masking.

At the time of writing several different masking techniques are in use. The color experts of GATF consider methods using four masks, one for each of the four separations, the most successful ones because "each mask may be made with one or two filters and adjusted in strength, thereby effectively correcting different sets of full-color inks, papers, and other conditions." [14]

The improvement and standardization of printing inks made more standardized and simplified masking methods possible. Kodak and Gevaert now manufacture multilayer films especially for masking. Masking can be done, by use of these special products, with a single mask instead of four masks, as mentioned above. The Kodak masking film is known as *Tri-Mask*, the Gevaert product as *Multi-Mask*.[15]

All masking systems aim of course at the same thing: better color fidelity of the printed reproduction. Changes in photographic densities on continuous tone negatives or positives are finally expressed as changes of the printing areas on the printing-image carriers and become therewith color changes in the printed image itself.

Photographic masking is a highly developed specialty. Reflection copy and transmission copy are masked by several different methods. Most masking for full-color printing is done with continuous tone separations, but it is also possible to combine masking, color separation, and halftone photography in one series of operations. This is the case in the Kodak Three-Color System.

We will not pursue this very technical subject any further. Let it be mentioned that photographic masking, like color separation, can be done in the camera, or with enlargers, or by contact printing. Readers who want to study the subject further will find that there exists a highly developed literature.

Photographic masking and manual color correcting. This unit should not be closed without mentioning that photographic and manual color correcting go hand in hand. In some cases handwork is done on the separation negatives, in others

on positives made from these negatives, or on the positives alone. In some plants positives are made on a specially treated photographic paper, which has good dimensional stability, but plates or films are more widely used for this purpose. Not all color correcting is done on continuous tone separations. Dot-etching, an important chemical color-correction method, cannot take place until the continuous tone images have been converted into halftone images.

Halftone Photography for Full-Color Reproduction

Full-color reproductions that will be printed either in collotype or in conventional gravure do not require halftone photography, but halftone photography is a necessity if the reproduction is printed in a method which must convert tonal images into halftones for the purpose of reproduction. As the vast majority of full-color work is done in one of these methods which include, as has been stated repeatedly, all of relief printing, lithography, some rotogravure methods, and screen process, halftone photography is an essential operation in most full-color jobs.

Direct and indirect color-separation methods. Halftone photography can be either done together with color-separation photography or as an independent operation. If color separation is combined with halftone photography, it is customary to designate this procedure as *direct* color-separation method and to distinguish it thereby from the *indirect* separation method where halftone photography takes place subsequent to color separation. These terms are apt to confuse the uninformed because the adjectives *direct* and *indirect* do not modify or describe the act of color separation itself (namely, the photographing of a colorful original through different color filters), but refer solely to halftone photography which is not mentioned at all in the term but must be inferred.

Both direct screening and indirect screening methods have their place in color-separation photography. Which method is actually selected depends on the reproduction task in hand. In the *direct screening method* a crossline, or now more frequently, a contact screen is used during color separation. Modern direct screening methods use masking quite successfully. Masks are handled differently for transmission copy and for reflection copy. (Transmission copy comprises color transparencies, reflection copy is on opaque material, as already explained.) Color transparencies are at present the majority of original images for color separation. Color-correcting masks are put on the transparencies, Ektachromes, for example, during color separation. In reflection copy such as paintings or color pictures on opaque material, the masks are mounted over the contact screen. Tri-Mask is used successfully for this purpose.

Courtesy Vulcan Photo Engraving Company

Operator at work on a Vulcamatic Precision Process Camera. This vertical camera is designed for direct color separation of transparencies. The camera is used in the darkroom, has preset timers and a punched register system.

In the *indirect screening method* color separation and halftone photography are not done together, and no screen is used during color separation. The products of color separation are continuous-tone records which can be color corrected by photographic masking and by retouching before they are converted into halftone images. Halftone photography for full-color reproduction is essentially the same as black-and-white halftone photography, but it has also some problems of its own. It can be done by means of the crossline screen, the contact screen, and in certain cases even with Kodalith Autoscreen film. The crossline screen must, as always, be used in the camera; the contact screen can be used in the camera and in contact printing; Kodalith Auto-

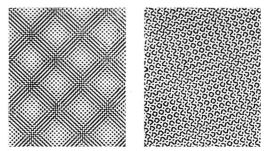

Courtesy Eastman Kodak Company

Two moiré patterns, greatly enlarged.

screen film can be used in the camera as well as in contact printing and projection.

The moire. One problem of halftone photography for full-color printing which is not usually present in black-and-white halftone photography is the danger of a *moiré* (pronounced *moawrey*) pattern, which needs a brief explanation. If various halftone images are printed in succession on the same paper, it can happen that the printed image shows a pattern which interferes with its appearance. This pattern is similar to a pattern that can be produced by passing fabrics through engraved rollers. As such a pattern is called "moiré" this name has also been applied to its undesired counterpart in halftone printing.

It has been found that moiré patterns can be avoided by *angling* the halftone screen. Angling means that the halftone screen is used at different angles for each of the several halftone images which belong to the same set of full-color negatives or positives. Crossline screens are, therefore, usually mounted in circular frame holders marked for angles, which makes it easy to set the correct angles accurately. Contact screen can be marked for the same purpose, or color transparencies are correctly angled for each color. Normally the screen angles are separated by 30° between black, magenta, and cyan. Yellow, which is less noticeable, is separated by only 15° from the magenta and cyan angles. Moiré can also be introduced in presswork by defective overprinting.

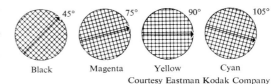

Courtesy Eastman Kodak Company

Example of different screen angles used in color-separation photography to avoid a moiré pattern.

Section 4:   Retouching, Dot-Etching, and Other Manual Techniques

Photographic intermediates, positives or negatives, must often be subjected to various manual treatments before they can be further used. The department where this kind of work is done is sometimes called the retouching department, or the dot-etching department, or the litho-art department. In some plants other departments such as the layout department or the stripping department, whose functions are explained in the following chapter, do some of the work which will be presented in this section.

In general terms it can be stated that manual treatments of photographic intermediates have the object of adapting these to their final purposes and of improving them where this is indicated. This kind of work is specifically called retouching, dot-etching, and opaquing. It is done by highly skilled graphic arts tradesmen who are actually reproduction artists. They are called *retouchers, dot-etchers, opaquers, litho-artists,* and more recently, *color-etchers.* Traditionally, the practice of color correcting differed in different printing processes. In offset lithography all color correcting must be done on the photographic separations before platemaking. No color correcting can be done on an offset plate. In photoengraving color correcting was done on photographic separations prior to exposure of the plate and also on the plate itself after etching. Modern production methods have changed practice and at present most color correcting is done, as in lithography, before the plate is made. In gravure too, most color correcting is done on photographic intermediates, usually on continuous-tone positives. Re-etching of plates or cylinders may be needed if the press proof is unsatisfactory.

The color-etcher works with such hand tools as artist's brushes, stumps, crayons, gravers, and airbrushes whereby they apply various kinds of media, dyes, inks, and photographic chemicals as the case may demand. These reproduction artists need high manual skills, thorough experience, and a good understanding of the nature of their work—photography and densitometry in particular as related to color rendition.

Extensive manual color-correcting can become quite expensive. Contemporary reproduction practice, therefore, tends to replace manual techniques whenever possible with photographic masking and electronic color-correcting methods.

Retouching

Retouching is applied to several rather divergent operations. In this manual we reserve the term "retouching" for the adjusting and changing of densities on continuous-tone photographs. Such other operations as the correcting of imperfections and flaws of photographic intermediates which are often also known as retouching are discussed under the heading of opaquing.

You understand of course that the changing of densities aims at a change of proportions between printing and non-printing areas of the final printing image carrier. These in turn control either the tones or the colors of the printed image. The retoucher and, in particular, the color retoucher or color-etcher, must consequently be able to interpret densities in terms of final colors. This is not easy to learn and requires natural talent besides training experience and a thorough familiarity with color charts.

Color charts are an important aid to the color etcher. These charts co-ordinate dot sizes in the several color-printers with the final color. Such charts enable the color etcher to produce dots of the required sizes, or values. Dot size can also be related to the densities on the continuous-tone separations in indirect separation procedures.

Outline of retouching. Generally speaking, the retoucher determines first which densities certain critical areas of a job should have on the different separation photographs. In this determination he is guided by his experience and by printed color charts. Then he measures these areas with a densitometer, and thereafter he makes the required adjustments which can be in various areas on one or several separation photographs. The adjustments can consist in either *increasing* or in *decreasing* the existing densities. (Other names for this work are *adding densities, intensification,* as well as *subtracting densities* and *reduction.*) In addition to the change of densities in general, retouching often includes the adding or diminishing of detail densities and possibly even the complete elimination of detail.

It is possible to do the retouching of continuous-tone photographs either on positives or on negatives. As the densities of positives can be directly related to the future printing areas and therewith to the colors of the final printed image, positive retouching is preferred in most cases to negative retouching. If the product of the camera is a negative, the making of a positive may precede retouching. In some methods the retouched positive must be converted back into a continuous-tone negative for halftone photography; in other cases the positive itself can be used.

Techniques of retouching. Now we proceed to some techniques commonly used for retouching of continuous-tone intermediates. These can be conveniently divided into methods using photographic chemicals, methods using various colorants, and methods using mechanical tools. Methods using photographic chemicals and those using mechanical tools serve mainly for the diminishing of densities, whereas methods using various colorants are primarily used for the opposite purpose. It is of course always possible to change from negative to positive and vice versa and thereby to obtain the opposite result. Increases in the densities of a negative will appear as decreases if the negative is converted into a positive, and the same holds true for positives if they will be converted back into negatives.

A retoucher at work. The original artwork is at the left; the separation film to be retouched is on top of the light table.

All this may sound quite confusing to the inexperienced. But if you think about it, you will realize that going back and forth from positives to negatives and back again offers most valuable possibilities to the retoucher. He can, for example,

make general density changes on the negatives, then convert these into positives and do the local retouching on these. Such an approach is often elected when several units of different sizes are to be made from one set of separation photographs.

Reducing of photographic densities. Treating a photographic halftone image with chemicals in order to reduce its densities is called *etching* by the trade; if this treatment is given to large areas it is called *flat etching*, if it is given in various stages to local areas it is called *staging*. The areas of the plate or film which are not to be reduced are protected from the chemical agent with a resist which is applied to them by painting with artist's brushes. Flat etching is done in a tray. There the photographic plate or film is immersed into a chemical solution which may be, for example, *Farmer's Reducer*—a mixture of potassium ferricyanide and hypo, strongly diluted with water—or a different agent known as *ceric sulfate*. These solutions are capable of dissolving the photographic image on plates or films. As the action is rather rapid, the time for which the photographic intermediates may remain in the reducing solution is quite critical. Immediately after removal from the tray, the film or plate is rinsed in water and then measured with a densitometer. This whole cycle of treating, watering, and measuring may need one or several repetitions until the desired result is obtained. Local reducing can be done directly on the photographic plate or film by applying the reducer with artist's brushes.

Reducing densities with hand tools such as the scraper is usually done after chemical reducing. This operation requires skill and patience. It is employed for the improvement of highlight and shadow detail but not for larger areas.

Adding to photographic densities. Density can be added in various ways. Among them are airbrushing, treatment with dyes, the use of graphite pencils, and painting with opaque. Which of these techniques is selected depends entirely on the case and on the personal preferences of the retoucher. The *bath technique* is indicated where the photographic intermediate either needs all-over intensification, or where large areas which can easily be defined and separated from the rest by protective coatings must be intensified. In this technique the plate or film is immersed under agitation in a tray containing a solution of the dye or dye mixture. The material is kept in the tray for a short time, rinsed and measured by a densitometer to find out whether it has come up to the desired density. If

not, the whole procedure is repeated until it produces the required result.

Airbrush retouching is rather difficult, but it is very useful for work which requires tonal gradations. The application of retouching dyes by painting is tedious work in which the retoucher is careful to avoid overintensifications. Detail, finally, can be retouched with pens, quills, graphite stumps, and pencils of different hardness.

Dot-Etching or Color-Etching

Dot-etching is a method of tone and color-correcting which is more widely used in lithography than in other printing methods. It has the purpose of controlling the dot size and therewith the density of halftone images on photographic intermediates. Dot-etching is usually done on halftone positives. These can be used without further conversion for the photomechanical production of certain types of lithographic image carriers, in particular for deep-etch plates. For other types, such as lithographic surfaces plates, for example, negatives are required. In these cases dot-etching is usually done on positives from which negatives are then made by contact printing.

Reducing area densities. Dot-etching can reduce area densities by decreasing the size of individual halftone dots, but we cannot produce equivalent intensification as it is not possible to materially increase the size of halftone dots by chemical treatments. Intensification must therefore be provided by the retouching of continuous tone intermediates, prior to halftone photography. The extent to which dot sizes are reduced depends on the job in hand. If all or most of the needed tone and color correcting must be achieved by dot-etching, reductions of 40 and 50 per cent in the size of dots may be necessary. If the continuous tone material was adjusted by photographic masking and retouching prior to halftone photography, dot-etching can be much less extensive.

The densitometer, a key instrument in dot-etching. Dot-etching can be done on halftone images made either with the cross-line screen or with the contact screen. The procedure is essentially the same as described above for reduction by etching, and the densitometer is again the main control instrument. It indicates where changes must be made and to what point these changes should go. Once this is established the best dot-etching technique can be selected. This may be either flat etching or staging and etching. As the etching

solution is usually the aforementioned Farmer's Reducer, and as the two techniques are basically the same, we do not need to discuss the subject again. For the sake of completeness it might be added that it is possible to intensify the periphery of halftone dots with chemical treatments. But these have very limited effects and are therefore not often given.[16]

Fake Color Process

Fake color process is a colloquial designation for various procedures which could perhaps better and less odiously be named imitation full-color printing. In this kind of color printing the original is mostly a black-and-white photograph or a black-and-white wash-drawing. The subject may be anything; in catalog work it is often some kind of merchandise, either by itself or in an attractive setting which may include people having the functions of models. In greeting cards the subject is usually a design. It is obviously much less expensive to arrive at this kind of original for color reproduction than at a good full-color original.

This kind of original image cannot be converted into a set of image carriers for full-color printing by color separation. But various areas of such an original can be translated into colors which can be reproduced either by the three full-color inks alone, or supplemented by black. This effect can

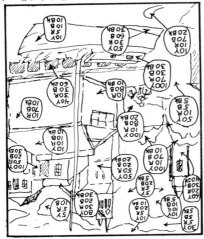

Courtesy Graphic Arts Technical Foundation

Diagram of charted color values in preparing separations for fake color printing. The letter "Y" means yellow. "R" means red, "B" means blue, and "Bk" means black. The figures next to the letters indicate per cent values of halftones.

be created in various ways. In some cases a commercial art studio will provide a color guide by indicating the desired colors of various areas in terms of an existing color chart. But it is also possible to transmit the merchandise which is the crux of the particular color job to the printer or photoengraver who will in turn employ specialists in this type of work for the determination of the various color areas.

If we compare the approach taken by fake color process with that of full-color printing, we notice an interesting difference. In full-color printing the work proceeds from the original color image. All adjustments have the purpose of assuring the fidelity of the final printed image. In fake color process the direction is reversed. Here the obtainable colors are recorded on the color chart. The different color areas of the original black-and-white pictures are marked accordingly, and the various color printers must have the values listed in the color chart.

The color-etcher, the retoucher, and the camera man must co-operate in this kind of work. In photoengraving some of the etching is even done on the metal itself. But we do not intend to lose ourselves in the intricacies of fake color process! It is merely added that the derogatory label should not lead to the assumption that the results of imitation full-color printing must be always poor. It is, on the contrary, rather surprising how adequate and economical such reproductions can be if produced by competent craftsmen.17

Opaquing

As you know from our introductory remarks on retouching, opaquing has the purpose of correcting flaws and imperfections in photographic positives or negatives. This is the sense in which the term opaquing is used in some branches of the graphic arts, especially in gravure. In lithography, opaquing means in addition also a number of other operations which are not performed in other branches of printing at the same production stage and therefore not included in the meaning of the term. As we assume that you will most likely meet the term "opaquing" in the expanded meaning as current in lithography, it is here explained.

Practically every photographic intermediate needs more or less correcting by opaquing. It happens often that camera negatives of line copy, such as type or line drawings, have *pinholes* or other flaws. These are eliminated by painting with an opaque medium, known as *opaque*. The operation itself is often called *spotting;* it is usually done on top of a light table. Sometimes the opaquer must repair broken lines in photographic inter-mediates, and he may even be called upon to do repairs of damaged halftones. Many smaller plants have no retouching and color-etching departments. There the opaquer must in a pinch be able to do many of the jobs that were discussed under the heading of retouching.

An opaquer at work on a negative. He blocks pinholes and repairs damaged images.

Finally it may be the task of the opaquer to add *register* and *trim marks.* Register marks indicate the correct fit of successive printed images, or serve for the proper positioning of images to be reproduced in multiples. Trim marks are guides for folding and trimming of the printed sheets. Both kinds of marks are production aids and must not appear on the final product.

Chapter V

Printing-Image Carriers

As you already know, printing processes are grouped in this manual in accordance with the characteristic differences of their printing-image carriers. This method of classification recognizes the far-reaching influence of image carriers which will be noticed by you in many chapters of this book. Since printing presses, printing inks, and printing stocks must be well attuned to the image carriers with which they are to be combined for image transfer, or presswork, the chapters where these subjects are presented cannot be understood without a grounding in the present subject.

At this point a brief listing of some of the more generally important features of image carriers seems to be in order. These are nine: (1) the nature of a printing-image carrier can have a significant influence on the appearance of the printed image; (2) not every image carrier can be used to print on every material; (3) various kinds of image carriers need differently constituted printing inks which vary in many characteristic respects; (4) the application of ink differs for different types of image carriers; (5) different ink application requires different inking mechanisms on the press and therewith leads to more or less radical differences in printing press construction; (6) not all image carriers can be printed at the same press speeds; (7) the number of impressions that can be made with different image carriers is subject to wide variations; (8) different image carriers have widely differing production costs; and (9) various types of image carriers are not only differently made but also differently assembled for presswork. This list is rather long though it covers merely the most obvious points.

One item is, nevertheless, best discussed immediately. We refer to differences in the appearance of printed images produced with different kinds of image carriers. Such differences were in the past quite pronounced but have become less noticeable in our own time. Modern printing technology has the tendency of leveling these historic differences. Not every kind of image carrier differs, consequently, from every other kind in each of the foregoing nine points.

The leveling process as regards appearance of the final printed image is particularly advanced in letterpress and offset lithography. At present, either method is usually capable of reproducing the same original images or, as the trade says, the same art-and-copy, with perfectly satisfactory results. When two or more different printing methods can produce equally acceptable results, appearance differences yield their controlling position to other considerations; among them are availability of equipment, speed of delivery, and last, but certainly not least, price.

In this chapter you find a systematic treatment of the most important image carriers and the methods by which they are produced. The chapter consists of six sections. Section 1 is a survey of all image carriers here discussed and of their manufacture; Section 2 presents an elementary introduction to photomechanics and to the various forms in which photomechanical methods are used in different printing processes and methods. The following four sections are each devoted to one process group, subdivided into its several methods. Section 3 covers relief printing; Section 4, intaglio printing; Section 5, planographic;

and Section 6, porous printing. It might interest the reader that this chapter is not limited to image carriers for industrial printing, or for printing as a business, and that printing-image carriers for fine-art printing are also described.

The total number of printing-image carriers discussed in this chapter amounts to several scores. This large number and wide range of differences in printing-image carriers is mainly due to modern specialization. It indicates to what extent printing, this ancient art of communication, has learned to cope with the never ending challenge posed by a constantly changing contemporary civilization.

Section 1: A Survey of Printing-Image Carriers

The manufacturing methods by which printing-image carriers are produced can be divided for the purpose of a systematic discussion into the following six different groups: (1) manually made image carriers, (2) mechanically made image carriers, (3) photomechanically made image carriers, (4) electrochemically made image carriers, (5) image carriers made by means of electronics, and (6) image carriers made by means of electro-statics. Actually, these divisions are not quite strict as several methods are often used in combination for the production of various types of image carriers. You will nevertheless find our grouping practical, as it emphasizes the most distinctive manufacturing processes by which each kind of image carrier is made.

Manually made printing-image carriers. All graphic reproduction processes were originally based on handmade image carriers. The skills needed for their fashioning were drawing, carving, engraving, etching, and tusching, to mention some. Although many of these skills are still useful in modern printing production, they are being replaced with increasing frequency by mechanical, chemical—and most recently—electronic processes. Quite often the field of application of manual skills has shifted from preparing the printing-image carrier itself to the improving of intermediate products such as photographic negatives and positives which are needed in a more mechanized production of image carriers. Retouching, dot-etching, and opaquing, which were all discussed in Chapter IV, are examples of the place which manual skills still have in modern image-carrier technology.

Hand composition is perhaps the most frequently used contemporary manual technique in the preparation of image carriers. Although the bulk of our composition is done by machines, hand composition still plays a vital role in various assembly operations and will remain a real necessity for a long time to come.

Limitations of manually made printing-image carriers. Even though it is possible to use manually made printing-image carriers in all printing processes they are at present not generally used in industrial printing. The reasons for this change are not difficult to find. Handmade image carriers are much too costly, much too limited in their scope, insamuch as they cannot reproduce photographs, and are much too vulnerable to be usable for quantity production of printed material. Such image carriers as woodcuts, wood engrav-

Courtesy Presentation Press

A screen-process film cutter at work making a knife-cut stencil. The stencil forming material, knife-cut film, is placed over the original artwork and the film cutter traces selective areas with his knife on this transparent material. The printing areas are removed after cutting, the non-printing areas are adhered to the porous screen where they block the pores of the stencil cloth.

ings, hand-tooled or hand-engraved lithographic stones, and etched or engraved plates, which were the pride of generations of craftsmen, have all but completely disappeared from the contemporary scene of industrial printing. Even now it may be expedient at times to solve exceptional printing problems by means of hand-crayoned lithographic plates or hand-engraved dies, to give some examples, but these instances are rare exceptions. In mid-twentieth-century America, handmade image carriers are confined to the fine graphic arts which serve for artistic self-expression rather than industrial production.

The only printing process in which handmade image carriers are still widely used for industrial printing is screen-process printing. Screen-process printing uses several kinds of handmade image carriers. Some are of rather limited scope, but those made by the knife-cut film method have remained quite important in screen printing. Such image carriers can be particularly economical for the reproduction of line artwork, but they are not suitable for tonal images such as wash drawings and photographs.

Mechanically made printing-image carriers. Under the heading of mechanically made printing-image carriers we include those that are produced by casting, by hot or cold molding, by pressing, or by means of a pantograph. Most mechanically made image carriers belong to various methods of relief printing, but image carriers made by means of the pantograph serve for one method of intaglio printing. Mechanical means such as scribing and stylus punching are part of electronic equipment for the making of certain kinds of image carriers. But as these are activated and directed by electronics they are discussed in the last unit of this section under the heading of "Printing-Image Carriers Made by Means of Electronics and Electrostatics."

Mechanically produced image carriers for relief printing fall into two categories: hot-metal machine composition is the first and duplicate printing plates the second. All hot-metal machine composition is brought about by the casting of molten metal in molds and type matrices. In duplicate platemaking, the processes are more numerous and involved. Each of the many different kinds is arrived at by a different production method and with different materials. Electrotypes, for example, are primarily made by means of electrochemical methods; but they also require molding, casting, finishing, and machining;

stereotypes require casting and machining; rubber and plastic plates require molding of thermosetting and thermoplastic materials as well as finishing of the molded plates.

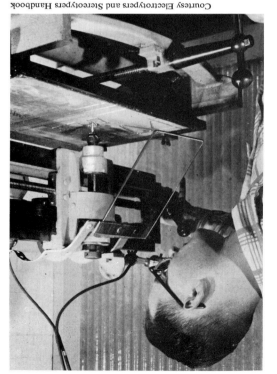

Dead metal is removed from an electrotype plate by routing.

Intaglio printing uses several kinds of mechanically made image carriers. These include pantographically made image carriers. These include pantograph engravings, engravings made with geometric lathes, and siderographs. Pantograph engravings, which require much less skill than handmade engravings, are common in steel die-stamping. Our national currency is printed partly in intaglio and partly in letterpress. Intaglio image carriers for stock and bond certificates, as well as those needed for the printing of our paper money, are often decorated by means of the geometric lathe which produces scrolls and other patterns that are not only very effective but also extremely difficult to imitate. Siderographs are another kind of mechanically made image carriers. They are still sometimes used by the Bureau of Engraving even though the majority of duplicate plates for intaglio printed currency is at present made electrochemically. Nor should it be omitted that

mechanically made cylinders have a place in the printing of textiles, wrapping papers, and wall-papers, as well as that of plastics by gravure.

Depending on the interpretation given to the word "mechanical," it can be said that plano-graphic and porous printing also utilize mechanically made image carriers. Direct-image plates, for example, which are used in lithography, can be prepared by typing on a typewriter, or on type-writer composing-machines, as well as by image transfer made either with proof presses or with production presses. And screen-process printing, finally, can use especially adapted pantographs for the making of knife-cut film image carriers.

It is correct that some of these methods are not generally practiced at the time of writing, but they may conceivably acquire more importance in the future.

Printing-image carriers made by means of photomechanics. First it should be explained that the term "photomechanical" is somewhat mis-leading as it "denotes processes in which by the action of light upon chemical substances a print-ing surface is prepared from which a large number of impressions can be made on a printing press."[1] Said more simply, photomechanics are methods for the making of printing-image carriers by means of light-sensitive materials.

Photomechanics comprise a number of related production methods for the making of image car-riers which are used in all four process families and in many of the different methods into which we subdivide each process family. Manually and mechanically made image carriers are very limited in their detail. They are, as repeatedly mentioned, incapable of reproducing photographs and other continuous-tone images. Photomechanics enable us to overcome these limitations. Practically all reproductions of continuous-tone images are made by means of photomechanics; the main ex-ception is halftone engraving done with elec-tronic equipment.

As photomechanics have a key position in our contemporary image-carrier technology, they must be more extensively discussed than methods of a more limited scope. It should also be under-stood that various photomechanical methods dif-fer in certain respects from each other, but that they have, nevertheless, a substantial common basis. A good understanding of this basis is a prerequisite for every discussion of specific photo-mechanical methods. For this reason, the subject is here divided into a general exposition of photo-mechanics and into specific photomechanical methods. The general exposition of photo-mechanics is the subject matter of the following section; specific photomechanical methods are presented in later sections under the heading of each type of image carrier for whose production they serve. This arrangement will not only lay a good foundation but it will also help to avoid otherwise inevitable repetitions.

At this point we shall merely identify various photomechanically made image carriers by name and relate them to the printing methods where they are used.

Courtesy The Beck Engraving Company

Etching of gravure plates requires attention to indi-vidual plate areas. The etcher manipulates the etchant with an etching pad.

To begin with relief printing, photomechanical methods are most important in the making of pictorial image carriers, known as photoen-gravings. The main function of photomechanical methods for photoengravings are two: one is to distinctively identify the future printing and non-printing areas of the image carrier; the other is to serve as a resist during the etching of the metal. But not all pictorial image carriers for relief printing that are made by photomechanics are photoengravings. It is also possible to make original photomechanical relief image carriers from plastics and photopolymers. Among such image carriers are duPont Dycril plates and Kodak Relief Plates.

Photomechanical image carriers for intaglio printing are either gravure plates or gravure cylinders. Here, too, photomechanics serve to distinguish the printing and the non-printing areas from each other. But in all intaglio methods em-ploying cells of varying depths, photomechanical processes have an additional and most important

function: they are the means by which these depth variations are controlled.

Photomechanical image carriers for plano-graphic printing can be divided into two broad groups, those for offset lithography and those for collotype. As photomechanically made offset lithographic plates exist in several variations, it is necessary to distinguish at least three kinds: (1) surface plates, (2) deep-etch plates, and (3) bimetallic plates. This division seems to be lacking in systematics as bimetallic plates can be made either as surface plates or as deep-etch plates. But bimetallic plates of either kind have many common characteristics and are therefore classified by themselves. In surface plates photomechanics serve not only for the identification of the printing image; these methods also provide the actual image areas on the plate. In deep-etch and in bimetallic plates, photomechanics have mainly the purpose of distinguishing the printing areas from the non-printing areas on the image carrier. In collotype plates, photomechanics have two functions similar to those in gravure methods with varying cell depth. Here, as always, photomechanics differentiate the printing areas and the non-printing areas of the image carrier. In addition, photomechanics make it possible to control the varying film thickness of the ink image and thereby the values of the printed collotype image. Photomechanical image carriers for porous printing are known as photographic screens. Here photomechanics are again needed for differentiation of the printing areas from the non-printing areas of the image carrier.

Printing-image carriers made by means of electrochemistry. It is possible to produce image carriers by electrochemical deposition of such metals as copper, nickel, and chromium. Even though the reverse approach, namely, electrochemical removal of metals is also possible, the latter process is not generally considered practical for the making of printing-image carriers. Electrochemical processes can be either the principal methods for the production of image carriers, or they can be used together with other manufacturing methods, such as photomechanics, for example. Electrochemistry is needed for the making of several kinds of image carriers. It plays a decisive role in the manufacturing of electrotypes, one of the most widely used kinds of relief duplicate plates. There image and non-image areas are both brought about by means of electrodeposition. Electrotypes pass through many different sub-

sidiary operations but these are much less characteristic for electrotyping than is electrochemistry. If photoengravings are made by electrochemical removal of metal, the process is called *electric etching*. Electric etching is, as mentioned above, not generally practiced.

Electrodeposition of metals plays a considerable, though not a decisive part, in the production of many intaglio and some planographic image carriers. Gravure plates, which consist of copper, are often plated with nickel or chromium after etching to improve their wearing qualities. Gravure cylinders are usually made by copperplating; after etching they are often chromium plated for the purpose of extending their life expectancy.

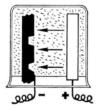

Courtesy Electrotypers and Stereotypers Handbook

Diagram of electroforming. The copper is at the left and the mold, on which the electrotype shell is formed, is at the right in the plating tank.

Electrotypes, stereotypes and, in special cases, photoengravings can be chromium plated for the same purpose. Plating is also used in the making of bimetallic lithographic image carriers, where it serves the purpose of distinguishing the printing areas from the non-printing areas of plates.

Printing-image carriers made by means of electronics and electrostatics. In the more recent past it has become possible to convert original images directly into relief printing-image carriers with electronic equipment specially developed for this purpose. Such image carriers are at the time of writing used mainly for low-priced picture reproduction and have proved especially practical for the relief printing of newspapers. The great promise held by electronic engraving machines is illustrated by the fact that it has become possible to produce sets of color-corrected printing-image carriers for full-color reproduction with electronic engraving machines. But the art of making image carriers by means of electronics is still very young and relatively undeveloped.

Image carriers made by means of electrostatics are at the time of writing not generally used in the

printing business, though it is not only possible but also very economical to make certain kinds of lithographic plates by one electrostatic process, known as *Xerography.* Such plates have secured for themselves a place in office-duplicating.

At the Ninth International Educational Graphic Arts Exposition in 1959, one could see a very ingenious application of another electrostatic method, the *Electrofax* process. The prototype of a camera there exhibited was capable of converting original images directly into the final image carrier for lithography by means of the Electrofax process. Like electronics, electrostatics is still a very young art in its application to the making of printing-image carriers. But electrostatics may possibly play a great role in the future.

Section 2: Introduction to Photomechanics

As mentioned earlier, photomechanics has made it possible to arrive at image carriers capable of reproducing continuous-tone images, photographs in particular. Photomechanical processes are as significant for the reproduction of pictures as type is for the printing of reading matter. In the course of the last thirty years or so, photomechanics has experienced a constant growth that has led this group of methods way beyond their original task of picture reproduction. Photomechanics has, in that time, revolutionized printing technology by achieving the union of pictures and reading matter in one and the same printing-image carrier. At present, there exist photomechanical methods for the production of image carriers embodying both pictures and reading matter for each process family.

The common denominator of photomechanics. All photomechanical methods are based on the ability of light to rapidly change the physical properties of certain chemicals in a very pronounced manner. The words to be stressed in the preceding sentence are *rapidly* and *very pronounced.* These two points distinguish a small number of substances from the great variety of matter which is affected in some way or other by light, though neither rapidly nor decidedly enough to be usable for photomechanics.

Materials for photomechanical coatings. The materials originally most important as film formers of photomechanical coatings were natural organic substances, such as asphalt and shellac, and natural organic colloids. Among the latter were egg albumin, casein, gum arabic, and gelatin. As a result of synthetic chemistry new materials such as polyvinyl alcohol, methyl cellulose, and photopolymers replaced natural materials—completely or partially—for certain purposes. The light sensitivity of many materials **must be improved by sensitizing.** Some materials are sensitized by compounding with diazos or with solutions of sodium, or potassium, or ammonium bichromates. "In the graphic arts, solutions and coatings consisting of soluble salts and organic colloids are generally called bichromated colloids."[2] The Dycril plate, developed by duPont "is called a *photopolymer* because when exposed to ultraviolet light, it polymerizes or becomes insoluble."[3] *Diazo* compounds are products of chemical manufacturing and serve as light-sensitive ingredients of coatings for presensitized plates as well as of wipe-on materials.[4]

Exposure to light changes solubility of photomechanical coatings. If one wants to make a bimechanical coating material, a solution of chromated colloid coating material, a solution of albumin, gum arabic, or gelatin and a solution of bichromate are thoroughly mixed and then coated on a support which may be paper, plastic, glass, or metal. Light affects such a coating in many ways, one of which is of particular significance for us. This is a decrease in solubility if the dry coating is exposed to strong light. *Where such a coating is shielded from light, it remains soluble in water of a given temperature, but where it is exposed to strong light, the solubility of the coating changes substantially. The exposed areas of the coating become insoluble in water of the same temperature in which this coating was soluble before exposure to light.* This phenomenon is the basis of most photomechanical processes, even though the coating materials may differ, and water may be replaced by another solvent.[5]

This change in relative solubility makes it possible to separate and identify the printing and the non-printing areas of the future printing-image carrier and thus to differentiate between the two. For this result, the coated photomechanical material must be combined with a transparency and then exposed to light. The transparency may be a glass plate, a photographic film, or even a

transparent paper on which the printing and the non-printing areas are distinguished by the fact that one kind is opaquely recorded while the other remains more or less transparent.

Positive and negative transparencies. As explained in Chapter IV, we call a transparency where the future printing image is opaque, a *positive*, and where it is transparent, a *negative*. In most cases, photographic intermediates such as negatives or positives are used as transparencies. But transparencies need not be photographs; opaque drawings or type proofs on a transparent or translucent material are also suitable as transparencies for photomechanics.

Transparencies control area changes in solubility after exposure. What happens when a light-sensitive coating is exposed together with a transparency? Obviously, the opaque areas of the transparency will stop the light, whereas the transparent areas will let it pass through the transparency onto the photomechanical coating beneath it. Wherever the coating is struck by light, it will be relatively insoluble at the following development, whereas it remains soluble in the light-protected areas. The nature and temperature of the solvent depend, of course, on the particular coating, but the principle remains the same.

Photomechanical stencils. The result of this kind of photomechanics is called a photomechanical *stencil*. The exposed areas of the light-sensitive coating are more or less completely retained on the base material, whereas the unexposed ones are more or less completely removed from the base material during development. Photomechanical methods resulting in stencils are used for line and halftone images.

Continuous photomechanical layers of varying hardness and thickness. However, photomechanical methods are not limited to line and halftone transparencies; they can also be used with continuous-tone transparencies as needed in certain gravure methods and in collotype. Continuous-tone transparencies are almost always made photographically. Here, variations of tone are a consequence of variations in the optical density of the developed photographic emulsion. Where a transparency is more dense, less light can reach the light-sensitive coating during exposure, and where the transparency is less dense, more light will pass through it. The result is a continuous photomechanical layer in which different areas are differentially hardened and thereby differentially changed in their solubility. During development,

the less hardened and hence more soluble areas are removed to a greater extent than the harder and more insoluble areas. This kind of photomechanical image is called in this manual a *continuous photomechanical layer of varying hardness and thickness*.

Every photomechanical method has its own materials and techniques. These must be appropriate to the specific manufacturing process by which an image carrier is made. The image carrier, in turn, must obviously suit the needs of the printing method for which it is to serve. Differences in photomechanical procedures are best understood if they are related to the image carrier and the printing method for which they are intended; these will be discussed later.

The main phases of photomechanics. It will be much easier for you to understand the descriptions of specific photomechanical methods in the following sections if you are familiar with the general workings of photomechanics. For this purpose the subject is here divided into six broad operational groups. These are: (1) preparation of the light-sensitive coating material; (2) selection and preparation of the carrier material; (3) application of the light-sensitive material to the physical image carrier; (4) exposure of the light-sensitive coating; (5) development of the exposed photomechanical coating; and (6) final role of photomechanical images in the production of image carriers.

All photomechanical production passes through these six main phases, but not necessarily through each phase in the order listed above; nor must all of these operations be executed in the same

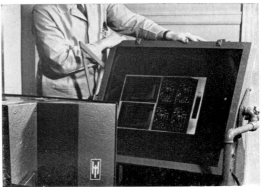

Courtesy Eastman Kodak Company

Craftsman operating a vacuum printing frame in which the plate and transparency are exposed to strong light during photomechanical platemaking.

plant. Phases one, two, and three, for example, are completely eliminated from the lithographer's and photoengraver's point of view if he uses presensitized plates. This obviously means that they were executed in advance at the supplier's plant and have already been completed when the presensitized material arrives at the lithographic or photoengraving shop or plant. (It should be noted that presensitized plates for lithography and those for photoengraving are not the same.)

Direct and indirect photomechanical methods. As to the order of operation, this differs markedly for *direct* and *indirect* photomechanical methods. In direct photomechanical methods, the light-sensitive coating is applied to the physical image carrier prior to exposure; in indirect methods, this coating is either only exposed, or exposed and developed on a temporary support, but not on the carrier material. The exposed, or the exposed and developed, light-sensitive material is, thereafter, transferred to the physical image carrier. Indirect photomechanical methods are often classified as *transfer methods*. Photoengraving, lithographic platemaking, and collotype use direct photomechanical methods exclusively, whereas gravure and screen process can utilize both direct and indirect methods.

Preparation of the light-sensitive coating material. We can divide photomechanical coatings into two groups: coatings that are light-sensitive without further treatment and coatings that require treatment in order to become light-sensitive. The treatment by which a photomechanical coating is made light-sensitive is called *sensitizing*.

Depending on their nature, some light-sensitive coating materials can be formulated by rather simple operations such as the dissolving and mixing of various chemicals, whereas others may require complex manufacturing procedures. Take, for example, albumin surface plates which were in a rather recent past widely used in lithography. The light-sensitive coating for these plates is generally compounded by a skilled craftsman within a lithographic plant. But presensitized lithographic plates, which are now the most common lithographic plates, require extensive chemical manufacturing which is beyond the scope of lithographic craftsmen and shops.

Some photomechanical coatings can be stored for only a few hours or days if they are already sensitized. They are, therefore, supplied by the manufacturer in an unsensitized state in which they have a much longer shelf life. These coatings

are sensitized either immediately before use, or for very short storage periods. The most important items in this group are *carbon-tissue* and several screen process materials. Carbon-tissue is used in the making of plates and cylinders for gravure and for photographic screens. It is sensitized by treating with solutions of bichromates; similar bichromate solutions are used for the sensitization of other photomechanical coatings especially formulated for the making of similar screen-process image carriers.

The equipment needed for the compounding and application of factory-made photomechanical coatings is too technical for discussion in this manual. The equipment used by graphic arts plants for the formulating of photomechanical coatings consists of scales, graduates, simple chemical instruments such as hydrometers, and various hand tools.

Selection and preparation of the carrier material. The choice of the carrier material depends on the nature of the final printing-image carrier. Most photomechanical image carriers have metals as their base. Screen process uses image carriers made of silk, synthetic fibers, or metal cloth; some presensitized lithographic plates are coated on paper. The kind of metal to be selected depends not only on the nature of the image carrier but also on the practice preferred in a particular plant.

Courtesy American Photoengraving

Application of a light-sensitive coating to a metal plate in a horizontal whirler. Most shop-coated plates are coated by whirling, either in horizontal or in vertical whirlers.

Zinc, copper, magnesium, and aluminum are materials most commonly found as bases for photomechanical printing-image carriers.

The preparation of the material can be very simple and may consist merely in cleaning or polishing; it may, on the other hand, require a series of more intricate operations, such as the graining and counter-etching of lithographic plates; or it can be a complete manufacturing process in itself, like the electrochemical plating of rotogravure cylinders. The equipment needed for this phase varies accordingly as you will see in the following sections where each of these different image carriers is individually discussed.

Application of the light-sensitive coating material to the physical image carrier. If the light-sensitive material is a solution, and if the physical carrier is in sheet form, whirling is the most common method of application. At present, wipe-on coatings are widely used in lithography; less frequently employed techniques include roller coating, and flowing-on. Scraping-on and brushing is used in certain specialty applications. If the physical carrier is a cylinder, special coating equipment is required for this operation. And, finally, if the light-sensitive material is a film coated on a temporary support (which is usually the case in gravure and screen process) it must be applied to the carrier by various techniques combining pressure with softening of the material.

Whirlers are found in all photoengraving and many lithographic platemaking shops. They are factory-made and usually power-driven, and they may be equipped with heaters and fans as well as with controls for temperature and air-exchange. Coating of cylinders is done with specialized equipment, and so is the *laydown* of carbon-tissue, as its transfer to the cylinder is technically called.

Exposure of the light-sensitive coating. Exposure has the purpose of identifying or determining the relative positions of the printing and the non-printing areas on the future image carrier and of making it possible to clearly distinguish each of these two kinds of areas from the other. For this purpose, the coated and light-sensitive material is exposed through the appropriate transparency to strong artificial light.

Exposure techniques differ for direct and for indirect photomechanical methods, for carriers exposed in sheet form, and for cylinders. Material that is processed in sheet form is exposed in vacuum printing frames, while cylinders need rotary exposure equipment. The light source can be one of several; carbon arc lamps are most commonly used because they produce the kind of light which is most effective for the purpose. Electric timers and integrating light meters are valuable aids for controlling this operation.

Development of the exposed photomechanical coating. Developing may either immediately follow exposure, or it may be preceded by one or more intervening steps; it may be done with water of varying temperatures or with other solvents. Solvents and temperatures depend on the specific photomechanical method selected. During development the unexposed areas of the most common types of photomechanical coating are removed. (In positive diazo coating the exposed areas are removed, whereas the unexposed areas remain on the carrier.) In some cases the removed areas will be the future printing areas; in others they represent the non-printing areas.

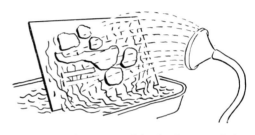

Diagrammatic illustration of the development of photomechanical coatings. The unexposed areas of such coatings remain water soluble and are washed away.

The equipment for developing is rather simple. It, too, varies with the kind of photomechanics employed. Some coatings can be developed in trays similar to those used for photographic development. For other coatings, special development sinks are needed, which sometimes are equipped with temperature-control mixing valves.

The developed photomechanical image is either a stencil or a continuous photomechanical layer of varying thickness and hardness. Photoengraving, lithography, some gravure methods, and screen-process printing employ photomechanical stencils. Other gravure methods, of which the so-called conventional or straight gravure is the most important, and also collotype, need photomechanical layers of varying thickness and hardness.

Final role of photomechanical images in the production of image carriers. Photomechanical images do not have the same function in all methods of image carrier production, but are used in two different ways. A photomechanical image becomes either part of the final printing image carrier or it functions as an intermediate element in the production of the image carrier. In the latter case it is usually removed after serving its purpose. Presensitized and wipe-on offset plates, as well as those for collotype, are two examples of the first kind; photoengravings and deep-etch plates are examples of the second.

In the making of photoengravings, gravure, and bimetallic lithographic plates, the developed photomechanical stencil acts as a resist during the operation of etching. In the making of deep-etch plates it has a similar function, as you will see in the discussion of lithographic plates. The equipment needed for the production of the final image carrier varies from method to method. It is discussed as part of the individual presentations in the following sections of this chapter.

Section 3:   Relief Printing-Image Carriers

Relief image carriers are classified in this manual either as original materials or duplicate plates. Original materials comprise various kinds of metallic (and, rarely though, wooden) types, handmade image carriers such as woodcuts, wood and rubber engravings, photoengravings, and electronically made engravings. Duplicate plates can be made from original materials, from previously made duplicate plates, or from a combination of both. Duplicate plates include stereotypes, electrotypes, molded rubber plates, and plastic plates. Each of these different groups of image carriers has its own purpose, and each must conform to the requirements of the relief printing method where it will be used. In this section, we shall study the above-mentioned kinds of image carriers with the exception of type which is the subject matter of Chapter II.

Handmade Relief Image Carriers

For hundreds of years, until the invention of photomechanics, relief printing relied on manual skills for the conversion of pictures into printing-image carriers. Pictorial image carriers were for several centuries mainly woodcuts and, later, wood engravings. Metal engravings and etchings were also used, but much less so. Engraving is a technique that obviously lends itself much better to the making of intaglio than to that of relief image carriers where all non-printing areas must be removed. More recently, rubber engravings and linoleum cuts were added to the historical group of handmade relief image carriers.

In our time, wood and metal engravings are primarily made for fine-art printing. Rubber engravings, on the other hand, are suitable for long press runs; therefore, they can play a certain role

in flexographic printing of bold line and area design. Wood engravings still have a place in industrial printing, but as they are much too delicate

A primitive 15th century woodcut, taken from John Jackson, A Treatise on Wood Engraving, *London 1839.*

for long-run printing, wood engravings serve mainly as original material for duplicate plates such as electrotypes and stereotypes, which become the actual image carriers for presswork.

Woodcuts. Woodcuts are made either from planks or from blocks of various woods, clean pine, for example. The design or picture is either drawn directly on the wood, or made on a thin paper which is then pasted face down on the wooden block. The artist converts this wooden block or plank into a relief image carrier by removing the wood in the non-image areas with knives and gauges. Gauges are tools typical for woodcutting; they are V- or U- shaped for cutting grooves and channels.

Since the attention of the woodcutter is concentrated on the printing areas which will appear usually in black ink on the printed sheet, woodcutting is often called *black-line engraving.*

Wood engravings. Wood engravings are made of fine-grained hardwoods such as boxwood or maple, with the printing image engraved on the end grain of the block. The artist or engraver

A wood engraver at work. The wooden block is on a sand bag because the sand bag facilitates maneuvering of the block during engraving. Taken from John Jackson, A Treatise on Wood Engraving, *London, 1839.*

works with the graver, or burin, rather than with the tools of the wood cutter. In his design he concentrates on the non-image areas which will appear as white lines in the printed image. For this reason, wood engraving is often called *white-line engraving*. White-line engravings can produce very detailed images. As these are more robust than halftone images and also of considerable attractiveness, they are sometimes preferred to photographs for newpaper reproduction of advertising material.[6]

Linoleum and rubber engravings. Linoleum has no grain and is softer than wood; it is, therefore, easier to cut and engrave. Linoleum blocks are mostly made from so-called battleship linoleum. They are used for fine-art printing primarily, but can also offer economical solutions to some printing problems, particularly on jobs that will not be produced in large quantities. Rubber engravings can be made of several materials, such as natural or synthetic rubber, as well as of specially manufactured products which consist of a top sheet of resilient material laminated to a canvas base. The design is transferred to the surface of the rubber either by manual skills or by means of photomechanics. Cutting and engraving of linoleum and rubber blocks is similar to wood cutting or wood engraving and is done with similar tools.[7]

Photoengraving

Photoengraving is one of the industrial arts whereby original images such as drawings, paintings, photographs, and letter forms can be converted into relief printing-image carriers. Photoengravings are used in all methods of relief printing, either directly in the press, or as original material for the making of duplicate plates. Even though photoengravings are limited to relief printing, many techniques originally developed for photoengraving have been modified and applied to the making of image carriers for other printing processes, just as techniques originally developed for other purposes have been successfully applied to photoengraving.

Advances in photoengraving. The contemporary changes and advances in printing technology which permeate all branches of the industry are particularly pronounced in the field of making pictorial relief printing-image carriers, a field traditionally dominated by photoengraving. These changes and developments can be divided for our purposes into two groups. In the first we place general improvements in the manufacturing of photoengravings, whereas the second group of developments has the object of creating new and more or less radically different image carriers for relief printing. Photoengravings have retained their position as the most widely used original pictorial image carriers for relief printing and are here discussed in some detail. The most important more recent improvements in the making of photoengravings are included as a matter of course in these discussions. Some of the new products of photoengraving are discussed under the side head "Wrap-Around Plates," and the final unit contains descriptions of image carriers made by engraving machines which are, strictly speaking, not part of photoengraving in the traditional meaning of the term. This unit is headed "Electromechanical Engravings."

Classification of photoengravings. The photoengraving industry has developed a generally accepted plan for the classification of its products. This plan is embodied in the *Standard Scale for Photoengravings* and in the *Standard Scale for Color Process Photoengravings*.[8] These scales were designed for estimating and charging. Consequently, they include many minute definitions of subsidiary operations and are a most valuable tool for all practically concerned with the subject. For the purposes of this manual their detailed discussion is much too burdensome. We have condensed and simplified these classifications and divide photoengravings into the following five main groups: (1) line etchings in one color, or in black-and-white; (2) halftone etchings in one color; (3) combinations of line and halftone etchings in one color; (4) sets of photoengravings for multicolor (or flat color) printing either in line or in halftone, or in line-and-halftone combinations; and (5) photoengraving sets for full-color printing, usually known in the printing and photoengraving industry as sets of four-color process plates.

Points of importance for the planning of photoengravings. At this point it should be mentioned that photoengravings are made from different metals and by different production methods, depending on their final use. Photoengravers expect to be informed by their customers of all details concerning the conditions under which photoengravings will be used. Some of the pertinent detail is here enumerated: (1) whether the photoengraving will be used directly in the press or as an original for duplicate platemaking; (2) if it is to be used for the latter purpose, then the type of duplicate plate to be made should be indicated; (3) the kind of press on which either the photoengraving or the duplicate plate will be printed; (4) the paper on which the job will be printed; (5) the screen ruling wanted; (6) which ink will be used in production; (7) in case of full-color engravings, whether they will be printed wet or dry; (8) whether color bars should be shown on proofs; and (9) the nature of the final printed product.

These are some of the more common considerations; in special cases, it may be advisable for the printer to discuss the job in even more detail with the photoengraver. Many printers and photoengravers follow the "PIA Standard Photoengraving Specifications Manual" which was developed by the Magazine Printers Section of Printing Industry of America and "has been prepared in association with and approved by the American Photoengravers Association and the National Association of Printing Ink Makers."[9]

The Main Manufacturing Stages of Photoengraving

The production of photoengravings can be divided into six main stages: (1) photography, (2) photomechanics, (3) etching, (4) finishing, (5) routing and blocking, and (6) proofing. We will first provide you with a brief explanation of the purposes which these six main stages have. Thereafter, the more generally important operations will be described in some detail.

Explanation of the main production stages. Photography converts continuous-tone and full-color images into printable images and provides the requisite transparencies, usually photographic negatives, of line and halftone images. These negatives are used in photomechanics for the distinctive identification of printing and non-printing areas, as already explained in the preceding section. This identification is made on the carrier by means of a photomechanical *resist* which protects the metal in the printing areas from the action of the etchant during the phase of etching. There the non-printing areas of the carrier are dissolved by the etchant and thereby removed.

In the next phase of *finishing*, the image carrier is corrected, improved, and prepared for its final use. During *routing* the inside bearers, meaning relatively large metal blocks in the non-image areas, are mechanically removed. If the engraving is made solely as an original image carrier for duplicate platemaking, the bearers are not routed as they are needed for duplicate platemaking. They are often stamped "dead metal" or marked with an "X" to indicate that these areas will be removed, usually by routing, from the duplicate plates. If the engraving is made for use in the press, it must of course be routed. *Blocking* has the purpose of bringing the engraving up to its proper height for presswork. Finally, *proofing* consists in taking prints from the completed engraving, thereby making it possible to evaluate the final product. These prints, known as engraver's proofs, also serve as a guide for the making of duplicate plates and for presswork.

Photography and Stripping for Photoengraving

As graphic arts photography is extensively discussed in Chapter IV, it is here sufficient to remind you that all copy must be converted into negative transparencies for the purpose of photomechanical image identification. The product of photography is usually a negative on film. Glass plates, which were in the past generally used, have practically disappeared since the introduction of dimensionally stable films. The photographic negative may be a line or a halftone image, and it may either read right (namely from left to right) or read wrong (from right to left). Negatives are assembled for common photoprinting by an operation known as *stripping*.

Photoengraving uses two essentially different stripping methods for two rather different kinds of products: *traditional stripping* is one, and *wrap-around stripping* is the other. Traditional stripping is used for the production of photoengravings other than wrap-around plates. The products made by traditional stripping are either placed in a typeform or on plate bases for direct use in the press or they serve as original material for duplicate platemaking. In all cases these products, our customary photoengravings, do not need assembling during their manufacturing process as the assembling is done during page makeup and

Courtesy American Photoengraving

In photoengraving, many small negatives are grouped together for common exposure to the sensitized metal plate. A transparent, wax-coated plastic sheet serves as a temporary support.

lockup, prior to presswork. Wrap-around plates are essentially different as they are single-unit, or integral, image carriers, combining many pages in imposition order on a single plate. Stripping for wrap-around plates has the purpose of assembling all images that will print from the same plate. This kind of stripping must be done prior to exposure; you will meet it again in the unit on wrap-around plates.

Traditional stripping for photoengraving. This operation has several purposes. One of them has already been mentioned. It is the combining or *ganging-up* of negatives for common photo-printing and etching. After etching, the *flat* of metal containing many ganged-up engravings, which may be 18 × 24 inches, to mention a commonly used size, is cut apart or sawed apart in order to separate the engravings into individual units. Each engraving is finally used independently, without regard to other engravings which may have happened to be made on the same flat.

Reversal of reading direction and combining of several images. A second reason for stripping lies in the necessity of turning the negatives in order to change their reading direction. All image carriers to be used for direct image transfer—and relief printing is, with rare exceptions, done by direct printing—must read wrong (or from right to left), in order to produce a printed image that will have the correct reading direction, namely, from left to right. If the negatives are taken through an image-reversing prism, or are exposed through the film base, they already have the reading direction required in photoengraving and turning is not necessary. A third purpose of stripping may be to combine various image elements in the same engraving, line and halftone images for example.

The stripped assembly is known as a *flat;* it is usually of the same size as the metal from which the engravings will be made. Neither the size of metals nor that of flats is standardized throughout the industry. Merely as an indication it is mentioned that flats for traditional photoengravings are often assembled in a size of 18 × 24 inches.

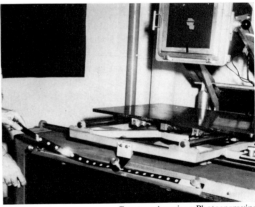

Courtesy American Photoengraving

A step-and-repeat machine for producing photographic negatives with many images of the same kind. High accuracy is obtained by the use of precision punched metal tapes which control the position of images in both directions.

Wet and dry stripping. In a not too distant past the negative material for stripping used to be a shop-made light-sensitive coating, known as wet-plate collodion. This method has been superseded by stripping with strip films supplied by several manufacturers of photographic materials. "Stripping films contain more layers than do ordinary films. A thin *adhesive layer* which softens in water allows the image-bearing layer to be removed. The very thin support layer, or 'skin' serves as a stable support for the emulsion layer while it is being stripped."[10] Stripping with strip film can be done either wet or dry: in wet stripping the wet film membrane is transferred from the temporary support onto a final support which may be either a sheet of glass or plastic; in dry stripping the developed film is dried on its temporary support from which it is later separated by peeling for transfer to its final support.[11]

Photomechanics for Photoengraving

Photomechanics have a dual function in the making of photoengravings: one is the distinctive identification of the printing and the non-printing areas of the plate; the other is the protection of the printing areas during etching against the action of the etchant. To be suitable for photoengraving, a light-sensitive coating must satisfy a number of requirements. It must adhere firmly to the plate metal on which it is coated, it must afford sufficient protection against the action of the *etchant*, and it must be capable of recording very minute detail. Other properties are not less important but more so for the specialist than for us.

Photoengraving tops and their application. Light-sensitive coatings are known as *resists* or as *tops* in the photoengraving industry. The names of various tops are also used for identification of the photomechanical method for which they are used. Before we discuss these, it should be mentioned that all types of light-sensitive coatings are directly applied to the plate metal in photoengraving; that the coated and dried metal is then exposed, together with a negative transparency, to intense light; and that the exposed plate is developed and variously heated in order to thoroughly protect the image areas with the photomechanical resist, while the non-image areas are laid bare for etching, the step to follow. The equipment for this phase of photoengraving consists of whirlers, vacuum printing frames, arc lamps and burning-in ovens in the main, supplemented by such utensils as may be needed for a particular photomechanical method.

The five more commonly used photomechanical topping methods are: (1) the cold-enamel process, (2) the bichromated-albumin process, (3) the glue-enamel process, (4) polyvinyl alcohol, and (5) KPR resists.

Courtesy American Photoengraving

A multiple-unit negative, made on a step-and-repeat machine, is checked on a precision line-up table.

The cold-enamel process. The cold-enamel process is used on zinc and on magnesium. The light-sensitive coating used to be an alkaline solution of shellac, sensitized with bichromate. This solution is applied to the metal by whirling. After the coating has dried, it is exposed through a negative transparency in a vacuum frame. After exposure, the top is developed at room temperature. A mixture of alcohol and water to which methyl violet (a violet-blue dye) usually has been added serves as developing agent. The exposed image appears after development in the color of the dye.

The word "cold" in the name of this resist refers to the fact that this top does not need burning-in when zinc is selected as the plate metal, whereas other tops do. But if the engraving is made of magnesium, then cold top is usually burned in. Burning-in improves the adhesion of the developed coating to the metal and also its resistance to the etchant.[12]

The bichromated-albumin process. The bichromated-albumin process preceded the cold-enamel process and is now widely replaced by the latter. But the process is still used for line and coarse halftone work on zinc, as well as for special purposes. The light-sensitive coating solution of this process contains either egg white or dried egg albumin, sensitized with bichromate. The metal plate is coated by whirling, then dried and exposed as already described. After exposure, but prior to development, the exposed surface is rolled up with black etching ink. The etching ink serves later as an adhesive for the etching powder. Because of the rolling-up with black ink, this process is commonly referred to as *ink-top* in the trade.

Development consists in bathing the rolled up plate in tap water. The water penetrates the ink-top and loosens the adhesion of the unexposed coating areas, which float off the plate metal together with their ink surface. After development, the plate is dried; then it is dusted with topping, or etching, powder. This operation is necessary to make the photomechanical image sufficiently resistant to etching. The etching powder, a fusible material, sticks to the ink-top but not to the metal surface, from which it is removed by rubbing with a dry cotton wad before the dusted plate is heated. Heating has the purpose of fusing the etching powder with the ink in the image areas. Even this brief description can explain why the ink-top is declining in its importance: it is cumbersome and time-consuming.

The glue-enamel process. The glue-enamel process, known in the trade as *enamel-top* or as *hot-top*, is a most important method for the making of high-quality copper halftone etchings. It is not used on zinc, but can be used on magnesium. More modern methods compete with the glue-enamel process, but at the time of writing the enamel-top still retains a position, primarily in copper engravings for full-color printing which may need manual color correcting.

The glue-enamel process is based on an aqueous solution of fish glue, sometimes in combination with albumin, sensitized with bichromate. This solution can be prepared by photoengraving craftsmen. At present, though, shop-made coatings are less widely used than commercially available preparations. The metal surface is first cleaned, then coated, dried, and exposed as already described. Development takes place in running water, which must be temperature-controlled. A dye is added to color the image and thereby makes it more visible. The developed plate is dried and then burned-in at a temperature of approximately 650°F. A properly burned-in plate is of chocolate-brown color. Since the glue-enamel process produces excellent resists, it is still used for quality work.

Polyvinyl alcohol resists. Polyvinyl alcohol is a synthetic organic compound which can be dissolved in water and sensitized with bichromates. Such a solution of polyvinyl alcohol can serve as a photomechanical coating resulting in an acid resist. Coating, exposure, and development of polyvinyl alcohol resists do not differ from other resists. But polyvinyl alcohol resists have the advantage that they need not be heated as high as glue-enamel resists in order to make them sufficiently acid-resistant. This is a great advantage, particularly where magnesium is to be used as the plate metal. Polyvinyl alcohol resists are consequently widely used for magnesium etchings.[13]

KPR resists. KPR resists are supplied by the Eastman Kodak Company; the letters KPR stand for Kodak Photo Resists. This coating material contains light-sensitive resinous materials dissolved in organic solvents. One of the advantages of KPR resists is that the coated metal can be stored for future use. KPR-coated plates are exposed like all others, but must be developed with organic solvents. The developed coating is burned-in at temperatures lower than those needed for glue-enamel tops. The burned-in coating is impervious to acid and alkalies but not to certain organic solvents.[14]

Electrofax resists. Even though the resists to be described in this unit are not commercially available and at the time of writing still in their developmental stages, they are of sufficient general interest to warrant a brief discussion.

Electrofax is an RCA trade-mark for an electrostatic or electrophotographic process. "The photosensitive element in this system is a mixture of a powdered photoconductor and a resin binder, which may be easily coated on practically any base, from paper or plastics to a metallic sheet. Such a coating is insensitive to light unless electrically charged, but attains usable, photographic properties when an electrostatic charge is placed upon its surface."[15]

The charged Electrofax coating can be exposed either by contact printing or in the camera. In this coating "we have a photosensitive surface

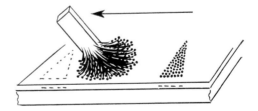

Diagram of magnetic brush development. Ferromagnetic particles adhere to a magnet somewhat like bristles to a brush, which explains the term magnetic brush. Electrofax material is developed by passing a magnetic brush over it. The resin toner particles, carried by the magnet, have a positive charge and are attracted by the negative charges of the exposed Electrofax areas.

which is thousands of times more sensitive to light than the conventional photoresists. There is adequate sensitivity for printing by projection with a camera. It is, therefore, possible to think of a printing plate made with enlargement from microfilm and with screening at the same time."[16]

Development and fixing of the Electrofax image do not require complex equipment but can be accomplished with simple hand tools. The resist image is formed on the exposed Electrofax plate by brushing its surface with a special magnetic brush containing finely divided particles of a pigmented resin. The particles adhere by electrostatic attraction to the charged image areas of the plate but do not adhere to the uncharged non-image areas. The adhering resin particles are then fused by heat into a resist. The unprotected non-image areas are exposed to the action of the etchant in the customary way.[17]

Etching for Photoengraving

Etching is the production phase by which the photoprinted metal plates are converted into relief printing-image carriers. The principle on which etching is based is quite simple. As you probably remember from your chemistry classes, most metals can form soluble compounds with certain acids. Applied to etching as an operation in the manufacturing of image carriers, this means that we can remove plate metal in the areas which are not protected by the resist from the acid or other etching agent, called generically *etchant*. As several metals are used in the photoengraving industry, and as each of them is etched in a different manner, and as each has different characteristics, we must begin our discussion of etching with photoengraving metals.

Photoengraving metals. Zinc, copper, and magnesium are the three commonly used photoengraving metals. None of them is used pure, though, for photoengraving but all are alloys containing small amounts of other metals. Brass, too, can be used for line and halftone engraving. But as it mainly serves for stamping and embossing dies, it is disregarded in the following discussion.

Zinc alloy is used in the United States for line and coarser halftone screen engravings. Even though zinc is considered in Europe and elsewhere suitable for fine halftones and for full-color work, it is in this country not generally accepted for these purposes. Zinc is the least expensive photoengraving metal; it has a relatively low melting

Courtesy American Photoengraving

A rotary power-driven brush and an abrasive powder are used in preparing photoengravers metal for application of the light-sensitive coating.

point and changes its structure and physical properties when heated to higher temperatures. Therefore, it cannot be used for glue-enamel tops which must be burned-in at a high temperature. The etchant for zinc alloy is nitric acid.

Copper alloy is generally considered the metal that must be used for highest quality engravings. It is the most expensive photoengraving metal, is harder than zinc, and has a melting point close to 2000°F. whereas that of zinc is under 800°F., "permits burning-in of glue prints without damaging the metal, and the tough nature of the glue photoresist withstands the scrubbing and brushing required during re-etching or local correction

Courtesy American Photoengraving

After the photomechanical resist, which will protect the printing areas from the etchant, is burned-in, the plate is de-scummed in preparation for etching.

of tone values in the halftone print."[18] The etchant for copper is a solution of *ferric chloride*, also known as *iron chloride* or *perchloride*.

Magnesium alloy, the newest photoengraving metal, is harder than zinc though less hard than copper. Its specific gravity is much less than that of either zinc or copper and it etches much faster than zinc. The etchant for magnesium is the same as for zinc, namely, nitric acid, but it is used more dilute than in the etching of zinc.[19]

Etching, the crux of photoengraving. Etching is a decisive operation in the manufacture of photo-engravings. Unless this point is clear in the reader's mind, he will not be able to understand the reasons for several other operations which are needed in the making of photoengravings. For this reason, and also because great advances have been made in etching, this subject is discussed in more detail than other phases of photoengraving.

The depth of photoengravings. If the principle of etching does not pose any problems, controlling the operation itself certainly does. In order to be suitable as relief image carriers, photoengravings must have the proper depth. This depth is the distance between the level of the printing surface and the non-printing areas of a photoengraving. The depth of photoengravings varies for line and halftone engravings. Line engravings that are to be used on high-finish papers are usually etched to a depth of approximately 0.020 inch; those made for flexographic printing and for printing on rough papers have a depth of 0.040 inch and more.

Halftone engravings are etched to different depths depending on the screen ruling number (a

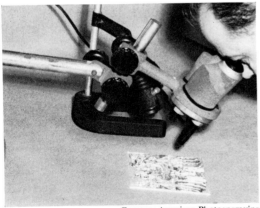

Courtesy American Photoengraving

A photoengraving technician examines the side walls of an etching with a binocular microscope. The microscope is tilted to permit precise viewing of side walls.

120-line or a 133-line screen, for example) and the purpose of an engraving. The lower the screen ruling number, the deeper the engraving must be etched. There is also a second kind of depth variation to be considered, namely, the variations for highlights, middle tones, and shadows within each halftone engraving. In a 133-line screen engraving, for example, the highlights ought to have a depth of 0.0029 inch, the middle tones 0.0020 inch, and the shadows 0.0014 inch.[20]

If you look at these figures you will notice that highlights need much more depth than middle tones and these more than the shadows. *As the etchant does not know the difference between printing areas and non-printing areas, it attacks the metal not only depthwise, as wanted, but also sidewise which is not wanted at all.* If the action of the etchant is left uncontrolled, the area, or size, of dots is considerably reduced until etching has progressed to its required depth.

The main problem of etching. The main problem of etching is to maintain the correct dot or line area at the correct etched depth. Historically, until the middle of this century, this problem was more or less satisfactorily solved by a combination of two techniques: one is known as *compressing the scale*, the other as *successive four-way powering*. Compressing the scale is a photographic technique whereby halftone negatives are so prepared that they allow for area losses incurred during etching. An example will explain how compressing the scale is applied. Let us assume that the highlight halftone dots of a finished engraving are supposed to be of a 10 per cent value, or to be 10 per cent dots. If we would record this dot size on the metal prior to etching, we would find that we have no usable dots left after etching. The acid would have dissolved the small 10 per cent dot area more or less completely during the time needed to attain proper depth of etch. Area losses explain why halftone dots must be recorded larger on the metal than they are finally wanted. This result is obtained during halftone photography in the preparation of the negative that will serve for photoprinting. Our final 10 per cent dot might have a 40 per cent value at the beginning of etching.

Four-way powdering. In cases where depth of etch was insufficient, the etcher resorted to four-way powdering in order to protect the printing surface against losses. In this method, etching is done in several stages, known as *bites*, and the already etched depth is protected after every bite from further action of the etchant. The material used was originally *dragon's blood*, a natural resin imported from the Malay Archipelago; later it was replaced by other fusible resins.[21] After each bite, the etcher applies powder to all four sides of the engraving. This he does by successively powdering and fusing side after side. The powder protects the sides of the engraving after fusing against the action of the etchant. The process of four-way powdering requires skill and is, of course, rather time-consuming.[22]

Disadvantages of four-way powdering. This technique of protecting the sidewalls during etching has numerous disadvantages. Depending on the job in hand, etching has to be done in many bites. Five are by no means rare, and four-way powdering is, to be sure, required between each bite. But slowness is not the sole drawback of this method. It may happen that the resulting engravings have sidewalls that are unsuitable for electrotyping because they trap the molding material. Since large numbers of photoengravings are made as originals for electrotypes and other duplicate plates, this defect can be rather serious.

In addition, four-way powdering is of limited effectiveness. It protects the sidewalls of engravings to a great extent but does not always prevent noticeable reductions of dot areas. This condition was generally recognized and more or less effectively corrected by the already mentioned compressing of the scale. Highlight and middletone dots have to be sufficiently larger on the negative to compensate for reduction of dot areas during etching. Finally, it was often left to the skill of craftsmen to obtain the desired quality results by manual correcting which utilizes chemical as well as mechanical techniques for adjusting the dot sizes.

The etch-factor and its meaning. Even though the problem of area loss, or *color loss*, by etching has existed since the beginning of photoengraving, etching had not been systematically studied until 1945 when this task was committed to Battelle Memorial Institute by Photoengravers Research, Inc., an industry organization. In particular it was found necessary to express the relation between vertical and horizontal etching in an objective numerical manner.

Such an expression became possible by the introduction of the etch-factor concept. "The etch-factor is a number that may be used to express color or image area loss. It is computed by dividing the depth of etch (in thousandths of an inch)

by the amount of side etch observed. The etching depth and side etch are measured microscopically. The average etch-factor observed in ferric chloride etching in a tray is about 3.5, while etching machines yield smaller etch-factors, such as 2.5. As the color loss of an etching procedure decreases the factor increases; an etch-factor of 5 indicates less color loss than an etch-factor of 3."[23]

The etch-factor is an important tool that makes it possible to evaluate and objectively compare not only various methods of etching but also the effects of variables on the detail of operation. This concept continues to play an important part in etching research.

After this somewhat extensive discussion of the problems of etching, we turn to a description of the operation itself, beginning with conventional etching.

Conventional etching of photoengravings. Conventional etching of photoengravings can be done in many ways. The most primitive etching method employs open etching tubs which were once hand rocked and are at present power operated. Well-equipped plants use etching machines of various designs which differ for zinc and for copper etching. It is also possible to remove the metal electrochemically by using the plate to be etched as the anode of the system. Electrochemical metal removal is known as electrical or an electrolytic etching; it is not widely used in the United States. Etching is a critical operation which has been extensively studied during contemporary research.

Courtesy American Photoengraving

A photoprinted metal plate, bearing many independent images for common etching of photoengravings, is inserted into a powderless etching machine.

The chemical composition of the etching bath, its temperature and the manner in which the etchant is applied to the metal, not to forget the length of time of etching, all influence the final results.[24]

Powderless etching of magnesium and zinc. Even though conventional etching methods are still used at this time, they are progressively replaced throughout the industry by powderless etching. In the opinion of some the more traditional photoengraving methods, which are sometimes also honored by calling them basic, are still of great practical importance and should not be considered outmoded by more recent innovations. In the mind of others, powderless etching should be recognized as a substantial advance, and its contributions to contemporary photoengraving should be emphasized.

The first metal for which powderless etching was developed was magnesium. The Dow Chemical Corporation originated this method and it hence became known as *Dow-Etching*. In order to appreciate the achievement of powderless etching we must remember that *in conventional etching the two functions of removing unwanted plate metal and of protecting the already etched sidewalls are executed independently* and by different methods. As explained, the plate is first etched to a certain depth, then it is removed from the bath and powdered or *banked*, as the protecting of etched sidewalls is often called. Thereafter, the plate is etched again, taken out again, banked again, and this procedure is repeated as often as necessary. To sum it up, conventional etching is done by alternating etching and protecting the already etched areas.

Dow-Etching functions in an entirely different manner; here *both banking and etching take place simultaneously*. Two elements are combined to this effect. One is a change in the composition of the etching bath; the other consists in the direction in which this bath is applied to the metal. "The etching bath is an emulsion which must be used in an agitated state."[25] It contains in addition to nitric acid several film-forming chemicals. These form an acid resistant film on the surface of the plate. The etching machine is specifically designed for Dow-Etching and applies the etchant by splashing. To understand its arrangement, it is helpful to keep in mind that the surface of the plate, which is the same as saying its printing area, is at a 90° angle to the sidewalls of the engraving which must be protected. The etching machine is built in such a manner as to splash the etchant

with great force at the non-image areas. "When the fluid strikes the non-image areas of the plate it does so at nearly a 90° angle, and there is apparently enough force to break the film, and etching of the metal takes place."[26] But the force exerted by the etchant against the sidewalls of the metal is obviously much less as the sidewalls and the direction of the etchant are practically in the same plane. "When the fluid strikes parallel to the sides of the image, there is insufficient force to break the (protective) film and no etching can occur. *The net result is that the chemical additives more or less powder the plate continuously.*"[27] The Dow patents and method cover both magnesium and zinc etching, but Dow-Etching is not suitable for the etching of copper.

Powderless etching of copper. Powderless etching of copper was developed partly by Battelle Memorial Institute and partly by the Georgia Institute of Technology for Photoengravers Research, Inc. It is a patent-protected method that differs essentially from Dow-Etching but resembles the Dow process in several points. One is that here, too, banking and etching are done concurrently. The other is the mechanical similarity of powderless copper etching and Dow-Etching. Powderless copper etching, like Dow-Etching, "involves the breaking up, by the force of the

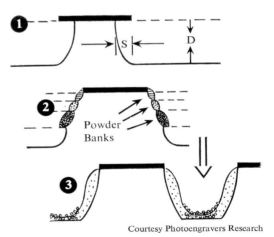

Courtesy Photoengravers Research

Comparative diagrams of conventional and powderless etching of copper: (1) shows undercutting in conventional etching; black plateau represents original width of resist, "S" sideward etching, "D" depth of etch; (2) shows three stages of powdering; (3) shows powderless etching. The arrow indicates direction of etchant; protective banking agent remains unbroken at the sides but gets broken at the bottom thereby permitting depthwise progress of etching without undercutting.

etchant propelled against the plate surface, of the protective deposit in the areas where etching is to occur."[28] As can be seen from the accompanying diagram, the etchant "breaks up the film so that etching can take place in the 'bottoms' or open areas, and flushes the material sideways to accumulate as a protective bank along the sides of the relief characters. Because the etchant strikes the 'banking agent' deposited on the sidewalls at a large angle, it does not have sufficient force to dislodge the material from these areas and sidewashed etching is inhibited. As etching proceeds, the accumulations on the sidewalls of adjacent printing elements build toward each other, until the deposits finally meet, filling the etched hole, and effectively stopping direct attack on the metal in that area."[29]

The similarity between the Dow process and powderless etching of copper does not include the chemicals added to the etchant nor the formation of the banking agent. The additives for powderless copper etching enter into a chemical reaction with copper compounds and can "under conditions analogous to those obtaining in the powderless etching bath, produce a variety of insoluble metal-organic compounds." The additives for powderless copper etching are commercially available. "The powderless copper etching baths used commercially have these basic components: (*a*) dilute ferric chloride, the etchant, (*b*) GT-1 or PERI 13a, the film former or primary additive, and (*c*) other secondary additives to modify bath performance."[30]

Finishing and Blocking of Photoengravings

The etched material is inspected and, if necessary, subjected to various correcting and finishing operations. In some cases these are performed by hand tooling, in others by additional local etching; often etching and hand tooling are combined. Some finishers specialize either in hand tooling or in etching; others do both. Practice varies in different regions of the United States and even in different shops within the same region. In the past, photoengravers relied much more than now on hand finishing for the final quality of halftone and full-color engravings. Fortunately, much of the time previously spent in finishing can now be saved due to highly improved techniques.

Beveling and routing. Beveling provides a slanting flange at the edges of the engraving. Routing

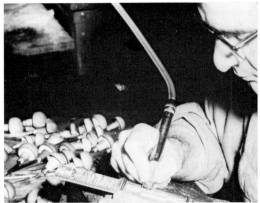

Finishing or "spotting" an engraving with the aid of an air turbine high-speed burr. Note the conventional finishing tools in the background. Each finishing tool is needed for a purpose and each has its own particular shape.

removes the larger areas of unwanted metal in the non-image areas which can be more economically eliminated by mechanical tools than by etching. But this dead metal is usually not removed when the engraving serves as an original for duplicate platemaking because then it is needed as a bearing surface during molding.

Blocking. Blocking has the purpose of providing the necessary printing height for the completed engraving. Photoengravings that will be printed as part of a type form must be mounted on a base to type height (0.918 inch). Those that are used on plate bases are mounted on a metal sheet to the required height, usually 0.152 inch. The mounting material can be wood, metal, or plastic; the engraving can be attached by nailing to wood, or with a thermosetting cement if the base is wood, metal, or plastic. Photoengravings to be used as molding patterns are in general left unmounted.

Proofing of Photoengravings

Proofing is a most important step in photoengraving because proofing makes it possible to evaluate the quality of the completed photoengraving; proofing also provides the printer and the maker of duplicate plates with a guide for their work. The engraver's proof must consequently always be taken with a view to the actual conditions under which a job is produced.

Proofing poses less of a problem in black-and-white and in multicolor jobs than in full-color reproductions, particularly if the engraving sets for full-color printing are to serve as originals for duplicate platemaking. All long-run work such as national magazine advertising, mail-order catalogs, and package printing—to mention some of the more common examples—is printed from duplicate plates if it is done by letterpress. The proofing of photoengravings has great practical importance. Even though the main discussion of proofing in all printing methods is in Chapter VI, Section 8, some problems related to the proofing of photoengravings are briefly explained at this point.

The proofing of full-color photoengravings presents two difficulties; one is the proofing of unrouted engravings; the other is the matching of wet-on-wet production printing on proof presses.

The problem of proofing unrouted photoengravings. First we consider the problem of proofing unrouted engravings. You already know that routing of large metal areas is omitted in photoengravings which serve as originals for duplicate platemaking because the dead metal has an important function during molding. When such unrouted engravings are proofed on ordinary proof presses prior to routing, the dead metal areas are inked together with all other relief areas. Consequently, the ink images corresponding to the shapes of the dead metal appear as disturbing color blotches on the engraver's proof. It is customary to present these proofs to the printer's customer (normally an advertising agency or a national advertiser) where they are often submitted to business executives who unfortunately often know very little about printing. Proofs showing blotches of color are not desirable in this situation because they distort the impression of the design in the eyes of the untechnical viewers.

Proofing on presses equipped for frisketing. This objectionable situation can be avoided if proof presses equipped with a frisketing mechanism are used. Here the unrouted and inked dead metal areas are automatically covered before image transfer takes place. The result is a proof that is not disfigured by blotches of ink transferred from the dead metal.

The problem of proofing for wet-on-wet printing. We now discuss the second difficulty, the matching of wet-on-wet printing production conditions by the photoengraver. In wet-on-wet printing, the sheet is printed in one pass through the press with all four, or possibly more, color inks. If the engravings have been proofed on single-color proof presses, the ink may either have already set or it may even have more or less completely dried between each of the four applications. It is impossible for the printer to match the results of such engraver's proofs in actual wet-on-wet production. For this kind of work, photoengravers have special proof presses that simulate the conditions of wet-on-wet printing and permit the taking of representative color proofs.

Proofing of all engravings must not only be done with the appropriate kind of proof press, but also on the same papers and with the same inks that will be used for production. Proofs that are made under different conditions and that cannot be matched in presswork are a source of disappointment for all concerned: the printer, the printer's customer, and finally the photoengraver himself who endangers his relations with the printer by careless proofing.

Wrap-Around Plates

Wrap-around plates are among the latest additions to letterpress technology. Until the advent of wrap-around plates letterpress did not have original printing-image carriers of large sizes suitable for rotary printing. Type and photoengravings were either used as parts of type forms on flatbed and platen presses or as original materials for the making of curved duplicate plates for rotary presses. Other relief printing methods developed various kinds of flexible plates, but these, too, were duplicate plates as a rule.

The needs of the letterpress field were aptly expressed by Mr. Robert Downie of Marathon, a pioneer in wrap-around printing, when he said: "What we want are fast applied, direct printing plates. We want them to go on the press fast because we want to reduce makeready. We want them to be low relief and direct printing to reduce cost."[31] These requirements are met for certain purposes by wrap-around plates.

It takes much less time to make wrap-around plates than it takes to make conventional photoengravings and duplicate plates from them. Powderless etching has made it possible to etch larger plates and to etch them faster than conventional engravings can be etched. It has also been found possible to print from much shallower plates than conventionally etched engravings. But it must be pointed out that it is not always possible to use shallow-etched plates on presses that were not designed for printing with wrap-around plates.

As a rule such presses must be adapted for this purpose, and not all presses may be suitable for such adaptations.

Characterization of wrap-around plates. The term wrap-around is relatively new and it is used differently by different people. Some classify all integral, or single-unit, image carriers as wrap-around plates and include offset and gravure plates, and even gravure cylinders, in their definition of wrap-around plates. The majority seems to prefer the term for relief printing-image carriers that are shallow etched and of the single-unit kind. Wrap-around is used in this sense in the present manual.

Various kinds of wrap-around plates are differently constituted. Some kinds consist of a single metal throughout, others have a different metal as the printing surface and as the base. Still others do not use metal as a printing surface but either a photopolymer or a plastic material; the base is steel or plastic in these plates. Wrap-around plates are made in different thicknesses and with different maximum depth of relief. Different makes of wrap-around plates are processed on different equipment.

The whole field of wrap-around plates is still in flux. Some plates have been in use for many years, others for a shorter time, and still others are in the stage of pilot plant operation. DuPont Dycril, a photopolymer plate, is available as a wrap-around plate and also for printing on plate bases with flatbed-cylinder presses and for printing with rotary letterpresses.

In this unit you find discussions of four kinds of wrap-around plates: (1) single metal wrap-around plates, (2) the duPont Dycril plate, (3) the Kodak Relief Plate, abbreviated KRP, and (4) bimetallic wrap-around plates, specifically the TI-Plate.

Single metal wrap-around plates. Single metal wrap-around plates are mainly, though not exclusively, etched by powderless etching. Zinc, magnesium, and copper plates may be chromium plated in order to increase the wearing potential of these plates. The plate metal must be provided with a resist which does not need to be of the same toughness as in conventional etching. The etching time is much shorter for shallower plates than for deeper-etched engravings. This decrease in etching time permits the use of less tough resists.

The coated and dried plates are next exposed together with the photographic negatives. This operation requires an entirely different assembly

of intermediates than conventional photoengraving. As wrap-around plates are single-unit image carriers, all intermediates must be properly positioned for exposure. The technique for this operation is stripping as it is practiced for lithography where single-unit plates are the only existing kind. For wrap-around printing the stripper assembles all negatives in imposition order as a flat, exactly like a lithographic flat. A discussion of stripping of this type is provided in Section 5, "Planographic Image Carriers" of this chapter.

Photopolymer plates. As mentioned in Section 2, the term "photopolymer" is a generic one. It comprises the materials of which the Dycril plate consists. The term has found general acceptance

Courtesy The Beck Engraving Company

A platemaker attaches a Dycril plate to the plate cylinder of a rotary exposure unit. The plate cylinder, with plate and negatives in vacuum contact, is then inserted into the exposure unit at the right for rotary exposure.

in the industry; unfortunately, its meaning has been broadened by some to include such materials as bitumen, gelatin, casein, shellac, and others which are all used in various photomechanical coatings. In this manual we prefer the distinction between natural materials which happen to be susceptible to photopolymerization and materials specifically designed for this purpose. *Hence we reserve the term "photopolymer" for synthetics capable of photopolymerization.*

The field of photopolymers is young and far from settled at the time of writing. Many developments are in progress in this country and overseas. Since there is, at the time of this writing, no other photopolymer plate commercially available in the United States than the duPont Dycril plate, we turn now to a brief discussion of this product.

The Dycril plate. What effort it takes to develop a new printing-image carrier is illustrated by data concerning the time and money expended by duPont on the Dycril plate. It took eight years from the inception of this project in 1949 to 1957 until commercially acceptable plates were ready for experimental introduction to the industry; and it took four more years, until 1961, before duPont opened a "full-scale plate manufacturing unit at the company's Parlin, New Jersey, plant. DuPont has invested more than $10 million over a twelve-year period in Dycril, including research and development carried out at Parlin and Wilmington, Delaware, and at the company's printing plate laboratory in Philadelphia.[32] For comparison it is mentioned that the Lithographic Technical Foundation was originally endowed with $750,000. In 1925, when the endowment was made, that was considered an enormous sum by many graphic arts people. At an interest rate of 6 per cent, the original endowment afforded an annual budget of $45,000.[33] Graphic Arts research and development has certainly changed in the last 35 years!

The making of Dycril plates. Now to the mechanics of making Dycril plates. These can be divided into four steps: (1) conditioning, (2) exposure, (3) washout, and (4) drying. Conditioning consists in placing the Dycril material in an inclosure which is filled with carbon dioxide. The inclosure can be a conditioning cabinet; large-size plates are conditioned in their shipping containers. Conditioning time varies; for heavier monomer-coated plates, it is 24 hours. For the larger, thinner wrap-around plates, it is less or may be omitted entirely. The purpose of conditioning is to remove oxygen which may have been absorbed from the air by the photopolymer during storage, as oxygen has a retarding influence on the speed of the plate.

Exposure is done either flat or rotary under vacuum contact. Rotary exposure is optically controlled in order to produce the desired shape of supporting structure below the printing surface. The negatives for Dycril must be prepared exactly to the specifications set forth by duPont. After exposure, the plate is put either in a flat or a rotary washout machine. There the non-image areas, which remained unpolymerized, are washed away by a warm alkaline spray. Finally, drying is done in a mild stream of warm air.

Kinds of Dycril plates. Dycril material is available in many thicknesses for printing on machines

with flat beds, for rotaries, and, as already mentioned, for wrap-around printing. The processing equipment was developed by duPont though it is not manufactured by the company itself but by several concerns which are active in the making of similar equipment.

Dycril plates can be used on plate bases, they can be mounted on wood or metal bases for type forms, and they can be curved prior to exposure for rotary printing. For wrap-around and indirect relief printing curving is not required. Cold rolled stereotyping mats can be made in quantity from Dycril plates by the customary methods. Vinylite molding for electrotyping can also be done, but it is necessary to follow exactly the manufacturer's instructions as to temperature and pressure. Dycril plates can be somewhat deformed by heat and pressure, a point that should be kept in mind when they are used for molding.

DuPont Dycril plates are available in a number of types. In this context it is sufficient to mention only a few. Type 25, which is 0.025 inch thick, has a maximum depth of approximately 0.010 inch, and Type 30, which is 0.030 inch thick and has a maximum depth of approximately 0.015 inch. Both Type 25 and Type 30 are on flexible steel. Type C is on Cronar and exceptionally thin; it has a total thickness of 0.015 inch and a maximum depth of approximately 0.007 inch. Type C is intended for indirect relief printing on standard offset presses. These three types of Dycril plates are made in a variety of sizes up to 40½ × 76 inch.

The Kodak Relief Plate. In 1963 a new kind of wrap-around plate became available for letterpress and indirect relief printing. This is the

Courtesy Eastman Kodak Company

Operator inserts an exposed and developed Kodak Relief Plate into the KRP Processor for removing the unwanted plastic in the non-image areas.

Kodak Relief Plate, abbreviated KRP, which was designed for rotary presses. The KRP consists of four layers which are from top to bottom: (1) a silver halide emulsion, (2) a white pigmented layer, (3) a relatively thick layer of modified cellulose acetate plastic, and (4) a sheet of lacquered steel.

The functions of these four layers are the following: The top layer of a silver halide emulsion is needed for plate exposure and for forming a resist. The white pigmented layer enhances the contrast between exposed and unexposed areas thereby enabling the platemaker to inspect the plate prior to development and to make corrections if necessary. The layer of cellulose acetate serves as the final relief printing image of the plate, and the sheet of lacquered steel provides a flexible support.

Processing the KRP. The KRP can be immediately used for exposure without any pre-treatments. The silver halide emulsion gives the plate its speed, but the plate can safely be handled in yellow light, gold fluorescent lamps, for example. The plate is exposed together with negatives to arc lamps or in a photocomposer. The exposure time depends on actually used equipment; it may be as short as 15 seconds and as long as 3 minutes, to indicate a range.

The exposed plate can be inspected prior to development thanks to the visible image formed during exposure and to the white pigmented layer underneath. The inspected plate is next developed whereby the silver halide is reduced to metallic silver and the emulsion is chemically insolubilized in the areas which will serve as a resist during etching. The non-resist areas remain soluble and "are washed away with hot water." After completion of development "the plate is drained and dried in a warm-air cabinet." Development and drying require a total time of approximately 5 minutes. At this stage unwanted printing areas can be easily removed.

The plate is held on the rotating drum of the KRP Processor by permanent magnets. Arranged around the outside of the drum are the successive stations for scrubbing, heating, and cooling of the plate during the processing cycle. An oscillating moving endless belt does the actual removal of the plastic in the non-printing areas. Each cycle removes approximately 0.001 inch of acetate; a processing time of 20 minutes is required to achieve full depth of the plate.

Reading matter, line illustrations and half-tone images as well as large reverse areas are all handled alike. The pyramidal shape of the halftone dots gives strong support to the printing surface, or relief areas, of the plate and makes the plate suitable for molding and duplicate platemaking.

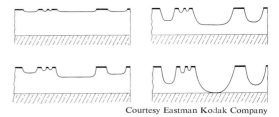

Courtesy Eastman Kodak Company

During processing the cellulose acetate layer of the Kodak Relief Plate is progressively removed, down to the steel base, as shown in the last diagram.

Sizes, thicknesses, and depths of etch of Kodak Relief Plates. At the time of writing this plate is available in three kinds. One kind is made up to a size of 30 × 60 inches, has a thickness of 0.017 inch, and a depth of 0.007 inch. The other two kinds are available up to a maximum size of 40⅝ × 60 inches; one has a thickness of 0.025 inch and a depth of 0.011 inch, the other is 0.030 inch thick and has a depth of 0.016 inch.

The KRP is attached to the plate cylinder of the press like other wrap-around plates by clamping its head and tail. It has good ink release and can be used for runs of medium length in direct letterpress and for considerably longer runs in indirect relief printing.

Bimetallic wrap-around plates. The TI-Plate is the latest addition to wrap-around plates. This plate is in actual use in some plants producing magazine covers and other color work; it was developed by Metals and Controls, Inc., a division of Texas Instruments, Incorporated. (TI are the initials of this company.) The TI-Plate consists of a top layer of photoengravers zinc alloy which is bonded to an aluminum base. The plates available at the time of writing are 0.032 inch thick and have a 60 per cent zinc and a 40 per cent aluminum layer. TI-Plates are not presensitized and must be coated with a suitable acid resist prior to exposure. Coating can be done either on flat or on cylindrical equipment, but etching must be done curved. The maximum depth of etch is down to the aluminum which is not affected by the etchant for zinc. After etching, the resist can be removed

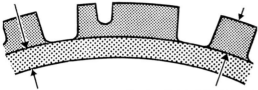

Courtesy Metals & Controls, Inc.

Diagram of the TI-Plate. The TI-Plate is a bimetallic wrap-around plate; the top layer is photoengravers zinc bonded to an aluminum base.

and the plate can be chromium plated for long-run jobs.

The TI-Plate material is available in widths up to 18 inch by any desired length. The manufacturer is field-testing 0.050 inch material having a 0.030 inch zinc and a 0.020 inch aluminum composition. Metals and Controls, Inc. are also producing a copper-aluminum plate in quantity. This version is used for fine screen full-color plates that are shallow etched.[34]

Electromechanical Engravings

Contemporary advances in electronics have made it possible to arrive at relief printing-image carriers by means of what has been called electronic engraving machines or electro-mechanical engraving. The term *electromechanical*, which is more used overseas than in this country, is well chosen as it parallels photomechanical and by replacing the word *photo* with the word *electro*, the name is hinting at an essential characteristic of these new methods. In electromechanical engraving the original image is directly converted into printing-image carriers without any intermediate products. The product of conversion and the capacity of various systems and models differ; generally speaking, electronic engraving machines can produce line and halftone image carriers of the same or different sizes as the original images as well as engravings for full-color printing.

The field is still in flux and far from settled. In the United States two systems are in practical operation. One is the domestic Fairchild line of electromechanical engraving machines. The other line of equipment is imported from Germany and known under the trade-mark of *Klischograph*. We restrict our description to these two systems because they appear to be firmly established in the American printing industry.

Fairchild electromechanical engraving machines. These machines are manufactured in a number of different models each for a particular purpose. The equipment is either sold or leased. Among the users are newspaper plants which do not have their own photoengraving departments, especially non-metropolitan publications, but also printers and photoengravers.

The first model, known as the *Scan-A-Graver*, was introduced in 1947 or in 1948. "Essentially the machine is a lathe with two rotating cylinders on a common shaft. The copy to be engraved goes on one cylinder and a sheet of special plastic goes on the other. The copy is scanned by a 240 cycle light, and the reflected light is picked up by a photomultiplier from which it is transmitted to an amplifier. The reflected light varies according to the copy—a highlight area giving a strong light reflection or signal and a shadow area a weaker light reflection or signal. The amplifier builds up the signal and feeds it to a powerful electromagnetic cutter head where it is translated into mechanical motion."

"This mechanical motion drives an incandescent stylus with a pyramid point into the plastic on the engraving cylinder. For every pulse of the reflected light from the copy, and there are 240 a second, there is a corresponding movement of the heated stylus into the material. Highlight area signals cause a deep penetration so that a large crater is burned in the plastic, and shadow area signals cause a shallow penetration with a smaller crater of less depth being burned. The area not burned away forms the printing surface of the halftone."[35]

The scope of the Fairchild equipment was greatly expanded by the development of the *Fairchild Variable Response Unit*. As explained above, "the Scan-A-Graver produces an electrical signal which is related to the tones of the original copy. Consequently, it is possible to take this signal and alter it in any way desired before it is used to actuate the engraving stylus. Where the desired response curve (or modification of tonal values) has been found that will for example give the best reproduction of very contrasty copy, such as flash pictures, this response curve can be exactly duplicated whenever the need arises."[36]

The principles of the Fairchild Variable Response Unit were combined with some of the basic features of the Scan-A-Graver in a machine of greatly enlarged scope, the Fairchild *Scan-A-Sizer*, introduced in 1955. There the copy to be scanned lies flat on a table. It can be enlarged or reduced, modulated in its values and even distorted when desired. The Variable Response Unit is at present no longer manufactured.

Fairchild engraving machines can be equipped with six equivalents of halftone screens from 60 to 110 lines per inch. Some models have two screens, others only one; some are capable of stepless enlargement and reduction, others can handle

Courtesy Fairchild Graphic Equipment

The Scan-A-Graver Journalist is an electromechanical engraving machine. This model can engrave line and halftone plates for relief printing. Engravings can be same size or enlarged in two fixed ratios. Halftone dots are equivalent to those of an 85 line screen.

certain predetermined proportions or produce only engravings of the same size as the original art work.

The Klischograph. The Klischograph line of electromechanical engraving equipment is manufactured by Dr. Rudolf Hell in Kiel, Germany, and imported into the United States. This firm is also known for their wire transmission equipment and for their line of color scanners. Our description concentrates on the Vario Klischograph K181, which is a unique piece of equipment. The

K181 can process both reflection and transmission copy, and makes color corrected separations for full-color printing including under-color removal. It can use six different screen rulings from 65 to 133; enlarges four times and reduces down to one-third; and engraves a plate up to 12 × 16 inches. "All this in one operation. Most standard materials can be used such as copper, zinc, magnesium, aluminum, or plastic."[37]

The K181 Vario Klischograph comprises two units. One does scanning and engraving; the other is a control cabinet where "the electronic signal produced by the photo-cells in the scanning head are suitably corrected and modified before being fed to the engraving system."[38]

The original image is placed on a table and held there by vacuum for scanning. The plate material is positioned on another flat surface and also held by vacuum. "These two tables are arranged in such a way that the picture table holding the original image can move under the engraving table. The latter is hydraulically driven at a speed which remains the same independent of picture dimensions and in turn drives the picture table. The scanning and the engraving heads are connected by an adjustable lever. Thereby the scanning head moves correspondingly faster or slower than the engraving head at each line feed. A stylus engraves the plate material with pyramid shaped dots."[39]

If separations for lithography are wanted, these can also be made on the Vario Klischograph by using the plastic engraving material. The separations, which can be either negatives or positives, take the place of photographic color-separations. The Klischograph separations are then contact exposed to photographic films, and these films serve for platemaking.

Other electronic engraving machines are either still in developmental stages or not sufficiently used in this country to justify description.[40]

Duplicate Plates

Duplicate plates are extremely important relief printing-image carriers. They can be divided into the four types of stereotypes, electrotypes, plastic plates, and rubber plates. Before we begin their individual presentation, we will briefly identify several most distinctive features of duplicate plates in general.

Duplicate plates save make-over expenses. Duplicate plates make it possible to preserve the

original material such as composition and photo-engravings; thereby they obviate expensive make-overs of these original materials. In some cases either the original material or the original images may even be irreplaceable. Old type faces, for example, may no longer be available, or the artwork of a job may have been lost.

Duplicate plates can be curved and used for long-run printing. All long-run printing is based on rotary presses. As type forms must be used flat and cannot be curved, they cannot serve for rotary printing. Their place is taken by plates which can be supplied as curved image carriers. Some kinds of duplicate plates are made either flat or curved, others can be made flat and then curved, still others are sufficiently flexible not to need separate curving as they will conform by their own flexibility to the curvature of the impression cylinder.

Duplicate plates have excellent wearing qualities. Excellent wearing qualities is a second requirement for long-run printing. Duplicate plates rate highly in this respect; they have a much longer press life than the original material from which they are made. A chromium-faced electrotype, for example, will last ten times as long as the photoengraving from which it was made.

Duplicate plates permit the combining of many different original elements in a single image carrier. Foundry types, Monotypes, slugs of type, wood engravings, photoengravings, and, if necessary, already existing stereotypes and electrotypes can all be combined for duplicate platemaking. The result is a single-unit plate made from a multitude of individual pieces.

Duplicate plates can be made of rubber and plastics. Rubber and plastics are materials which are not suitable for typesetting and photoengraving. But some methods of relief printing—flexography for example—cannot use image carriers consisting of metals but must have for their particular purposes more resilient materials such as natural or synthetic rubber. The only way to obtain such image carriers is by duplicate platemaking, which is consequently an absolute necessity for these printing methods.

Duplicate plates make it possible to print multiples of the same subject either at the same press run or at different times and different places. The printing of large quantities of package material by *ganging* (meaning in the printer's language combining) a considerable number of units for the same press run is one example. The printing of national advertisements in many different newspapers or magazines, and often at different times, is another.

Duplicate platemaking can correct some defects of the original material. Special techniques can be used to correct some defects of original materials during the manufacturing and finishing steps of duplicate platemaking. Examples are improvements in the uniformity of printing level and print-ing height, repair of nicks and scratches, removal of edges that would print unsatisfactorily. In addition, allowances can be made for stretch or shrinkage in special printing applications. Finally, some kinds of duplicate plates can also have makeready incorporated.

Some duplicate plates are much lighter and less bulky than original material. This feature is important where plates must be stored for later reprinting. Plastic duplicate plates, for example, which are widely used in book printing, occupy much less space than the original type forms from which they were molded. Duplicate plates are also much less heavy than these, a fact not to be forgotten.

After this characterization of duplicate plates, we turn to descriptions of the manufacturing processes by which they are made and we begin, in historical order, with stereotypes.

Stereotypes

Stereotypes were invented during the second half of the eighteenth century and are therefore the oldest type of duplicate plates. In spite of their age, they are still very important at present because practically all relief-printed metropolitan daily newspapers are printed with curved stereotypes. Stereotypes are also used to some extent in book printing and in the production of short-run trade magazines. For these purposes stereotypes are usually used flat rather than curved.

The two branches of the stereotyping industry. The stereotyping industry is customarily divided into two branches: one is stereotyping as a part of newspaper production; the other is stereotyping as part of the printing service trades. In the first case, stereotypes are manufactured by newspaper plants for their own needs; in the second, stereotype trade shops supply printers, publishers, and national advertisers either with matrices for stereotyping or with flat stereotypes.

Matrices, called *mats* by the industry, are intermediate elements in the production of stereotypes but they are also independent items of commerce. Publishers of syndicated material for newspapers (such as their comic pages) and national advertisers provide local newspapers with stereotyping mats from which flat stereos are cast to be incorporated in the page form of the newspaper prior to molding of the whole page. Stereotypes are manufactured in two main stages. The first stage consists in mat-making; the second, in casting. During mat-making an intaglio replica of the original relief material is produced. The product of this phase is a *matrix*, or *mat* for short. During the second phase, the molten stereotype metal is cast in the intaglio mat and thereby becomes a relief printing-image carrier.

Mat-making is done in five steps: (1) assembling of the type-form for mat-making, (2) registering for color work, (3) molding including drying or baking, (4) separating the mat from original material and (5) trimming the completed mat after separation.

Assembling for mat-making and registering. For newspaper stereotyping, the type form is locked up in the composing room in the size of the newspaper page. For commercial mat-making the stereotyper assembles a variety of materials, often belonging to different jobs, for common molding. Registering is a necessity in color work, which is customarily done in four different inks and therefore requires four different mats. The black form is usually the key form; the other forms are fitted to it by taking an ink impression of the black form on a transparent material and by using this print as a guide for registering.

Molding of stereotyping mats. Molding is the next step in mat-making. Molding has the purpose of producing an intaglio intermediate from the original relief image carrier. The material for this intaglio intermediate is also known as a mat. (As the same word is used for both the material for molding and the molded intaglio intermediate produced by use of this material, confusion can easily result.) The mat-making material is a manufactured pulp sheet, consisting of cellulose fibers with a smooth-coated malleable surface.

The mat is placed face down over the type form and the relief image of the original material produces the intaglio image on the mat during molding. Molding can be done by use of pressure alone, or by pressure and heat in combination. Cold-molded mats can be produced either in a roller-type press or in a flat platen hydraulic press. Molding by heat and pressure takes place in hydraulic presses equipped with heating devices. Here, the mats are baked during molding and are, therefore, known as *direct-pressure-baked* mats as distinguished from *cola-rolled* or *cold-pressed* mats.

Direct-pressure-baked mats possess better detail than *rolled* or *cold-pressed* mats. Direct-pressure-baked, "plastic impregnated mats provide the best medium for stereotype casting of

Roller molding of stereotype mats. The molded mats serve as intaglio intermediates for casting of stereotype plates which have their printing areas in relief.

flat or curved mats. Pressure and heat help to retain dimensional stability as well as depth and fidelity."[41] Finally, it is mentioned that one of the oldest molding methods, *brush molding*, is still used where the original material must be molded without the application of mechanical pressure. The molding material, a specially prepared paper, "called a flong, is made by pasting together several sheets of strong tissue paper and thick blotter-like paper with a prepared paste."[42] This flong is put in a moist state on the original material and molded by beating it with a stereotype brush, a special long-handled bristle brush.

If the mat is a combination of several units that will be cast as separate stereos, it is trimmed accordingly. Mats made for immediate casting pass through at least four additional operations. These are: (1) packing, (2) scorching, (3) casting, and (4) finishing.

Packing of stereotyping mats. During packing the non-printing areas of the mat are supported, or built up, from the back for casting unless *packless* stereotype mats are used. Hand packing of stereotype mats is necessary in standard mats as the non-image areas would otherwise not retain the molded depth in the final stereotype. As hand packing is time consuming, and as time is of particular importance in newspaper printing, a method of molding is needed that either totally eliminates or at least considerably reduces hand packing. One solution to this problem is a "two-piece packless mat. This consists of a standard mat backed up with a sheet of special plastic material. Upon molding and forming under heat the two pieces have the property of being joined into one. The formed mat has a thermosetting property which permits placing it in the plate casting box without hand packing."[43]

Cast stereotype plates are removed from an automatic casting machine.

Craftsman removes a pre-shrunk stereotyping matrix from vacuum forming equipment. The pre-shrunk matrix is used for casting of curved stereotype plates.

Scorching of stereotyping mats. Scorching is the next step; it is done in gas-fired or electrically heated ovens and has the purpose of relieving the mat of excess moisture which would cause trouble during casting. Scorching results in a shrinking of the mat. The extent of shrinkage can be sufficiently controlled.

Flat casting of stereotypes. Stereotypes can be cast either flat or curved. Stereotypes that will be used as image carriers for platen or flatbed-cylinder presses must of course be flat cast. Flat casting is also needed in the newspaper field for the conversion of supplied stereotyping mats into intermediates. Such flat cast stereotypes are assembled together with type and possibly photo-engravings in the type form which in turn is molded for the making of the final curved image carrier. Flat casting is done in a casting box where the mat is surrounded with bearers. The workman

ladles the molten metal by hand into the box which he puts in a vertical position for casting.

Curved casting of stereotypes. Curved casting requires modification of some of the preceding steps. In the newspaper field scorching is designated as *forming the mat*. This operation has the purpose "to position the printing surface of the mat and to dry, shrink, and form the mat."[44] The equipment for this step is a *vacuum former*. The vacuum former is provided with a semi-cylindrical cover which has an electrically heated vacuum chamber where the mat is held in the correct curved position during forming. The formed and shrunk mat is trimmed and then put in the casting machine where the curved stereotype is cast.

A number of different types of casters is available; fully automatic machines are capable of producing completely finished stereotypes, which are usually also automatically beveled for attaching to the plate cylinder of the newspaper press. Each stereotype represents a full-size newspaper page. Papers that have very large editions must be printed simultaneously on several presses, requiring several stereotypes of the same page. Usually, all these can be cast from a single mat.

Finishing of flat stereotypes. Flat stereotypes that have been cast ganged-up are cut into individual units, shaved for proper height, and when necessary improved by hand tooling. The completed stereotype can also be nickel or chromium plated, whereby its wearing qualities are considerably improved. If stereotypes are to be used in type forms, they are mounted to type height (0.918 inch) and are then ready for further use. Stereotypes may be incorporated in a newspaper page for common molding, or they may serve directly for printing on the press.

Electrotypes

Electrotypes are the elite of duplicate relief image carriers because they combine highest quality, greatest precision, and exceptionally long press life. Electrotypes are used for three different purposes: (1) directly as printing-image carriers for letterpress printing; (2) as pattern plates for the making of additional electrotype molds, newspaper mats, rubber or plastic plates; and (3) as embossing and stamping dies in short-run binding jobs. Electrotypes can be made either flat or curved; their printing surface may be one of the following three metals: copper, nickel, or chromium. Finally, electrotypes may either have premakeready incorporated or be without it.

The manufacture of electrotypes can for our purposes be divided into four broad production stages: (1) molding, (2) electroforming, (3) backing, and (4) finishing. Molding comprises several operations and results in the *electrotyping mold*. This mold is an intaglio intermediate made by means of the original relief material. The mold is next used in electroforming. This operation produces the *electrotype shell*, which comes about through the electrodeposition of metal in the intaglio mold. Upon removal from the mold, the electrotype shell presents the printing image of the final electrotype in relief.

The back of the shell is traditionally filled with hot molten electrotype metal during the casting operation. More modern backing methods for curved electrotypes use lightweight plastics instead. The backed electrotype is a sturdy and rigid image carrier. It passes through several additional finishing operations, which have the purpose of insuring the quality of the electrotype and of preparing it for the press.

Each of the four main stages comprises several operations and can be executed in various ways. Depending on the kind of electrotype desired— flat or curved for example, and on the molding and casting process selected, the detail of production varies considerably.

Molding can be done by one of four different methods depending on the molding material selected. These four methods will be discussed under the headings of (1) wax molding, (2) lead molding, (3) Tenaplate molding, and (4) hot plastic molding.

Wax molding. Wax molding is one of the oldest molding methods. Since it is no longer extensively practiced, we shall discuss it but briefly. A wax composition is formulated in the electrotyping shop. While molten, it is poured onto metal backing sheets. Upon cooling, this wax layer is shaved to about one-quarter-inch thickness. This composite of wax layer and metal backing sheet is called a *wax case;* it is the molding material. Next, the intaglio intermediate is formed by pressing this wax case with the original relief material in a molding press. The surface of the molded case is made electrically conductive by graphiting which prepares it for electroforming.

Wax molding is cumbersome and lacks in the ability of rendering fine detail in comparison with lead molding and other contemporary molding methods. It further is handicapped by the required graphiting which is a dirty operation as the extremely small particles of graphite cannot be effectively confined to the mold where they are wanted but find their way to many other objects and also to the body of the workman where they are rather objectionable.

Lead molding. Before the development of hot plastic molding, lead molding was employed wherever fine halftone detail was to be molded. "Because of the high pressures required (8000 lbs. per square inch), this process cannot be employed for molding subjects containing type metal. It is, however, sometimes used for making molds of previously fabricated electrotypes that contain type matter."[45]

The molding material is a thin sheet of pure lead, approximately 0.04 inch. As lead is an electrical conductor, lead molds do not need to be made conductive but "to prevent the lead mold from sticking to the form, both are lightly dusted with molding graphite. In some cases a dilute solution of grease in a solvent is applied instead of graphite."[46] The lead mold is further chemically treated prior to electroforming in order to facilitate separation of the formed shell from the mold. Lead molds cannot be used for repeated electroforming.

As to the value of lead molding in contemporary electrotyping, opinions are divided. Some hold that the quality of lead molding is still supreme, others believe that hot plastic molding is at least equal to lead molding in quality and highly superior in economy and all-around suitability.

Tenaplate molding. Tenaplate is proprietary molding material that consists of a thin aluminum

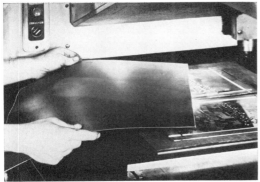

Craftsman putting a sheet of thermoplastic material, usually vinyl, over the original material to be electrotyped. After the vinyl is pre-heated it will be molded together with the preheated type form in a molding press, resulting in an intaglio mat.

foil which serves as a base for a layer of a wax-rubber coating. "When a type form is molded in such a sheet, the metal deforms to a considerable extent, but the exact impression is taken by the wax surface. The net result is a more accurate reproduction of the original type face, and bench operations are minimized."[47] Tenaplate must be made conductive for electroforming; Tenaplate molds cannot be re-used.

The main advantage of Tenaplate is that it does not require highly elevated temperatures for molding. For this reason, Tenaplate molding is often designated as cold molding. Actually, Tenaplate is heated approximately 10 to 15 degrees above room temperature; the type form is preheated approximately 40 to 50 degrees above room temperature and molding is done without further heating. The material is available in roll form and permits economical and fast molding.

Hot plastic molding. Hot plastic molding is based on a thermoplastic molding material such as Vinylite, for example. This method is therefore often called Vinylite molding. (Vinylite is a trademark for a product manufactured by one company; the generic name of the plastic molding material is vinyl chloride-acetate copolymer.) "Plastic electrotype molding was introduced in 1942 and was the most significant development in the electrotyping industry in 75 years. The use of a thermoplastic resin sheet for molding has practically obsolesced wax and lead molding."[48]

Hot plastic molding is capable of accurately rendering the finest detail. The molds can be re-used for repeated electroforming of the same sub-

ject. They are lightweight and save shipping costs, and the plastic material can be simply flattened after electroforming and re-used for the molding of other forms.

Several techniques are found in the industry for the molding of plastic sheets. First, both the type form and the plastic materials are preheated, then the preheated form and the plastic sheet are assembled and put in the molding press, heated and then molded under pressure. The molded assembly is removed to a cooling unit which may or may not be part of the molding equipment. After cooling the plastic mold becomes rigid again. The mold is separated from the type form and next made electrically conductive.

Silver spraying. Cold and hot molded materials are usually made electrically conductive by silver spraying. The mold is first treated with a sensitizing solution of a tin compound and then sprayed by means of a double-nozzled spray gun which discharges a silver solution from one nozzle and a chemical reducing agent from the other. These solutions react chemically on the prepared mold by forming an extremely thin film of metallic silver. This silver coating is an excellent electrical conductor; the intaglio mold can now be used for electroforming.

Electroforming. Electroforming is an electrochemical process whereby such metals as copper and nickel can be deposited to a controllable thickness on the conductive surface of a mold by the agency of an electric current. This process takes place in large plating tanks where a num-

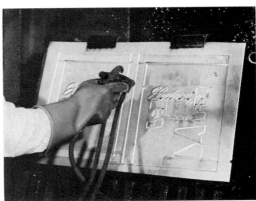

The molded vinyl sheet is silver sprayed with a double-nozzle spray gun. This operation deposits a thin film of silver on the mold and thereby makes the unconductive mold conductive on its surface for electroforming.

The electrotyping mold with the attached electroformed copper shell is removed from the plating tank.

ber of molds are suspended for common electroforming in a so-called *plating bath*. The plating metal, copper or nickel, is connected to the positive terminal of the current source, the molds to the negative, and the metal is electrodeposited on the mold surface until the shell has reached the required thickness.

Nickel electros, sometimes called steel electros, are first placed in a nickel-plating tank where a thin layer of nickel is deposited directly on the mold. The mold is then transferred to a copper tank for the formation of the shell. Nickel is usually deposited in a thickness of 0.0005 to 0.001 inch; the thickness of the copper shell varies between 0.008 and 0.015 inch. Chromium-surfaced electrotypes are known as *chrome plated*. Here the chromium is not deposited during electroforming but as a separate step on the otherwise already completed nickel electrotype.

After the shell has attained its prescribed thickness, the mold, together with the adherent shell, is removed from the electroforming tank. Next, the shell must be separated from the mold. Wax molds, lead molds, and cold-molding sheets are either completely destroyed during their separation from the shell or they are too much damaged for re-use. Plastic molds are the only ones that remain suitable for repeated electroforming.

Backing of electrotypes. The electroformed shell is much too fragile for extensive handling, not to speak of its fitness for use as a printing-image carrier. The shell must therefore be strengthened and made more substantial. This is achieved by a

series of operations including tinning and backing, or casting, of electrotypes. The otherwise prepared shell is "placed face down on a flat glass table, and soldering fluid is brushed over the back or non-printing surface. This fluid serves as a flux for the tin-foil strips which are then laid over the brushed surface."[49] Tin foil or plated tin serves to bond the copper shell with the backing metal. A brief outline of tinning follows.

Tinning of electrotypes. The shell with the tin foil on the back is then heated, thereby completely tinning the back surface of the shell. While this tinned film is still molten, the molten electrotype metal is applied. An intimate bond between the backing metal and the shell is hereby insured. Some electrotypers electrodeposit a film of tin on the back of the copper shell before removing the shell from the mold instead of using tin foil. Electrodeposited tin is coated with a liquid flux before applying heat to melt the tin.

Flat and curved electrotypes. Electrotypes can be flat or curved. For printing on flatbed-cylinder presses and on platen presses, flat electros are needed. For rotary presses electros must have curvatures corresponding to those of the plate cylinder of the press. Curved electros can be made in various ways. One of them is by cold curving of flat electros; other methods employ curved casting.

Backing of flat electrotypes. Flat electros are backed by putting the shells in a backing pan which is heated to a temperature sufficient for melting of the tin coating or foil. "A small ladle of molten electrotype backing metal is then poured over the hot tinned surface of the shell. This backing metal acts as an intermediate coating between the melted tin on the shell and the full amount of backing metal which is immediately

Pressure casting, one of several methods whereby the electrotype shell is backed, or made rigid and sturdy.

flowed on the shell. The cast is solidified by drafts of forced air directed both on the top of the cast and the bottom of the pan."[50]

Curved cast electrotypes. Backing of curved cast electrotypes can be done in several ways. We mention centrifugal casting and casting in the vacuum casting box. "Centrifugal casting of the shells in the curved position is one of the most effective means of eliminating the stretch that normally occurs in the cold curving of a flat electrotype. This ingenious process has made possible a dimensional stability that adds materially to the printing quality of electrotypes."[51] Casting in the vacuum casting box is based on equipment similar to that used for the curved casting of stereotypes. The shell is put next to a perforated half-round vacuum holder of the proper curvature. The vacuum forces it into the proper position in which it is then cast. The vacuum also removes the air and other gases from the metal and thereby improves the structural characteristics of the backed electrotype.

It should be mentioned that major variations in the diameter of plate cylinders require correspondingly curved casting equipment. For this reason, curved casting is more often done by large printing plants which have standardized equipment than by electrotyping companies which service the whole industry and are called upon to supply electros of different curvatures.

Lightweight electrotypes. Electrotypes cast with electrotype metal, which contains more than 90 per cent lead, have a rather high specific gravity. As the weight of electrotypes presents many problems on high-speed rotary equipment, efforts were made to manufacture electros of a lower specific gravity. Several lightweight electros are available. One is a laminated plate. For this purpose, "the curved electrotype is shaved to an over-all thickness of about 0.085 inch and attached by means of a thermosetting adhesive to a curved aluminum blank about 0.160 inch thick."[52] Another approach is taken in the *Bista* plate which combines a copper shell with a plastic backing. "The material backing up the shell to required press thickness is a specially compounded plastic weighing only a fraction as much as the lead alloy employed in the casting of an electrotype. The result is a press plate weighing only 15 per cent as much as its lead-backed counterpart."[53]

The *Color Line* plate is another lightweight electro. It is quite similar to the Bista plate. Both the Color Line and the Bista plate can have a curved or perforated aluminum sheet incorporated in the plastic backing. This perforated metal unit can also constitute the back (meaning the surface with which the plate is attached to the plate cylinder of the press) of the curved electro. The metal sheet provides added ruggedness and a stable means for attaching plate hooks. (Electrotypes are attached to the plate cylinder of the press by either external or internal lockup.)

Courtesy Electrotypers and Stereotypers Handbook

Shaving an electrotype plate. This operation removes excess metal from the back of the electrotype, thereby bringing the thickness of the final plate within the required close tolerance.

Finishing of electrotypes. Finishing is a most important phase of electrotype production. It includes a variety of operations that aim at producing a printing plate of perfect quality. The backed plate is first *rough-straightened* with a planing block and then passed through the *roughing machine* or so-called *shavers*. Then the plate is *bumped* in a *bumping* press that straightens it further. The electro is further improved by several hand-tooling operations which require high skill. The purpose of this step is the raising of the printing image wherever this may be needed. Often these operations are done after the electro has been proofed and the proof marked with the required corrections. Last, the hand-tooled electro is given a final shaving which determines its correct printing height.

Flat electros that will be used on rotary presses are first curved and then routed. The large metal areas that are removed by routing must remain undisturbed during curving. Their prior removal would weaken the electros during curving.

Flat electros are readied for use on the press in several ways, depending on the kind of assembly selected for presswork. If they are to be put on plate bases, electros are usually beveled for attaching with hooks. And if they will become part of type forms, electros must be mounted type high. Mounting can be done on wood or on metal. On wood, electros can be either nailed or cemented with thermoplastic adhesives; on metal, they may be either soldered or cemented, similar to their cementing on wood. Curved electros can be *scarfed*, or milled on their backs, for attachment to the plate cylinder of the press by tension lockup devices.

If a printing surface of chromium is required, both flat and curved electros are finished, routed, and beveled before they may be plated. Chrome plating is the last and final operation in this case.

Pre-madeready electrotypes. Before closing this introduction to electrotypes, two more points should be mentioned: the use of so-called pre-madeready electros (meaning electrotypes in which makeready has been incorporated) and the proofing of curved electrotypes. Pre-madeready electrotypes are treated by the electrotyper for printing pressure differentiation. In many printing plants, though by no means in all, it is considered good practice to differentiate the printing pressure for the highlights, the middle tones, and the shadows of the printing image. This can be done by raising or depressing the respective tone areas of the image carrier. The middle tones remain at the customary printing level, the highlight areas are somewhat depressed beneath this level, and the shadow areas are somewhat raised. Several pre-makeready systems are available. In principle, they all exert pressure on the electro which may be sandwiched between a specially prepared face-mat and a corresponding back-mat registered in exact position. The back-mat is then removed and the back of the electro is shaved while the face-mat is still in position. After the face-mat is removed, the treated electrotype has a smooth back and its printing surface the required differentiated height.

Proofing of electrotypes. Flat electrotypes can be proofed on the same kind of presses as photoengravings; curved electrotypes must be proofed on rotary equipment. Essentially, proof presses for curved electros are rotary printing machines which have facilities for the fast change of curved electrotypes. (Proof presses for curved electrotypes are described in Chapter VI, Section 8.)

Rubber and Plastic Plates

Rubber and plastic plates are relative newcomers to the printing industry. Their growth developed during the last twenty-five years; they are at present widely used not only in flexographic printing but also in many other fields. Molded rubber or elastomeric plates "are called flexible plates whether they are made from natural or synthetic rubbers or of a plastic resin."[54] Flexible plates are with the exception of engraved rubber plates duplicate image carriers.

Fields of application for rubber and plastic plates. Rubber and plastic plates can be used for many different purposes. Among them is bag printing, the production of business forms, package printing on papers and plastics, printing of envelopes, books, tags, foil wraps, wrapping papers, and wallpaper. In the newspaper and magazine industry plastic plates are not used for printing but for the same purpose as advertising mats and electros.

Five common characteristics of plastic and rubber plates. Even though plastic and rubber plates are made of different materials and serve different purposes, they are presented together because of their many common points. Some of these are: (1) light weight in comparison with metal plates, (2) similarity of production inasmuch as either kind is manufactured by molding and remolding, (3) simplicity of curving, (4) limitations in the rendering of fine halftone images, and (5) excellent durability. But not all kinds of rubber and plastic plates have all of these characteristics under all conditions, as will be seen presently.

Thermoplastic and thermosetting plastics. Before we enter into a presentation of the manufacturing processes for plastic plates, a short explanation of the difference between *thermoplastic* and *thermosetting* plastics will be found helpful. *Thermoplastic* is the designation of such plastics as will soften when heated and harden again during cooling. This softening and hardening process can be theoretically repeated indefinitely with the same material. *Thermosetting* is the designation of such plastics as will soften *only once* when heated and then harden permanently. These plastics cannot be softened again by heating. Even though flexible plates can be made from either kind of materials, the vast majority consists of thermoplastic rather than thermosetting plastics.

The two main production stages in the manufacturing of rubber and plastic plates. Rubber and

A craftsman examines a thermosetting mold made from original material. Thermosetting molds are intaglio intermediates for molding of rubber or plastic plates.

A rubber plate, having its printing areas in relief, is separated from the intaglio thermosetting mold after molding is completed.

plastic plates are manufactured in two main stages. The first stage has the object of making an intaglio mold, called matrix, from the original relief material. The second stage consists in the molding of the final relief plate in this intaglio mold. As two molding operations are necessary, the making of flexible plates is often designated as the molding and remolding of duplicate plates.

The molding of plastic matrices. The molding material for matrix molding is *Rogers* board, a rigid board impregnated with a thermosetting resin, usually of the phenolic family. "Two types of matrices are used: the plain matrix which is adequate for most printing conditions, and the non-shrink matrix, which is utilized when the printing design calls for critical register work."[55] The plain matrix consists of a single sheet of Rogers board, the non-shrink matrix has a thin sheet of perforated metal sandwiched between two such sheets. Obviously, thermosetting resins must be used for the molding of matrices.

For molding, the type form, pattern plate, or "engraving is covered with a sheet of matrix material and then placed in a hydraulic press, or vulcanizer. Bearers, or stops, are inserted alongside the relief material covered with the plastic sheet. These stops are calculated to give the matrix its required thickness when the press is closed down. At first, the press is closed down just enough so that its heated plates can soften the matrix material." The pressure is gradually increased until the softened thermosetting material is pressed deep enough into the relief image to mold it completely in all its detail. The maximum pressure is maintained "for about ten minutes to allow the plastic to polymerize (i.e., to harden)." The completed matrix is cooled, removed from the relief material and, after minor operations, ready for remolding of rubber or plastic plates.

The molding of rubber plates. Rubber plates are made either of natural or of synthetic rubber. Natural rubber is more generally used than synthetic rubber. Often, the solvents present in a given ink formulation control the selection of the plate material. "Natural rubber resists the destructive action of some solvents better than does synthetic rubber while with other solvents synthetic rubber offers greater resistance."

The molding of rubber plates can be done with the same equipment and along the same lines as the molding of thermosetting matrices. "Sheets of rubber are laid on the matrix and together they are placed in the same kind of press used to mold the matrix. The rubber is first softened by a momentary application of heat, then squeezed and held under the pressure until it forms to the matrix. After removal from the press the rubber plate is stripped from the mold, allowed to cool, and then trimmed."

Vulcanization and its effects. During molding, two things happen simultaneously: one is the forming of the relief image; the other is the concurrent curing, or *vulcanization*, of the rubber. Vulcanization changes many properties of rubber; we mention merely two, its resistance to solvents and its hardness, because these are most important from the printer's point of view. The hardness of rubber plates "is measured by various systems, the most common on which is the Shore A scale. The usual hardness of a plate used in

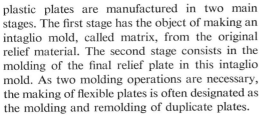

flexography measures from 45 to 55 durometer on the Shore A scale. However, a plate 0.125 inch thick will read harder than a plate 0.250 inch thick though manufactured with the same compound." The term *durometer* indicates the unit of hardness measurement; the *Shore A* scale refers to a generally accepted testing method described by the American Society for Testing Materials (ASTM).

The molding of plastic plates. Most plastic plates are made of Vinyl compounds which are thermoplastic. A number of somewhat different molding techniques are used. We briefly describe one of these. The thermosetting matrix is coated with a releasing agent, the proper bearers are selected and the granular plate charge is applied over the matrix in a uniform layer sufficient to obtain the desired plate thickness. Then this assembly is placed in the molding press, the press is closed and minimum follow-up pressure is applied for a period of two to four minutes with platen temperatures of 270° to 290°F. At the end of this preheating period, sufficient pressure is applied slowly to close the press tight on the thickness bearers. Molding pressures range from 700 to 2,000 pounds per square inch. Maximum pressure is held for 30 to 60 seconds. Then the molding assembly is removed to a water-cooled chilling press where it is cooled for approximately two minutes under pressures of ten to fifty pounds per square inch."[56]

The finishing of rubber plates. Rubber plates are "trimmed free of flash or excess rubber by shearing or cutting with a foot shear or another suitable tool. Non-printing areas can be relieved in plate construction having metal or fabric base by cutting and stripping away the material of the non-printing plate areas."[57]

If rubber plates are molded to a thicker dimension than the correct one, this can be corrected by grinding. "The grinding of rubber plates after molding is sometimes employed to bring the plate down to within the plus-minus 0.001 inch tolerance in thickness. But excessive grinding of a plate (more than one or two thousandths of an inch) materially reduces its printing quality by introducing high 'edges' in the printing design."[58]

The mounting of rubber plates. The flexographic industry distinguishes six kinds of mountings: (1) plainback plates, (2) sticky back plates, (3) precured plates, (4) brass-back plates, (5) design rollers, and (6) plate-mounted cylinders.

The *plainback* plate has no backing at all and is used with mounting machines that apply adhesive to the plate cylinder immediately before mounting. Plainback plates are used for general work where size and register of the printed image are not extremely critical. In the *sticky back* plate a double-faced pressure sensitive adhesive is bonded

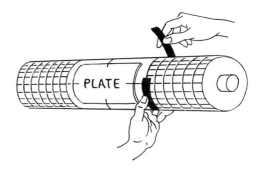

This diagram shown that sticky back and rubber plate are lined up with scribed lines on the cylinder and that the edges of the sticky back are reinforced around the cylinder. (Adapted from Mosstype literature.)

to the rubber plate. This plate is made for hand mounting. The *precured plate* "is a laminated construction molded to a permanent curve that approximates the curve of the cylinder on which it will be used. It is a shrinkage-controlled plate intended for applications where accuracy of printing size and color register is critical and where the normal size variations of standard plates are not acceptable." The *brass-back* plate is a rubber plate vulcanized to a sheet of spring brass. It is made-ready and precured and has a rubberized sheet of fabric attached to the brass saddle to prevent the plate from creeping on the cylinder. *Design rollers* are plate cylinders that have rubber plates permanently vulcanized to their surface. They are primarily made "for continuous all-over patterns, single or multicolor, as used on gift wraps, trade-mark wraps, box coverings, security papers, liner board for corrugated, and various specialty paper products. *Plate-mounted cylinders* are made the same way as design rollers, but for non-continuous designs. They are used for very long printing runs as they make it practical to run at high speeds yet retaining accuracy of printing."[59]

Finishing of plastic plates. Under this head we discuss a number of operations which are necessary to prepare plastic plates for use as image carriers. Like other duplicate relief image carriers plastic plates can be used flat and curved. Flat plates may be either printed on plate bases or as

A molded plastic plate is trimmed to size with foot-operated hydraulic shears.

part of a type form. "Finishing operations consist of trimming the flash, or excess material, from the plate, routing, beveling and where necessary, grinding, or shaving the back of the plate to obtain accurate plate thickness." Finally, after shaving "plastic plates are leveled by softening the plate at an elevated temperature and cooling against a smooth surface."[60]

Curved plastic plates are made by softening the flat plates and by putting them on a convex saddle that has the same curvature as the plate cylinder of the press where they will be used. This saddle is heated to approximately 145°F. The upper platen of the curving equipment has a concave counterpart, faced with a layer of sponge rubber. "The softened plate is placed backside down on the saddle against a guide bar and the press is closed quickly. Pressure is maintained for 30 to 60 seconds when the plate becomes rigid and maintains its curved position."[61]

The limitations and advantages of plastic and rubber plates. Plastic plates are capable of producing images containing medium and fine halftones, but thermoplastic plates soften under heat. Unfortunately, it is possible to generate such temperatures during presswork as to make plastic plates suffer, particularly if the printing ink contains solvents or other ingredients that can attack the plate material. Rubber plates are more limited in their ability to render tonal detail than plastic plates. They are, consequently, used for coarse to medium halftones.

The advantages of plastic plates are, on the other hand, quite impressive. "Lightness in weight, long-wearing surface, excellent ink transference, low cost, speed of manufacture, and machineability are the principal advantages of plastic plates."[62] Both types of plates are most valuable contributions to relief printing technology.

Section 4:   Intaglio Printing-Image Carriers

Intaglio printing is divided into a number of different printing methods. Most of these have their own characteristic image carriers. Our explanation of intaglio printing-image carriers is accordingly grouped into the following three parts of (1) fine-art intaglio image carriers; (2) image carriers for steel-die engraving and for banknote printing; and (3) gravure plates and cylinders.

Fine-Art Intaglio Image Carriers

The base material for fine-art intaglio image carriers is a metal plate, usually copper. This plate can receive the intaglio printing image by hand tooling or by chemical treatments, or by a combination of both. Various kinds of treatments result in printed images of different aesthetic qualities. Line engraving, drypoint, and mezzotint are made by hand tooling, whereas etching, soft-ground etching, aquatint, and sugar-aquatint are made by chemical methods. If chemical and hand tooling techniques are combined, fine-art printers speak of *mixed mediums*. Stipple and crayon engravings are examples of combination methods.

Line engraving. In line engraving, the act of creating the visual image and that of producing the intaglio printing image are one. The artist either sketches the main lines of his composition directly on the copper plate with a lead pencil, or he makes a tracing from a previously prepared paper sketch. Then he takes to his engraving tools and designs or draws as he engraves. The tools he uses are gravers, burins, and scrapers of various shapes. All these are made of steel, set in wooden handles. For smoothing unwanted fine lines or scratches, the artist can use the burnisher, or a snakestone, and engravers' charcoal.

Intaglio line engraving, taken from S. T. Prideaux, Aquatint Engraving, London, 1909. (Reproduced same size from 133-line photoengraving.)

Drypoint. In drypoint the metal plate is scratched with a pointed hand tool. The intaglio image consists of the turned-up metal, the so-called *burr* behind which the ink is deposited. The plate metal is usually copper; steel, brass, aluminum, and zinc can also be used for drypoint but the softer metals do not yield as many impressions as do copper and steel. The cutting or scratching point may be steel, diamond, sapphire, or ruby jewel set in metal. Drypoint is distinguished by the quality of its lines, and requires great skill on the part of the artist printmaker.

Mezzotint. Mezzotint is the fine-art intaglio method closest to contemporary industrial gravure methods. Like a conventional gravure plate, a mezzotint plate consists of a large number of small individual cells. But these are not as regular and as small as gravure cells, nor are they the result of photomechanics and etching. The mezzotint cells are produced by hand tooling. The whole plate surface is roughened with a *mezzotint rocker*, a hand tool with many hardened steel teeth. The plate, usually copper, is worked with the rocker in all directions until it is evenly covered with intaglio cells. If a print is taken at this stage it shows an all-over ink coverage.

The printing image is created by controlling the depth and the presence of the burr in all image areas. Where the metal burr is completely removed, no ink will remain on the plate; where the

burr is reduced, less ink will be caught than in the areas that have a full burr. The artist must work from black to white. For the white areas, he uses scrapers of various shapes which remove the burr completely. He achieves his tonal effects with the burnisher by flattening the burr to the required degree. If the artist wants to roughen the plate locally, he can do so with various *roulettes*.

Etching. The word etching is apt to cause confusion; therefore, it must be briefly explained in its several meanings. Etching as a verb means the treatment of metal (or other substances) with chemical agents in which the material is soluble. These agents were traditionally called *mordants;* contemporary literature prefers the term *etchant* which is now more generally used than the older word mordant. Etching as an operation is part of many intaglio printing methods.

The etching ground protects the plate from the etchant. Where the etching ground is removed by the artist, the plate is laid bare and thereby becomes accessible to the etchant.

Etching as a noun signifies both the print produced by a certain intaglio method and the method itself. Other intaglio methods in which etching as an activity is important are not called etchings but have their own names such as *soft-ground-etching, aquatint,* and *sugar-aquatint.* The method described under the heading of etching is the oldest of all intaglio methods based solely on chemical action for producing the intaglio printing image. Etching is used to achieve the same results as line engraving while avoiding the difficulties of this medium. The basic thought behind etching is rather simple; the artist can restrict himself to the familiar drawing and leave the hard work of removing the metal to the acid.

A metal plate, usually copper, but also zinc and

iron, is first completely covered with an acid-resist. Then the artist removes this resist wherever he wants to create a printing image. Where the metal is unprotected, the acid will attack and remove the metal, thereby producing an intaglio area. The longer an area is exposed to the acid, the deeper and wider will the image be etched.

Intaglio etching, taken from S. T. Prideaux, Aquatint Engraving, *London, 1909. (Reproduced same size from 133-line photoengraving.)*

Controlling the progress of etching. Control of the duration for which various areas are exposed to the etchant is an essential aspect of all etching methods. This control can be obtained in various ways; one of them is known as *staging*. The etching operation is divided into several stages known as *bites*. After each stage, such areas as are already completely etched are staged-out by protecting them with an acid-proof resist.

Softground etching, taken from S. T. Prideaux, Aquatint Engraving, *London, 1909. (Reproduced same size from 133-line photoengraving.)*

Softground etching. Softground etching is a method whereby textured and crayon-like effects can be produced. The etching ground for this method does not become hard nor does it adhere strongly to the plate. This type of etching ground is sticky and can be easily lifted by drawing on paper put over it, by textured objects, or by the etcher's fingers. Such manipulation removes the ground sufficiently to give access to the etchant. Otherwise, this method does not differ from the above-described etching.

Aquatint. Aquatint is a tonal intaglio method. It is not only important as a fine-art printing method but also as a forerunner of halftone printing in general and of photogravure in particular. Aquatint produces the counterpart of mezzotint cells, though with a difference. In mezzotint, the plate is mechanically roughened; in aquatint a corresponding effect is produced by etching. For this purpose the metal plate is dusted all over with an acid-proof resin powder. Then the dusted plate is heated until the resin melts and attaches itself as tiny globules to the plate. These globules act as a resist during etching. The etcher controls the intaglio printing image by *stopping-out*, or by protecting, an area with an acid-resist and by varying the etching time of different areas.

Sugar-aquatint. Sugar-aquatint is a variation of the aquatint method which enables the artist to paint positive rather than negative images. As a painting medium on the plate he uses a compound that contains sugar to a certain extent. With this medium he creates the positive image on the plate. Then the whole plate is covered with acid-resistant varnish and when dry immersed in water; the varnish film is sufficiently porous to permit passage of the water to the image areas. These lift from the plate and carry the varnished areas above them along in the process. Thereby the plate is laid bare in the image areas. It is now treated like any other aquatint plate, as already described.

Stipple and crayon engraving. Both of these methods aim at the reproduction of tonal values and are in a sense intaglio halftone methods. In both methods etching and engraving are combined, though with certain differences which are too technical to be discussed in this manual. The plate is covered with a hard etching resist which is punctured with various fine-pointed tools for etching. After the plate is etched it is finished by hand engraving. Stipple and crayon engraving are only two of many possible combinations open to the intaglio print-maker.[63]

Image Carriers for Steel-Die Engraving and for Banknote Printing

Intaglio printing-image carriers for steel-die engraving and banknote printing were traditionally the result of manual and mechanical production methods. In the second third of this century the U. S. Bureau of Engraving and Printing introduced the electrolytic plate for banknote printing, and more recently it became possible to make plates for steel-die engraving by photoengraving techniques. Even though the last two mentioned kinds of image carriers reduced the importance of traditional plate-making methods for steel-die engraving and banknote printing, these methods are still of interest. In the following you find brief explanations of seven methods whereby intaglio plates are made for steel-die engraving and banknote printing: (1) hand engraving, (2) engraving with the ruling machine, (3) engraving with the geometrical lathe, (4) pantograph engraving, (5) die sinking, (6) plates made by electro deposition (known as electrolytic plates), and (7) plates made by photoengraving techniques.

Hand engraving. The first step in engraving is the transfer of the original image, or design, to be reproduced to the surface of the plate metal. This original may be a detailed drawing or it may be just a rough layout, depending on the nature of the job. The engraver can transfer the layout by making a tracing, by drawing, or by photoprinting, to mention some of the many existing techniques. The plate metal may be copper, but it is usually soft steel for production work. Hand engraving requires very high manual skill. It is done with various burins, or gravers, and the engraver observes and controls the progress of his work with a magnifying glass. For reasons of economy, hand engraving is limited to such design elements as cannot be reproduced mechanically.

Engraving with the ruling machine. For the laying of tints and for the making of decorative designs the engraver can use an engraver's ruling machine. This machine is equipped with a movable base for the plate and a diamond cutting head which can be spaced by a mechanical precision arrangement. The plate is covered with a resist in the areas to be ruled, and the cutting head scratches this resist, thereby laying the plate metal open to the action of the etchant during the etching operation which follows engraving.

Engraving with the geometric lathe. If you look at the border which frames each United States

dollar bill you will find an exceedingly fine pattern similar to that of the very finest lace. Each denomination of our money has a different pattern which helps to distinguish it from other denominations. These borders are made by means of an ingenious mechanical device, called the geometric lathe. In this precision machine a cutting point is actuated "through an elaborate system of gears, cams, and indexing mechanisms."[64] This machine can produce a practically infinite variety of patterns which are extremely difficult to imitate. The geometric lathe is therefore a most important designing tool in the protection of currency as well as other securities against forgery.

Engraving with the pantograph engraving machine. This kind of engraving is generally done in the engraved stationery field. The pantograph engraving machine produces tracing of letters from a master pattern. The operator traces the outline of the letter, or other image, on the master. A diamond follower reproduces this outline on the sur-

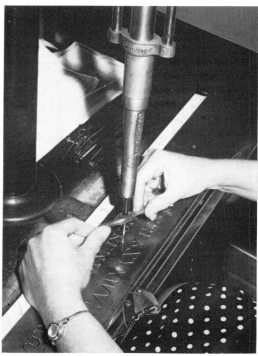

Courtesy Mr. Austen Pomerantz, Philadelphia

Steel-die engraving with a pantograph machine. You see the operator tracing the outline of letters on a master plate. The die itself is on top of the pantograph, not shown in this picture.

face of a die which is coated with an etching resist. The machine is manually operated and not power driven. It can reduce the size of letters in a wide range, say between 20 per cent and 2 per cent of the letter size on the master. Reduction comes about by mechanical linkage. Some models are capable of changing the proportions of letters and can therewith produce slanted letters, or italics, extended and condensed letters from one and the same pattern.

Standard patterns, or master plates, for a widely used model of a pantograph engraving machine "measure from 3¼ inches to 3⅜ inches wide and 18 inches long. As a rule they are manufactured on high carbon steel anywhere from 0.050 inch to 0.065 inch thick. They are often chromium plated to prevent them from rusting. The master plates which are offered for sale by the supply houses usually contain the capitals, smaller letters, and numerals for the particular style. Average script master plate letters have capitals 1 inch high and lower case letters ⁵⁄₁₆ inch high."[65]

Die-sinking. Very small type can be engraved by means of die-sinking. A set of sinking dies comprises the necessary letters and figures of a certain type design in the proper size. Each character is a separate steel die with the image in relief. These dies are known as punches. The die-sinker indicates the position of the future intaglio image on the plate and then produces this image by placing each punch in its correct position on the plate and by tapping the punch with a hammer. Thereby the relief image of the die is sunk into the steel plate. It goes without saying that die-sinking is a highly skilled operation.

Hardening and duplicating of intaglio steel dies. The completed steel die may be case-hardened before it is used for long-run printing. If duplicates of the die are needed, as is the case in the printing of our national currency, these are sometimes made by a process technically known as *siderography.* The hardened original steel die is first used for the making of a relief intermediate, a steel roller. Then this intermediate steel roller is hardened and thereafter functions like a punch. The image borne by the relief roller is duplicated as an intaglio duplicate image by pressing the roller into a plate of soft steel. The product of this operation is the final steel die. This die must be hardened prior to use, and it may be chromium-plated in addition.

Electrolytic plates for banknote printing. Siderography has been largely replaced in the United States Bureau of Engraving and Printing by an electrolytic process for duplicating steel engravings. The face of the full-size steel engraving is treated with a separating medium and then placed in a plating solution. During plating, a relief mold, known as *Alto*, is formed which consists of iron with a nickel surface. In turn, the face of this also is coated with a separating film and then placed in a plating solution where a thin surface film of nickel is electrodeposited. This film is the surface of the future *Basso* or duplicate intaglio die which is built up by electrodeposition of iron. The completed Basso is removed from the plating tank, ground smooth, welded to a steel backing plate, and finally chromium plated. This plate is suitable for long production runs as it can be re-chromed several times; as it can also serve for the making of many duplicate Bassos, the process is very efficient.

Intaglio plates made by photoengraving. Photoengraving is a most important method of making original image carriers for letterpress and other relief printing methods. Since photoengraving is extensively discussed in the preceding section, it is merely mentioned at this point that the relief printing areas are protected by a photomechanical resist and that the non-printing areas are etched away to the required depth by dissolving the unwanted metal with an etchant. The same principle can be applied to the making of intaglio plates for steel-die engraving. The difference is that now the non-printing areas are protected and the printing areas are bare. The etchant removes the metal in these areas whereas the surface of the plate remains at its original height. Steel-die engravers found that photoengraved intaglio plates add considerable latitude to steel-die engraving. This platemaking method makes it possible to convert drawings or reproduction proofs of type into the requisite image carriers without hand engraving.

Gravure Plates and Cylinders

Many people like to distinguish sheet-fed and roll-fed gravure printing by designating the first as photogravure and the second as rotogravure. This division is somewhat misleading as both sheet-fed and roll-fed gravure are based on photography and photomechanics and as both are executed on

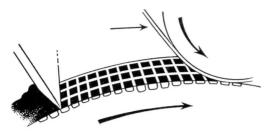

Diagram showing transfer of ink image to stock in gravure. At the extreme left the plate or cylinder surface is shown flooded with ink; the doctor-blade wipes the top surface and leaves the ink in the cells undisturbed. The ink image is transferred to the stock under high pressure exerted by the impression roll.

rotary presses. To add to the conundrum it must be mentioned that the term *photogravure* was originally reserved for a gravure method that did not use a controlled pattern of gravure cells but protected some of the plate metal from etching by dusting with acid-resistant powder—a technique that resulted in an uncontrolled or random pattern. This, the original Klič method of photogravure, is no longer used as a production process.

For these reasons, and as there is essentially but little difference between them, it is most expedient to discuss gravure plates and gravure cylinders together. For our purposes the subject matter is presented under seven headings which identify the main production stages of gravure plates and cylinders. These are: (1) preparation of plates and cylinders, (2) photography and retouching, (3) layout, (4) photomechanics, (5) etching, (6) plating, and (7) proofing.

Preparation of Gravure Plates and Cylinders

Image carriers for gravure are either plates or cylinders. Plates are used for sheet-fed gravure, cylinders for rotogravure. Gravure plates consist of refined copper, have a highly polished surface, and are approximately 0.020 inch thick which makes it possible to wrap them around the plate cylinder of the press. Gravure plates need no particular preparation but should be free of surface defects. "If the plate has deep polishing marks or other defects, it should be polished with engraving coal, using kerosene, water, or machine oil as a lubricant. To be effective, the polishing must be continued for a considerable time."[66]

It should be mentioned that gravure plates are much less used than gravure cylinders. Gravure plates are the image carriers for jobs

printed by sheet-fed gravure and they are also used for the proofing of material which will finally be printed with cylinders, a technique widely used in advertising production.[67]

We turn next to the commercially much more important subject of cylinders for rotogravure and their preparation.

Construction of gravure cylinders. "There are two types of rotogravure printing cylinders: the permanent shaft cylinder, having either a shaft running through the body of the cylinder or fabricated trunnions welded at each end, and the mandrel or cone-type cylinder. Both the permanent shaft and the mandrel designs have their distinct   advantages   and   disadvantages."[68] Roughly speaking, permanent shaft cylinders permit highest accuracy but are heavier and more difficult to store than detachable shaft, or mandrel type, cylinders. The latter are widely used for package printing where cylinders must be stored between runs.

Metals for gravure cylinders. Cylinders can be made of iron, steel, copper, and aluminum. "Selection of the material is greatly influenced by length, diameter, weight, wall thickness, and deflection tolerances. Ends are usually fabricated of steel bar and plate or steel shaft pressed through the cylinder body."[69]

Size of gravure cylinders. The size of gravure cylinders is determined by the press and by the nature of the job. The length of the cylinder depends on the press alone; the diameter depends on the design of the press in publication printing where cylinders with fixed diameters are used; in package printing where variable diameter cylinders are customary the nature of the job controls this dimension. "For regular publications cylinders are often up to 70 inches long by about 10 or 12 inches diameter. Cylinders for packaging vary greatly in size from the very small, about 7 inches long by 2 or 3 inch diameter up to massive cylinders 80 or more inches long with a diameter of about 17 inches. These variations are due to requirements for specialized printing and especially for inline production operations where dimensions are related to the operations which follow printing."[70] More recently much larger presses were built. There exists, for example, at least one publications press that prints a web 102 inches wide and that has cylinders of a 107-inch face. Still larger presses are used for the printing of vinyl floor covering. These are capable of printing material up to 144 inches in width,

Copper plating of cylinders. The image forming metal of gravure cylinders is copper. As the body of most gravure cylinders consists of other metals, they must be covered with copper before they can be used as image carriers. Copper deposition is done electrochemically in a plating tank. The thickness of the copper deposit "varies greatly with the circumference, length, and construction of the cylinder. The larger the cylinder, the greater the deposit, ranging from 15-thousandths on the side on laboratory cylinders to 50-thousandths on the side for large 86-inch face publication cylinders."[71] These figures refer to solid copper deposits. Other authorities mention 20 thousandths as a most usual thickness of such copper deposits. *Thin deposits*, known by their inventor as Ballard cylinders, have copper deposits of 6 thousandths of an inch.

The Ballard Process. In the Ballard Process the thin skin deposit is loosely adhered to the bulk of the cylinder surface "but is firmly attached at the bare ends. After the cylinder has been etched and printed, the copper skin is removed by cutting and then pulling it off."[72] Ballard cylinders are more used in publication printing than in package printing as "it is generally supposed that a skin deposited cylinder will not stand up to a very long run on the machine so well as a solid cylinder."[73] On the other hand, Ballard cylinders offer considerable advantages, "the two primary ones being the elimination of grinding, or turning off, of the old etching and allowing exact size cylinders for color work."[74]

Finishing of gravure cylinders. Under this head we discuss the turning, grinding, and polishing of solid deposit cylinders. "Ordinary thick deposits (as distinct from skin or Ballard deposits) are deliberately formed to have a greater diameter than is required in the finished cylinder. They may be brought to the required diameter and be given a relatively smooth surface by turning on a lathe with a hard tipped tool, a diamond, for example. The wheel-grinding technique may be used for trueing and rough grinding of fresh deposits and for removing etched work. Finishing is completed on the grinding machine with a fine abrasive material or a grinding stone. Final polishing can also be accomplished on a buffing machine."[75]

The completed cylinder must have the specified diameter within the permissible tolerances as close cylinder tolerances are "of prime importance for the control of color register and web tension."[76] In the GTA Cylinder Gauge the industry

Courtesy The Beck Engraving Company

A copper-plated gravure cylinder is polished to a high luster before it is used as an image carrier.

has an instrument that permits accurate measurements of cylinders within 0.0005 inch, greatly contributing to cylinder precision.

Photography and Retouching for Gravure

Essentially, photography for gravure does not differ from other kinds of graphic arts photography. The function of photography is the same in gravure as in all other printing processes: photography must provide intermediate records of the original images to be reproduced as required for the making of the printing-image carrier. But photography for gravure is more complex and can be executed in more variations than other branches of graphic arts photography.

This is so for two main reasons: one is the necessity of providing the bearing surface for the doctor-blade; the other is the fact that gravure is capable of reproducing continuous-tone images in three principally different ways. As the necessity of providing the bearing surface for the doctor-blade is closely related to the principle selected for the reproduction of continuous tones and as photography and photomechanics play decisive roles in the methods selected, a few explanatory comments are in order.

Three ways of reproducing continuous-tone images. Gravure is distinguished from all other printing processes by its ability to reproduce continuous-tone images in three different ways. The first is by changing the amount of ink in various areas by having *cells of constant areas and varying depth.* This principle underlies conventional, or straight, gravure. The second is by changing the relations between printed and not printed areas by having *cells of constant depth and varying areas;* this approach is based on halftone photography. Methods using halftone photography are classified in this manual as intaglio halftone methods. (In the gravure industry the term *reverse halftone* is frequently used.) The third way by which gravure can reproduce continuous tone images is by a combination of intaglio halftones and changes in the amount of ink to be deposited. This result is obtained by providing *cells of varying depth and varying areas.* Conventional gravure, which is at the time of writing still widely used, is the only method that is not executed by several proprietary methods. Straight intaglio halftone printing and the combination of intaglio halftones with changes in cell depth can be done by many methods. Most of these are proprietary processes, more or less protected by patents. Practically all of these many different gravure processes differ from each other in several production phases particularly in the photographic procedures by which they must be executed.

Gravure processes. As you will immediately see, there exists a considerable number of so-called gravure processes or methods. These processes are sometimes designated by the names of their inventors or by the type of dot employed. Generally speaking, the subject is too technical for discussion in our manual, but as many people are bewildered by these different processes a few explanatory comments should be found helpful. We will therefore mention the names of some of these processes and briefly classify them according to the three principles on which gravure image carriers can be based. This identification will be followed by a brief discussion of three representative processes, one for each of the three kinds.

There is first *conventional gravure,* which is based on cells of constant area and varying depth. The *Henderson Process* is an example of a straight intaglio halftone process based on cells of varying areas and constant depth. All other processes mentioned here are combinations of intaglio halftones and variations in cell depth. The oldest

of these is the *News-Dultgen Process,* still widely used at present. Others are the *Round Dot,* the *Dultgen-Hard Dot,* the *Gresham-McCorquodale,* the *Lateral Dot,* the *Art Color Hard Dot,* the *International-Wattier,* and the former *Dr. Kott-Alco Process,* now known as the *Hurletron Process.*[77] Even though a technical discussion of these processes and methods is not intended in this manual, the reader might find it helpful to distinguish between two gravure dot patterns: one is the checker-board pattern; the other is the so-called lateral dot formation. The older gravure processes fall in the first category; the more recent ones in the second.

Photographic differences of various gravure processes. Photographically, conventional gravure requires continuous-tone intermediates; straight intaglio halftone methods require halftone intermediates; and most mixed processes require both continuous-tone and halftone intermediates. The continuous-tone intermediate is needed for variations in cell depth, whereas the halftone intermediate provides dots, and hence cells, of varying areas. Mixed processes obtain their halftones either by use of a cross-line screen, by a contact screen, or by special screens developed for a particular process. The same holds true for intaglio halftone methods. In intaglio halftone methods and in mixed processes, the bearing support for the doctor blade is provided by the solid areas between halftone dots; in conventional gravure this support is obtained by a separate step known as screening. This step is part of photomechanics and should not be confused with screening for halftone photography.

The three representative gravure processes to be briefly characterized in this unit are (1) conventional gravure which is later described in more detail, (2) the Henderson Process, and (3) the News-Dultgen Process.

Conventional gravure. Conventional gravure is based on continuous tone photography which may or may not include color separation photography depending on the nature of a reproduction job. Type images are, of course, prepared by line photography. Continuous-tone negatives are usually retouched before they are converted into positives and these are often again retouched before they are passed for exposure. Continuous-tone positives are suitable for controlling depth variations of gravure cells but they do not provide for the *lands,* or bearing surfaces, needed for the doctor-blade. These must be incorporated by a

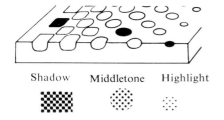

Shadow   Middletone   Highlight

Diagram of a gravure image carrier made by the original Dultgen Process. *This process combines varying the areas of cells with varying their depth.*

separate operation, namely, the already mentioned gravure screening as distinguished from halftone screening. Gravure screening is discussed further in the unit on photomechanics.

The Henderson Process. The Henderson Process is a straight intaglio halftone method. The inventor wanted to achieve two simplifications over conventional gravure. "First he wanted a cylinder engraving means which would eliminate carbon tissue as the material for transferring a design to a cylinder ready for etching; and second, he wanted a screening technique that would provide for a uniformly etched cylinder by the use of a single Baumé strength ferric chloride."[78] This result is achieved by using a halftone positive, prepared as specified by the inventor, as intermediate and by coating the cylinder with a photoengraving resist. Six units of equipment built to the inventor's specifications are available for the execution of the process. Even though there are some variations in depth between cells of different sizes corresponding to larger or smaller halftone dots, these are incidental. There is no continuous-tone intermediate used, and as the resist is incapable "to control the rate of etch from shadow to highlight, the depth of etch is fairly uniform."[79] The Henderson Process is limited in scope and mainly used for package printing.

The News-Dultgen Process. The News-Dultgen Process, at present often called the *Dultgen Soft-Dot Process* to distinguish it from the more modern *Dultgen Hard-Dot Process,* "was one of the principal factors that contributed so much to the rapid increase in four-color gravure advertising in newspaper supplement and magazine printing." The News-Dultgen Process combines a continuous-tone positive and a halftone positive made from the same negative. The halftone image is so adjusted that the shadow areas have almost, but not quite, a checkerboard pattern which provides the necessary bearing surface for the doctor

blade. The continuous tone positive is used to control cell depth of the halftone areas. The Dultgen Process simplified cylinder-making, made it possible to achieve greater uniformity in the etching of multiple images and of duplicate cylinders, "without at any time sacrificing detail and full tonal range of the copy. In addition, its halftone screen formation permits extensive cylinder or plate correction with safety while at the same time assuring greater printing uniformity and longer cylinder life."[80]

The Dultgen Hard-Dot Process. Finally a few words on soft-dot and on hard-dot Dultgen. Halftone photography for the Dultgen Process cannot be done as customary. "Because gravure dots must never touch or overlap, Dultgen had to design a special halftone screen and set up a new practice for handling exposure and development. *The dots produced by this screen are called "soft dots" because they lack a sharp rim on their outer edge.* Dultgen dots terminate in a gradually shaded-off vignetted edge. Since in etching this dot the well (or cell) gets rough on the edges and does not print clean, detail is adversely affected. The Dultgen Hard-Dot Process corrects this fault. By a different technique of exposing and using high contrast material, a sharp opaque dot is obtained."[81]

These examples must suffice. They show clearly the relationship of the nature of a process to the problems of providing the necessary bearing surface, uniformity of cylinder-making, and the photographic techniques needed for this process. We turn now to our next subject, which is layout for gravure.

Layout for Gravure

Both photogravure plates and rotogravure cylinders are single-unit, or integral, printing-image carriers. The photographic intermediates must therefore be assembled in the exact position in which they are intended to appear on the image carrier. This assembly and the planning for it are called *layout* in the gravure industry. Layout corresponds to stripping in lithography and to imposing and lockup in letterpress.

Some consideration for gravure layouts. The first step in preparing a gravure layout is the development of a detailed position plan for all material to be placed on the same image carrier. In publication work where the size of pages and their arrangement is rather standardized, such plans are not very often changed, but in package and other custom printing each job requires its own position diagram. Single-color, or monotone, jobs pose fewer difficulties than full-color reproductions because in the latter the layout for full-color printing must also consider the correct position of each color image in relation to all other images.

Two other points should be mentioned. One is that tonal images and line images, which include of course type images, are usually not assembled together but in two separate units. Care must be taken that the images of both units will fall in their proper places. The other point is connected with the subsequent operation of photoprinting. In many cases, the assembled images are photoprinted on a material known as carbon-tissue. Carbon-tissue will be discussed in the following unit on photomechanics for gravure, but at this point we must anticipate two pertinent items. One is that carbon-tissue must be transferred to the final image carrier, the other is that carbon-tissue, in larger units especially, requires very careful handling for the high dimensional stability which is necessary for full-color jobs.

Pin register systems. In any case the assembly of positives must be made with greatest precision, particularly for full-color printing. Various methods are used for precision assembly during layout. These are called generically *register systems.* "In the 'pin,' 'stud,' or 'lug' register system, two projecting pins are attached to the margin of the positive assembly. In the simplest application of the idea, the carbon-tissue has holes punched in it to engage the pins on the positive at the time of exposure. In a more refined application of the idea, a thin flat strip of metal bearing punched holes is temporarily attached to the carbon-tissue before exposure. Lug register methods have been developed largely because of the tendency to put work down in relatively small units on the cylinder because of the difficulty of maintaining dimensional stability of large sheets. Lug register, properly used, allows of work being laid with great accuracy."[82]

The cabriolet system. Three point register systems have become a valuable addition to registering techniques in color work particularly. The original three point register system, the so-called *cab* system, is now briefly described. "The word 'cab' is derived from the French word cabriolet, meaning carriage. Our cab is actually a carrier plate. The three-point system is necessary because

the glass plates used for color work have bumpy edges. Therefore a metal angle is equipped with two triangular metal points along one side and one such point on the adjacent side. Now all plates touch only at the same three points. Since the glass edges affect the register, the photographer must also have similar points in his camera kit."[83]

Impositions are related to the nature of the printed product. The detailed layout or plan for the assembly of publication printing and book work, generally known as imposition, depends— as already stated in a similar context—primarily on the available folding equipment, and is therefore discussed together with folding for all other printing processes in Chapter X. The layout for custom-made jobs depends entirely on their nature. In package printing the subsidiary conversion processes by which the printed material receives its final shape must be carefully considered. These may consist in die-cutting, slitting, laminating, embossing, and so forth. Some of these operations are briefly explained in Chapter X.

The layout sheet. After the scheme of assembly is determined, an exactly drawn diagram known as the *layout sheet*, or *layout*, for short, is made. This layout sheet serves as the basis for the assembly of the positives to be combined in one image carrier. In the past gravure positives were usually photographic glass plates. These were superseded by films when stable film bases became available

Photomechanics for Gravure

Photomechanics for gravure often appear to the beginner to be complex and a little confusing. But if you keep firmly in mind what functions photomechanics have in the production of gravure image-carriers, you will not find the subject too difficult. You want to remember that gravure can obtain tonal reproductions either *by depositing ink films of varying thickness in different areas* of the printed image or *by varying the size of intaglio halftone dots*, or, finally, *by combining both techniques*. Technically, this is achieved either by varying the depth of cells, or by varying the area of cells, or by varying both cell depth and area.

The crucial role of cell depth and cell area. It should be unnecessary to explain again that variations in cell depth imply variation in the ink quantity held by these cells and that these quantity variations will be noticed after image transfer to the paper as variations in color values. Nor does it need further explanation that intaglio half-tones, which serve the same purpose as do other halftones, will produce tonal images on the printing stock and that a combination of both, namely halftones and variations in cell depth, cannot fail to have the same end result.

Diagram showing the relations between cell depth and values of printed images in conventional gravure. Shallower cells transfer less ink than deeper ones. Differences in ink quantity account for differences in image values from light to dark.

Photomechanics and the structure of gravure cells. Close control of both depth and area of gravure cells is therefore essential for all gravure methods. Treating the image carrier with an etchant removes the required amounts of metal where it should be removed and thereby produces the gravure cells. Photomechanics provide the guide and control for the etching operation. Both the cell areas and their depth can be decisively influenced by the photomechanical image which is either formed on the surface of the image carrier or transferred to this surface after having been formed independently. By what means this result is achieved is our next topic.

In Section 2, "Introduction to Photomechanics," it is explained that we distinguish two kinds of photomechanical images: (1) stencils and (2) continuous photomechanical layers of varying hardnesses and thicknesses. It is also explained that stencils serve for the making of intaglio halftone image carriers, whereas images of varying hardness and thickness serve as resists in the etching of gravure cells of varying depth.

A firm grasp of the difference between these two photomechanical products is a prerequisite for the understanding of photomechanics for gravure. *In photomechanical stencils, the light-sensitive coating is either completely hardened or not hardened at all, with no significant variations between these two extremes.* During development of the photoprinted coating, all hardened areas remain on the supporting surface and all unhardened areas are washed away.

In continuous photomechanical layers of varying hardness and thickness, the light-sensitive coating is variably hardened throughout and changed in its solubility to various degrees in various areas. In some areas the coating is harder; in others it is less so. After development, such a coating still presents a continuous uninterrupted film, but it is a film of varying hardness and thickness. The hardness and thickness variations of this film depend on the amount of light to which a given area is exposed; areas exposed to more light are more hardened than areas exposed to less light. These variations in the physical properties of the resist influence the extent to which a given etchant can pass through it or permeate it and etch the metal underneath.[84]

The hardness and thickness of the developed photomechanical coating plays a decisive role in the etching of gravure image carriers with cells of varying depth. *As a simplified generalization, it can be said that the depth of cells is inversely related to the hardness and thickness of the photomechanical film.*

Resists for gravure and their functions. The photomechanical film serves as a resist during the etching of the intaglio image carrier. You may remember that photomechanical resists are also used for the etching of relief image carriers such as photoengravings or wrap-around plates. In these cases the resists are stencils that uniformly protect the image areas of the metal from the action of the etchant, but in gravure methods having cells of varying depth, the resist has a different function. Here it protects various metal areas not uniformly but to varying degrees from the etchant, depending on its own hardness and thickness in any given area. The harder and thicker the resist, the more an area is protected from the action of the etchant; the more an area is protected, the less it will be etched. Conversely, the less an area is protected from the etchant the deeper will the cells be etched. The *lands, bridges,* or *posts,* as the metal areas between cells are called, must consequently be completely protected, whereas the deep shadows, which require the deepest etched cells, are least protected from the etchant.

Gravure can use two kinds of materials for the making of resists with varying hardness and thickness; the oldest is carbon-tissue which is manufactured by several companies. The other material is a much more recent development by the E. I. duPont de Nemours Company sold under the trade name of *Rotofilm.* Even though these two materials differ significantly in their composition, either of them is suitable for the making of gravure image carriers with cells of varying depth. Gravure image carriers of uniform depth can be made with resists similar to those described for photoengraving and lithography.

Our presentation of gravure photomechanics is divided into the following five points: (1) carbon-tissue, (2) Rotofilm, (3) photomechanics for conventional gravure, (4) photomechanics for methods having cells of varying area and varying depth, and (5) photomechanics for intaglio halftones of uniform depth. We begin with carbon-tissue, the classic material of photomechanics for rotogravure.

Preparation and exposure of carbon-tissue. Carbon-tissue consists of a mixture of gelatin, plasticizers, pigments, and similar ingredients, which is coated on a paper base. Gelatin is, as you already know, one of the several colloids that can be sensitized by bichromates and thereby made light-reactive. Carbon-tissue is not light-reactive until it has been treated with a solution of bichromates; it is either sensitized shortly before use or sensitized and then stored under refrigeration for future use. Practice is not uniform; some plants store sensitized tissue for a few days, others up to six weeks.[85]

After sensitizing, carbon-tissue is dried and then used for photoprinting by exposing it to strong lights together with a gravure screen or a photographic transparency in a vacuum frame. The tissue is relatively thick; during exposure it is hardened to different degrees in its depth, depending on the amount of light received by vari-

Removing the backing sheet of exposed carbon tissue is a step in its development. The tissue itself adheres to the gravure copper plate, the backing sheet is discarded. Notice the images, due to exposure, on the removed backing sheet.

ous areas. Exposure is regulated in such a manner that the hardening action does not go all the way down to the paper base on which the tissue is coated. A layer of unhardened, easily soluble gelatin must remain close to the support. The detail of exposure depends on the gravure process used. It is not the same for conventional gravure and for combination methods using intaglio halftones together with variations in cell depth.

Laydown and development of carbon-tissue. After exposure the tissue is transferred, gelatin side down, to the wetted gravure image carrier, a plate or a cylinder, in one of several techniques, either manually or mechanically. This step is known as *laydown* and the machines used for this purpose are called laydown machines; they are equipped with precision positioning devices. The laid-down tissue is next developed with hot water. The water penetrates the paper backing and melts the unhardened layer of gelatin close to it. The backing paper can now be removed and the tissue is further treated with water until the image is completely developed. Then the image carrier with the developed tissue on its surface is dried and subjected to several manual operations by which it is prepared for etching. Carbon-tissue is a very critical material that must be handled with care and closely controlled in each of the many operations through which it passes, from storage to the final etching of the image carrier.

Rotofilm. Carbon-tissue was the only material that could be used for the making of photo-

Laydown of carbon tissue on a gravure plate. Plate and exposed carbon tissue are put through a mangle. The plate is slightly wetted to make the tissue adhere.

the printing image. "A typical etching schedule for monotone conventional gravure would show a heavy first acid being poured on for four minutes; next acid for five minutes; third acid for five minutes; fourth, four minutes; fifth, three minutes, for a total etching time of twenty-one minutes. A sixth acid may be used for a minute or two on the lightest tones if it is necessary."[89]

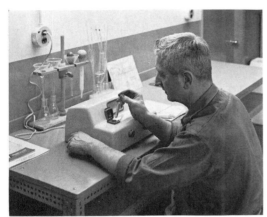

Laboratory technician testing the strength of an etchant.

Type and other line images may or may not be etched together with tonal images in conventional gravure. Sometimes both kinds of images are present in the same resist. If type is to be etched separately, it is usually etched first and the tonal images are protected against the action of the etchant by *painting-out* with an acid-proof material. After the type is etched, the type areas are protected in the same way as were the tonal images, and the tone areas are now made accessible to the etchant by removing the protective coating with a solvent. Another method uses two different resists, one for type and the other for tonal images. The tissue bearing the type images is laid down first, the rest of the image carrier is protected, and the type is etched. Then the tissue with the tonal images is laid down in register with the type areas, and the tonal images are etched after the type images have been protected.

Etching of combination gravure image carriers. The etching of combination image carriers is less critical than the etching of conventional gravure plates or cylinders. The more the tonal effect is due to variations in cell areas and the less to variations in cell depth, the simpler etching becomes. In the News-Dultgen Process where the cell areas

are limited to 50 per cent dots, four to five etches are customary. "Dultgen etching for newspaper or publication work may take as little as 12 minutes using 4 acids about 2½ minutes apart whereas monotone brown conventional may take as long as 25 minutes."[90] In some other mixed processes where dots up to 70 per cent are possible, three and sometimes merely two etches are sufficient.

Etching of intaglio halftone gravure image carriers. These image carriers do not vary the depth of cells and can therefore be etched in a single operation. The density of etches is, of course, not the same for conventional gravure, combination methods, and intaglio halftone image carriers. Methods using a smaller number of etches begin with a much less dense etchant than is used in conventional gravure.

Etching Techniques

Traditionally etching of gravure plates and cylinders is left to highly skilled and well-experienced craftsmen who perform their work with simple equipment. But during the recent past many efforts were made to improve etching methods and to control etching by application of science to this phase of gravure. At the time of writing, traditional etching is most likely still dominant but several new methods are already well advanced and cannot be omitted from a discussion of the subject. Terminology is rather undeveloped in this area. For most gravure people there exists (or existed until very recently) only one kind of etching and therefore no need for distinctive terminology. Without any intention to introduce lasting terms, but solely for the purpose of organization, several descriptive terms which were taken whenever possible from the literature are used in the following discussion. First you find a brief characterization of the customary etching technique. This is headed as traditional etching; next, a two-stage etching machine process is described under the heading of the *Art Color Etching Process*, then comes the *Detroit Gravure Automatic Etching Process*, and finally the *black-light one-iron etch* is described.

Traditional etching. Traditional etching is done without the aid of mechanical equipment. The cylinder is placed in an etching trough and slowly rotated either mechanically or manually during etching. Each of the different etching solutions is prepared beforehand, ready in its own jug. The etcher pours the etchant from these jugs; as it

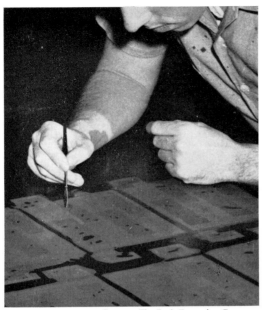

Courtesy The Beck Engraving Company

A skilled craftsman applies an acidproof resist to those plate areas that must be protected during etching. This operation is called staging.

flows off the cylinder it is collected in another jug under the trough. An etcher must of course be a highly skilled and equally experienced craftsman. He must be able to judge the results of etching and to modify etching as the case may need it. This he does by changing the duration of various baths, or even their order, and by local application of the etchant with an etching swab, for example. After completion of etching, the image carrier (plate or cylinder) is hosed with water; the resist is removed and the product is carefully inspected prior to proofing or press work.

The Art Color Etching Process. This etching process was developed for the etching of cylinders made by the Art Color Hard-Dot Process, a combination process of intaglio halftones and differentially etched cell depths. The Art Color Etching Process uses a two-bath etching machine where every detail is most carefully controlled. The etchant is directed by an air bubble burst to the cylinder which is automatically rotated at a controlled speed and automatically reversed in its direction every 30 seconds. "At the end of the first etch the cylinder is lifted while the second tray slides underneath. At this point the cylinder is kept rotating so that an even coat of etchant remains on the cylinder."[91] After completion of

etching the cylinder is automatically rinsed with temperature controlled water. The inventors state among other advantages of this system that they have put the skill of etching on a scientific basis, that they have absolute control over etching and etch conditions, and that they can duplicate cylinders so that each unit will be like others etched by this process.

The Detroit Gravure Automatic Etching Process. This process combines the principle of etching with etchants of varying Baumés, or concentrations, with extremely accurate timing and measuring devices. "The etching machine we have is not just an etching machine. In a broader sense it is an etching computer. All of the customer's requirements are reduced to time units and numbers. These units are dialed on the control panel. At this point the machine is completely automatic except for pushing the start button." A controlled amount of etchant of a predetermined specific gravity and controlled temperature is used for etching. The etchant is diluted as required by the job in hand. "In using the continuous dilution procedure not one, two, three, or four different Baumés are used, but an infinite number."[92]

The black-light one-iron etch. This designation is not understandable without explanation. "Black-light is a sort of a popular name. It's a poor name. The energy is not black nor is it light. Technically it is energy from 3,200 angstroms to 4,000 angstroms. It is known as ultraviolet, near ultraviolet."[93] This explains black-light. One-iron etch, the second component of this mysterious heading is a single bath etchant made of iron perchloride. The compounding of black-light and one-iron etch expresses the relatedness of photomechanics and etching, which characterizes this new method of arriving at cells of differing depth with a single bath.

This method was first publicly presented by Ernest Wattier at the 1960 convention of the Gravure Technical Association in New York City. In the course of experimental work which had the object of producing a one-bath etch, it was found that replacing the customary carbon arc lamps with black-light fluorescent tubes for the exposure of continuous tone positives made it possible and practical to replace conventional etching techniques requiring a number of different etching solutions by a single etching bath.[94] In the following year it was reported that this method was used successfully with certain modifications for actual cylinder production by a large gravure plant.

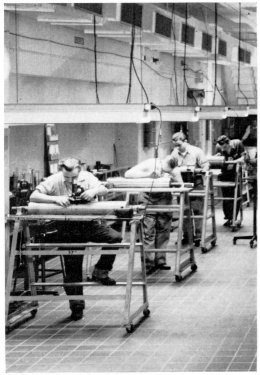

Gravure finishers at work on rotogravure cylinders. These highly skilled craftsmen give cylinders the final touch of quality. For inspection they use a special rotogravure microscope.

This process relieves the etcher of the responsibility for the quality of etching. The etcher pours the etchant as customary, but neither adjusts nor manipulates the concentration and duration of various etches nor does he treat the cylinder locally by swabbing. "His judgment is exercised only at the tail end of the etching to decide when the etching is complete."[95]

These three items show that the gravure industry is in the process of developing modern industrial methods for better controlled and more scientific etching. At this point we leave the subject of etching and sketch briefly the following operations of proofing and if necessary, re-etching of plates and cylinders.

Proofing and re-etching. The etched image carrier is inspected and if it passes inspection it may either be proofed or be put on the press without proofing. Gravure plates are usually proofed on production presses. Single-color gravure cylinders, called "monotone cylinders," as you may remember, are not usually proofed; but cylinders for full-color printing are. Proofing can be done either on production or on proof presses.

The proofs are examined, marked where improvements are wanted, and the image carrier is corrected accordingly. If cells are too shallow, the plate or cylinder is either locally or completely re-etched. The top surface, which provides the support to the doctor-blade, is carefully protected during this operation. If certain areas are etched too deep, this condition can be corrected by locally treating the lands of the cells with abrasives or by burnishing. Other techniques for correcting cells that are etched too deep include spot electroplating and the application of lacquer to the bottom of cells, thereby reducing their total volume. After correction, the image carrier may or may not be proofed again, depending on the nature of the work and the standards of a plant. (Proof presses and proofing techniques are discussed in Chapter VI, Section 8.)

Chromium Plating of Gravure Cylinders

Cylinders intended for comparatively short runs do not need chromium facing but those made for long production runs do. The life of a cylinder

A gravure plate is lifted out of the plating tank after chromium plating.

depends, according to Cartwright and MacKay, on at least seven variables, namely (1) hardness and grain structure of copper, (2) screen ruling and ratio, (3) depth of etching, (4) doctor action, (5) composition of the ink, (6) type of ink duct, and (7) the paper on which the work is printed. "With so many factors it is difficult to estimate the number of impressions an unfaced cylinder will give. In general, it has been found that unfaced cylinders for publication printing can be expected to print 60,000 to 100,000 copies on a web rotary with open ducts. The life of a cylinder is much greater on a machine with an enclosed duct if suitable ink is used, and editions up to 500,000 have been reported."[96]

"It is now usual to chromium face all cylinders used for packaging, but non-faced cylinders are often preferred for moderate editions of publications. The cylinders are generally used only once and it is desirable to avoid the expense and delay associated with facing."[97] Chromium facing is like copper plating an electrochemical process. Chromium is much harder than copper, nickel, or iron which two metals may also be used for the facing of gravure cylinders.

Advantages of chromium plating. The thickness of the chromium facing is governed by the nature of the work. "For tone subjects made with a 175 screen a thickness of 0.0002 inch is satisfactory, but for coarse screen work the thickness may go to 0.5–0.7 thousandths."[98] Chromium facing contributes many desirable features to gravure cylinders besides increasing their life expectancy. It makes for "a low coefficient of friction between the contact edge of the doctor-blade and the face of the cylinder; has a leveling effect on the cylinder surface resulting in a clean wiping action by the doctor-blade; and further facilitates ink release from the cylinder cells to the web. But the most important feature of chromium faced cylinders is that these can be replated with chromium when the cells lose depth and therewith color as a result of cylinder wear."[99]

Length of run obtainable with plated gravure cylinders. Finally a brief comment on the length of run to be expected from chromium-faced cylinders. Keeping the earlier mentioned variables in mind, much depends on actual operations. But "under good conditions, a minimum of one million copies, or impressions, may be expected from a gravure cylinder and larger editions are not uncommon. On the other hand, coatings sometimes break down at an early stage, necessitating stripping and re-depositing."[100]

Section 5:   Planographic Printing-Image Carriers

The common denominator of planographic printing is the already stated fact that the printing areas and the non-printing areas are essentially in the same plane on planographic image carriers and that the two different kinds of image areas are chemically treated to be either ink-receptive *and* water-repellent, or water-receptive *and* ink-repellent. The ink receptivity and water repellence of the printing areas and the water receptivity and ink repellence of the non-printing areas must be maintained by dampening the plate at every printing cycle.

Our introduction to planographic printing-image carriers consists of three units: (1) image carriers for stone lithography, (2) image carriers for offset-lithography, and (3) image carriers for collotype. We do not discuss image carriers for direct lithography under a separate heading because these are essentially the same as offset-lithographic image carriers. On the other hand, it should be explained that collotype image carriers differ in some important respects from other planographic image carriers. They are nevertheless presented in this section because collotype image carriers are more related to planographic than to any other kind of image carriers.

Diagram of printing and non-printing areas of a lithographic plate. The solid black areas are ink receptive and water repellent; the areas having droplets are ink repellent and water receptive.

Image Carriers for Stone Lithography

With the perfection of offset lithography stone lithography lost all commercial importance in the United States and serves now almost exclusively in this country for fine-art printing. The printing-image carrier is a lithographic stone, usually imported from Bavaria which traditionally supplies the best kinds of lithographic stones. The artist can create his design directly on the stone or he can work on a specially treated paper which is known as lithographic transfer paper because images drawn on it can be simply transferred to a lithographic stone. But many artist printmakers believe that a fine-art lithograph should be directly drawn and otherwise created on the stone itself. At this point it should be mentioned that stone lithography is a direct printing method by which, as in all other direct methods, the reading direction of the image is reversed during press-work. The artist must keep this fact in mind when he creates the image, particularly when he combines reading matter with pictures or drawings.

The making of image carriers for stone lithography can be divided for our purposes into three phases: (1) the preparation of the stone, (2) the creation of the printing image, and (3) the treatment of the image and non-image areas for ink receptivity and water-repellence and vice versa.

The preparation of lithographic stones. Graining is the first step in the making of lithographic stone image carriers. Graining has several functions. One of them is the removal of an existing printing image, another is to provide the texture necessary for drawing on the stone. This texture is known as the *grain;* it has technical functions as well as aesthetic ones. For graining, the artist places the stone face up on a table, makes a watery mixture of an abrasive on the image-bearing surface, places another stone face down on the first stone and rubs and pushes the top stone back and forth in different directions on the bottom stone until the latter is smoothly ground.

The creation of the printing image. After the stone is ground and otherwise prepared, it is ready for the making of the printing image. Lithography is so popular with artist printmakers because it permits the creative artist an almost unlimited range of effects which can be obtained with a variety of techniques including

Artist painting on the surface of a lithographic stone. The painted areas become ink receptive and are the future printing areas; the blank areas are treated to repel printing ink and become the non-printing areas.

drawing, painting, scratching, engraving, and spattering, to mention some of the more commonly used ones. The lithographic artist draws with special ink-receptive lithographic crayons, available in various degrees of hardness. If he wants to paint he can use lithographic tusche. Both are media which produce water-repellent and ink-receptive images on the stone after it is treated with an acid rinse.

Treating a lithographic stone. After the artist has created the printing image, the stone is chemically treated to improve the ink-repellence and water-receptivity of the non-image areas and, separately, to improve the ink-receptivity and water-repellence of the image areas. The first treatment is traditionally known as etching, and the second as rolling-up. The word "etching" is inexact, and modern technical literature prefers the term *desensitizing* to it. Desensitizing is done by brushing a chemical solution on the stone. Rolling up is done by applying a special greasy ink to the image on the surface of the stone.

The preceding description is most sketchy. The making of a lithographic stone image carrier is a highly developed art of which we here present only a brief outline.

The finished stone is then proofed, and thereafter either retouched or completely reworked until the artist printmaker feels that it is ready for printing. The artist, or the lithographic printer, can modify the inking of the stone and of the printing pressure in order to obtain certain aesthetic effects.

Image Carriers for Offset Lithography

Offset lithography is in our own time the commercially most important planographic printing method. Compared with it, all other planographic methods are almost insignificant. This fact alone would justify a more extensive treatment of offset lithographic image carriers than that accorded to image carriers of less used printing methods. But there are two additional reasons for a more detailed discussion of this subject. One is that the growth of offset lithography depended primarily on improvements in the making and in the quality of image carriers; the other reason is that there exists now such a wide variety of offset plates—to use the common industry term—that the field is somewhat confusing to the uninitiated and therefore needs explaining.

Following the general plan for the discussion of image carriers, we will first review the principal stages by which original images are converted into lithographic plates; then we will discuss different kinds of plates, their purposes and also their different properties.

The Main Manufacturing Stages of Lithographic Plates

Most lithographic plates are made by means of photomechanics but some are also made by other methods such as direct image transfer or electrostatics. The latter kinds are mostly, though not exclusively, used for office duplication and are at the time of writing not too important in the lithographic business. The production of lithographic plates made by photomechanics can be divided into the following five main stages: (1) photography, (2) litho-art, (3) stripping, (4) platemaking, and (5) proofing.

Photography for Lithography

The functions of photography are essentially the same wherever image carriers are made by means of photomechanics. The detail of operation differs, of course, for different types of image carriers, but this detail is in all cases outside our discussion. As you may remember, photography has the object of converting original images into printable images and of providing transparent intermediates for photomechanics. These points are extensively discussed in Chapters III and IV. It should be mentioned that the literature on photography for lithographic printing is exceptionally well developed, primarily by the Graphic Arts Technical Foundation.

Litho-Art

The department where the products of the camera department are further processed is usually known as the litho-art or as the color-etching department. This department must not be confused with *creative* art departments which can also be found in some lithographic plants. From the lithographer's point-of-view the creative art department has the function of rendering art-and-copy preparation services, whereas the litho-art department is a part of lithographic manufacturing. In the litho-art or color-etching department we find, consequently, highly skilled lithographic craftsmen, whereas commercial artists and designers are employed in a creative art department.

The term "litho-art" is not clearly defined; it is a catch-all for a variety of operations all of which use artistic abilities and skills of varying degrees. The craftsmen who work in the litho-art department or in the color-etching department must have the ability to handle pencil and brush, inks, and various other media. They must be capable of interpreting various images and they need a keen sense of tonal values. Admittedly they are not functioning as creative artists but they must possess a highly specialized kind of imaginative power which is essential for their work.

It should be mentioned that not every lithographic plant needs its own litho-art department. Often the stripping or the opaquing department is called upon to perform some of the operations discussed in the following. But first a few words on the layout and equipment of this department.

The layout and equipment of the litho-art department. The main value of the litho-art and color-etching department lies in the skill of its craftsmen. The equipment is rather simple and light if compared to that used in other departments of a lithographic plant. This equipment varies according to the size of a litho-art department and also according to the functions exercised in a specific department.

In a well-equipped litho-art department we find artist's stands and stools and easels for placing the copy. Light tables equipped with a diffusing surface and with registering devices are used for a variety of purposes, among which are the squaring of negatives, ruling, opaquing, and the adding of register and other reference marks. For dot-etching special sinks or stands are available.

Tools and materials used in litho-art departments. Among the optical instruments used in a litho-art department are various kinds of densitometers, magnifiers, and collimators. (Collimators are optical instruments with which the vertical alignment of transparencies can be checked.) The tools of the litho-artist or, as he often is called, *color-etcher*, consist of pencils, brushes, paper stumps, litho crayons, ruling pens,

Courtesy Eastman Kodak Company

A litho artist at work. The original art is at his left for comparison. He retouches a color separation which is on the tilted light table. To avoid touching the separation he uses a movable hand rest; his tools are on a tabouret at his right.

needles, scrapers, frisketing knives, and similar items. Airbrush equipment may also be used for retouching and vignetting. The materials used by litho-artists include opaquing liquids, lithographic tusche, dyes, photographic reducers, staging lacquers, and resists.

Finally, the litho-art department should be well illuminated. Illumination plays a very important role in the judging of color, as you know from our Chapter III. The work of the litho-artist consists to a great extent in the evaluating and comparing of color and in the adjusting of minute tonal differences. The light in which he works is therefore critical, and the illumination of this department is carefully planned.

The seven main tasks of the litho-art department. A litho-art department may have all or some of the following seven tasks: (1) translating customers' art into reproducible form, (2) correcting flaws in the product of the camera, (3) correcting flaws in press plates, (4) supplementing the work of the camera department, (5) correcting of tone, (6) correcting of color, and (7) tusching of plates. Each of these seven main functions is here merely briefly identified as a more extensive discussion is provided in Chapter IV, Section 4.

Translating customers' art into reproducible form. It happens often that artwork not quite suitable for offset-lithographic reproduction must, nevertheless, be used for a specific job. In such cases the litho-art department may have to modify or adapt the copy for the necessities of the lithographic process. Services of this nature are not generally rendered, but they are nonetheless worth mentioning.

Correcting flaws in the products of the camera. Like everything else, the products of the camera may turn out at times to be defective. If the defects are minor, they can be corrected by the litho-artist. Pinholes or other defects in opacity are opaqued; closed-in areas are opened up by scratching or scraping with needles or scrapers.

Supplementing the work of the camera. Not all desired effects are solely obtainable by photography or obtainable by it in the most economical manner. Some effects are best brought about by the skilful hands of a lithographic artist. Among them are silhouetting and vignetting, ruling, and others. Vignetting makes a subject fade out very gradually into its background; silhouetting does the contrary, it makes the subject stand out in clear definition; ruling may be necessary in the production of business and other forms. All these and similar tasks can be performed by manual skills directly on negatives or positives.

Correcting of tone. Correcting of tone is a very important step in halftone work for quality single-color as well as for full-color reproduction. Retouching and dot-etching are the most frequently used techniques for tone control. Both of them are explained in Chapter IV, Section 4.

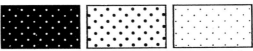

Courtesy Graphic Arts Technical Foundation

Diagram of changes in dot sizes, effected by dot etching.

Correcting of color. The subject of color correcting is extensively discussed in Chapter III and Chapter IV. Here it needs merely to be mentioned that color correcting is partly done in the camera department by photographic masking and partly in the litho-art department by manual methods, such as dot-etching.

Stripping for Offset Lithography

Stripping plays a steadily increasing role in the conversion of original images into image carriers for offset lithography. As the stripping department of a lithographic plant has, generally speaking, two different functions that are not discharged by corresponding departments in other printing methods, the purpose and place of lithographic stripping is often misunderstood. These two different functions are (1) the supplementing and adapting of photographic negatives or positives, and (2) the assembly of these intermediates for photomechanical plate making.

Before we identify the most important functions of stripping, it must be remembered that different kinds of work require different stripping techniques. It is therefore expedient to speak of stripping either as of black-and-white, or as of multicolor, or as of full-color stripping. Other distinctions are made according to the purpose of printed jobs such as publications, labels, books, and greeting cards, for example. None of these kinds uses exactly identical stripping techniques, but their detailed discussion is, as can be expected, too technical for our purposes. Keeping all these differences in mind we can, nevertheless, arrive at a practical division of the subject by distinguishing six main tasks of stripping for offset lithography. But before we discuss these, a brief description of the layout and equipment of the stripping department is presented.

The layout and equipment of the stripping department. The stripping department is, as already mentioned, closely related to the platemaking department. Very often both departments share the same general working area and utilize some of the required equipment together. Like all other departments, the stripping department of a lithographic plant is differently equipped, according to its size and purposes.

Some very simple stripping departments may have no other furniture than stripping and work tables; more completely equipped departments will have layout and line-up tables in addition.

Color stripping requires high precision equipment. In some large stripping departments one can find darkrooms for contact printing and double-negative-printers for the combining of several negatives. Troughs for development, whirlers, vacuum printing frames, and arc-lamps may belong either to the platemaking department or to the stripping department, but they are a necessity for color stripping in every case.

Stripping departments equipped for special work of a recurring nature may have specially designed equipment. Pegboard assemblies, for example, are used for standardized layouts in publication printing and are usually especially designed for the kind of work to be done.

The stripping department is responsible for the correct assembly of the stripped flat and of the press plate and therefore very much concerned with the precision of its work. It uses several kinds of magnification devices and various precision tools for measuring.

The material used in the stripping department consists of different kinds of photographic film, plate glass, plastic sheets, goldenrod paper, and a variety of proprietary products that are used for layout and assembly. Some of these materials are suitable for scribing or engraving, others have top layers that can be cut with special knives and stripped for assembly. The coatings or top layers of scribing or knife-cutting films are often transparent and dyed to a color that blocks actinic—or blue—light.

The six main tasks of stripping. It is practical to divide stripping into the following six groups of tasks: (1) the planning of the press plate, (2) contact printing, (3) tint-laying, ruling, scribing, and retouching, (4) preparation of the support for

Courtesy Graphic Arts Technical Foundation

Layout of a lithographic plate planned for uniform ink distribution.

stripping, (5) adapting and fitting of photographic intermediates for assembly, and (6) the assembly of the stripped flat. Each of these tasks is now individually discussed.

The planning of the press plate. The planning of the press plate is a rather responsible step in printing production. Among the many points to be considered in this operation are the kind, size, and grain of the paper; the type of press plate; the ink distribution on the press; and last, but certainly not least, the binding and finishing methods whereby the printed sheet—or web—is converted into its final form and shape, which may be a book or a display, or any one of many different printed products.

Planning for the assembly of the final printing-image carrier is a necessary step in printing production. In larger companies, planning is handled by fully staffed planning departments. In smaller companies this function is delegated to highly experienced supervisors or craftsmen. As planning is intimately related to the binding and finishing of the printed sheet, the subject is discussed for all printing methods in Chapter X, together with other aspects of binding and finishing. In letterpress, both the plan for, and the operation of, assembling the final image carrier are known as imposition, as you may remember. In lithography, the word "imposition" or the equally frequently used term "layout" signifies the plan for assembly; the act of assembling itself is known as stripping; the product of stripping is called the stripped *flat*.

The imposition layout. The imposition or layout must indicate the size of the sheet, the size of the plate, gripper distance for plate and for sheet, printing area, and location marks for each of the units to be assembled. All of these indications refer to assembly and presswork. Many jobs need additional information pertaining to trimming, folding, binding, mounting, die-cutting, and other operations, depending on the nature of a job.

Planning of the imposition or layout must, of course, also consider the type of press plate to be made, and that some types of plates are made from negatives and others from positives. The assembly techniques for both are similar in principle but they differ in execution. But before the intermediate material can be finally assembled it is subjected to several preparatory operations, to which we now turn our attention, beginning with contact printing.

Contact printing. Photographic contact printing is a very important stripping technique, particularly for color work. Contact printing does not require a camera; the equipment for it consists of a vacuum printing frame, a light source, and possibly an interval timer. The resulting contact print is always of the same size as the intermediate element used for contact printing. The contact print may have the opposite area identification of the intermediate used for contact printing, meaning that it is a negative when made from a positive, or a positive when made from a negative. But it is also possible to make negatives from negatives and positives from positives by various photographic techniques.

Courtesy Eastman Kodak Company

Loading a vacuum printing frame for contact printing. The vacuum frame is connected to a light integrating meter which assures that the calculated light is in fact delivered.

Contact printing can be executed either in the darkroom or with the equipment used for plate-making. In all cases the intermediate element for contact printing and the light-sensitive material are exposed to the light source in close contact with each other, mostly in a vacuum printing frame. Various light-sensitive materials can be used for contact printing; some are of greater, others of lesser speed; different light-sensitive materials require shorter or longer exposure times and weaker or stronger lights.

The purposes for which contact printing is used may be broadly grouped into four: (1) auxiliary operations in color work, (2) combining of several intermediates into a smaller number of units, (3) making of several duplicates of the same intermediates for common assembly, and (4) photographic proofing techniques.

Tintlaying, ruling, scribing, and retouching. Tintlaying, ruling, scribing, and retouching are all done manually by skilful craftsmen. These techniques are used to provide some feature or other

Courtesy Technical Trade School, Pressmens Home

Craftsmen stripping a flat on a light table for offset lithography.

on photographic intermediates with a view to obtaining various effects in the most economical way.

Tintlaying produces tonal values by mechanical means rather than photographic ones. The effects obtainable by tintlaying, or as this operation is also called, *bendaying*, are limited. The subject is explained in Chapter IV during the discussion of tonal reproduction and does not detain us here. Ruling is mainly done on positives; it produces lines and is particularly needed in forms and tabular work. Ruling is done with a ruling pen and a *liquid opaque*. Engraving and scribing have the same purpose as ruling and are mainly done on negatives where these techniques are used to remove the opaque silver deposit. The engraved or scribed lines thereby become transparent.

Opaquing and staining are techniques for stopping the passage of light through negatives and positives. They are needed for various reasons, one of which is the elimination of imperfections in the intermediate material. The stripper corrects these by applying a liquid opaque with artists' brushes to negatives or positives wherever needed.

Preparing the support for stripping. The stripped flat can be assembled on sheets of different materials. The most common supports for assembly by stripping are four: (1) goldenrod paper, (2) acetate sheets, (3) vinyl sheets, and (4) polyester sheets. In addition to these materials there are several proprietary products on the market, suitable for cutting, scribing, or engraving.

Different supports vary considerably in their dimensional stability. Goldenrod paper and acetate sheets are least stable, vinyl and polyester sheets are much more so, and plate glass is most

stable of all. These differences in dimensional stability are the main reasons why goldenrod paper and acetate sheets must not be used for close register stripping and why stripping for color is usually either done on vinyl or on polyester sheets. When the work must meet very exacting tolerances, some strippers still prefer plate glass.

Goldenrod paper is mainly used for black-and-white and for multicolor stripping and it needs no particular preparation, but vinyl or polyester plastic sheets and plate glass do. These three materials are used only for critical color work. The techniques of stripping critical color work are known as vinyl or polyester *blueline* stripping or as *blueglass* stripping. Before vinyl sheets and plate glass are used for stripping they can be covered with a light-sensitive coating which makes them suitable for contact printing; this coating results in blue images, hence the names "blueline" and "blueglass." (The availability of stable base films has greatly decreased the use of glass plates in color stripping.)

In close color stripping, individual blueline supports are needed for each flat. These may be three, four, five, or even more, depending on the job in hand. During contact printing, each of the blueline supports is provided with images serving for the exact placement of intermediate elements, usually photographic positives.

Adapting and fitting of negatives and positives for common assembly. Adapting of negatives and positives is necessary where a number of individual intermediates must be combined during assembly. It happens often that each of them is of proper quality if examined individually, but that they are not suitable for combining without some adaptation, particularly at adjoining areas. For reasons of handling, the material of which intermediates are made must always be larger than the image recorded on it. This excess material may need elimination when the intermediates are assembled. Cutting the material to size may entail retouching and opaquing for proper fitting.

Assembly of the prepared material for platemaking. The final assembly can be quite simple but it can also be rather complex; it can consist of a single unit or of a considerable number of units, and it may be an assembly of negatives or of positives, depending on the type of press plate for which the assembly is prepared. Some plates are made by a single exposure for the whole plate area, others by exposing parts of the plate area in succession. Successive exposure can be made by a

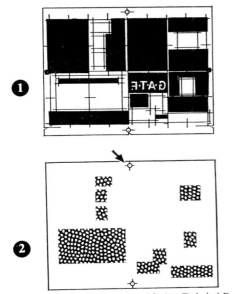

Courtesy Graphic Arts Technical Foundation

Two flats as needed for a two-color job. The line flat (1) has the layout; the halftone flat (2) does not need a layout as the halftones were positioned by putting them over the line flat on a light-table.

special machine known as a *photocomposing machine* or *photocomposer* (not to be confused with a photographic typesetting machine) or it can be done by manual techniques. As if all these variables were not enough to confuse an uninitiated person, assembly methods vary also for different register requirements.

Various kinds of stripped flats. The stripped flat is the final product of the stripping department. It must contain all elements needed for platemaking. Among these are various controls needed for platemaking and for presswork such as the *GATF Sensitivity Guide*, and, for full-color printing, *color blocks* or *color patches*, as they are also called. Goldenrod flats are very commonly used in single color and non-critical multicolor jobs. The goldenrod paper is opaque and serves as a support for the assembled photographic intermediates. These are first correctly positioned and then attached to a sheet of goldenrod paper; thereafter, the stripper cuts windows in the goldenrod paper where it covers the image areas of the photographic intermediates.

Blueline and blueglass flats are made for close register work, because, as already mentioned, goldenrod is lacking in dimensional stability. Some of these assemblies use photographic nega-

tives or positives, others are made by the use of stripfilm. Stripfilm is a photographic material whose image-bearing photographic film is extremely thin and therefore is temporarily attached to a thicker material for handling. After developing, the thin image-bearing film is separated from its heavier temporary support and transferred to the blueline or blueglass flat.

Pegboard assemblies. Finally, a few words on pegboard assembly techniques. These are mainly found in publication and catalog printing, where standardized page sizes and press-sheet layouts are possible. Here "the pegboard assembly method provides a rapid and accurate means for positioning and combining films. The pegboard method requires a set of two or three holes to be punched in each film in accurate relationship to the subject detail. The pegboard on which these punched films are assembled has a number of duplicate sets of positioning pins (pegs) that are so located as to provide the desired layout."[101] Pegboard or pin register systems often include the equipping of cameras and vacuum frames with pegs or register pins, whereby great economies may be obtained.

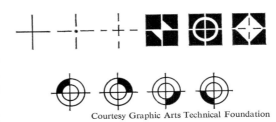

Courtesy Graphic Arts Technical Foundation

Various kinds of commonly used register marks. Bottom row shows differently coded marks for the first, the second, the third and the fourth color plate.

Platemaking for Offset Lithography

Platemaking is the final phase in the conversion of original images into lithographic printing-image carriers. The product of lithographic platemaking is a single-unit or integral image carrier where all images are completely assembled as they will appear on the printed sheet or web.

Contemporary lithography commands a wide range of plates. Platemaking for lithography can be a rather complex operation, particularly when the plates to be made must be suitable for long runs of full-color printing or other intricate work, and still more so if the plates are large and contain a sizable number of individual units. Let us illustrate this statement with two examples. On the one hand we may have a single-color job, to be run on a 17½- × 22½-inch sheet in a quantity of 5,000 impressions. The plate for this kind of a job usually does not pose any problems; platemaking is for this and similar simple cases just routine work. On the other hand, we may have a catalog job of many hundreds of pages, all to be printed in full color for the pictures and in black for the reading matter. The quantity is rather large, say 850,000, the page size 9 × 12 inches. This job would be printed on a sheet sufficiently large for 32 pages and hence measure 50 × 74 inches approximately. Such a job poses rather different problems. Not only must each of the pages be perfectly positioned in relation to all other pages, but the images of each plate must also correspond to the images of each of the other three plates, and the detail of all images is, of course, much more critical than the detail of our first-mentioned small-size single-color job. It goes without much explaining that the equipment and the skill needed for platemaking of the last described, very intricate type, are of a much higher order than those needed for the small plate.

We have a similar situation when we consider the conditions under which contemporary lithographic plates are used. The principle of lithography has remained the same and is rather simple, but it is by no means so simple to apply these principles to the needs of modern high-speed printing and to produce plates suitable for it.

Application of the lithographic principle to platemaking. In order to understand the complexities of contemporary lithographic platemaking, we might recall that lithography is based on the fact that oil and water do not mix under certain conditions. Colloquially, this can be expressed by saying that lithographic ink must be *water-shy*. This formulation satisfies half of the problem, namely, that the image, or printing areas, of the plate must be ink-receptive and water-repellent. But it does not solve the whole problem, which includes the non-image, or non-printing areas, as well as the image, or printing areas, of the plate. The non-printing areas of the plate must become just as *ink-shy* as the printing areas must be printed with *water-shy* ink.

Why must this be so? Assume for a moment that the non-image areas would be ink-receptive, and you can immediately see that then the whole plate would be covered with ink and that printing would become impossible. You will agree that ink

repellence of non-image areas is truly a precondition for lithographic printing. As both the image and non-image areas are on the same level of the plate and not on different levels as in relief and intaglio printing, these two kinds of areas must be distinguished by their receptivity to and repellence of ink.

The preceding outline has disregarded the finer points of the subject in order to convey the generally most important facts. Now, when you may be assumed to understand these, it must be added that lithographic inks have a limited tolerance for moisture, as is more fully explained in the unit on "Inks for Offset Lithography" in Chapter IX, Section 5. It must be further added that the conditions under which lithographic printing can take place are apt to change as the press run progresses and that they need careful watching, as you will see in the discussion of lithographic presswork in Chapter VII.

Lithographic platemaking is a highly developed industrial art. Platemaking comprises a number of steps that serve this purpose. Unless you understand the nature of the problem you will always remain puzzled by the variety of treatments which are part of lithographic platemaking.

The magnitude of the problem with which lithographic platemaking was confronted can be appreciated if we realize that the surface of a lithographic plate is far from robust and consists—with the exception of bimetallic plates—of photomechanical coatings that are reinforced with ink and other substances presumed to be of long-wearing quality. The conditions of modern halftone printing make high-precision plates an absolute necessity. In 133-line halftones, which are commonly used in the reproduction of black-and-white photographs, each square inch consists of almost 18,000 individual units. Practically each of these 18,000 units is further divided into a printing and a non-printing area, and the proportions of these two kinds of areas varies for different tones, or values, of the picture. Dividing a lithographic plate into printing and non-printing areas of such minute sizes, and, consequently, of an enormous number of such divisions is quite an undertaking! Nor should the difficulty of keeping such a plate in perfect state during presswork be underestimated.

Specialization in contemporary lithographic platemaking. Modern lithographic technology provides us with many different kinds of lithographic plates. This variety may seem at first confusing, but it exists for very good reasons. Every year brings new expansions for lithography and every new conquest becomes a new challenge for better and more efficient lithographic production methods. Long runs pose different problems than short runs; high-quality requirements must be approached along other lines than run-of-the-mill work where economy counts more than anything else. As the plate occupies a key position, different types of plates were obviously required and consequently also developed. Some are on paper, others on zinc or aluminum, still others on steel. As plate materials vary, so do image-formation methods and techniques. Once you realize which purpose a plate must serve, you also understand why it exists and why it differs from others. Variety, the scare for the beginner, becomes a most desirable condition for the well-informed specialist who knows how to use it.

Review of Contemporary Lithographic Plates

Lithographic platemaking has experienced many new developments in the last quarter of a century. The field is far from static, and new platemaking methods are constantly being developed by various research and business organizations. One of the less desirable effects of this thriving growth is terminological confusion. As plates were developed they were named without regard for a systematic nomenclature. If growth is very vigorous, the variety of names can become confusing. After a certain time, the most advanced workers in a given field feel a need for systematization and begin to coin new terms. Wholesome as this endeavor is, the immediate result is, alas, not less confusion but more, because now people begin to use two groups of terms—the old unsystematic names side-by-side with the new systematic ones. Lithographic platemaking is at the time of writing in this unenviable situation.

Some plates are known by the material of the image carrier; others by chemical substances used for image formation; still others by trade names or some characteristic feature. We will follow the terminology preferred by the Graphic Arts Technical Foundation, and divide the subject into surface plates, deep-etch plates, and bimetallic plates.

Surface plates. The term *surface plates* was coined by the Graphic Arts Technical Foundation when the traditional designation *albumin plates* became inaccurate and therewith misleading.

Albumin is an organic colloid which is better known under the name of egg white. Egg albumin was widely used for photomechanical plates and the name albumin plate became widely known. More recent developments introduced other organic colloids for the same purpose, and GATF consequently suggested the name *surface plate* as a more indicative group designation. All surface plates have one feature in common: the printing areas are on the surface of the image carrier.

The class of surface plates comprises several types. Historically, *albumin* plates were the first. These plates were usually coated in the lithographic shop or plant. They were not objects of commerce prior to platemaking itself. Albumin plates have lost all importance in contemporary platemaking. They were more or less completely superseded by various novel developments which reached maturity in the last decade, primarily by presensitized plates.

Presensitized plates. Presensitized plates have become the most popular plates in the lithographic industry. The reason for their wide use is that "presensitized plates are the acme of simplicity in platemaking."[102] Presensitized plates are manufactured by several companies and are available in a wide array of sizes and thicknesses. The base material is usually aluminum, but plates for relatively short runs are made with less expensive paper or foil mounted board. Presensitized lithographic plates have many advantages if compared with shopmade surface plates using bichromates as sensitizers.

Shop-coated surface plates (and the later described deep-etch plates) must be exposed shortly after coating. Within a short time, varying "from a few hours to a couple of days, depending on the relative humidity and the temperature, ordinary coatings harden over the whole plate, and it is impossible to get an image on the plate. (This change in plate properties is technically known as *dark reaction*.) A coating for a presensitized plate must be light-sensitive and still have such a slow dark reaction that plates can be processed at least six months after they are coated. Certain diazo compounds fill these requirements."[103] Diazo compounds are organic whereas bichromates are inorganic substances. The chemistry of diazos and related materials is a highly technical subject. Fortunately it is entirely possible to make good presensitized plates without knowledge of this branch of organic chemistry.[104]

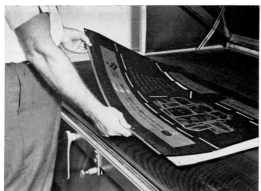

Photographic negative assembly over a 3M Type S presensitized offset plate for common exposure in a vacuum frame. Exposure hardens the image areas of the plate; the non-image areas are removed during development.

From the printer's point of view presensitized plates can be divided into negative-working and positive-working ones. *Negative-working presensitized plates* are exposed with photographic negatives. Exposure results in a chemical change of the exposed areas. "The important thing for lithographic platemaking is that the light-changed diazo coating is not soluble in the developer solution, while the part of the diazo coating which was not exposed to light is soluble in the developer." Development is followed by treating the plate in order to make the image areas ink receptive. The medium for this purpose must of course be repelled by the non-image areas of the developed plate. After the plate is gummed up with a solution of gum arabic it is ready to be put on the press.

The *positive-working presensitized plates* are particularly interesting because in this kind of plates the unexposed areas remain impervious to the developer whereas the exposed areas are soluble in it. Compared with negative-working presensitized plates and plates having bichromated coatings, such presensitized plates show an opposite result. This kind of behavior makes it possible to make a positive image on the plate by exposure through a positive. Positive-working plates are being used in many plants and trade shops for the proofing of full-color images.[105] Full-color jobs are usually printed with deep-etch plates which are made from photographic positives. The same positives that will be used in the making of the final press plate can be used for proofing with positive-working plates.

Another aspect of positive-working presensitized plates is worth mentioning. Such plates, and plates made with similarly acting wipe-on coatings, can be used for the reproduction of tonal values without halftone photography, a feature previously exclusive with collotype. "The optical V principle of the plate grain controls the amount of ink printed in different tone values. The detail of printed images is much sharper and color tints are purer than by printing halftones."[106] At the time of writing screenless printing with positive-working presensitized plates is much less used than the much older and well established collotype printing. (Image carriers for collotype are discussed in the final unit of this section.)

Presensitized plates are made by a number of manufacturers using different coating materials. Most of the later discussed bimetallic plates are also supplied presensitized.

Another type of surface plates, the so-called *wipe-on* plates, is very widely used. Wipe-on plates act similar to presensitized plates, but they are not supplied to lithographic plants with a light-sensitive coating. These plates are coated in the lithographic platemaking department by lithographic craftsmen. The coating material is supplied by various manufacturers, ready for application. Coating of the plate metal is done by wiping, hence the designation "wipe-on."

If lithographers want to do their own coating, they can use other light-sensitive materials, such as KPR for example. The letters KPR stand for

Development of a presensitized 3M Type S offset plate. The unexposed non-image areas are removed from the plate during development; the hardened image areas remain on the plate. After development the plate is rinsed clean with water.

and materials used in making them are essentially the same."[109] Bimetallic plates using positives are preferred by many for high-quality, full-color printing jobs.

Bimetallic plates have longer press life. Comparing bimetallic plates with deep-etch plates, particularly with copperized aluminum plates, we notice that bimetallic plates have much heavier copper deposits in their image areas. This difference accounts for the longer life of bimetallic plates, as it permits them to withstand better and longer the abrasion inevitably encountered during the printing process. Bimetallic plates can produce extremely long runs, going into the millions, whereas deep-etch plates are selected for runs in the hundreds of thousands of impressions.

The layout and equipment of the platemaking department. Stripping and platemaking are closely related operations; both departments have, therefore, often a community of working area and equipment. Wherever possible the platemaking department is air-conditioned, more for technical reasons than for the convenience of the platemakers. Humidity and temperature fluctuations are most undesirable conditions for producing plates of uniformly high quality.

Equipment for lithographic platemaking. The equipment of a platemaking department depends on the specialization of a lithographic company, the kinds of plates to be made, and also on the size of the department. Some companies purchase their plates from lithographic trade shops. These companies may not even maintain platemaking facilities. Other companies use presensitized or wipe-on plates exclusively. In platemaking departments maintained for these methods, the equipment will consist of light tables for checking the stripped flats, working benches, vacuum printing frames, and carbon-arc lamps.

In platemaking departments of companies that produce deep-etch and bimetallic plates, the equipment comprises many additional items. To begin with the preparation of the metal plate, we must mention the graining department where used plates are reclaimed and prepared for re-use. (Graining is at present not so much done by lithographers as by trade shops.) Even though tub graining is only one of several methods, it is still preferred by many for long-run image carriers.

Lithographic platemaking departments that handle the compounding of light-sensitive coatings need scales, graduates, hydrometers, and other laboratory items. Other than wipe-on coatings are usually applied by whirling, and whirlers of different size and construction are available in larger plate rooms as a matter of course. Exposure of coated plates is done either in vacuum frames or in step-and-repeat machines. (The terms "photocomposing machine" and "photocomposer" are in general use for the same equipment, but apt to cause confusion with non-metallic typesetting machinery.) Step-and-repeat machines permit higher precision in the positioning of multiple images on the same plate and are, therefore, particularly important where large plates must be made to close tolerances.

Equipment for deep-etch and bimetallic plates. Where deep-etch plates are made, the equipment includes special deep-etch developing sinks, and where bimetallic plates are made that use chromium as the non-image metal, *down-draft* tables are needed to remove etching fumes.

In addition to the above-listed appointments, companies specializing in certain fields often have platemaking equipment of particular design. To mention one such case, lithographers who concentrate on the printing of twenty-four-sheet posters use very powerful projection cameras for exposure instead of the customary exposure by contact printing.

The Four Main Phases of Lithographic Platemaking

Lithographic platemaking is a complex and highly technical subject, as you must have realized from the preceding units. It is, of course, not the purpose of this manual to burden you with detail which is of greatest value to those who are active in this area, but only confusing to the reader who is looking for general or background information.

On the other hand, we can gain a good insight into lithographic platemaking by concentrating our attention on its essential elements rather than on confusing detail. We have therefore divided the subject into four main phases: (1) selection and preparation of the base metal for the plate, (2) photomechanics for lithographic platemaking, (3) formation and protection of image areas, and (4) formation and protection of non-image areas.

Selecting the base metal for lithographic plates. Paper stock and many metals are suitable as base materials for lithographic plates. Paper stock can be used for direct-image and presensitized plates which come ready for exposure to the platemaking department. The same holds true for presensitized plates on a metal base and for proprietary brands of bimetallic plates. In all these cases the platemaking department is not concerned with selecting and preparing the base material, as these tasks are already taken care of by the manufacturers of such plates.

For plates that are made from the bottom up in the platemaking department of a lithographic plant or a trade shop, the platemaking department has a choice between aluminum and zinc, the most widely used plate metals, and the much less popular stainless steel. For surface plates coated in the platemaking department, zinc is first and aluminum second in rank of preference; for deep-etch plates aluminum dominates the field. Stainless steel is also used for deep-etch plates, particularly where its excellent size-holding qualities are needed—in metal decorating, to mention one example.

Graining and counter-etching. Preparing metal plates for coating can be divided into two groups of operations. Graining is one, counter-etching the other. Graining has the two purposes of making already used plates fit for new service and of providing a structure of minute hills and valleys on the plate surface whereby the water-receptivity of the plate is increased. Graining can be done in several ways. In tub graining the metal plate is oscillated in a graining machine with metal balls, known as marbles, on its surface together with an abrasive water mixture; in brush graining, a more recent development (possibly merely a revival and refinement of an older technique) electrically rotated brushes take the place of marbles.

If graining roughens the plate surface, *counter-etching* and so-called *pre-treatments* clean and deoxidize the plate thoroughly and condition the plate surface for proper adhesion of the light-sensitive coating that is needed for photomechanical image formation.

Photomechanics for lithographic platemaking. Photomechanics has been sufficiently explained in Section 3 of this chapter that we merely want to refresh your memory. We will, therefore, repeat that photomechanics comprise three steps: (1) coating, (2) exposure, and (3) development of the light-sensitive coating. During coating the plate surface is covered with a light-sensitive film. The coated plate, which is dry at this stage, can be either combined with a stripped flat for exposure or be put in a step-and-repeat machine.

During exposure the exposed areas become relatively insoluble due to the action of the light used in this step. This difference in solubility produces the photomechanical distinction between the future image areas and non-image areas. The third group of operations, development, leads to the photomechanical stencil.

These operations are not the same for surface plates and deep-etch plates. To begin with, the coatings for either type are different. In addition, surface plates are exposed to negative transparencies, whereas positives are needed for deep-etch plates. Nor is development the same. Surface plates are first *rubbed down* with *developing ink* and then treated with water, whereas deep-etch plates are not rubbed down but are immediately developed with a specially formulated chemical solution. Last, but not least, the resulting photomechanical stencil has an entirely different function in either case. In surface plates this stencil remains on the plate surface as the final printing image. In deep-etch plates the stencil acts as a resist for the etching and formation of the printing image. Once this task is accomplished, the stencil is destroyed and disappears from the plate.

Formation and protection of the printing image in lithographic plates. The detail of image formation and protection depends on the specific method selected. Generally speaking, the most important requirements for well-formed and durable lithographic printing images are three: (1) maximum adhesion to the surface of the image carrier, (2) very high immunity to water, and (3) strong resistance to abrasion. If the printing image loses its adhesion it is said to *walk-away;* if it loses its immunity to water it is called *blinding.* Surface plates use lacquer, developing ink, or asphaltum for image protection, whereas *non-blinding* lacquers serve for this purpose in deep-etch plates.

Formation and protection of non-image areas in lithographic plates. The formation and protection of both kinds of plate areas, namely, the printing and the non-printing areas of the plate, goes hand-in-hand in lithographic platemaking. As both areas are practically on the same plate level every action on one kind of area influences at the same time the other kind. Therefore, action on one type of area and protection of the other type are most closely related. In addition the non-image areas have also certain problems of their own. These are, generally speaking, to increase the gap between the ink and the water-receptivity of the non-printing areas. The non-printing areas must be avidly water-receptive so as to be thoroughly ink-repellent at the same time. Various steps of platemaking are needed for this result. The already mentioned desensitization, pre-treatments, and post-treatments are steps in this process, and, therefore, important parts of platemaking.

This concludes our discussion of lithographic platemaking. We turn next to proofing, a group of operations which serves to control the progress and results of image conversion for lithography.

Proofing for Offset Lithography

Offset lithography uses a large number of different proofing techniques. These confuse the beginner unless he learns to understand the essential task of lithographic proofing. This task can be clearly defined as one phase of quality control. The variety of existing proofing methods corresponds to the variety of quality control problems; it came about in the effort of coping most effectively with each of the many different tasks that are lumped in this general term of quality control. It does not need lengthy explanations that the least expensive and least time-consuming method must be used in every specific case. What does need explanation is why we have so many different lithographic proofing techniques, wherein they differ, and for what purpose they are applied.

Differences in proofing techniques are related to the vast differences in products manufactured by offset lithography. Length of run, complexity of jobs, level of required quality are some of the points that come immediately to mind. But there are also more specific technical reasons that are related to image conversion for offset lithography, to the nature of the image carrier, and to available proofing equipment. In the following you find a brief introduction to contemporary proofing practice. The subject is divided into (1) proofing as part of running, (2) photomechanical proofing in monochrome, (3) photomechanical proofing in full-color, (4) proofing on proof presses, and (5) proofing on production presses.

Proofing as part of running. Many lithographic plates are put on the press without being proofed first. In simple single- and multi-color jobs, it is usually considered sufficient to inspect the progress of image conversion at each critical juncture and to check the final plate carefully before it is transmitted to the pressroom. There the first printed sheets are inspected again, and if this final inspection is passed, the job is *run off* immediately, as the pressman says.

In more difficult jobs this simplified procedure

may be too risky, and proofing of one kind or another may be instituted as part of production procedure. In such cases proofs are usually submitted to customers for their okay, not without first being inspected by competent plant personnel.

Photomechanical proofing in monochrome. Photomechanical proofing in monochrome is mainly used for single-color and for multicolor work, either by itself or in conjunction with full-color images. Photomechanical proofing in monochrome can be done on three kinds of materials: blueprint papers, brownprint papers, and diazo papers. "Blueprint paper is exposed to arc light together with negatives, in most cases a stripped flat, in a vacuum printing-frame. The result is a photomechanical positive proof, showing the image areas in dark blue on a more or less white or light blue background."[110] Brownprint papers, which are also known as Van Dyke, Solar, silver print, and print-out papers, "are used for making positive photomechanical proofs from negative flats." Diazo papers, finally, are also known as Ozalids and whiteprints. These, too, are exposed to strong light by contact printing. But whereas blueprints and brownprints are developed in water and therefore not dimensionally stable, diazos which are developed with ammonia fumes "do not change their size during development."[111] Another point worth mentioning is that diazo produces positive prints from positive flats which can be desired in proofing for deep-etch plates.

Finally, a few comments on the information provided by photomechanical monochrome proofs: "Blueprints afford sufficient information on three aspects of accuracy; that of the assembled material, its position, as well as of the imposition. As to the fourth kind of accuracy with which proofing is concerned, namely, the accuracy of *internal register*, or fit, blueprints may or may not be sufficiently indicative. Brownprints afford information on all aspects of accuracy, not only that of the assembled material, its position and imposition, but also that of internal register or fit, in multicolor jobs. This feature we owe to the peculiar way in which the brownprint image is created that permits us to identify various flats on the same brownprint in different tonal values. Diazo prints, finally, afford information on all aspects of accuracy other than internal register or fit. For proofing of internal register, brownprints remain unsurpassed."[112]

Photomechanical proofing in full-color. This method of proofing is mostly, though not exclusively, used as a quality control method during image conversion for full-color reproductions. It is practically impossible to visualize the final product of color separation and color correction without the aid of some color proofing method. "At the time of writing several photomechanical proofing systems in full-color are available. All such systems have their value in the hands of the well-informed worker who knows their nature and limitations. But none of them produce true replicas of the future pressprint."[113]

Our discussion is limited to two types: diazo foils and pigmented light-sensitive formulations. Diazo foils are available in a number of colors as well as in hues corresponding to those of our full-color inks. Some brands of diazo foils can be used with positives; others are suitable for photographic negatives. Each of the color printers is contact printed with the corresponding color foil which consists of a thin transparent plastic sheet bearing the colored image. After exposure and development, the foils are superimposed in register and viewed together. Pigmented light-sensitive coatings can be either wiped-on or whirled on plastic surfaces which are used as counterparts of three full-color inks. The dried color coating is exposed together with the color printer, developed, and the dry color prints are finally again combined by superimposing for common viewing.

Proofing on proof presses. During the discussion of proofing of photoengraving sets for full-color printing, it is pointed out how difficult it is to arrive at proofs of full-color engravings which are truly indicative of the final wet-on-wet production run. Proofing for lithographic reproduction faces obstacles not less severe than does proofing for letterpress printing.

Some of the difficulties lie in the absence of wet-on-wet proof presses for lithography; others are related to the fact that lithographic plates are single-unit image carriers and that we do not have proof presses large enough for the proofing of final press plates in the sizes in which they are often needed for actual running. A lithographic plate may be host to a large number of images of the same kind and size, in the printing of labels or folding paper boxes, or to a number of different sizes as is usual in point-of-purchase display jobs. Such plates may be as large as, say, 54 × 84 inches and must be proofed on the press on which they will be finally run.

The proofing of full-color reproductions is, again, more critical than that of other jobs. Often special plates destined for proofing exclusively and not for production are made of such jobs and printed on proof presses or small production presses. If the job needs corrections, these are made on the photographic intermediates, mainly positives, before they are used for the making of the final press plate. (An extensive discussion of proofing is in Chapter VI, Section 8.)

Proofing on production presses. This kind of proofing was already mentioned in the preceding paragraph. It could also have been discussed under the head of proofing as part of running, the first division of this subject. For several reasons, this type of proofing, which refers to proofing of complex and large-size jobs is briefly discussed by itself. As there exists no proofing equipment for large-size plates and as there are no wet-on-wet four-color proof presses, the content and state of the actual press plate is unknown in its critical detail until the plate is put on the press. Even such images as were proofed individually on proof presses will not necessarily appear identically under production conditions but rather vary to a degree that depends on the detail of the case, particularly on differences between actual proofing and production equipment. Proofing such jobs on the press on which they will finally be printed affords more information than all previous proofing steps. Often proofs so produced are submitted to the customer for final okay, or a customer's representative is invited to the printer's plant to approve the first press sheets before the job is run off.

This concludes our discussion of proofing which has again shown how intimately related all phases of production are and how the detail of each specific problem or task controls the selection of the best quality control procedure for it.

Image Carriers for Collotype

Collotype is a rather esoteric printing method; it is commercially insignificant if compared with offset lithography. Yet collotype is, perhaps surprisingly, the oldest existing printing method that uses photomechanically produced printing-image carriers.[114] Unfortunately, collotype is not suitable for long-run printing as the paper abrades the image carrier with which it is in direct contact during each impression. This abrasion limits the useful life of collotype plates to approximately

5,000 impressions. Collotype can also be done by indirect image transfer. This method is called offset collotype; it is at the time of writing not a generally used production method. Collotype is primarily distinguished by being able to reproduce continuous-tone images without converting them into halftones. This feature of collotype was unique in planographic printing until the advent of positive-working presensitized plates and similarly functioning wipe-on coatings. At the time of writing screenless printing with presensitized plates is still in its beginning whereas collotype has been successfully practiced in the United States and Europe for a long time.

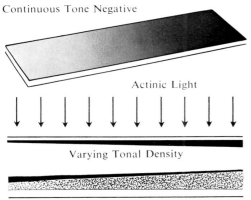

Courtesy Presentation Press

Diagram of collotype principle. The optical density of the continuous-tone negative increases from left to right. Less dense areas let more light pass than denser areas during exposure. The collotype coating is accordingly more hardened under the less dense areas and less hardened under the denser negative areas. The more hardened plate areas accept less moisture and swell less than the less hardened areas. More hardened areas accept more ink than do the less hardened ones.

The most distinctive feature of collotype combined with the ability of this method to deposit exceptionally strong layers of ink accounts for its reputation as a high-quality reproduction medium. Many reproductions of fine art subjects, including art books and prints of paintings, are printed by collotype. Many experts consider it a great advantage that collotype achieves reproduction of continuous-tone images without halftone photography. It is emphasized that this fact is of particular importance in full-color printing and the attendant masking for color-correcting. The absence of screened images permits photographic masking techniques that cannot be used with half-

tones. Collotype masking techniques employ multiple exposures onto the several printing plates from continuous-tone masks. These methods are considered very valuable and highly practical by industry specialists.

Exactly how collotype achieves reproductions of continuous-tone images is disputed. It seems that the tonal qualities of collotype prints result from the interaction of two related items. One is generally called *reticulation;* the other is *varying ink receptivity.* A strong magnification of collotype prints shows peculiar random patterns whose individual elements are much smaller than the dots obtained by halftone screens of such rulings as are commonly used for good commercial reproductions. The other point, variations in the thickness of the deposited ink film, is not as easy to demonstrate. Some leading practitioners of collotype firmly maintain that variation in the thickness of the ink film is the main reason for value differences in collotype. This opinion is not shared by others who credit reticulation exclusively for the functioning of the collotype plate.

At this point it should be added that collotype has no literature to speak of, especially if compared with offset lithography. Before the questions concerning reticulation and selective ink-receptivity can be conclusively answered, new research will have to be made.[115]

After this brief general introduction, we turn to an equally brief description of contemporary practice in the making of collotype plates. The subject is divided into the following points: (1) image conversion, (2) coating the collotype plate, (3) exposure and development, and (4) the character of the collotype plate.

Image conversion for collotype. Image conversion for collotype is very similar to that for offset lithography. The main difference is that collotype does not need halftone photography, whereas offset lithography does. Image conversion begins with photography which may include color separation and photographic masking for color correcting. Line and continuous-tone images are photographed on different films, as usual. The product of the camera is inspected where necessary, improved by retouching and, of course, corrected for minor flaws. The approved continuous-tone negatives are assembled for platemaking in various techniques, often similar to those used for the same purpose in offset lithography.

Coating the collotype plate. As there are no presensitized collotype plates available, all collotype plates are shop-coated. The base material for rotary collotype plates is usually aluminum, but monel plates have also been successfully used. In Europe, where collotype is still printed on flat-bed presses, the plates are usually made on heavy panes of plate glass. The light-sensitive coating is formulated by plant personnel; throughout the industry its detail is considered a valuable trade secret. From the unfortunately very unsatisfactory literature, it can be gleaned that one or several kinds of gelatin, glycerine, and other plasticizers and bichromate may be present in such formulas. The plate is coated in a whirler, preferably equipped with fan and heater.

Exposure and development. The coated and dried plate is exposed to continuous-tone negatives in the usual manner. The equipment consists of vacuum frames and carbon arc lamps or other suitable light sources. After exposure, the plate is developed, or washed out, in water to remove the excess of bichromate.

The character of collotype plates. The final plate is distinguished by the fact that its whole area is continuously hardened to varying degrees. This continuous difference in plate hardness corresponds to the density differences in the continuous-tone negative to which the plate was ex-

posed. The densest areas in the negative stop all light and therefore the plate is least hardened in these places. In other places, light will pass to varying degrees and the plate will be harder or softer accordingly. The plate is treated with a solution of glycerine, whereby it swells. "The image will take up glycerine and water in proportion to the amount of tanning produced by the light which passed through the negative on exposure."[116] When this plate is inked, the shadow areas which absorb least moisture will accept ink more readily than the middletones which swelled more and hence are less ink-receptive. The highlight areas, finally, contain most moisture and are, hence, almost completely ink-repellent.

Collotype plates differ in another essential point from other planographic image carriers. They need not be dampened in every printing cycle, and collotype presses have, therefore, no water fountains and dampening rollers. But the moisture content of the pressroom must be kept over 55 per cent relative humidity in order to keep the plate sufficiently moist for printing. After printing about 1,000 sheets, the press is usually stopped and the plate is sponged with a solution of glycerine and water. The glycerine acts as a humectant for the moisture content of the plate.

Section 6:   Image Carriers Made of Porous or Foraminous Materials

The process family of porous printing comprises two methods: One is screen-process printing and the other is serigraphy. (The term porous is not used in the screen-process industry; the reasons for its selection are explained in Chapter I, Section 5.) The difference between screen process and serigraphy is less technical than one of

purpose: screen-process printing is the industrial method, serigraphy serves for printmaking. It might be interesting to note that porous printing is widely used for office duplicating in the form of mimeographing. Office duplicating is outside the frame of this manual and we turn immediately to a discussion of image carriers for screen process.

Printing-Image Carriers for Screen-Process Printing

Screen-process printing uses a large number of techniques for the making of screens as the industry calls its printing-image carriers. Since the image carrier consists of a porous, or foraminous, material, the printing image is brought about by controlling the pores of the image carrier, a silk screen. Wherever the pores are left unobstructed, ink will pass through the screen and be deposited on the printing stock over which the screen is positioned during image transfer. And

conversely, where pores of the screen are blocked, no ink will pass through it onto the material to be printed. Image conversion has always the task of blocking the pores and never that of opening them as the structure of the porous cloth must remain undisturbed for printing. This fact should be noted because it accounts for limitations imposed upon screen-process printing in the reproduction of extremely small detail, fine halftone images in particular.

Screen process is more a picture printing and decorating process than a process suitable for the reproduction of reading matter in bulk. This is not to say that even small types are not well reproduced by screen process. In many instances the printing of small type is essential. Larger type and display lettering are, of course, parts of most promotional printing. But screen process is not used for the production of books, magazines, and newspapers, where body type is predominant.

Among the many products printed by screen process are posters, displays, greeting cards, wrapping papers, and many other items needed for promotional purposes. Screen process is also used for the decorating of bottles, for many other objects ranging in size from large metal drums to tiny compact cases of metal or plastics.

Image conversion for screen-process printing has a wide range of techniques at its command. Many of these are highly specialized as they were developed for the solution of specific problems. In this manual we want to concentrate on the two most widely practiced image-conversion methods which are knife-cut film techniques and photographic methods for screen-process plates.

Knife-cut Film Image Carriers for Screen-Process Printing

The knife-cut film method is an ideal medium for the image conversion of line and area originals for screen-process printing. Apart from the historical importance of the knife-cut film method for screen-process printing this technique has remained one of the two most widely used platemaking methods for screen process.

Knife-cut film techniques are based on various proprietary materials which are known by their trade names and are available as articles of commerce. Knife-cut films consist of two different layers: one, the top layer, is a specially formulated colored coating; the other, the temporary support, can be either a transparent paper or a clear plastic sheet. The top layer is attached to the temporary support by means of pressure-sensitive adhesives. Even though the top layer is colored, the whole assembly is nevertheless quite transparent.

Courtesy Presentation Press

Adhering a knife-cut film stencil in screen process. The top surface of the stencil is sealed to the stencil cloth with a solvent. The craftsman works with both hands; one hand applies solvent with a soaked rag, the other hand immediately blots excess solvent with a dry rag.

The making of knife-cut film stencils. If this film is placed over an original image, the image can be seen quite distinctly through it. This material is converted into a resist that will block the pores of the image carrier by tracing the outlines of the original art work with a special knife. The platemaker is a highly skilled craftsman known as *film-cutter* in the trade. After cutting, he peels the future printing areas from the temporary support, leaving all non-printing areas undisturbed. The cut and stripped film is often called a *stencil* in the trade.

The next operation is performed by either the film-cutter or by another skilled craftsman who is usually called a *set-up man*. He transfers the non-printing areas from the backing sheet of the knife-cut film to the bottom of the image carrier by an operation known as *adhering the film*. The shaped material, stripped of its image areas, is placed with its top coating upside under the image carrier. Then the screen is brought into contact with the top layer of the material and the film is sealed to the underside of the carrier cloth. This is achieved by treatment with a solution containing carefully blended organic solvents, commonly known as *adhering liquid*, which softens the top of the film and thereby fuses it to the fibrous cloth which serves as image carrier. After adhering, the image carrier is lifted and the temporary support is re-

Courtesy M & M Displays, Philadelphia

Stripping a knife-cut stencil. The screen-process craftsman removes cut stencil material in the printing areas.

moved. The adhered top layer, or film, serves as a resist that blocks the non-printing areas of the image carrier and leaves the pores of the printing areas open.

Strong points and limitations of knife-cut film stencils. Knife-cut films are surprisingly wear-resistant. It is possible to produce many thousands of impressions with knife-cut film image carriers; in some instances it took more than 50,000 impressions before the resist needed replacement. The knife-cut film technique is most effective in jobs where large areas or bold lines dominate, it becomes marginal as small detail increases, and it is not usable at all for halftone reproduction. But it should be mentioned that most film-cutters have very high skills and at their best can perform almost incredible feats with their knives, such as cutting 10-point type to perfection.

Photographic Image Carriers for Screen-Process Printing

This discussion of photographic image carriers for screen-process printing must, unfortunately, begin with an apology for inexact terminology. The heading should not be photographic but photomechanical as most of the image carriers to be discussed under this head are products of photomechanics. If the term "photographic screen" is nevertheless used (contrary to the terminology followed in this manual), it is done for the simple reason that "photographic screen" is generally accepted whereas "photomechanical screen" is not customary in this industry. As an afterthought it might be added that in one case at least, the term photographic screens is correct: screen-process image carriers made with duPont Screen Process Film can be made directly in the camera, and therefore may justly be classified as photographic screens. (*The word "screen," when used in conjunction with screen process, always means image carriers, and never—as it does so often in the graphic arts industry—screens for the making of halftones.*)

General exposition of photographic screens. Screen-process printing technology includes a wide variety of photomechanical methods and materials for the production of image carriers. These can be conveniently divided into directly sensitized screens on one hand and transfer methods on the other. Before we begin with our presentation of individual methods a few general comments are in order. All photomechanical

screen-process image carriers must provide a resist in the non-image areas and leave the screen unblocked in the image areas. As the resist comes about by exposure of light-sensitive coatings, all screen-process transparencies must be clear in the non-image areas and opaque in the image areas. This type of transparency is already known to you as a positive. Since the image areas are opaquely recorded on a positive, the light-sensitive coating is not reached by the exposure light; hence it remains soluble and is washed out during development, whereas the non-image areas which have become relatively insoluble remain after development and form the required resist. Another point worth mentioning is that most photomechanical methods for the making of what the trade calls *photoscreens*, are executed by contact printing. The only exception is duPont Screen Process Film which can be processed either by contact printing, or in the camera, or by projection with an enlarger.

Our review of photomechanical resists, or stencils, for screen-process printing is restricted to the more commonly used methods and materials. These are the following six: (1) sensitized screens, (2) carbon-tissue methods, (3) unsensitized films, (4) presensitized films, and (5) the duPont Rotofilm Method.[117]

Sensitized screens for screen-process printing. Sensitized screens represent historically the first application of photomechanics to screen-process printing in the United States; they are well described in the first book published in this country on screen-process printing in 1926. In this method the image carrier is coated with a light-sensitive formula either by brushing, or scraping, or whirling. The coating material is either shop-formulated or bought from screen-process supply houses. Such coating materials contain either gelatin or, more lately, polyvinyl alcohol as their main film-forming ingredient together with a solution of bichromate and various additives.

Sensitized screens are not as much used in shops and plants specializing in printing for advertising displays, greeting cards, wrapping papers, and similar items as they are in other fields of specialization. Directly sensitized screens are more important where screen printing is an adjunct of a given manufacturing process and they play a considerable role in the screen printing of textiles, wallpapers, toys, dials, printed circuits, and other industrial objects. The coated screen is exposed to a positive, then washed-out, inspected, and where

A screen-process platemaker inspects a combination screen-process screen having both knife-cut film and photographic stencil areas. After inspection this screen is lacquered to block the remaining non-printing areas.

necessary retouched and reinforced before it is used for printing. Such precision screens as needed in the electronics industry are usually made of stainless steel cloth. But stainless steel cloth is very costly and therefore too expensive for screens serving merely for decorative purposes. These are usually made of silk or other fibers.

Among the disadvantages of sensitized screens is the necessity for special exposure equipment and, in the case of silk or other fibrous materials, the difficulty of reclaiming the image carrier for future use. For this reason sensitized screens are more efficient in long production runs than in such kinds of screen-process printing as need repeated and very fast changeovers.

Carbon-tissue methods for screen-process printing. Carbon-tissue is a pigmented coating of colloids and plasticizers. This coating is an article of commerce and is not light-sensitive when it is delivered. The first step in making a carbon-tissue resist consists, therefore, in the sensitizing of the tissue by treating it with a solution of bichromate. Carbon-tissue can be converted into resists by two methods. One is known as the *wet method*, the other as the *double-transfer method*. In the wet method the sensitized but still wet tissue is combined with the positive, and exposed while the tissue is still wet. In the double-transfer method the sensitized tissue is dried, exposed to the positive, then placed on a temporary support and thereafter developed. In the wet method this step is eliminated because the transparency serves here as the temporary support. After development in hot water, which removes the unhardened tissue

in the image areas and preserves it in the non-printing areas (thereby resulting in the required stencil or resist), the still wet tissue is adhered to the bottom of the image carrier. After drying, the tissue is anchored in the porous cloth and the temporary support can be removed without damage to the resist.

Unsensitized films for screen-process printing. Carbon-tissue is capable of producing very excellent results but requires precision and skill on the part of the craftsman who does the work. For this reason various suppliers developed special films for photographic screens (sold under different brand names) which are much simpler to handle. These films use plastics as their backing sheets; their coating can be sensitized by brushing with a solution of bichromate which is compounded with alcohol to speed drying. In order to avoid double-transfer such films are usually exposed through the backing sheet. Some of these unsensitized films have an intermediate layer of cement between the backing sheet and the photomechanical coating. Thereby development becomes a much less critical operation, as the smallest particles of this coating are kept in place by the cement and protected from being floated away.

Presensitized films for screen-process printing. These films are essentially of the same construction as the preceding group of materials, with the difference that they do not need sensitizing prior to exposure. They are therefore preferred by screen printers who use photomechanics only in rare cases and who want to spend as little effort as possible on preparatory operations. Presensitized films of this kind do not have silver-halide emulsions and require approximately the same exposure times as do shop-sensitized films.

DuPont Screen Process Film. This method is based on *Rotofilm*, a photomechanical material developed by the duPont Company originally for gravure as an improvement over carbon-tissue. In our discussion of gravure image carriers we met Rotofilm in conjunction with the Alco process; now we meet a similar product again as a medium for making screen-process resists. DuPont Screen Process Film has a silver-halide emulsion of great speed. For this reason it can be exposed directly in the camera or by projection as well as by the customary contact printing. The exposed film is chemically developed; thereby the non-image areas become relatively insoluble whereas the image areas are washed out. The resulting resist is then transferred to the bottom of the screen.

Printing-Image Carriers for Serigraphy

Serigraphy is the name of screen-process printing when it is used for fine-art printmaking. Many a new printing method is at the beginning considered a cheap substitute for one or another of the well-established methods. When screen-process printing was new, some people thought of it as a cheap replacement for the more expensive and well-established lithographic method. (It is amusing to remember that in the beginning of the nineteenth century lithography in turn was in the minds of many people merely a cheap substitute for the high status engraving. Times change indeed, and so do the reputations of printing methods.) When screen-process printing was first used on a larger scale for fine-art printing during the big depression, artists wanted to avoid the odium attached to the name of screen process and were looking for a different name. "The name 'Serigraph' was originated for this medium by Carl Zigrosser, Curator of Prints at the Philadelphia Museum of Art, on the occasion of an exhibition of silk screen prints held at the Weyhe Gallery in New York City. Seri (silk) and graph (to draw) is the obvious derivation of Serigraph, which seems an expressive and suitable name for the silk screen process when employed in the fine art field."[118]

As in all other fine-art printing methods, in serigraphy, too, the artist printmaker makes the image carrier by hand and uses only simple hand-tools for this purpose. Various artists prefer different serigraphic techniques. In the following you find brief explanations of two of them: the tusche method and stippling.

The tusche method of making image carriers for serigraphy. Image carriers for serigraphy have basically the same functions as all other porous image carriers. The non-printing areas of the screen must be blocked and only the image areas must remain unblocked and therewith open for passage of the ink. This result can also be obtained if the artist paints directly on the screen with a film-forming medium suitable for blocking and impervious to the ink to be used. But direct painting has severe drawbacks: the artist must paint the non-image areas, that is, he must not paint what he wants to see printed but must paint around what he wants to show in print. For this reason, artists prefer a method where they can make image carriers by painting the image areas and where the blocked non-image areas are obtained with more mechanical techniques.

The tusche method is a satisfactory solution for these requirements. It derives its name from the painting medium used in its execution, which is a lithographic tusche that can be supplemented by lithographic crayons if desired. In the tusche method the screen is first sized in order to permit painting on its surface, then the artist creates the image by painting and drawing, not to mention other techniques of endowing the screen with various textures. Next the screen is coated with a blocking medium which must be repelled by the painting medium. If lithographic tusche is used as painting medium, glue can serve as blocking medium as it will be repelled by the fatty lithographic tusche which is, of course, water-repellent.

Courtesy Presentation Press

In serigraphy the artist printmaker works with crayon and brush on the screen, creating his design as he works. Often he is guided by a sketch placed under the screen.

After the glue has dried, the lithographic tusche is, of course, removed with an organic solvent such as turpentine. This solvent does not attack the blocking medium but removes the painting medium from the image areas which thereby become unblocked and suitable for ink passage. In some variations of this method, the image medium is replaced with a specially prepared formula.

Stippling for screen-process printing. Stippling is a technique that lends itself to the obtaining of relatively coarse vignetting, or fading-out, effects. The artist works with various rather stiff brushes and a blocking medium such as glue or lacquer. The quality of the result depends entirely on the skill of the artist; very outstanding effects have been obtained in this manner but inexperienced people can be rather disappointed by this technique. Stippling is used in both serigraphy and screen-process printing. In the latter method it has often the function of supplementing knife-cut film image carriers by softening their sharp outlines.

Chapter VI

Printing Presses

Printing presses are the production machines of the printing industry. They are the equipment for presswork, the stage in which printed images are produced in the required quantity. Even though this quantity may vary within wide limits, depending on the purpose and end use of the printed product, the presses which are characteristic for contemporary printing are essentially mass production machines designed to cope with the demands of a mass production society. These demands comprise a vast diversification of printed products and cause a corresponding diversification of printing presses. Great as the differences between various kinds of presses are, it is nevertheless possible to isolate a number of basic features that must be present in all modern printing presses.

Contemporary printing presses must provide ten basic facilities. They must permit: (1) the secure positioning of the printing-image carrier, (2) the correct application of printing ink to the image carrier, (3) the precise positioning of the printing stock, (4) the making of the impression whereby the ink image is transferred from the image carrier to the printing stock, (5) the removal of the printed stock from the printing unit immediately after image transfer, (6) the storage of blank or partially printed stock in a quantity sufficient to maintain presswork, (7) the continual or continuous conveyance of printing stock to the position required for making the impression, (8) storage of printing ink in a quantity sufficient to maintain presswork, (9) regulating the printing pressure to suit different job conditions, and (10) temporary storage of the printed material.

This listing is far from complete. Depending on the nature and purpose of a press, the mechanisms for these ten essentials must be supplemented by a smaller or larger number of others. Some provide the power necessary for operation, some have the function of adjustment or regulation, some are needed for correct and often split-second timing, and some for protection of the operator and the equipment itself. The detail of these many mechanisms depends not only on the purpose of a given press but also on its particular make. In keeping with the general plan of this manual the basic features of press components will be explained in the present chapter, disregarding particular makes as much as possible and practical.

   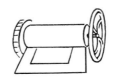

The five minimum facilities of printing presses are: (1) provision for secure positioning of printing-image carrier; (2) facilities for application of printing ink; (3) devices for precise locating of paper; (4) implements for applying pressure, and (5) space for removal and temporary storage of printed sheets.

This chapter is divided into eight sections: Section 1 is a survey of standard presses for all printing methods, Section 2 is devoted to printing units, Section 3 describes the closely related inking units, Section 4 explains sheet feeders, Section 5 does the same for roll-feeding equipment and for web controls, Section 6 discusses deliveries of sheetfed and roll-fed presses, Section 7 introduces you to drying methods and drying equipment, and Section 8, the last, deals with proof presses and proofing.

Section 1:   A Survey of Printing Presses

The following survey of printing presses has the purpose of acquainting you with the large variety of available standard equipment. It is organized by printing processes and methods and divided accordingly into the four main categories of (1) presses for relief printing, (2) presses for intaglio printing, (3) presses for planographic printing, and (4) presses for porous or screen-process printing. Each of these four process families is further divided, as always in this manual, into its several methods. These are usually explained as to their main purpose and general characteristics before the variety of available equipment is described. You, the reader, might keep in mind that the variety of presses changes constantly. Every so often some kinds or sizes of presses are discontinued by their manufacturers and new kinds and sizes are put on the market. But discontinued equipment still exists in thousands of printing plants. It has neither become useless nor necessarily obsolete and often proved to be especially suitable for certain kinds of work. Even though it is not possible—and in many instances far from desirable—to describe or mention all such equipment, there are some instances when it is necessary to do so.

Several terms used throughout this section are here introduced and explained if they need explanations. To give you some idea at which speeds presses can be operated, their *maximum rated speed* is usually indicated. In sheetfed presses the maximum rated speed is expressed as the number of impressions per hour, abbreviated as i.p.h. In roll-fed presses, which are used for web printing, speed is also expressed as the number of printed feet per minute, abbreviated f.p.m. In sheetfed presses the size of a press means its *maximum sheet size;* in roll-fed presses two terms are used to indicate the size limits of the printed product: the *maximum web width* characterizes one dimension and the *cut-off* does the same for the other. In some instances press equipment is designated in this manual as single-purpose or single-product machinery to distinguish it from less specialized all around presses which are called here multi-purpose machines.

This seems to be the right point to emphasize the difference between maximum rated speed and actual *operating speed.* Maximum rated speed should not be confused with average operating speed, nor should it be assumed that every job can be printed at maximum rated speed. The actual operating speed depends on the nature of the job in hand; it may be considerably less than maximum rated speed. Maximum sheet size is much less subject to fluctuations than actual press speed, but it happens that certain jobs are more efficiently printed on a smaller than maximum sheet. The detail of the job and the kind of stock are important points in this respect, as well as in determining the actual operating speeds of presses. The maximum sheet size is sometimes assumed to be the maximum printing area of a press. This is a mistake, since the *maximum printing* area is somewhat smaller in both directions than the maximum sheet size.

This section deals exclusively with standard production equipment. Presses for specialty printing are not covered because their detailed discussion would exceed the available space, but the last unit of this section provides a brief general discussion of specialty printing and its variety.

Presses for Relief Printing

Relief printing is in this manual subdivided into the four printing methods of (1) letterpress, (2) newspaper relief printing, (3) flexographic printing, and (4) indirect relief printing. All of these methods are based on image carriers which have their printing areas in relief, or above their non-printing areas. Apart from this common factor, the four methods differ widely in their image carriers which, although all in relief, are made by different manufacturing processes and for different purposes. Nor do all four methods of relief printing employ the same inks, print on the same stocks, and produce the same end products. The broadest method of the four is letterpress printing. This method comprises multi-purpose equipment, which is needed in the service business, as well as single-purpose equipment, which is designed to produce specific kinds of products. Newspaper relief printing serves but rarely for other purposes than to print and fold newspapers. The presses used in this method are, hence, single-purpose equipment. Flexography, too, is a highly specialized method used primarily for package and business forms printing. Indirect relief printing in its present form is the newest of our four relief methods. It has its single-purpose machines, for forms printing for example, but multipurpose equipment is also, and increasingly, used in this method for job-and-commercial printing.

Letterpress Printing Machines

Those who are not familiar with the history of graphic reproduction are often puzzled by the great diversity of available letterpress printing equipment. They wonder why there are more kinds of printing presses for letterpress than for any other method, and they are even more surprised when they find out that letterpress equipment is available for the efficient production of any quantity in any size and number of colors, from the relatively small and slow hand-fed presses on which a few hundred sheets of stationery are printed in the neighborhood shop to the giant multicolor web perfecting presses which produce millions of general-interest magazines in full color at incredible speeds.

The explanation of the unique breadth of letterpress is threefold. One part of the answer is historical, the second part is related to the nature of metallic composition, and the third to the intrinsic nature of letterpress and its stability in particular. Historically, letterpress is the original method of printing; it has existed more than five hundred years. Lithography, which is approximately one hundred sixty years old, is the second oldest printing method, and contemporary offset lithography is a mere fledgling, as printing processes go, with its 50 or 60 years of age. Gravure is not much younger than letterpress as a fine-art

printing method, but as an industrial process it has approximately the same age as offset lithography.[1] Most other widely used printing methods are still younger even if they can establish an older pedigree. What counts in this context is not the earliest event with which a printing method can be connected, but the time at which a method began to see general use. Some printing methods did not attain maturity before or even after World War II.

If you keep in mind that all printing methods other than letterpress were originally picture reproduction methods incapable of reproducing reading matter in bulk, then you will understand the difference between them and letterpress which was, until the perfection of photomechanics at the turn of the nineteenth century, the only method capable of printing reading matter in bulk. Consequently, it was the task of letterpress to develop the means whereby the needs of society for communication by printing would be satisfied, whatever these needs were, whether they entailed the printing of a few copies or of large runs. The history of printing explains the incredible diversification of letterpress. The same facts explain also why so many of the early printing presses for other processes resemble their contemporary letterpress counterparts: other processes followed the patterns developed by letterpress, which was then identical with printing.

The second fact that is too often not fully appreciated in a time when photographic image conversion is widely used is the ability of letterpress to print directly from type. Under certain conditions, of which shortness of run is the most convincing, printing directly from type is more efficient and more economical than any other reproduction procedure. To summarize, history accounts for the diversification of letterpress; the intrinsic stability of letterpress during the press run for its pre-eminence in long-run printing; and the fact that letterpress is the only printing method capable of printing directly from type makes it a most economical method if a job consists more or less completely of reading matter and the run is relatively small.

Historic letterpresses. The traditional wooden hand press, which was in general use from the inception of printing in the middle of the fifteenth century until the second quarter of the nineteenth century, had two flat surfaces as its printing unit: one of them was a thick stone, surrounded by a sturdy wooden frame which projected beyond its top surface; the other was a thick wooden board, sometimes faced with an iron plate. The first member, called the "coffin," served for positioning of the type form; the second member, called the "platin," had the function of applying the required printing pressure. During the nineteenth century the wooden hand press was superseded by iron hand presses of different constructions. Power-driven presses outmoded iron hand presses which disappeared as production machines in the later decades of the nineteenth century, but were used as engravers' proof presses well into the twentieth. One of them, the Washington hand press has become a collector's press; it is still used by hobby printers.

Printing units consisting of two plane surfaces, though arranged entirely different than in hand presses, are still used in contemporary letterpress printing. But such presses represent only one of three basic designs which are used in the construction of presses for the letterpress industry.

The three kinds of contemporary presses for letterpress. The three kinds of contemporary presses for letterpress are: (1) platen presses, (2) flatbed-cylinder presses, and (3) rotary presses. Platen presses have two flat surfaces, the bed and the platen. As they have a flat bed, they can use type forms. But they are not the only kind of presses that can print directly from type; platen presses share this capability with another kind, flatbed-cylinder presses. The printing unit of flatbed-cylinder presses consists of a flat bed and a cylinder which takes the place of the platen. This cylinder is called the *impression cylinder* or, though less generally, the *paper cylinder*. The third and last kind of printing presses for letterpress, rotary presses, has no flatbed at all. The flatbed of platen and of flatbed-cylinder presses is now also replaced by a cylinder, known as the *plate cylinder*. Rotary presses have, hence, two cylinders, the plate cylinder and the impression cylinder. The image carriers for rotary presses must be curved in order to correspond to the contour of the plate cylinder. Such image carriers are either duplicate plates or, most recently, thin curvable image carriers known as wrap-around plates which are made photomechanically and by etching. Platen and flatbed-cylinder presses serve for the production of short and medium-length runs whereas rotary presses are, generally speaking, used for high-speed mass production printing.

Purposes and kinds of platen presses. Platen presses are the smallest and least complex of all widely used letterpress printing machines. They

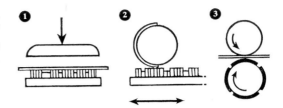

In platen presses (*1*) the platen and the bed are flat; in flatbed-cylinder presses (*2*) the bed is still flat but the platen is replaced by an impression cylinder; in rotary presses (*3*) the plate cylinder takes the place of the flatbed, and both members of the printing unit are cylindrical.

are frequently found in small unspecialized printing businesses. Platen presses are used for many different purposes. Among them is the printing of paper and paperboard, envelopes, embossing, steel-rule die-cutting, and gold leaf stamping. Most platen presses are sheetfed, either by hand or by feeding machines. Hand-fed platen presses are often called *open presses;* platen presses equipped with mechanical feeders and deliveries are classified as *job automatics*. Platen presses can also be roll-fed. Roll-fed platen presses are used for forms printing and other kinds of specialty printing.

Sizes and speeds of platen presses. Platen presses are manufactured by several companies in the United States and are also imported from Europe. Their size varies from a minimum sheet size of approximately 7¼ by 12½ inches to a maximum sheet size of 18 by 24 inches. Presses capable of handling sheets of 10 by 15 inches, 12 by 18 inches, and 14½ by 22 inches are quite popular. The speed of automatic platen presses ranges between 1800 and 5000 i.p.h. depending on size and purpose of a specific model.[2] Not all platen presses are of the same construction. The most important construction principles are discussed in the section on printing units.

The main difference between platen and flatbed-cylinder presses. Flatbed-cylinder presses were up to World War II the most important letterpress printing machines for medium-length runs, say, up to 50,000 impressions. They are capable of printing directly from type as well as from duplicate plates and can handle sheets of much larger sizes than platen presses. The main difference between platen and flatbed-cylinder presses is the fact that platen presses make the impression of the whole area covered by the printing-image carrier at the same time, whereas flatbed-cylinder presses do so in small increments. The area which is under pressure extends all the way across the image carrier and may be only a fraction of an inch wide. This area is called the *impression nip* and differs in width for presses of different sizes. Flatbed-cylinder presses are consequently capable of printing much larger areas without requiring the impression power that would be needed by platen presses of the same size.[3]

Horizontal and vertical flatbed-cylinder presses. The principle on which flatbed-cylinder presses are based, which is the interaction of an impression cylinder with a flat surface, proved exceptionally fruitful in the development of printing presses not only for letterpress but also for stone lithography. Designers of printing presses tried a considerable number of variations in which these two elements, the bed and the cylinder, were made to function. Many of these combinations are of historical interest only; some versions of flatbed-cylinder presses which remain of contemporary importance will be described in the section on printing units. Here it is merely mentioned that the larger size flatbed-cylinder presses are of horizontal construction, meaning that the type form is positioned horizontally, or parallel to the pressroom floor. But flatbed-cylinder presses can also have their type forms in a vertical position and are then known as vertical presses.

Various kinds of horizontal flatbed-cylinder presses. Flatbed-cylinder presses are available as three different kinds: (1) as *single-color presses* which print one side of the sheet in one color in one pass through the press; (2) as *two-color presses* which print one side of the sheet in two colors in one pass through the press; and (3) as *perfecting presses*, or *perfectors*, which print both sides of the sheet in one color in one pass through the press. In 1962 all domestic press manufacturers ceased to build horizontal flatbed-cylinder presses; but vertical flatbed-cylinder presses and some horizontal models for die-cutting are still made in the U.S.A. One American press builder makes horizontal flatbed-cylinder presses in Europe and imports them in the United States; several European press manufacturers continue to make this kind of equipment and to offer it also in the United States.[4]

Sizes and speeds of single-color flatbed-cylinder presses. Single-color flatbed-cylinder presses were built in the United States in a large variety of constructions and sizes in the course of many decades. To list all or most of them would be use-

less dead weight, as many models disappeared in the course of time. In 1962, prior to their discontinuation, single-color flatbed-cylinder presses were built in the United States in six different sizes. The smallest press then built takes a maximum sheet of 12 by 18 inches; the largest press then built can handle a maximum sheet of 42 by 56 inches. Among the most popular models is a vertical press that prints a 14 by 20 inches maximum sheet and horizontal presses that can handle a 20 by 26 inches, a 21 by 28 inches, and a 28 by 41 inches maximum sheet. The maximum rated speed of single-color flatbed-cylinder presses built in 1962 in the United States varies for different sizes and makes; it runs from 2,250 i.p.h. in the largest listed size up to 5,000 i.p.h. in smaller sizes.[5]

The preceding listing of single-color flatbed-cylinder presses does not contain a number of models that were discontinued some time before 1962. Many of these older models are still in operation throughout the country, particularly presses that can print larger sizes. Two such models seem to be worth adding. One can print a maximum sheet of 46 by 64½ inches and has a maximum rated speed of 1,750 i.p.h.; the largest model worth mentioning can handle a sheet 50 by 73½ inches at a maximum rated speed of 1,600 hourly impressions.

Sizes and speeds of two-color flatbed-cylinder presses. In 1962, two-color flatbed-cylinder presses were built in the United States in three different sizes. One model takes a maximum sheet of 21 by 28 inches and is rated at a maximum hourly speed of 4,600 two-color impressions, the second model can print a sheet of 27½ by 41 inches at a maximum rated hourly speed of 3,750 two-color im-

Courtesy Technical Trade School

Instructor explains the operation of a two-color flatbed-cylinder press.

pressions, and the third handles a sheet of 38 by 56 inches at a maximum rated hourly speed of 2,250 impressions.[6] Older presses were made in a number of different sizes. Here we mention merely one which was designed to print a maximum sheet of 46 by 69½ inches at a maximum speed of 1,800 i.p.h.

Sizes and speeds of flatbed-cylinder perfecting presses. This class of presses was discontinued before 1962 and is not even mentioned in the 1962 Buyers Guide of *Printing Production* magazine. Before these presses were discontinued they were made in three sizes. The smallest perfector printed a sheet of 37 by 52½ inches at a maximum rated speed of 1,900 impressions; the next model had a maximum sheet size of 40 by 55½ inches and a maximum speed rating of 1,800 impressions, and the largest flatbed-cylinder perfector goes up to a maximum sheet size of 45 by 68½ inches and prints at a maximum rated hourly speed of 1,600 impressions.[7] Older presses went up to a maximum sheet size of approximately 51 by 74 inches and had a maximum rated hourly speed of approximately 1,500 impressions. Some of these large presses are still in operation.

The Miehle Vertical. The Miehle Vertical is the most widely used vertical press in this country. Its maximum sheet size is 14 by 20 inches; the maximum rated speed is 5,000 i.p.h. The press is equipped with automatic feeder and delivery. The Miehle Vertical is mainly used in job-and-commercial printing and is often classified together with platen presses that have mechanical feeders and deliveries as a job automatic press. The Miehle Vertical is the only kind of flatbed-cylinder printing press still manufactured by the Miehle Company, Division of Miehle-Goss-Dexter, in Chicago.

Presses for Rotary Letterpress

All rotary presses have printing units that consist of two cylinders: one is the plate cylinder and the other is the impression cylinder. Type forms cannot be curved, as already explained, and rotary presses therefore cannot use type forms as their printing-image carriers. The image carriers for rotary letterpress machines are either curved duplicate plates, mainly electrotypes, or photomechanically made thin curvable image carriers including metal wrap-around plates, Dycril photopolymer plates, and Kodak Relief Plates.

The purpose of rotary letterpress equipment. Rotary presses are much more efficient than platen or flatbed-cylinder presses. The rotary principle permits a continuous uninterrupted motion in the same direction, resulting in much higher press speeds since it eliminates the time-consuming and cumbersome reciprocating motion of flatbed-cylinder presses. Rotary presses are, therefore, a natural choice for longer press runs and a necessity in mass production printing.

It is often asked which quantity, or run, of a job can be more economically printed on rotaries than on flatbed-cylinder presses, always assuming of course that it was decided to do a particular job in letterpress. Unfortunately, it is not possible to answer this question without considering the nature and the detail of the job in hand. Generally speaking, jobs requiring more than 50,000 sheets of the same kind will be more economically produced on rotary than on flatbed-cylinder presses. In dubious cases, all costs of a job must be considered before a decision can be made. One of the most important cost elements is the cost of printing-image carriers, another is that of press preparation. Image carriers can be type forms for flatbed-cylinder presses, but must be either duplicate plates or wrap-around plates for rotary presses. The efficiency of rotary presses is of course much higher than that of flatbed-cylinder presses but it may be insufficient to compensate for the additional cost of plates and for higher costs of press preparation due to the higher hourly cost rate of rotary presses. Everything depends on the actual conditions under which a decision must be made, and the figure of 50,000 impressions cannot be used mechanically. The advent of wrap-around plates tends to reduce plate costs but rotary presses built for printing with electrotypes cannot handle wrap-around plates without mechanical changes.

Various kinds of rotary letterpress equipment. Rotary letterpress machines can be either sheetfed or roll-fed. Sheetfed presses are used as multi-purpose equipment in job-and-commercial printing and in publication printing of specialized, or limited-interest, magazines which are produced in editions that exceed the range of flatbed-cylinder presses but are not sufficient to warrant printing on roll-fed presses. National general-interest magazines such as *Time, Life,* and *McCall's,* as well as mail order catalogs and other long-run jobs are printed on especially designed roll-fed magazine presses. Even though letterpress is a most important method in the field of magazine printing, it is by no means the only method which can be used for this purpose. Rotogravure and, lately, web offset are also used for the production of national magazines and catalogs.

Unit-type and common impression cylinder presses. Rotary presses can be based on two different construction principles. One is the *unit-type* design in which every color is printed by an individual printing unit consisting of a plate cylinder and of an impression cylinder. The other construction principle is that of a *common impression cylinder* for two or more plate cylinders. These two principles are used for presses in various processes, in letterpress as well as in offset lithography and in flexography. Either construction principle can be applied to sheetfed and to roll-fed presses. Sheetfed presses for letterpress are usually designed for the printing of one side of paper, paper board, or other stock, whereas roll-fed presses are usually perfecting presses which print both sides of the sheet or web in one pass through the press.

Number of colors, sizes, and speeds of sheetfed rotaries for letterpress. Sheetfed rotaries of the unit type are made in 1, 2, 3, 4, 5, and 6 colors for one-side printing. These presses are made in two sizes. The smaller models have a maximum sheet size of 42 by 60 inches; the larger models can handle sheets 52 inches (or more recently 54½ inches) by 76 inches. The rated maximum speed varies for presses with different numbers of color units between 3,000 and 6,500 i.p.h. for the smaller models and between 2,750 and 6,000 impressions for the larger ones. Unit-type perfectors are made as single-color and as two-color presses for a maximum sheet size of 52 by 76 inches; the maximum rated speed of single-color perfectors is 6,000 i.p.h., that of two-color perfectors is 5,500. The larger models can be equipped with sheeter-feeders which sheet paper rolls as part of presswork.

Presses of the common impression cylinder construction are made for sheetfed letterpress printing either as two-color or as five-color presses. Two-color models are made in three sizes: the smallest takes a maximum sheet of 36 by 48 inches and has a maximum rated speed of 7,000 i.p.h., the next size takes a maximum sheet of 40 by 59 inches and has a maximum rated speed of 6,000 i.p.h., and the largest model is built for a maximum sheet size of 48 by 72 inches and rated at a maximum speed of 5,000 i.p.h. All two-color presses have single deliveries. Five-color common impression cylinder presses are built in three sizes:

the first two handle the same sheet sizes at the same maximum rated speeds; the largest five-color model can handle a maximum sheet size of 48 by 71 inches and has a maximum rated speed of 6,000 i.p.h. Five-color presses are equipped either with a single or a double delivery. Double deliveries are mainly needed on presses used for the printing of paper boards.[8] It bears mention that not all sheetfed rotaries found in actual plant operation conform to the sizes, number of color units, and speed ratings mentioned here. Some plants may have presses that differ in one or more of these points because their presses may have been built for a particular kind of work.

Our next subject is wrap-around presses, the latest addition to sheetfed letterpress equipment.

Wrap-around presses. Wrap-around presses are relatively new, and the field is still in flux. Consequently, we do not have a generally accepted terminology. Some consider every press built to use wrap-around plates as image carriers a wrap-around press. Since wrap-around plates can be made either for direct or for indirect relief printing, some prefer to limit the designation

Courtesy Downingtown Paper Company

A two-color Harris Wraparound *press for printing of paper board. Since paper boards are much thicker than papers, the press is on a raised foundation whereby additional space is provided in the feeder as well as in the delivery.*

wrap-around press to presses for direct printing. In this manual indirect relief printing is treated as method different from letterpress, and we are at this point describing only direct printing wrap-around presses. Wrap-around presses are available as single-color and as multicolor presses from a relatively small single-color model that prints a maximum sheet size of 23 by 30 inches to such large installations as six-color presses for the printing of maximum sheet sizes of 43 by 60 inches. Between these two extremes there are presses that can handle a maximum sheet of 25¾ by 38½ inches, and those that print a maximum sheet of 36 by 49½. The maximum rated speed of single-color presses for 23 by 30 inch sheets is 8,000; that of presses handling 25¾ by 38½ inch sheets is 7,500, and the maximum speed of larger presses is rated by their manufacturer at 6,500 i.p.h. Wrap-around presses cover, as these data demonstrate, a wide gamut of production facilities.

Magazine presses for letterpress printing. Finally, we come to the giants of the letterpress industry: roll-fed multicolor perfecting presses which are known as *magazine presses* according to their main product. (As mentioned before, gravure and web offset are also used for magazine printing.) Magazine presses are usually built to specifications and are single-purpose equipment. The number of plants operating such presses is comparatively small, but the economic importance of magazine printing is great nevertheless. A roll-fed magazine press can be either of unit-type or of common impression cylinder construction. Practically all magazine presses are perfecting presses; common impression cylinder presses are equipped with two printing units, one for each side of the web of paper. Magazine presses may have up to six plate cylinders for each side of the web, and may hence be capable of printing the web in a total of 12 colors. The format of the final product for which a magazine press is designed determines the dimensions of the press. Magazine presses may deliver from 32 to 192 pages per revolution. The width of the web and the diameter of the plate cylinder depend on the format of the printed product. Webs can be run at a maximum rated speed of 2,000 f.p.m.

Magazine presses are enormous machines. The printing units themselves are merely a part of this equipment. The feeding unit, which usually harbors three rolls of paper and is, in the most modern presses, equipped for completely auto-matic connecting of a new roll to the expiring one, creates an almost endless band of paper. The delivery end of the press is, if possible, even more impressive. Here the web is cut and folded to the required number of pages. The folded product can be stitched, imprinted, and pasted wherever any of these operations is required.

It is clear that magazine presses must be perfectly co-ordinated in all their functions. They are usually provided with driers to insure the drying of ink at the tremendous speed at which they are operated. Drying is followed by cooling, or chilling, the web to the proper temperatures. Many controls are needed on these presses. Mass circulation magazines use much full-color printing, and the web must be under strict control as to its tension and position at all times. The control panels of modern magazine presses indicate the progress of production by means of electrical signals to those in charge. It is obviously not possible to follow presswork on magazine presses simply by eye as can be done on less fast and less complex equipment.

Relief Printing Presses for Newspaper Printing

Until very recently the term "newspaper press" was not only generally accepted but also free of ambiguity. Practically all newspapers were printed on newspaper presses which used relief printing-image carriers. These were type forms for short-run papers and duplicate plates, practically always curved stereotype plates, for long runs. Metropolitan newspapers were, and still are at present, printed in this manner. In the end of the fifth decade and in the beginning of the sixth decade of this century, web-offset printing was successfully introduced into the newspaper field, and a considerable number of smaller newspapers, as well as some larger weeklies, are at the time of writing printed by web offset. Since web offset is a newcomer in the newspaper field, some of those who are in favor of this method for newspaper printing object to the term "newspaper press," when used in the traditional sense of relief printing, as discriminatory and inexact. These people maintain that web-offset presses designed for newspaper printing are just as much entitled to be called newspaper presses as the traditional equipment. For this reason the qualifying adjective *relief* is added in this manual wherever misunderstanding could be caused by using the term newspaper printing without this qualification. To make things quite clear it is expressly stated that newspapers can be produced by several different printing methods, including web offset and rotogravure as well as by relief printing.

Newspaper presses are single-purpose machines. Contemporary newspaper presses are designed to manufacture a single product: the newspaper. Even though newspapers can be produced by means of other equipment, newspaper presses are not, generally speaking, suitable for other purposes. Hence they are seldom used for anything but the production of newspapers and such products as can be used in newspaper-like quality. Roll-feeding, the assembling of several webs, and folding are integral parts of newspaper printing. Newspaper presses of any kind—for relief printing, rotogravure, or offset lithography—always include roll-feeding equipment and a folder. The word "folder" signifies, in newspaper printing, the machinery which converts printed webs into the final product. Folders used in web printing perform many other operations in addition to folding. (Newspaper folders are described in Section 6.)

Requirements for newspaper printing equipment. The design of newspaper presses cannot be understood without an explanation of the necessities of newspaper publishing. The first consideration is, of course, economy. American newspapers are exceptionally inexpensive and even though advertising revenue is instrumental in maintaining the low price of our newspapers, efficiency of production is nevertheless indispensable. Paper and ink are the two most important materials used in newspaper printing. They are crucial cost elements, and as they are consumed in immense quantities, the use of the least expensive types of these materials is mandatory. In *newsprint* the industry has an inexpensive paper and in *news ink* an inexpensive ink.

Immediacy and speed of production are paramount requirements in newspaper printing. Immediacy refers to the time it takes to convert the news into printing-image carriers and to get the press running. Speed means in this context the time needed to produce a given number of newspapers after the press is started running. Both points are closely related. An additional necessity is flexibility of the equipment. Flexibility is not needed for changing the size of pages, which remain the same for long periods of time at the same newspaper, but it is needed for changing the number of pages which varies considerably for different seasons of the year and different days of the week. The fluctuations in the number of pages are mainly caused by fluctuations in advertising since many newspapers try to maintain a certain ratio between advertising and editorial space. The result is that on some days newspapers have fewer pages than on others. It is not uncommon for a newspaper to have thick issues with three or four times as many pages as their thin issues.

Standardization of page sizes in the newspaper industry. The newspaper press is designed to cope with all these necessities. If we compare newspaper production with commercial or job printing done on sheetfed presses, we must first keep in mind that the product of newspaper printing has always the same page size. The page size differs for standard, or full-size, newspapers and for tabloids. Full-size newspapers have mostly pages of one of the three following lengths: $21\frac{1}{2}$, $22\frac{3}{4}$, $23\frac{9}{16}$ inches. The width of pages is less standardized and varies between, say, 15 and 17 inches. The page size of *tabloids* is one-half of a standard size page, and may be 15 to 17 inches long and approximately $11\frac{3}{4}$ inches wide. The decisive point is not the exact page size, but the fact that the page size remains the same for a long time once it is adopted for a given paper. This makes it possible to standardize everything to a much greater extent than in the service business where sizes differ from job to job.[9]

Brief description of newspaper presses for relief printing. As mentioned repeatedly, newspapers can be printed by other methods than relief printing, but in this unit we are discussing presses for newspaper relief printing. All but the smallest newspapers are printed on rotary web perfecting presses. The printing unit of such presses consists of two printing couples, one for each side of the paper web. Rotary newspaper presses use curved stereotype plates as their image carriers, each occupying either the whole or, much more frequently, one-half of the circumference of the plate cylinder. As plate cylinders are either 2 or 4 pages wide, a printing unit can produce a maximum of 16 standard size pages, 8 on one side and 8 on the other.

If a newspaper has more than 16 pages, or if it is printed in a quantity which is too large to be produced within the time available for printing, more than one printing unit must be employed. Actually, large metropolitan newspapers employ presses with a number of units, usually seven or eight, depending on the needs of a specific paper. Each of these units prints, of course, its own web of paper. But webs of paper are far from being newspapers, and our next subject is how these webs of paper are further processed to make newspapers out of them.

Reasons for folding of newspapers. Some of the problems encountered in newspaper printing can perhaps be easier understood if we consider the form in which a newspaper is handed to the customer. Standard, or full-size, papers consist usually of a number of sections. Each section has several sheets containing 4 pages, 2 on each side. The number of sheets is not fixed but can vary. Several such sheets are folded together the long way of the page. It is also possible that sections contain sheets of paper having the width of a single page instead of that of 2 pages. Such sheets have one printed page on each side of the paper and do not need folding the long way. Standard newspapers consist of several sections in sequence; these sections are folded across their width whereby the folded paper becomes equivalent in size to half a page. In tabloids, which have individual pages half the size of standard size papers, the whole paper is one unit and does not consist of sections. Each leaf of a tabloid contains 4 pages, 2 on either side of the paper; all pages are in sequence, and the tabloid is folded only once in the middle between page pairs. Tabloids have, therefore, only a single fold.

A standard size newspaper, which usually consists of more than one section, is folded two times; a tabloid has no sections and is folded only once.

Next it must be explained how the newspaper press makes the final product from rolls of blank newsprint. We assume that the printed product is a standard size paper. The maximum web is 4 pages wide, containing 2 pairs of pages on either side. As mentioned before, each plate cylinder bears 8 stereotype plates—two rows of 4 plates across the plate cylinder. Since there are 2 plate cylinders, one for each side of the web, the total number of printed pages is 16 per revolution of the cylinder. The next and every following revolution produces, of course, the same printed result. Assuming that our newspaper consists merely of 16 pages, the 16 pages which are printed on the web in two rows of 8 pages each, must now be given the form of a newspaper. The 4-page wide web must obviously be reduced to the customary 2-page newspaper width. This is accomplished by slitting the web in the center, resulting in two printed webs, each 2 pages wide. Each of the 2-page wide webs has 8 pages, 4 on one side and 4 on the other. These two webs must be put together and the two groups of 8 pages, which are still connected one above the other, must be cut and put in proper sequence. In addition, the newspaper must be folded lengthwise whereby it becomes an unfastened book whose pages can be turned by the reader; it must further be folded in half for handling and selling.

The preceding discussion does not intend to describe the detail and the exact order of operations; it has only one purpose: to explain that there is a lot more than printing to contemporary newspaper production. Nor is the continuous printing of rolls, without which mass production printing is not possible, a simple thing. It requires, at its highest technological level rather complex, fully automatic roll-feeding equipment which involves substantial capital investment. You can see that the printing unit, which is between the feeding and the folding equipment, is merely a part of the newspaper press.

The different position of folding in sheetfed and in web printing. Printers experienced in sheetfed printing but not in web printing do not consider folding a part of presswork but of binding. And when printers who are experienced in sheetfed printing only hear of several printing units in sequence, they think automatically of multicolor presses capable of printing several colors on the same sheet of paper. Contrariwise, those who are interested in the printing of newspapers think first of additional webs when they speak of additional printing units. If a newspaper is to be printed in more than black, color printing is an added problem to that of handling the required number of webs. The problems and techniques here described are not only met in newspaper printing but exist also, though in somewhat different forms, in other web-printing methods. As web printing has become an important field in job-and-commercial printing, which was in the past exclusively done on sheetfed equipment, this discussion should be of interest to all who want to familiarize themselves with web printing.

Various kinds of newspaper relief presses. After this introduction to newspaper printing we turn to a brief discussion of various types of newspaper presses. In grouping newspaper presses, we can distinguish the following seven kinds: (1) *flatbed-cylinder presses*, meaning presses that print rolls of paper on both sides from type forms rather than from plates; (2) *tubular* or *cylindrical presses*, meaning rotary presses "that use curved plates, cast in the form of a slotted cylinder. The cylinder is slotted to permit sliding the plate past the bearing support on the press"; (3) *semicylindrical presses*, namely, "rotary presses that use curved plates that cover about one-half of the plate cylinder"; (4) *deck-type presses* which "have the printing couples—plate cylinder and impression cylinder—arranged one above the other"; (5) *unit-type presses* that "have the printing couples arranged horizontally along the floor rather than vertically. The unit is a separate element. Each unit has two printing couples with additional plate cylinders available"; (6) *single width presses*, a type of press that "prints a web 2 standard newspaper pages wide, which is the minimum width for a newspaper press"; and, finally, (7) *double width presses* which "can print a web 4 newspaper pages wide, or any smaller width down to a single page."[10]

The purposes of various kinds of newspaper presses. It is obvious that these classifications do not all refer to the same points but describe various aspects of newspaper presses. As a summary it can be said that flatbed-cylinder presses are used by papers with the smallest circulation, in the United States primarily by local weeklies. The vast majority of urban daily newspapers are printed on rotary presses. Tubular presses, which have a much smaller production than semicylindrical presses, print only 1 page around the cylinder and are only made 2 pages wide. They obviously produce much less than semi-

cylindrical presses which have 2 pages around the cylinder and are either 2 or 4 pages wide. (If they are 2 pages wide, they are single width, and if 4 pages wide, they are double-width presses.) The terms "unit type" and "deck type," finally, describe the manner in which the several units are arranged. Deck-type presses are historically much older than unit-type presses. The difference between these two types is not only one of space utilization but also of importance for roll-feeding, which differs in kind for either type of press.

The meaning of "impression" in newspaper printing. The printing unit of newspaper presses, like that of all other types of presses, is discussed in some detail in the following section on "Printing Units." But one item is singled out at this point because it is most significant for the difference between newspaper relief printing and other relief-printing methods. This difference lies in the handling of the impression cylinder. The function of the impression cylinder is in newspaper printing to provide "a smooth resilient surface against which the web is pressed by the plate." In the opinion of newspaper technicians "printing is a process of making impressions from an inked surface," and the impressions of relief newspaper presses "are made by the plate pushing the newsprint into the resilient surface on the impression cylinder. Printing is done by impression; the ink records the impression."[11] This description of newspaper printing indicates one of the most salient differences between letterpress and newspaper printing. In letterpress the image carrier should, ideally, never make an impression in the sense in which this word is used in the preceding quotation. In newspaper printing the paper is actually pressed into the resilient surface of the packing which is embossed by the plate. *The reason for using a soft packing in newspaper printing is simply that soft packings require no work before printing can begin whereas hard packings need careful press preparation.*

Letterpress technology makes every effort to avoid an impression in the sense in which this word is used in newspaper printing but even in the best magazine work a very slight impression is made on the packing. These differences in the transfer of the ink image are not the only ones between newspaper relief printing and magazine printing. In newspaper relief printing the ink dries by absorption, and forced drying equipment is not needed. In high-speed letterpress web printing, the ink must be dried by application of heat and air to the web which passes through forced-drying installations.

Flexographic Printing Presses

Flexographic printing can be done for a number of different purposes; one of its main fields of application is the printing of package materials. Paper boards, aluminum foils, papers of different weight and quality such as wrapping papers and the semitransparent, or translucent, glassine papers, and plastic films of many kinds are among the stocks most frequently used for flexographic printing. Even though sheetfed flexographic presses exist, these are a small minority which can be neglected for our purposes. The overwhelming majority of flexographic presses are web presses with feeding equipment for rolls of stock. Another generalization can be made: most flexographic presses are built for printing of the stock on one side only rather than for perfecting the web.

Characteristic points of flexographic presses. In describing flexographic presses, the following items are usually specified: (1) type of press; (2) number of colors that can be printed in one pass through the press; (3) maximum width of the web; (4) kind and maximum length of repeat; (5) kinds of stocks that can be printed by the press in question; (6) kind of feeding equipment provided; (7) kinds of operations to which the printed web must be subjected at the delivery end of the press; and, finally, (8) maximum speed at which a given press can be operated. Additional points may refer to drying and cooling equipment as well as to various means for controlling the tension and the register of the printed web. Most of these items are now briefly explained.

The three types of flexographic presses. Flexographic presses are "broadly classified in three categories or types: (1) stack; (2) central or common impression drum, and (3) inline presses."[12] In *stack-type presses* two or more printing and inking units are vertically arranged on one or both ends of the main press structure. Presses of this kind resemble the deck-type newspaper relief press. "The main drive frame usually contains one common "bull gear" that drives the color sections through separate gear trains."[13] Four-color stacks are most common, but presses can be built from one printing and inking unit up to eight and more of them. Similar to other web presses, stack-type flexographic presses can be equipped as double-enders for the perfecting of a web that

is one-half of the maximum web width of the press.

The second type of *common impression cylinder presses* for flexography is in principle quite similar to those used in letterpress and in offset lithography. Several plate cylinders, from two up, are combined with a single impression cylinder which becomes the biggest cylinder on the press and is therefore often called a *drum*. The central cylinder "may be as large as 5 or 6 feet in diameter. This is a good press for thin stocks, cloth, papers without much body, or a material that wrinkles or stretches easily because such materials cannot be webbed over long distances without re-enforcement. The central cylinder press will give better register than the stack-type press but there is more difficulty in drying of inks between the units when overprinting is necessary."[14] There is also less of a possibility to control the position of the web in its sideways motion. "Normally, printing on both sides of the web is not practical on a central impression cylinder press with a single drum. A more common method is to connect either a stack-type press or another central impression-drum press inline for perfecting the web."[15]

The third type, *inline presses*, can also be considered as unit-type presses. Each printing unit which consists of an impression cylinder and a plate cylinder is separate, and unit follows unit on the same level. The number of units depends on the purpose of a press. The web travels from color unit to color unit in a straight line. Perfecting the web can be accomplished by using the press as a double-ender as mentioned under the head of stack-type presses. The term "inline" is used in a second sense throughout the converting industry, in gravure not less than in flexography. Inline equipment manufactures more or less finished end products and does printing as well as the required converting operations. Among inline presses are machines that produce paper bags, envelopes, die-cut and sometimes windowed paper folding-boxes, and paper napkins, to mention just a few.

Number of colors and width of web. Flexographic presses are made by a considerable number of domestic manufacturers, and some equipment is imported from Europe. Domestic equipment of standard construction has one to six plate cylinders. Stack-type presses have frequently two, four, or six printing units; central impression cylinder presses are also made in the same range of color units, and so are unit-type presses. The

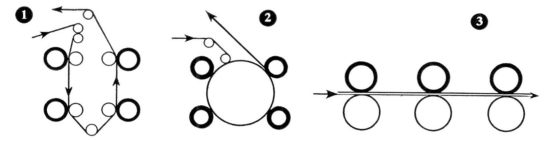

The three types of flexographic presses. Diagram (1) is a stack type, (2) a central, or common, impression cylinder type, and (3) an inline press.

maximum width of the web varies between 4½ inches for label printers, and 95 inches for the printing of paper. Within this range one can find 18, 24, 28, 36, 38, 40, 44, 48, 52, 55, and 60 inch models. Flexographic presses for printing of toilet tissue are made upwards of 100 inches wide.[16]

Length of repeat. Our next point, the length of repeat, needs a brief explanation. The word "repeat" was originally used in the description of continuous patterns, such as printed in wallpapers and textiles. There it refers to the length of the pattern which is the design unit and is repeated over and over again. In flexography, repeat is defined as "the printing length of a plate cylinder, determined by one revolution of the plate cylinder gear."[17] Narrower presses have usually shorter repeats than wider ones. Most flexographic presses are built to permit changes in repeats; a very frequently listed range of repeats is from a minimum of 9, 10, or 12 inches up to a 36 inch maximum. Changes in the length of repeat can be either of the fixed-increment type or all-size repeats. The *fixed-increment type* depends on the number of teeth in the gear of the impression cylinder; *all-size repeats* can vary without limitations within the range of the press. Changes in repeats are here accomplished by means of various mechanical arrangements rather than by changing of gears.

Speed of flexographic presses. The speed of flexographic web presses is like that of all web presses expressed in linear feet per minute abbreviated f.p.m. Flexographic presses are built at present for speeds up to 1,000 f.p.m. More modern machines run faster than older models. Ratings of 300, 400, 500, and 600 f.p.m. can be seen frequently. The maximum rated speed of a press must, of course, not be confused with the actual speed at which a specific job can be run. Actual running speed depends on the detail of a job and can be considerably less than the rated maximum speed.

Feeding and delivery equipment. Flexographic presses are mostly roll-fed; sheetfed presses exist but they are very seldom used. Roll-feeding machinery can hold one or several rolls of stock. The expiring roll can be connected to a new roll in various ways that are discussed in Section 5, which is devoted to roll-feeding for all kinds of web presses. The printed web of paper can be either sheeted, or rewound into a roll, or completely converted into the final product such as paper bags, for example. Some inline presses have coating and laminating equipment, and they may be connected to die-cutting and stripping machines. (For various kinds of deliveries see Section 6.)

Kinds of stock for flexographic presses. Among the most common stocks for flexography are many kinds of paper including glassine (a translucent paper), plastic films, paper boards, foils, and many others. Some presses are built for particular stocks, such as papers, or lightweight boards, or films; others can handle all of these materials. But the latter kind is obviously not as efficient for a particular kind of stock as machines designed for a narrow range of similar stocks.

Drying, cooling, and web control equipment. High-speed web printing in several colors necessitates equipment for the forced drying of inks. Such equipment must be supplemented by cooling or chilling units, particularly if the printed web is to be rewound. The web of material must be carefully controlled in its tension and in its position across the press. (Equipment for web controlling is discussed in Section 5; that for forced drying in Section 7.)

The swing-out feature. Some stack-type flexographic presses are equipped for "swing-out." This feature is an interesting one not found on other than flexographic equipment. The plate cylinder is divided into two units, each half the width of the full-size cylinder. The same is done with the fountain and with the intermediate inking roller. The impression cylinder is of course full size and not divided. This construction makes it possible to keep one part of the divided rollers running and to swing the other part out for preparing the changeover from one set of plates to the next.

The swing-out feature is mainly used for the printing of milk containers which, though manufactured in huge total quantities, may nevertheless be produced in relatively small individual orders. Orders which require changes of plates for different brands are usually planned for printing on the same stock and for taking advantage of the swing-out feature. The width of the stock is half, or less, the full width of the press. When one set of plates is running, the swing-out feature makes it possible to prepare the press for the change in brand. As this preparation takes place without stopping the press, the swing-out feature is an important economy factor. Even though swing-outs can be built for other than stack-type presses and for all-size repeats, they are mainly used on stack-type presses with fixed increment repeats.

Presses for Indirect Relief Printing

Together with all other relief printing methods, indirect relief printing uses printing-image carriers on which the printing areas are raised above the non-printing ones. The main difference between this method and others of the same process family is that the ink image is not transferred directly to the printing stock but indirectly. The image carrier transfers the ink image to a rubber blanket which in turn transfers it to the paper or other stock to be printed.

Since indirect image transfer is widely practiced in contemporary lithographic printing, which has become generally known as offset printing, indirect relief printing was for a long time called "dry offset" printing. The word "dry" refers to the fact that the plate is not dampened in indirect relief printing whereas it must be dampened in offset lithography; the word "offset" indicates, of course, indirect image transfer. In 1962 Miehle and duPont coined the term "letterset," a combination between *letter*press and off*set*, for indirect relief printing. Dry offset of the past and

contemporary letterset are based on the same principle but differ widely in actual performance, and a new name for this method was therefore selected to emphasize the progress made in indirect relief printing.

Indirect relief printing was first developed by the U.S. Bureau of Engraving and Printing for the production of long runs as needed for tax stamps, U.S. Savings Bonds, and other items. The Bureau, which makes its own image carriers and printing inks for security reasons, developed a thin metal wrap-around plate with a low relief, suitable for printing on offset lithographic presses after their plate cylinder was adapted for the thickness of such plates. "Early records show that the Bureau ordered its first press (a Harris offset model S8L) with the plate cylinder ground to accept the thick 0.025 inch 'high-etch' offset plate late in 1919."[18] To avoid misunderstandings it is explained that the words "high-etch" compare the depth of etch on relief plates used on this press not with that needed in other relief plates, which are much deeper etched, but with high-etched lithographic plates which are much less deeply etched than traditional relief plates. (High-etched lithographic plates are not generally used, but are made for special purposes such as the lithographic printing of overall tints and patterns on bank checks.) Indirect relief printing has been in successful operation uninterruptedly since 1919, or for more than 45 years, in the U.S. Bureau of Engraving and Printing in Washington, D.C.

During the 1950's, when printing with flatbed-cylinder presses became unsatisfactory to many letterpress printers because of long press down-

Courtesy duPont Company

In this picture a Type C Dycril *plate is put on the plate cylinder of an offset press for indirect relief printing. The plate has a total thickness of 0.017 inches and is on a clear polyester film base.*

times and slow press operation, strong interest was generated in dry offset. The subject became controversial when some printers achieved the results desired by them, whereas others were disappointed by their experience. In the last ten years, substantial progress was made in this field, not only by the introduction of shallow-etched metal plates, photopolymer plates, and etched plastic plates, but also in other respects, better blankets in particular. Until 1964 wrap-around plates were too thick to be put on most offset presses built for the customarily thinner offset plates, but all American press builders were prepared to supply offset presses with plate cylinders sufficiently undercut for printing with wrap-around plates. When letterset began to be widely publicized, approximately in 1962, some press manufacturers built all their offset presses with plate cylinders undercut for wrap-around plates. Such presses can be used either for offset lithography or for indirect relief printing. In 1964 duPont announced that Dycril plates were also manufactured in a thickness that permitted their interchangable use with customary thin offset plates without need for undercutting the plate cylinders of older offset presses.

The whole field is in flux, and terminology is still unsettled. Some feel that *wrap-around* should be limited to direct image transfer and that "letterset" should indicate indirect printing. But it is a fact that wrap-around plates can be made for either purpose. In this manual wrap-around is selected as a generic term for thin relief printing-image carriers, and indirect relief printing is also used generically. Both terms are strictly descriptive and neutral, and this is the reason for their selection. The final decision, if there ever is a final decision on terminology, will be made by industry usage when the field will be more settled.

It is unnecessary to describe the sizes, maximum rated speeds, and number of colors of indirect relief printing presses. As explained, presses for indirect relief are either sheetfed or roll-fed offset presses, and those are extensively described in the present section. It might be added that the dampening unit of lithographic presses is not needed when they are used for indirect relief printing. If presses are used for both offset lithography and indirect relief, and if the changeover from one method to the other is rather frequent, the dampening rollers are simply disengaged. When presses are used for protracted periods of time for indirect relief, the dampening unit is usually removed from the press.

Intaglio Printing Presses

In this manual intaglio printing is divided into three methods: (1) steel-die engraving and banknote printing; (2) sheetfed gravure; and (3) rotogravure. Rotogravure, in turn, can be further divided into publication printing, package printing, and specialty printing. As you will see from the following descriptions, printing presses for intaglio printing range from small hand-fed presses to huge and complex manufacturing equipment designed for high-speed mass production. Various methods of intaglio printing have often very little else in common than the fact that they employ printing-image carriers in which the printing areas are present in a sunken or intaglio form, whereas the non-printing areas are on the surface of the image carrier. All intaglio methods must force the ink into the image areas which consist of intaglio recesses, or of small cells. Application of the ink cannot be restricted to the image areas but includes inevitably the non-image areas which are on the surface of the printing-image carrier. For this reason inking requires one or several additional steps whereby the unwanted ink is re-moved from the non-image areas. The manner in which inking and removal of the excess ink is performed depends on the viscosity, or body, of the ink used for a particular intaglio printing method.

Just as presses and printing inks are not the same for all intaglio methods, so do the stocks which are used on them differ. These include a variety of papers, from the inexpensive grade on which newspaper supplements are printed to paper of good or highest quality for sheetfed gravure. Paper of exceptional characteristics is especially made for the printing of our currency and U.S. government bonds. These, as well as our postage stamps, are printed by the U.S. Bureau of Engraving and Printing on intaglio presses. Intaglio printing is one of the main package printing methods. Lightweight paper boards, metallic foils, and many kinds of plastic films are printed in rotogravure for packaging. (This is not to be interpreted as if package printing could not be done by other methods. Flexography, letterpress, offset lithography, and other methods are also used for package printing.)

Presses for Steel-Die Engraving and Banknote Printing

Steel-die engraving and banknote printing are here grouped together because they use printing-image carriers of a relatively similar nature and heavy bodied inks. But the final products of either method are quite different and so are the presses on which printing is done. Steel-die engraving prints relatively small sheets of paper or light-weight paper board, and its products are mainly items of engraved stationery such as letterheads, envelopes, calling or visiting cards, and social announcements. Boxtops and labels for high prestige consumer goods may also be printed in this method. Another field for steel-die engraving is the greeting card industry, and so is the engraving of certificates for schools.

Banknote printing is not too well known to the general public but one of the products for which it is used is probably the most generally appreciated of all printed items: money. But money is not the only product turned out by this method. Other products of banknote printing include stock and bond certificates as well as traveler's checks. In the United States the printing of paper money, U.S. government bonds, and postage stamps is not done by private enterprises but by the U.S. Treasury Department. The Bureau of Engraving and Printing has its manufacturing facilities in Washington, D.C.[19] Several privately owned American banknote printers produce currency, government bonds, and postage stamps for foreign countries as well as stock and bond certificates for domestic and foreign corporations.

General description of presses for steel-die engraving. Presses for steel-die engraving, also known as die-stamping or as steel-die embossing presses, are not manufactured in the United States but imported from Europe, England in the main. Die-stamping presses are available in a number of different sizes. The smallest press takes a maximum die of 2½ by 4 inches; the largest, one of 8 by 12 inches. There are also models for maximum die sizes of 3 by 8 inches, 4½ by 9 inches and 7 by 11 inches, as well as several others. The maximum size of the paper or board to be processed by these presses is considerably larger than that of the die. Most die-stamping presses can handle standard 8½ by 11 inches letterhead sheets, and the stock size may go up to 10 by 14 inches or 15 by 17 inches, for example. The hourly speeds with which die-stamping presses can be operated are rated between 1,500 and 3,600 sheets, depend-

ing on the size and make of a press. Die-stamping presses are either hand or mechanically fed. Some installations have drying equipment attached in order to speed the production of the printed product. Most die-stamping presses are sheetfed, but there are also roll-fed presses in existence.

General description of presses for banknote printing. Presses for banknote printing are not standardized but usually made to order. Banknote printing combines a number of different operations of which intaglio printing is one, typographic or letterpress printing another, and numbering the third. The U.S. Bureau of Engraving and Printing used to print all dollar bills on flatbed presses, which permitted the production of 18 bills on one sheet of paper. These presses processed moist paper and were much slower than the later developed 32-subject rotary intaglio presses on which 32 bills were printed on a single sheet of paper. The new presses have the advantage that they can print on dry, unmoistened paper. The dry process was instituted in 1957 in the Bureau. "In contrast to the wet process which has been in use in the printing of United States paper currency for approximately 95 years, the dry process provides for a relatively high degree of dimensional stability in the paper and simplifies subsequent trimming and cutting operations."[20] Most recently the Bureau has introduced rotary presses for the printing of dollar bills.

Non-governmental printers of banknotes and securities use the dry-printing method primarily. Presses for this type of work are made in sizes varying from 18 by 25 inches to 27 or 30 inches. Most manufacturers of banknotes and security certificates have their own press designs and often build these presses in their own plants. For this reason it is not possible to give generally valid specifications for this type of presses. Intaglio presses for commercial banknote printing are usually single-color rotary presses. The printing-image carrier is an electrolytic intaglio plate, as described in Chapter V. Rotary intaglio presses are automatically fed and have automatic deliveries. Their speed is in the range of 2,000 to 3,000 i.p.h. If the printed sheet is not exposed to forced drying, it is either racked or otherwise separated from other wet sheets to speed drying and to prevent some of the still wet ink from leaving unwanted marks on other sheets. This unwanted ink transfer is called either rubbing-off, or setting-off, or offsetting in the trade. For security reasons and protection against tampering, banknote printing

Courtesy Bureau of Engraving and Printing

New high-speed, rotary intaglio press for the dry printing of U.S. currency. Each sheet has 32 notes; design on either side is printed in intaglio; serial numbers, seals, series year, and signatures are printed in letterpress. Printing inks are manufactured by the Bureau, paper by private contractors under strict Government control.

requires an exceptionally strong impression whereby ink particles are forced deep into the paper fiber. Some banknote printers are of the opinion that printing ink for securities should contain abrasive particles which facilitate ink penetration into the paper.

Sheetfed Presses for Gravure Printing

Sheetfed gravure is not nearly as popular in the United States as it is in Europe. For this reason the demand for gravure presses is rather small, and sheetfed gravure presses are built by only a single domestic press-manufacturing concern, whereas in Europe a number of press builders are active in this area.[21] The relatively rare use of this method in the United States is regrettable since the quality of sheetfed gravure at its best cannot be surpassed by other printing methods, especially in reproductions of photographs and fine art subjects.

Description of sheetfed gravure presses. All sheetfed gravure presses are rotary presses. The printing-image carrier can be a cylinder, but in the U.S.A. it is usually a relatively thin plate of etched copper which may be chromium plated for long press runs. This etched copper plate is clamped to the plate cylinder. The cylinder is inked and the excess ink is removed by a doctor blade prior to image transfer. Domestic presses are available as

single-color, two-color, three-color, and four-color presses which print only one side of the sheet. The maximum sheet size is 29 by 43 inches; the presses are operated at between 3,000 and 6,000 i.p.h., depending on the nature of the work. European presses are manufactured in a variety of sizes up to a maximum sheet size of 41 by 55 inches. Many of the European designs are made with a view to combine single-color sheetfed gravure presses into multicolor presses by adding a number of individual units in sequence. Sheetfed gravure presses are usually equipped with driers through which the sheet passes after it has received the required number of impressions; then the dry sheet is delivered and stacked as usual.

Differences between sheetfed and rotogravure presses. As you will see in the following unit, rotogravure presses are divided into publication and into package-printing presses, omitting those for specialty printing. These two kinds of rotogravure presses differ from one another and also from sheetfed gravure presses. Here we will mention a few characteristic points. First, sheetfed presses are much less fast than rotogravure presses; another difference is in the manner in which the two members of the printing unit, the plate cylinder and the impression cylinder, are driven in sheetfed presses; a third difference is in the manner of inking which is related to differences in ink viscosity and to the different speed of operation. Fourth, it might be mentioned that sheetfed presses are built with a plate cylinder of a fixed diameter whereas presses for package printing are built to permit the use of cylinders which may vary in their diameters within the range of the press.

Since these differences lead us into our following subject they deserve brief explanations. "In rotogravure only the engraved cylinder is driven, the impression roller being rotated by the friction of the web of material which it squeezes against the engraved cylinder. In sheetfed gravure the plate cylinder drives the impression cylinder, so that the plate cylinder and the impression cylinder are in positive relationship to each other at all times. Actual impression is produced by packing or building up the impression cylinder for the exact amount of pressure required to produce the perfect print."[22] Sheetfed gravure presses operate not only much more slowly than rotogravure presses and have much better control over the relations between plates and impression cylinder, but they are also capable of depositing thicker

Web Flow Chart of a
CHAMPLAIN
Heavy Duty Model B-28
Flexogravure Printing Press

Champlain Model B-28 Flexogravure printing equipment is of heavy duty construction and suited to printing by either the rotogravure or flexographic process, materials ranging in weight from light paperboard up to materials .035" in thickness at operating speeds of 1000 feet per minute.

A turnover unwind reel stand is normally used for support of the paperboard roll in one of two alternate positions. This type of roll stand is capable of lifting a roll of paperboard from the floor which eliminates the need for overhead handling equipment, reduces the time needed for roll changes, and also provides for continuous press operation when it is used in conjunction with an automatic web splicing mechanism which, as the roll runs out, "butt splices" the trailing end of the expiring roll to the lead end of a new roll of material.

Paperboard rolls as received from the mill may be eccentric, telescoped or have characteristics that will cause variations in press web tension. To counteract such conditions, which adversely affect printing register, the incoming web is metered through a pre-feed unit and into a "free loop" from which it is side-guided and then fed to the first color station of the press by a constant tension feed unit. Printing stations can be arranged to print on either side of the web (face or back printing) and any number of units, in keeping with printing requirements, up to a total of eight stations can be provided.

Ink drying is accomplished by passing the web through a balanced air system unit type dryer, following each printing impression. Heat medium for heating of air can be either steam, gas or electricity. Extended dryers are used for the drying

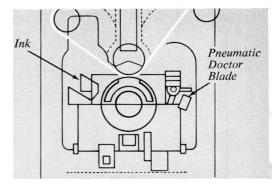

❶ *GRAVURE carriage with etched cylinder, doctor blade assembly and ink applicator. Carriage construction principle makes rapid changeover possible.*

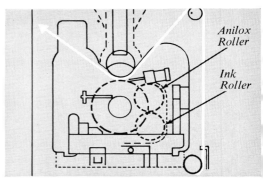

❷ *FLEXO carriage with flexo plate cylinder, ink roller and Anilox roller. Flexo carriages and gravure carriages are interchangeable.*

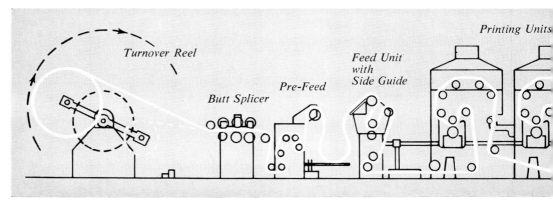

of unusual materials, and most frequently on the last printing station which is normally used for the application of an overall lacquer coating.

A web pull unit, located following the last color station, serves to convey the printed web from the printing section of the press to the delivery, and further functions to isolate the effects of rewinding and splicing or other transfer disturbances from being transmitted back to the color units and thus adversely affecting color registration. Three types of delivery units can be used inline with Corsair color units: roll rewind, web-fed cutter-creaser for the die cutting of folding cartons, or a rotary sheet cutter.

Companion "light duty" flexographic printing equipment, Champlain's Model B-29, is also available, and is similar to the equipment described herein but intended primarily for the printing of paper, other light materials, and various films. It has the additional feature of being able to utilize an embossing carriage which, when substituted for a rotogravure printing cylinder or flexographic plate cylinder carriage, permits embossing "inline", and thus adds this flexibility to the equipment's overall versatility.

Printing or plate cylinder carriages for either rotogravure or flexographic printing can be used with the Champlain Model B-28 or B-29 color unit. By withdrawing a complete carriage from a color station, all parts that are exposed to ink become completely accessible for rapid clean-up and changeover. Where duplicate gravure or flexo carriages are available press down-time is held to a minimum.

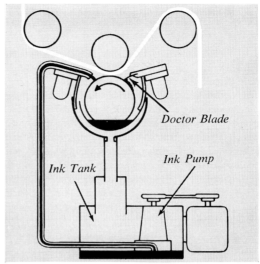

3 *Ink pump, tank and ink applicator showing flow of ink to etched gravure cylinder. The web is printed where gravure cylinder and impression cylinder are closest.*

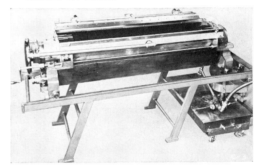

4 *Gravure cylinder carriage with doctor blade, ink applicator, ink pan, bearings and their housings, splash shields, and side register adjustments. Every part exposed to ink is removed for offpress makeready.*

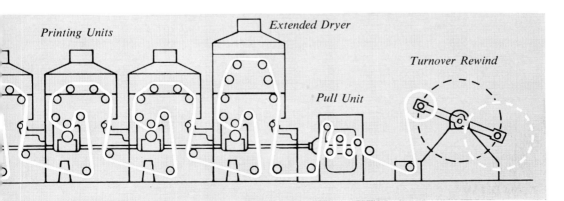

or more intense ink films. "In sheetfed gravure the inks can and do carry a much larger amount of pigment and resin binder, and usually a much slower and less volatile solvent is used, as drying of the printed sheet is nowhere nearly as critical as it is in rotogravure." [23] The possibility of using cylinders of different diameters contributes greatly to the flexibility of package gravure since it enables gravure to print repeats of different length on the same press. (Rotogravure presses for publication printing, on the other hand, have cylinders of a fixed diameter.) To avoid misunderstandings, it is added that sheetfed gravure does not need to print sheets of maximum size but can produce any size within the minimum and maximum sheet size of a specific press.

Finally, it should be noted that in the United States sheetfed gravure presses are often used as proof presses and not as production presses. For many rotogravure jobs in full-color, plates are made from the color separations and proofed on sheetfed presses. For actual production, the approved separations are then used in the making of rotogravure cylinders. To be sure, there are also several kinds of proof presses for rotogravure in existence. (These are described in Section 8, "Proof Presses," together with proof presses for all other printing methods.)

Presses for Rotogravure Printing

All rotogravure presses are roll-fed machines. They can be divided three ways according to their final products: (1) publication presses for the printing of newspaper supplements, magazines, catalogs, and similar products; (2) presses for the production of package printing on paper, paper boards, plastic films, foils, and other stocks; and (3) specialty presses which are much too numerous for inclusion in this manual.

General description of rotogravure presses for publication printing. Rotogravure presses for publication printing are among the giants of printing equipment and resemble in many respects presses for newspaper relief printing, letterpress magazine presses, and web-offset presses. Like all presses for long-run publication printing, rotogravure presses are equipped with roll-feeding machinery which permits semiautomatic or fully automatic connecting of the expiring web to a new roll of paper. Such presses have a smaller or larger number of printing units and are capable of printing four or more colors on each side of the web. But they differ in one essential point from presses for newspaper relief printing, letterpress perfecting presses for magazine printing, and blanket-to-blanket web-offset presses. *In rotogravure each color must be dried before the next color is printed.* Rotogravure presses have, consequently, a drying unit after each printing unit. The folders of rotogravure presses for publication printing are more or less the same as the folders of corresponding web presses in other printing methods.

The web travels at a speed of 1,500 f.p.m. (more or less), and the cylinder may make 25,000 and more revolutions per hour. In 1960 a magazine press was installed in the plant of Standard Gravure Corporation in Louisville, Ky., which was then considered the world's largest publication press. This press can print 8 magazine pages across the cylinder and 4 pages around it, or a total of 32 pages per revolution. Its cylinder has a width of 107 inches and it can print on a web of 102 inches. The pressroom has a 26-foot ceiling and needs about 100,000 cubic feet of air per minute for the drying and exhaust system. The press is approximately 20 feet high and has 14 units. It is equipped with two folders, and can print and stitch 50,000 copies of "Parade," a newspaper supplement, per hour.[24]

Even though this press was considered the biggest at the time of its installation, other presses which belong in the same category are by no means uncommon. Some of them are used for catalog work, to give a different example, "and will produce as many as fifteen million catalog pages for a big mail order house in a single hour. For this purpose 1,100,000 pounds of paper are processed during each 24 hours, through printing, binding, trimming, wrapping, and shipping operations. In the same 24-hour period a total of 309,-760,000 printed pages in from one to four colors are produced in the plant of the Chicago Rotoprint Company."[25]

Rotogravure presses for publication printing are usually built to specifications and are not available as standard models. It is to be understood that for the sake of economy many parts of such presses are the same and used in different combinations by the designers and manufacturers of this kind of equipment. But this does not mean that standardized rotogravure presses are available on the market.

General description of rotogravure presses for package printing. For package printing such mammoth equipment as may be used for publication printing is often less practical. There are, nevertheless, many rather substantial installations in existence for the purpose of package printing. As an example we mention the manufacturing facilities installed at the Gardner Division of the Diamond-Gardner Corporation at Lockland, Ohio, a suburb of Cincinnati. This plant has several rotogravure presses for the printing of paper board which print 26, 42, and 44 inches wide webs respectively. "The presses are more than 100 feet long. In one continuous operation each press prints, cuts, and creases cartons, producing them from a continuous roll of paper board, in widths from 26 to 44 inches. Speeds are such that one press can produce 150,000 cigaret cartons, 50,000 soap cartons, or 30,000 bottle carrier cartons per hour."[26]

Package printing has certain problems of its own. One of them is the necessity of storing gravure cylinders for reruns. A large gravure plant for package printing must be equipped to store a substantial quantity of cylinders, and such storage requires considerable space and a well-planned internal organization. In one package-printing plant the cylinder storage racks, located close to the press area and the shipping dock, go 10 feet high and hold more than 1,000 gravure cylinders. The storage racks are so designed that any cylinder may be stored or removed without moving any other. Speaking of storage facilities, it might be added that the racks for ink storage are four tiers high with a capacity for 505 ink drums (each drum holds 55 gallons) or more than 27,000 gallons of ink. The same plant can store more than 97 million completed cartons and of course as many rolls of unprinted paper board as are needed for uninterrupted production.[27]

Web width and cylinder diameters of standard gravure presses for package printing. Not all installations for package printing are of giant size. The largest installations are usually especially designed, but there is a substantial number of standardized presses for package printing in gravure available and in actual operation. Most of these are multicolor presses which are usually combined with such finishing equipment as is needed for producing the final product for which the installation was made. In some plants gravure and flexographic printing are done in combination on the same press.

Rotogravure presses for package printing are available in a number of different web widths beginning with 15 inches and going up to 55 inches, to mention some figures. As already stated, package presses can handle cylinders of different sizes. Each model has its own minimum and maximum cylinder circumference. Cylinder circumferences on smaller presses may have a minimum of 10 inches and a maximum of 20 inches. Larger presses go up to 18 or 20 inches as the minimum cylinder circumference and may be able to handle 36 inches or even 50 inches as the maximum. There are also some special presses built for rather narrow webs of 2, 3, and 4 inches. These presses may have minimum cylinder circumferences of 5 to 6 inches and maximum circumferences between 9 and 11 inches.

Speeds of gravure presses for package printing. The maximum rated speed is expressed, as in web printing throughout, in linear feet per minute; it varies between 750 and 1,500 f.p.m. Actual running speed depends on many factors. Among them are size and make of the press, the number of color units, whether the job is printed on one side only or on both sides, the kind of stock to be printed, the kind of ink to be used, the type of drying equipment, and last but not least, the detail of the job in hand.

Perfecting on gravure presses for package printing. Presses for package printing are usually not built for printing on both sides of the stock. But it is nevertheless often possible to print both sides of the web on such presses either by using the double-ending method where the actual running web is only half of the maximum web width, or by means of a reverse box which is manufactured by several press builders. One or more printing units of multi-unit presses are then used for the printing of the second side of the web which can be of maximum width on presses equipped with reverse boxes.

Deliveries of gravure presses for package printing. Rotogravure presses for package printing can be equipped with different types of deliveries, depending on their purpose. Among them are *rewinds*, delivering rolls of the printed stock; *sheeters*, which cut the printed web into individual sheets; and *cutter-creasers* which die-cut and crease lightweight paper board resulting in folding cartons from which the waste is usually already removed by the equipment. (Various kinds of deliveries are discussed in Section 6.)

Presses for Planographic Printing

In this manual, planographic printing is divided into three methods: (1) direct lithography, (2) offset lithography, and (3) collotype or photogelatin. Direct lithographic and collotype presses are not standard products, but are only made to order in the United States. The dominant, and practically the only method of planographic printing, is offset lithography.

Explanation of the offset principle. Offset lithography is an indirect printing method. In direct printing methods the printing-image carrier is inked and the resulting ink image is directly transferred, or impressed, onto the printing stock where it becomes the printed image. In offset lithography the ink image is not transferred to the stock but applied to an intermediate surface, called the blanket. From the blanket the ink image is then transferred again, now to the stock where it becomes the final printed image.

Therefore, offset lithographic presses need three members for their printing units, whereas the printing units of direct printing presses have only two members. As offset lithographic presses are of rotary construction, these members are: (1) the plate cylinder which carries the printing-image carriers, (2) the blanket cylinder on which the blanket is mounted, and (3) the impression cylinder, or paper cylinder, where the printing stock is positioned. During each revolution of the press the ink image is produced on the plate cylinder, transferred to the blanket cylinder, and finally applied to the printing stock which is carried by the impression cylinder.

Offset lithographic presses are best divided into the two broad groups of sheetfed and roll-fed or web-offset presses. We begin our discussion with the first group, sheetfed offset lithographic presses.

Sheetfed Offset Lithographic Presses

Presses based on the principle of offset lithography are used not only by printers but also for office duplication. Some people draw a sharp line between presses for office duplicating and those built for industrial printing. But it is difficult to do so because presses for office duplicating are also used in many smaller printing businesses. It might be interesting to mention that in the United States more than 150,000 small offset presses are running in offices or reproduction departments of various organizations according to estimates of well-informed people. There are no generally agreed

characteristics for classifying offset lithographic presses either as office duplicators or as machines for printing as a business, but most office machines cannot print sheets larger than legal size paper, which is 8½ by 13 inches. These presses are considered by us office duplicators and are not included in our discussion of offset lithographic presses.

Sheetfed offset lithographic presses are available in a number of different sizes as single-color, two-color, three-color, four-color, five-color, and six-color presses. Most of these presses print one side of the sheet only, but there are also sheetfed offset perfecting presses on the market. The size of sheetfed presses refers as always to the maximum sheet that can be handled by a press.

Single-color sheetfed offset presses. Single-color sheetfed offset presses are at the time of writing available in 32 different sizes. Their maximum sheet size ranges from 11 by 15 inches up to 54½ by 77 inches. Among the more popular sizes are 17½ by 22½ inch, 23 by 29 inch, 25¾ by 38 inch, 43 by 60 inch models in addition to the already mentioned smallest and largest size. Single-color presses are made by several domestic press builders and also imported from Europe. Competition is rather lively in this field. This can be seen from the many variations in which some press sizes are offered. As an example it is mentioned that presses in the 36 by 49 inch size are available as 49½, 49⅝, 49¾, and 50 inch models. Each of these differs in the 49-inch dimension merely by

Courtesy Technical Trade School

Pressman inspecting a sheet during running of a single color sheetfed offset press.

one-eighth or one-quarter of an inch. Whatever else this example may suggest to readers in favor of standardization, it certainly demonstrates the wide choice available to American printers.

Multicolor sheetfed offset presses. In multicolor presses the number of available models is less large. Domestic two-color presses range from a sheet size of 20 by 26 inches up to 54½ by 70 inches; three-color presses come in two sizes, 43 by 60 inches and 54 or 54½ by 77 inches. These sizes are also the only ones in which domestic four-color, five-color, and six-color presses are offered. Imported presses add to the number of multicolor presses on the market.

Sheetfed offset perfecting presses. Until the end of the 1950's, few sheetfed offset perfecting presses were in operation in the United States. Since that time their popularity has greatly increased due to the Miller multicolor-perfecting design. This design makes it possible to print either a second color on the same side of the sheet or to perfect it by printing on its other side. Miller multicolor-perfecting presses are made in two sizes. The smaller model can print a maximum sheet size of 23 by 36 inches; it is available as a two-unit press, meaning that the press will either print two colors on the same side of the sheet or that it will print one color on either side. The larger model can print a maximum sheet of 25¾ by 38½ inches. It is available as a two-, three-, four-, five-, and six-unit assembly, capable of printing sheets in one, two, three, or more colors on one side and of perfecting them in a number of colors depending on the total number of units. In addition to Miller offset perfecting presses there are also other makes available.

Speeds of single-color offset presses. The press speeds mentioned in this brief discussion are always maximum rated speeds as specified by the manufacturers of presses. It may be repeated that the maximum rated speed is not identical with the actual operating speed. The operating speed depends not only on the speed limit for a given press but also on a number of different factors, particularly the nature of the job, the required quality level, and the kind of stock on which a job is printed. Papers for offset printing range from the very thin Bible papers up to paper boards as needed for the printing of folding cartons; different kinds of stock usually require different running speeds.

The maximum rated press speed depends not only on the make of presses but also on the time

of their construction. Older presses run less fast than more modern ones. The contemporary smaller presses for sheets of 11 by 15 inches and 17½ by 22½ inches are rated around 7,000 i.p.h. Medium sizes such as 23 by 29 inches and 25¾ by 38 inches models can run at hourly speeds of 7,500 to 8,000 impressions. As the size of presses increases, their speed diminishes to some extent. The 36 by 49 inch models are rated at 6,500 i.p.h. and very large models, such as 43 by 60 inch and 54½ by 77 inch presses, can be operated at a maximum rated speed of 6,000 i.p.h. Generally speaking, the trend is to higher speeds, and the maximum speed figures for presses built in one year may be superseded by next year's models.

Speeds of multicolor and perfecting sheetfed offset presses. The speed of multicolor presses depends like that of single-color presses on size, make, and age of presses. As a rule, two-color presses are rated at higher speeds than four-color presses of the same size. The maximum speed rating of large size domestic multicolor equipment is between 6,000 and 6,500 i.p.h., that of medium-size models runs approximately to 7,000 or 7,500 i.p.h. Multicolor perfectors have a maximum speed rating of 6,000 or 7,000 perfected sheets per hour.

Web-Offset Presses

Web-offset presses are made for a number of different purposes. For us it is practical to distinguish the following four groups: (1) web-offset presses for job printing, (2) web-offset presses for publication printing, and (3) web-offset presses for newspaper printing. Web-offset presses are in addition widely used in various branches of specialty printing, particularly in forms printing.

Points considered in describing web-offset presses. For description of web-offset presses the following eight points are usually considered: (1) type of press, (2) number of printing units, (3) maximum web width and cut-off, (4) speed of the press, (5) kind of roll-feeding equipment, (6) kind and capacity of drying equipment, (7) kind of delivery, and (8) web controls and other accessories. Each of these points is briefly explained in the following, and more extensive discussions will be found in subsequent sections.

Types of web-offset presses. Web-offset presses can be either non-perfecting or perfecting presses. Non-perfecting presses are much less common than perfecting web-offset presses. Non-perfecting web-offset presses are more used in forms printing

The MILLER *Multicolor-Perfector Offset Presses*

The Miller Multicolor-Perfectors are sheet-fed off-set presses which provide the option of printing either on one side or on both sides of the sheet on each press run. The choice of straight color print-ing or perfection operations is made possible by a series of three transfer cylinders between the im-pression cylinders of the printing units.

These consist of a normal, skeleton-type trans-

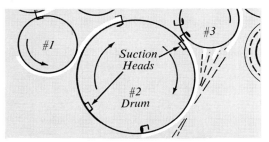

The transfer cylinders between units may be set either for straight color printing or for perfecting.

fer cylinder, a double-sized transfer drum with facilities to carry two sheets at a time, and a third transfer cylinder which is denoted as the "perfect-ing cylinder" because of its paramount impor-tance to the perfecting operation. By adjusting or interchanging gripper operating cams and setting the press to prescribed timing marks calibrated to sheet size, these cylinders are caused to either carry the sheet straight through the printing units for color printing on one side or tumble any size sheet within the complete range of the press to print on both sides. Changeover time from straight color printing to perfecting or vice versa is usually accomplished in fifteen minutes or less.

The Miller Multicolor-Perfectors are available with from two to six printing units. The sheet transfer mechanism which provides the option of straight color printing or perfecting may be placed between any of the units to suit the require-ments of the individual plant.

Sheet Flow in Straight Color Printing

After the sheet is initially side-registered, it is fed into the grippers of the first impression cylinder by a feed roll register system, and is printed on the top side. Through a normal lead-edge grip-per transfer, the #1 transfer cylinder receives the printed sheet from the impression cylinder and forwards it to one of the sets of grippers on the large #2 transfer drum.

At the tangent point of the #2 transfer drum and the #3 transfer cylinder one set of grippers in the #3 transfer cylinder takes the sheet by the leading edge directly from the #2 transfer drum. The sheet is then forwarded to the next unit and all the way to delivery in the normal manner.

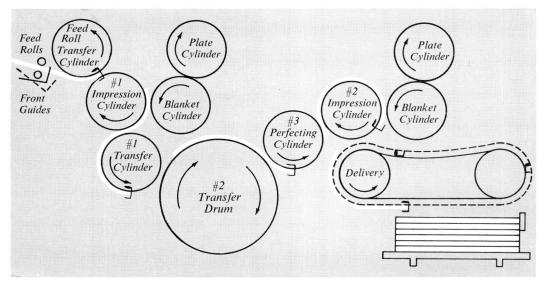

Sheet Transfer in Perfecting

The diagram on this page shows the sheet flow through a two-unit press, set for perfecting to print one color on each side of the sheet.

The sheet is carried in the same manner as in the straight printing operation until it reaches the tangent point of the #2 drum and the #3 transfer cylinder. As the sheet is carried on the #2 transfer drum, suction heads positioned to the tail of the sheet take hold and slide back by piston action to draw the sheet taut around this drum. The #2 transfer drum continues to hold the sheet by lead-edge grippers until the tail of the sheet is grasped by a series of grippers on the #3 perfecting cylinder, accepting the sheet from the suction heads. As indicated in the detailed diagrams, the sheet is transferred to a second series of grippers in this cylinder and thence to the next impression cylinder for the back-up print.

Although the sheet is taken by the trailing edge during the perfecting operation, front-and-back register is always maintained to the original gripper edge. Compensation for inaccuracies of sheet length or squareness of cut is made by more or less gripper bite at the #3 perfecting cylinder.

To maintain a sharp print, free of ink smudges, the impression cylinders after the perfecting transfer are equipped with ink repellent coverings to minimize a build-up from the first-down side.

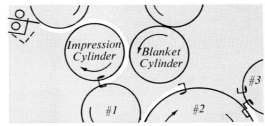

A lead-edge gripper transfer takes the sheet through #1 to #2 transfer cylinder. At cylinder #3 the tail edge is grasped, stripping the sheet from suction heads. (See below)

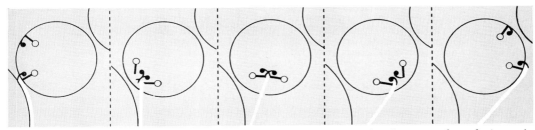

Detail of motions of grippers in the gap of cylinder #3; the sheet is transferred to a second set of grippers, in preparation for proper gripping by the next impression cylinder.

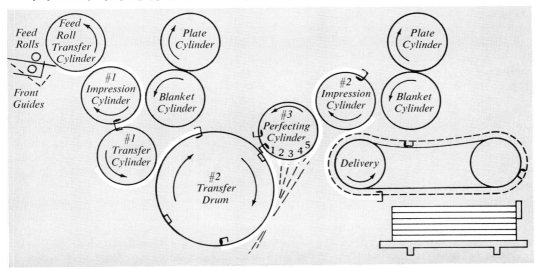

than for any other purpose; their printing units have the customary three elements of sheetfed offset presses, namely, a plate cylinder, a blanket cylinder, and an impression cylinder. In job-and-commercial printing, non-perfecting presses are but rarely used and then "for high-speed production of small hand bills, throwaways, etc., printed on one side and in a standard size such as 8½ by 11 inches."[28]

Most web-offset presses can print both sides of the web, usually in more than one color. Web-offset perfecting presses are made in three basically different kinds of constructions: (1) presses that have the customary three elements of sheetfed offset presses for every printing unit, (2) presses that have a common impression cylinder for several plate and blanket cylinders, and (3) presses

without impression cylinders. In this type the web passes between two blanket cylinders for every printing unit, and the blanket cylinders for one plate cylinder serve at the same time as impression cylinder for the opposite unit and vice versa. Presses equipped with individual impression cylinders are often called unit-type or "open" web-offset presses. Sometimes the term "rubber-to-metal" is used in addition, referring to the blanket cylinder, which is covered with rubber, and to the impression cylinder, which has a metal surface. Presses with common impression cylinders are described as "drum type" or as "semi-drum type" and are also of the rubber-to-metal kind. Presses completely without impression cylinders, finally, are called "blanket-to-blanket" or "rubber-to-rubber" machines.

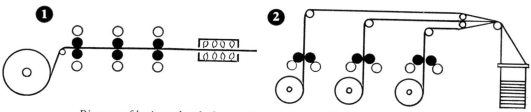

Diagram of horizontal and of vertical arrangement in blanket-to-blanket web offset presses. Horizontal arrangement (1) is typical for commercial color printing. Here the web moves in a straight line through all color units and is heat dried before folding. Vertical arrangement (2) is often used in newspaper printing although many small newspapers are printed on presses with a horizontal design. In single-color newspaper printing several webs are printed and folded without heat drying. In either kind of press several webs can be used, printing one or several colors.

Each of these three types of web-offset presses has its own characteristics, its own advantages, and also of course its own limitations. Each of these three kinds is more suitable for some applications than for others. Generally speaking, *unit-type* or *open presses* are used primarily in forms printing, often in conjunction with rubber plate printing, numbering, or other operations. *Drum-type presses* are sometimes employed in publication printing. For perfecting they have two drums, each serving as the impression cylinder for all colors of one side of the web. After the web is printed on the first side it is passed through drying and chilling equipment before the second side is printed. These presses are substantial pieces of machinery, usually designed for the printing of a standardized product rather than for job-and-commercial printing. *Blanket-to-blanket presses* are the most widely used kind of web-offset presses. They can be either single-product or multiple-purpose machines. Many magazines and news-

papers are produced on blanket-to-blanket presses, but such presses are also widely used in job-and-commercial printing. Blanket-to-blanket presses are less expensive to build than the other two kinds because they have no impression cylinders.

Number of printing units. The number of printing units depends entirely on the purpose of a press. Equipment for publication printing may have four and possibly more printing units for each side of the web. But this is not a generally valid statement as everything depends on the kind of product a web-offset press is intended for. Blanket-to-blanket presses are usually equipped with at least two perfecting units. This number can be increased to three, four, and many more.

Maximum web width and cut-off. Web offset presses are built in a considerable number of different web widths. The range is from the narrowest models having a maximum web width of 17½ inch up to 72 inch and even 90 inch wide presses. Between these extremes there is a wide available

The COTTRELL *Model V-22 Web-Offset Newspaper Press*

Available in models with up to six perfecting units, in-line, the Model V-22 will produce a 24-page standard size newspaper (48-page tabloid) at speeds of up to 22,000 papers per hour.

As the web leaves the white roll, its speed is monitored by a semi-automatic friction braking system to insure controlled web-feed. Before the web enters the printing unit, it is threaded through a variable speed infeed mechanism which accurately meters the proper amount of paper into the printing unit. Infeeds maintain exact web tension and assure maximum register control between units. Each perfecting unit of the Model V-22 will print—in black or spot color—four standard news pages or eight tabloid across both top and bottom of the web. Four color spot or process work can be produced by running the web horizontally through four perfecting units. After the printing operation, the webs are associated in the gathering section (top of former) and are fed onto the former nose. Two adjustable pinch rollers, located at the bottom of the former, accurately form the web or webs around the nose and provide pulling power to deliver the web to the folder's cutting cylinder. After the web or webs wrap the cutting cylinder and cut-off is made, the signature is transferred by means of a tucker blade into the jaws of the folding cylinder. The signature, half-folded, wraps the folding (jaw) cylinder until contact is made with stripper fingers which assist in delivery to the folder's creeping belt. In the case of quarter-folded products the signature is fed to the ¼ folding table where fold is made by a cycloidal rotary tucking blade and then fed into a fan slowdown and the creeping belt delivery.

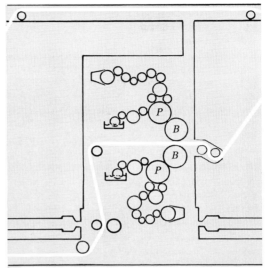

1 Blanket-to-blanket printing unit including the inking and dampening systems.

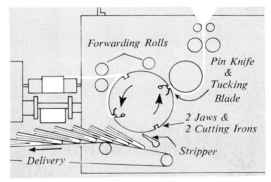

2 After passing the former folder the webs are cut then folded either once or twice depending on whether its a half or quarter folded product.

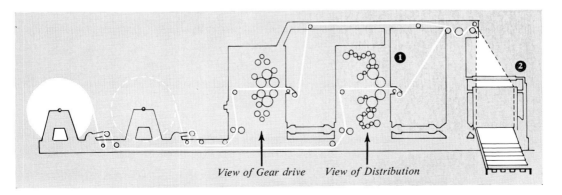

View of Gear drive   View of Distribution

choice. Among popular presses we find web widths of 30, 36, 38, 40, 50, and 64 inches. The circumference of the plate cylinder determines the image length that can be printed on a web-offset press. This dimension is called the "cut-off." The width of the web can be varied within the limits specified for each make of web-offset press. But the cut-off is not changeable, and the length of the cut-off is always the same on the same press. The actual length of the cut-off is naturally related to the width of a press. As a rough guide, it can be assumed that the cylinder circumference, or cut-off, is between 60 and 70 per cent of the maximum web width. One press with a web width of 38 inches has a cut-off of 22⅔ inches, another press of the same web width has a cut-off of 25½ inches. One 50 inch press has a cut-off of 35 inches, whereas another 50 inch press has one of 43 inches. These examples show that the ratio of width and cut-off is not uniform and must be ascertained for each press model.

Speeds of web-offset presses. The maximum rated speed of web-offset presses varies widely, depending on the purpose of the equipment and also on its make and age. At present, standard domestic web-offset presses are rated by their manufacturers from 500 to 1,500 f.p.m. Assuming a press with a 24 inch cut-off, a 36 inch width, and an operating speed of 500 f.p.m., the production of such a press is equivalent to 250 sheets per minute, or to 15,000 i.p.h. of a sheetfed press. If a press with a 36 inch cut-off and a web width of 50 inches is operated at 1,500 f.p.m., the production of this press equals 500 sheets 36 by 50 inches per minute or 30,000 sheets per hour. These figures are multiples of the production obtainable with sheetfed presses, even if we consider that web-offset equipment, like sheetfed presses, cannot be run at its maximum rated speed at all times.

Roll-feeding equipment. High-speed web printing needs many subsidiary units of equipment besides the press. These items represent a very substantial capital investment. Roll-feeding can be done on several technological levels, depending on the speed of the press and its purpose. The feeding equipment may be a relatively simple roll stand for a single roll or two rolls, and it may be fully automatic equipment that connects the web from roll to roll without any other manual work than that of placing successive rolls of paper into the feeding equipment and preparing them for feeding. Between these two extremes there are several kinds of equipment for roll-feeding which

vary in the degree to which they must be manually operated. (Roll-feeding is discussed in Section 5.)

Kinds of drying equipment. Depending on the quality level of the finished product and on the speed with which a press must be run, equipment for forced drying may or may not be mandatory. Several different drying systems are in use for web-offset printing. The capacity of a drier must, of course, match the output of the press. Drying equipment can be used in several ways. In blanket-to-blanket presses the drier is at the end of the press and dries both sides of the web prior to delivery; in drum-type presses there are usually two driers, one after the first side is printed and the other after the web is perfected. As the web comes out of the drier at an unsuitably high temperature, drying is usually followed by chilling whereby the temperature of the web is lowered. (A discussion of drying equipment is provided in Section 7.)

Several kinds of deliveries. Deliveries of web-offset presses vary according to the end product. In presses for book and publication printing, as well as in many installations for job-and-commercial work, the delivery is a folder. The folder for web printing does a number of different operations besides folding proper. It delivers signatures which may be identical with or part of the final

A web of white paper being folded lengthwise on the former folder of a web-offset press.

product. In newspaper printing, for example, the product coming off the folder is usually ready for use, whereas in book and magazine work the signatures delivered by the folder need further processing before the final product stage is reached. Folders are not the only kind of deliveries. There are several others such as sheeters, rewinds, and inline deliveries for the die-cutting of folding cartons, to give one example. (Web deliveries are discussed in Section 6.)

Web controls and other accessories. Web-offset printing is widely used for reproductions of full-color jobs, particularly in the printing of publications, and in job-and-commercial printing. As press speeds rise, controlling of the web becomes increasingly critical. If each of the four different color images which are needed in full-color printing is not in its correct position, the final product is more or less impaired, possibly to the point of complete uselessness. Web control equipment has the task of providing continuous and, ideally, fully automatic adjustment of the running web for proper position. Other items that can be mentioned in this place are devices for automatic control of ink feed, and various controls related to speed, the tearing of the web, and to the safety of the operating personnel, as well as that of the equipment. (A number of web controls is discussed in Section 5.)

This brief listing of the main features of web offset presses can be summarized by saying that web-offset printing is most efficient for press runs of some length, particularly for runs where changeovers are limited to the change of plates but do not require a change of inks nor a change of stock. Sheetfed presses, on the other hand, are most efficient for producing a variety of work in short and medium length runs, where repeated changeovers of plates, ink, and stock are needed. It might be added that web-offset presses are manufactured by several concerns in the United States and that this country is a leader in web offset. Sheetfed offset presses are imported into the United States to some extent from Europe, but our web-offset presses are predominantly built in this country.

Presses for Screen-Process Printing

Screen-process printing is the only contemporary printing method which is still executed by hand printing in many shops. There are also a number of screen-process printing presses on the market. These differ widely in their design, their purpose, and their degree of complexity. For our brief survey, the subject is divided into five different groups: (1) hand printing tables without any mechanical advantage, (2) one-hand squeegees, (3) flatbed presses, (4) cylinder presses, and (5) rotary screen-process presses. A few words on each of these five kinds will explain their nature, purpose, and relative efficiency.

Hand printing tables for screen-process printing. Hand printing tables for screen-process printing are simple wooden tables with either a level or a slanted top on which the screen is placed for printing. Some shops prefer "setups" consisting of a plywood base to which the screen is attached with sturdy hinges, others attach the screen directly on the top of the printing table. There are also mechanical hinging devices available which are fastened to the table top and permit speedy attachment and removal of screens by a clamping action.

Feeding and removal of the stock is of course done by hand in this method of printing. The screen, which serves both as image carrier and as ink fountain, must be out of the operator's way during delivery. During the act of taking the impression, the screen must be directly above the printing stock. In order to separate screen and

A hand printing table, New York Style, for screen process. The springs, suspended from the gallows, are attached to hooks on the screen during printing.

printing stock after the impression, the screen can have a simple leg on one side, or it may be attached to counter weights. Some hand printing tables are built with wooden gallows to which expansion springs are attached. These are connected to the screen with hooks and so balanced that they hold the screen away from the bed for feeding and delivery, but can be brought into printing position with a small effort.

Image transfer is obtained by pushing the ink across the screen with a squeegee. For extremely large sizes and for very viscous inks this operation requires two men, one at either end of the squeegee. Smaller and medium-size jobs printed with an ink of low viscosity are handled by a single squeegee man.

One-hand squeegees. One-hand squeegees, also known as one-man squeegees, were introduced to eliminate the second worker on the squeegee and to improve the smoothness of squeegeeing. A number of different constructions is on the market, but essentially all one-hand squeegees are similar inasmuch as they all are guided on one end by a metal member and are pushed at the other end by the operator. One-hand squeegees may or may not provide a mechanical advantage or be counterweighed.

Flatbed presses for screen-process printing. The screen-process industry differs in its terminology from the letterpress industry. Flatbed presses for screen process have two flat surfaces, a flat bed and a flat screen. As the paper or other printing stock is placed on the bed, the flatbed in screen process is equivalent to the platen in letterpress printing. But as the bed is stationary and does not exert pressure, it also differs functionally from the platen. Terms accepted in other branches of the graphic arts cannot be simply transplanted into this industry, which has its own distinctive technical characteristics.

There are several makes of flatbed presses for screen process on the market. They are equipped for continuous operation but may also be controlled by the operator to print individual cycles when required. Feeding and delivery is often done manually, but there also exist delivery units, known as "take-offs," which can be attached to flatbed presses. These delivery units remove the printed stock mechanically to conveyor belts which are usually connected to drying equipment.

Flatbed presses for screen-process printing are made in a number of different sizes, beginning with a maximum sheet size of 11 by 16 inches and going up to a maximum sheet size of 52 by 72 inches in the largest models. Their rated maximum speed is in a range of 800 to 1,800 impressions per hour, depending on size of press and its make.

Cylinder presses for screen-process printing. Cylinder presses for screen-process printing combine a flat printing-image carrier and an impression cylinder. The impression cylinder has here the same function as in other presses, namely, to carry the printing stock in the correct position during the making of the impression. This kind of press is at present the technically most advanced equipment for screen-process printing. Cylinder presses are mainly used for paper, lightweight paperboards, and other relatively thin stocks which can assume the curvature of the cylinder. For the printing of rigid boards and other rigid materials up to a certain thickness, some press models can be equipped with special attachments. Rigid stocks can of course be handled by flatbed presses which have two flat surfaces.

Cylinder presses for screen process are manufactured in a considerable number of models; the smallest will print a 13 by 20 inch sheet, the largest one of 52 by 76 inches. To mention some of the many sizes in which these presses are built, there are models taking a maximum sheet size of 20 by 26 inches, 25 by 38 inches, 35 by 45 inches, and 44 by 64 inches. The maximum rated speed depends on size and make. The smallest size can be operated at a maximum rated speed of 3,000 i.p.h. and the largest size has a maximum rated speed of 1500 i.p.h. All cylinder presses for screen process are single-color presses; wet-on-wet multicolor printing is not feasible in screen-process printing since the sheet must be dried after each color before it can receive the next impression. Feeding of cylinder presses is either done by hand or by sheet feeders.

Rotary presses for screen-process printing. At the time of writing there are no rotary screen-process presses on the market. But there exist some such installations which were developed for particular purposes. Since rotary printing is used in other applications of porous printing (such as mimeographing), rotary equipment may conceivably be also introduced into the screen-process industry. At this point it is worth mentioning that drying is much more responsible for the relative slowness of screen-process printing than the lack of fast printing equipment. (Driers for screen process are discussed together with all other driers used in the printing industry in Section 7.)

Presses for Specialty Printing

In a not too distant past the term "specialty printing" was applied to printing businesses which were not engaged in job-and-commercial printing or in the printing of books and publications. As so often, the name has remained even though conditions have changed. Our own time is a time of specialization in printing not less than in other fields. If printing may be compared with medicine, the general medical practitioner is similar to the printer who serves the public at large, or does job-and-commercial printing. Due to constantly increasing specialization, both the general practitioner and the printer who engages in every kind of work needed by the community have also become specialists, namely, specialists in rendering an unspecialized service.

Under these conditions it is practically impossible to draw exact lines of demarcation whereby specialty printing is separated from other branches of the printing industry. Some people suggest that specialized machines, as distinguished from those used in general, could be the decisive point for classifying certain businesses as specialty

Courtesy Bureau of Engraving and Printing

General view of Giori Press No. 1. *This press is a multi-color sheet-fed stamp press; it prints three colors with one pass through the press using three different ink fountains and three different inking-in rollers rotating in synchronization with a single printing plate.*

printing. But equipment alone is no sufficient indicator for specialization. Many differently specialized businesses use the same equipment though in different ways according to their specialization. Printers specializing in color cards, for example, can use the same kind of presses which are found in the plants of printers who specialize in the printing of advertising and sales promotion material, or they may use entirely different, specialized machinery. The human factor is often much more important than the physical plant in the specialization of printing businesses.

There are many end products which cannot be made without specialized machinery. As mentioned in the introduction to this section we distinguish single-purpose and single-product equipment from multiple-purpose and multiple-product machines. Newspaper presses are an example of single-purpose machines; sheetfed standardized presses for letterpress or offset lithography exemplify multiple-purpose equipment. It could be asked why newspaper presses or presses for steel-die engraving and banknote printing are included in our discussion of presses, whereas equipment for forms printing and for metal lithography are omitted because they are here classified as presses for specialty printing. The reason is that newspaper printing is a most important and generally recognized branch of printing and that many items of equipment which are now widely used in

Courtesy Rutherford Machinery Company

One of several models of Rutherford *steel tape rule printing machines; various models can print from one to four colors. Printing is done in dry offset; tape may be flat, convex, or concave. Accuracy is kept within ±0.001 inch per foot.*

the printing industry were originally developed for newspaper printing. Roll-feeding and folders for letterpress, rotogravure and offset lithographic web printing are all based on machines originally devised for newspaper printing. The reasons for inclusion of steel-die engraving and banknote printing are entirely different. These methods are the successors of plate printing, one of the classic graphic arts, and their products are customarily associated with printing. But the writer is aware that competent industry people may differ with him on these points and consider his decisions arbitrary.

This general discussion raises another point. There are several kinds of printing which are traditionally completely outside the printing industry and were never included even in "specialty printing." Reference is made to the printing of floor coverings, textiles, and wallpapers. The printed images of these products are of course not reproductions of reading matter, but fall into our second broad class of pictures, which includes designed patterns. The equipment used is different from that used in the graphic arts industry but it has also many points in common. For some purposes relief printing-image carriers are used, for others intaglio methods or screen process is more suitable. The printing of floor coverings, textiles, and wallpapers is of great economical importance. It gives work to a large number of people and its end products have a high dollar value. Should these industries be omitted from a discussion of specialty printing or should they be included?

Courtesy Virkotype Corporation

View of a pressroom combining offset printing and thermography. Each press is connected with a conveyor to the thermographic equipment which performs all operations automatically on an endless variable-speed conveyor matching the speed of the press to which it is connected.

As you can see, the subject of specialty printing is full of problems. It is also very vast; so vast indeed that it would take a book in itself to do it justice. For this reason, and considering the purpose of the present manual, it was decided to omit detailed descriptions of presses for specialty printing and to restrict this unit to a brief general discussion of specialty printing.

The following remarks are less systematical than enumerative. Specialty presses use all printing processes and methods, often in combinations which were especially devised to suit the tasks in hand. One of the largest branches of specialty printing is *forms printing* for which a number of manufacturers have developed standardized machines. They may combine offset printing with numbering done in letterpress, perforating and also slitting. Other operations may include spot carbonizing, interleaving, assembly of several webs, and tipping.

A somewhat similar situation exists in raised printing or *thermography*. In this field standard presses are supplemented with specialized automatic equipment to produce stationery, calling cards, social announcements, and other similar items. Thermographed products look like embossed ones; the printed images are raised in a relatively high relief on the printing stock. This effect is obtained by using the printing ink as an adhesive for resinous powders which may be uncolored or pigmented and combined with bronzes or aluminum powder if gold or silver prints are desired. The printed sheet is dusted with the appropriate powders when the ink is still wet. The pow-

Courtesy Bureau of Engraving and Printing

Making of gum for postage stamps at the Bureau of Engraving and Printing.

der adheres only to the printed areas; the excess powder is removed and then the sheet is exposed to heat. Now the resin melts and fuses with the ink on the paper. As soon as the sheet leaves the heat zone the resin solidifies, and the result is a raised, glossy printed image.

Another most recently developed group of specialty printing methods is based on electrophotography and on electrostatics; some of them will now be described if ever so briefly. (An explanation of the principles of electrophotography and electrostatics is included in Chapter I, Section 6, and should be consulted by interested readers.) Map printing is an outstanding example for the solving of special problems by electrophotography. The *electrostatic map printing press* was developed for the U.S. Army Engineer Geodesy, Intelligence and Mapping Research and Development Agency by the Harris Intertype Corporation. First a single-color press was made for experimenting, and in 1965 a five-color press was installed for production. Whether this equipment is properly called a printing press or an electrophotographic machine will not be discussed here. But it should be mentioned that it does not have most of the units customarily associated with printing presses and that there are no printing-image carriers.

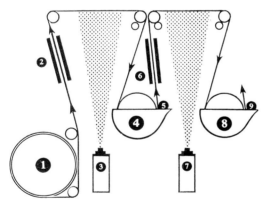

Diagram showing two units of the five-color electrostatic map printing machine. The roll of zinc oxide coated paper (1) is unwound; the paper is charged at (2) exposed on the fly by the first projector (3) and the exposed image is colored in the development tank (4). Excess developer is removed at (5) before the web leaves the tank. Next the paper is charged again at (6) exposed to the positive of the second color (7) developed with the second color developer (8), and squeegeed (9) to remove excess developer. The whole cycle of charging, exposure, and color development takes place five times, resulting in a map printed in five colors.

The material that serves as printing stock is a special paper, coated with a photoelectric surface. Each color requires electric charging, exposure, and electrostatic development whereby the exposed image areas are made visible in the selected color. The colors used are not those of full-color printing but black, brown, green, blue, and red. Exposure is by projection, on the fly; the exposed material is 70 millimeter film; the image is approximately nine times enlarged. Register is obtained by tying exposure to marks printed on the web as a result of preceding exposure. The web is 30 inches wide; the equipment can produce 2,000 five-color maps, 22½ by 30 inches, per hour. Set-up time is approximately 30 minutes; a sheeter is part of the machine.

Since *Remak Electrograph Color Proofing* is based on the same principles it is mentioned next. The materials for this process are zinc oxide coated paper and liquid electrostatic developers, which are both discussed in Chapter I, Section 6. The equipment provides an electric charging unit, facilities for time controlled contact printing, and four trays for immersion development in the four full-color inks, yellow, magenta, cyan, and black. The electrostatic sheet of paper is first charged, then exposed to the positive, thereafter immersed for electrostatic development. This cycle is repeated three more times in four-color proofing. Finally the proof is sprayed with a clear lacquer.

At this point another electrostatic color proofing process must be mentioned: the *3M Brand Electrocolor Process*. The material for this process is a sheet of polyester film to which a thin layer of aluminum is applied by vacuum evaporation. The aluminized side of the plastic is then coated with zinc oxide, presenting a smooth white surface for image reception. Processing is done in especially designed equipment, the 3M Brand Electrocolor Processor. Separation negatives are placed in a pin register frame outside the equipment, the frame is swung in for contact printing. After exposure the frame is swung away and the colorant is electroplated; then the material is washed and dried automatically by the Processor. The same procedure is followed for each of the four separations. The result is a full-color proof on a single material; this proof is laminated with a clear plastic for handling and enhancement.

Finally a few words on *electrostatic stencil printing*. This method is used for the decorating or marking of objects that cannot withstand printing pressures. Electrostatic stencil printing differs

3M Brand Electrocolor Processor. *This machine can make black-and-white or color pictures up to a print size of 8½ × 11 inches. It does not use silver halide material but a white zinc oxide surface on which colorants are deposited electrolytically.*

from electrophotographic map printing in a number of points. There is no photoelectric material such as zinc oxide coated paper used in this method. Other differences are the use of a printing-image carrier and dry powder colorants, such as described in the discussion of Xerox photo copying in Chapter I, Section 6, rather than liquid dispersions as used in map printing.

Electrostatic stencil printing uses a screen of metal cloth as a printing image carrier. Here, as in screens for screen process, the actual image areas remain open but the non-image areas are blocked. The dry powder is placed in the screen and acquires a negative charge. At some distance from this screen is a conductive back plate which has a positive charge. The object to be marked or decorated travels between screen and back plate and the charge is carefully adjusted to make the dry powder traverse the distance or gap between the

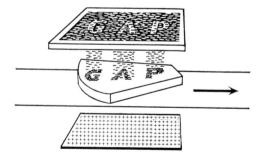

Diagram of electrostatic stencil printing, also called "gap" printing. *The object is moved through an electrostatic field between a wire screen, serving as printing-image carrier, and a charged back plate. The ink is dry electrostatic powder of a charge opposite to that of the back plate, transferred to the object by a carefully adjusted charge. (The powder is agitated to go through the screen.) After transfer the powder is fixed to adhere like ink to the printed object.*

two. (Electrostatic stencil printing is for this reason also called "gap printing.") As the powder moves perpendicular to the screen, random shaped objects can be so decorated. The deposited powder is finally fastened to the object by solvent vapor or heat. Like all electrostatic printing methods this one, too, is in flux and new developments are to be expected.

Metal decorating is an important branch of package printing. It is done on special offset lithographic presses, supplemented by a number of other machines such as coaters and conveyorized baking equipment. The package industry has many other needs for specialty printing. Metal tubes for the cosmetic and other industries must be coated and decorated, various objects made of plastics must be identified by printing rather than labeling.

Many consumer goods are decorated by one printing method or another. These include glass bottles for various industries, cosmetics in particular, but also glassware for household and restaurant use, ash trays for advertising; plates, cups, saucers, and other crockery; place mats and

Courtesy Miehle-Goss-Dexter

Printing and decorating of sheet metal is an important phase of metal can production. This picture shows the end of the oven in which the printed sheets were baked, a Dexter oven stripper, waxer, and a 9,000-lb. heavy duty pile delivery.

paper napkins. If you use a carpenter's ruler, a tape measure made of cloth, or one made of steel, you handle items produced by specialty printing.

Then there is the enormous number of finished products that must be identified for information of the consumer; and there are many intermediate products which need printing of a simple kind for the smooth flow of manufacturing. The shoe, clothing, electronics, and electrical industries are but a few of the many that utilize printing for these purposes. Printing for such purposes is usually called "marking" rather than printing.

Marking is done by necessity in the plant where the object to be marked is manufactured rather than in a printer's shop. Among marked industrial items are products of the electronics industry and coded electrical wires. Among consumer goods are shirts and shoes, medical capsules and ampules, and even small chocolate candies. Practically everything that enters your field of vision is printed in some way or other, from the vitamin bottle that you handle at breakfast to the dial on the alarm clock that you set late at night.[29]

Section 2:   Printing Units

The printing unit is the heart of every printing press. It is the unit that produces the impression, as the printer calls the transfer of the ink image to the printing stock, and therewith the final printed image. The construction of printing units depends primarily on the nature of the image carrier which will be used for making the impression, but the nature of the image carrier is by no means the only factor that must be considered in the design of printing units. Not less important is the over-all purpose of a specific press model, whether it will be sheetfed or roll-fed, the kinds of stocks and inks that are needed for presswork, and other considerations. As inking and the storage of ink are very closely related to printing units, the inking unit is often considered a part of the printing unit and therefore included in the description and discussion of the printing unit. For the purpose of this manual it seems preferable to divide the two subjects; inking units are therefore separately discussed in the following section.

Two generally valid points should be made in this brief introduction to printing units. The first point is that all printing units have at least two different members. One serves for the positioning of the printing-image carrier, whereas the other exerts the pressure necessary for transferring the ink image from the image carrier to the printing stock. The second generally valid point is that many kinds of printing can be done either by direct or by indirect transfer of the ink image to the stock. Indirect image transfer is called "offset printing" in the printer's vernacular. To avoid misunderstanding, it is added that the term "offset printing" is in contemporary printing language practically synonymous with lithographic printing. Indirect relief printing, which is gaining ground, is called by some dry offset and by others letterset. Gravure can also be printed indirectly, but this is done only rarely, and as to porous printing, our fourth process group, it is doubtful whether it can be executed at all as indirect printing; at present screen-process printing is done by direct printing exclusively.

In the following discussion we adhere to the division of printing processes into relief, intaglio, planographic, and porous or screen-process printing. The printing units for different processes and methods are presented in this order.

Printing Units of Presses for Relief Printing

Relief printing comprises four methods: letterpress printing, newspaper relief printing, flexographic printing, and indirect relief printing. Even though all of these methods use printing-image carriers on which the printing areas are raised above the non-printing areas, letterpress and newspaper printing are the only two printing methods that can use type forms, though only on presses equipped with a flat bed. Rotary letterpress printing is done with duplicate plates on some kinds of presses and with wrap-around plates on others. Rotary presses for newspaper relief printing use curved stereotype plates; flexography and indirect relief printing are done on rotary presses and cannot print with type forms. The image carriers for flexography are rubber plates, those for indirect relief are wrap-around plates. Many considerations enter into the design of printing units. One of them is the nature of the printing-image carrier which will be used in a press, another is the purpose of a press.

Printing Units of Presses for Letterpress Printing

As mentioned in the preceding section, letterpress printing machines are divided into three kinds: platen presses, flatbed-cylinder presses, and rotary presses. All three kinds can be either sheetfed or roll-fed. As roll-fed platen presses fall in the group of specialty presses and roll-fed flatbed-cylinder presses in that of equipment for newspaper printing, they are not discussed in this unit which is devoted to generally used sheetfed platen and flatbed-cylinder presses. Rotary presses, on the other hand, can be either sheetfed or roll-fed and are classified in both versions as generally used letterpress equipment; therefore their printing units are here discussed.

Platen presses. The general purpose of platen presses is explained in the preceding section. Here you are merely reminded that platen presses are used for short-run printing of smaller sheet sizes. The printing-image carrier of platen presses is usually a type form. The printing unit of platen presses consists of two members which are both plane surfaces, called the *press bed* and the *platen.* Customarily, platen presses are divided into three kinds according to the principle of their construction. These three kinds are: (1) clamshell platen presses, (2) Gordon-type platen presses, and (3) universal or sliding platen presses. The differences are primarily in the movement of the platen

Courtesy New York School of Printing

Students operate Heidelberg platen presses equipped with automatic feeders and deliveries.

(which exerts the requisite printing pressure) as can be seen from the following brief descriptions.

In the type of *clamshell platen presses* the press has a vertical stationary bed, and the platen is hinged to it along its lower edge. The impression is made by closing the platen against the bed. Although it is quite simple in operation, the mechanism is unsatisfactory for heavy forms, meaning type forms having a high ratio of printed area to the total paper area, because it exerts greater pressure near the hinge than it does at the top edge. The clamshell mechanism is now used only on platens of small size.[30]

In the *Gordon-type platen press*, which is named after its inventor, "the platen moves by cam action from a horizontal open position where the sheet is fed to a closed vertical position where the sheet is printed. The bed which holds the type form stands vertically at the top of two long legs which are pivoted at the extreme bottom of the press frame. The bed moves forward as the platen closes so that the print can be made. After the impression has been made, the bed moves back for passage of inking rollers and the platen opens for delivery of the printed sheet."[31] This design is possibly the most commonly used kind of platen press in the United States. It is manufactured by two American companies as well as by several European ones.

The third type of platen press, known as *universal, or sliding, platen press*, is much heavier and more powerful than Gordon-type presses, not to speak of clamshell platens. It is used for the printing of heavy type forms as well as for steel rule die-cutting and embossing. Certain models of this press are built solely for these purposes and are not equipped with an inking unit. The platen of this machine is moved by cam action from the horizontal feeding position to a vertical position exactly parallel with the bed which is vertical and stationary. Heavy sidearms slide the platen forward on two tracks into contact with the bed for impression.[32]

A few words on the two members of the printing unit of platen presses will explain their functions. The bed of platen presses is either completely stationary or almost so. Its main function is to serve as a stalwart support for the printing-image carrier which must be maintained exactly in its vertical position throughout presswork. The type form is fastened, or locked up, in a sturdy metal frame, called the chase. "When the chase is put to the bed of the press, it is held in position by two lugs on the bottom of the bed which fit into grooves at the foot of the chase, and at the top by a clamp which is hinged to the top of the bed, holding the chase by spring tension."[33] The platen is the moving member of the printing unit, and it carries the paper or other printing stock during the printing cycle. For correct placement of the stock guides are provided on the platen, and grippers insure the separation of the printed paper from the type form. The force with which the platen presses the paper against the inked type form is considerable. "For each square inch of an ordinary type form to be printed, 75 pounds of pressure is necessary, and solids require even more. When the number of square inches in the form is multiplied by at least 75 pounds, it may be seen readily that the press must be constructed solidly to withstand such pressure."[34]

Platen presses and flatbed-cylinder presses. Flatbed-cylinder presses preceded platen presses by several decades. When the first flatbed-cylinder presses were built (around 1810) by Friedrich Koenig in London, the wooden hand press was still extensively used and iron hand presses were just becoming popular. As already mentioned one member of the printing unit of the wooden hand press was called the *platin.* (This spelling distinguishes it from our own platen.) Wooden and iron hand presses differ from contemporary platen presses in many ways, most conspicuously in the arrangement of their printing units. In hand presses the printing unit is horizontal whereas it is vertical in modern platen presses.

But hand presses and platen presses have one congenital disadvantage: the printing pressure is applied to the whole area of the type form at the same time. Platen presses are therefore limited in the size of type forms that can be printed with a single impression. The flatbed-cylinder press overcame this limitation by an ingenious new construction principle. The impression cylinder replaced the platin of hand presses. This cylinder supplies the required pressure as it turns on the type form; it is therefore never in contact with more than a small strip across the form. This strip is of course constantly changing during the impression. It is known as the "impression nip."[35]

The original purposes of flatbed-cylinder presses. Flatbed-cylinder presses were originally designed for two purposes: the printing of books and the printing of newspapers. Book printing is still done on flatbed-cylinder presses, but they were relatively soon too slow for the needs of newspaper printing and were superseded in the course of the nineteenth century by the much faster rotary presses. Flatbed-cylinder presses are one of the most fruitful inventions in the field of letterpress printing and they dominated not only book printing but also the job-and-commercial letterpress business for approximately 150 years.

The construction principle of combining a flat bed with a cylinder permits a wide range of different types of flatbed-cylinder presses. Many of the possible solutions are of historical interest only but several versions of flatbed-cylinder presses remain of contemporary interest and are here briefly described. These are (1) two-revolution presses, (2) single-revolution presses, (3) stop-cylinder presses, and (4) stationary bed presses.

Two-revolution flatbed-cylinder presses. In the United States, two-revolution presses were the preferred kind of flatbed-cylinder presses since Miehle presses appeared on the market. In the last few decades during which flatbed-cylinder presses were still built in the United States, American press manufacturers built two-revolution presses primarily if not exclusively. In two-revolution presses the impression cylinder makes two revolutions during each printing cycle, and the flatbed, too, makes two strokes performing a reciprocating motion during each cycle. The image carrier, a type form or an assembly of flat plates, is inked two times, once on each stroke. In the impression phase of the cycle the cylinder bearing the stock rotates in contact with the bed. After the impression is made, the cylinder is automatically lifted from the bed and now rotates out of contact with the bed. During this rotation the printed sheet is delivered by the cylinder. At the same time the bed reverses its stroke until it has arrived at its original position. Then the next printing cycle begins again.

The two-revolution press construction has many advantages which were particularly useful for American conditions. Not only is the two-revolution press a rather stable machine, it is in addition also well suited for the printing of large sheets in runs which were considered rather long before mass production printing in the contemporary sense became a necessity. Runs up to 50,000 or 60,000 sheets were, and possibly still are, quite practical for two-revolution presses. The feeders and deliveries of two-revolution presses can hold bigger piles of paper than flatbed-cylinder presses of other constructions. Nor is it necessary to lift piles of stock to the feeder on the press. The feeder and the delivery of two-revolution presses are at different ends of the press and rest on the floor of the pressroom; the sheet travels in a straight line from the feeder through the press, directly into the delivery. This general layout is not arbitrary but closely related to the construction principle of two-revolution presses.

The two-revolution construction principle was successfully used for two other kinds of presses besides single-color flatbeds. One kind comprises two-color presses on which the sheets are printed in two colors on the same side of the sheet in one pass through the press. The other kind is known as perfecting presses or perfectors; it prints the sheet in one color on each of its two sides in one pass through the press.

Single-revolution and horizontal stop-cylinder presses. These two kinds of presses were not popular in the United States after the introduction of Miehle flatbed-cylinder presses. In the late nineteen fifties and sixties both kinds became again interesting to American printers, as modern European designs entered the market. Single-revolution presses are imported from Germany, horizontal stop-cylinder presses from Italy. Both kinds of presses are most effective for the printing of shorter runs and smaller sheet sizes than those that can be printed on two-revolution presses. Single-revolution and horizontal stop-cylinder presses have feeder and delivery on the same end of the press, one above the other. This general layout is space saving but the capacity of feeder and delivery is smaller than that of two-revolution presses, particularly of those that can take a whole skid of paper in the feeder.

The printing cycle of single-revolution presses and of horizontal stop-cylinder presses differs from that of two-revolution presses. The impression cylinder makes here one revolution in each cycle, whereas the bed makes two strokes. After the sheet is printed, the cylinder either stops for a brief interval (in stop-cylinder presses) or continues its rotation (in single-revolution presses) during that part of the cycle in which the flatbed is returned. Whereas the cylinder is lifted during the return stroke of the bed in two-revolution presses, it is not lifted in single-revolution and stop-cylinder presses but has a portion of its gears cut away, thereby permitting the passage of the bed on its return stroke.

Vertical stop-cylinder presses. The best known press of this construction is the Miehle Vertical, a

Courtesy Heidelberg Eastern

The feeder and delivery of a Heidelberg press. The feeder is above the delivery at the same end of the press.

domestic flatbed-cylinder press which is still manufactured in this country. This kind of press is mainly used for short runs of smaller size sheets and is, as mentioned before, often classified together with mechanically fed platens as an automatic job press. The main difference between vertical and horizontal flatbed-cylinder presses is that in the Miehle Vertical the bed is not in a horizontal but in a vertical position. Consequently "the bed moves up and down, but its travel is in an opposing direction, and the bed and cylinder, together with the adjacent parts, are counter-balanced one with the other."[36]

Flatbed-cylinder presses with stationary beds. Flatbed-cylinder presses with stationary beds are used for two widely differing applications. One is the printing of newspapers from type forms, the other is the proofing of relief printing-image carriers. In such presses the impression cylinder performs two motions; one is a rotary motion, the other is a reciprocating motion which has the object of traversing the whole length of the flatbed for making the impression. In newspaper presses the impression cylinder prints in one direction only; it is lifted out of contact with the bed in its return stroke, but in some proof presses the impression cylinder exerts pressure on both strokes.

The drive of flatbed-cylinder presses. Flatbed-cylinder presses have one construction problem which is absent in all rotary presses, namely, the kind of drive whereby the reciprocating, or back-and-forth, motion of the press bed is accomplished. The type of press drive is not only important for the speed of flatbed-cylinder presses, but has also an influence on the quality of the impression. It is not difficult to understand that the reciprocating motion of the flatbed poses greater problems than the rotary motion of the cylinder. The flatbed carries the type form which can weigh several thousand pounds in large sizes. This heavy bed with the type form must be moved two times in every printing cycle, and every move requires a reversal in direction. The movement must be as fast as possible and the press must not experience shocks during bed reversal, which means that the acceleration and deceleration of this considerable mass must be perfectly controlled. It is also necessary that the action of the bed must be timed with the action of the cylinder. Several generations of press designers have wrestled with these problems in this country as well as in England, France, and Germany.[37]

The bed of flatbed-cylinder presses. Next we turn to a brief description of the two members which are the printing unit of flatbed-cylinder presses. These are, of course, the flatbed and the impression cylinder. Let us first consider the bed of the press. This is a flat, even surface on which the form is placed for printing. It is supported by two, three, or four roller tracks evenly spaced across the press. Four bed gibs are attached by lock screws near each of the four corners of the bed to prevent sidewise movement of the bed itself. On each side of the bed are the bed bearers which run the entire length of the bed and are about 2 inches wide. Bed bearers vary for different press makes and models but are not higher than 0.918 inch, the standard height of type in the American Type System. The register rack, the last item mentioned in this brief description of press beds, is bolted to the side of the press. Its purpose is to insure perfect register between the impression cylinder and the bed while the press is on impression. The cylinder gear segment and the register rack must mesh more or less tightly.[38] It remains to be mentioned that the press bed is provided with a reference line for the correct positioning of the form. This line is scribed on the bed and usually known as the deadline.[39] "At no time should any of the printing matter extend beyond the deadline. As the deadline marks the extreme ends of the cylinder grippers in relation to the form, the sheet must extend about one-fourth of an inch to provide the necessary gripper bite."[40]

The impression cylinder of two-revolution presses. The impression cylinder is equipped with a number of items of which we mention the cylinder gear segment, the cylinder bearers, the cylinder grippers, the cylinder packing clamps, the cylinder reels, the cylinder brush, and the cylinder bands. Each of these items will be briefly identified as to its function. The *cylinder gear segment* meshes, as mentioned in the preceding paragraph, with the register rack of the press bed. Rack and gear segment are adjusted "to start the cylinder and bed together at exactly the same point at the beginning of each impression."[41] The *cylinder bearers* are sturdy steel rings on both ends of the cylinder and serve as riding members in contact with the bed bearers. They are important as reference guides for the packing of the impression cylinder. (Packing of impression cylinders on flatbed-cylinder presses is explained in Chapter VII, Section 2.) The *cylinder grippers* are small metal fingers which open and close automatically. The paper is inserted between them and, after closing, the grippers clamp, or pinch, the edge of the inserted sheet. The strip of the sheet which is inserted between the grippers is known as the *gripper bite* and cannot be printed. The next two items are related to the packing of the cylinder. The packing is attached with the *cylinder packing clamps* and tightened with the *cylinder reels*. (Their function is explained in Chapter VII, Section 2.)

Cylinder brush and cylinder bands, finally, have the purpose of smoothing the sheet on the cylinder and of holding it to the cylinder before it receives the impression. The *cylinder brush* presses the air out between the cylinder and the paper and also takes care of minor wrinkles in the stock; *the cylinder bands* hold the sheet in position. It is further mentioned that the cylinder is driven from the main drive which drives the bed, that the press has a mechanism by which the impression cylinder

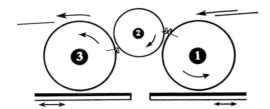

Diagram of a two-color flatbed-cylinder press. The sheet is fed to impression cylinder (1) and printed in the first color. Then the sheet is removed to the transfer cylinder (2) and in turn transferred to impression cylinder (3) for printing of the second color.

is lifted from the bed in the second, or delivery, revolution, and that the cylinder can be taken off impression during running by the *cylinder trip*. All these and many other points cannot be discussed in the available space.[42]

Two-color flatbed-cylinder presses. All domestic two-color flatbed-cylinder presses are two-revolution presses. Two-color presses have two type forms, two impression cylinders, and one transfer cylinder. The sheet is fed to the grippers of the first cylinder and stays on this cylinder for the first impression. Then the printed sheet is transferred to the grippers of the second cylinder by the intermediate transfer cylinder. On the second impression cylinder the sheet receives the second color impression and is thereafter delivered.

The construction of two-color presses utilizes each of the two strokes of the bed for the printing of one color. During each stroke one cylinder is on impression and the other is off impression. With every bed reversal the cylinders alternate in their position. During each cycle one sheet is printed in two colors. Each of the two impression cylinders has its own packing and overlay. Two-color presses can be used for both multicolor and full-color printing. If full-color jobs are printed on two-color presses, the sheets must be put two times through the press as full-color printing is usually done in four colors, one of which is black. This kind of full-color printing is called *two-and-two printing* to distinguish it from *dry-printing*, which is done on single-color presses and from *wet-printing* (or wet-on-wet printing) which is done on four-color presses. (Four-color presses are not built as flatbed-cylinder presses but are rotary printing machines.)

Full-color printing is often done from electrotypes rather than from original photoengravings which are mounted type high. The bed of flatbed-cylinder presses can be adapted for the printing of electrotypes or other flat duplicate plates, as well as for Dycril photo-polymer plates, by equipping it with plate bases. Duplicate plates for flatbed-cylinder presses are usually 0.152 inch high. Plate bases are needed to supply the difference between the height of duplicate plates and the printing height of type forms which is 0.918 inch. A number of different makes of plate bases are available. All provide "a system of movable hooks which grip the bevelled edges of the plates, bringing them into position of exact register and holding them accurately in place during the press run."[43]

Perfecting flatbed-cylinder presses. Perfecting flatbed-cylinder presses produce a sheet which is printed on both sides. Perfectors are of the two-revolution type, have two type forms and three cylinders. Two of them serve as impression cylinders, the third—also called the *skeleton cylinder*—turns the perfected sheet prior to delivery. The sheet is first printed from one form on one side. During the delivery stroke of the first impression cylinder the one-side printed sheet is transferred to the second impression cylinder. This cylinder prints the second form after the reversal of the bed; now the printed sheet lies with its printed side on the packing of the second impression cylinder and has its blank or unprinted side outward, ready for the printing of the second form.

Perfecting presses were made in large sheet sizes and were in the past widely used for book work and other printing jobs which were done by printing large sheets in medium-length runs. These presses produce satisfactory results in an economical manner, particularly if the printing matter consists of type and line engravings. They are not suitable for the reproduction of high-qual-

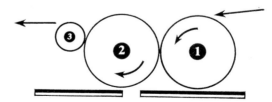

Diagram of a perfecting flatbed-cylinder press. The sheet is fed to impression cylinder (1) for printing the first side. Then it is transferred to impression cylinder (2), the printed side toward the cylinder, and printed on the other side. After the sheet is perfected it is turned by the skeleton cylinder (3) prior to delivery.

ity halftone images. At present the trend is away from printing with flatbed-cylinder perfectors, but there are still many of them in active service in the United States, not to speak of other countries.

Printing units of rotary letterpress presses. Printing units of rotary letterpress equipment consist of two members: the *plate cylinder* and the *impression cylinder*. Rotary presses are built in two different basic designs either as unit-type presses or as common impression cylinder presses. In unit-type presses, each printing unit consists of a plate cylinder and an impression cylinder. In common impression cylinder presses, a single large impression cylinder is combined with a number of plate cylinders which are arranged around its perimeter. Both designs of printing units, the common impression cylinder construction as well as the unit-type construction, can be built for sheetfed and for roll-fed or web printing.

In the recent past a third kind of press design for direct letterpress printing was introduced by the Harris-Intertype Corporation. This kind of press is known as "wrap-around press," a designation that is correct, yet capable of producing misunderstandings. Wrap-around plates are image carriers that can be used on rotary presses without requiring prior curving. As Harris wrap-around presses are built for such image carriers, their name is correct. Misunderstandings can arise if it is assumed that wrap-around plates cannot be used on presses of a different construction. This assumption would be incorrect as such plates can be used on other rotary presses as well. These may be designed either for direct or for indirect relief printing. The characteristic feature of Harris wrap-around presses is in their inking unit. This point will be explained in the next section where inking units are discussed.

A number of different image carriers are generally used in rotary letterpress. Among them are electrotypes, stereotypes, rubber and plastic plates, and wrap-around plates of different nature. Not all of these many image carriers can be attached to the plate cylinder in the same way, and plate cylinders differ consequently in their construction. Electrotypes are used for high quality, long-run jobs on sheetfed or roll-fed presses. Rubber plates have an important place in the printing of paper-covered books which are consumed in huge quantities. Wrap-around plates are used for both sheetfed and roll-fed letterpress printing; stereotypes and plastic plates are not as generally used but serve more for special tasks. Nor is the method of attaching the same for all kinds of plates. Electrotypes, for example, are individually assembled on, and attached to, the plate cylinder; rubber plates are usually preassembled on a support which is placed together with the plate assembly on the plate cylinder; wrap-around plates, finally, are single-unit plates which arrive assembled in the pressroom and do not need assembly prior to attachment on the plate cylinder of the press. The essential features of plate cylinders for each of these three kinds of image carrier will now occupy our attention.

Rotary plate cylinders for electrotypes. These plate cylinders must be designed for long-run printing, which amounts to countless millions of impressions during the life of the press. Such plate cylinders are usually made of solid steel. They are equipped with bearers on both ends which serve as the rolling surface and ride in contact with the bearers of the impression cylinder. Depending on the make of presses, they are undercut to varying degrees. In letterpress and offset the *undercut* of the cylinder is the difference between the diameter of the cylinder and that of the cylinder bearers. It provides the space needed by the image carrier, in this case curved electrotypes. Electrotypes can be attached to the plate cylinder in two

Courtesy duPont Company

Lockup of a precurved Dycril *plate on the plate cylinder of a rotary press. The pressman tightens a plate hook with his right, holding the plate with his left hand.*

different techniques. One is known as "compression" lockup, and the other as "tension" lockup. Both kinds of lockup require cylinders which have precision milled grooves. These grooves run either parallel to the diameter of the cylinder or they run diagonally across the surface of the plate cylinder. Compression lockup is the older technique of attaching electrotypes to the plate cylinder. The electros are beveled on their edges and fastened to the plate cylinder with hooks, which are anchored in the cylinder grooves and grip the edges of the electros.

Compression lockup and tension lockup. Compression lockup is satisfactory in newspaper relief printing and in sheetfed letterpress but can cause grave problems in web printing when the equipment is operated at very high speeds. The Springdale Laboratories of Time, Inc., studied high-speed rotary letterpress printing and reported significant findings: "As we increased press speeds, particularly above 1,200 f.p.m., our number of cracked plates increased violently. Normal operation would indicate a cracked-plate expectancy of three or four per form on a 128 plate press with a press count of about 4,000,000. As we edged press speeds up to 1,500 f.p.m., and then up to 1,750 feet or better, we ran into some occasions where we would crack 50 or more plates on a form comprising 128 plates. This was not only expensive, but very dangerous, since cracked plates are usually the ones that fail and are thrown off the press."[44] The investigation made by Springdale Laboratories showed that "as speed increased, the plate came off the cylinder further and further. This lifting of the plate off the cylinder is referred to as *plate breathing*."[45]

This and several other shortcomings related to compression lockup can be eliminated by tension lockup. For *tension lockup* the electrotype "is scarfed or milled on its underside, and special hooks adjustably movable in grooves are used to engage these scarfed grooves and pull the plate tightly to the cylinder."[46]

The centrifugal force on plates increases considerably in high-speed printing. At speeds of 1,500 to 1,600 f.p.m., "a plate which weighs ten pounds becomes a 400-pound object on the periphery of the cylinder. That puts a tremendous load on the cylinder. The centrifugal effect is such that when the web goes under impression the plate is running through a rolling mill bite; when it comes off impression, centrifugal force tries to throw it off with considerable force, and this is the

reason for plate failure. In tension systems that are strong enough and that are designed to hold the plate down snug, it becomes, in effect, an integral part of the cylinder. The force is there but it does not result in any mechanical motion."[47] The discussion of tension lockup has been more extensive than might have been expected. But the subject offers itself to an exposition of some problems related to high-speed printing which should give the interested reader a better idea of the difficulties and obstacles to be surmounted.

This general description of plate cylinders for electrotypes can be concluded by mentioning that certain reference lines are scribed on the cylinders which may include indications for the positioning of electros on single-product presses. Different press models provide different adjustment facilities which are outside this general discussion.

Plate cylinders for rubber plates and for wrap-around plates. Rubber-plate printing on the one hand, and wrap-around printing on the other, are adaptations to letterpress of flexographic and offset lithographic printing respectively. The plate cylinders for these two kinds of presses do not need separate description, as they are merely variations of those explained under the following headings of printing units for flexography and offset lithography. We turn next to a discussion of impression cylinders for rotary letterpress.

Impression cylinders for rotary letterpress. Four different kinds of impression cylinders for rotary letterpress can be distinguished: (1) impression cylinders on sheetfed unit-type presses, (2) impression cylinders on roll-fed unit-type presses, (3) impression cylinders on sheetfed common impression cylinder presses, and (4) impression cylinders on roll-fed common impression cylinder presses. All impression cylinders for sheet-fed printing must be equipped to hold the sheet during the impression and to release it in a manner which depends on the design of the press in question. In unit-type presses the sheet is printed on a different impression cylinder for each color. In common impression cylinder presses the sheet remains on the same impression cylinder during all color impressions made on the same side of the sheet. In the first-mentioned type of presses, the sheet must be transferred from one impression cylinder to the next, and this must be done as often as the sheet moves from printing unit to printing unit until it is finally delivered. In the second type of presses, the sheet does not travel to another impression cylinder for each color on the same side, but is removed from the common impression cylinder only when it is delivered. Impression cylinders for sheetfed presses cope with these tasks by a number of features which include grippers, as well as transfer, skeleton, and delivery cylinders depending on the make of a specific press.

In roll-fed presses, or web printing, the travel of the web is not controlled by the impression cylinder which is therefore not equipped with grippers and other features serving for the positioning, transfer, and delivery of printed sheets. These functions are in high-speed web printing assumed by a number of web-control devices. But all impression cylinders for letterpress are undercut for the packing and equipped with bearers which are the riding surfaces for a single plate cylinder, or, in common impression cylinder presses, for several plate cylinders.

Next, we must dwell, if every so shortly, on the differences between unit-type impression cylinders and common impression cylinders. The first kind can take a conventional letterpress makeready. (The meaning of "letterpress makeready" is explained in Chapter VII, Section 1.) The second kind cannot take any makeready for differential printing pressure because the sheet remains in the same place on the impression cylinder during all successive colors. Presses of this kind, particularly those used for high-speed color printing, require a different approach to regulate printing pressures. (This subject is discussed in Ch. VII, Section 2.)

Printing Units of Presses for
Newspaper Relief Printing

Printing units for the relief printing of newspapers can be divided into three basically different kinds: (1) printing units of flatbed-cylinder presses for newspaper printing, (2) tubular printing units, and (3) semicylindrical printing units. The first kind, flatbed-cylinder presses, uses type forms as image carriers; the other two kinds print from curved stereotype plates. Tubular presses and semicylindrical presses can have their printing units arranged in two different patterns which are known as deck-type and unit-type respectively. Another distinction is made according to the number of standard newspaper pages which can be printed side by side on the same printing unit. Single-width presses print webs two pages wide; double-width presses can handle webs that permit the printing of four standard size pages side by side.

The following discussion will explain the three basic types of printing units for newspaper relief printing and relate them to the kinds of presses, purposes, and products for which they are best suited.

Printing units of flatbed-cylinder presses for newspaper printing. Flatbed-cylinder presses for newspaper printing are not discussed in other sections of this manual. Therefore a brief description of these presses is included in the explanation of their most characteristic unit which is the printing unit. Flatbed-cylinder presses are used for the production of short-run newspapers. As these presses print with type forms, the capital investment for stereotyping equipment is avoided and the expenses of making plates are saved. Flatbed-cylinder presses for newspaper printing are roll-fed and have newspaper folders. Their maximum rated speed is 3,500 i.p.h.; their maximum number of pages is either 8 standard or 16 tabloid pages. If two such presses are operated in series the number of pages can be doubled.

In the United States roll-fed flat-bed cylinder presses for newspaper relief printing were built by the Goss Company, Division of Miehle-Goss-Dexter. These presses are known as Cox-O-Type presses. Even though Cox-O-Type presses were discontinued in 1966, many of them are still in operation. For this reason they are briefly characterized here. The main difference between Cox-O-Type presses and flatbed-cylinder presses for sheetfed printing is in the motion of the two members of the printing couple. In two-revolution and stop-cylinder presses, the press bed makes a reciprocating motion and the impression cylinder is stationary but performs a rotary motion, "whereas both flatbeds of the Cox-O-Type press are stationary while the two impression cylinders reciprocate as the continuous web moves through the press."[48] It should be noted that the web is continuous but the motion of the web is not. During the impression the web is stationary. The impression cylinder carriage, to which part of the inking system is attached, travels over the stationary bed on which the type form is located. The traveling mechanism is called the "crosshead." It performs a reciprocating motion in combination with a rotary motion of the impression cylinder and the inking rollers which are part of the crosshead. The two type forms are arranged on two different levels. The form for inside pages is underneath the form for outside pages. Both forms are printed at the same time.

"The Cox-O-Type is a single-acting press, printing only on one stroke of the crosshead. Cylinders are on impression when the crosshead is moving away from the ink fountains, but the rollers ink the forms on both strokes of the crosshead. When the crosshead moves toward the ink fountain, the lift cam raises the impression cylinders off the type forms, allowing the web to travel between the cylinders and the forms." During the impression period the web of paper is, as mentioned, stationary. The slack of the web is absorbed by an equalizer mechanism. Each press is equipped with a roll stand and one folder. The roll stand is at one end of the press; the folder at a right angle to the press, and the web is redirected by means of turning bars.

Our next subject is printing units of rotary presses for newspaper relief printing. Since terminology differs in the newspaper industry from that used in other branches of the printing industry the meaning of several commonly used terms will be explained first.

The meaning of printing couple, deck, unit, and press in newspaper printing. A plate cylinder together with its impression cylinder and inking system is called a "printing couple" in newspaper pressrooms. A printing couple prints the web on one side. Two printing couples which print both sides of the web are called a "deck" on deck-type presses, and a "unit" or a "printing unit" on unit-type presses. A newspaper press combines roll-feeding equipment, a differing number of decks or units, and a folder. Modern pressrooms for large metropolitan newspapers have one, two, or more rows of presses of the unit-type construction. The basic press equipment includes the press drive and a number of different controls.

Meanings of the term "undercut" in newspaper printing. The term "undercut" has a different meaning in the newspaper industry on the one hand and in the letterpress or lithographic industry on the other. This difference stems from a different construction of printing units. Each member of the printing unit of rotary presses for letterpress is provided with bearers. But neither plate cylinders nor impression cylinders of newspaper presses have bearers. Bearers are, as mentioned in the description of impression cylinders of flatbed-cylinder presses, rims of hardened steel on either end of the cylinder which serve as riding surfaces and as important reference guides during press preparation. On rotary presses equipped with bearers, as well as on impression cylinders of flatbed-cylinder presses, the undercut means the distance from the metal surface of the cylinder to the bearer surface. In newspaper printing three undercuts are recognized: "(1) on the plate cylinder the undercut is equivalent to the thickness of the stereotype plate; (2) on the impression cylinder the undercut is the distance from the steel surface of the impression cylinder to the printing surface of the plates, and (3) the combined distance from the surface of the plate cylinders to the surface of the impression cylinder. The third undercut is known as the steel-to-steel distance in the newspaper industry."[49]

Printing units of tubular presses. The terms "tubular press" and "semicylindrical press" may put uninformed readers off the right track as the presses so named are neither tubular nor semicylindrical. The adjectives tubular and semicylindrical refer to the kinds of plates for which these presses are designed. (The naming of presses by characteristic features of their plates confirms the key position of image carriers, if such a confirmation is still needed.) Both tubular and semicylindrical presses are rotary presses. The image carriers of tubular presses are slotted cylinders; those of semicylindrical presses are semicylindrical plates, meaning that each plate is approximately one-half of the cylinder circumference. The printing couples of either kind of presses consist of a plate cylinder and an impression cylinder.

Tubular presses are used for shorter runs than semicylindrical ones. "The tubular press prints one standard newspaper page around the cylinder per revolution and is usually 2 pages wide."[50] Some 4-pages-wide tubular presses were built but they have not been commercially successful. It might be mentioned that in many shops the tubular plate is known as a "stove-pipe," which it resembles. Tubular presses are built as unit-type as well as deck-type presses. Unit-type tubular presses can also be made for run-of-paper, or ROP, color printing. For this purpose they may have a common impression cylinder for two plate cylinders or a total of two cylinders per unit. A unit-type tubular press for ROP requires two such units for the printing of each 2 standard size newspaper pages.[51]

The plate cylinder of tubular presses may or may not be of solid steel; plate cylinders for tubular presses are "undercut to allow for the thickness of the plate. The undercut will be 0.4375 inch for a $7/16$ inch plate, or 0.375 inch for a $3/8$

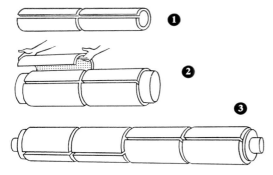

Plate cylinders of tubular newspaper presses (1) have two plates across the cylinder; those of single-width semicylindrical presses (2) have four plates, two across and two around the cylinder; and the plate cylinders of double-width presses (3) have eight plates, four across and two around the cylinder. Each plate prints one standard size newspaper page.

inch plate which is most common."[52] After the plate is put on the press, it is positioned around the plate cylinder by the margin bar which fits in the slot of tubular plates. But this operation does not attach the plate to the plate cylinder; attaching the plates is a separate step known as lockup.

The plate cylinder of tubular presses may be equipped either for compression or for tension lockup. In compression lockup, the plate is engaged on the beveled edge of its circumference by several clips similar to the hooks described in the discussion of compression lockup for letterpress printing. These plate clips push, or force, the plate against a fixed ring on the plate cylinder. Since this action results in a compression of the plate, this type of lockup is classified as compression lockup. "On tubular presses where the plate on the far side of the press must slide over the clips, a recess is cut in the plate cylinder to permit the clip to retract and then withdraw into the recess."[53] After the plates are on the plate cylinder, the clips can be tightened by the pressman from one end of the plate cylinder, which is on the "near side" of the press, as pressmen call the working side of the press to distinguish it from the other side known as the "far side" of the press. (The near side is also called the "plating side" and the far side the "gear side" of the press.)

Tension lockup and the impression cylinder are essentially the same on tubular and on semicylindrical presses. These two points are part of the description of semicylindrical presses which are the typical presses for metropolitan newspaper printing.

Printing units of semicylindrical presses. Printing units of semicylindrical presses are usually much more substantial than those of tubular presses. The latter are built to print not more than 4 pages per revolution. Single-width semicylindrical presses can produce 8 pages per printing unit and revolution, and double-width presses using semicylindrical plates can produce twice that number, or 16 pages. The plate cylinder of double-width semicylindrical presses is built to permit placement of 8 plates in two rows of 4 plates. Each row goes across the width of the plate cylinder, and one row of plates follows the other around it. Four-page wide presses are the widest generally used, but single-width presses, which have two full-size plates across the cylinder are also frequently built. In addition "a few presses have been made with cylinders that are one, three, or five pages wide. A four-page wide press may have a plate cylinder that measures 72 inches from end to end. There is no standard dimension for the end-to-end distance since page widths vary from one newspaper to another."[54]

Tension plate-lockup on newspaper presses. Several systems of tension lockup are used in the newspaper industry. Some manufacturers prefer one kind of designation, others another. The systems differ in detail but not essentially, whether they are called tension plate-lockup or underside plate-lockup. "With either type of lockup the operation is essentially the same. Four pockets are milled in the underside of the plate. When the plate is placed on the cylinder a set of fixed fingers grips the pockets on the trailing edge of the plate. When the lockup is closed, the movable fingers grip the pockets at the leading edge of the plate to pull the plate around the cylinder."[55] Tension lockup was originally developed for high-speed newspaper printing. After this method of lockup had proved its value it was introduced in high-speed letterpress, particularly in web printing done by magazine presses. The functional differences between compression lockup and tension lockup are explained in the preceding discussion of printing units for rotary letterpress and need not be repeated.

Margin guides and margin bars. Both margin guides and margin bars refer to non-printing areas of the plate cylinder. Margin guides control the margins of a full-size newspaper page in the short direction; margin bars do the same in the long direction. "The compression-type lockup provides for the side-lay location with a center ring on semicylindrical presses, and an end ring on tubular presses. The rings are fixed to the press so that the plates can be located accurately. The under-plate lockup has pins in the cylinder to locate the position of the plate. The compression-type lockup permits the plate to slide around the plate cylinder. To hold the plate in position, a steel bar is bolted to the surface of the plate cylinder. This bar is known as the margin bar, head bar, head stop or plate stop."[56]

Impression cylinders of newspaper presses. The impression cylinder has the function of supporting the web during the transfer of the ink image from the plate to the web. The essential difference between newspaper relief printing and letterpress is explained in Section 1. This difference is best expressed in the different packing of impression cylinders for newspaper printing and for letterpress. The packing of newspaper presses is soft whereas that of high-quality letterpress is hard. The effect of the packing on speed of operation must be emphasized. Newspaper printing requires many plate changes during the press run. The customary soft packing makes it possible to change plates without any delay caused by adjusting the packing. Plate changes do not require any work on the impression cylinder if the packing is soft; a hard packing as used in magazine printing, for example, would cause considerable delays at plate changes and is therefore not practical in newspaper printing. (The packing and related preparatory steps in letterpress are discussed in Chapter VII, Sections 1 and 2.)

Impression cylinders for newspaper presses may be either of solid steel or of a steel surface supported by structural elements. "The dimensions of the impression cylinder are given in terms of the length and width of the newspaper page. The page length is known as the 'cut-off.' The diameter to which the impression cylinder is machined is equal to the diameter of the packed cylinder minus the amount for undercutting. An impression cylinder is undercut to allow for the thickness of the blankets. In general, semicylindrical presses are undercut 0.125 inch while tubular presses are undercut 0.156 inch."[57]

The packing of newspaper presses. The printing surface of the impression cylinder is not steel but consists of an assembly of several softer materials. The materials used for covering the impression cylinder are chosen to give it a smooth resilient surface and are known as blankets and the draw sheet. Blankets are made of felt, rubber, cork, or a combination selected. A felt blanket over a cork blanket results in a soft packing, whereas a combination of a rubber and a cork blanket will give a firmer packing. The choice of packing material depends on the job in hand. Softer packings compensate for defects in the plate and inaccuracies of the press; harder packings are conducive to sharper printing than soft ones.[58]

The last items to be mentioned in this brief description of impression cylinders are various devices serving for the tightening of the blanket with which impression cylinders are equipped. One attaching and stretching device is the *one-reel arrangement* which "has a set of pins and a reel rod to hold the blankets. The reel rod is a slotted steel shaft to which a piece of canvas has been attached. To blanket the press, the leading ends of the blanket and the draw sheet are punched and placed over the pins. The trailing ends are left free while the canvas on the trailing end of the draw sheet is pinned to the canvas flap on the reel rod. The draw sheet wrapped around the reel rod provides the necessary strength to pull the draw sheet taut."[59]

This ends our description of printing units for newspaper relief printing. Our next subject is an exposition of printing units for flexography, the third method by which relief printing can be done.

Printing Units of Flexographic Presses

Flexographic printing is, like letterpress and newspaper relief printing, predominantly done by direct image transfer, and the printing units for this method consist, consequently, of two members, the plate cylinder and the impression cylinder. One of the strong points of flexographic presses, which they share with rotogravure presses for package printing but not with presses for other printing methods, is that plate cylinders of different diameters can be put on the same press. The range within which plate cylinders may vary in their diameter depends on the design of a press and must, of course, be ascertained for each press by those who want to take advantage of this feature. To avoid misunderstandings, it is emphasized that flexographic plate cylinders do not vary in their width or end-to-end dimension.

The printing units of flexographic presses are therefore designed in such a manner that plate cylinders can be quickly exchanged. The second member of the printing unit is, as always in direct printing, the impression cylinder which is not exchangeable but a permanent part of the press. It might be interesting to note that the terminology used in describing flexographic printing units is somewhat different from that used in other branches of the graphic arts, letterpress printing in particular. The plate cylinder is sometimes named "type cylinder" or "form cylinder," and the impression cylinder is called by some "platen cylinder." All these terms can contribute to misunderstandings. In the older literature plate cylinders were called type cylinders, then referring to type images rather than to physical type. But in contemporary American printing literature this term is not used. Names like "type cylinder" or "form cylinder" or "platen cylinder" are misleading. Uninformed people could assume that physical type is used on a type cylinder and that type forms are the image carriers for form cylinders. As you know, neither type nor type forms can be curved, and these misleading terms would best be avoided. The printing-image carriers of flexographic printing are, as explained in Chapter V, "Printing-Image Carriers," either original or duplicate rubber plates. The images present on such plates can be type images and pictures in any combination.

Construction of plate cylinders for flexographic printing. There are three kinds of plate cylinders for flexographic printing which can be grouped according to their construction into integral, slip-on, and demountable types. *Integral* cylinders can be constructed with the journals, ends, and bodies all welded together as one unit. In the *slip-on* construction, the cylinder body and gear are slipped over a bar of cold-rolled steel and then locked with set-screws; in the *demountable* type of cylinder construction, the cylinder body can be separated from its ends. The concentricity of cylinders is held within ± 0.001 inch.[60]

It should be said that the adjective integral is used in abbreviation of the more precise integral shaft. The differences between variously constructed cylinders lies in the manner in which the cylinder body and the shaft are joined more than in any other single construction feature. Integral-shaft cylinders can be of a "one-piece solid construction where the entire cylinder—plate surface and shaft ends—is formed from a solid bar of steel. This type of cylinder obviously offers the maximum in rigidity—but it is very costly and, in large sizes, its weight makes it a real problem to handle it in the pressroom."[61]

Demountable plate cylinders are much easier to store, an important feature in all work that needs reruns. Demountable cylinders can be classified in three categories: those with internal adapters, those with external adapters, and those with no adapters at all. Demountable *cylinders with internal adapters* are hollow tubes with heads, or ends, bored for a single shaft which is slit through and fastened with set-screws. Such cylinders are either quite difficult to assemble or practically not concentric and therefore not suitable for precision printing. Demountable *cylinders with external adapters* are also hollow tubes with a variety of different heads shaped to accommodate cone or plug-type adapters bored for a sliding fit or a straight-through shaft. Such cylinders are widely used but they pose problems in maintaining their concentricity.[62] In the third category of *demountable cylinders without adapters* are the "D-Mount" cylinders. Here "the cylinder and shaft are assembled like integral cylinders. That is, the separate cylinder tube is first heated to make it expand, using special electrical expanders provided for this purpose. Then the tube is fitted over the shaft and allowed to cool. But unlike integral cylinders the "D-Mount" tube is not made of steel; it is made of a light metal with a different coefficient of expansion. This permits disassembly simply by the re-application of heat which causes the tube (but not the shaft) to expand, thus freeing it for removal."[63]

Description of plate cylinders for flexographic printing. Functionally, the plate cylinder of flexographic presses does not differ from other cylinders that serve for the assembly of relief image carriers. But there are, nevertheless, many differences between flexographic plate cylinders and those on rotary letterpress machines. To mention one of the most obvious, the plate cylinder (and also the impression cylinder) of flexographic presses is not equipped with bearers which are an essential feature of presses for letterpress printing as well as of those for offset lithography. Another point worth mentioning is that the image carrier can be either directly assembled on the plate cylinder, in which case it serves for multiple unit assembly, or it can be preassembled on a support and then put on the plate cylinder like an integral, or single-unit image carrier.

Individual plate assembly is done by means of pressure-sensitive adhesives and not by clips or hooks. The plate cylinder therefore does not need milled grooves which must be provided where clips or hooks are used for attachment of individual plates, as in letterpress equipment and newspaper presses for relief printing. Flexographic plate cylinders are scribed across and around the cylinder surface with guidelines for the positioning of plates. The cylinder diameter must take account of the thickness of the plates which may be, to give an example, 0.125 inch for a rubber plate to which the required double-faced adhesive is bonded. Even though flexographic cylinders do not have bearers, it is nevertheless said that they are "undercut" for the plate thickness, but not precisely, as a certain amount of pressure is needed which is provided by a somewhat larger radius than cylinder and printing plate would have if there was no need for this additional pressure.

Single-unit plates are thicker than individual sticky-back rubber plates, and the plate cylinder must be correspondingly undercut. Single-unit flexographic plates are known as *brass-back plates* because the rubber plates needed for common presswork are permanently vulcanized to a sheet of spring brass. Such plates can be made in several variations and are either punched or notched for correct placement on the plate cylinder. Where plates with holes are used, the cylinder is equipped with corresponding location pins. Brass-back plates "are secured to the cylinder by means of hold-down bands that fit over the exposed brass sides. Made of stainless steel, these bands are designed for specific cylinder diameters and have a series of teeth that engage a latch at the opposite end. They are tightened and locked, as well as unlocked, by means of a special gripper tool."[64] Not all flexographic presses have plate cylinders. On some models the plate cylinder is replaced by what the industry calls impression bars. The *impression bar* is "a small diameter rod or bar, supported by a back-up member of sufficient rigidity, mounted in place of the impression cylinder for running certain types of work, porous tissue for example."[65]

The swing-out feature. As mentioned in Section 1, some stack-type flexographic presses are equipped for swing-out of the plate cylinder. The plate cylinder may be either an uninterrupted unit of full cylinder width or it may consist of two parts, each one-half of the full width. If the plate cylinder is divided, then the ink fountain and the intermediate inking roller are also divided to match the width of the plate cylinders. The impression cylinder is a permanent part of the press and, of course, not equipped for swing-out.

The swing-out feature enables the pressman to prepare one-half of the cylinder, or possibly the whole cylinder, for the next run by swinging it away from the running press. The swing-out feature has the advantage that the plated cylinder can be brought into its correct printing position by a simple swing-back motion and that running can continue without costly delays.

Impression cylinders of flexographic presses. The impression cylinder is here, as in other printing methods, "the roller or cylinder which backs up, or supports, the web at the point of impression."[66] Flexographic presses are either built unit-style where each plate cylinder has its own impression cylinder, or as drum-type presses with a common impression cylinder for two or more plate cylinders. Impression cylinders differ in several respects from those used in rotary letterpress machines. As mentioned in the preceding description of plate cylinders, flexographic presses do not have bearers. The distance between plate cylinder and impression cylinder is, consequently, not adjusted by taking the bearer contact as a guide, but by calipering. Nor do impression cylinders for flexographic printing have a packing which serves in letterpress printing for placement of overlays and for adjusting the diameter of the impression cylinder to the changing thickness of different printing stocks. In flexography these adjustments are made by moving the impression cylinder, usually by turning a hand wheel which may or may not be tied in with a gage indicating the position of the cylinder.

Printing Units for Indirect Relief Printing

Presses for indirect relief printing are usually adaptations of offset lithographic equipment. Their printing units consist of three members: the plate cylinder, the blanket cylinder, and the impression cylinder. Conversion of offset presses for indirect relief may or may not require grinding down of the plate cylinder to increase the cylinder undercut, depending on the model of the press and the thickness of plates to be used. If a press is operated for both indirect relief and offset lithography, the dampening plate rollers are disconnected for indirect relief, but if a press is used exclusively for indirect relief, it does not need a dampening unit at all. Since the printing unit of offset presses is discussed at considerable length later in this section, printing units for indirect relief do not need further description.

Printing Units of Presses for Intaglio Printing

Under this head we discuss the following four kinds of printing units: (1) printing units for steel-die engraving, (2) printing units for banknote printing, (3) printing units for sheetfed gravure presses, and (4) printing units for rotogravure.

Printing Units of Presses for Steel-Die Engraving

Presses for die-stamping, or steel-die engraving, differ from other presses for intaglio printing in several points. One is that the printing-image carriers for steel-die engraving are flat and not rotary; another point is that steel-die engraving results in a printed image which has not only the qualities of the usual ink image but is, in addition, in relief or on a higher plane than the printed stock itself. This effect is obtained by forcing the stock, paper or lightweight board, into the cavities of the image carrier. The printing units of die-stamping presses—and the presses themselves—are designed with these two features in mind.

Die-stamping presses are powerful platen presses. The two members of the printing unit are arranged in a vertical position, the bed above the platen. The deeply engraved plate is fastened to the press bed which is stationary, whereas the platen moves up to bring the printing stock into contact with the engraved plate. The platen serves, as usual, for the positioning of the printing stock and as its support during the impression. In die-stamping the platen is the place where the counter, or relief unit, is prepared, which is needed in conjunction with the intaglio image carrier for giving the printed product its distinctive embossed character.

As it is neither intended to discuss die-stamping in all its phases, nor to describe presswork of this method, a brief description of the counter and its preparation, as well as that of the printing cycle of die-stamping presses, is here included.

The counter-force for die-stamping. The generally used word "counter" is not related to the action of counting, but is an abbreviation of *counter-force;* this term can also be abbreviated by calling it the "force." People active in the trade have, of course, no problems with this terminology, but outsiders are in a different position. "The counter, or force, as used on the die-stamping press is an especially prepared pad of cardboard, rubber-coated cloth and similar materials by means of which the paper is forced into the engraved lines of the die. In Europe it is called the force, but in the United States it is called the counter and referred to as such. The counter is built by the press operator upon the removable steel block at the pressure end of the ram. The perfection of the die-stamped work largely depends upon the proper preparation of the counter. Therefore, *before* the counter is prepared, the shape of the lines, the width of the lines and other characteristics of the die should be considered."[67] The pressman prepares the counter by pasting counter-board or other suitable materials to the platen in the image areas, thereby adding considerable pressure, or counter-force, when the actual impression is made. The non-image areas are relieved of this pressure by cutting the excess of the counter away. The making of the counter is (in more complicated work particularly) a task that requires experienced and highly skilled craftsmen. This brief description must suffice, and we turn to our next subject, the printing cycle of die-stamping.

The printing cycle of die-stamping. After press preparation is completed, running can begin. Die-stamping uses highly viscous inks which are applied to the whole surface of the plate, its non-

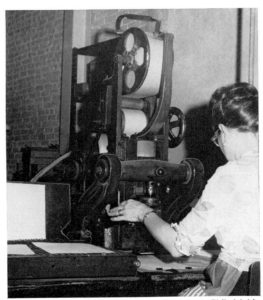

A platen press for die-stamping in operation. This press is hand fed; the paper for wiping the intaglio plate is in a roll on top of the press.

printing areas as well as to its recessed printing areas. After the ink is forced into the intaglio areas, the excess must be removed from the plate surface. This requirement is not peculiar to steel-die engraving but exists in all intaglio printing methods, even though the manner in which inking and the removal of excess ink is accomplished differs for methods using inks of high viscosity and for methods in which the inks are of low viscosity, or rather fluid. Removal of excess ink is either known as doctoring or as wiping. The term "doctoring" presupposes a doctor blade and is therefore not applicable to die-stamping which does not use doctor blades but wiping pads; the term "wiping" is used in all intaglio methods, often synonymously with doctoring.

In die-stamping, the plate is inked and wiped whereby the excess is removed from the plate surface. Then the plate is ready for making the impression. Inking and wiping are done automatically by the press, but the feeding of the printing stock is mostly done manually. (As mentioned in Section 1, there also exist automatic feeders for die-stamping presses.) The pressman or his assistant puts the stock to the guides on the platen which is already equipped with the counter. Then the platen moves upward, the impression is made, the platen goes down into its original position, the printed sheet is manually removed, and the cycle is repeated until the job is completely run off.

Printing Units of Presses for Banknote Printing

Banknote printing is the second intaglio method that uses highly viscous inks. But at this point its similarity with die-stamping ends. Different from steel-die engraving, banknote printing is done on rotary presses whereas the former uses platen presses. An additional dissimilarity is that banknote printing does not aim at a three-dimensional printed image and therefore does not use counter-forces which are necessary in steel-die engraving.

Modern banknote presses are rotaries. Their printing unit consists of a plate cylinder and an impression cylinder. The plate cylinder and the impression cylinder are usually provided with bearers which have the same functions as bearers on rotary letterpress or offset lithographic presses. The plate cylinder resembles that of offset presses, as it, too, has a cylinder gap in which the plate, a single unit image carrier, is fastened with clamps. The impression cylinder is covered with rubber

and holds the sheet in cylinder grippers during presswork. (The mechanisms whereby the highly viscous printing ink is applied to the plate and whereby excess ink is removed from the non-printing plate surface, are described in Section 3, "Inking Units.")

Printing Units of Sheetfed Gravure Presses

Sheetfed gravure is done on rotary presses by direct image transfer. The printing unit of sheetfed gravure presses has two members, a plate cylinder and an impression cylinder. Overseas, sheetfed gravure is also done with rotogravure cylinders. Presses designed for the printing with etched cylinders rather than plates have, of course, no plate cylinders. In the United States such presses are not generally used. In this country sheetfed gravure presses usually have printing units consisting of a plate cylinder and an impression cylinder.

The plate cylinder of sheetfed gravure presses. The plate cylinder of sheetfed gravure presss is constructed of steel and must be quite sturdy. It is undercut to the extent required by the thickness of the actual printing-image carrier, and has a cylinder gap where the plate is attached at head and tail, meaning at both ends, with a clamping mechanism. The cylinder gap is then covered in order to prevent ink from seeping into the gap. As the cylinder rotates constantly in the ink fountain, its ends must seal tightly, otherwise ink would flow into the cylinder.

The impression cylinder of sheetfed gravure presses. The impression cylinder has a rubber blanket of high compression and abrasion resistance as its top surface. It has a cylinder gap which

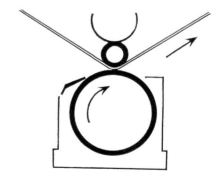

Rotogravure printing unit. The etched cylinder rotates in the ink; the web passes between the doctored cylinder and the impression roll. Above the impression roll is the heavy pressure roll.

houses, as usual, the gripper mechanism that clamps the sheet during the impression. One of the differences between sheetfed gravure and rotogravure is that the impression cylinder of sheetfed presses is undercut and can be packed. The packing makes it possible, by patching or similar techniques, to influence the printing pressure of different plate areas, whereby sometimes noticeable quality improvements in the final printed image can be attained.

Printing Units for Rotogravure Presses

The term rotogravure is in the United States synonymous with roll-fed gravure printing. In rotogravure the printing unit does not have a permanent plate cylinder. Here the etched cylinder serves two functions at the same time. It is the printing-image carrier and it is so constructed that it is also its own support, thereby obviating the need for a separate, independent plate cylinder. Presses for package printing are designed to permit printing with cylinders of differing diameters. Rotogravure presses for publication printing do not need this facility and are built for cylinders that cannot vary in their diameters.

Printing units of rotogravure presses have two additional members: one is a rubber-covered impression roll, the other an uncovered heavy steel "back-up roll." The web rides between the etched cylinder and the covered impression roll. It is kept in perfect contact with the cylinder by the setting of the back-up roll which forces the rubber-covered impression roll to provide this contact over the whole length of the cylinder. This arrangement is typical for rotogravure printing units.

Printing Units for Planographic Presses

Of the three kinds of planographic methods which we distinguish in this manual, direct lithography and collotype are, as repeatedly mentioned, numerically unimportant. The main planographic method is, at present, offset lithography which must be divided into sheetfed and roll-fed, or web-offset printing. The printing units for these two methods will occupy the following discussion.

To begin with, it must be repeated that offset lithography is an indirect printing method, whereas all of the methods described so far, with the exception of indirect relief printing, are direct printing methods. In direct printing methods, the inked image carrier, and the printing stock make contact during the impression, and the ink image is directly transferred from the image carrier to the stock under pressure. Printing units for direct printing have consequently two members which are in rotary presses the plate cylinder and the impression cylinder.

In indirect printing, image carrier and printing stock do not make contact. Here the ink image is transferred from the image carrier to a temporary support, known as the "blanket"; then the ink image is transferred again, this time from the blanket to the printing stock where it appears as the final printed image. Printing units for indirect presses have for this reason three members: (1) the plate cylinder, (2) the blanket cylinder, and (3) the impression cylinder. These three members of the printing unit can be arranged in a number of different designs. As you will see later in the discussion of printing units for web-offset printing, it is even possible to construct presses where the same member serves as the blanket cylinder for one side of the web and as the impression cylinder for the other side of the web which is on such presses perfected, or printed on both sides, at the same time.

The comments made so far apply, with the necessary changes, to all indirect printing methods. Offset lithography differs from other methods not only because it is an indirect method but also because the distinction between printing and non-printing areas is not made mechanically but chemically. The manner in which this distinction is made is explained in Section 3. At this point it is best to concentrate on the advantages of offset printing and on the reasons which account for its success.

The advantages in lithography of indirect printing. In Chapter V, "Printing-Image Carriers," it is made clear why image carriers for lithography other than bimetallic plates are much less robust than those used for letterpress and gravure. Lack of sturdiness is particularly noticeable in such lithographic plates as have photomechanical top layers. If such plates are used for direct printing, they suffer strongly from the abrading effect of printing papers. Lithography was for more than a hundred years a direct printing method with image carrier and paper making contact during the impression. Lithography was in this period

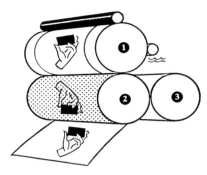

Diagram of indirect, or offset, printing. In indirect printing the printing unit usually consists of three cylinders: (1) the plate cylinder, (2) the blanket cylinder, and (3) the impression cylinder. The ink image is transferred from (1) to (2) and from (2) to the paper which is carried during the impression by (3) the impression cylinder. Plates for indirect printing have the same reading direction as the final print. Since the ink image is split twice, the final ink film is thinner in indirect printing than in direct printing where the ink image is split only once.

of its development principally a picture printing method and it was, generally speaking, not suitable for long production runs. This limitation of lithography was overcome by the introduction of indirect printing. In indirect lithographic printing the blanket is interposed between plate and printing stock, thereby eliminating direct contact of the plate with the paper and all attending disadvantages of this direct contact.

The great progress in printing technology during the second quarter of the twentieth century has made it possible to produce lithographic plates which are incomparably more sturdy than the traditional hand tusched or photomechanical ones. In bimetallic plates, the image areas are present in the form of one metal which is ink receptive and water repellent, whereas the nonimage areas consist of a different metal with reverse properties. But such plates are much more expensive than plates of lesser intrinsic sturdiness. Most lithographic jobs are still printed from plates that cannot stand the abrasion to which they would be exposed in direct lithography.

Indirect printing has other considerably important advantages which will now be briefly explained.

Five reasons for the success of indirect lithographic printing. The reasons for the great success of indirect lithographic printing can be briefly enumerated: (1) The blanket protects the plate, as already explained, because it is soft and resilient. Longer plate life makes longer printing runs

and faster printing possible. (2) The ink film is split twice in indirect printing, once between plate and blanket and again between blanket and printing stock. Thinner ink films are conducive to more faithful reproductions of fine or minute detail than thicker ink films. (3) Coated papers caused, until rather recent times, many problems because the paper coating is affected by the fountain solution which is applied to the plate in every printing cycle. These problems are considerably diminished by the interposition of the blanket. (4) The resiliency of the blanket makes it possible to transfer fine halftone images, such as made with a 133-line screen, to rough-surfaced papers which cannot be used for fine halftones in direct-printing methods. This capability is an important one, particularly in promotional printing and that of greeting cards where papers with antique finishes are often preferred for aesthetic reasons. (5) The double reversal in the reading direction due to the interposition of the blanket makes it possible to have right-reading plates. In all direct-printing methods the image carrier must read wrong or from right to left. During image transfer the reading direction is reversed and the printed image reads correctly from left to right. In indirect transfer there are two reversals of reading direction. A right-reading image carrier deposits a wrong-reading ink image on the blanket. When this image is transferred to the printing stock, it is reversed again in its reading direction and appears as a correct, or right-reading printed image. Right-reading plates are easier to check than wrong-reading ones. All these features contributed, singly and in combination, to economy, and they also enhanced the appearance of indirectly printed lithographic products.

After this general explanation of indirect printing, we can turn to the description of printing units beginning with those for sheetfed presses.

Printing Units of Sheetfed Offset Presses

As described in Section 1, "Survey of Printing Presses," sheetfed offset presses are made for the printing of one to six colors in a large range of sizes. Each of the several companies that manufacture offset presses has its own specific designs, and a four-color press of one make may differ substantially in its design from a four-color press for the same sheet size but built by another company. These construction differences are of great interest to specialists but not to those who want to become familiar with the fundamentals of offset presses. For this purpose it is best to describe the printing unit of a single-color press which is the basic press of the industry. Such a printing unit consists of: (1) the plate cylinder, (2) the blanket cylinder, and (3) the impression cylinder.

The plate cylinder of sheetfed offset presses. The plate cylinder is so named because the printing-image carrier, commonly known as an offset plate, is borne by this cylinder during presswork. The plate cylinder "is generally, but not always, the uppermost cylinder of the three. It is placed here because it is most accessible in this position and because it is easier to design an inking system for the top of a cylinder than for the side or bottom. The plate cylinder should be the most accessible because more work is done on it, and it is more frequently examined than the others."[68] Our description of plate cylinders for sheetfed offset presses is limited to a few remarks on the construction of the plate cylinder, its bearers and undercut, and on the cylinder gap and its function.

The construction of plate cylinders must be rugged; the cylinder has a cast body which is machined to its diameter within close tolerances. At the two ends the cylinder is usually equipped with rings of hardened steel which are the *cylinder bearers.* These are the riding surfaces of the plate cylinder and have corresponding bearers on the blanket cylinder. "The diameter of the bearer is the effective diameter of the cylinder. The body of the plate cylinder is ground to a diameter that is smaller than the bearer diameter. The difference between the height, or radius, of the body surface and that of the bearers is called the undercut. The purpose of the undercut is to provide space for

Plate cylinders of modern offset presses are usually equipped with fast-acting clamps. These can be operated with a simple pin wrench as held in the hand of the pressman. Various adjustments of the plate such as stretching, shifting, or cocking the plate are made with the same pin wrench while the plate remains locked in the clamps.

the thickness of the plate plus a certain amount of packing."[69] Presses for different sheet sizes have not only cylinders of different diameters but also of different undercuts. Smaller plates can be made of thinner sheets of metal than larger plates. Thicker plates need deeper undercuts.

The body of the plate cylinder is not a complete cylinder in the geometrical sense since part of it is cut away. This cutaway part is called the cylinder gap. On sheetfed presses the *cylinder gap* occupies a substantial part of the cylinder body. Depending on the model and make of a press, this gap takes up "one-fourth to one-third of the periphery. On some presses the cutaway section is as much as half the cylinder."[70] The cylinder gap is much larger on sheetfed presses than on web-offset equipment. The cylinder gap contains the plate clamping mechanism and provides the necessary space for the two clamped ends of the plate. Both ends of the plate must be attached to the plate cylinder and the plate must be pulled "tight against the cylinder body. Different makes of presses have different designs but they all accomplish the same thing."[71]

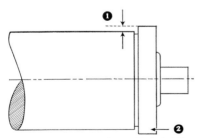

❶

❷

Plate cylinders and blanket cylinders of offset presses are undercut and usually equipped with bearers at both ends. The undercut (1) provides space for plate and packing; the bearers (2) are the riding surfaces of plate and blanket cylinders.

The blanket cylinder. The blanket cylinder rides directly in contact with the bearers of the plate cylinder which is driven from the blanket cylinder. It resembles the plate cylinder in many points, not only in its general construction but also because it has bearers, is undercut to provide room for the thickness of the blanket, and has a cylinder gap. The cylinder gap of the blanket cylinder has no clamping mechanism but holds one or two reel rods which are used for the stretching of the blanket.

The blanket cylinder is between the plate cylinder and the impression cylinder. It must therefore be independently adjustable to each of these two cylinders. "When the pressure is said to be 'thrown off,' meaning that no image transfer is

Courtesy Miller Printing Machine Co.

Offset presses can be adjusted for stocks of various thicknesses by changing the position of the blanket cylinder relative to the impression cylinder. You see the hand of the pressman turning a worm drive with a wrench. The dial, calibrated in thousandths of an inch, and the pointer guide the pressman in making the required adjustment.

to take place from the plate to the blanket, the blanket cylinder is moved away, or backed away as the trade expression goes, from the other two cylinders, the plate cylinder and the impression cylinder. Even though the distance is not great it is sufficient that plates may be put on, washed, inked or gummed without getting the blanket dirty."[72] Backing off is done by means of eccentric bushings which are part of the press.

A second need for adjustment of the blanket cylinder is related to variation in the thickness of the printing stock and to variation in the height of the blanket packing. "In some presses these adjustments are made by moving the impression cylinder in or out. In other presses the impression cylinder remains in the same place having no adjustment. In this case the blanket cylinder movement is accomplished with another pair of eccentric bushings placed outside the bushing used for backing off the blanket cylinder. A change of adjustment made between blanket cylinder and impression cylinder by these bushings does not affect the pressure setting against the plate made by the inside bushings."[73]

The impression cylinder. The impression cylinder is sometimes known, like its counterpart in letterpress, as the paper cylinder because it serves for positioning and supporting of the paper during the printing cycle. The impression cylinder is similar to the other two in many points of construction, but it does not have bearers and is not undercut. "In fact the surface occupied by the bearers on other cylinders is generally undercut on this cylinder. The cylinder gap accommodates the gripper bar that actuates the cylinder grippers which clamp the printing stock during the impression."[74] Some models have impression cylinders with polished steel rings on their ends. But these rings are functionally not bearers as they do not serve as riding surfaces. "The impression cylinder ends are, nevertheless, generally known as bearers in the lithographic industry. They are used for the alignment of the impression cylinder, though merely as reference points. The alignment is made by setting the space between the bearers of the blanket cylinder and the ends of the impression cylinder so that they are exactly equal at both ends."[75]

Composition of blankets for offset printing. In offset lithography, the blanket is in a key position as it must receive the ink image from the plate and transfer it to the paper or other printing stock. Blankets are made in various thicknesses and constructions, as well as with different top layers that must be suitable for the kind of ink with which a specific job will be printed. "Up to World War II, natural rubber was nearly exclusively used for the top surface of offset blankets. Since then blankets made of synthetic rubbers, first of Neoprene and then more and more of Buna N, have replaced the prewar blankets and are here to stay."[76] Natural rubber blankets were the only available kind of blankets until synthetic rubber was developed. Natural rubber blankets served the offset industry well during its formative stages, which is not to say that they were free of trouble even with the comparatively slow-drying inks used then, which were based on linseed oil vehicles. Natural rubber blankets became soft, sticky, and lost their resilience. To keep them in good working shape, elaborate blanket care was a necessity. With mounting press speeds and the introduction of fast-drying inks based on synthetic varnishes, natural rubber blankets swelled or embossed, caused inks to tack up and to dry on them. When synthetic rubber blankets were developed that were free of these defects, natural rubber blankets were abandoned by the industry.

At present the top surface of blankets is synthetic rubber, usually Buna N, which can be compounded to suit specific requirements of resistance to oils, solvents, and abrasion, and can also be varied in its hardness or resilience. Next a few words on the construction of blankets.

The construction of blankets for offset printing. Blankets for offset printing "consist of two, three or four plies, or layers, of fabric laminated by means of thin layers or rubber. The fabric is made from long staple cotton and treated in order to restrict its stretch to less than two per cent. This laminated structure is covered with an approximately 0.020 inch top layer of rubber compound. The final thickness of the blanket depends on the number of fabric layers, plies, and amounts to 0.055 inch for two-ply, 0.065 inch for three-ply and 0.075 inch for four-ply blankets."[77]

The blanket is subjected to a number of preparatory steps before it is put on the blanket cylinder. There it covers the whole surface of the cylinder body. The two ends of the blanket are either attached to one or to two reel rods which are housed in the gap of the blanket cylinder and serve for tightening the blanket.

But blankets covering the whole cylinder surface are not the only existing kind. In the more recent past, a removable and disposable blanket

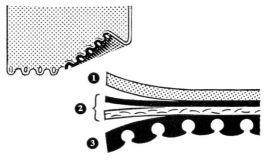

The 3M offset blanket does not have a fabric base. It consists of three parts: (1) the printing surface (rubber), bonded to the core (2) which supplies strength, and (3) the waffled springy rubber bottom which adds smash resistance.

made its appearance on the market. "This blanket consists of two parts: (1) a rubber-impregnated fabric carcass similar to the ordinary blanket; and (2) a compressible, fibrous top member, coated with a rubber composition on the surface. Each part is about 0.032 inch thick or half the thickness of an ordinary blanket. The top member is coated with a pressure-sensitive adhesive on the back, so that it can be attached to the carcass on the press. An interesting feature of the method of application is that the top member is not under tension. When damaged it can be readily removed and a new top surface attached to the carcass."[78]

Printing Units of Presses for Web-Offset Printing

Essentially, the functions to be performed by printing units of web-offset presses are the same as those performed by their counterparts on sheetfed offset presses. This is to say that the printing unit of web-offset presses must be fit to position the plate correctly and to attach it securely; that it must effectively make the transfer of the ink image from the plate to the blanket; and that it must support the paper during the making of the impression at the pressure needed for transfer of the ink image from the blanket to the stock. But if the essential functions are the same, their actual execution differs considerably in sheetfed and roll-fed offset presses. As pointed out in Section 1, "Survey of Printing Presses," web-offset presses are made in three different construction patterns: (1) presses which have individual plate, blanket, and impression cylinders for each color; (2) presses which have a common impression cylinder for all color units that print on the same side of the stock (such presses have two impression cylinders if the web is to be printed on both sides); and (3) presses which have individual perfecting units consisting of two plate cylinders and two blanket cylinders. In this kind the blanket cylinders serve also as impression cylinders, and impression cylinders are therefore eliminated. The third-mentioned construction, known as the *blanket-to-blanket* press, has become the generally most preferred kind of web-offset press. For this reason we concentrate on a description of the printing unit of blanket-to-blanket presses.

Printing units of blanket-to-blanket presses. The printing units of blanket-to-blanket presses are perfecting units; this means that the stock is printed on both sides in one pass through the press. Printing units of blanket-to-blanket presses can be arranged either horizontally or vertically. The horizontal design is used mainly in presses for newspaper printing; the vertical in presses for high-quality color printing as needed in books, catalogs, and advertising material. But it must be added that there are no sharp dividing lines; many newspaper presses have vertical arrangements of printing units and color work is done successfully on presses of the horizontal design.

If we look at a web-offset press of vertical design from top to bottom we see first a plate cylinder, then a blanket cylinder which is followed by the second blanket cylinder, and the last member is again a plate cylinder. The two plate cylinders are on the extremes, the two blanket cylinders are between them, and the web of paper runs in the center, between both blanket cylinders. Each of the two blanket cylinders transfers the ink image received from its plate cylinder to the paper surface which is in contact with it. At the same time it provides the necessary support and counter pressure for the running web. Blanket cylinders of blanket-to-blanket presses act, as already mentioned, also as impression cylinders. Why they can assume the function of the impression cylinder becomes understandable by comparing impression cylinders for sheetfed and for web-offset printing.

Impression cylinders on sheetfed presses are equipped with gripper mechanisms for positioning and holding the sheet during presswork. But it is obviously not possible to use the same mechanism for a web of material. The web cannot be positioned by grippers but must be handled entirely differently. (This subject is explained in Section 5,

"Roll-Feeding and Web Control.") The impression cylinder of web presses is therefore unencumbered by a gripper mechanism and has merely the functions of supporting the web and of providing the pressure for the impression. These functions can be effectively discharged by a pair of blanket cylinders if they are properly arranged.

The plate cylinder of web-offset presses. The main difference between plate cylinders of sheetfed presses and of web-offset presses is in the cylinder gap. On web-offset presses the cylinder gap is kept down to the smallest possible size, usually well under an inch. The reason for such a small cylinder gap is economy of paper. As the web of paper continues to run not only where the plate prints but also where it is merely clamped, and since the advanced paper web is of the same length for each press revolution, a large cylinder gap means simply that much more wasted paper. Paper wastage is, of course, intrinsically incompatible with the purpose of web-offset printing: economy. Web offset is a high-speed mass-production method, and even the smallest increase in the cost of the finished product due to waste must be avoided as much as possible; paper waste is one of the problems with which all kinds of web printing are concerned, particularly in high-fidelity full-color work.

Reducing the cylinder gap to a minimum is essential for preventing paper waste. Like every other solution of a problem in complex equipment, this too can cause new problems. The reduced cylinder gap of web-offset presses leads to much smaller plate cylinders on web-offset presses in comparison with sheetfed ones for the same printing area. This reduction in plate diameter can mean in certain cases that the plate may need precurving before it can be put on the cylinder, and the narrowness of the cylinder gap requires that the two ends of the plate, its head and its tail, must be bent precisely to fit the plate-clamping mechanism. Each company that manufactures presses has plate bending and curving fixtures which are designed to meet the requirements of its own press designs. On some bending jigs, vacuum is provided to hold the plate during bending. It is important that the plate be held tightly at this operation because bulges can cause variations in the position of the bend.

Adjustments of plate cylinders on blanket-to-blanket presses. Plate cylinders of blanket-to-blanket web-offset presses may be provided with circumferential adjustment, lateral adjustment, and also with cocking or skewing, which means slightly tilting the cylinder out of its true position in which its axis is parallel to the axis of the blanket cylinder. Cocking or skewing is done to counteract minor errors in plates or in the clamping of plates on the plate cylinder.

Blanket cylinders of web-offset presses. These cylinders differ from blanket cylinders of sheetfed presses primarily in the manner whereby the blanket is attached to the cylinder. This difference is a consequence of their narrow gaps which must evidently correspond to the gap of the plate cylinder. To properly anchor and stretch blankets on the cylinders of web presses, it is necessary to attach metal strips on each end. This operation can be done either in the printing plant or in the plants of blanket manufacturers. The blanket strips are inserted into the cylinder gap, and the blanket is then tightened with the means that are provided on the press. Blankets for web-offset presses are essentially not different in their construction from blankets for sheetfed offset lithographic presses. Web-offset presses run at higher speeds, and their blankets must be of high abrasion resistance; they must also withstand the solvents which are among the ingredients of heat-set inks, and they are usually harder than the blankets of sheetfed presses.

Printing Units of Presses for Screen-Process Printing

Screen-process printing other than specialty printing can be done by three different kinds of presses, as explained in Section 1. These are (1) hand presses, (2) flatbed presses, and (3) cylinder presses. The printing units of each of these kinds are briefly explained in the following.

Printing Units of Hand Presses for Screen-Process Printing

It is almost misleading to speak of printing units when discussing hand presses for screen process. Hand presses and printing units are in this method practically identical. If the term "printing unit" is retained, then this is done for the reason that the essential functions of printing units of screen-process equipment can be clearest understood in this elementary form. The points here discussed are (1) three basic kinds of screen process printing units for sheetfed hand presses, (2) the functions of squeegees, and (3) different techniques of handling squeegees.

Three basic kinds of screen-process printing. Hand printing is done in three different forms in screen process, each variation being needed for a different purpose. For sheetfed printing the image carrier, a screen-process screen, must be moved onto the printing stock and away from it. This motion is usually made by pivoting a stationary screen attached at its back to the bed by hinges or a similar arrangement. The squeegee and the printing stock are moved by a stationary operator. The same arrangement is used, with certain modification, to be sure, on flatbed presses for screen process. Cylindrical objects, such as bottles, are printed with a reciprocating screen and a stationary squeegee by a stationary operator. The

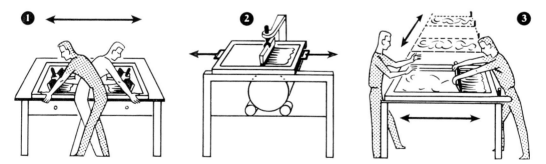

Three basic forms of screen-process printing. In (1) the operator uses a squeegee with a single handle; in (2) the squeegee is stationary, the cylinder rotates either through friction with the moving screen or by mechanical means; in (3) two operators print with a squeegee that must be pushed with both hands. Hand printing of sheets is done by method (1); cylinder presses and bottle printing are based on (2), and (3) is followed in textile and wallpaper printing.

cylindrical object to be printed rotates by frictional contact with the moving screen. The printing of bottles is outside the frame of this manual and not further discussed. The reason for mentioning this variation is that it shows the principle on which cylinder presses are based in its elementary form. The third variation of screen printing is used for the decorating of webs of material, fabrics, plastics, and paper among them. In this variation the web of material is spread on long tables, sometimes exceeding 100 feet in length. The screen is carried by one or two workers who register it to preset stops, make the impression and continue walking and printing until the job is completed. This variation is the elementary form of screen-process printing in the textile, wallpaper, and plastics industries. It is like bottle printing classified as specialty printing and hence outside our manual and here mentioned only for the sake of completeness.[79]

Sheetfed hand presses for screen process. Screen process is the only branch of the printing business that uses hand printing as a matter of course for many purposes. The printing unit for hand printing consists of a screen-process screen, a base, and a squeegee. The screen serves as image carrier as well as ink fountain. The second member of a hand printing unit is the base on which the stock is fed to guides. At its simplest, the base is a sheet of heavy plywood, though some bases, known as *vacuum bases*, have a different construction. They consist of a plenum, or air compartment, which is attached to a low-pressure, high-velocity exhaust. The top of this plenum is a hard-surfaced board, drilled with many small holes. This board serves as the feeding surface and the vacuum acts through its holes on the fed stock, holding it down on the bed after the impression is made. In many jobs separation between the screen and the stock does not need a vacuum base but can be accomplished by simple mechanical means.

The screen itself is attached to the base in such a manner that it can be simply put in the exact printing position and that it can be equally simply moved away from the base after the impression is made when the base must be accessible for delivery of the printed sheets and for feeding of the next sheet. To this effect the screen may be attached with hinges to the base and with metal chains and extension springs to the gallows of the hand press, to mention one of several possibilities.

The third member of the printing unit is the **squeegee**. It combines several functions for whose performance a number of implements are needed in other printing methods.

The three functions of the squeegee. In screen process the printing image is brought about by forcing ink through the open pores or meshes of the screen directly onto the surface of the stock to be printed. The ink image and the printed image are therefore inseparable, if one may speak of an ink image at all in porous printing. Pushing the squeegee, or squeegeeing, has at least two and often three functions. In all cases it distributes the ink across the surface of the screen and forces it at the same time downward on the stock. This effect is obtained by either pushing or pulling the squeegee at an acute angle with the screen. The third function of squeegeeing may be the forcing of the image carrier down into contact with the stock when the printing technique is *off-contact* printing.

Two different techniques of pushing a squeegee. The hand printer, known as "squeegee man," as "squeegee pusher," or "pusher" for short, pushes the squeegee either from one side of the screen to the other or from front to back. (Differently designed squeegees are needed when the pushing is done from side to side and when it is done from back to front.) For each printing cycle the squeegee man reverses the direction of the squeegee stroke unless he must give the job a double push. On large size jobs, a single man may not be strong enough to apply the required printing pressure. Where single-hand squeegees are available such jobs can be printed by one man; where they are not available a team of two men, consisting of a squeegee man and a helper, is needed. The squeegee man, usually an experienced craftsman, is in the lead. He determines the angle of the squeegee and the speed of the push; the helper adds pressure at the other end of the squeegee.

The printing pressure depends on two factors: the viscosity of the ink and the fineness of the stencil cloth. The finer the cloth, meaning the more orifices, meshes, or pores it has per square inch, the greater is the required printing pressure, assuming constant ink viscosity. The same general rule can also be applied by taking ink viscosity as a variable. In this case the printing pressure changes with the viscosity, other conditions being equal. Inks of higher viscosity need higher printing pressures than inks of lower viscosity.

Under these conditions inking is functionally inseparable from printing, and the printing unit is practically also the inking unit in screen process.

The following discussion of mechanical screen-process presses will show that this is so not only in hand printing but also in printing with screen-process machines. In screen-process printing, inking takes place at the point of image transfer.

Printing Units of Flatbed and of Cylinder Presses for Screen-Process Printing

Both kinds of mechanical screen-process presses are based on design principles already explained. The printing unit of flatbed presses has a moving squeegee whereas that of cylinder presses is stationary.

Printing units of flatbed presses for screen process. Flatbed presses for screen process are used for the printing of papers, foils, rigid boards, and other stocks. Their printing units consist of a flat base, a carriage for the screen, and a mechanism for moving the squeegee across the screen. The stationary base is usually equipped with vacuum for holding the stock during the impression. The carriage makes a reciprocating motion, usually from the back of the press to its front, and then returns again to the back. The squeegee also makes a reciprocating motion, usually though not necessarily in the same direction as the carriage. Most large size presses can be operated either continuously or intermittently, as "cycling presses." If they are functioning intermittently, the operator starts the press for each cycle with an electrical switch. Printing by individual cycling is often needed for large sizes of stock which may be cumbersome to feed and remove.

The printing cycle of a typical flatbed press for screen process has five phases: (1) the stock is fed to guides on the stationary flatbed by the operator; (2) the carriage brings the screen into printing position above the stock; (3) then the impression is made by the squeegee which moves mechanically across the screen thereby pushing the ink through the screen onto the sheet. After the impression is made, (4) the carriage returns to its original position, away from the bed of the press. Finally, (5) the printed sheet is removed either manually or mechanically. After the stock is removed the cycle begins anew with the feeding of the next sheet.

Printing units of cylinder presses for screen process. The printing units of cylinder presses consist of an impression cylinder, a carriage for the screen, and a squeegee. In this construction, the screen carriage and the cylinder move, but the squeegee is stationary. The cylinder has grippers that clamp the stock during the impression, and it is also equipped with a vacuum holding-segment to prevent the sticking of the printed sheet to the bottom of the screen. Since screen-printed images must be dried prior to stacking, the printed sheet is delivered to a conveyor and then subjected to drying of one kind or another. Cylinder presses have the highest production capacity of all screen-process presses. Their full potential requires forced drying equipment of a corresponding capacity for its realization. (Forced drying is discussed in Section 7; presswork on flatbed and on cylinder presses for screen process is described in Chapter VII, Section 5.)

Section 3: The Inking Unit

The ultimate purpose of the inking unit can be easily identified as the formation of the correct ink image on the printing-image carrier. The ink image is either transferred to the printing stock or to the blanket. In all direct-printing methods this transfer is immediately made to the stock; in indirect methods such as offset lithography and indirect relief printing, the blanket is interposed between image carrier and stock. In both direct and indirect printing, the ink image becomes the final, or printed image, when it is transferred to the stock during the making of the impression.

The inking unit is consequently closely related to the printing unit, so much so that many writers do not recognize it as a separate unit but treat it

as part of the printing unit. For the purposes of this manual, which is not written to teach operational skills but to develop understanding, it is preferable to discuss inking units separately rather than to make the explanation of printing units more complex. Another advantage of independent explanation is the possibility to discuss functional and equipment characteristics of inking units together and thereby to save repetition in the discussion of inking units for different printing methods. Three points appear to be of sufficient general interest for an introductory discussion. These are (1) the relations between printing inks and printed images, (2) the functions of roller-operated printing units, and (3) printers' rollers.

Relations Between Printing Inks and Printed Images

The printed image consists in all printing methods with the exception of newspaper relief printing of a dry colored ink film. If this ink film is black, the meaning of the printed text and the appearance of photographs is conveyed to the reader by contrast. The black ink absorbs most of the incident light, whereas the white paper reflects most of it. Black pigments absorb more light than other pigments. For this reason reading matter is usually printed black. The difference between absorbed and reflected light, which is only another way of expressing contrast, makes it possible for the human seeing apparatus to recognize printed images and for the human mind to grasp their meaning. In color printing the situation is somewhat different. Here the several color inks cause selective absorption and reflection of the incident light. The result is that we now see color images. (Color printing is explained in Chapter III.) Printing ink plays, as you will agree, a most important part in printing production. The final printed images must be more or less exact in color and shape. Even minor distortions of printed letter forms may impede reading and may deprive reproductions of photographs and other continuous-tone pictures of their aesthetic appeal.

It could be asked why this reminder is offered prior to the discussion of inking units, as these points seem to be related to printing inks and their quality rather than to printing units. This objection is much less valid than it appears. The quality of the printed image depends not only on the quality of the ink itself, but also on the handling of the ink on the press, on the skill with which the inking unit is set and maintained. Even though the ultimate purpose of printing inks is more or less the same in all existing printing methods, the means by which the desired result is accomplished are not always the same. The main differences are rooted in the nature of printing-image carriers and in the speed of press operation.

It is not too difficult to understand that inks for different printing processes must have different basic characteristics. Inks to be printed by relief methods must be fit to form the ink image on the top of the image carrier which consists of a large number of smaller or larger individual plateaus separated by gorges of varying depth—the nonprinting areas. In fine halftone printing, these plateaus are so small that they may not be recog-

nized by the unaided eye, and they are not separated by steep clefts but by mild, shallow valleys. Ink must not be applied to these minute nonprinting areas, but must be deposited on the printing areas exclusively. It must, ideally, assume the shape of each of these tiny dots without spilling over their edges or staying away from them and without distorting or reducing their areas. Compare these kinds of requirements with those of gravure. In gravure the printing ink must fill the cells of the image carrier, little craters in the landscape of etched plates or cylinders, more or less similar to the gorges that divide the plateaus of relief printing. These cells, which may be extremely small, are the printing areas of gravure image carriers whereas the top surface is nonprinting and hence not supposed to be covered with ink. It is obvious that the inking units, as well as the printing inks which are applied by these inking units, must be radically different in both methods.

These two examples could be supplemented by others, since every printing method has problems of its own in the formation of the ink image. Further, inking units for the same printing methods, say for letterpress, differ according to the speed with which a press is run. It is explained in Chapter IX, "Printing Inks," that the body, consistency or, to say it technically, the viscosity of inks must be decreased as the speed of printing increases. This means that inks for printing on hand-fed platen presses, which are the slowest kind of contemporary letterpress machines, are much more viscous than those for letterpress printing of magazines on high-speed web presses. The differences in viscosity influence of course the construction of inking units. Generally speaking, inks of higher viscosity are needed for letterpress printing and offset lithography; newspaper printing and most applications of screen printing use inks of a medium viscosity, lower than that of the group first mentioned; flexography and gravure, finally, use inks of a much lower viscosity, which are quite fluid at room temperature.

Another reason for explaining the functions of inking units is their share in the total power consumed during presswork. It will be surprising to many readers that in large publication presses for letterpress printing the inking unit "takes about 80 per cent of the horsepower needed."[80] That things are not much different in inking units for much less viscous inks may be somewhat unexpected, but "it has been shown that in large flexographic presses as much as 75 per cent of the driving effort is absorbed by the inking rollers."[81]

The construction of inking units depends on a number of different considerations. Some are related to the viscosity of certain types of ink, others to the nature of the printing method and the manner in which printing ink is applied to the image carrier or transferred to the printing stock.

Printing rollers are the main components of inking units of letterpress presses, equipment for newspaper relief printing and other relief printing methods, and of machines for planographic printing. Some methods either do not use printing rollers or use them in a modified form, often in conjunction with other features of their inking units. But the foregoing printing methods are so widely diffused and have such a wealth of different kinds of presses that the functions of their inking units are best explained before inking units of different kinds are discussed. The same holds true for printing rollers, the main components of such inking units.

Roller-Equipped Inking Units

Inking units which consist of an assembly of different printing rollers may differ in their construction, but it is nevertheless possible to identify five essential functions which all such inking units have in common. These five functions will next be discussed.

The five essential functions of roller-equipped inking units. The five essential functions of inking units equipped with printing rollers are: (1) storage of printing ink in adequate quantity, (2) metering of the ink as required by the progress of printing, (3) transportation of the ink from the storage space to the printing-image carrier, (4) distribution of the ink film, and (5) application of the properly conditioned ink film to the image carrier.

Storage of printing ink on the press. Storage of printing ink refers in this context obviously not to general storage of materials but to the storage of such quantities of ink as are needed for the job in hand. It may, of course, occur that storage tanks are directly connected with inking units which are part of single-product equipment and consume always inks of the same quality and color. Examples of such arrangements can be found on newspaper and magazine presses. But the storage compartments of presses for multiproduct printing, sheetfed ones in particular, are simple metal receptacles known as the "ink fountain." These receptacles are filled by emptying the content of ink pails in which the ink is delivered in varying smaller quantities by ink manufacturers. Larger quantities of inks are shipped in drums, and inks for newspaper printing as well as those for other methods not included in the present discussion may even be delivered in tank cars which are emptied directly into storage tanks.

Metering of ink from the storage compartment. At each impression a certain amount of ink is consumed. This amount of ink varies depending on the nature of the image carrier, the size of the printed sheet, the kind of printing paper or other stock, and last but not least, the quality of the ink itself. Whatever this consumed quantity may amount to, it must in any case be continually replaced. This replacement is one of the functions of the ink fountain. The construction and functioning of an ink fountain is now explained, taking the ink fountain of a sheetfed single-color offset press as a typical example. "The ink fountain of offset lithographic presses is a V-shaped reservoir that holds the supply of ink. One side or part of the side is a metal plate of spring steel. This is called the "fountain blade." The other side is formed by the surface of a metal roller called the "fountain roller." The *fountain roller* is turned intermittently, the ink side moving downward."[82] The fountain roller carries a film of ink which varies in thickness according to the setting of the fountain blade. The *fountain blade* is set by means

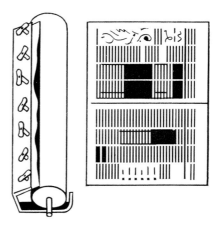

Diagram showing the relation between the setting of the fountain blade and the metering of ink for different columns. Columns with heavy solids need most ink; the corresponding areas of the fountain blade press less against the fountain roller thereby leaving more ink on the fountain roller than where the blade is tightened.

of thumbscrews placed behind it in short intervals. When a thumbscrew is tightened it presses on the fountain blade and thereby reduces the space between the fountain blade and the fountain roller; this is the same as saying that the thickness of the ink film left by the blade on the roller is reduced. This adjustment varies the ink feed across the press according to the demands of the plate. Another adjustment varies the movement of the fountain roller; it determines how large the area of the surface on the fountain roller is that will be covered with ink during each cycle of the press.

The fountain roller, also called in the pressroom the "fountain ball" (a reminder that inking was for a long time done with ink balls), is an all-metal roller. The next roller is the "ductor" or "ductor roller." (The ductor roller should not be confused with the duct roller, a term used in the United Kingdom for the fountain roller; the fountain is there often called the ink duct.)

Transportation of the ink film. Every roller which turns and is in contact with another roller transports some ink. But only one member of the inking unit has transportation as its exclusive task. The other rollers have different tasks and transport ink films coincidentally. The *ductor roller* is the only roller that has no other function but the transportation of the ink from the fountain roller to the distributing system. (In presses where the ink is pumped from storage tanks to the fountain, this operation is also classified as transportation.) "The ductor, a soft covered roller, oscillates between the ink fountain roller and the upper drum or its riders."[83] With the ductor roller you are introduced to soft-covered or resilient kind of rollers, which must be distinguished from steel rollers (or other "hard" rollers) such as the fountain roller. "It is a common and useful procedure to alternate the two types (metallic and resilient rollers) so that like rollers do not touch each other."[84] The ductor roller is mounted in such a way that it can make a swinging motion from the fountain to the distributing system and back again.

Inking systems with ductor rollers feed ink intermittently to the distributing system; inking systems in which the ductor roller is replaced by a stationary roller provide continuous ink feed. In the Goss continuous ink feed system the fountain roller has spiral grooves; the ink-film is transferred to another spiral-grooved roller set at the proper distance from the fountain roller. This second roller does not swing but is stationary. The ink film is fed to the lower distributing drum by a rubber transfer roller which is between the spiral grooved roller and the distributing drum.

Distribution of the ink film. The spreading of the ink film until it becomes sufficiently thin for application to the printing-image carrier is called "distribution," and the rollers by which this result is accomplished are known as "distributing rollers" or as "distributors," for short. "In the distribution phase ink is transferred from steel rollers to rubber rollers and vice versa until finally an ink film is deposited on the form. On the roller system of the press the ink is discontinuously sheared. Longitudinal shear caused by the so-called roller vibration is also present. The shearing stresses to which the ink on the rollers is subject are very high."[85] You may remember that approximately 75 per cent of the total power consumed during presswork is needed for operating the inking unit. Now it may be added that the ink distributing system gets the lion's share of the power needed for driving the inking unit. Some of the required power serves to split the ink film; another part is used to break up the ink particle structures, an important function of the distribution system. A large part of the energy is dissipated as heat. The heating of inking rollers will occupy our attention in the next unit on printers' rollers, but at this point an explanation of roller vibration is in order.

The distributing section of the inking unit comprises both soft and hard rollers. (In lithography steel rollers are copper-plated for reasons explained in the discussion of inking units for offset lithography. Lithographic presses may also be equipped with non-metallic hard rollers, made either of nylon or of ebonite.) Some steel or other hard rollers and the drum are vibrators. The drum is merely a hard roller of larger diameter to which the ductor roller transfers a band of ink from the fountain roller. *Vibrators* make two motions at the same time: one is the rotation of the roller, the other is an axial movement, known in the pressroom as oscillation, which moves the vibrator in the direction of its axis back and forth. The distance traversed axially depends in its maximum on the design of the press; on smaller presses it is rather short, say in the order of an inch. The importance of the lateral shearing action accomplished by vibration is mentioned already. But vibrators have also a second function: the lateral movement prevents "the ink from printing in longitudinal rows that appear like a cornfield."[86] Other steel rollers are known as "idlers"; they ride on resilient rollers and may or may not require a setting of their pressure, depending on the design of a specific inking unit.

In the preceding paragraph it is explained that a considerable amount of energy is dissipated as heat in the distributing section of a press. This point is important and should be remembered in the following unit which is devoted to resilient rollers. Steel rollers also get hot during running, but the consequences of heating are much less grave for steel rollers than for resilient rollers, particularly if an ink contains solvents injurious to the material of which a soft roller is made.

Application of the ink film to the printing-image carrier. The properly conditioned ink film is finally applied to the image carrier where it forms the ink image. The rollers for this purpose have a metal core which is always covered with resilient materials; they are called "plate rollers" or "form rollers." The number of form rollers and their diameter depends on the design of a press. Smaller platen presses may have but two form rollers, whereas offset lithographic presses have usually three or four.

Depending on the nature of the image carrier, various areas need more ink or less ink. Areas which have solid color backgrounds need most ink. Next comes display type, bold face in particular. Body type, in which reading matter in bulk is composed, needs less ink than display type but more ink than halftone images. Ink control can be troublesome. As you may remember from the explanation of ink metering, the amount of ink is determined by the setting of the fountain blade for various areas. And you may also remember that ink control is limited to one direction of the sheet only. Good planning will avoid situations where extremely heavy and extremely light ink coverage is needed within the same ink-control area, since the same band of ink cannot be thin and thick at the same time. Unfortunately, mutually contradictory requirements cannot always be avoided and compromises must be made. In such situations, the experience and sense of balance of a pressman will show itself.

After this identification of the main functions performed by inking units consisting of rollers, we turn to a discussion of printers' rollers, the materials of which they are made and the methods by which they are manufactured.

Printers' Rollers

Hard rollers, which are primarily though not exclusively made of steel, are part of the press and do not need frequent replacements, but soft-covered, or resilient, rollers are subject to much greater wear and tear and must consequently be renewed more often. In keeping with the general trend of contemporary specialized technology, "it has not been possible to develop any one roller that will meet the requirements of all possible conditions. This accounts for the various types of rollers in use and the need for special rollers within each type."[87] Before we begin a discussion of different types of resilient rollers, a brief description of their main characteristic requirements is in order.

Characteristic requirements of printers' rollers. Four generally valid characteristics are set forth for printers' rollers: "(1) *physical durability*—the resistance to friction, heat, and atmospheric conditions; (2) *ink receptivity*—the ability to accept and distribute ink and not to be greatly affected by it; (3) *ink stability*—the compatibility of solvents and other ingredients contained in printing inks and the roller compound itself; and (4) *hardness or softness*—the resistance to indentation or yielding under pressure by the roller."[88]

All these requirements are self-explanatory. It might be added that they also apply to steel or other hard rollers. "The ink must thoroughly wet metal as well as rubber to distribute well. Failure to wet the rollers completely will cause improper distribution."[89] An interesting list of "properties ideally required by printing rollers" is printed under the head of "General Desiderata for Printing Rollers" in the *Printing Ink Manual* published by the Society of British Printing Ink Manufacturers.[90]

The seven main kinds of printers' rollers. "There are seven types of printing rollers which have attained commercial prominence in varying degrees: (1) gelatin or composition rollers, (2) leather rollers, (3) vulcanized oil rollers, (4) natural rubber rollers, (5) synthetic rubber rollers, (6) plastic rollers—notably those made of polyvinyl chloride, and (7) cast synthetic rubber-like rollers—notably made of polyurethane. These seven kinds of rollers are listed approximately in the chronological order of their appearance in the printing industry."[91] Each kind of roller has its own purpose; some of them will now be explained.

Gelatin or composition rollers. Composition rollers, which are also known as gelatin rollers and as glue-composition rollers, are the oldest kind of inking rollers supplied by roller manufacturers to letterpress printers. Like all other soft-covered rollers, they consist of a metal spindle (which is usually supplied by the press manufacturer) covered with a layer of composition. This composition contains three main ingredients: water, glue or gelatin, and glycerin alone or in combination with similar substances. "The glue used is extracted from the trimmings of cow hides. Its gelatinous consistency gives body to the roller materials but it lacks the property of retaining its resiliency upon exposure, since it gives up its moisture rapidly."[92] Glycerin is the ingredient of composition rollers that prevents loss of moisture and keeps the rollers soft and resilient. "Glycerin occurs in animal and vegetable oils and fats which are glycerin esters of fatty acids. Most of it comes as a by-product from the soap industry. Where pure, it is a colorless, syrup-like liquid, odorless with a pleasant bittersweet taste."[93] Glycerin is hygroscopic, meaning that it attracts moisture from the air. Composition rollers are cast in a multiple mold machine under pressure. This machine is called a casting gun or Gatling gun. (The multiple casting machine resembles the multiple firing gun invented by the American R. J. Gatling, about 1860.)[94]

Composition rollers are made in various qualities and as summer and winter rollers. They can be used on presses for letterpress printing operated at comparatively slow speeds. But they are not sufficiently durable to withstand continuous high-speed rotary press operations as they are subject to softening and to melting. Composition rollers are affected by water and are consequently not suitable for offset lithography. It must be added that composition rollers are also made as non-meltable rollers which are more precisely designated as melt-resistant ones. "Unlike the glue-glycerin composition roller which can withstand heat up to approximately 90° to 95°F. before melting, the non-melt roller can withstand heat of approximately 120° to 125°F. before expanding and pulling apart."[95]

Leather rollers. Leather rollers are the classical rollers for lithographic presses. In a past when composition rollers were the only other existing kind, leather rollers were generally used as soft-covered rollers in the inking system of lithographic presses. Since the advent of other waterproof rollers, these have more or less completely replaced the leather roller. But even a decade ago, leather rollers could be found among the form rollers which apply ink to the plate in offset presses because "leather has no peer as a 'hickey' roller. Leather rollers will pick up and hold dampener lint, paper dust, dried ink, etc., thus keeping the plate free of hickies."[96] Leather rollers are hand sewn from selected cow or elk hides, pulled over metal spindles which are padded with several layers of flannel or a rubber base. Then leather rollers are "ground on a lathe to bring up the nap and the type of grain desired—fine, medium, or coarse. If specified, the leather is further prepared by applying lithographic varnish to its surface."[97] Leather rollers are expensive, have a short life on high-speed equipment, are difficult to break in and to clean.

Vulcanized oil rollers. Vulcanized oil rollers were developed for replacement of leather rollers in response to the demand by the offset lithographic industry. "The roller maker's first answer to this demand was the vulcanized oil roller. This roller was much easier to use than the leather roller, and therefore attained commercial prominence fairly soon after its introduction."[98] Until the development of vulcanized oil rollers, all rollers were made of natural materials. Vulcanized oil rollers introduced synthetic materials in this industry. "About 1915 in the U.S.A. a method was discovered that very much increased the tensile strength of factice, which is a weak, rubber-like material made by reacting of the cold vegetable oils such as linseed, rape, cottonseed, or soya oil with sulfur chloride. The essential features of the new method were the removal of air from the composition and the addition of strengthening varnishes. It took some five years to perfect a printing roller based on the new composition but ever since it enjoyed considerable popularity under the trade name *Ideal*."[99]

Vulcanized oil rollers are made by a process that can be called centrifugal casting, as the liquid compound is solidified between a core and an outer tube which rotate at high speeds of approximately 2,000 revolutions per minute. After completion of casting, the roller "is removed from the mold and ground to size and concentricity in a lathe or grinder."[100] Vulcanized oil rollers are not affected by water, but they are affected by heat-set inks and have several other limitations. The vulcanized oil roller "achieves best results with linseed oil base inks; to a limited extent for distributor positions and to a lesser extent for ductor positions."[101]

Natural rubber rollers. Natural rubber rollers swell when they are used with such oils and solvents as are part of most inks for letterpress and lithography. This fact excludes them from many applications. Natural rubber rollers are less affected by the ingredients of news inks and were widely used in newspaper relief printing in the past when press speeds were slower than on modern presses.

Natural rubber rollers for high-speed newspaper printing appeared in the early 1920's. The first natural rubber rollers were compounded with glue and organic resins. A later development was the natural rubber roller compounded with vulcanized oil. Both these rollers served the newspaper industry until World War II, and some newspapers were still using them in the late 1950's. At the time of writing, practically all high-speed newspaper presses are equipped with synthetic rubber rollers.

Courtesy Ideal Roller and Manufacturing Co.

Mixing and milling of individual roller compounds.

Synthetic rubber rollers. Synthetic rubber rollers were developed with a view to retaining some of the main advantages of natural rubber rollers and to reducing or eliminating their disadvantages. Synthetics may be compounded to meet almost any specific requirements. This is their basic advantage. Synthetic rubber rollers are made from a number of different chemical compounds such as Thiokol, Neoprene, Buna N, to mention some trade names.

Ingredients of synthetic rubber rollers. In addition to various synthetic rubber compounds five main kinds of ingredients are needed in the manufacturing of synthetic rubber rollers. These are: (1) vulcanizing chemicals, (2) accelerators, (3) antioxidants, (4) softening agents, and (5) extenders. Each of these kind is now briefly identified as to its purpose. (The names of chemicals are only added if it may be safely assumed that they have some meaning to non-chemists.) *Vulcanizing chemicals* are needed for vulcanizing the rubber. Vulcanization is the process of treating rubber under heat to change it from a permanently plastic state to an elastic state. After vulcanization rubbers become more or less impervious to certain solvents and are much less affected by heat. The most widely used vulcanizing chemical is sulfur; it is replaced by zinc oxide in vulcanizing Neoprene. *Accelerators* have the purpose which their name implies. Without an accelerator vulcanization may take several hours at the same temperature at which it can be done within twenty minutes by addition of certain organic accelerators. An added advantage is that less sulfur is needed and that diminution of sulfur is conducive to product improvements. The life of vulcanized rubber is affected by oxidation particularly if rubber is exposed to air. *Antioxidants* are chemicals that counteract oxidation and retard the aging of rubber. (Organic chemicals that are used as accelerators and antioxidants are not named because their names are meaningless to nonspecialists.) *Softening agents* have many purposes. They are introduced to ease the processing of vulcanized rubber and to improve desirable properties of the final product, tack, flexibility, and resistance to aging among them. Mineral oils, waxes, and organic synthetic chemicals including plasticizers can be named as softening agents. *Extenders*, finally, are inorganic fillers which modify the physical properties of the final product without affecting vulcanization. Properties that can be influenced by extenders include color, strength, hardness, and elasticity as well as resistance to abrasion, to tearing, to various liquids and gases.[102]

Manufacturing of rubber rollers. The manufacturing of natural and synthetic rubber rollers is a complex process. It includes the calendering or rolling into sheets of the thoroughly mixed rubber formula, its application to a core by laminating or spiraling, and curing or vulcanizing (for which the spiraled rubber remains on its core) after

Courtesy Ideal Roller and Manufacturing Co.

Packing synthetic rubber rollers into vulcanizer.

some preparatory steps. The cured roller is subjected to grinding and polishing before it can be used on a printing press. Synthetic rubber rollers have "good physical properties, including heat and abrasion resistance, are not appreciably affected by changes in temperature and humidity, and have several other strong points such as resistance to practically all kinds of inks with the exception of those made of rubber base, and not the least, adequate strength and durability for presses which are operated at high speeds."[103] In the time since World War II many new and improved versions of synthetic rubber were developed in this country; compounding techniques were refined and so were the manufacturing methods of synthetic rubber rollers. In consequence of these developments synthetic rubber rollers are generally used for high-speed letterpress, newspaper, and web offset printing. The detail of their formulation depends on the actual conditions in which synthetic rubber rollers must perform.

Plastic rollers. Plastic rollers were developed in attempts to find an acceptable printing roller which can be manufactured by casting because casting can be done with lower labor costs than methods requiring complex handwork, including grinding and polishing. "Of the many plastic materials, polyvinyl chloride (PVC) and the polyurethanes have shown the most promise for use in the manufacture of printing rollers."[104] Modern formulations of PVC rollers are successfully used on sheet-fed offset lithographic presses because "they retain their resiliency and possess all the good cleaning properties of Urethane rollers as

well as presenting a surface toughness almost comparable to Urethane."[105]

Cast synthetic rubber-like rollers. The main item in this class is rollers made of polyurethane. Polyurethane was mentioned in the preceding class as a plastic. But "it is increasingly difficult to differentiate between plastics and rubbers and the term 'elastomer,' meaning a rubber-like substance, is becoming more widely used. An elastomer which, by virtue of its general chemical constitution is known as polyurethane, has proved very suitable for printing rollers."[106] Polyurethane rollers are marketed under various trade names in different countries; in the United States they were originally introduced under the name of "Extron."[107]

The manufacturing of polyurethane rollers is not done by handwork like that of rubber rollers, but "by casting in molds, in a process very similar to and in many ways less complicated than the original composition casting process. While the raw materials are currently quite expensive, large volume production should result in substantial decreases of costs in the future. Labor costs required are low in the making of polyurethane rollers in comparison to those connected with the making of rubber rollers."[108]

Both PVC and Urethane rollers have a controversial status in the industry. But there seems to be general agreement on one point: these rollers are not, at present, suitable for high-speed web printing. When used for this purpose Urethane rollers lose their elasticity in a relatively short time. At the time of writing Urethane rollers have found some use on letterpress proof presses and other relatively slow presses as well

Courtesy Ideal Roller and Manufacturing Co.

The vulcanized, or cured, rollers are ground to the required diameter and finish, inspected, tested, and protected for shipment.

as on coating machines. Polyurethane rollers "are cast and essentially non-porous; can be washed easily and are more abrasion resistant than synthetic rubber rollers of the same hardness. They are excellent with rubber base inks but useless in conjunction with moisture set inks."[109] The future will tell whether Urethane rollers can be developed that retain their intrinsic advantages and overcome their limitations.

The preceding discussion covers the essential points of elastic inking rollers but does not include dampening rollers. Dampening units are closely related to inking units of offset lithographic presses and are discussed together with them.

Inking Units of Presses for Relief Printing

Inking units of the already described construction, consisting primarily of a train of printing rollers, are used in letterpress, newspaper relief printing, and indirect relief printing. Even though there are many differences in the construction of inking units in presses for these printing methods, they are nevertheless similar in principle. The only exception is the inking unit on Harris wrap-around presses which is based on an entirely different approach to inking of shallow-etched relief plates. Flexography, the fourth relief printing method, uses printing inks of a much more fluid nature, and inking units of flexographic presses are therefore quite different from those found on presses for other relief printing methods.

Inking Systems for Letterpress Presses

The inking systems for all kinds of letterpress printing machines are essentially the same, with the exception of the inking system for Harris wrap-around presses. There are, nevertheless, a few items which might be mentioned as characteristic for various kinds of presses used in letterpress printing.

The inking system of platen presses. Open platen presses and job automatics are equipped with inking units comprising a fountain with the requisite fountain roller and fountain blade, a ductor roller, and a number of rollers which serve for distribution of the ink and for the inking of the type form. All of these are familiar items to readers who have absorbed the information presented in the introduction to this section.

The most conspicuous difference between domestically built platen presses and other letterpress printing equipment is their ink disk. The *ink disk* is a "flat, circular plate above the bed. Its purpose is to distribute the ink in a thin, even film over the rollers. To do so, it turns clockwise a few inches during each cycle of the press, thus presenting a consecutively different portion of its surface to contact the rollers and spread the ink."[110] If very small quantities of ink are needed, these are not put in the fountain but directly on the ink disk by the pressman who uses an ink knife, or spatula, for this purpose. Not all platen presses are built with ink disks; the popular Heidelberg platen press has an ink drum instead. Without wanting to go into burdensome detail, it might be mentioned that the soft rollers on open platen presses are usually composition rollers, whereas those on fast job automatics are often synthetic rubber or vulcanized oil rollers.

Inking systems for flatbed-cylinder and rotary presses. The inking systems for these kinds of presses differ greatly in their detail. But here, where we are not concerned with specific press models and makes, we may be rather brief and merely point out that "all inking units are similar. They consist of an ink reservoir or fountain, a series of rollers to distribute the ink, and rollers to transfer the ink to the forms. The shorter flatbed-cylinder presses generally use a 'pyramid style' of roller arrangement with no ink plate or a very small one. The longer presses use an 'ink plate' to transfer the ink from the distributor rollers to the form rollers."[111] Rotary presses do not use ink plates but an ink drum. Their rollers are of particularly heavy construction and, as they are built for high-speed presses in large sizes, they also have larger diameters. The soft-covered rollers on slower flatbed-cylinder presses are usually composition rollers which work excellently with oil-based inks. High-speed rotary presses are generally equipped with synthetic rubber rollers.

The inking system of Harris wrap-around presses. Harris wrap-around presses are for direct relief printing from shallow-etched metal plates or from photopolymer plates. The image carrier is so thin that it does not need precurving prior to placement on the plate cylinder. Harris wrap-around presses strongly resemble offset presses. They have, nevertheless, an entirely and radically

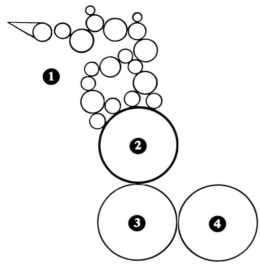

Diagram of a Harris Wrap-Around *press. The drumlike, single ink roll (2) is characteristic for this kind of press. This single ink roll applies the ink to the shallow etched wrap-around plate on the plate cylinder (3). The sheet is carried by the impression cylinder (4). Above (2) you see the ink fountain and the roller train (1); note that four rollers, comparable to plate, or form rollers, on other presses apply ink to the drumlike ink roll.*

different inking system. Whereas offset presses have three or four relatively small form rollers, Harris wrap-around presses ink the whole surface of the relief image carrier with a single large inking drum. No area of the image carrier is inked more than once. This method of inking is unique, and it makes it possible to overcome many difficulties which are encountered when shallow-etched relief plates are inked by several form rollers in succession.

The inking system itself comprises the usual elements of fountain, fountain roller, fountain blade, and ductor roller, as well as a distributing system. The form rollers are, of course, eliminated and replaced by a single large roller which resembles the blanket cylinder of offset lithographic presses. (Actually this large inker receives the ink supply from four idlers which are equivalent to the form rollers.)

Inking Units of Newspaper Relief Printing Presses

News inks, the inks for newspaper relief printing, differ in composition as well as in viscosity from letterpress inks. Their composition is such that they do not form a dry ink film, a feature advan-

tageous to the inking system of newspaper presses. To avoid misunderstandings it is added that news inks dry through absorption of their vehicle by newsprint, the paper on which newspapers are printed. (The composition of news ink and its manner of drying is explained in Chapter IX, "Printing Inks.") Like every other branch of the graphic arts, newspaper printing has inking problems peculiar to itself. These can, perhaps, best be appreciated by an explanation of the "color" of a newspaper.

The meaning of "color" in newspaper printing. The inking unit of newspaper presses must enable the pressman to print papers which are consistently of the same color. The word "color" is used in a sense peculiar to the newspaper industry. "Color in the pressroom usually refers to the amount of ink that is applied to each column of the newspaper. Each page and each column should be the same shade of black or gray. The amount of ink needed to obtain the desired color will vary with the type, design or photograph on the page. A page with all the same type—the classified section for example—will take the same amount of ink across the page, while a page with large solid type on one side and an open ad on the other side will take different amounts of ink across the page."[112]

Black and gray newspapers. Each newspaper has its own standards for the kind of color wanted. (A more precise term than "color" would be the value of black printed images.) This standard must of course be met in presswork. The newspaper industry distinguishes black and gray papers. "The black or darker papers are considered more attractive since the contrast of the printed area with the white paper is greater. A gray paper which loses something in appearance has certain production advantages. An appreciably smaller amount of ink is needed to print a gray paper."[113] In addition to the saving there is also less tendency for offset, or set-off.

Generally speaking, the inking system of newspaper presses is less complex than that of web presses for magazine printing. This is perhaps due to the fact that the printed quality of newspapers is not as critical as that of magazines, since newspapers are cheaper and are bought more because of their content than their appearance. Newspaper presses must be built to avoid the smallest delays in getting ready for running, and are in certain points more advanced in the constructions of their inking units than other presses.

Conventional inking systems of newspaper presses. In common with inking units in letterpress and offset lithography, newspaper presses have inking units with fountains, fountain rollers, and fountain blades. The fountain blade is, on older presses, adjustable with thumb screws, one for each column of the paper. In newspaper printing the column is the smallest ink-control unit. Depending on the position of the fountain roller and the fountain blade, two kinds of fountains are distinguished; the older kind is called "undershot," the more modern kind, "overshot." In both types the fountain blade is adjusted with thumbscrews which run, like the fountain itself, across the whole width of the press. "This arrangement required the pressman to reach into a deck-type press, under the arch of some unit-type press, or between the units, to turn the thumbscrews. The overshot fountain gave better control over the ink, but there were many hazards. To eliminate the hazards of setting color, metal rods that extended to the side of the press were attached to the thumbscrews. The pressman could then raise or lower the fountain blade by using a key to turn the ends of the rods. With this arrangement, colors could be adjusted rapidly while the press was running."[114]

More recently, ink control of newspaper presses was further mechanized by two systems in particular. One is the Goss Colortrol and the other is the Hoe system of column control.

The Goss Colortrol. In the Goss Colortrol, the pressman adjusts the ink for each column by the Colortrol panel which is on the outside of the press, and thereby freely accessible. "The control panel for the Colortrol is located waist high on the operating side of each unit. Each individual column adjustment across the entire width of the ink fountain is extended to this central panel. Individual toggle type electrical switches, one for each corresponding column, are located in this panel and are identified with column numbers for each of the four pages across the fountain. The switches engage the selected column adjusting screws through a coil, magnetic clutch, worm gears on a shaft and a set of worm gears which are located in the fountain knife plates. Ink feed for the entire system is adjusted by turning a single hand wheel located just below the Colortrol panel."[115] The pressman can make the required adjustments completely from the outside by operating the electrical positioning devices and by turning a handwheel.

The Hoe inking system of column control. In the Hoe system of column control an ink pump is provided for each page width and there are individual ink pump pistons for each column. These pistons are variable in their strokes and feed the required ink volume through flexible hoses to orifices in the ink rail through which the ink is distributed directly on the inking cylinder. Electrical control means are provided on the operating side of the unit to permit regulation of the amount of ink to be metered by each piston for each column of the page. The indicating dial is calibrated for reading of adjustments under high-speed operating conditions. The ink pump drive is connected directly to the drive of the printing unit, and this arrangement synchronizes the speed of the press and the speed at which ink is fed. "There is also a master control button for uniformly increasing or decreasing the stroke on all of the pump mechanisms over the full page at one time."

The ink is forced-fed from centrally located large storage tanks, automatically strained and continuously circulated through the closed looping system to supply each of the pumps mounted on each printing unit. This forced-feeding system conditions the ink for application and prevents clogging of the feeding system and contamination of the ink because paper and other foreign matter are removed from the system by timely straining.[116]

These two systems of ink control show the great advances made in newspaper presses, particularly in the metering of ink. These systems may point into the direction that press building for other methods may take in the future. But it must not be forgotten that news ink does not form dry films and is therefore singularly suitable to be handled in the described manner. Inks that do form dry films would pose a number of additional problems to the designers of similar inking units on web equipment for magazine or for offset lithography. The printing inks for these methods do not dry by absorption alone but by physico-chemical changes in the printed ink film, and such inks would clog small pumps and orifices.

Inking Units of Flexographic Presses

Flexographic presses have inking units which are much simpler than those for other relief printing methods. The reason for the comparative simplicity of inking units for flexography lies in the fluidity of flexographic inks. Fluid inks do not need distribution prior to their application to the image carrier. Thereby the whole distributing mechanism which must be provided by inking systems for more viscous inks is completely eliminated. Another important difference is in the metering of flexographic inks in comparison with viscous inks which are needed for letterpress and offset lithography.

The printing and inking unit of a flexographic press has an ink fountain with a rubber-covered fountain roller (1), a metal roller (2), a plate cylinder (3), and (4) an impression cylinder. The printing stock receives the impression between the plate cylinder and the impression cylinder.

Inking units for modern flexographic presses consist of three members: (1) the ink fountain, (2) the fountain roller, and (3) a roller for applying ink to the printing-image carrier. The fountain roller is covered either with natural rubber or with synthetic rubber, depending on the kind of ink to be printed. The roller used for ink application is commonly known as the "form roller." It is a metal roller which has the function of metering in addition to that of applying ink to the image carrier.

The ink fountain of flexographic presses. Depending on the design of a press, the ink fountain may or may not be part of the storage tank. Some ink fountains, particularly those of very fast presses may need cooling; in other designs cooling is done not in the fountain, but in the storage tank. Overheated ink is undesirable and so is overcooled ink. Some consider the troubles related to controlling the cooling of inks worse than the possible disadvantages of overheating, provided the press is operated with the proper care. Cooling of the ink tank can be accomplished in different ways. The ink tank can be made with a double bottom through which cooling water is circulated.[117] Double bottoms are only one of several possible solutions of the cooling problem;

there are also ink tanks equipped with copper coils through which the cooling water is circulated. The fountain of a flexographic press has a fountain roller. This roller is soft covered and applies ink directly to the form roller.

The form roller of flexographic presses. The second roller of flexographic inking units is a metal roller that applies the ink received from the fountain roller to the printing-image carrier, which is an assembly of rubber plates. Flexographic presses can also be constructed without fountain rollers by placing the plate roller in the fountain where it is partly submerged in the ink during its rotation. Plate rollers of flexographic presses do not have a smooth, flat surface but are treated in one of several ways to receive cavities of varying areas, shapes, and depths for holding the required quantities of ink. In some models, those without fountain rollers in particular, but also in models which are equipped with fountain rollers, "excess ink would be doctored off with a doctor blade."[118] The doctor blade of flexographic presses is in principle the same as that of gravure presses and therefore not discussed further. (A description of the doctor blade and its mechanism is provided under the heading of "Inking Units for Rotogravure Presses.")

The form roller can be made by sandblasting, by etching, and by engraving. Etched rollers are called "Anilox" rollers, a protected trade name; engraved rollers are often called knurled rollers. *Anilox rollers* are "etched across the full face with 150 to 300 lines per inch to a specified depth, usually two to four thousandths of an inch. This type of roller gives better ink distribution and provides a more solid contact with the plates. Each time the plate strikes the Anilox roller the same quantity of ink is transferred. Some shops have, in recent years, become proficient enough at

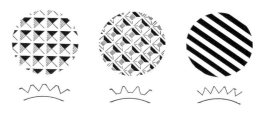

Three kinds of flexographic form, or plate, rollers. The form roller applies ink to the assembly of rubber plates. The first diagram shows the normally used pyramid cell structure; the second quadragravure cells, which hold more ink, and the third tri-helicoid cells, used for highly viscous coatings.

sandblasting to produce a sandblasted steel inking roller which is then copper plated and ultimately chromium plated to produce a uniform ink transfer surface."[119]

The structure of the cell itself is not without interest. The "*pyramid screen* is normally used in flexographic printing. The cell is a true inverted pyramid as can be seen from the accompanying diagram. Sometimes two other types of cells are used. One is the *quadragravure cell*, which is actually a bucket-shaped cell that will carry anywhere from 20 to 40 per cent more ink for the same screen count than the pyramid screen. This type of screen is normally used for direct application where the form roller is running in the ink fountain and doctored with a blade. Lastly, there is the *tri-helicoid cell* which is made by line engraving. Rollers engraved with tri-helicoid cells are not used for printing but rather for coating applications of asphalts or highly viscous heat seals. Such rollers have actually no discrete cells with four walls but narrow channels or cells with two walls only. With heavy viscous materials that will not release from four-walled cells, this screen will do the job."[120]

The development of Anilox rollers is an example of the successful transplanting of printing techniques from one printing method to another. When flexography was still in its formative stages, another already well-established printing method used inks of a similar consistency. This was of course gravure, rotogravure in particular, which also prints with rather fluid inks. The rotogravure principle was applied to flexography in the development of Anilox rollers. In rotogravure an etched cylinder, on which intaglio cavities represent the printing areas, rotates in the ink tank. As the top surface of the cylinder consists of non-printing areas, the excess ink must be re-moved, and this is done with a doctor blade which scrapes the surface of the cylinder.

The original Anilox unit consisted of a fountain in which the etched cylinder rotated directly in the fluid ink without a fountain roller. The surface of this etched roller was scraped by a doctor blade before it transferred the ink to the plate cylinder. "The original Anilox method with the doctor blade had several practical limitations, among which was the fact that the press could not be reversed or backed up without damaging the doctor adjustment or the surface of the Anilox roll, not to forget that on one side of the press the doctor blade assembly was in an inaccessible position. Furthermore, most flexographic pressmen were not adept at setting the doctor blade; in addition, excessive wear was experienced on both doctor blade and engraved roll, and the blade was apt to pick up and hold dirt, fibers, and lint, causing much streaking when this occurred."[121] The final Anilox system operates without a doctor blade and has proved itself successful in operation.

It remains to be mentioned that some presses are designed for printing either in flexography or in gravure. These presses must permit rapid changeover of one or several units from one method to the other. Their inking units are built with this purpose in mind.

Inking units on relief presses for indirect printing. Relief presses for indirect image transfer were previously known as presses for dry offset and are at present often called letterset presses. Their inking units are in principle the same as those for offset lithography, though without the dampening unit. As inking units for offset lithography are extensively discussed in a later part of this section, we turn immediately to our next subject, inking units for intaglio printing.

Inking Units of Presses for Intaglio Printing

The inking of intaglio printing-image carriers can be divided into two related stages. The first is the putting of ink into the intaglio cells, or recesses, which are below the surface of the image carrier. In the process of putting ink into the intaglio areas, the surface of the image carrier is inevitably also covered with ink. As the top surface consists of the non-image areas which must not print, the following stage has the purpose of removing this unwanted ink from the non-printing areas on the surface of the image carrier. The means whereby ink is put into the printing areas differ for highly viscous and for fluid inks, and so do the techniques employed to remove ink from the non-image areas.

Our discussion has two units: one covers inking units of presses for steel-die engraving and banknote printing which use high viscosity inks, the other inking units of sheet-fed and rotogravure presses which apply fluid inks.

Inking Units of Presses for Steel-Die Engraving and Banknote Printing

Both steel-die engraving and banknote printing need highly viscous inks. These are forced into the incised areas of the image carrier by heavy rollers. In banknote printing the inking unit consists of an ink fountain, an ink agitator, a fountain roller of steel, and a fountain blade with the usual arrangement of thumbscrews. The fountain roller is followed by a rubber roller that transfers ink to the vibrator. This roller combines, as always, a rotary motion with an axial motion. The vibrator of presses for banknote printing is a steel roller of large diameter; it is followed by the form roller, a soft-covered roller with a top layer of synthetic rubber. This roller applies the ink film to the printing-image carrier. After the image carrier is inked, the excess of ink is removed from the plate surface with a doctor blade and the removed ink is collected in a pan for reuse. But the doctored surface of the image carrier is not yet completely free of ink and must be further cleaned. The residual ink film must be removed, which usually requires two, and even three, operations. First, the image carrier is wiped by paper which moves back and forth and is consumed to the extent of approximately 10 to 15 per cent of the plate dimension for every impression. Then the wiping paper is mechanically turned and its other side wipes the plate clean in a second position. Other arrangements utilize two or three independent rolls of paper: the first fulfils the function of wiping; the second and the third that of polishing the printing plate. The paper for wiping and polishing is usually a creped kraft paper.

Inking Units of Presses for Sheetfed and for Rotogravure

The inks for sheetfed gravure are not quite as fluid as those for rotogravure. As the speed of sheetfed gravure presses is also less than that of rotogravure presses, more time is available for the inking and doctoring of the plate. Even though image carriers for sheetfed gravure can rotate directly in the ink reservoir, this procedure is not found as practical with plates as it is with cylinders. Plates are better inked by means of a fountain roller, whereby ink seepage between the plate and the plate cylinder is avoided. Another place in danger of ink seepage is the cylinder gap of the plate cylinder which is protected by a tight-fitting cap.

Inking units of presses for sheetfed gravure. Inking units of presses for sheetfed gravure by means of plates as image carriers have a fountain, a fountain roller, and a doctor blade. The fountain or "ink roller rotating within the open ink fountain floods the plate surface as the press goes into operation. As the plate cylinder rotates, a doctor blade brought into close contact across the face of the plate wipes the ink from the plate surface. The ink remaining in the etched wells is then transferred to the paper which is fed one sheet at a time and is pressed against the plate by a rotating rubber blanketed impression cylinder."[122] This brief description is sufficient for inking units of sheetfed gravure presses which have small commercial importance in this country. Here rotogravure dominates the field, and the inking units for rotogravure presses are therefore more extensively discussed.

Inking units of rotogravure presses. The most significant point of inking units for rotogravure is that they have extremely few components. Inking units of different press designs vary in their detail, but essentially they consist of an ink reservoir and a doctor-blade mechanism. The ink reservoir and the fountain, or either, may or may not be water cooled. The fountain of rotogravure presses is more or less completely enclosed and leaves only that space open which is needed for the gravure cylinder to make contact with the moving web of stock.

The gravure cylinder "rotates through a bath of ink which does two things. First, it thoroughly washes out the etching during every revolution and, secondly, it insures a complete filling of the ink cells in the etching. As each portion of the etching approaches the point of impression, the surplus ink is first removed with an auxiliary blade set close to, but not touching, the cylinder. Then final doctoring is done by a thin steel blade held in a separate holder which is clamped into a full-length bar support to keep the blade in constant rigidity. The blade is held at a steep angle and is located as close to the point of impression as the web path will permit. The arms carrying the doctor blade holder are raised or lowered through a worm and gear arrangement by means of a hand wheel and are spring counterbalanced. This gently acting device removes the danger of inadvertently dropping the doctor blade onto the cylinder and the possibility of thereby injuring the etched cylinder or the blade itself. Doctor blade pressure is adjustable at either end, from zero to maximum. Pressure is indicated by two dials, allowing operators to control the blade adjustment. The doctor blade reciprocating drive crank has a fixed radius to provide a basic 1¼ inch stroke. However, to spread out end stroke effects, means are provided so that at each stroke the extremity is displaced with respect to the mean position. This displacement arranges gradually to either side of the mean position, but the 1¼ inch stroke always remains constant."[123] The preceding description pertains to a Hoe gravure publication press. As each model and make has its own distinctive features, other makes may differ in detail, but for the purposes of this manual such differences are of no consequence. This description conveys the general features of inking units for publication presses, possibly in more detail than really required.

In rotogravure presses for package printing, a somewhat different arrangement can be found. Here, too, the inking unit consists of an ink tank and the connected fountain in which the gravure cylinder rotates. In Champlain rotogravure presses which are widely used for package printing, "the engraved cylinder is flooded with ink from an applicator and dipped into a secondary bath to cover its surface completely, filling the minute cells. As the cylinder revolves further, the surplus ink is wiped off by a doctor or wiping blade, leaving the surface clean but permitting the ink to remain in the cells (filled to surface level, in correct proportion to their depth). Since the inking system is self-flushing, it will prevent any foreign material or lint picked off the web from remaining on the cylinder surface and thus marring the print."[124]

Inking and Dampening Units of Offset Lithographic Presses

An offset plate must be dampened and inked in each printing cycle. The inking unit has the usual functions of roller-operated inking units and provides the image carrier with the requisite ink film. The dampening unit applies a controlled amount of fountain solution to the plate and thereby insures that the non-image areas of the plate remain ink repellent during the following inking of the plate.

The Inking Unit of Offset Presses

Inking units of offset presses are roller-equipped. Since such inking units are described in the introductory part of this section, merely a brief recapitulation is needed at this point. The inking unit consists of an ink fountain with fountain blade and fountain roller, a ductor roller, the ink distributing section comprising vibrators and soft-covered rollers as well as riders, and the form or plate rollers which transfer the properly prepared ink film to the surface of the plate. The only item left for explanation is the reason why steel rollers are often copper-plated on lithographic presses. Steel rollers "accept ink very well when the steel is clean and when the ink is applied before any desensitizing material, such as gum arabic, has a chance to come in contact with the steel."[125] Desensitizing solutions are applied to the plate to make the non-printing areas of the plate ink repellent. "But as the press operates, the ink sometimes 'strips' from the steel rollers. It has been found that the tendency for rollers to strip is

much less if they are covered with copper. Some presses are now equipped with steel rollers which have been electroplated with copper. This is the best method since the copper layer is the heaviest; the GATF research department also developed a method for the chemical deposition of copper on steel rollers."[126] Most recently, copper-plated cylinders have been successfully replaced in some installations with nylon, hard rubber, and ebonite rollers.

Soft-covered rollers are extensively discussed in the introductory part of this section under the head of "Printers' Rollers." At this point it is merely mentioned that sheetfed offset presses are usually equipped with synthetic rubber rollers or with PVC rollers. Synthetic rubber rollers are also used on web-offset presses since they withstand heat-set inks. The traditional plate rollers of lithographic presses are leather covered; they remain unsurpassed in their ability to prevent "hickies," but are not often used on contemporary presses. (Leather rollers are discussed in the unit "Printers' Rollers.")

We turn without delay to a discussion of the dampening unit which is an element most characteristic of lithographic presses.

The Dampening Unit

The dampening unit has the purpose of keeping the non-image areas of the plate water receptive and ink repellent. It is a press unit that requires careful handling and is considered by some the

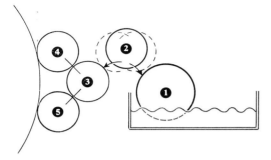

The conventional dampening system of an offset press consists of a dampening fountain with (1) a fountain roller; the ductor roller (2) supplies fountain solution to the vibrator (3); (4) and (5) are the two plate dampening rollers that dampen the offset plate prior to inking.

main source of printing troubles in lithography. Dampening and inking are interdependent operations. "The offset pressman has to learn to control ink and water (as the fountain or dampening solution is called in the pressroom) and to balance one against the other for good results."[127] The dampening unit has attracted the interest of many ingenious people who have developed a number of different technical approaches to dampening.[128] At present there are several dampening systems in operation. Some of them are briefly described in the following.

Different dampening systems. Our discussion begins (1) with the conventional dampening system; then follow (2) paper dampeners and 3M dampening sleeves, (3) the Mullen air doctor dampening system, (4) the Dahlgren dampening system, (5) the Harris-Cottrell continuous brush water feed system, (6) the Levey flap roll dampening system, (7) the Goss dampening system, and (8) the Dampen-Orr system. This listing and the brief descriptions of various dampening systems have merely the purpose of indicating to the reader that dampening is a much investigated subject and to indicate some of the lines followed in contemporary development work. The listing is of course neither complete nor is an evaluation of different dampening methods intended.

Conventional dampening units. Conventional dampening systems consist of a reservoir for the fountain solution, called "water fountain" or "water pan," and five rollers. These are the fountain roller, which is partly immersed in the reservoir, the ductor, the vibrator, and two form or plate rollers. Some fountain rollers are cloth-covered and some are felt base. They carry a film

of solution up to the ductor. The *ductor roller* is a molleton-covered roller that oscillates back and forth from the fountain roller to the vibrator and carries moisture from the fountain roller to the vibrator. (Molleton is the name of a thick cotton fabric, similar to flannel, having a long nap.) The length of time during which the ductor remains in contact with the fountain roller determines the amount of water that it feeds to the vibrator. The *vibrator* is a bare, power-driven roller and drives the dampening form rollers by surface contact. Like all other vibrators it makes two motions: one is rotary, the other is from side to side at the same time. This motion is technically called "axial vibration." It equalizes the water feed to some extent and has the purpose of preventing water streaks around the circumference of the form rollers. These are molleton-covered rollers which contact both the vibrator and the lithographic plate.[129]

Paper dampeners and 3M dampening sleeves. Molleton-covered rollers have certain disadvantages. Among them is their short life, the fact that they pick up grease in the image areas, and that

Pressman sliding a 3M dampening sleeve onto a roller. The roller with the sleeve is then thoroughly wetted whereby the sleeve shrinks and fits the roller.

they get dirty with ink stains and consequently need frequent washing and replacement. Some of these disadvantages are eliminated by the use of paper dampeners instead of molleton-covered rollers. The rollers themselves remain the same; the main difference is that their top layer is now paper instead of molleton. Dampening rollers consist of a metal body and a cover of cloth or rubber which acts as a cushion for the top layer. Paper dampeners are made by winding a ribbon of vegetable parchment paper "on the rubber rollers and maintaining an even spiral across the entire length of the roller. When paper rollers have been properly set, one can obtain the finest distribution of water."[130] A different cover for dampening rollers is manufactured by the 3M Company and sold under the trade name "3M Dampening Sleeve." This sleeve "is a perfectly round, rigid fiber tube of special construction. It is seamless and made to replace paper and cloth covers on dampening form rollers. This sleeve is not made of paper but from synthetic fibers and is actually stronger wet than dry."[131]

The Mullen air doctor dampening system. The Mullen system is made in a number of different versions, all based on the same general approach to dampening. The Mullen system does not attempt to apply an exact minimum quantity of fountain solution to the plate. It puts a controllable excess of fountain solution on the plate and reduces this excess of fountain solution to a minimum in the non-image areas by directing a narrow band of compressed air to the dampened plate. As both image and non-image areas are exposed to this air band, the image areas are completely dried of fountain solution that may have adhered to them. Application of the fountain solution and the removal of its excess take place before the plate is inked. (The name "air doctor" is analogous to the steel "doctor blade" which removes excess ink by wiping of gravure cylinder.)

The original Mullen system uses a metal fountain roller, set at such a distance from the plate that dampening takes place without the roller's touching of the plate. The air doctor comprises two elements: one is the effusor and the other a vacuun chamber. The effusor "air pressure chamber is designed to produce maximum efficiency in directing the air stream. The vacuum chamber is positioned in relation to the air pressure chamber and the angle of the *effusor* as to most efficiently remove the excess water."[132] Later versions of the Mullen system eliminate the vacuum chamber or

make further changes by adding a transfer roller. "This system has been used on a number of sheetfed presses but so far as is known, no installations have been made on a web press."[133]

The Dahlgren dampening system. In this system the fountain solution is not directly applied to the lithographic plate but indirectly. "The Dahlgren system applies regulated plate moisture to the first ink form roller which transfers it to the plate."[134] The idea of applying moisture to the inking system rather than directly to the plate is not new; the Dahlgren system is different from similar ones because earlier indirect dampening systems applied the fountain solution to ink distributors whereas the Dahlgren system applies the fountain solution to the first ink form roller, which transfers it to the plate without going through intermediate rollers.

The Dahlgren system is composed of several major parts. Among them is a stainless steel water pan, a circulating pump and reservoir assembly, and three special rollers. One of them is a chromium-plated transfer roller which is treated to be permanently water receptive. This roller is the transfer or metering roller. Metering is done by adjusting the distance, or nip, between it and the rubber-covered fountain roller. The fountain solution is transferred from the chromium-plated transfer roller directly to the rubber-covered form roller. "For high speed web presses and for large multicolor sheetfed presses, the Dahlgren system provides a refrigeration system for maintaining a stable temperature of the fountain solution."[135] These are some of the essentials of the Dahlgren system. "The dampening solution used in this system contains about one fourth alcohol. After a stop of the press, the ink-water balance can be re-established in two or three sheets."[136] The almost instantaneous re-establishing of the ink-water balance is a most important feature in web-offset printing which has high press speeds and commensurate paper waste with conventional dampening. It should be added that inks containing pigments soluble in alcohol must be avoided in all systems which have alcohol in their fountain solution.

The Harris-Cottrell continuous brush water feed systems. The Harris-Cottrell system replaces the ductor of conventional dampening units with a rotary brush. The old molleton-covered ductor still causes some trouble while it feeds water from the pan roller to the vibrator. It also picks up a trace of ink and feeds it back to the pan roller and to the water in the pan. Recently this was eliminated on one type of system by installing a brush to take the place of the ductor. This brush contacts the pan roller but not the vibrator. It flips water over an air gap from the ends of the bristles so it remains free of ink and the pan roller stays clean.

The Levey flap roll dampening system. This is another continuous feed system which is designed for web-offset printing. "In the Levey Flap Roll, the fountain roller is filled with canvas loops or flaps that contact the vibrator roller. As with the brush system, the flap roll responds quickly to changes in demand for fountain solution."[137]

The Goss dampening system. The Goss dampening system is used on the "Suburban" and the "Urbanite" web presses manufactured by Goss, a division of Miehle-Goss-Dexter, for the offset printing of newspapers. "This system is similar to the conventional one except that the moisture is fed directly from the water pan roller to the distributor without doctoring. It would be expected that this system would respond to changes in demand for moisture but would suffer from the same problems as the conventional system with regard to water droplets and restoring the ink-water balance."[138] There is a difference between the dampening system for the Suburban and for the Urbanite press. The former has a single form roller for application of moisture to the plate, the latter two of them.

The Dampen-Orr system. The Dampen-Orr system is the latest dampening system. It was introduced during 1964 and is mainly used on sheetfed presses. In this system the two molleton-covered rollers of conventional dampening systems are replaced by a single rubber-covered roller which has two rubber "trucks" mounted on either end of its spindle. There is also a special ductor roller furnished which is a precisely ground rubber-base roller, covered with a treated fabric to provide even water distribution and faster response to the water control setting. The conventional water pan roller and vibrator are utilized with this system. The "trucks" mounted on either end of the plate-dampening roller are driven by the bearers of the plate cylinder, whereby a true speed relationship results between the plate-dampening roller and the plate surface. This method of driving the dampening roller serves to avoid skidding of the dampening roller on the plate and is conducive to better print quality. The usual "running in" of molleton-

covered rollers is eliminated. The Dampen-Orr system uses alcohol in its fountain solution; inks that bleed in alcohol must therefore be avoided.[139]

This concludes our survey of different dampening systems. But before we turn to the next subject, two items which are not tied to particular dampening systems deserve a brief description. These are water stops and water levelers.

Water stops and water levelers. Water stops and water levelers can be used with conventional dampening systems or with those of different construction. *Water stops* control the amount of water carried by different areas of the pan roller. They enable the pressman to vary the plate moisture in one direction of the plate, according to the distribution of image and non-image areas of a

Baldwin Circulation Water Levels *circulate, filter and maintain the level of the fountain solution automatically.*

specific plate. *Water levelers,* finally, keep the level of the fountain solution in the water pan constant, and thereby control the rate at which the fountain solution is fed to the entire plate.

Inking units for screen-process printing. The discussion of inking units for screen-process printing can be very brief. Screen-process printing does not have independent inking units: the ink is carried in the screen which serves as both image carrier and fountain; the ink is transferred by the squeegee which provides the necessary printing pressure and is therefore classified as part of the printing unit. In some screen-printing machines, ink spreaders or ink funnels are used which could be considered parts of inking units. But generally speaking, screen process does not have independent inking units at all.

Section 4:   Sheet Feeders

The third of the four main units of printing presses is the feeding unit. It has the function of storing the stock to be printed, which may be either sheets or rolls of material, and of positioning it correctly for making the impression. The other three press units, the printing unit, the inking unit, and the delivery unit, are each the subject matter of a single section, but the feeding unit is here discussed in two sections: sheet feeders and sheet feeding are discussed in the present section, whereas roll feeding and the related web control is the subject matter of Section 5. One reason for discussing these two kinds of feeding separately is their lack of common equipment, or even equipment elements. Another reason is that roll feeding is needed for a much wider range of stocks than sheet feeding. Most sheet feeders handle primarily, if not exclusively, paper and paper boards. Feeding units are sometimes used for the feeding of metallic foils laminated to paper and, most rarely though, for the feeding of plastic materials. Roll feeding is of course also a most widely applied method for feeding of paper and paper boards; methods for package printing,

such as flexography and rotogravure, use foils and plastics to a great extent. These materials, and others too, are printed in substantial quantities by web printing which requires roll feeding.

The present section is devoted to sheet feeders exclusively. Roll feeding and the related web control are the subject matter of the next section. Since paper was historically made in individual molds that produced individual sheets, sheet feeding preceded roll feeding which did not become practical until approximately one hundred years ago.

The subject of sheet feeding is here divided into three major portions: (1) hand feeding, (2) automatic feeding of platen presses, and (3) automatic feeding of presses equipped with impression cylinders. The third group includes rotary presses, which have, as you know, printing units consisting of two cylinders, and also flatbed-cylinder presses, which combine a flat printing-image carrier with an impression cylinder, sometimes called the paper cylinder.

Since hand feeding is the oldest feeding technique and affords many valuable hints for mechanical or automatic feeding, our discussion begins with it.

Hand Feeding

Hand feeding, at present practiced only in certain methods but not in general, was the rule for approximately four-hundred-fifty years of printing history. Hand feeding is much too slow to satisfy the needs of fast-moving presses which devour more sheets in an hour than a man can feed in the longest work day. Hand feeding is prohibitively expensive and therefore only used where its versatility counts more than its cost and where automatic feeding is either impractical or equipment for automatic feeding has not been developed. In the production of very short runs and in jobs that require longer press preparation in conjunction with short runs or with materials difficult to feed, hand feeding has still a place. But it is a precarious place of dwindling size. Hand feeding is not used anymore in contemporary letterpress printing exceeding a few hundred sheets, nor in sheetfed offset lithography and

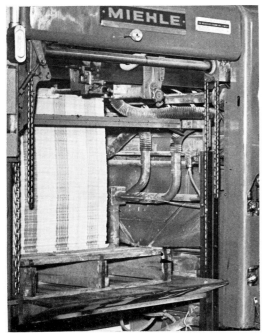

Courtesy Miehle-Goss-Dexter

A skid of paper in the pile feeder of a large Miehle offset press.

gravure. It still has its place in presswork done with open platen presses, in steel-die engraving, collotype, screen-process printing, and in some kinds of specialty printing.

Sheet Flow of the
ORIGINAL HEIDELBERG
Platen Press

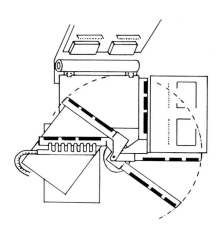

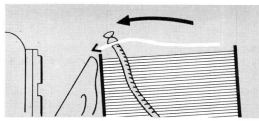

1 *The sucker bar lifts the top sheet from the feed pile. An air blast is directed into the feed pile from the front and sides of the feeder.*

2 *The rotating gripper takes the sheet from the sucker bar and transports it across the platen.*

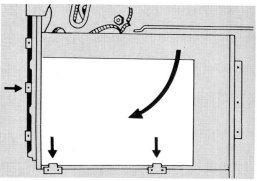

3 *In this position the gripper releases its tension on the sheet and allows the two bottom register guides to move the sheet obliquely to the side guide where accurate register is accomplished.*

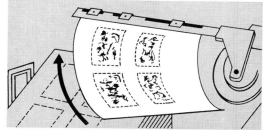

4 *After impression, the gripper again closes on the sheet and moves the sheet into the delivery. A traveling air blower follows the sheet into the delivery assuring maximum stability even on tissue.*

The Original Heidelberg Platen Press is a high-speed job press designed to print the normal run of small job printing. In addition, this press is capable of performing such operations as perforating, numbering, die-cutting and embossing. The range of stock is from tissue to 10 ply cardboard. A similar model press accomplishes roll leaf stamping and hot embossing.

The Heidelberg obtains its high speed and high impressional strength by employing a stationary type bed and a swinging platen driven by a toggle-lever system. Attached to the swinging platen is a rotating gripper head carrying two mechanical feed grippers. Each gripper serves the same function; it takes the sheet from the sucker bar that lifts the top sheet from the feed pile and transports it 90 degrees into printing position. After impression takes place the same gripper peels the sheet from the printing form and transports it another 90 degrees to the delivery pile. At the time the sheet is released by the gripper in the delivery, the opposite gripper is picking up a sheet in the feeder to commence another printing cycle.

This system means that there is no hesitation of the platen in the open position. The sheets are being fed simultaneously with the closing of the platen and remain on impression for one-sixth of the entire cycle.

A description of hand feeding could be omitted at this place because hand feeding is part of press-work which is discussed in the next chapter. There is, though, a good reason for describing some of the techniques whereby sheets of paper are hand fed: hand feeding must cope with the same tasks as automatic feeding and is therefore well suited as an introduction to automatic sheet feeders. These are not the same for all kinds of printing equipment, but since sheet feeders for presses that have an impression cylinder are of greatest industry-wide importance, the following description of hand feeding is limited to that on presses of this nature.

Hand feeding on presses equipped with impression cylinders. Two kinds of presses fall in this class: flatbed-cylinder and rotary presses. Both kinds were hand fed in the past. We have chosen to describe hand feeding on an offset lithographic press, but could have just as well selected a flatbed-cylinder press since hand feeding, and also automatic feeding, of either kind is essentially the same. "In the feeding by hand the first thing the feeder must do is to separate the top sheet from those under it. To do this he wears a rubber finger-tip on one finger or has a glycerin pad for moistening this finger on the feed board. With a light touch of the finger he buckles the corner of the top sheet; he uses his thumb for a stop or a snubber. When a bulge is formed, he continues the pinching action and grasps the sheet. The next thing he does is to give the sheet a quick waving action that sends a wave of air beneath the sheet to float it. He then guides the sheet which floats on air, down to the front stops, and registers it to the three guides. Automatic feeders use the same general principles."[140]

If we want to identify the operational features of hand feeding, we can name these: (1) the separation of individual sheets from the pile of stock, (2) the forwarding, or advancing, of the sheet to the registering device, and (3) the registering or exact positioning of the sheet for printing. We will meet these three functions again in the discussion of automatic sheet feeders. Feeding of sheets on presses that have impression cylinders is completely divorced from the delivery of the printed sheet. This operation is usually performed in some way by the press itself.

Automatic Feeders for Platen Presses

Automatic feeders for platen presses are distinguished in several points from feeders for presses having an impression cylinder. The most obvious point is that feeders for platen presses are mechanisms which take care of both feeding and delivery, whereas the feeders on presses equipped with impression cylinders are completely independent of the delivery which is a different unit. Another point worth noting is that feeders for platen presses must place the sheet directly on the platen in its correct position, whereas feeders for presses equipped with impression cylinders register the sheet outside the printing unit in such a manner that it can be mechanically inserted into the gripper mechanism of the impression cylinder.

The following discussion is divided into four points: (1) the Chandler & Price feeder, (2) the Kluge Automatic Press feeder, (3) the Original Heidelberg feeder, and (4) special feeding attachments to platen presses. The first two feeders are automatic feeders of domestic manufacture, the third feeder is imported from West Germany. The fourth point includes a number of attachments for the feeding of envelopes and for the handling of bulky stocks.

The Chandler & Price feeder. The Chandler & Price Company of Cleveland manufactures several models of platen presses which differ also to some extent in their feeders. On Chandler & Price "Craftsman" presses the feeder is in front of the press, but the delivery is on the side at a right angle to the feeder. "Four separate functions are performed by the Chandler & Price automatic feeder during each cycle of the press: (1) the feeder separates one sheet from the top of the unprinted pile of paper; (2) the feeder arm lifts the sheet forward into the bottom guides and releases it; (3) a swinging register fork grasps the sheet and moves it sideways into contact with the side guide; (4) after the impression the delivery arm descends, lifts the printed sheet and deposits it on the delivery table. Both the feeder and delivery arms use vacuum suckers to grasp the sheet."[141]

The Kluge Automatic Press feeder. The Kluge Automatic Press feeder is a part of platen presses manufactured by Brandtjen & Kluge in St. Paul, Minn. It differs from Chandler & Price feeders mainly in the arrangement for storing the paper in the feeder; the stock does not lie flat but stands on its edge in the Kluge feeder. The feeder is on top of the press, the printed paper is removed to a delivery table where it does not stand on its edge but lies flat as usual. "Unprinted sheets are held standing on their edge on a feeder table at the upper front of the press. Each sheet is carried from this table to the guides and, after being printed, is delivered to a table located under the feeder table. The actions which the feeder performs during each complete cycle of the press are: (1) the feeding arm, which is swung from an overhead support, grasps the bottom of a sheet that is separated from the front of the pile by an air blast, raises the sheet slightly to aid the separation from the second sheet, and pulls forward to complete the separation; (2) in an arclike swing the feeding arm begins its travel forward rapidly, decreasing its speed as it approaches the guides, releases the sheet at the guides and returns as the platen starts to close; (3) a finger holds the sheet at the bottom guides, moving down and off the sheet slowly, while the side guide moves toward the sheet to touch it and push it sideways into accurate register; (4) after the impression the delivery arm approaches the back margin of the sheet in a raised position, lowers to grasp the sheet, withdraws the sheet and deposits it on the delivery table. Both the feeder and delivery arms utilize vacuum suckers to grasp the sheet."[142]

The feeder for Original Heidelberg platen presses. The feeder for Original Heidelberg presses is again a horizontal feeder. It is placed in front of the press and the delivery table is next to it. A distinguishing feature of the Original Heidelberg feeder is the arrangement by which the sheet is fed and removed after printing. The sheet is carried from the feeder table to the platen by a rotating gripper. This gripper remains on the sheet in all but hairline register work during the impression period and removes the sheet onto the delivery table after it is printed. A modification of this method of positioning the sheet is required for hairline register. Then the sheet is released for a brief moment from the gripper and pushed toward

a side guide for final positioning. After taking the impression, the same gripper closes again and removes the sheet as if it had been printed in it. "The actions which the feeder performs during each complete cycle of the press are: (1) vacuum suckers lift the top sheet which has been separated from the pile by an air blast and hold the sheet for transfer to the gripper; (2) the gripper grasps the sheet, then makes a one-quarter turn down and to the right until it holds the sheet parallel to the right-hand edge of the platen; (3) the gripper holds the sheet in this position while the platen closes and makes the print; (4) as the platen opens, the gripper swings through another one-quarter arc to the right and upward until the printed sheet is directly over the delivery table; (5) the gripper opens and drops the sheet onto the delivery table. At the same moment the second gripper is picking up the next sheet to be carried into the press."[143]

Special attachments to platen presses. Platen press feeders can be equipped with a number of special purpose devices. It is, for example, possible to feed two sheets at the same time, provided they are of the same thickness and together do not exceed the maximum size of the sheet. Another often-used attachment is the die-cut envelope feed table. This attachment makes it possible to feed envelope blanks of an irregular shape and therefore not suitable for the standard feeder. If envelopes, heavyweight papers, and paper boards are to be printed in relatively large quantities, the use of the standard delivery is not practical, and it can be replaced with a continuous delivery which makes it possible to remove the printed product as it comes off the press. Most press manufacturers provide also other attachments, but these are too specialized for our discussion.[144]

Sheet Feeders for Flatbed-Cylinder and Rotary Presses

The kind of feeders to be discussed in this unit are used on presses that have impression cylinders. Since such presses are the vast majority of all sheetfed presses, these feeders are generally known as sheet feeders, disregarding the fact that the feeders of automatic platen presses also feed sheets of paper. Sheet feeders are practically the same for letterpress, indirect relief printing, offset lithography, and sheetfed gravure though they differ in the detail of construction and operation depending on make and age of various models. The

subject of sheet feeders is divided into four major portions: (1) general exposition of sheet feeders, (2) sheet separation and forwarding, (3) sheet registration and insertion, and (4) descriptions of various kinds of sheet feeders.

General Exposition of Sheet Feeders

The steadily mounting importance of sheet-feeding equipment, its perfection, and increase in speed are a response to the quest for ever higher and faster production, the most characteristic trend of contemporary printing. "The automatic devices for feeding the paper into presses opened up a new era of speed and lifted the direct rotary and offset presses out of the 1,500 sheets-per-hour-class into the 3,000 impressions-per-hour-class. Speeds have been mounting steadily ever since; speeds of over 7,000 impressions per hour are common today. The speed of offset presses is no longer limited by the feeder but by the registering devices. The automatic feeder was not universally accepted by all press manufacturers and lithographers for many years after its invention, but by 1920 it had become standard equipment on all offset presses."[145] One of the consequences of the development work resulting in different kinds of sheet feeders is the lack of a clear, descriptive terminology. The customary traditional terminology poses no difficulties to those active in the field but is often puzzling to others. For this reason the discussion is opened by a systematic classification of sheet feeders.

Classification of sheet feeders. Sheet feeders are classified by two characteristic features: one is the quantity of paper that can be stored in the feeder and the manner in which additional paper can be added; the other feature is the construction of the forwarding mechanism and the manner in which the sheets are forwarded to the press. If the paper is stored in large piles, which may be whole skids of paper in larger models, the feeder is classified as "pile feeder." Until very recently the reloading of pile feeders required interrupting of presswork. This interruption is not necessary with "continuous feeders" which take a much smaller amount of stock but can be reloaded while running. Classifying feeders by their forwarding mechanisms, we have two different kinds: the more recently developed "stream feeders," which forward the sheets in an underlapped stream, and the older types of feeders which forward a single sheet from the pile to the press in each cycle of the press.

Originally all feeders had the same forwarding mechanism, whether they were pile feeders or continuous feeders. In that period the names "pile feeder" and "continuous feeder" were clear and distinctive. This situation changed when stream feeding, and the forwarding mechanism which makes stream feeding possible, became widely used. Now it was necessary to use a different designation for stream feeders and for those that do not stream feed. Then various distinctive adjectives were introduced to modify the word "feeder." Some industry people speak of "sheet-by-sheet" feeders, or of "successive" sheet feeders in contrast to stream feeders. In this manual many machines and processes which were originally unique but later lost this position, are labeled "conventional" or "traditional," thereby distinguishing them from newer developments serving similar purposes though in different ways.

It is worth noting that both pile feeders and continuous feeders can be built either as traditional, sheet-by-sheet, feeders or as stream feeders. Theoretically this means that designating a feeder solely by its forwarding characteristics still leaves open whether it is a pile feeder or a continuous feeder. Practically this is not so, since in the pressroom pile feeders are the rule and continuous feeders the exception. Therefore, you will find that sheet feeders are discussed disregarding the distinction between pile feeders and continuous feeders. This distinction is losing its importance because most modern presses are equipped with pile feeders which can be reloaded while in operation. Such feeders are actually "continuous pile feeders" and are so named in this manual.

Another recent innovation in sheet feeding is the introduction of sheeting machines that sheet rolls of paper to the required size (which can vary within certain limits) as part of feeding. These machines are mainly used with stream feeders. In this manual they are classified as "sheeter-feeders" to distinguish them from other sheeting machines which are used by paper mills and paper converters, and also from "sheeter-deliveries" which sheet the printed web and are part of the delivery system of many web printing installations.

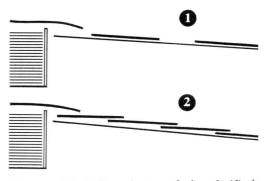

Diagram of single file and stream feeding. In (1) the sheets are fed single file with a distance between them; in (2) the stream fed sheets move in an underlapped stream.

Traditional and stream feeders. Traditional sheet feeders are, as already mentioned, sometimes called sheet-by-sheet or successive sheet feeders. In both types, traditional and stream feeders, the sheets are successively separated, forwarded, and registered. The difference between traditional and stream feeders is that in a stream feeder the next sheet is started toward the press before the preceding sheet has cleared the pile. *In stream feeders the sheets go down the feed board in an underlapped stream, whereas traditional sheet feeders forward the sheets to the press single file, with space between each sheet.* The advantage of a stream feeder is that the speed, or velocity, of the sheets moving toward the press is reduced in proportion to the amount of overlap of the sheets in the stream. Stream feeding permits higher press speeds without requiring sheet velocities as high as those needed in conventional feeding at the same press speed. As will be seen in the operational descriptions of sheet feeders, forwarding and forwarding mechanisms are technically the main points of difference between traditional and stream feeders.

Sheet Separation and Forwarding

All modern sheet feeders for printing presses operate by a combination of vacuum and air blasts whereby the two principal functions of sheet separation and of forwarding are performed.

Preliminary sheet separation. The top sheet must be separated from the sheets remaining in the pile. (Every sheet to be printed becomes sooner or later the top sheet, just as it was part of the pile before sheet separation.) Sheet separation is done in two stages; the first is preliminary separation, the next is final separation. Preliminary separation takes place only at the edge of the sheet. (The separation edge is the *rear edge* in stream feeders and the *front edge* in traditional feeders.) Preliminary separation is generally accomplished by "combers" (which are small driven wheels with beads forming their outer surface) or by air blast against the top edge of the pile, or by a combination of combers and air blasts, accompanied by suction-cup separators that complete the lifting of the entire edge of the top sheet. Both combers and air blasts have the function to compel a slight separation of the top sheet at the points where the lifting suckers touch it. Combers and air blasts counteract any tendency of the vacuum from the suckers of "striking-through,"

or penetrating the top sheet and exerting suction on one or more sheets underneath. *Striking-through* would result in lifting not only a single sheet but two or more sheets, which must not happen.

As the edge of the top sheet is lifted away from the pile, especially at high speed, a void is created under the sheet which must instantly be filled with air. If it is not instantly filled with air, the partial vacuum created by lifting of the top sheet will tend to lift and disturb the following sheet. This disturbance is prevented by a variety of means, including air blasts, flipper springs, brushes, and other mechanical devices, and one or more "foot clamps" or "goosenecks" that hold down the upper sheets of the remaining pile and prevent their shifting out of position during forwarding. Some types of foot clamps also serve as air nozzles and pile-height detectors.

When the entire edge of the topmost sheet is raised free of the pile under control of the suction separators and the following sheet is held firmly in position on top of the pile by the foot clamps—or on small feeders by a single foot clamp—preliminary separation is completed. Next comes final separation and forwarding.

Final sheet separation. During final separation the entire remaining and as yet not completely separated area of the sheet is floated on a film of air. This floating the total sheet on air is accomplished by blasting strong jets of air under the edge of the sheet held up by suction separators. The faster the press is operated the stronger these air blasts must be, since it is essential that the top sheet be completely separated over its entire area prior to forwarding. The completely separated sheet is ready for forwarding. But before this operation is described a brief explanation of the decisive difference between stream feeders and conventional feeders will be found helpful by many readers.

Forwarding mechanisms of traditional and of stream feeders. When the differences between those two kinds of sheet feeders were first mentioned, it was pointed out that technically these differences are mainly expressed in the forwarding of sheets and forwarding mechanisms. Now we are ready for their explanation. In stream feeders, the forwarding suckers are located at the rear edge of the sheet. The sheet is actually urged forward by the movement of blast air under the sheet and merely restrained and controlled in its motion by the swinging forwarders at the rear edge. *Being located at the rear enables the for-warders of a stream feeder to pick up and com-mence forwarding the succeeding sheet as soon as the top sheet has advanced a few inches.* The sheets are forwarded into the feeder rollers in an under-lapped stream, and the forwarding and separating mechanism have virtually a full press cycle in which to perform their function.

In traditional, sheet-by-sheet, feeders, the for-warders are usually located near the leading edge of the pile and pull the sheet into the feed rollers or onto the feed board. In consequence of this location the forwarding mechanism cannot go to work again until the entire sheet, which is in the process of being fed, has cleared the pile. *Forward-ing mechanisms separating the leading edge of the sheet must perform all their functions in a small fraction of the press cycle—actually in that portion of the cycle which is represented by the space between sheets.* This space can be clearly seen on traditional sheet feeders.

Forwarding of sheets. The pile of paper in the feeder is separated from the press itself by the feedboard, often called "ramp," which connects the press and the paper pile. The separated sheet is first forwarded a few inches into the bite and control of feed rollers by means of swinging or reciprocating forwarder suckers. Now the sheet has left the pile and arrived at the ramp. The ramp is an inclined plane which contains means for the forwarding and the registration of the sheet. These differ for different models, but in general the sheet is moved down the ramp by forwarding rollers and pull-in wheels, as well as by a series of tapes.

In traditional feeders the sheets move down the board singly and with some space between each sheet. The sheets must therefore move a distance which is equivalent to the maximum sheet length plus the space separating sheet from sheet. This distance must be traversed by each sheet during each press cycle; the sheets must therefore move at high speeds, particularly on larger or faster presses. In order to prevent the sheets from strik-ing the front guides with too much force, a *slow-down mechanism* must be employed on sheet-by-sheet feeders. When stream feeders initially re-placed traditional feeders, slowdown mechanisms were no longer needed since the lapped stream of sheets made it possible to reduce forwarding speeds. This situation has changed; presses are op-erated much faster, and, at present operating speeds, the speeds of sheets even in a stream are

such that slowdowns are needed again. In addition to slowdowns, introducers are needed to control the introduction of sheets to the front guides. *Introducers* usually consist of reciprocating vacuum shoes or moving guides, possibly in combination, operating from beneath the feed board on the leading edge of the sheet as it ap-proaches the front guides,

Sheet Registration and Insertion

The forwarded sheet must next be registered and inserted in the gripper mechanism which attaches the sheet to the impression cylinder for making the impression. Registration and insertion must make sure that the sheet will be correctly posi-tioned during image transfer. It is customary to distinguish three different registration and inser-tion systems: (1) the three-point guide system in combination with tumbler-grippers, (2) the feed-roll system, and (3) the swing-gripper system.

We begin the explanation of sheet registration and insertion with a brief description of the first mentioned, the three-point guide system in com-bination with tumbler-grippers because its under-standing "is essential to a better understanding of other systems."[146] First we turn to a discussion of side guides, which determine the register of the sheet sideways, and of front guides, which align the sheet at its gripper edge and determine the front margin. After the explanation of guides fol-lows that of tumbler-grippers.

Side guides and front guides. As mentioned be-fore, two kinds of guides are needed for register-ing the sheet. Their total number is at least three and may be as high as five: one side guide and two, three, or even four front guides. Side guides can be of different constructions. They either pull or push the sheet in order to register it. For the regis-tering of paper, "pull guides" are preferred, whereas "push guides" are used for exceptionally thick papers and for paper boards. The construc-tion of front guides varies for different registration systems. "In the simple three-point register sys-tem, the guides are mounted on a shaft which is above the feed board. The guides can be moved sideways along this shaft in order to properly balance the particular size of the sheet being run. The guide itself is essentially a flat face-plate. In the simple three-point register system, the sheet is held to its guides until the impression cylinder grippers take hold. At this time the front guides, or stops, are lifted out of the path of travel of the sheet. Where the three-point register system is

Pressman adjusting the side guide of a sheet-fed press. In this close-up the right hand of the pressman is on the hand crank (outside the press guarding) which is turned for fine adjustment. His left hand is on the pull-type guide itself. Not shown in the picture is the two-sheet caliper, or choke, which throws the press off impression if more than a single sheet is fed. The choke is adjustable for different papers.

supplemented by an insertion device, the general principles of construction are similar. However, in these cases the front guides are generally constructed so as to drop down, clearing the forward part of the sheet after the gripper on the insertion device takes hold of the sheet."[147]

Both front guides and side guides are rather limited in the extent to which they can be moved; the exact figures depend of course on the make and model of a press, but the move made by pull guides for registering is usually a fraction of an inch. "There is a good reason why the movement of any front guide is limited to not much more than ⅛ of an inch. It is because moving the guide will change the amount of bite that the gripper gets. On some presses the bite can be changed from 3/16 to 5/16 inch without getting into trouble. Any less bite than the safe minimum, and the sheet may pull out of the grippers; any more bite than the safe maximum, and the sheet may be misregistered or torn by some of the grippers."[148] The gripper bite is of interest not only to press-operating personnel, but also to people who design printed material and to those who plan its production.

The tumbler-gripper system. The three-point guide registration system is often combined with the tumbler-gripper system for holding the sheet to the impression cylinder. Tumbler-grippers are housed like other kinds of cylinder grippers in the gap of the impression cylinder. They are called "tumbler" because they are operated by a mechanism that opens them a full half turn and tumbles them closed. There is no insertion device to put the sheet into the gripper openings. The grippers are tripped and grab the sheets as they go by. Presses that do not employ tumbler-grippers must have an insertion device to carry the sheet to the cylinder. This device inserts the edge of the sheet into the gripper opening. There are two generally used types of insertion devices: the feed-roll and the swing-gripper type.[149]

The feed-roll insertion system. The decisive feature of feed-roll registration is "over-feeding." *Over-feeding* means that the sheet is forwarded at a higher speed than the surface speed of the cylinder on which the gage pins are located. This higher speed, or over-feeding, assures that the gripper edge of the sheet is firmly registered against the gage pins or cylinder stops when the grippers close on the sheet, thereby achieving perfect front register. The following description explains how the feed-roll system works.

The sheet is preregistered and side-guided as it comes down the feeder ramp. "While the sheet is at rest, it is firmly gripped in its preregistered position by being pinched between upper and lower feed-rolls or cams. The front guides then drop down or lift up (whichever the case may be). As soon as they are clear, one set of feed-rolls starts rotating and positively drives the sheet against

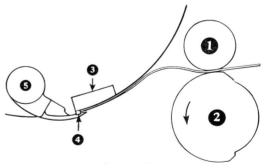

Diagram of feed roll system. The pre-registered sheet is propelled between upper feed roll (1) and lower feed roll cam (2) against the register bar (3) and register stops (4) on the transfer cylinder. The cylinder grippers (5) secure the sheet on the cylinder and transfer it to the impression cylinder in register position.

gage pins which are located either on an intermediate cylinder (sometimes called a feed or transfer cylinder) or on the impression cylinder. When the sheet is inserted into the grippers, it is held against these cylinder stops until the impression cylinder, feed cylinder, or transfer cylinder grippers have closed firmly on the sheet. Where an intermediate feed or transfer cylinder is used between the feed board and the impression cylinder, complete control of the sheet is maintained by having the grippers of the intermediate device positively grip the sheet while the impression cylinder grippers close on it. For a short distance of travel, both sets of grippers are actually holding the sheet."[150] The fact that the sheet is held by the grippers of both cylinders for a brief moment during transfer from one cylinder to another is a common one; you will meet it again in the discussion of deliveries of high-speed sheet-fed presses.

The swing-gripper insertion device. The swing-gripper insertion device is a bar of grippers swung in an arc from a shaft running across the press. The sheet comes down from the ramp and is stopped by the front guides. The gripper bar, with the grippers open, is ready for the sheet which enters their opening. The sheet is side-guided; then the grippers close, the guides move out of the way, and the gripper bar swings toward the gap of the impression cylinder, accelerates and inserts the gripper edge of the sheet into the cylinder gripper opening. As the bar contacts the stops on the cylinder, the cylinder grippers close. For an instant, both sets of grippers hold the sheet. Then

the swing-grippers release the sheet and the bar swings back to its receiving position, ready for the next sheet.[151]

Each of the described registration and insertion systems is capable of doing a good job. Which of these systems is used on a given press depends on considerations related to the design and construction of a press.

Description of Various Kinds of Sheet Feeders

In the two preceding units you were acquainted with the essential functions of sheet feeders. But there are many other points of interest in addition to sheet separation, forwarding, and registration. These will now be discussed. Even though we must concern ourselves mainly with pile feeders as the most widely used kind of sheet feeders, this unit contains brief descriptions of sheeter-feeders and of two widely known continuous feeders.

Several important features of pile feeders. Some of the more important features generally present in pile feeders are here briefly characterized. The pile of stock must be continually raised to the extent to which stock is fed. *Automatic pile-raising mechanisms* take care of this task. They include several controls. "First is the automatic pile-height control which maintains the pile at the correct height for continuous feeding. Second is the control for raising and lowering the pile by power and third, the manual raising or lowering system."[152] The pile-height control is commonly called the *pile-height governor;* it is adjusted at the setting, or preparing, of the feeder for a particular run. Pile feeders are usually equipped with several

Courtesy Miller Printing Machinery Co.

Pressman adjusting the register bar of a sheet-fed offset press. The register bar of this model can be moved in or out and bowed (concave or convex) by adjusting three calibrated dials. You see the pressman as he adjusts the dial closest to him by turning a screw with the small Allen wrench in his hand. Another dial is in the center and a third (not shown) at the other end of the bar. The grippers across the bar are shown in a closed position; during operation the grippers open when the sheet, driven by the feed rolls, arrives for final registration.

means for discontinuing feeding. Some of them are automatic, others are manually operated. Here we merely mention one automatic safety device, the two-sheet caliper. The *two-sheet caliper* prevents two sheets from going through the press at the same time. This safety device is set to pass a single sheet, and as long as single sheets are fed the two-sheet caliper remains inoperative. But when two sheets are fed together, most two-sheet calipers trip the press—meaning that it is taken off impression—shut off the power, and apply the brake. The two-sheet caliper, or two-sheet detector, is often called the "choke" by pressmen. Other calipers "may be built into the side guide; they trip the press if a sheet is not where it should be when the impression cylinder grippers come into their taking position."[153] Some automatic sheet detectors operate completely mechanically, others use vacuum or are based on electrical devices.

The feeder must be perfectly timed with the press; changes in speed must be made for both press and feeder at the same time. As vacuum and air blasts play a key role in the separation and forwarding of sheets, feeders are equipped with one or more pumps for air pressure and vacuum.

The capacity of sheet feeders. The capacity of the feeder depends on the design of the press. Domestic letterpress equipment has large feeders, whereas some European presses which are not built for long-run printing have less capacious feeders, as you may remember from the description of single-revolution flatbed-cylinder presses. The number of sheets held by a feeder varies for thicker and thinner papers. Pile feeders for large presses take skids of paper which may weigh one ton or more, depending on sheet size and kind of paper.

The reloading of pile feeders. Older pile feeders were not designed for reloading during running. On such feeders presswork must be interrupted for reloading the feeder and also for emptying the delivery. The most modern feeders are continuous pile feeders which can be reloaded without press stoppage. But it is also possible, as will be explained immediately, to equip conventional pile feeders for continuous feeding.

A main reason for developing continuous pile feeders. The spread of high-speed offset lithographic presses gave the impulse to the development of continuous pile feeders because in lithography interruptions of presswork are not only losses of production but can also become

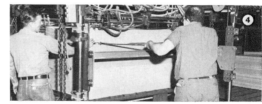

Courtesy Miehle-Goss-Dexter

Some steps in continuous pile feeding: In (1) reload rods are inserted to support the paper in the feeder. In (2) all rods are in, the operator switches feeder controls to reload position. Then (3) a new load of paper is placed in the feeder. In (4) the reload bars are removed. The feeder continues feeding during all operations.

harmful to printing quality. Each interruption may cause a more or less serious disturbance of the ink-water balance which is essential in offset lithography. (Ink-water balance is explained in the discussion of lithographic presswork, Chapter VII, Section 4.)

These disadvantages are avoided by continuous pile feeders, since the press is not stopped during their reloading. The means whereby standard pile feeders can be equipped for continuous feeding are relatively simple. "On some of the smaller presses thin rods are fastened to a flat bar at one end and sharpened to a point on the other, forming a sort of square fork. When all but approximately a thousand sheets have been fed, the fork is inserted in grooves that have been cut in the top of the elevator board. The rods are now under the paper and rest on supplementary elevator bars. The sheets continue to feed and rise when the elevator proper is lowered and reloaded. When loading is complete, the new pile is raised until it contacts the rods. The rods are then pulled out and feeding continues with no interruption."[154] The detail of operation is not the same for small and for large presses but the general principle is. As continuous loading of the stock has the purpose of avoiding stoppage of the press, "there is little reason for making the loading of feeders continuous if the press has to be stopped for unloading the delivery. So, small presses with such feeders have the same general idea built into the delivery. The large presses generally employ a double delivery where delivered sheets may be switched from one pile to the other."[155]

Sheeter-feeders. Rolls of paper are less expensive than sheeted paper, and on presses which consume quantities of the same paper, it has been found economical to introduce equipment whereby rolls of paper are sheeted to the size required for the job in hand. The sheeted paper is then fed to the press as usual. Such equipment is classified as sheeter-feeders in this manual; other names met in the literature are "web-sheet feeder" and "roll-sheet-feed" or "roll-sheet-feed system." In such a system "the sheets cut from the web pass over the regular feeder and go directly to the forwarding rollers. From then on, the sheets are handled by the usual method. When the roll feed is not used, it is merely disconnected. It can be set up to handle single or double rolls. The sheets are overlapped as they go down the feeder ramp, the same as in stream feeding. So all the advantages of the stream feed system are retained. This method of

roll-sheet-feed will operate at the highest speed that the press will register and print."[156]

The above-described method sheets the roll of paper and feeds the sheeted paper in the direction of the sheet passage through the press, by-passing the regular pile feeder altogether. This arrangement restricts the system to feeding of sheets cut from the roll with paper grain "short," meaning that the paper grain is parallel to the direction of sheet feeding. Paper with grain short is in some cases disadvantageous. (Paper grain means the direction of paper fibers; the subject is discussed in Chapter VIII.)

"Another type of web/sheet feeder has recently been developed for medium size offset presses wherein the roll feed and sheeting mechanism is at right angle to the press. The sheeter produces an overlapped stream which passes over the pile feeder, around a drum, and thence into the regular pile feeder where it forms a small pile only a fraction of an inch high under the feeder separator mechanism in the same position as the top of a standard pile. The sheet feeder then separates and forwards the top sheet of this small pile into the press in the normal manner, while the pile is continuously replenished from beneath by the roll sheeter."[157]

This unit cannot be ended without mention-

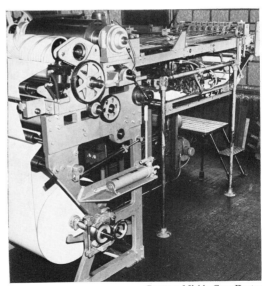

Courtesy Miehle-Goss-Dexter

A Web/Sheet Feeder that sheets a roll of paper and permits feeding grain long as customary in offset lithography.

ing two continuous feeders which have no provisions for storing large piles of paper. Such feeders were the only kinds of continuous feeders before continuous pile feeders were developed.

The Cross and the Christensen continuous feeders. Continuous feeders feed from an overlapped bank of sheets fanned out on a board. One of the most popular continuous feeders was the Cross feeder, so named after its inventor. The Cross feeder is no longer used on presses because it is a sheet-by-sheet feeder and for this reason not fast enough for contemporary press speeds. However, the Cross feeder is still widely used in the bindery for the feeding of folding machines. (Folders are described in Chapter X, Section 4.) The Christensen continuous feeder is used on some modern high-speed presses, as it is a stream feeder based on the same principles of sheet separation and forwarding as other stream feeders. It is not necessary to discuss these two continuous feeders in the present context; their distinguishing feature and principal advantage is no longer important in the pressroom since the introduction of continuous pile feeders.

Section 5:   Roll Feeding and Web Control

The feeding unit of presses for the printing of paper, paper boards, and plastics is either a sheet feeder or roll-feeding equipment. As explained in the section on sheet feeders, the feeding unit has the functions of storing the printing stock in the required quantity on the press and of positioning it for making the impression. Roll feeding is the feeding method used in web printing where continuous webs of stock are processed. Roll feeding and web controls are interrelated subjects and are therefore combined for discussion in the same section.

Web printing is done in many printing processes and produces many different products. National magazines of general interest are web printed in letterpress, rotogravure, and offset lithography. All metropolitan newspapers are produced by newspaper relief printing, smaller newspapers increasingly by web offset. Another most important field for web printing is package printing which uses many different stocks. Package printing on paper and paper boards is done in letterpress, flexography, rotogravure, and web offset, whereas package printing on plastic films is done in flexography and rotogravure, as a rule. Magazines that are part of Sunday newspapers and therefore called "newspaper supplements" are printed in huge quantities by rotogravure.

But web printing, and roll feeding with it, is not restricted to mass-production printing of publications and package material. It can also be used for the printing of books, catalogs, and advertising material. Web printing is further important in several kinds of specialty printing, forms printing in particular. Even though much web printing equipment is designed as single-product machinery, web printing is also used in the service business. Many job-and-commercial printing plants have web-offset presses.

Each printing method has its own characteristics, but these are of lesser importance for roll-feeding equipment than the requirements inherent in the manufacturing needs for different products. Such requirements express themselves in the design and in the selection of various kinds of roll-feeding equipment and probably even more in the kinds of web controls incorporated in particular installations.

The following explanation of roll feeding and web controls is divided into seven units: (1) introduction to roll feeding, (2) equipment for roll feeding and splicing, (3) margin control in roll feeding, (4) tension controls, (5) web break and web splice detectors, (6) web controls for high-speed full-color printing, and (7) ink controls in full-color printing and web viewers.

Introduction to Roll Feeding

Roll feeding was originally developed for the production of metropolitan newspapers by relief printing; other applications of roll feeding are based on equipment originally designed for newspaper production. It is not difficult to find the reasons why the newspaper industry pioneered in the development of roll feeding. Newspaper printing is perhaps that branch of the printing industry which has intrinsically the tightest production requirements. On the one hand, a newspaper should be printed as late as possible because it must include the news up to the very latest moment; on the other hand, the newspaper must be available for sale at the customary time at which the public is ready to buy. The newspaper business is traditionally an exceptionally competitive business. At present, fewer papers compete for readers in the same area, but radio and television have become new and rather serious competitors. As these media can convey the news to the public without much delay, almost instantaneously, newspapers feel constrained to strive for inclusion of the very latest news. The time when the papers must be on the street is fixed, and there are only two ways in which this need for inclusion of later and ever later news can be satisfied. One is shortening the distribution time, the other is increasing the speed of production. Since the speed at which rolls of paper can be fed to the Moloch press depends not the least on roll-feeding facilities, roll-feeding equipment occupies a key position in newspaper printing. Designers of roll-feeding machinery have devised a number of different roll-feeding methods, depending on different speed requirements and on differences in the length of the press run.

Relations between roll-feeding equipment and length of press run. The length of run is the controlling factor in the selection of roll-feeding equipment. Length of run and production time are closely related in newspaper printing; short-run papers obviously have less tight production schedules than metropolitan dailies. Newspapers having small editions that can be produced with a single roll of paper per printing unit need the least complex roll-feeding equipment. As the number of rolls needed per printing unit mounts, more complex roll-feeding equipment becomes necessary. This relation between length of individual runs and roll-feeding equipment exists in all kinds of web printing.

Number of papers yielded by rolls of newsprint. This point will become clearer if we consider the number of papers which is yielded by a roll of paper. "Rolls of newsprint vary from 36 to 40

inches in diameter. A 40-inch roll will print about 13,500 to 14,000 newspapers. A full-size roll is four standard pages wide, and the width of rolls varies from 60 to 72 inches, depending on the format of a newspaper."[158] The number of newspapers which can be printed from a roll is, as you see, rather small. Many American newspapers published in larger cities have editions of several hundreds of thousands. As the standard roll prints approximately 14,000 papers of 16 standard pages, a simple calculation shows that approximately seven rolls are needed for each hundred thousand papers, always, of course, per printing unit. Multiply this figure by the number of printing units, which can easily be seven or more, and you get an inkling of the problem presented by roll feeding. But the full magnitude of this problem will not be appreciated until it is realized that the putting of each new roll into feeding position requires the connecting of the expiring roll with the new roll. If the whole press must be stopped, even for a very short time, whenever a new roll is needed, efficient long-run printing is simply out of the question. The many-page, long-run American metropolitan newspaper could not exist under such conditions. Depending on the total number of rolls to be fed for the whole press run and depending on the time element, various kinds of roll-feeding equipment are employed.

Various kinds of roll-feeding equipment. The simplest type of roll-feeding arrangement provides for a single roll of paper for each printing unit. This kind of roll-feeding equipment is called a "roll stand." The next kind is feeding machinery that holds two rolls. One is actually fed and the other is ready for feeding when the first roll is consumed. The "two-roll stand" reduces the time needed for press shutdown but does not eliminate interruption in production. "The efficiency of the

   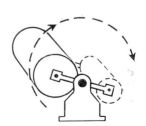

Single roll stands, double roll stands, three-roll reel stands and two-roll turnover reel stands are four kinds of roll-feeding equipment. The first two require stoppage of the press and manual splicing or pasting; the second two make either semi-automatic or fully automatic pasters without press stoppage.

rear mounted roll stand decreases rapidly when the circulation goes beyond the number of papers that can be printed with three consecutive rolls of newsprint. For roll stands designed to take a 40-inch roll this would be approximately 40,000 papers."[159]

Roll stands were superseded by "reels" (short for reel stands) as carriers of paper rolls. The word reel was originally used for a revolvable device on which yarn or thread is wound. It is usually a frame consisting of a horizontal axle with spokes radiating from the hub near each end and horizontal bars on slats connecting these in pairs."[160] Reels for the feeding of paper rolls are giants if compared with those for yarn. They hold either two or three rolls which are resting on their spokes, known as "spiders."

Reels make it possible to supply the press with a flow of paper on several technological levels. In the simplest form, the press must be stopped for joining the new roll to the expiring one; on a technically higher level are systems which permit uninterrupted production and are operated by the pressman. Systems that function without intercession of human beings are fully automatic and are on the highest technological level. All rolls must be prepared for the step of joining the expiring web to the new one, or of "making the paster," as the trade calls it. Roll preparation varies somewhat for different methods and different systems of pasters. (The word paster is now used to indicate the equipment that makes the connection between the two webs. As mentioned before, this connection and its making is also called paster. Trade terminology is often puzzling for the tyro, but it must be remembered that such confusion is much more likely in writing and reading about a subject than in doing the work. The working situation makes such misunderstandings much less likely.)

Equipment for Roll Feeding and Splicing

The following discussion concentrates on the methods whereby rolls of stock are connected for continuous printing. But it must be pointed out that roll stands and reels are also equipped with various devices that are related to speed control of the moving web and that the proper speeds of the expiring roll and of the new roll are essential for mechanical splicing. At this point we do not broach the subject of web control, which is for the sake of simplicity deferred to a following unit where tension controls will be described. But it

should be understood that mechanical roll splicing cannot be done without such controls.

Our discussion of roll splicing is divided into the following five points: (1) roll preparation, (2) manual splicing of rolls placed on roll stands, (3) manual splicing of rolls placed in reels, (4) semi-automatic pasters, and (5) fully automatic pasting systems.

Roll preparation for feeding. The roll of paper is first placed in the roll stand or the reel and firmly secured in the correct position. Then the roll is prepared for pasting, or as this operation is also called, "splicing." Pasting can be done by hand or by mechanical equipment. For hand-pasting, the new roll of paper is prepared "by tearing a straight edge, a 'V' nose or a 'W' nose. With a 'V' or 'W' nose the leading edge has one or two triangular points to help lead the web-through the press."[161] When the running roll is close to its end, the press is stopped and the web is severed from the roll, usually by tearing, and attached to the new roll either with an adhesive or with gummed tape. Roll preparation for automatic pasting is not uniform; it depends on the system used on a press. Generally speaking, it follows the same lines as preparation for hand-pasting. In addition to V or W noses, timing marks or timing devices are needed for automatic pasters. Some of this detail will be mentioned in the following descriptions of pasting systems.

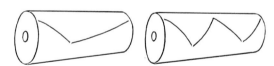

The paper roll at the left is prepared for splicing with a "V" nose; that at the right with a "W" nose.

Manual splicing of rolls placed on roll stands. Roll stands are used for web printing of relatively short production runs. Roll stands cannot be equipped for mechanical splicing. Wherever they are the feeding equipment, the press must be stopped for joining the new roll to the expiring one. Roll stands can be equipped for holding either one or two rolls. Stands holding two rolls save the delay which is caused by placing the next roll on the stand and therefore permit shorter interruption of running than single-roll stands. Roll stands are also known as "unwind stands" or as "spindle stands." The reason for the name "spindle stand" is that the roll is supported by a steel shaft or spindle, which goes through the core of the roll.

The techniques of splicing vary. In newspaper printing where several printing units, each requiring its own roll of paper, are needed, splicing poses problems different from those met in other kinds of web printing where only a single web passes through the press. This is usually the case in package printing. A web press for package printing may have several printing units, but these are needed for multicolor or full-color printing on the same web.

In newspaper printing the whole press must be stopped when only one of the several rolls needs splicing. Repeated stopping can be strongly reduced by an interesting technique: "To eliminate a number of stops during the run, the press is usually started with new rolls. All of these rolls will expire at nearly the same time, so the press is stopped and new rolls are spliced to the web. At the end of the day's run, the unused portions of rolls, called 'butts,' are replaced with full rolls. The butts are stored until enough have accumulated to rewind into a 36- or 40-inch diameter roll. Rewinding takes place on the roll stand. An electric motor is attached to the spindle that is holding the butt, usually one that was left in the press for this purpose. Another butt is spindled and placed in the roll stand. After the splice has been made, the electric motor is started which will wind the paper to the 'rewind' roll. Several butts are spliced and rewound. When the 'rewind' roll reaches a 36- to 40-inch diameter, it is ready for use in the press."[162]

Manual splicing of rolls placed in reels. Reels can be either part of the press structure or they can be independent units having their own pedestals. The second kind is more common than the first. They may be equipped to hold two or three rolls of stock. Reels for long-run production, such as needed for metropolitan newspaper printing, usually hold three rolls. One is the "running roll"; the second is the roll prepared for splicing, often called the "ready roll"; and the third roll, usually known as the "loading roll," is the roll which will take the place of the ready roll and be prepared for splicing when the second roll becomes the running roll. Each of the three rolls is individually supported by two arms of the spider, one on each end.

In package printing, reels often differ in physical size, progressing from a small two-roll unit handling 9-inch rolls of cellophane (which may or may not have provisions for inserting of turn-over arms for flying splicing) to heavy-duty roll stands capable of handling four rolls up to 72 inches in diameter, weighing 2,000 pounds or more per roll. But while they vary in size, the function of all reel carriers remains basically the same: "to support the roll and its core shaft on antifriction bearings and to supply a braking or holding force to prevent the roll from running away at a red button stop."[163]

For manual splicing the press must be stopped, whether the roll of stock is on a stand or in a reel. Reels not equipped for mechanical splicing save time as the new roll can be put into running position by a simple rotary motion. But the great advantage of reel stands is not realized unless they are combined with mechanical splicing equipment.

Semiautomatic pasters. In all pasting or splicing systems the new rolls must be put into the reel stand, and they must be prepared for splicing in accordance with the system used. There are, though, substantial technological differences between systems that must be timed by the pressman and those which do not require timing. The first kind of equipment is here classified as semiautomatic, the second as fully automatic pasters.

The distinction between semiautomatic and fully automatic pasters is not new but it is not always made in the industry. There semiautomatic pasters are either called "automatic pasters" or "flying pasters." The invention of the flying paster was a great event in roll feeding, which became thereby much more efficient. Since the introduc-

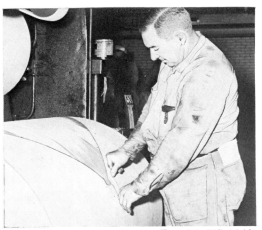

A paper roll is being prepared for automatic splicing.

tion of the flying paster more mechanized pasters have been developed which can be considered fully automatic, whereas flying pasters are semi-automatic equipment.

Semiautomatic pasters can perhaps be best explained by describing the Wood Autopaster which was introduced in 1931. This invention made it possible to run high-speed newspaper presses "at full speed during the printing of the entire edition, thus ending the stoppages, delays and large paper waste which were inherent factors in paper replenishment."[164]

The Autopaster (and other mechanical pasters as well) "includes devices for (1) bringing a new roll up to surface speed of the web prior to splicing, (2) pressing the old web against the new roll to make a splice, (3) severing the old web after the splice has been made, (4) moving the web pressing and web severing devices to the inoperative position, and (5) automatically rotating the reel with the newly spliced roll so that it bears against the tension straps and is controlled thereby in the tension of the web."[165]

Operationally, the following steps are required. First the second roll must be prepared for splicing. This step includes unwrapping, inspecting, and the cutting of a W nose which must be precisely positioned. "The roll is then indexed with two Autopaster tabs, one each at the bottom of the W nose. The other ends of the tabs are attached to the next course of the paper on the roll. The tabs are supplied with a dry adhesive coating and are moistened before application. The operator thereafter applies glue or another adhesive to the leading edge of the roll. Often he puts a small colored flag at the top of the W nose and extends this flag over the edge of the roll, which serves as a signal for the pressman at the delivery end of the press. The flag makes it easier to locate spliced papers, which are not saleable, and to remove them. Then the new roll is put in position for splicing. For this purpose the pressman has a roll positioning gauge."[166]

The operator must also time the splicing mechanism, and he must watch the decreasing diameter of the roll as it comes near the point of expiration. "When the running roll reaches approximately 6 inches in diameter, the operator presses the button *Lower*. This energizes a complex mechanism which moves the arm with the brush for pressing web to web into operative position and brings the new roll up to web speed. The operator watches the expiring roll and when there is approximately

¼ inch of paper left on the core, he presses the button *Paste*. This causes the brush to drop the web against the rotating roll and, as the glued W comes into contact with the running web, the two Autopaster tabs which have the purpose of keeping the roll together when it is brought up to speed are broken and the new web is attached to the old one. Within less than one revolution thereafter the knife automatically severs the old web, the brush returns to its inoperative position resetting the brush and knife for the next splice, and the reel automatically takes the newly spliced roll forward until it bears against the tension controlling straps. Then the reel stops automatically in its proper position."[167] Now the third or loading roll has become the second roll. A new roll is loaded in the empty spider arms, and the whole process of preparing the second roll for splicing begins anew.

The Wood Autopaster was the first of its kind, but many other equipment builders for the newspaper industry developed similar pasters. Among them are Cline, Goss, Hoe, and Scott who manufacture semiautomatic pasters which have each their own particular features. These are highly technical and therefore not discussed.[168]

Fully automatic pasters. As was described in the operational discussion of the Wood Autopaster, the pressman must perform a number of operations. "He must visually calibrate, or guess, the diameter of the expiring roll and initiate the changeover sequence by setting the paster switch and by pushing the changeover button. In some machines he must manually lower the paster arm into pasting position and he must operate the paster switch to make the splice, again visually calibrating, or guessing, the expiring butt diameter. Lastly he must raise the paster arm to its inoperative position following the splice."[169]

All these manual operations are eliminated by fully automatic pasters. Here we will briefly explain the workings of the equipment manufactured by R. Hoe & Co., of New York City, but it should be understood that other manufacturers of pasters have also developed fully automatic machines. The Hoe "fully automatic reel uses two tachometer generators, one of which supplies a signal proportional to press speed and the second a signal proportional to the speed of the expiring roll. These two signals are combined in the control circuit to give a diameter measuring signal which can be preset to automatically start the changeover sequence at a given diameter of the expiring roll and to actuate the pasting mechanism at the desired butt size."[170] Fully automatic pasters do not require other operative steps than roll insertion, roll preparation, and removing the cores of expired rolls.

Margin Control in Roll Feeding

Rolls of printing stocks must be placed in the feeding equipment in such a way that the printed image will be correctly positioned on the web. Roll-feeding machines are provided with facilities for this purpose. The means whereby rolls are adjusted for the correct sideways printing lay, or position, is called "side margin control" or "margin control" for short.

Margin control is accomplished by moving the roll of printing stock across the width of the press. The roll must of course be originally positioned in the feeding unit as correctly as practical, and margin control should be required merely for fine adjustment. Margin adjustment can be done on three levels: (1) manually, (2) hydraulically, and (3) electronically. In the following you find brief explanations of manually and hydraulically operated margin controls. Electronic margin control is primarily used for high-speed full-color printing and therefore discussed in the unit "Web Controls for High-Speed Color Printing" in the paragraph headed "Web guiding controls."

Manual margin control. Manual margin adjustment is done in roll feeding with roll stands. The means for such adjustments are rather simple. The roll is, as you may remember, supported by a strong shaft or spindle on which it is fastened at both ends. This spindle is connected to a threaded shaft and can be adjusted in its axial direction. The member that is fastened to the spindle and provides the means for moving the spindle is the "brake shoe," which is threaded itself and through which the threaded adjustment shaft runs. The threaded shaft itself can be turned by a simple handwheel in either direction. The rotary motion of the threaded adjustment shaft is translated into an axial motion by the inside threading of the brake shoe.

Hydraulitically operated margin controls. Hydraulically operated margin controls are used on reel stands. These controls are often called "automatic, but they are actually remote control systems. An electric motor pumps hydraulic fluid against one end of the reel shaft to move the rolls of newsprint in one direction. To move the reel

shaft in the opposite direction, the motor is reversed to pump the hydraulic fluid against the other end of the shaft. On some of the older reels a mechanical arrangement was used to move the reel shaft. The electric motor is controlled from a two push-button station control box. For each reel there is usually a margin station control box on the folder, on the unit, and at the reel stand. With the mechanical arrangement a crank can be used at the reel to move the reel shaft."[171] The preceding description is mainly valid for newspaper presses. Other kinds of web printing equipment may use hydraulic systems for margin control or accomplish the same result by different means.

Tension Controls of Web Presses

Control of web tension is one of the crucial points in web printing. "If printers were able to have only one perfect feature in a web press, that feature unquestionably would be a perfect web-tension system. Without it, constant control of register cannot be obtained nor maintained by either the printing units or in any subsequent in-line operation."[172] It has been said that web tension is a necessary evil in the operation of web presses for newspaper printing. "It is an evil since paper is relatively weak. It would obviously be less subject to breakage if the paper could be allowed to run into the printing units without subjecting it to any tensional strain whatsoever. However, web tension is necessary because it has not yet been found practical to operate a web press without tension on the paper. When there is no tension on the web, the print appears blurred for there is more paper pulled through the printing couple than required by the circumference of the impression and plate cylinders. The web or webs become loose traveling through the press and tend to walk or slide sideways, resulting in spoiling the printed product as the fold will be uneven and the cutting knives will not cut in the prescribed margins."[173]

Tension controls can be divided into manual, automatic, and electronically operated systems. The last kind, which is used in full-color web printing, is discussed together with other controls for high-speed color printing. In this unit you find brief descriptions of some manual and automatic web tension control methods. Most of the methods here described are used on newspaper presses for which they were originally developed. Some of these systems for controlling web tension were later applied to other kinds of web printing.

Manual control of web tension. Manual control of web tension is used on roll stands only and cannot be part of high-speed systems which need continuous adjusting of web tension. Manual control of web tension is often classified as core tension, since the controlling element acts on the shaft by which the roll is supported. (This shaft or spindle goes completely through the core of the roll.) In this type of tension control, brake shoes are used which are loosened or tightened with set screws. The extent to which they are adjusted is left to the judgment of the operator. Tightening increases tension and loosening has the opposite result.

Automatic tension control systems. Automatic tension control systems can be grouped into four: (1) core tension systems, (2) driven belt tension systems, (3) stationary belt tension systems, and (4) hydraulic tension control systems. Each of these four will be briefly explained.

There is first the automatic core tension system, called the *Jones Tension System* or the *Jones Tension Governor*, after its inventor, Thomas Jones.[174] This system combines the action of a floating roller with the action of brake shoes, as described under manual tension controls. Here the brake shoes are of course not manually tightened or loosened but by a number of mechanical devices such as levers and dash pots which are changed in their settings according to the position of the floating roller; this roller responds to changes in web tension and applies the corrective measures automatically. The Jones system can be used on reels but it is more widely found on web presses with roll stands, many of them serving other purposes than newspaper printing.[175]

The next system is the *driven belt automatic tension system*. The driven belt system uses either a leather or a composition belt that travels at a slightly slower speed than the surface speed of the roll. This belt exercises tension control by a braking action which depends in its extent on the contact area between the belt and the roll of the printing stock. The extent of this area can be influenced by lowering or depressing the belt in relation to the roll. This action, in turn, can be connected to a floating or "dancer" roller as in the Jones tension control system. Driven belt tension control systems do not scuff the surface of the paper, or scuff it less than the next described stationary belt tension control system. For this reason reels and pasters of presses for high-

Courtesy *The Bulletin*, Philadelphia

This picture shows how driven belts apply pressure to the paper roll thereby producing the required braking action.

grade magazine work involving coated or highly finished stock are equipped with running belts if they use belts for tension control.

In the *stationary belt tension system*, the belts are approximately 4 inches wide and made of copper or brass. The braking action comes about by their direct contact with the outside surface of the

Courtesy Miehle-Goss-Dexter

This picture shows how stationary belts apply pressure to the paper roll thereby producing the required braking action.

roll to which the stationary belts apply a varying amount of pressure. The pressure variations are initiated by a floating idling roller which rides on the web. "As the idling roller rises, due to the increased pull on the web, an electrical circuit or an air system decreases the pull on the stationary belt to release the roll. As the idling roller drops due to a slack web, the electric circuit or the air system increases the amount of pull on the belt to decrease the rate of rotation of the roll of newsprint. An idling roller and an electrical or air control system is also used with driven belt tension systems."[176]

The final group, *hydraulically operated tension control systems*, is not used on newspaper presses but widely in package printing, especially by gravure. Package printing has a fundamentally different web control problem from that in newspaper production. In the latter the printing stock is always the same disregarding unintended variations in the manufacturing of paper. But such variations are held within close tolerances. In package printing, a wide variety of materials must be handled, ranging from the thin plastic films to the much thicker laminated foils, and even to lightweight paper boards. Since the Champlain Constant Tension System is widely used in package printing, it is described as an illustration of hydraulic tension control methods. (There are, of course, also other tension control systems available for package printing.)

The basic assumption of the Champlain Constant Tension System is that the ideal tension under which the web should be fed into the press must be determined for each kind of stock and the "weight of the dancer roll must be twice the amount of the tension needed to have each side of the web carry its full load. In turn, this dancer roll is connected through linkage through the control valve of a hydraulically operated variable speed unit, which in turn drives the feed or metering rollers. Thus the feed rollers meter the correct amount of the web necessary to keep the dancer roll suspended and operating at a free-floating position. The dancer roll is solely supported by the web in this position imparting the correct preset tension to the web."[177]

Champlain published a table of basic dancer roller weights based on long experience. This table indicates the weight of the dancer roller per linear inch of web width for various printing stocks. The weight is from ½ to 1 pound for cellophane and other plastic materials; 2 pounds for paper up to a basis weight of 40 pounds; 3 pounds for paper above the basis weight of 40 pounds; for paper board up to 0.012 inch thick each linear inch of dancer rollers should weigh 4 to 5 pounds; for boards from 0.012 to 0.024 inch thickness this weight goes up to 6 pounds; and over 0.024 inch it becomes 7 pounds per linear inch of web width.[178]

The stop tension system. This system differs functionally from tension control systems since it does not have the object of controlling web tension during operation but has the only purpose of protecting the web from breaks when the press is suddenly brought to a complete stop, called "red button stop" in the industry. Due to its momentum, the roll of newsprint would continue to unwind without a stop tension control system. "The mechanics of the arrangement will vary with the type of tension system used. The effect in each case is the same. When the red button stop occurs the rotation in the roll of newsprint must be decreased at the same rate that the rotation of the printing couple decreases. If the roll of newsprint is stopped too rapidly, a web break will occur or if the roll of newsprint is stopped too slowly, the newsprint will unwind faster than it can be taken by the printing couple. The stop tension system must be adjusted with the press braking system to insure that the decrease in the speed of the press is the same as the decrease of the roll."[179]

Web-Break and Web-Splice Detectors

Web-break detectors are safety devices without which high-speed web printing would be impossible. Webs of paper can break or become torn for a number of different reasons. Considering the speed with which high-speed web printing progresses, the quantity of paper fed by the feeding equipment would be large and highly injurious if the press continued to run until the accident was noticed by operating personnel and the press was stopped by them.

The web that is fed after a web break has occurred will damage plates and particularly blankets, which are needed in newspaper relief printing and in web-offset printing. Other damages are waste of paper and loss of press time for getting the press again into running condition after a web break.

The function of web-break detectors. Web-break detectors are known under various names; but regardless of their trade names, they all have the same tasks. "The function of the detector is to reliably and faithfully stop the press each and

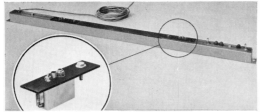

Courtesy Web Press Engineering, Inc.

A photoelectronic web break detector system. Web breaks are detected by reflected light, the sensors are from 2 to 6 inches above the web, out of contact with it.

every time a web break occurs. Although many ideas and innovations have been tried and worked on over the years, the simplest and most accepted method of detecting a web break in newspaper printing is still the arm and shoe riding on the web. When a break occurs, the shoe moves beyond the normal web pass and trips a switch which, in turn, stops the press. In the more recent web-break detector systems, the arm and shoe are made much lighter and do not depend on gravity as did the formerly used heavy arm and shoe for tripping the switch which controls the motor and shuts the power off. In these constructions gravity is replaced by a spring adjustable in its tension."[180]

Ultrasonic and electric eye web-break detectors. Ultrasonic web-break detectors were introduced by Meredith Printing, Inc., Des Moines, Iowa. This equipment is considered by its developers much more sensitive than the usual mechanical devices for web-break detection, as it is capable of detecting "slight tears at the edge of the paper web. Such a tear would mean the beginning of a complete web break and consequent risk of wrap up. Tearing of the web is detected by two ultrasonic units mounted on opposite sides of the web. A tear in the web is indicated by the closing of the sound path between the transmitter and receiver sensors which closes the control relay and shuts down the press."[181] Other modern web-break detectors use "photo electric devices with a light shining against the web. When a break occurs, the light activates the photo electric cell on the other side of the paper and a red button stop results."[182]

Web-severing devices and web impellers. Unfortunately, the mere stopping of the press is not sufficient for full protection. Two supplementary devices may be needed to insure the complete safety of the press. These are web-severing devices

and web impellers. First, a brief description of *web-severing devices.* "Web-severing devices are knife arrangements located directly under the unit or at the point where the web feeds into the printing couple. The purpose of the web-severing device is to cut the web when the web-break detector drops. If the web-severing device was not installed on the press, the paper being fed from the roll to the printing couple would continue to feed newsprint into the printing couple until the press came to a stop. This could take as many as fifteen revolutions of the printing couple, so there could be 15 layers of paper between the plate and the impression cylinder. At 0.003 inch layers of paper (which is the average thickness of newsprint) there would be 0.045 inch of paper between the plate and the impression cylinder. An increase of this size would result in damage to the plate, to the blankets of the impression cylinder or, possibly, to the press. The web-severing device keeps the amount of newsprint available for wrapping to a minimum."[183]

Now to the web impeller and its protective function. "The *web-impeller device* is a rubber wheel which carries the web away from the printing couple when the web break occurs. The rubber wheel is held just above the web as it goes over an idling roll. When the break-detector contacts close, a solenoid pushes the rubber wheel against the web to hold the web against the spinning idling roller. The momentum of the spinning idling roller carries the web away from the printing couple. This device keeps the printed web from wrapping back into the printing couple."[184]

Web-splice detectors. Splices are apt to cause trouble during printing, and spliced paper cannot be part of the final product which becomes unfit for sale if it contains splices. For this reason some presses are equipped with automatic impression-throwoffs and with splice detectors. "*Automatic impression-throwoffs* are used in conjunction with automatic pasters or with splice detectors. They automatically lift the impression when the splice passes the printing unit and automatically return the impression after the splice has passed. Automatic impression-throwoffs avoid both damage of the impression cylinder blanket by the splice and the pulling apart of the splice by the blanket. Splice detectors may also be used as a signaling device to the pressman working at the folder end of the press. He will remove products which have splices from the final delivery.[185]

Web Controls for High-Speed Full-Color Printing
High-speed and high-quality color printing has some problems which do not exist in newspaper printing, especially if it is done with black ink only. For this reason a separate discussion of web control in color printing is indicated. The problems and methods of coping with them are not exactly the same in all kinds of color printing. But it is nevertheless possible to divide the subject into three points which are of general validity: (1) various kinds of register in web printing, (2) automatic register controls for color and cut-off, and, (3) web guiding systems.

Various kinds of register in web printing. In full-color web printing, the following five kinds of register need to be distinguished: (1) side margin register, (2) back-up register, (3) cut-off register, (4) web-to-web register, and (5) color register. Some of these five kinds of register are not only important in web printing but also in the printing of sheets. These are back-up and color register as well as side margin register in its functional meaning, even though the term itself is not used in sheetfed printing. In black-and-white newspaper printing of more than a single web, four of the aforementioned kinds of register must be considered. The only exception is of course color register. In package printing which is usually done on one side only though predominantly in several colors, we count three kinds of register; color register is among them but back-up register and web-to-web register may be eliminated. All five kinds of register are present in multiweb color printing for promotional purposes, catalogs and magazines disregarding the printing method selected for a particular job.

Each of these five kinds of registers is now briefly explained. The *side margin register* refers to the correct positioning of printed images across the width of the web. The *back-up register* is concerned with the position of printed images on both sides of the web in relation to one another. Both sides of the printed web must have matching side margins as well as matching head and foot margins. The third kind of register, *cut-off register*, is needed in jobs that are sheeted or that are folded directly on the press. Cut-off register indicates the precise location of the cut which must be made across the web. In package printing, where webs may be rewound or subjected to inline conversion, there may or may not be a cut-off register. Cut-off register may be replaced by other kinds of register which refer to the specific con-

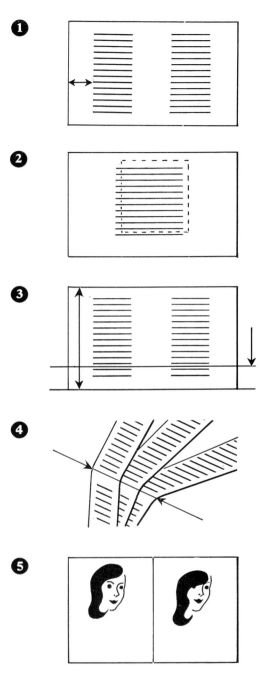

Five kinds of register in web printing: (1) side margin register, referring to position of printed images relative to edge of web; (2) back-up register, referring to correspondence of images printed on either side of web; (3) cut-off register, referring to correct position of cut-off; (4) web-to-web register, referring to position of associated webs; and (5) color register, referring to position of successive colors.

version operation; die-cutting and creasing of paper folding-boxes, for example. In all cases the location of printed images must be in correspondence with inline or fabricating methods, otherwise the final product would be disfigured, if not completely useless.

The fourth kind of register in our list is *web-to-web register*. This kind of register is of great importance in newspaper printing and in signature work, particularly in the printing of booklets and publications for which several webs are needed. As you will read in the discussion of folders which are integral parts of some web printing equipment, often several webs must be combined—or *associated*, to use the trade term—prior to folding and cutting. Web-to-web register refers to the correct relative position of several webs. The head and foot margins as well as the side margins of all associated webs must be the same. If they are not the same, the folded signature will not be properly aligned in the best case; in the worst case, some of the pages may be cut through the text rather than at the end of the foot margin. Obviously, improper web-to-web register is not acceptable and may lead to the complete waste of a job. *Color register*, finally, refers to the relation of colors printed successively one over the other. There are usually four different inks printed in full-color reproductions: yellow, magenta, cyan, and black. (In many pressrooms the magenta ink is traditionally called "red," and the cyan ink "blue." The difference between magenta and red, and between cyan and blue is explained in Chapter III.) The tolerances permissible in full-color printing are more or less critical. Successive color images must be exactly positioned, and the amounts of inks to be deposited should, ideally, not vary after inking has been properly regulated.

Automatic register controls for color and cut-off. Automatic color register controls have the object of assuring the correct lay, or position, of color images. A complete control system for full-color printing must, in addition, provide controls for correcting irregularities of ink supply during the press run. Color register includes control of the web in both dimensions, in its length as well as across its width. At this point we concentrate on control systems for the proper lengthwise image lay. As proper lay of images in the direction of the web is a prerequisite for correct cut-off, the two subjects are so interrelated that they are best discussed together.

Controls for color register and cut-off are based on the electric eye. Even though electric eye register control systems differ widely in the detail of their construction and operation, all systems make provisions for the four basic requirements needed for color control. These are: (1) measurement, (2) comparison, (3) computation, and (4) correction. "The measuring element in the automatic register control system is the photoelectric 'web scanner' which scans a register mark printed on the web. The 'error detector' is the control unit or computer which determines the time-space relationship of the register mark with the desired position and generates an error signal or correction signal which operates the compensator motors to effect the required change in register."[186]

Detecting and measuring of the error in register are only preliminary steps for its correction. "There are two basic methods of adjusting register between successive prints. One is by changing the amount, or length, of the paper web between two adjacent printing units. The other is by changing the angular positions of the printing cylinders in adjacent units relative to one another."[187] The first method is called "web-compensation" and requires a compensator roller, the second method is called "cylinder compensation" and does not influence the length of the web but the position of the printing member of the press. This method uses a combination of gears.

The needed adjustments are made by correction motors. A "correction motor is a simple, reliable induction motor without brushes and fitted with a brake to prevent overshooting. It is coupled through a reduction gear box to the register mechanism of the press. This mechanism may be a movable roller which alters the length of paper between printing units, or it may change the angular position of the printing cylinder through a differential gear. Electrical impulses from the control cubicle cause the motor to make quick and accurate correction."[188] The preceding description refers to Crosfield color register control equipment. Other register control systems may differ in certain technical points, but all aim at the same result.

Our next subject is *cut-off register*, often also called *print-to-cut register*. This kind of register refers to the relation between the printed images and the cuts which must be made across the web either in sheeting or folding. "Print-to-cut register of sheeters and folders presents a serious problem in multiweb-offset presses. A large percentage of waste can often be traced to misregister at the cut. The webs have traveled through a drier, and some change has taken place in the length of each pattern. Also, the shrinkage is not uniform throughout the entire roll and will vary from one part of the roll to another. Tension changes can cause stretching or even slipping of the web. In addition, the cutting action of the cutting cylinder or knife can produce a pulling effect which can change from cut to cut. The greatest percentage of cut-off misregister occurs during start-ups, slowdowns, and at paste cycles. Any sudden change in tension will produce errors. When the press is up to speed, the cut-off register holds fairly well, and not as many corrections are required."[189]

Cut-off controls are installed on the delivery end of the press on both sheeters and folders. They are essentially based on the same principles as register controls. The register marks are read and interpreted by the control equipment, and correction is made by adjusting the length of the web prior to cutting.

Web guiding controls. Where color register control systems are installed, these can include the control of the side margin, but there are also independent web guiding systems available which have acquired particular importance in the flexographic industry, especially in package printing. Web guiding systems eliminate or reduce waste because they permit "buying roll stock just wide enough for the job. In fact, when running jobs two, three, or four wide, slitting can be done on the press prior to rewinding with no trim on the outer edges. A separate slitting operation is thereby saved."[190] Automatic web guiding equipment resembles in its essential points the already described color control systems. "The elements of web guiding, or side register control systems, as they are sometimes called, are: (1) an error-sensing device; (2) a power source; and (3) controls to transmit error signals and corrective forces. Error-sensing mechanisms vary in their design as the application requires. When the operation requires that a guideline be followed, a photoelectric scanning head is used. It is possible to use air pressure or vacuum-type sensing heads exclusively in a plant, by starting at the press with automatic guides, thereby positioning the print accurately with respect to the edge of the web. In succeeding operations the edge of the web can be used as a guideline, making its printing unnecessary. Vacuum-type sensing kits generally transmit a signal in the form of changing pressure to a diaphragm as the web moves to cover or partially cover holes in the error-sensing head. The signal is then amplified and controls the movement of an air or hydraulic cylinder which does the work of moving the unwind roll or changing the position of the guiding roll."[191]

Ink Controls in Full-Color Web Printing and Web Viewers

The quality of the printed image depends to a great extent on the correctness of ink application. This is particularly true in full-color printing. Ink controls which adjust the printed ink deposit are used on high-speed web printing equipment where a continuous control of ink is often indispensable.

Low- and high-viscosity inks need different control systems. Automatic ink-control systems are different for control of low viscosity inks and for those of high viscosity. Letterpress and offset lithography use high viscosity inks whereas low viscosity inks are typical for gravure and flexography. The viscosity of letterpress and offset inks for high-speed web printing is considerably lower than that of letterpress and lithographic inks formulated for printing on sheetfed presses, but there is still a strong difference in viscosity between letterpress and lithographic inks for web printing on the one hand and flexographic and gravure inks on the other. These differences in viscosity account for differences in the equipment for ink control.

Explanation of electronic ink control. The function of all automatic ink controls is similar. "Basically all of these controls act like a self-calibrating densitometer installed on the press. The scanning head measures the density of the colors that have just been printed and compares the density of the print to an established density of the approved color, preset into the controls. The controls then average density readings for consecutive revolutions and correct the color density."[192]

Inks for gravure which are, as you know, very fluid, can be adjusted "by actually changing the pigmentation of the gravure ink mixture. If the color becomes too light, ink is added, and if the color becomes too dark, extender is added. The controls compensate for cylinder wear, doctor blade wear, paper absorbency and even for variations in the color of the paper itself."[193] A number of different control systems is available; among them is the Crosfield Idotron which is designed for fluid inks. Letterpress and offset inks are much too viscous for the aforementioned method of color adjustment. Therefore the Crosfield Inkatron, which is designed for color control of viscous inks, "changes the over-all amount of ink being transferred from the ductor roller to the form rollers. It maintains an even ink film thickness and will increase the amount of ink being transferred when the color lightens, and decrease the over-all amount when it darkens."[194]

Both Crosfield color control systems use a scanning head which reads color patches. "A rotary shutter, driven synchronously by the timer, makes the scanning head function only in that area of the web on which the color marks are printed. Signals from these color marks are picked up by the scanning head once every cylinder revolution. The normal position for mounting is after the last color unit of the press, and one head will handle up to six different colors simultaneously. It has been designed to operate in areas where explosive fumes are a hazard."[195]

Each ink tank of gravure ink is equipped with a device to measure viscosity. This device is connected to the main control panel and "electrical signals are produced which are proportional in strength to viscosity changes and these changes are recorded on the control panel. A change in viscosity above a predetermined value causes the solenoid valve to open and inject into the tank sufficient solvent or ink to return the viscosity to normal."[196]

The Inkatron, which is based on original research initiated by the Printing Packaging and Allied Trades Research Association (PATRA), Leatherhead, England, makes automatic density readings throughout the whole press run and maintains a consistent ink density throughout the entire run. It is equipped with a scanning head, a control cubicle, and relays which operate the solenoids or electric motors which adjust the feed of the inking rollers. "For every cylinder revolution the signal from the scanning head is passed to the computer in the control cubicle. The computer selects from the signal voltages proportional to (*a*) the white of the paper; (*b*) the ink density of the color; and (*c*) a black. The computer now compares the white-to-ink density measurements with the white-to-black measurements and from these values derives a steady voltage which is always proportional to the ink density, regardless of the lamp brightness or the phototube sensitivity. This voltage controls the meter indicating ink density. It also controls the relays which operate the solenoids or electric motor which adjust the feed of the inking rollers."[197]

Web viewers. High-speed package printing has many problems of its own. One of them is related to the fact that printed webs are frequently rewound in package printing rather than subjected to inline fabricating after they leave the press. "However, the increase in press speeds created the problem of checking register and printing quality of the fast-moving web while the press was in operation. Unless the operator stopped the press, he saw nothing but a blur as he looked at the web. With sheetfed presses or where the printed material is folded, sheeted, or fabricated inline, it is possible to examine printing quality at the delivery end of the press and to check color and register. With material being rewound, this is impossible."[198]

The problem of inspecting high-speed webs in motion prior to their rewinding "was solved with the development of web scanning or viewing equipment which produces a stationary image and permits inspection of printed material without slowing the web travel and cutting production speed. Not only can register be checked, but color variations can be seen so that ink color and viscosity adjustments can be made to correct any

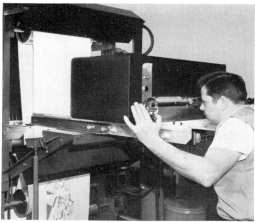

Courtesy National Laboratories and Manufacturing Corp.

Web viewers are needed when the printed web is rewound. In the Scan-A-Web *a system of rotating mirrors produces the effect of optically stopping the moving web. This makes it possible for the pressman to inspect the running web.*

deficiency. There are three basic types of web viewers: (1) viewers with a single oscillating mirror; (2) viewers with a revolving drum multiple mirror; and (3) viewers with a stroboscopic light—a light synchronized to go on and off at high speed to correspond with the press revolution speed."[199] With web viewers, the pressman can inspect the web in any desired area; magnification devices are often built into the equipment, and he is in a position to judge the printing quality of the web almost as well as if he were inspecting printed sheets. Web viewers have consequently become important adjuncts of high-speed package printing equipment.[200]

Section 6: The Delivery Unit

The delivery unit is the last unit of printing presses. The sheet or web is first fed by the feeder or by roll-feeding equipment, then it passes through one or several printing units bearing image carriers inked by the corresponding number of inking units. The printing unit performs the impression, or as it can be said in terms of images, applies the printed image to the stock. After this image is applied, printing in the sense of image transfer is completed. In sheetfed presses the printed stock passes directly into the delivery, in web presses the web is either delivered without drying or first put through forced drying equipment.

The final press unit is called by printers the delivery. Deliveries can be divided into two major kinds, those for sheetfed presses and those for roll-fed ones. Deliveries of roll-fed, or web presses, are not all the same. The printed web may be rewound at the delivery for later fabrication, or for combining with another printed web, or for subsequent printing on its other side on a newspaper press. This kind of delivery is called either "rewind delivery" or "rewind." Another kind of web delivery cuts the printed web into sheets; it is called "sheeter delivery" or simply "sheeter." Then there is the "folder delivery" or the "folder" which assembles a number of printed webs into a newspaper or delivers signatures of books or periodicals. Folder deliveries are needed in newspaper printing, magazine work and job-and-commercial web printing. Finally, the printed web can be delivered "inline," meaning that it is converted by fabricating as printing progresses.

The present section comprises therefore five units: (1) deliveries on sheetfed presses, (2) rewinds and sheeter deliveries, (3) folder deliveries for newspaper relief printing, (4) folder deliveries on magazine and on web-offset presses, and (5) inline deliveries.

Deliveries of Sheetfed Presses

Not all kinds of presses have mechanically operated deliveries. In hand-fed platen presses, the pressman removes the printed paper with his left hand and places it on a delivery board which has no mechanical elements whatsoever. Flatbed-cylinder presses, which were the mainstay of letterpress printing for the past 75 or 80 years, had originally no delivery units. "In the days of hand presswork fly boys were often employed to take the printed sheets off the tympan to expedite the work for the pressman. On the first power presses, the delivery of the printed sheet was done by boys until a mechanical fly was devised."[201]

Four kinds of deliveries for sheetfed presses. The constant demand for faster presses, which necessitate ever higher precision, has changed deliveries not less than other units of the press. The four kinds of deliveries here discussed are: (1) the fly delivery, (2) the carriage delivery, (3) the tape delivery, and (4) the chain delivery. The *fly delivery* is completely outmoded and can be seen at present mainly on direct lithographic presses converted for collotype. "It is usually a large frame of long sticks or fingers attached to a bar which moves on an axis, receiving the printed sheets from the impression cylinder and turning them over upon a receiving table."[202] Carriage deliveries and tape deliveries are outmoded because they are too slow and because they do not permit precision sheet control. In both the carriage and the tape delivery, the sheet is removed from the impression cylinder with sheet lifters, or "shooflies," and stripper fingers. In the *carriage delivery* the sheet is put on the delivery pile by a reciprocating carriage, in the *tape delivery* by a series of conveyor tapes. The only important contemporary type of delivery on presses equipped with impression cylinders is the chain delivery.

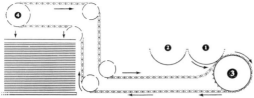

Chain delivery of a sheet-fed offset press. The chain delivery consists of two endless chains carrying correctly spaced gripper bars which deliver the printed sheets face-up. The sheet is held by the grippers of the impression cylinder (1) and receives the impression from the blanket cylinder (2). Then it is transferred to the gripper bar of the delivery at the transfer cylinder (3). This cylinder has two sprockets which drive the chains. When the sheet is in delivery position the grippers open automatically, and the chains return at (4), the front wheels. The unnumbered rolls are supporting idlers.

The chain delivery. The chain delivery is the only type of delivery which proved to be suitable for high-speed flatbed-cylinder and rotary presses. It can be operated quite fast and permits excellent sheet control. As offset lithographic presses are at present the fastest sheetfed presses and as they have high precision chain deliveries, their deliveries will be here described. (Chain deliveries are also used in flatbed-cylinder and rotary presses for letterpress as well as in presses for other printing methods.) "The function of the delivery mechanism is to carry the sheets forward from the impression cylinder and deliver them face up on a pile properly jogged. The chain delivery consists primarily of two endless chains carrying gripper bars which are spaced so as to bring a bar in position to receive a sheet at every press revolution. A skeleton cylinder, carrying two sprockets, provides the power for driving these chains."[203]

The sheet is held by the grippers of the impression cylinder during printing. After the impression the printed sheet is transferred to the delivery gripper which comes around the skeleton cylinder into transfer position. During transfer the sheet is held for a fraction of a second by both the impression cylinder gripper, which will release it, and the delivery grippers, which have already closed. The sheet is therefore always under control. Firm sheet control is especially necessary in offset printing where some part of the sheet is usually still held on the blanket when its edge is transferred to the delivery grippers. Loss of control could mean that the sheet remains on the blanket, or is torn, instead of being removed from

it. How precise the transfer must be made can be illustrated by a simple calculation. Contemporary sheetfed offset presses have maximum rated speeds ranging between, say, 6,000 and 10,000 sheets per hour. This means that 100 to 170 sheets must be delivered per minute.

When the sheet is in the proper position for being deposited on the delivery pile, the grippers open mechanically, the sheet drops on the pile and must next be "jogged," or straightened. *Joggers* are simple mechanical devices consisting of three power-driven plates which act on three sides of the delivery pile. They are timed with the delivery mechanism and act at each revolution of the press by moving toward the delivered sheets, thereby pushing each new sheet into its proper position. After making contact with the pile, these three jogging plates move back from it; they return for the jogging of the next sheet.

Double deliveries and continuous deliveries. Some high-speed presses, particularly those for the printing of large size sheets in many colors, are provided with two delivery units, called double deliveries. These can be used in two ways. In one method, each of the two deliveries receives every other sheet, thereby giving the ink a little more time to set. The disadvantage of this method of operation is that both deliveries become filled at the same time and that the press must be stopped for removal of the delivered piles. If continuous operation is desired, the double delivery is used in

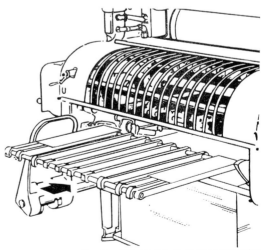

Continuous delivery of a sheet-fed offset press showing the sheet catcher.

succession. After one delivery is filled, the printed sheets are directed to the second delivery unit; the full unit is emptied and made ready to take the place of the second unit when it, in turn, will be filled.

Continuous delivery can also be accomplished by equipping a conventional delivery in a manner similar to that described in Section 4 under the head of continuous pile feeders. "Bars are inserted to hold a top lift of sheets long enough to allow a pile to be taken out and an empty platform to be put in. This makes it unnecessary to stop the press every time a pile is changed. A system of continuous feeding and delivery is especially helpful when running card stock."[204] The most modern presses have continuous deliveries just as they have continuous feeders.

Sprayers. Sheetfed presses often have sprayers at their delivery ends. Sprayers have the purpose of preventing wet ink transfer from the front of printed sheets to the back of the following sheets. This result can be accomplished either by wet or by dry sprays. In wet sprays, solutions of waxes and gums are vaporized and applied to the sheets; in dry sprays, a small amount of powder is sprayed on each sheet. "A few spray particles distributed over every square inch of the sheet prevent the next sheet from making an early and intimate contact with the wet printed image. The powder does not dry the ink, and an excess of powder does not improve drying. All that is needed is enough powder grains to help trap air between sheets. The air does the setting and drying by supplying oxygen to the ink; the spray gives the ink the necessary time by holding sheets apart for a short period."[205]

Rewinds and Sheeter-Deliveries

These two kinds of deliveries are here discussed under the same head because they are the least complex of all web deliveries. Rewinds are used primarily in package printing when the printed web must pass through fabricating operations which are not done inline for one reason or another. One example is the combining of different plastic webs by laminating. Rewinding is also needed for preprinted webs which must be perfected and combined with other webs on a newspaper press. Such webs are color advertisements, usually printed on one side in rotogravure, or possibly web offset. The other side of the preprinted web is perfected on a regular newspaper relief press, and the perfected web is combined with other webs for folding on standard newspaper folding equipment. For this reason the color-printed web is rewound in such rolls as can be handled like rolls of blank paper on newspaper presses.

Sheeter-deliveries cut the web into individual sheets. Such deliveries are needed in many branches of web printing. Sometimes rewind deliveries are operated in conjunction with slitters which trim the web on both edges or divide the full-width web into two or more narrow webs. Slitters are also widely used in folder deliveries.

Rewinds. Rewinding is done on roll stands which resemble those described under the head of roll feeding. The stock unwound from the roll at the feeding end of the press passes through the printing units and is again made into a roll by rewinding. But the problems related to each of the two operations, unwinding and rewinding, are not exactly the same. The roll to be unwound

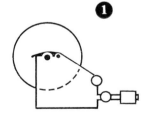 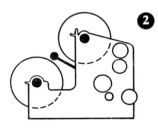 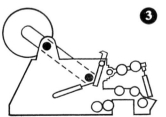

Courtesy Bobst-Champlain, Inc.

Diagrams of three different rewinds. The single roll rewind (1) is a basic unit for handling of paper and paper-backed foil. The hydraulic drive provides uniform roll build-up. The dual shaft, multiple core rewind (2) is used for rewinding paper, foil and plastic films after slitting. This model permits continuous operation. The continuous turnover rewind (3) is designed for rewinding of lightweight thin plastic films. Rewinding of such films requires highly sensitive controls to insure correct hardness and other essential characteristics of the rewound roll. This model has automatic web splicing.

arrives at the printer's or converter's plant in the proper condition. (It is often the product of rewinding in the plant of the manufacturer who supplied the stock.) For unwinding, the printer is less concerned with the roll than with the web, its tension and position in particular. In rewinding, attention must be concentrated on the new roll itself. "The basic function of a good rewind is to produce a straightly rewound roll without telescoping, wound to the desired tightness. This tightness will depend upon the material run or the type of printing thereon. The other function of the rewind is to rewind the web to the maximum diameter of the master input roll—for all types of materials from cellophane to paper board."[206] This wide range is necessary in rewinds for package printing; rewinds for preprinted paper webs do not need the same flexibility.

The tension of the rewound stock is particularly critical in plastic films because these can be easily distorted; distortion can be troublesome in subsidiary fabricating operations. "The tension of plastic materials must not exceed one pound per linear inch of web width and must be maintained throughout the roll."[207] The problem of maintaining constant web tension is too technical for a detailed discussion. Generally speaking, the rewind roll increases its tension as its diameter grows. As every revolution of the press and of the rewound roll adds stock to the latter, rewinding cannot be left to itself but must be well engineered and controlled. A number of different methods are used for the operation of rewind stands. Here we merely mention one of them which is often found in package printing, the Champlain "hydraulically operated constant-tension unit for uniform winding of large ranges of diversified materials."[208]

Sheeter deliveries. Deliveries that sheet the printed web are needed for a number of purposes. In package printing, for example, gift wrappings that are produced in large quantities may be web printed and then sheeted to the standard size in which such items are usually sold in retail stores. Another example is the sheeting of web-printed covers for widely distributed magazines. Some magazines with a large circulation print the insides of the magazine on lighter paper than that of its cover. In such cases the covers must be printed by themselves, usually on a different press than the inside signatures. The web on which the covers are printed must be sheeted before the magazine is bound.

As web presses are built to be run at high speeds, sheeter deliveries must be high-speed machines too. Depending on the purpose for which they are used, they may need adaptability for the sheeting of different kinds of materials, or they may be permanently used for a single kind of stock. Sheeters attached to presses for package printing belong in the former group, whereas those for magazine production fall in the latter. Sheeters must, further, operate at close tolerances in relation to the cut-off of the press. The cut-off is fixed in web printing equipment for letterpress and offset lithography; it is usually variable on gravure and flexographic presses for package printing. Sheeters for variable cut-off equipment must be adjustable for the length of cut-off within the range of the printing equipment with which they are combined.

Sheeters are made by several concerns and in various designs. We are limited to a brief characterization of a single sheeter and have selected one for package production. This sheeter is based on "the single rotary knife cutting-head system, consisting of a rotary blade (set on a shear angle) which passes a stationary knife and produces a scissor action to sever the web cleanly."[209]

Slitters. If the final sheet size is of the same width as the web, severing the web across its width produces the required result. It may also be necessary to divide the width of the web or to remove its edges in addition to sheeting. Such tasks are performed by rotary knives which are called "slitters." Slitters can be used as part of rewinding as well as of sheeting. They are of different construction for paper and plastics on the one hand, and for heavy-weight materials such as paper boards on the other. Where slitters are used for trimming the edges of the web, the delivery is usually equipped with a scrap duct which removes the scrap, shreds it, and transports it after shredding to a disposal unit.

Folder Deliveries of Newspaper Relief Presses

At the outset of this unit it must be made clear that the newspaper industry does not use the term "newspaper relief printing," and that it is not customary to speak of folder deliveries in any branch of printing. The reasons for introducing the term newspaper relief printing were explained in Section 1; speaking of folder deliveries has the purpose of emphasizing that folders discussed under this head are part of the press equipment in contrast with folders that can be independently operated. These are used in the bindery and discussed in Chapter X. It must further be repeated that the term "folder" comprises in web printing all machinery that follows the last printing unit, or when forced drying is needed, the last drying unit. (Newspaper printing does not usually require forced drying, but many other high-speed methods of web printing do.)

As mentioned during the discussion of roll feeding, the web unwound from a single roll can at the most produce 16 pages of a standard, or full-size, newspaper. Many newspapers consist of multiples of 16 pages, and many webs do not contain 16 different pages but two sets of the same 8 pages; a newspaper press must therefore print and combine several webs, which may at times be rather numerous. In single-color newspaper printing, each printing unit has its own web, and these webs must be handled by the press in such a manner that the final result is our customary newspaper. The equipment for the handling of webs can be best explained by a general description of its purpose.

The functions of newspaper folders. The folder has the task of making complete newspapers from a number of different printed webs. Assuming that the final product is a standard size newspaper, the folder must be capable of performing the following seven operations: (1) the folder must assemble the several webs in correct order, (2) it must be equipped to fold the assembled webs in the direction of the web, (3) it must sever individual newspapers or newspaper sections from the web, (4) if required, it must be capable of inserting sections in the proper order, (5) the final newspaper consisting of one or more sections must be folded in half, (6) the folded newspapers must be moved away from the press, and (7) they must be mechanically counted.

The part of the folder where several webs are associated is the "roller-top-of-former," or RTF for short. The long fold of the web is made by the "former plate"; severance of the web and folding of newspaper sections is done by a pair of interacting cylinders which are called the "cutting cylinder" and the "folding cylinder" respectively; removal of the folded newspaper is accomplished by the "delivery fan" and the "delivery conveyor"; the count, finally, is indicated by the "kicker."

Straight runs and collect runs. Before we begin the description of the various elements which are combined in folders for newspaper printing, two technical terms must be explained. These are "straight runs" and "collect runs." Both of these terms are needed in the printing with semicylindrical presses which have two rows of plates attached to the plate cylinder. The number of plates may be either two or four per row, but this difference is immaterial for the discussion of straight and collect runs. The point that makes a difference is whether the two semicylindrical plates which together cover the circumference of the cylinder are

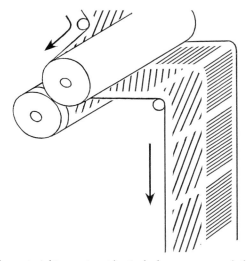

In a straight run, two identical plates are around the plate cylinder and all successive pages of the web are the same.

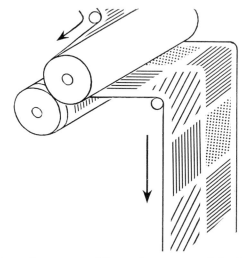

In a collect run, two different plates are around the plate cylinder and successive pages alternate on the web.

for the same pages or not. If two following plates are image carriers for the same page, the arrangement is known as a "straight run"; if each of the two following plates is for a different page, the run is called "collect." (Two adjacent plates in the same row are of course always different in the printing of standard size newspapers.)

The two or four plates which are side by side across the length of the plate cylinder result in two or four rows of printed pages in the running direction of the web. If the plate cylinder is plated with two identical sets of plates, one following the other, each of the two rows are the same. This kind of imposition is characteristic for a straight run. If the plate cylinder is plated with two different sets of plates, the printed web will not repeat the same page in sequence, but will have two different pages in alternation in the direction of the web. This kind of web with alternating pages is characteristic for a collect run.

Product differences of straight runs and collect runs. As already mentioned, a newspaper often consists of a number of sections. A straight run produces in each revolution of the press two identical newspapers, whereas a collect run produces newspapers consisting of two different sections. If the press is equipped with two formers, one above the other, four sections can be produced by the equipment without resorting to hand-inserting. Not all newspapers have the same attitude toward sectioning. In the Eastern United States single-section newspapers seem to be more often desired than in the Middle West and in the West. There the preference is more generally for multisection papers.

The controlling position of available press equipment. Whether a paper is run "straight," resulting in a single unsectioned product, or "collect," producing a two- or four-section paper, depends ultimately on the press equipment available in a given plant. Within the capacity of this equipment there is freedom of choice, but in many situations freedom of choice does not exist and the press equipment becomes the controlling factor; choice is overruled by necessity. Two examples will explain such situations. First we assume a press consisting of seven units, each unit capable of 8 pages (two times) in a straight run or of 16 pages in a collect run. If such a press is to be used for papers up to 56 pages, these can be unsectioned. But if the paper must contain a larger number of pages it must be printed on the existing equipment as two sections.

Just as freedom of choice is limited for those who prefer unsectioned papers it is also limited for those who prefer many sections. It was already mentioned that it is possible to produce on the press papers consisting of four sections. If a larger number of sections is desired, additional sections need hand-inserting, a delaying and expensive operation. Hand-inserting cannot always be avoided, particularly not in Sunday papers which consist of more sections than sectioned weekday papers. The magazine section of Sunday papers is often printed in rotogravure and supplied to the newspaper by concerns specializing in this kind of printing. Several other sections of Sunday papers are printed on newspaper presses, but they are printed during the preceding week and ready for inserting when the topical parts of Sunday papers are coming off the presses. Another reason for hand-inserting is the geographical limitation of certain sections which is a consequence of the gaining importance of suburbia.

Some reasons for sectioning of newspapers. American newspapers cover a considerable number of different fields. Some parts of newspapers are of general interest, others appeal to different reader groups. During the week these group interests are often satisfied by a single page or by a few pages which are not necessarily in different sections. But our Sunday papers expand the coverage of special-interest material substantially and may consist of many different sections. The number and the size of these sections varies from paper to paper, depending on local conditions and editorial policy. The main section, or sections, of a newspaper has general-interest information and features the daily news. An editorial or political section may be devoted to reviews of the past week's events, editorials, and the opinions of a number of political commentators. In larger cities newspapers may have cultural sections where motion pictures or new plays as well as concerts are reviewed. In the travel section the subject matter is traveling and vacations; in the women's section items pertaining to the running of a home; in the real estate section, housing; and in the sports section, outdoor and other competitive sports. Some papers have sections filled with classified advertisements, and, more recently, a book review section has been added by a few large papers. Each of the different sections carries in addition to editorial material display advertisements that are of interest to the readers of each particular section.

American newspapers can be rather voluminous, on Sundays in particular. "The largest paper ever printed probably was the September 13, 1964, issue of the *New York Times*. That issue, a Sunday paper, came 754 pages and used 4,814 tons of newsprint. The *New York Daily News* on Columbus Day, 1964, had 800 tabloid pages, but the total included 11 suburban editions; no issue included more than one of the suburban editions, of course. Other exceptionally large papers, published Thanksgiving, 1964, were the *Houston Chronicle* with 300 pages, the San Jose, California, *Mercury*, 148 pages; the Orlando, Florida, *Sentinel*, 254 pages, and the St. Louis *Globe-Democrat*, 168 pages."[210]

A reader particularly interested in one subject would have to wade through many pages before he could find what he wanted to read if the paper was not divided into sections. Sectioning is equally important to advertisers who want their advertisements placed where they will be noticed by prospective customers. Travel ads are therefore put in the travel section, homes for sale or apartments for rent in a section devoted to housing, and so on.

Each of several sections consists of a number of pages, depending primarily on the amount of advertising carried in a section. These sections are inserted into other sections. The mechanics by which individual webs are assembled and converted into newspapers are now to be explained,

The roller-top-of-former. The roller-top-of-former, or RTF, is the topmost unit of the folder.

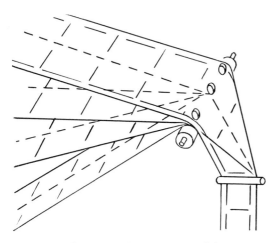

A number of printed webs are associated for common folding above the former plate on the roller-top-of-former (RTF). The webs are held together by small rollers, called trolleys, or propellers.

As already mentioned, "the roller-top-of-former pulls all of the webs to be folded together into the folder. This is the first time that any of the webs travel over a common roller. The bringing together of two or more webs is known as the association of webs."[211] The roller-top-of-former derives its name from its location above the former. It is a driven roller of a larger diameter to which the webs are held by a number of undriven, small diameter, knurled rollers which are called either "trolleys" or "propellor rollers." From the RTF the webs move to the former.

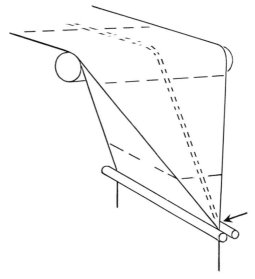

Former folders are used for giving standard size newspapers their lengthwise folds. The two-page wide web is pulled down the former plate (a triangular, sloping metal surface) until both edges of the web meet at the guide rolls. In actual practice a number of webs is associated for common folding. Former folders are typical newspaper equipment; they are also used in magazine and commercial web printing.

The former folder. The former folder, or former plate, has the task of giving standard size newspapers their long fold which separates opposite pages and makes an unbound or unfastened book of the newspaper. This fold is made not on individual papers but on the associated running webs. Webs must therefore be 2-page wide when they arrive at the former plate. Webs of double width can be slit in half and angle-barred whereby they are put on top of the other half. Both halves are then folded on the same former. On many double-width presses the web is split in the center of the roller-top-of-former by circular slitting knives, and each of the 2-page wide webs is folded by a separate former folder. The former folder is a metal plate in the shape of an isoceles triangle. The base of this triangle is next to the roller-top-of-former and parallel with it. This plate points down, and its pointed end is called the nose, which explains the name "nose folder." The nose of the former is not part of the rigid plate, but a spring-loaded separate member which may or may not be adjustable when the number of associated webs changes.

The former plate has a fixed angle of incline which amounts to approximately 60 degrees. As the webs go down this triangular plate, their edges are gradually moved toward each other from the originally spread out position where the two edges are in the same plane and completely separated. At the nose of the former the two edges of the webs touch; the webs are now completely folded. They are guided around the former by a pair of idling rollers, the "guide rollers," which are at the nose of the former. Following the guide rollers there is one or several pairs of nipping rollers which are driven rollers and have two purposes: one is to guide the web during folding, and the other is to crease the folded web. These rollers are also known as "pinching rollers" or as "pinchers" or as "nips."

Balloon formers. Larger presses are often equipped with balloon formers. These make it possible to double the number of sections that a press not provided with such formers can produce. "On a single-width press which has one regular former, a balloon former will produce an additional section for a straight run. On a double-width press, which has two regular formers, two balloon formers can be added to produce a total of four sections on a straight run, or eight sections on a collect run."[212] Balloon formers are simply duplicates of regular formers placed above them. They have of course their own roller-top-of-formers.

Cutting of the web and folding in half of full-size newspapers. We have followed the assembled, or associated, webs through the former where they received their long fold and through the guide and nipping rollers which guided and creased the folded web. Now we are at the point where the web must be cut into individual newspapers or into newspaper sections. The cut product must be folded in half in order to be saleable. The fold now to be made is called the "right-angle fold" because it is at a right angle to the long fold made

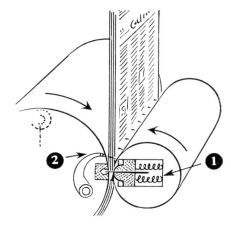

Diagram of the cutting action on newspaper presses. The lengthwise folded webs are cut by interaction of the folding cylinder (left) and the cutting cylinder (right). First the running folded webs are pressed against the folding cylinder by the spring-loaded cheekwoods (1) of the cutting cylinder, and the saw-toothed knife makes the cut. Immediately thereafter the tail of the webs is engaged by the pins (2) of the folding cylinder. (The saw-toothed edge and the holes made by the pins can be seen on the printed newspaper.)

on the former. The machinery which does the cutting and the right-angle folding consists of two elements: one is the cutting cylinder and the other is the folding cylinder. These two cylinders work together.

The cutting cylinder. The cutting cylinder cuts the web after it passes the nipping rollers. Cutting cylinders can have either one or two knives; those equipped with one knife cut a single paper per revolution, those equipped with two knives cut two papers per revolution. A cutting cylinder with one knife has a circumference equal to the length of a single full-size newspaper, whereas a cutting cylinder with two knives has a circumference which is equivalent to two lengths, or to twice the circumference, or cylinders with a single cutting knife.

The cutting cylinder "is a metal cylinder with a knife box and a set of pins. The knife box holds the sawtoothed knife, on each side of which are the spring-loaded 'cheekwoods.' As the cutting cylinder rotates, the web is pulled between it and the folding cylinder. When the knife box arrives at the web, the cheekwoods on one side of the knife blade press against the web; then the knife presses against the web and the second cheekwoods do the same. The cheekwoods hold the web taut, and the knife which is between them pushes through the web and makes the cut."[213] The cheekwoods are spring loaded to prevent a resounding thump when the knife makes the cut. It is worth noting that the cutting edge is at all times a fraction of an inch above the surface of the cutting cylinder, ready for making the cut. This holds equally true for cutting cylinders with two knives.

The folding cylinder. "The folding cylinder makes the right angle fold in standard newspapers and the center fold in tabloids. It is a metal cylinder with a cutting rubber and a set of pins for each page length of the cutting cylinder. Two kinds of folding cylinders are used; one is known as the *two-to-one* folding cylinder, because it produces two completed newspapers for each revolution of the folding cylinder. This folding cylinder is combined with a single-blade cutting cylinder. The second kind is the *three-to-two* folding cylinder which produces three completed newspapers per revolution. This kind of folding cylinder is combined with a cutting cylinder that has two knives. The first figures "two" and "three" in "*two*-to-one" and in "*three*-to-two" refer to the number of newspapers folded, the second figures "one" and "two," to the number of blades in the cutting folder."[214]

Performance of folding cylinders. Two-to-one cylinders can be used either for straight or for collect runs. Here we describe their working in straight runs which is easier to describe than their operation in collect runs. As mentioned, cutting and folding cylinders work together and must therefore be synchronized.

For the purpose of description it is assumed, as a starting point, that a cut was just made. From here on the cutting and folding cycle consists of the following five phases: (1) the end of the cut web is pierced by the first row of pins of the folding cylinder, (2) the web is pulled around half of the circumference of the folding cylinder by the folding cylinder pins, (3) the cutting cylinder makes a full revolution in the same time (whereas the folding cylinder has made only half a revolution), (4) as the knife approaches the cutting rubber of the folding cylinder, the knife pushes through the web into the cutting rubber and makes the next cut. Now we have two different items on the surface of the folding cylinder: one is the completely free individual newspaper, the other is the remaining web which is fastened to the cylinder surface by the second set of pins of the folding cylinder. The folding cylinder continues to rotate as the pins release the newspaper and (5) the folding or tucker blade starts the fold by forcing the center of the newspaper between the two folding rollers that make the fold. Since the folding rollers operate at a higher surface speed than the surface of the folding cylinder, the folded product is immediately removed. During the second folding operation, the web which is pinned to the folding cylinder starts around the opposite half of this cylinder to begin the cutting and folding cycle for the next newspaper.

The whole cutting and folding operation is done with both cutting and folding cylinders in uninterrupted motion; it takes much less time than the reading of this description. The operation of two-to-one folders is less complex than that of three-to-two folders, if these are used for collect runs. Collect runs are made when two different newspaper sections are to be combined by inserting one section into the other prior to folding. The detail of this operation is not described. It is merely mentioned that the folding cylinder must hold the future inside section until the outside section is placed over it. Then both sections are folded together by the same kind of mechanism as is described above.[215]

Delivery fan and delivery conveyor. After the folded newspaper leaves the pair of folding rollers, it is moved into the delivery fan. This unit is an

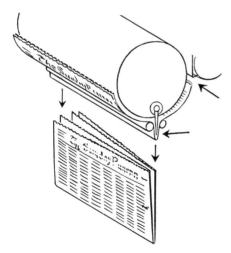

The cut newspaper receives its second, crosswise, fold by interaction of the folding cylinder and a pair of fold rolls. The tucker blade of the folding cylinder pushes the paper between the two fold rolls underneath the folding cylinder; at the same time the pins across the cylinder are withdrawn, thereby releasing the paper.

intermediate between folding rollers and delivery conveyor. Counting of newspapers is made easier by the "kicker," a metal arm which pushes, say, every 25th or every 50th paper out of line, thereby dividing the flow of papers into smaller batches. "In the smaller pressrooms, the 'packer boy' or 'fly boy' transfers groups of 25 or 50 papers from the conveyor to a cart, or to waiting newsboys. In larger pressrooms, a second conveyor, the mailroom conveyor, carries the newspapers from the pressroom to the mailroom, where they are counted, bundled, addressed, and sent to the trucks that distribute the bundles to the newsboys."[216]

Folder Deliveries of Magazine, Rotogravure, and Web-offset Presses

The term "folder delivery" is just as uncommon in the magazine, rotogravure, and web-offset industries as it is in the newspaper business. The reason for introducing this term is explained at the beginning of the discussion of folder deliveries of newspaper relief presses; the same reason applies to the subject in hand. But the reader should be aware that the equipment under discussion is simply known as "the folder" in the pressrooms of printing plants using magazine, rotogravure, and web-offset presses.

Publication printing by rotogravure is divided into the two branches of newspaper supplements and of the printing of high-quality magazines, catalogs, and advertising material. Web offset is also increasingly used for newspaper production on the one hand, and for high-quality printing of advertising and sales promotional material, books, and magazines on the other. Rotogravure presses for newspaper supplements and web-offset presses for newspaper printing have folder deliveries which are essentially the same as those in newspaper relief printing. These were discussed in the preceding unit; the present unit is not concerned with them but devoted to descriptions of folder deliveries other than those used in newspaper production.

Most magazine presses (which are as explained in Section 1, high-speed roll-fed letterpress printing equipment) and rotogravure presses for high-quality magazine, catalog, and advertising printing, as well as some web-offset installations are single-purpose machines. They were designed to produce a given product as efficiently as possible, and are often equipped with special features. Such presses are, generally speaking, not as flexible or adaptable for changing tasks than general-purpose equipment. Web-offset presses are more often than not designed for job printing, but there are also special-purpose web-offset presses in operation.

Folder deliveries of magazine and other single-product presses. Folders on letterpress, rotogravure, and web-offset presses designed for production of high-quality products differ from newspaper folders in the precision with which they can be operated. Such folders may or may not have former plates, which serve for folding the web in its running direction. If they use former plates, they differ mainly in the equipment that makes right-angle folds. The folding rollers of newspaper presses are replaced with "jaw folders" which are more precise in their action. If they use "ribbon folders" the former plate is not needed at all. (Both jaw folders and ribbon folders are described in the following discussion of folders for web-offset printing.) Folder deliveries may be capable of pasting, of wire stitching, and of making gate-folds or fold-outs, depending on the requirements of a particular publication. Such specialized points are here merely mentioned but not further discussed.

Folder deliveries of web-offset presses. The term "folder" signifies in the web-offset industry, as in all other branches of printing, all equipment following the last printing and drying unit. This equipment does not only folding but also performs other operations needed for converting the

Delivery end of a web-offset press showing the final folded signatures coming off the press.

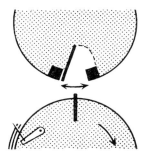 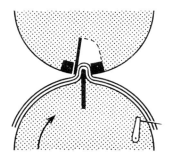 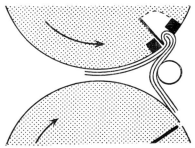

Diagram of jaw folding. Jaw folds are made by interaction of a jaw cylinder (top) and a tucking cylinder (bottom). In the first figure you see the jaw cylinder with the stationary and the operated jaw separated for folding. Opposite the gap you see the tucking blade and at the left, the pinned end of the signature. Next, the signature is pushed between the two jaws; the operated jaw closes and makes the fold. Finally, the folded signature is released from the pins in the tucking cylinder and moves along while being held between the closed jaws.

printed web into signatures. The choice of the folder depends on the purpose of the press. As you can read in the discussions of presswork, some web-offset presses are equipped with more than one folder and sometimes with a sheeter.

Purposes of different folder deliveries. For publication printing or for commercial work where "some flexibility in the delivered product is required, the former folder together with a chopper folder will produce a variety of folded signatures. To this can be added the double-parallel attachment which will make a two-up pocketbook size signature. There is a tendency to run lighter weight papers to help overcome increasing mailing costs. Web-offset presses printing Bibles, prayer books, and lightweight magazines usually are slower running presses with simple ribbon and chopper folders. Some people feel that ribbon or jaw folders are slower running than former folders of the newspaper type. However, on some of the more recent web-offset presses there are ribbon folders producing folded signatures at press speeds of 1,000 to 1,200 f.p.m., depending on the job."[217] The former folder is described under the head of "Folders for Newspaper Printing" and does not need additional discussion for web-offset printing. But there are several new terms which must now be explained. These are jaw folder, chopper folder, and ribbon folder.

Jaw folders. The first or lengthwise fold is made with former folders which are in the web-offset industry also called newspaper folders. With the exception of ribbon folders, which do not use formers, the web goes from the former folder into

the next folding unit, the jaw folder. A "jaw folder consists of three cylinders between which the web passes to make one or two parallel folds at right angles to the direction of the web travel. The lead edge of the web is caught on pins which carry it around the first cylinder. Halfway around, tucker blades on the cylinder force the center of the signature-to-be into folding jaws on the second cylinder. At the same time, a cut-off knife separates the tail of the signature from the web. The signature is carried around and released by the jaws, and the cycle continues. The signature can be passed to a third cylinder in a similar manner to make the second parallel fold."[218] The second jaw fold is made when the final product has a rather small size, publications of the digest kind, for example.

The chopper folder. From the jaw folder the product, which is now severed from the web, may pass to the next folder which often makes the final fold. (Digest-type products receive their final fold on the jaw folder and do not require further folding.) The mechanism of the chopper folder is similar to that used on knife folders for the folding of sheets. This mechanism consists of a folding blade and a pair of folding rollers. The unit to be folded is driven by conveyor belts, or tapes, against a stop. Then the chopper blade pushes it into the fold rollers which make the actual fold. The chopper fold is "also called a "cross fold" or a "right-angle fold." The fold can only be made following the first parallel fold and at right angles to it. This fold produces signatures that are 16-page multiples of the number of webs in the press, ¼ web width by ½ cut-off length."[219]

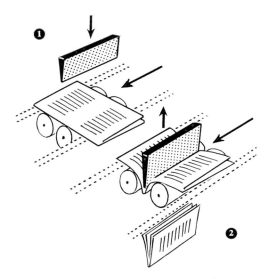

The chopper fold is made by interaction of a reciprocating tucker, or chopper, blade and a pair of fold rollers. In (1) the blade moves down on the signature which is in position for folding; in (2) the signature is already between the fold rollers and the blade moves up. The blade can also be carried by a cylinder if a rotary motion is preferred to a reciprocating one.

The ribbon folder. Some web-offset presses have ribbon folders. Ribbon folding does not require folding by a former folder for the first fold. Some presses equipped for ribbon folding have no former at all, others have formers as well as ribbon folders. The presence of a former gives the press more versatility. If a job is best folded by ribbon folding, the former folder simply remains inoperative, and if a job can be better or more economically done by use of the former folder this is equally possible. "Ribbon folders, generally speaking, produce a well folded signature but they require accuracy in setting and control for high speeds."[220] The ribbon fold is "often called an angle-bar fold. The web is slit into multiple ribbons, or narrow webs, which use angle bars to by-pass the former. The ribbons are brought together at the jaw folder for folding and cut-off into desired signatures."[221]

Inline Deliveries

Many package materials can be completed in a single pass through connected printing and fabricating equipment. Such installations are called inline because the fabricating equipment is arranged in a straight production line with the press. Inline deliveries are usually combined with web printing of package materials in rotogravure and flexography. Paper bags, for example, are frequently produced by inline flexographic equipment. Other examples are die-cut wrappers for razor blades and folding paper boxes. Such products can be either manufactured inline or, if they are web printed, rewound or sheeted and then fabricated in a separate operation.[222]

Inline deliveries are by their very nature single-purpose machines; a discussion of various kinds of this equipment is not possible within the frame of the present work. Here we are limited to a brief characterization of a single kind of inline delivery, the cutting and creasing of folding paper boxes. The following description is based on a Champlain cutter-creaser. (To avoid misunderstandings it is added that other cutter-creasers are also available for the same purpose.)

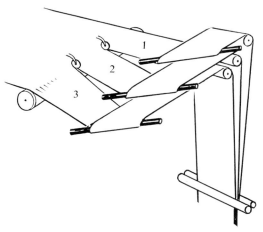

Diagram of ribbon folding. In ribbon folding the web is divided by rotary knives, called slitters, into several narrow webs or ribbons. These ribbons are associated in proper sequence and registered by angle barring. The associated webs are folded by jaw folders.

Description of an inline cutter-creaser. Champlain cutter-creasers have two plane surfaces, one is called the upper bolster; it is used for placement of the cutting dies and does the cutting by a brief reciprocating motion down and up again. The other surface is the stationary lower bolster; it has a cutting jacket on which the counter for the cutting and creasing dies is made. After the impression, the upper bolster returns to its feeding position and the cycle begins anew. "The continuous web is fed into the cutter-creaser by an intermittent feed roller actuated by a cam device. The feed unit is geared to meter the correct length of the web in one cycle of the cam, after which it comes to a rest, still maintaining control of the web. During this rest period of the feed roller and the web, the cutting knife and score rules cut and crease the carton and withdraw."[223]

Co-ordination between the continuously printed web and the intermittently operating cutter-creaser is achieved by an "automatic loop control gate," a "compensator roller" which provides for cut-to-print register, and an electric eye control system which adjusts the compensating roller.

After the stock has been die-cut, "the next cycle feeds the cut sheet into an intermittent belt section. At this time a kicker roller, synchronized to the speed of the stripper, parts the cut sheet from the solid web and feeds it in time to the pins in the stripping cylinder. The *stripping cylinder* has grooves that run around its entire surface. Into these grooves, pins can be placed to pierce the waste or scrap, meaning that portion of the stock which is not part of the carton. This scrap is led into a waste disposal system. When the stock is stripped free of scrap, the individual cartons are fed into a tab breaker that separates and ejects them onto a slow-moving belt where they are overlapped and carried to the take-off position. At this position, the completed cartons, which are printed, die-cut and stripped, can be removed, jogged, and stacked by press personnel for gluing or packing."[224] To give the reader an idea of the speed at which cutter-creasers can be operated, it is mentioned that modern models, producing a maximum sheet size of 36 by 36 inches have a maximum rated speed of cutting and creasing 250 sheets per minute. (A detailed description of inline carton production is provided in Chapter VII, Section 3.)

Section 7: Drying Equipment

Joseph Moxon who published the first English book on printing in 1683, tells us that in his time the printed sheets were dried in small batches from 17 to 24 sheets on drying racks, which were placed under the ceiling of the pressroom or, more frequently, of the printer's warehouse.[225] The main reason for the drying of printed sheets in small batches was that handmade papers required wetting with water before presswork; machine-made papers eliminated this necessity. Contemporary drying methods are exclusively concerned with the setting or drying of printed ink images. Progress in the formulation of printing inks and in the construction of presses is such as to make drying as a separate step unnecessary in many printing methods, particularly in sheetfed letterpress and lithographic printing. Sheetfed presses are often equipped at their delivery ends with sprayers or open flame heaters to which the printed sheets are exposed prior to stacking in the delivery pile. But sprayers and heaters are to be classified as accessories rather than as drying equipment.

Drying equipment is, nevertheless, needed in many branches of printing. There are two different reasons why the printed stock may need drying as a separate operation: one is the thickness of the deposited ink film which constitutes the printed image, the other is the speed of printing. Screen-process printing, sheetfed gravure, and steel-die engraving are methods which deposit much heavier ink films than letterpress or offset lithography. The printed ink film is not of the same thickness in screen process, steel-die engraving, and sheetfed gravure. These three printing methods have, nevertheless, one common characteristic: the sheet cannot be simply stacked as it comes off the press but must be individually dried. Even though sheetfed letterpress and offset lithographic printing does not need individual drying, high-speed web printing in the same methods requires drying as a separate operation prior to delivery. The reason for this difference between drying in sheetfed and in web printing is the much higher speed of web printing.

The general interest in drying and drying equipment is a result of the persistent trend to faster and more economical printing production. This trend explains the recent growth of web-offset printing which is often used for the production of medium-length runs in job-and-commercial printing. As long as web printing was not practiced by companies active in the service business, but only by those engaged in the production of exceptionally long runs, in magazine printing for example, the bulk of the printing industry had no reason to be concerned with drying methods and equipment. At that time, drying of webs printed at high speeds was the problem of a few magazine printers and publishers. The wide dissemination of web offset in the recent past changed this situation and has made printers conscious of drying problems. Since drying is a highly technical and also a new subject to most printers who are used to sheetfed printing, an exposition of drying fundamentals seems to be called for; this exposition must begin with the material to be dried—printing inks.

Printing inks and their relation to drying. Before we enter into a discussion of the techniques whereby printing inks are dried, a few explanatory words on the constitution of inks and the different ways by which they dry are indicated. The subject is extensively presented in Section 1, Chapter IX, "Printing Inks," under the head of "The Drying of Inks." The following remarks are condensations of this unit which should be consulted by everybody interested in drying fundamentals. To recapitulate briefly, the vehicle is the component of inks that determines how an ink will dry. Ink chemists distinguish seven kinds of drying actions, among them evaporation of solvents contained in the vehicle. Evaporation is here mentioned because inks for web printing are formulated, generally speaking, to have this kind of drying action. During drying the printing ink changes from the fluid to the solid state. In some kinds of inks, drying takes place in two stages. The first stage is the "setting" of the ink film, the second its hardening An ink film is set when it is sufficiently dry for the handling of the printed stock. During the stage of hardening the set ink film is thoroughly dried. Not all ink films dry in this manner. Neither do all inks pass through the stage of setting. As mentioned, most inks for high-speed web printing dry by evaporation of their solvents. Solvent evaporation can be speeded by applying heat and air, singly or in combination, to the printed sheet or web. The first stage in the drying of such inks is solvent evaporation, the second stage is solidification of the ink film. Where higher temperatures are used to speed solvent evaporation, the film-forming materials, which are usually thermoplastic, become more or less fluid during forced drying, and must be solidified by reducing the temperature of the stock. For this reason cooling, or chilling, of the web follows the application of heat. These brief remarks must here suffice.

Techniques for the drying of inks. As explained in Chapter IX, there are seven kinds of drying actions which can, singly or in combination, change a wet ink film to a dry one. For the purpose of the present discussion, the subject can be simplified by dividing inks into two broad groups depending on the methods by which drying is actually accomplished. One comprises *natural drying* methods, the other *forced drying* methods. In the first kind, which is also called *air drying*, the ink dries without need for subjecting the printed stock to extensive treatments, simply because it is in the nature of such inks that a thin printed ink film will sooner or later become dry. But natural drying is much too slow for high-speed web printing. In this kind of printing the wet ink image must undergo forced drying which consists in applying heat and air to the running web prior to its delivery.

Films of air-drying inks as applied in some printing methods are too thick for instant setting which is necessary for the immediate stacking of sheets as they come off the press. Sheets printed by these methods either need racking or some kind of forced drying. Sheetfed letterpress and lithographic printing do not need forced drying even at the high-press speeds at which contemporary presses are operated. Such presses usually have sprayers at their delivery ends. The spray coming from these accessories has merely the function of permitting air to remain for a brief time between sheets, thereby giving the ink a better chance for setting. (Sprayers are discussed in Section 6.)

The main difference between sheetfed and web printing is the speed at which web printing is done. The same kinds of inks which are satisfactory for sheetfed printing are unusable for high-speed web printing. As the essence of web printing is speed, inks are especially formulated for high-speed printing in conjunction with forced drying. All mass production printing, with one exception, is done on installations including forced-drying equipment. Web printing in letterpress, rotogravure, offset lithography, and flexography all belong in this class. The only exception is newspaper printing which does not need forced drying since news ink is dried by absorption.

But not all web printing has the same drying problems. Web printing of plastic films for packages poses problems different from those encountered in the web printing of paper. Nor does all web printing of paper have identical drying problems. These depend on a number of considerations including the speed of printing, the printing method, the kind of paper, and whether the web is perfected prior to drying or printed on one side only and dried before it is printed on the other. Drying equipment is usually designed for a specific purpose; equipment built for drying a variety of products must have more flexibility than installations needed in single-product manufacturing.

Our discussion of drying is divided into four units: (1) equipment for natural drying, (2) the role of heat, air, and ventilation in forced drying, (3) forced-drying equipment for sheetfed presses, and (4) forced-drying equipment for web printing.

Equipment for Natural Drying

As mentioned earlier in this section, the printed images of screen-processed and steel-die engraved products consist of such thick ink layers that it is not possible to stack the printed sheets without previous drying. The drying method selected depends on several considerations. Among them is length of run, kind of ink used and, of course, equipment available in a given shop or plant. Screen process and steel-die engraving can use several kinds of forced drying, as will be seen under the head of forced-drying equipment for sheetfed presses. But these two methods can also utilize equipment for natural drying which has the purpose of storing the printed sheet until the ink has either set or is completely dried. Once the ink reaches one or the other stage, the printed sheets can be removed from this kind of storage equipment and put in smaller or larger piles, depending on the nature of the job.

Equipment for natural drying is usually designated as "drying racks." Drying racks are made either of wood or of aluminum and may be rather primitive. A number of different types of drying racks are in use, and some of them will be briefly described. In addition to drying racks, mention will be made of wicket conveyors which are power-driven machines used in screen process for natural drying as well as for forced drying.

Shelf racks. Shelf racks are the oldest type of racks in the screen-process industry. They have a sturdy wooden base equipped with casters, and consist of an indefinite number of lightweight wooden shelves which are assembled into an upright structure as printing progresses. The "racker" or "take-off man" places as many sheets on top of the shelf as there have room. When the surface of a shelf is occupied, he takes another shelf and lays it on top of the preceding one. The shelves have simple spacers which prevent the printed stock from getting marred by the next shelf. After a time this stack of shelves becomes too high for the racker. It is then rolled away for

drying in a storage area of the shop. There it remains for a time which varies for various types of ink. Often the sheets remain in their racks overnight. When the ink is sufficiently dry for piling, the racker gathers his harvest by disassembling the stack of shelves, one after the other, removing the dried sheets at the same time. Shelf racks are among the least efficient drying racks and are restricted to short-run work.

Drying racks for cardboard. Counter and window displays are, generally speaking, printed directly on cardboard in screen-process printing. Hand printing and flatbed screen-process presses can handle cardboard of any required thickness, whereas cylinder presses are limited in this respect. In lithographic printing only thin, lightweight boards are usable, and cardboard displays are usually printed on paper which is later mounted to board as a part of display finishing. Screen process offers savings in the cost of stock because it uses, or can use, thick boards. Thick boards coated for screen process are made by board mills; lined boards are made by converters on equipment that uses individual sheets of board and rolls of paper. The cost of thick boards that are coated and the cost of lined boards is less than the combined cost of the paper for printing, the cardboard onto which it is mounted after printing, and the cost of individual mounting. But in longer runs the greater speed of lithographic presses more than outweighs the initial advantage of the much slower screen-process.

Screen-process businesses specializing in display work are usually equipped with drying racks designed for air drying of rigid sheets of board. Air drying and the related racking are more used for short runs than for long ones. Drying racks for cardboard consist of a varying number of immovable shelves, closely spaced and made of thin strips of wood which are fastened to a sturdy wooden structure equipped with casters. Drying racks of this kind are not articles of commerce but made to order; therefore they can vary considerably in their dimensions. By way of example it is mentioned that a cardboard rack may be 3 feet deep, 6 feet long, and have 50 shelves. The rack runs on casters and can be moved to a drying area after it is filled.

Drying racks for cardboard are not suitable for the handling of papers of the customary printing weights. It is not easy, and sometimes even not possible, to push printed lightweight paper into the narrow space which separates shelf from shelf. When cardboard racks must be used for the printing of paper they are usually lined with large sheets of board which can be pulled out and then permit the laying on of papers. Cardboard racks are more efficient than shelf racks as they save the time-consuming operations of assembling and disassembling of individual shelves. Cardboard racks are nevertheless not suitable for long-run work since the required handling is quite expensive.

Hinged drying racks. Hinged drying racks have a number of individual shelves which are hinged to a supporting structure in the back. The shelves are tilted upward when the rack is empty and brought into their horizontal working position as they are needed. The advantage of this kind of rack is that each shelf is completely accessible on its whole surface which permits full utilization of its area. The shelves are properly spaced to avoid contact with undried ink images. Removal of the dried material is done shelf by shelf, and each shelf is then tilted upward.

Wicket conveyors. Wicket conveyors are relatively new in the screen-process industry though they have been in use for a long time in metal decorating. (Wicket driers were introduced in the screen-process industry in the early 1950's.) Their main advantage is that the stock is not moved flat, occupying a maximum of space as in belt conveyors, but in an almost upright position where each sheet needs much less horizontal space. As the space needed for stock in belt con-

veyors is a multiple of the space needed in wicket conveyors, shorter conveyors permit air drying of the printed stock without occupying the excessive space which is needed for other air-drying equipment. Each printed sheet is placed individually into a wicket which is made of wire and tilted backward in order to support the stock. A metal structure carries the wickets which move continuously by a chain drive. Most wickets can be used on both trips, in their forward as well as in their return motion; others are unloaded when they arrive at the end of their forward motion. Wickets are more practical for heavier stocks such as cardboards or cover papers. Light-weight papers of large sizes tend to buckle, whereby the wet ink image may become smeared.

The Functions of Heat and Air in Forced Drying

Most forced-drying systems use a combination of heat and air, but there are some drying systems which are based on heat alone and do not use air for the drying of the ink film. In some drying systems, solvent vapors are removed by ventilation; in drying systems based exclusively on heat, the solvent vapors are burned as they leave the ink film. As heat and air can be applied in several ways, a brief discussion of these subjects follows.

Functions of heat in the drying of ink films. Heat may have two functions in forced drying. One is

Courtesy Advance Process Supply Company

A screen-process operator removes a printed paper board from the press and puts it in a wicket of the wicket dryer.

that practically all chemical and many physical processes progress faster at elevated temperatures than at room temperature. This holds true for drying by oxidation and polymerization in which many small molecules are combined into larger and more complex ones. But the application of heat for this purpose is not too important in forced drying of high-speed web printing since the speeding of oxidation and polymerization of film formers need higher temperatures than those to which paper can be safely exposed and longer times than are practical for high-speed web printing. (Inks drying by oxidation and polymerization are used in various fields, metal decorating and tin printing in particular. These inks are subjected to higher temperatures for varying times in baking ovens.) As most inks for web printing dry by the evaporation of their solvent components, heat is mainly needed to speed the change of solvents from their liquid state into their gaseous or vapor state. "Therefore, while some oxidation or polymerization may be used in heat-set inks, which are the dominant type of inks for web printing in letterpress and web offset, it is of secondary importance and the main drying process depends on evaporation."[226] Drying by evaporation is also the characteristic drying action for gravure and for flexographic inks, as well as for some kinds of inks for screen-process printing.

Different solvents have different boiling ranges, as explained in Section 3 of Chapter IX under the head "Classification of Solvents." Generally speaking, gravure and flexographic inks, and some screen-process inks, are formulated with solvents of a lower boiling range than inks for letterpress and web-offset printing. These differences explain temperature differences found in systems based on heat primarily for the drying of different kinds of web printing. "In gravure, most of the drying is accomplished between 100° and 175°F. in publications work and between 100° and 250°F. in package printing."[227] In letterpress and offset lithographic web printing, much higher temperatures are needed because heat-set inks must be formulated with solvents of a considerably higher boiling range than those suitable for rotogravure and flexography. These differences are rooted in the different means by which letterpress and web offset printing-image carriers are inked in comparison with the inking of rotogravure and flexographic image carriers. The temperature to which a web of paper is heated in web-offset printing is "anywhere from 250° to 350°F., depending on ink coverage and other particulars."[228]

British Thermal Units and calories. Heat requirements are expressed in the United States and other English-speaking countries in British Thermal Units, abbreviated BTU's. A British Thermal Unit is the amount of heat required to raise 1 pound of water 1°F. at its maximum density which is at 39.1°F. In countries using the metric system, heat requirements are expressed in calories. (Most people know calories only from dieting, but calories have many other uses, some of them related to our present subject, drying.) Most substances, including solvents, require a different amount of heat for raising the same quantity to the same extent in their temperature. This varying amount of heat required by different solvents is called the "specific heat" of solvents. These heat requirements are expressed, in the United States as in other countries, in calories which are calculated by using units of the metric system. In that system our pound is replaced by the gram (or by multiples of the gram), our degrees of Fahrenheit are replaced by degrees of Centigrade, and heat requirements are not expressed as BTU's but as calories. The *specific heat* of a solvent is the amount of heat required to raise 1 gram 1°C. In the same system the specific heat of water is 1.00 calory. Calories and BTU's can be simply converted; for some purposes the use of one system is more habitual, for other purposes the other system is preferred. In America total heat requirements of a drying system are usually expressed in BTU's.

Sources of heat for drying. Various sources of heat are available for drying. These can be classified into three, according to the way they transfer heat to the object. "Heat may be transferred from one body to another by conduction, convection, or radiation, or by a combination of these processes. Examples of each are common. *Conduction* occurs with direct contact, as when an egg is fried on a hot griddle."[229] *Convection* means indirect heat transfer from the heat source to another place, or to the object to be heated, by heating a liquid or gas, including air, which in turn transfers heat to its final destination. A hot-air heating system, as used for the heating of homes, is an example of convection. Heat transfer by *radiation* "occurs when radiant energy emitted by one body is absorbed by another. Wave lengths longer than those of the visible spectrum and shorter than those of radar are commonly used for heating."[230] The part of the electromagnetic spectrum which has wave lengths suitable for radiant heating is known as the near and as the far "infrared." "Because ordinary glass and the carbon dioxide in the air absorb most of the energy of wave lengths longer than 4,000 millimicrons, only wave lengths shorter than about 4,000 millimicrons are utilized in practice, though longer wave lengths may be emitted by infrared sources."[231] The range of infrared waves is nevertheless considerable, as it begins with approximately 700 millimicrons and goes up to approximately 4,000 millimicrons or 4 microns. Sources of heat radiation for industrial purposes are infrared or radiant heating lamps, as well as strips and bars that are electrically powered and controlled. Infrared waves can also be generated by high-frequency tubes.

The functions of air in forced-drying systems. Many forced-drying systems use convection either as sole drying medium or in combination with other forms of heat transfer. With the exception of open-flame drying where the solvent vapors are immediately burned by the flames, drying systems must be equipped with the proper kind of ventilation for reasons of safety. The drying action of inks that dry by evaporation results in vapors of the solvents which are forced to leave the printed ink film in the course of drying. These vapors are highly dangerous explosives unless their concentration in the air is kept below a certain point. The permissible concentration must be less than the explosive limit which is established for various solvents and can be looked up in the literature. Drying installations are normally designed with a high safety factor. "It is usually safe to figure that the solvent concentration should be under 25 per cent of the lower explosive limit."[232] This means that the amount of air is four times as much as theoretically required.

Calculation of the required air volume. This general discussion is illustrated by an example that demonstrates how the required air volume is calculated for a flexographic press. This calculation is based on a press speed of 700 f.p.m. and on a 24 inch wide web. It is assumed that the maximum possible ink consumption is 2 pounds per minute, and that the ink has a solvent content of 80 per cent, or that 1.6 pounds of solvent are applied per minute. "Then by referring to solvent factor tables, we determine the amount of air that is required to render this 1.6 pounds of solvent barely explosive. There we might find the figure of 2,000 cubic feet per pound of solvent as

the lower explosion limit. Multiplying the figure of 2,000 cubic feet per pound of solvent by the 1.6 pounds of solvent, which are the application maximum of our example, and multiplying the product by a safety factor of 4, we find the required air volume of 12,800 cubic feet of air (abbreviated cfm) per minute."[233] The figure of 12,800 cfm may not have too much meaning to the reader, but it is equivalent to the air content of a house 40 feet by 40 feet, or 1,600 square feet and 8 feet high. This volume of air must be applied to the web every minute during which it is running at full ink consumption.

High air velocity and its importance. Drying systems that operate by convection exclusively apply heated air to the web. Just as you know from your own experience that heat conduction can vaporize liquids, so do you know that hot air can achieve the same result. (If examples be needed, think of a steaming teakettle which shows heat conduction, and of drying the wash on a warm breezy day in the yard, which shows convection and is a non-industrial application of warm air drying.) Returning to drying technology, high air velocity systems are more effective than systems applying low velocities.

High-speed drying is a young branch of engineering, and our knowledge of the reasons for the effectiveness of high velocity driers is the result of recent, contemporary research. It was found that "webs moving at press speeds have a *boundary layer* of air securely held to the web and traveling at web speed. The protective action of these small air layers impede drying efficiency. A second barrier to high drying performance is saturation by ink solvent vapor of these boundary layers. A third, though less severe barrier, is the exuding of vapor from the drier as fast as it leaves the web. Even a low concentration of solvent vapor will frustrate the drying process."[234] Strong currents of air, usually heated, are therefore provided in many drying installations to remove boundary layers.

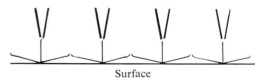

Surface

Courtesy Overly's Inc.

Diagram showing a series of nozzles, as used in high-velocity driers, and their effect on boundary layer.

Chilling of the dried stock. Most driers for web printing, and practically all driers for high-speed printing, contain in addition to heat and air applicators also chilling equipment. The resins, or film formers, of printing inks which dry by evaporation of their solvents are, as mentioned before, often thermoplastic, which means that heat changes their state from the solid to the fluid. Consequently, ink films which were dried by high heat may be quite soft and therewith rather vulnerable. The web must therefore be cooled after drying. Cooling is achieved by means of water-cooled rollers which are called "chilling rollers." Depending on the speed of printing and on the temperature of drying, a varying number of chilling rollers may be needed. *Chilling rollers* can be either of single shell or of double shell construction. "The plain single shell roll has an unrestricted cavity. Cooling water passes through the roll at relatively low velocity. This is commonly considered the least efficient cooling roll, having the widest variation of surface temperature, probably because of heat transfer coefficient of stagnant water in the roll ends. In the double shell roll, stagnant water is eliminated and water velocity is increased."[235]

Measuring the temperature of running webs. All drying systems are equipped with temperature controls for keeping the amount of heat to be applied to the printed stock within certain limits. These controls do not usually include the measuring of the web temperature but are designed for the correct operation of the systems themselves. But it may be necessary to determine the temperature of the running web since certain stocks, plastic films in particular, must not be heated beyond a temperature which depends of course on the kind of stock in question.

The temperature of the running webs is best taken by a pyrometer. The pyrometer combines two elements, a thermocouple and a potentiometer. The thermocouple has two wires of different composition, welded together at one end to form an open loop. When the two ends are at different temperatures the temperature difference produces a voltage difference across the open end of the loop. This voltage difference can be measured with a potentiometer, an instrument that measures extremley small voltages, also called millivoltmeter. Thermocouples and potentiometers are extremely sensitive instruments and the pyrometer is consequently a highly sensitive and quick temperature measuring device.

Forced-Drying Equipment for Sheetfed Printing

Letterpress and offset lithography, the two methods by which the bulk of sheetfed printing is produced, do not need forced-drying equipment. Contemporary inks for letterpress and offset lithography are fast setting and do not throttle the speed of high-speed sheetfed presses of these two methods. Forced-drying equipment for sheetfed printing is limited to three printing methods which are of secondary importance if compared with sheetfed letterpress and offset printing. These three methods are sheetfed gravure, steel-die engraving, and screen-process printing.

There are not many sheetfed gravure presses in operation in the United States, and some of them are not used for production printing but for proofing of color work that will be ultimately printed in rotogravure. Driers for sheetfed gravure are customary on multicolor presses. The drier is at the delivery end of the press and has the purpose of removing most of the solvents contained in gravure inks, thereby drying the printed sheet which could otherwise not be stacked in the delivery pile. Different from rotogravure, sheetfed gravure does not need thorough drying after each color, as the speed of sheetfed gravure printing is much less than that of rotogravure printing.

Drying equipment for sheetfed gravure. Inks for both sheetfed and rotogravure contain a high percentage of organic solvents. During drying, most of these solvents evaporate; the solvent vapors mixed with air present a serious explosion and fire hazard unless the vapor concentration is strictly controlled. Drying equipment for sheetfed gravure uses indirect, or convected, heat. The convection medium is air which is heated by radiation rather than by open flames. The sheet to be dried travels on a conveyor through a tunnel where hot air is blown on its printed surface. The solvent fumes mix with the hot air, and in some installations they are completely removed by an exhaust system. In other installations the air-solvent mixture is partly removed and partly recirculated and mixed with fresh air which is, of course, first heated to the proper temperature. Recirculation of air saves some of the heating costs and is therefore practiced whenever solvent concentration is sufficiently low.

Drying equipment for steel-die engraving. Most press runs in steel-die engraving are relatively short, and the printed area of steel-die engraved stationery is small, particularly in letterheads where most of the area must be left blank for the

Courtesy M & M Displays, Philadelphia

The infeed of a General Tower Drier, *connected to the delivery of a cylinder press. Normally the drier is completely enclosed; in this picture the operator holds the front plate up to show arrangement of shelves inside the drier.*

letter itself. These two points combined make rack drying practical and there are consequently not many forced-drying installations in existence in this industry. Inks for steel-die engraving do not contain large quantities of solvents, as inks for steel die engraving must be of a highly viscous consistency. Such inks dry primarily by polymerization which can be speeded by the application of heat. But the temperature must be controlled, otherwise it could become injurious to the paper. Drying by radiation is often found a practical approach. The heat source may be one of several available electrically powered radiators of heat. Most drying installations for steel-die engraving are custom made; their detail depends on the purpose for which they were built.

Drying equipment for screen-process printing. In the United States there are probably more drying installations for screen-process printing in operation than for other methods of sheetfed printing. The drying problem of the screen-process industry is rather complex for the following three reasons: First, the ink films deposited by screen-

process printing are exceptionally thick, varying between approximately 20 and 50 microns, whereas those deposited by letterpress have roughly 3 microns, and those resulting in offset lithography are between 1.5 and 2 microns in thickness. The next reason for the difficulty of drying in screen-process printing is caused by the printing of large sheets in many colors. Such sheets are not easy to dry, and drying equipment may need adjustments from one color to the next. A third reason contributing many variables in the drying of screen-process printing is the wide range of materials handled and a correspondingly wide range of printing inks, most of which have their own drying requirements. On the other hand, the speed of screen-process printing is much less than that of sheetfed letterpress or offset lithography.

In the course of time screen shops became more specialized, and at present the drying of screen printed paper and paper boards has become less of a problem. Most driers are for inks which dry by evaporation, and such driers generally incorporate the "jet" principle. This type of drier was developed for screen process by the Eastman Kodak Company which "donated the results of their work to the screen-process industry by making them public knowledge." The Kodak drier was based "on techniques which Kodak engineers had developed for high-speed drying of processed photographic film."[236] Jet driers use warm air which is forced through small orifices immediately above the sheet to be dried. The warm air "scrubs" the wet ink and removes its solvents by the action of the warm air. Jet driers are made by several equipment manufacturers in several versions. (The Eastman Kodak Company does not manufacture jet driers for sale.) Some driers have horizontal conveyor belts, others use wickets. There are also wicket driers which do not use the jet principle at all. Some installations move the wickets horizontally, others save floor space by using drying towers in which the wickets move vertically.[237]

Forced-Drying Equipment for Web Printing

Forced drying is a necessity in all high-speed web printing with the exception of newspaper printing. But not every kind of web printing can use the same kind of forced-drying equipment. Each installation must be designed considering a number of different points. The speed at which printing is to be done is the first and often most important point. Letterpress and gravure web printing can be done at maximum speeds of approximately 2,000 f.p.m. Web offset permits, at the time of writing, maximum speeds of 1,500 f.p.m., and flexography has a maximum of 1,200 f.p.m. But this does not mean that all presses are built for these maximum speeds nor that each job can be run at the rated maximum speed of a press. Drying equipment must therefore be designed to take care of the output of the press to which it will be connected and also to be suitable for the nature of the printed product and its quality requirements. Not every kind of drying equipment can meet each of these requirements.

Equally important is the ink to be dried by a given drier. Practically all inks for high-speed web printing dry by evaporation of their solvents. But solvent evaporating inks are not all the same. They differ in many points, particularly in the boiling range of their solvents, in the amount of solvents present in a pound of ink, and in the coverage or mileage of inks, which indicates the number of square feet that can be covered by one pound. (A concrete example how these data are used, with the exception of boiling range of solvents, is given in the preceding unit under the paragraph head "Calculation of the required air volume.")

Each solvent differs in some degree from other solvents, and each has its own evaporation characteristics. Some solvents, or solvent combinations, need more heat for evaporation than others. The safe proportion of solvent-to-air is of course not always the same, nor should it be forgotten that different inks do not necessarily contain the same percentage of solvents even if they are made for similar purposes.

The third variable is the printing stock and its differences. Web printing is done on a wide range of stock, including newsprint-like papers for gravure supplements, offset and book papers which may or may not be coated, various kinds of plastic films, and metallic foils, to mention the most widely used ones. Many of these stocks consume different amounts of inks, which are often especially formulated for a particular task. Last but not least, the space required by a forced-drying system must be considered. The trend in web printing has been toward higher speed and shorter drying equipment, thereby making greater efficiency of drying equipment a necessity.

Basic types of driers. As explained in the general introduction to drying, heat can be transferred by three different methods which are conduction, convection, and radiation. Driers can be based on each of these principles, singly or in combination.

In addition driers must have facilities for removing solvent fumes, and they must, finally, provide for chilling of the heated web and the ink layer on it.

Steam-drum driers. Driers which heat the web by conduction are used on common impression cylinder presses for multicolor printing. On such presses the web is printed on one side, dried and then printed on the other side, thereafter dried again and then delivered. Driers for this kind of press are often steam-heated cylinders, or drums. "Here high-pressure steam is applied to the drum, and the printed web is brought around the drum with the surface to be dried on the outside, being heated by contact to almost 270°F. The steam temperature in the drum is 300 to 350°F. In addition to that, air temperature of 500° to 700° F. is applied to the printed surface of the paper around the drum. Between the two (conducted heat and hot air), drying is accomplished. After the web leaves the drum, it is then passed over a series of chilling rolls to chill the paper as well as the ink and the resins in the ink."[238]

Steam-drum drying combines conduction of heat with convection. It is used in publication printing and has several advantages and, of course, also disadvantages. Among the advantages of steam-drum drying is that the paper web is kept flat, that the web is not distorted, that it permits close temperature regulation, and that it prevents scorching of the paper. Among its disadvantages is the high cost of installation, that it cannot be used for blanket-to-blanket web-offset presses, that it tends to soften and dull the printed image, and that the finished print appears flat on the paper rather than standing out on top. But it should be added that the last two points are controversial. Partisans of steam-drum drying do not agree that these two points are strongly noticeable and that they seriously detract from the advantages of steam-drum drying.

Flame driers. Flame driers are based on the principle of radiation. Such driers consist of a "continuous series of flames applied to the printed surface as the web goes from one end of the drying tunnel to the other. Here, flame temperatures of 2,000° to 2,500°F. are applied to the web, causing flashing of the solvents and burning-off of solvents as the paper travels through the drier. After the web passes through the drier, it is then brought immediately over a series of cooling drums so that the paper is brought back to a normal temperature of 80° to 100°F.[239] Flame driers have the disadvantage of applying higher temperatures to the paper than desirable. Flame driers are efficient and get solvent evaporation started almost immediately after the web enters the drying tunnel. But flame drying tends to dehydrate the web, to scorch it, and to curl its edges. Another disadvantage of flame driers is that the printed image may show blisters, on coated paper in particular.

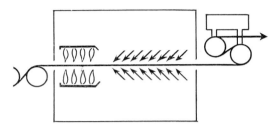

Diagram of an Offen *two-stage drier. The web is first exposed on both sides to flames and then to air. On its way to the folder the dried web is cooled.*

Multistage driers. Multistage drier is a term introduced by B. Offen & Company, builders of web drying equipment. Multistage driers are designed to retain some of the main advantages of flame drying and to eliminate their disadvantages. These driers combine flame drying with heated air drying, or radiation and convection of heat. "The printed web is passed into an insulated tunnel with grater rollers to support the web to bring up the temperature of the paper quickly so that the solvents in the ink can start to evaporate. Following the flame zone, the web then passes to a hot air drying zone. Here, air temperatures of 600° to 650°F. are applied directly to the web through a series of air knives. The application of the high velocity air tends to sweep the solvent vapors from the surface, causing rapid evaporation and rapid drying"[240]

Hot-air driers. As mentioned in the preceding unit on forced drying of sheetfed printing, the screen-process industry uses "jet" driers which dry the printed sheet by scrubbing it with hot air. Web printing must of course be equipped with driers that have a much higher capacity corresponding to the much faster operation of web presses. Hot-air drying without previous flaming is considered adequate for these tasks provided that it applies high air velocity. Hot-air drying systems for high-speed web printing are consequently often designated as "high velocity air driers." The temperature of the air is critical and should be kept as low as possible. While solvents are being extracted, the temperature of the resins and waxes (which are ingredients of printing inks) is also being raised, and they become almost fluid. Too much heat will cause these substances to be absorbed into the paper, lost into the atmosphere, or to be changed chemically. Excessive temperatures destroy gloss and rub resistance of the ink. High heat sources are efficient for quickly bringing materials up to temperature, but the higher the temperature supplied, the more critical the problem of adjust-

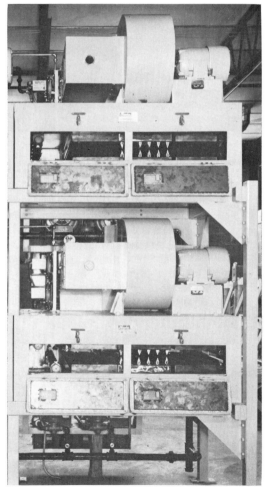

Courtesy Web Press Engineering, Inc.

A two-pass unit of an Otepka *high velocity hot air drier. Each pass can dry one web printed on both sides. (Webs pass through the compartments with the open flames.) Each unit is self-contained; two or more units can be used in sequence.*

ing to variations in the time the web is exposed to the drier and in materials to be dried."[241]

High-velocity driers have, like everything else, also certain disadvantages. One of them is that they may cause web flutter; others are their bulkiness and the high consumption of electrical energy needed for the operation of their blowers and other equipment. (Web flutter is particularly objectionable in the drying of perfected webs.)

High-velocity drying of perfected webs. The application of high-velocity hot-air drying to perfected webs (which are printed on both sides prior to drying) was made possible "by a new invention called the web stabilizer. In the words of its inventor, the *web stabilizer* uses air nozzles at close intervals to place the drying air in position to firmly support the web. In addition it tends to prevent the web from wrinkling in the web direction. Variations in web width have little effect on operation. Slight web tension must be maintained, less than one pound per inch, which is no problem on perfecting presses."[242] The new drying system is based on recently gained knowledge about mass transfer or the problems connected with the evaporation of liquids. Mass transfer "is simply the name physicists have given to the flow of molecules of a vaporized liquid substance from a surface to the air stream above the surface in the drying process. In their passage from the surface to the air stream, these molecules are obstructed by a thin boundary layer film of air on the surface. The flow of heat from the air stream to the surface is similarly affected by the boundary layer film. In both cases, the boundary layer film acts like a blanket of insulation to prevent flow. If the film is thick, high liquid vapor pressures are required to drive vapor molecules through the film in substantial amounts and high air temperatures are required to force heat through the film at good rates."[243] In the Gardner drier, high velocity of warm air is applied to the web by a number of nozzles designed to counteract the boundary effect.

Drying by radiation. Drying by radiation is at the time of writing not generally used. Many experiments were made with infrared lamps and with various heat-radiating panels. Infrared lamps proved highly successful in the baking of industrial coatings, for example in the baking of enamels applied to automobile bodies, but they were not found to be well adaptable to the forced drying of printed inks in web printing. This is so for several reasons, particularly because radiant heat produced by infrared lamps is not equally capable of drying differently pigmented inks. Different pigments, vehicles, and printing stocks react differently when exposed to infrared lamps. The effectiveness of radiant energy depends on the absorption rate of the emitted wave lengths by the ink to be dried. As an example it is mentioned that of a specific wave length "cobalt blue will absorb 86 per cent of the emitted radiation, chrome green will absorb 67 per cent, whereas chrome yellow will absorb only 59 per cent."[244] It is well known that in heat-set inks which are dried "mainly by radiant energy in certain ovens, the black ink dries faster than the colored inks because carbon blacks absorb heating rays much better than do the other colored pigments."[245] It does not take much explanation to make clear that a drying system which may produce vastly different results at the same setting from color to color is not too practical. In many instances the result may be either lack of drying or blistering after a color change with the same setting at which the drier produced perfect results before. Since operators of presses and drying equipment are not normally selected for their scientific background, they may feel helpless when they experience such difficulties.

Multifrequency heat radiation. Multifrequency heat radiation has the object of eliminating the problems encountered with radiant heat generated by infrared equipment that is limited to a narrow band of wave lengths. The desired result can be obtained by combining differently powered tubes which emit radiant heat varying considerably in wave length. "The wider frequency range in the effective radiant heat spectrum (2 to 20 microns) of a multifrequency thermal radiation source used in one installation for the drying of plastic films printed in flexography, allows more uniform absorption of heat rays by inks of various colors and composition than would be possible with heaters having a fixed or narrow output such as radiant lamps, metallic-sheathed heaters, and other heat sources. Over 90 per cent of the electrical power input to this multifrequency heat source is converted to useful high-thermal radiation. Transparent films allow most of the radiant infrared energy to pass through without absorption. Printed inks, however, absorb energy depending on their color, density and composition, and thus dry rapidly while the web remains relatively cool. The results obtained with multifrequency thermal radiation, consequently, sharply reduce chilling requirements."[246] At the time of writing multifrequency radiation is still in its experimental stage.

Section 8:   Proof Presses

Proof presses are needed for quality control and differ therefore functionally from production presses. Proof presses and production presses have several points in common and several other points in difference. Both kinds of presses need printing-image carriers, printing inks, and printing stocks; both kinds of presses produce printed images consisting of printing ink. But the manner in which the ink image is brought about and the manner in which image transfer takes place differ considerably between proof presses and production presses. Speed of operation, which is so essential in production presses, is not nearly so important in proof presses since these are not needed for quantity production but merely for quality control of image conversion and its final product, the printing-image carrier.

As you remember, the starting point of all graphic reproduction is art-and-copy, which represents the subject matter of printing. Art-and-copy must be converted into printing-image carriers before presswork can be done. The detail of image conversion depends, obviously, on the nature of the image carrier and on the process by which it is made. All image conversion methods need a number of production steps, and the result of each production step must pass one quality control test or another before it can be used further. These quality control tests vary greatly and may be rather informal, primarily based on the judgment of highly skilled craftsmen. Proofing on proof presses is, hence, one quality control method among many. Proofing may either be done as an independent operation or as part of presswork, and it may be required during image conversion in order to endow the final printing-image carrier with its proper quality.

All proofing on proof presses must be done from printing-image carriers. The image carriers used in proofing may or may not be the same as those used finally in the press for image transfer. Proofing of reading matter and proofing of pictures is usually done separately. (Practically all reading matter is proofed, whereas pictures other than full-color images are often printed without proofing.) In some instances the final image carrier is proofed on proof presses, but in many cases this step is either not necessary or not practical, and proofing of the actual image carrier is done at the beginning of presswork on the production press. Finally, it should be made clear that proofing on proof presses is the only quality control method by which printed images consisting of printing ink can be produced on other than production presses. Other quality control methods, based on photography and photomechanics, can also be used for the making of proofs in one or several colors. Such proofs differ from proofs made by means of proof presses in the chemical composition of their images which do not consist of printed ink films but of other substances.[247]

Our discussion of the subject is divided into four units: (1) introduction to proofing and proof presses, (2) proof presses for relief printing, (3) proof presses for intaglio printing, and (4) proof presses for planographic printing. Porous printing, the last of our four process families, does not use proof presses.

Introduction to Proofing and Proof Presses

Proof presses are machines for quality control, but the qualities to be controlled are not the same in all kinds of proofing. As you may remember we divide printing into two main kinds: one is the printing of reading matter, the other that of pictures. These two main kinds present entirely different image conversion problems. Reading matter, which is in most cases received by the printer as a typescript, must be converted into printing types by composition. As a rule, the appearance of the typescript, or "copy," submitted to the printer is completely changed during the process of composition. (In some instances of advertising composition, the composed images may purposely look like typed ones. But these are relatively rare and insignificant exceptions.) Pictures, which are meant by the word "art" in art-and-copy, must also be converted into printing-image carriers. Contrary to the result of converting copy, that of converting art aims at fidelity of the final printed images.[248]

Proofing of composition. Composition, or typesetting (the two words are used synonymously in the printing industry), converts reading matter into standardized letter forms. The many different methods by which this result can be attained are described in Chapter II, "Composition for Printing." For the present discussion it is relevant that metallic composition can be proofed on proof presses, whereas non-metallic composition must be proofed differently. The reason for this difference is the fact that non-metallic composition results in type images but not in physical type. The products of non-metallic composition cannot be inked and impressed, and are therefore not suitable for proofing on proof presses. Non-metallic composition is proofed by photographic or photomechanical methods before it is converted into image carriers.

Proofing of pictures. Image carriers made from pictures can be proofed either by themselves or together with reading matter. The equipment for proofing of pictorial image carriers depends on the printing method for which specific image carriers are made. In letterpress printing, presses for the proofing of composition differ from those needed for the proofing of photoengravings, particularly of photoengraving sets for full-color printing.

The dual purpose of color proofing. The purpose of proofing is, as already explained, quality control. But in full-color printing, quality control cannot restrict itself to making certain that the printing-image carrier to be proofed be of the required quality level. The image carrier is only a means, the end is the final printed product. Proofing must not only verify the quality of the image carrier, it must also provide a guide for presswork, the operation whereby the final printed images are produced. The compositor's, engraver's, and platemaker's proof must therefore satisfy two conditions: *the proof must be a conclusive guide for evaluation of the proofed image carrier, and it must be anticipatory of the image quality which can be obtained in presswork by means of the material used for proofing.* The latter point is of special importance in the proofing of pictures for full-color printing. If a proof made on proofing equipment cannot be satisfactorily matched in actual presswork, such a proof is misleading and can cause serious trouble between customer, platemaker or engraver, and printer. For this reason some people distinguish between anticipatory and actual press proofs, calling the first-mentioned kind "pre-proofs."

Problems attending pre-proofing. The requirement that a proof which is not made on actual production equipment should accurately anticipate the result of presswork is difficult to meet under the most favorable conditions, and more or less impossible under less favorable ones. Of the many reasons which account for these difficulties, we will explain merely the two most important ones. First, it must be understood that the printing-image carriers for proofing and those for actual presswork are often not identical, particularly not when printing is done on high-speed web printing equipment. The second difficulty is related to the intervals between the overprinting of successive color inks in proofing and in actual production. As these two points are important considerations in the proofing for several printing methods, they are here explained.

After a full-color job is proofed it can be seen whether the color separations need further correcting before they can be used for making the final printing image carrier. In this picture the reproduction technician is comparing proof and separations for further decisions.

Image carriers for proofing and image carriers for presswork. As mentioned in the preceding paragraph, image carriers for proofing are often not identical with those for presswork. This lack of identity exists in all mass production printing; it poses more problems in full-color subjects than in single-color or multicolor images. Full-color subjects pass through the stages of color separation and color correction which play no part in image conversion of single-color and multicolor images. As color separation and color correction need specialized skills and facilities not required for the conversion of single-color and multicolor images, full-color subjects are usually not converted together with other images but independent of them.

Some printing plants have their own color departments, others rely on trade engravers specializing in this type of work. In either case it is more expedient to proof full-color jobs individually than as part of the final image carrier. (An advertiser is obviously not interested in the looks of the many other pages printed together with his own advertisement but only concerned with the appearance of his own page or pages.) Full-color subjects are usually first proofed by means of plates especially made for proofing and not for presswork. The resulting proofs are submitted to the customer and after correction and approval the existing material is used for the making of the final printing-image carriers with which presswork will be done. Procedures vary, but for our purposes it is sufficient to distinguish two major divisions: one is the making of single-unit image carriers, the other is the making of multiple-unit or assembled ones.

Single-unit image carriers include wrap-around plates, either for direct or for indirect relief printing, plates for offset lithography, and rotogravure cylinders. Most single-unit image carriers are made photomechanically. As described in Chapter V, all photographic intermediates belonging to the same plate are assembled for common exposure. Such intermediates may be photographic negatives or positives, depending on the kind of image carrier wanted. The final result is a more or less large plate or cylinder for each of the color inks, usually four, with which the job is to be printed. To make the difference between image carriers for proofing and those for presswork still clearer, it is mentioned that the individually proofed full-color subjects (which may be single pages, two-page spreads, and possibly three-page foldouts) have now become parts of a single-unit image carrier which contains a large number of pages. The actual number varies depending on page size, capacity of press equipment, and other considerations. As an example large size general-interest magazines are often printed 32 pages or more to a single image carrier.

Multiple-unit, or assembled, image carriers often consist of a single plate per page and color. (The unit may be a different one, a carton or wrapper, for example, in package printing.) Multiple-unit image carriers are used in relief printing and consist of duplicate plates. For full-color rotary letterpress the plates are usually curved electrotypes made from flat photoengraving sets.

Even though the making of single-unit and that

of multiple-unit image carriers differs in many ways, for the point to be made in this explanation, both have one thing in common: they are not the same as the plates which were used to supply the customer with proofs.

Wet-on-wet printing, dry-printing, and two-and-two printing. Most full-color jobs are printed with four different inks. The appearance of the final printed image is not the same if each successive color ink is overprinted when the preceding ink film is still wet, and when it has either set or completely dried. With the exception of proofing on multicolor proof presses for photoengraving and on one kind of proof presses for rotogravure, proofing is done on single-color presses. In proofing on single-color presses, the time consumed for washup and press preparation is sufficient to permit each printed color ink, including black, to set before the next ink is applied. Truly accurate pre-proofing is therefore not possible if the job is produced by high-speed web printing. Since in web printing the inks are overprinted on wet ink films, this kind of printing is called "wet printing" or "wet-on-wet" printing in contradistinction to overprinting on set or dry ink films, which is called "dry-printing" in this context. Using these terms, it must be said that proofs for wet-on-wet printing are best made by wet-on-wet proofing and not by dry-printing.

Differences between printed images produced by dry-printed proofing and the images resulting from wet-on-wet presswork are most noticeable in web printing done at very high speeds. In sheetfed printing these differences are less pronounced since sheetfed presses are operated at much lower speeds. Shorter runs which do not need highest printing speeds, are often printed in both letterpress and offset lithography on two-color presses. Full-color printing on two-color presses combines wet-on-wet printing with dry-printing. The second and the fourth color ink are printed on the still wet ink films of the first-down and the third-down color, but the third-down color itself is dry-printed since the preceding two color inks had sufficient time to set, or possibly to dry, before the sheets were put through the second run. (The first-down ink is printed directly on the stock and does not present a problem.) This kind of color printing is often called "two-and-two printing." The letterpress industry has recognized the necessity for correlation of proofing and presswork. An important tool in this endeavor is the *PIA Standard Photoengraving Specification Manual for Let-*

terpress Printing from Electrotypes for Magazine, Catalog and Commercial Work, first published in 1950 and revised in 1962. This manual is the result of a co-operative effort in which the Magazine Printers Section of Printing Industries of America, the American Photoengravers Association, and the National Association of Printing Ink Makers participated.[249]

This introduction has the purpose of conveying to you that the proofing of full-color jobs is a task requiring considerable equipment, skill, and experience. The correct interpretation of full-color proofs needs experience combined with attentiveness to minute detail and keen color perception.

Proof Presses for Relief Printing

The process family of relief printing includes four different printing methods: (1) letterpress printing, (2) newspaper relief printing, (3) flexography, and (4) indirect relief printing. These four methods are served with three kinds of printing-image carriers: (1) metallic type and photoengravings, which are classified as original materials, (2) stereotypes, electrotypes, rubber plates, and plastic plates, which form the class of duplicate plates, and (3) shallow-etched metal plates or plates made of photopolymers, which are designated as wrap-around plates. Original materials are flat and non-curvable and must be proofed on presses equipped with a flat bed. Duplicate plates, which are made from original materials, can be either flat or curved. Curved duplicate plates may be either made flat and then mechanically curved or they may be curved as part of their manufacturing process. Wrap-around plates, finally, are flat and either assume the curvature of the plate cylinder when they are put on the press or may need pre-curving with curving jigs.

The variety of image carriers and printing methods accounts for the existing diversity of proof presses for relief printing. Flat printing-image carriers must be proofed on presses equipped with flat beds; curved image carriers must be proofed on rotary proof presses; and image carriers which are made flat and then curved can be proofed either when they are still flat or after curving. But curved-cast image carriers such as curved-cast electrotypes must be proofed on rotary proof presses. Wrap-around plates, which are approximately one-fifth as thick as flat electrotypes for flatbed-cylinder presses, cannot be proofed on existing letterpress proofing equipment if proofing is done with the object of evaluating plates for color work, but they can be proofed on flatbed proof presses for the mere purpose of reading.

Proofing techniques in the four methods of relief printing. Before we enter the discussion of various kinds of proof presses a brief rundown of techniques and equipment used for proofing in the four relief printing methods is in order. Letterpress uses predominantly flatbed proof presses. These are made for the proofing of composition and of photoengravings. Curved electrotypes are often proofed flat before they are curved, but there are also proof presses for curved plates. Wrap-around plates cannot be proofed on proof presses with a view to evaluating their quality. Newspaper relief printing uses the same equipment as letterpress for the proofing of composition and photoengravings. Curved stereotype plates are as a rule not proofed. Flexography has its own equipment, designed primarily for the assembly of rubber plates but also suitable for their proofing. (Rubber plates are duplicate plates made from composition and photoengravings. The original materials are proofed on letterpress proof presses prior to molding.) Indirect relief printing is based on wrap-around plates for which there is no proofing equipment, as already mentioned. If wrap-around plates must be proofed this is done on the actual production press.

Proofing tasks and proof presses in relief printing. Not all flat relief printing-image carriers can be proofed on the same kind of proofing equipment. The purposes of proofing differ and so do the machines which serve these purposes. The least exacting kind of proofing, requiring the least complex proofing equipment, is done to make sure that the composed matter is free of errors and imperfections. Proof presses for this purpose are called "galley proof presses." On the next higher level is the task of making reproduction proofs. Reproduction proofs are proofs of metallic composition, possibly in combination with photoengravings, serving for photomechanical production of printing-image carriers. Proof presses used for the making of reproduction proofs are precision presses, designed for the proofing of single-color photoengravings in line and in halftones as well as for making reproduction proofs. Such presses can be classified as single-color proof presses. The most exacting kind of proofing is that of proofing photoengraving sets for full-color printing. Presses which are designed to cope with the problems of proofing for high-speed printing are needed for this purpose unless the actual presswork is done on slow equipment. Such presses are here grouped under the head of multicolor proof presses. These three kinds of proof presses are all built for the proofing of flat material. Curved image carriers, electrotypes primarily, must be proofed on rotary presses which are available as single-color presses only and flexographic plates are proofed on equipment differing from that for other relief methods.

The following discussion of proof presses for relief printing is therefore divided into five points: (1) galley proof presses, (2) single-color proof presses, (3) multicolor proof presses, (4) proof presses for curved electrotypes, and (5) proof presses for flexography.

Galley proof presses. Galley proof presses are a necessity in metallic composition. Proofing is needed to make sure that the composed type matter corresponds faithfully to the original typescript and that it is free of mistakes, particularly in spelling and hyphenation, as the division of words is commonly called. Galley proofing does not only serve for ascertaining the grammatical correctness of composition, it also makes it possible to do the same for its typographic quality. Proofing permits identification of damaged characters, upside-down characters, letters of the wrong font or wrong point size, to mention a few examples of frequently occurring minor typographic defects. Of equal importance is the arrangement of the composed matter, and proofing makes it possible to verify whether type faces and sizes, length of lines, and word spacing (or when required, letter spacing)

Pulling proof of a type form.

are done properly and in accordance with customer instructions and the typographic rules to be followed in a particular composing room. (The cycle of composing, proofing, reading, and correcting of proofs, correcting of the composed matter and re-proofing is described in Chapter II, "Composition for Printing.") Galley proofing is an essential phase of metallic composition, and for this reason there are probably more galley proof presses in operation than any other kind of proofing equipment. (Proofing of non-metallic composition is, of course, equally essential. But as it is not done on proof presses, it is outside the present discussion.)

Two different constructions of flatbed-cylinder proof presses. Galley proof presses are flatbed-cylinder presses. The composed matter is placed on the flatbed, inked, and the impression is made by the impression cylinder which may or may not be equipped for carrying the paper on which the impression is to be made. Proof presses are built either with a moving bed or with a stationary bed. The *moving bed construction* is built on the principle of the two-revolution flatbed-cylinder press: the cylinder rotates in a stationary position and the bed makes a reciprocating motion. The other kind of proof presses with a *stationary bed construction* is built on the same principle as flatbed-cylinder presses for newspaper relief printing: the bed is stationary and the impression cylinder reciprocates, or moves back and forth over it. The reciprocating bed principle is used by several manufacturers of proof presses, Challenge Machinery Company, to mention one. The stationary, or rigid, bed construction is used by Vandercook & Sons; all Vandercook proofing equipment has stationary beds and reciprocating impression cylinders.

Various models of galley proof presses. Galley proof presses are manufactured in a number of different models which vary, apart from the basic construction principle, in the inking and in the positioning of the paper for the impression, as well as in the removal of the printed proof. At its simplest, proofing is done on presses which are hand-operated and do not have provisions for inking. This operation is performed by hand with an inking roller mounted in a simple metal holder equipped with a handle. Such a hand-inking roller is called a "brayer" by printers. Proof presses for hand-inking are usually provided with a metal plate for working the ink with the brayer until it is ready for application to the type. Then the galley is inked; next the paper is laid on the inked galley, and the impression is made by rolling the rubber-covered impression cylinder over it. Finally the printed proof is lifted by the operator from the galley. Reciprocating flatbed proof presses are also available for hand-inking. They have a stationary impression cylinder and are operated by a crank which is turned by the craftsman. The laying on of the paper and the removal of the printed proof are performed just as on hand-inked stationary bed proof presses. "The large, full size ink plate also serves as a cover for the cylinder and is removable for changing the packing. The bed is equipped with a removable galley plate, so that proofs can be made either while the type is in galleys or directly from type forms." [250]

On a somewhat higher technological level are presses equipped with a separate inking unit whereby hand-inking with the brayer is eliminated. Presses of this construction can be used for the pulling of galley proofs and of page proofs, but they are not designed for the taking of reproduction proofs. The press model here referred to has a stationary flatbed, an inking unit, and a separate, independent impression cylinder. The inking unit is moved by hand across the bed. This step is followed by laying on of the paper and by then manually moving the impression cylinder in the opposite direction for making the impression. "In the beginning of the operation the inking roller carriage is at one end of the press and the cylinder carriage on the other. With the galley placed in position on the bed of the press, the operator then brings the inking roller carriage across the form in one swift motion bringing the rollers to rest on the ink plate under the cylinder at the opposite end. The sheet is then laid down on the inked matter, and the cylinder pulled across to the opposite end to pull a proof. The press inks both ways and prints both ways of its travel, thereby making every motion count." [251]

Power-driven galley proof presses. Finally, we mention power-driven galley presses which are used in composing rooms of newspapers and particularly in book composition where large quantities of galley proofs are needed. Such presses can take either full-length galleys of type, or made-up pages, up to a size of 12 by 27 inches, and have automatic inking systems and power-driven impression cylinders equipped with grippers for holding the paper. These galley presses can be operated either in individual cycles or continuously. The production of electric galley proof presses may be as high as 40 proofs per minute. This large capacity is often desirable in book composition when advance editions for promotional purposes are needed. Of other valuable features found on such presses merely one is mentioned, namely, that they are equipped with automatic washup. [252]

Single-color proof presses. Under the head of single-color proof presses we describe precision proofing equipment used for the pulling of reproduction proofs of composition, photoengravings, and flat duplicate plates. The presses described under this head and under the following head of multicolor proof presses are manufactured by Vandercook & Sons. The reason for limiting these descriptions to the products of one firm is that a survey made by the International Typographic Composition Association in 1962 found "that 96 per cent of all presses reported in use for reproduction proofs are Vandercooks." [253] Vandercook distinguish between proof presses for galley proofs, or rough engraver's proofs, and presses "that would serve as testing instruments for accurately checking the printability of types and plates. Therefore, according to Vandercook & Sons, a machine for ordinary proofs should be designated as a proof press, while a machine capable of critically evaluating printing plates and type forms should be regarded as a test press." [254] This point of view explains why proof presses described in the following are designated as test presses by their manufacturer.

Wet-on-wet proofing of photoengraving sets for full-color printing on a Vandercook *test press equipped for frisketing.*

We describe the Vandercook Universal I Test Press since it is the most frequently used current model for pulling reproduction proofs. Like all other Vandercook presses it has a stationary, or rigid, bed and a traveling head which carries the inking system and the impression cylinder on which the paper is held by cylinder grippers. The press is made in a power-driven and in a hand-operated version. The maximum sheet size is 15¼ by 24 inches. A fully equipped press has automatic washup, a bed adjustable in its height, automatic sheet delivery, power-operated grippers with adjustable time delay, and an ink fountain. Automatic frisketing equipment and equipment for the printing of transparent plastics is also available. Another feature of this and other Vandercook presses is the optional "Positive Lockup Bar" which makes it possible to proof made-up pages with great speed. This feature is particularly useful in advertising composition.

The Universal I Test Press is adaptable for type-high material as well as for photoengravings and for electrotypes before they are mounted. This versatility is due to the bed construction which can be raised or lowered depending on the height of the material to be proofed.

The described press is only one of several comprising the Vandercook line of single-color proof presses. Nor are single-color proof presses solely made as stationary bed machines; they are also available as reciprocating-bed and stationary impression cylinder presses. These presses come in several models, and some of them have automatic inking systems. All American-made reciprocating-bed proof presses are hand-operated. The proofer turns a crank which moves the bed under the impression cylinder, thereby making the impression.[255]

Multicolor proof presses. Multicolor proof presses are designed for the proofing of full-color photoengraving sets. At the time of writing, such presses are made by Vandercook only. The problems attending the proofing of photoengravings for high-speed web printing are explained in the preceding "Introduction to Proofing and Proof Presses." You may remember that one of these problems is the making of an anticipatory proof that will permit duplication of the proofed images during presswork. Another problem of proofing derives from the fact that most full-color engraving sets are made not for printing in the press, but for the making of duplicate plates, usually electrotypes, which are the actual image carriers for presswork. Such sets of photoengravings have often relatively large non-printing areas. They are best not removed prior to electrotyping, and, as ink transfer from them is undesirable, multicolor proof presses are provided with frisketing devices. (The subject is discussed in some detail in Chapter V, Section 3, under the head "Proofing of Photoengravings.")

Internal and external proofing. Proofing of full-color engravings can be divided, like all other proofing, into internal and external proofing. *Internal proofs* are needed to guide craftsmen in the improving and correcting of engravings. When the engraver is satisfied with the result, *external* or *submission proofs* are pulled for approval by the customer. A third and most important purpose of proofing is to provide engraver's proofs, which are taken from engravings already approved by the customer, as a guide for electrotyping and, last but not least, as a guide for presswork. Full co-operation between photoengravers, electrotypers, and printers is consequently a true necessity.

Approximation of wet-on-wet presswork in the proofing of photoengraving sets. The main problem in the making of proofs for full-color printing is the rapidity in which successive color images are overprinted in actual presswork in comparison with the slower speed at which they can be proofed. This subject is familiar to you from the introductory unit and needs no further discussion. Since it is impossible to approximate the speed of wet printing (especially in high-speed magazine printing) with single-color proof presses, different proofing equipment was developed for this purpose. It is interesting to note that one of the largest printing and publishing companies was instrumental in this development. "Some time before America's entry in World War II, the Vandercook Company was commissioned by the Curtis Publishing Company of Philadelphia (the publishers and printers of the *Saturday Evening Post* and the *Ladies Home Journal* and other magazines) to design and produce a four-color high-speed test press that would be capable of delivering a finished four-color *wet proof* in the shortest practical period of time."[256] Vandercook had introduced in 1937 a completely power-operated two-color press and, interrupted by World War II, delivered its first four-color press in 1946 to the Curtis Publishing Company.

Vandercook High Speed 4-Color Test Presses. Vandercook presses for the proofing of full-color engraving sets are made in two versions. One model is the Vandercook Universal V High Speed 2- and 4-Color Test Press, the other is the Vandercook 30-26 Double 4-Color High Speed Test Press. The difference between these two models is that the first has two sequential printing stations, whereas the second press has four of them. Each printing station has its own independently adjustable bed, and each bed can be divided into two parts. Thereby it is possible to provide four differently adjustable beds, each one-half of the width of the undivided bed on a two-color press. The printing head has two inking units which can also be divided in half to correspond with the width of the divided beds. The printing head can therefore print four colors in a single pass, though not in sequence. First, a sheet is proofed in two colors; then the same sheet is proofed on the other half in the remaining two colors. At the same time a new sheet may be proofed in the first two colors. If this technique is used, every cycle of the press produces two impressions: one in two and the other in four colors.

The Vandercook Universal V High Speed 2- and 4-Color Test press can proof either "one 2-color set up to 29 by 25½ inches, impression time two seconds; or proof two 2-color sets up to 13½ by 25 inches, impression time two seconds; or proof one 4-color set up to 13½ by 25½ inches, impression time 20 seconds."[257] In proofing a set of engravings for full-color printing, two colors, say yellow and magenta, are proofed first. After refeeding, the remaining two color inks, cyan and black, are applied to the sheet. (The rotation of color inks, or their sequence, is not uniform. Proofing must be done in the same sequence that is selected for presswork.) The impression time for two-color proofing is rated by the manufacturer as two seconds, that for four-color proofing including refeeding is rated as 20 seconds.

The main loss in time occurs, as you can see, during refeeding. This operation is eliminated with four-color presses having four different printing stations. These presses are equipped with automatic delivery of the printed sheet on the feed board and with automatic frisketing, not to speak of many other features which permit adjustment and controlling of many factors of importance in proofing for wet-printing. The automatic frisketing feature makes it possible to proof unrouted engravings without showing ungainly ink blotches on the proof. The frisket is a paper stencil in which the printing areas are cut out, whereas

the unrouted non-printing areas are not. After inking the frisket is automatically positioned between the photoengraving and the paper before the impression is made. The frisket prevents ink transfer in the areas which are not cut out.[258]

Proof presses for curved electrotypes. Curved electrotypes must be proofed on presses equipped with an impression cylinder having the same diameter as the impression cylinder of the actual production press. The impression cylinder must, further, permit the attaching of electrotypes in the same manner (either by compression or by tension lockup) as they will be attached on the plate cylinder of the production press. As rotary letterpress equipment for printing with curved electros is often built to order, both impression cylinder diameters and thicknesses of plates may vary within wide limits. Consequently, trade electrotypers, who service many printing plants, are called upon to supply electros of varying thickness and curvature. This condition complicates the proofing of curved electros since differently curved electros cannot be attached on the same plate cylinder for proofing. For this reason electrotypers prefer to make proofs from flat electros before they are curved. This technique can obviously not be used for the proofing of curved electros which do not pass through a flat stage.

Large publication printing plants often operate their own electrotyping foundries. Since most of these plants standardize their equipment as much as possible, they need to consider few or no variations in the thickness and curvature of their electrotypes. The builders of equipment for publication printing in letterpress are usually prepared to supply matching proof presses to customers of their production presses. Various makes of proof presses for curved electros differ in their detail. In general they are built as single color presses only. Wet-proofing of curved electros is not customary.

The Flower Multi Diameter Proof Press. In 1962, the Flower Multi Diameter Proof Press for curved electrotypes was introduced. The main feature of this "press is that cylinders of different diameters can be interchanged on the basic press frame and bed assembly. This system eliminates the necessity of having an individual proof press for each diameter of plate manufactured."[259] The Multi Diameter Proof Press is a flatbed-cylinder press. The plate cylinder is housed in a carriage which moves across the flatbed on which the paper is positioned. The press can be either hand- or power-driven; the inking system is motor-driven. The plate cylinder can be equipped for compression or for tension lockup and adapted for the proofing of wrap-around plates.[260]

Proofing equipment for flexographic printing. Rubber plates for flexographic printing are either proofed on the production press or by means of proofing equipment which combines facilities for the mounting of plates and the taking of proofs. Several makes of proof presses for flexographic printing are available. For space reasons we can describe only one, the Mosstype Mounter-Proofer. This equipment is used for the dressing of the plate cylinder which will be ultimately placed in the production press bearing the required number of plates. In flexography, proofing is not done separately for each plate but for the assembly of all plates to be printed at the same time from the same plate cylinder. The Mounter-Proofer is manually operated and consists of a heavy stand which is equipped with a proofing cylinder, gears, control devices, and a flat plateholder. The plate cylinder of the production press is inserted into the Mounter-Proofer, and its own gear is meshed with the gear of the "proofing cylinder," as the impression cylinder is here called. The individual rubber plates are assembled in their correct positions on a plateholder which lays the plates from above on the plate cylinder. Precision measuring devices facilitate this operation and contribute to high accuracy. After the cylinder is dressed, the plateholder (which is counterbalanced) is swung out of the way for proofing. The plates are inked by hand with a roller, and the impression is made by turning the proofing cylinder with its handwheel.[261] Finally, it is mentioned that wet-proofing is not possible with the kind of proofing equipment described. But wet-proofing is much less needed in flexography since full-color printing is not nearly as frequent in this method as in high-speed letterpress, gravure, and web-offset printing.

Proof Presses for Intaglio Printing

Intaglio printing is in this manual divided into the methods of steel-die engraving, banknote printing, sheetfed gravure, and rotogravure. Of these methods rotogravure is the only one for which proof presses are built. In the other three methods, proofing is done on production presses, though not necessarily always as a part of press-work. The proofing problems in rotogravure are essentially the same as those in all other printing methods for mass production printing. In gravure,

too, the conversion of full-color images into printing-image carriers requires the most critical kind of proofing. For our purposes proofing can be divided into two kinds: one is the proofing of intermediates, the other is the proofing of actual rotogravure cylinders.

Industry practices as to the making and proofing of gravure cylinders are not uniform. Some gravure plants are prepared to handle internally both image conversion of art-and-copy as well as the making of cylinders. Other plants rely for these services on trade engravers from whom they buy their cylinders. Between these extremes we find companies that handle some phases of image conversion internally and use the services of trade houses for others. Many gravure printers who will internally handle single-color and multicolor art-and-copy including the etching of cylinders may not want to do color separation and color correction of full-color images, but rather buy these services outside. The products delivered to them by trade engravers consist of sets of color-separation positives and sets of progressive proofs showing the printed images which were obtained from image carriers made with the same color-separation positives. The proof-books become, assuming customer approval, the guides for cylinder etching.

In publication printing of gravure supplements, proofing is especially important. In this field, the customary procedure is to charge trade houses with the making of color separations and with proofing regardless of the facilities available in the plants where the supplements will finally be printed. The reason for this procedure is the desire for uniformity on the part of national advertisers who want to be sure that their advertisements will appear as approved by them in all regions of the United States. Syndicated gravure supplements are supplied by their publishers to newspapers from coast to coast and from Canada to Mexico. They are printed in huge quantities, and it is obviously neither practical nor economical to produce such quantities in a central plant and to ship the vast tonnage of printed paper all over the country. Printing of gravure supplements is, therefore, best done regionally by a number of gravure printing plants. Regional plants receive a set of gravure positives together with proofs of national advertisements which are frequently to be reproduced in full-color printing. The actual printing cylinders are made regionally, either by the cylinder-making department of the gravure printing plant, or by a trade engraver. These cylinders must be made to enable a faithful and uniform reproduction of the approved quality level during presswork. Ideally, the final printed images and the proofs provided with the sets of color separation positives should match.

Proofs of full-color advertisements for gravure are, hence, anticipatory or pre-proofs and resemble in this respect proofs of photoengravings for rotary letterpress printing with electrotypes. In both cases the image carrier used for proofing is different from the image carrier used for presswork. A very similar condition exists in offset lithography when submission proofs are not made from the final press plate but from individually proofed sets of color separation positives or negatives.

As already mentioned, proofing in rotogravure can be divided into that of proofing of intermediates (sets of color-separation positives) and that of gravure cylinders. The proofing of intermediates has four purposes: (1) quality control in the making of intermediates, (2) providing submission proofs which enable the advertiser to judge the appearance of his advertisement, (3) supplying those who are responsible for the quality of etched cylinders with a guide for the expected appearance of the final printed images, and (4) furnishing a guide for presswork. If the customer will not be shown individually printed proofs of his job but rather proofs made from etched cylinders, the purpose of proofing is the same in points (1) and (2); point (3) is eliminated but point (4), to provide a guide for presswork, remains valid. In all instances the crucial function of a proof remains the same. "A good proof is one that is consistent and accurately tells what results can be obtained from the etching and in such a manner that the production press-run can always duplicate the proof."[262]

Proofing of color-separation sets. As each subject for full-color printing may need individual treatment, all pages are proofed prior to cylinder making either by themselves or together with other subjects of similar nature. This practice is followed in both trade engraving plants and color departments of gravure printers. Proofing is quite often done on single-color sheetfed presses, but it can also be done on multicolor presses. The image carriers for proofing are copper plates which are much less expensive than gravure cylinders. "Gravure engravers and some printers make use of sheetfed equipment such as the large and small L & M English presses. This type of press is ideal

for running four-color proofs and progressives (which show each of the four separated color images by themselves and are often called *progs*) of one to four ads, or double spread pages of magazine or newspaper size."[263]

The following paragraphs refer to proof presses for the proofing of etched gravure cylinders which are the image carriers of rotogravure. Proofs of cylinders made for full-color printing are a link between an engraver's proofs made for submission to the customer and approved by him, and the final product to be printed on production equipment. In such cases the proofs of cylinders must, ideally, match two different kinds of images. One is the image present on the submission proof, the other is the image that will be produced by the press.

Various kinds of proof presses for rotogravure. The proofing of gravure cylinders is a task that poses different problems in jobs to be printed in a single color (or, as the industry says, in monotone), in jobs that use several colors, and in full-color printing. The proofing of single-color image carriers can be done on comparatively simple proofing equipment which may also be suitable for the proofing of multicolor jobs. The proofing of cylinders made for full-color printing is a much more difficult task requiring higher skill and more complex equipment.

Five different kinds of proof presses for gravure image carriers are used in this industry, even though some of them may be considered outdated at present. These five kinds of proof presses are: (1) the Klingrose proof press, (2) the Stoessel proof press, (3) Southern Gravure proofing equipment, (4) low-speed open fountain proof presses, and (5) the Cerutti multicolor, variable size proof press. The first three kinds of presses are mainly used for package printing; the last two serve for the proofing of cylinders in publication printing.

The Klingrose proof press. This press has been in use since the early fifties of this century. "It takes cylinders from 10 to 62 inches in width and consists of a large impression cylinder covered with a rubber blanket. The sheet of stock remains in fixed position while a number of cylinders are moved into contact and registered with it. A bead of ink of about three ounces is placed the length of the inverted doctor blade while one turn of the cylinder is made to transfer the ink to the stock. Single or multicolor proofs can be obtained in this manner."[264]

Courtesy The Beck Engraving Company

A group of Stoessel *presses which are used for proofing of gravure plates. These presses can also serve for producing small production runs.*

The Stoessel proof press. The Stoessel proof press was introduced at approximately the same time as the Klingrose machine. "This equipment was an improvement on the original idea of using a lay-down machine for proofing cylinders. In fact the equipment was sold for the combined use as both lay-down machine and also proof press. It is possible to make sets of progressive proofs with the Stoessl machine."[265]

Southern Gravure proofing equipment. The proof press developed by Southern Gravure is "a modification of the Klingrose press, providing for the engraved cylinder to be carried to the impression drum, and the entire operation of the press was motorized for faster production."[266]

The low-speed open-fountain proof press. This kind of proof press is used in mass production printing of publications, especially those carrying advertisements in full color. "When the majority of the cylinders to be proofed consist of full-color work which is done in four-color printing, more proofings will be required than in line work and in the printing of solid tone areas in one, two or three colors which do not overprint. This is particularly true where a large amount of advertising is involved. The exacting demands of advertising agencies and their clients must be complied with."[267] Low-speed open-fountain presses are web presses having usually four printing units. Their speed is in the neighborhood of 125 f.p.m., whereas that of production presses can be ten times as much and more. The ink fountains are open and can be connected to portable ink storage tanks. The press is not equipped with driers. "Normally, one proofing is sufficient for mono-tone and spot-color cylinders. Full forms of four-color editorial and advertising usually require three and sometimes four proofings to insure good balance and faithful color reproductions."[268]

The Cerutti multicolor variable size proof press. The Cerutti proof press is a relatively recent addition to proofing presses for rotogravure cylinders. This proof press is a web press capable of handling a web width of 102 inches on standard models. It has a four-roll stand for four different widths of paper. "Each printing unit has a high-speed steam-heated air-knife drier, pneumatic impression control, pneumatic-loaded doctor blade, elevating fountain, motorized differential gear box for length register control, manual side guide, and push button station. The variable size feature of the press enables it to handle cylinders of any face length up to 86½ inches, any circumferences from 16 to 51 inches, and virtually any length and diameter of cylinder shaft."[269]

Proofing was, and in some cases still is, one of the bottlenecks in gravure publication printing. Some companies still proof on production equipment, a rather expensive method of proofing as "it has been estimated that where proofing is performed on regular production presses, down-time cost can average up to $1,000 a day."[270] Even complex and costly proofing equipment is considered less expensive by competent industry people than proofing on large production presses which have an excessively high down-time rate.

Proof Presses for Offset Lithography

Offset lithography uses a number of proofing techniques; proofing with proof presses is only one of them. The generally most important proofing techniques for offset lithography are discussed in Chapter V, Section 5; at this point the subject is rounded out by descriptions of several models of proof presses for offset lithography. As in other printing methods proofing of full-color subjects is more important than proofing of single-color and multicolor jobs. Proofs of full-color subjects can be made on single-color and on multicolor production presses. Single-color production presses are used exclusively for proofing in some plants and by many lithographic trade shops. If multicolor presses are used for proofing then proofing is usually done at the beginning of the press run.

The three basic types of proof presses for offset lithography. Proof presses for offset lithography can be grouped into three basic types that differ mainly in the extent to which their operation is done manually. These three kinds can be classified as (1) hand proof presses, (2) power proof presses, and (3) automatic proof presses. All proof presses built at the time of writing are flatbed presses;

Courtesy Rutherford Machinery Company

An offset proof press with manual inking and dampening. The blanket cylinder is power driven. Plate and paper are next to each other on a plate bed and on an impression bed.

the paper for proofing and the plate to be proofed are side by side on the flat press bed. Automatic proof presses have usually two beds next to each other. One bed is sometimes called the paper bed, the other is the plate bed. Each bed can be individually adjusted in its height. These adjustments can be important features when different stocks and different kinds of plates are to be proofed or when proof presses are used as production presses for such items as dials and scales.

During operation the plate and the stock are stationary; the moving member is a proofing head of differing construction. Proof presses for offset lithography are built both in this country and overseas. Until 1964 domestic proof presses were manufactured by a single press builder, the Rutherford Machinery Company, a Division of Sun Chemical Corporation; in 1964 Vandercook & Sons, Inc., entered the field with a newly designed automatic press. The following brief descriptions of hand proof presses and of power proof presses are based on Rutherford equipment because these presses are the most widely used ones at the time of writing.

Hand proof presses for offset lithography. Hand proof presses are not equipped with dampening and inking units. The moving head bears a blanket cylinder in its carriage which is hand-driven. For proofing "the plate is lightly dampened with a sponge and while still wet with fountain solution, ink is applied with a hand roller. When the plate is fully charged with ink, the excess water is removed by fanning. Then the moving head with the blanket is rolled over the inked plate. Thereby the impression is picked up on the blanket cylinder which then deposits the ink image on the paper held by grippers on the impression bed."[271] At the time of writing, hand proof presses are built only in a single sheet size, 17 by 22 inches. In the past these presses were made in several sizes, and many larger presses for hand proofing are still in operation.

Power proof presses for lithography. Dampening and inking are done in the same way on power proof presses as on hand proof presses, since power proof presses are not equipped with dampening and inking units. The head bearing the blanket cylinder is not hand-driven but power-operated in this kind of press. "There are two advantages in the use of a power proof press: (1) the speed with which the blanket cylinder moves from the plate to the paper has some bearing on print quality and thickness of the final ink film. The power proof press enables the proofer to maintain a uniform printing speed and consequently to produce proofs of a higher quality and greater uniformity. (2) The increased efficiency of the power press makes longer proofing runs possible."[272] Power proof presses are made in three sizes: 24 by 28 inches, 30 by 36 inches, and 32 by 44 inches.

Automatic proof presses for offset lithography. Automatic proof presses are equipped with a

Proofing of an offset lithographic plate on an S & S *flatbed offset press. The moving head of this press is equipped for inking and dampening as well as for making the impression.*

dampening and inking system which is part of the moving head in addition to the blanket cylinder. They are designed to produce proofs which correspond to the prints made on production presses. "Uniformity of proof sheets is assured and production speed is increased enough to make short runs possible. Sheets are hand-fed, however. The speed of an automatic proof press is consequently much slower than that of a production press."[273] Automatic proof presses have many valuable features and controls. They can be used for printing on metal and other rigid materials which cannot be hand-fed by rotary offset presses built for printing of paper or metal decorating. Rutherford automatic proof presses are available in three standard sizes: 24 by 32 inches, 40 by 52 inches, and 48 by 62 inches. They "produce up to 200 prints per hour on paper, 300 per hour on metal."[274] Vandercook offers one size, the Vandercook 20-26 Flat Bed Offset Press which handles a maximum sheet of 21 by 27 inches. This press has many original features, among them an adjustment for the size of the printed image. "To take care of sheet stretch or shrink between colors, the print can be made up to ⅛ inch longer or ⅛ inch shorter than the size of the image on the plate by merely shifting one knob."[275]

Single-color proofing and wet-printing. All offset proof presses, domestic or imported ones, are single-color presses. In proofing for full-color printing, which requires usually four different plates and four different proofings, the time elapsed between subsequent color proofings is considerable. These intervals permit each proofed ink to set (and possibly even to dry) before the next ink is applied. This kind of proofing is similar to the production of full-color work on single color presses, and sometimes called dry-printing to distinguish it from wet-printing. In dry-printing the preceding ink film is either set or dry, but never wet when the next ink film is applied. Since not much full-color printing is done on single-color presses, single-color proofing is not a true anticipation of the final result obtainable on production presses. This problem is extensively discussed in the first unit of this section: "Introduction to Proofing and Proof Presses." Here it is merely repeated that the interpretation of a proof made on single-color presses as a means for guiding presswork in high-speed wet-printing requires experience and familiarity with the actual production equipment.

Neither of the two remaining printing methods, collotype and screen process, uses proof presses. Collotype is done on single-color presses and collotype plates are proofed on them, either as separate proofing runs or at the beginning of presswork. Screen-process printing utilizes hand printing for proofing: presswork may be done either by hand printing or on power-driven screen-process presses. Hand printed proofs are suitable in either case.

Chapter VII

Presswork

Presswork is the terminus on the long road from original images to printed images. It is the decisive test of the many production steps taken in the conversion of art-and-copy into printing-image carriers. During presswork these are combined with printing inks and printing stocks for image transfer which results in the final printed images. The actions of the press and the properties of image carriers, printing inks, and paper or other printing stocks must be carefully co-ordinated and adjusted for obtaining the proper result. In no other stage of printing production can the interrelatedness of all printing elements be seen as clearly as in presswork; in no other stage of printing production is it possible to observe how much the final result depends on the fitting of each component element to all others.

Presswork is done on a vast variety of equipment which differs widely in complexity and technological level. But all presswork has, nevertheless, one common characteristic: it is the most mechanized phase of the graphic arts, the mass production phase of contemporary printing. All preceding steps have the object of image conversion and result either in a unique printing-image carrier or in a small number of duplicates, usually not exceeding a few dozens. Presswork is the only phase of printing which produces identical products in large quantities, ranging from thousands to tens of thousands, to hundreds of thousands, going often into the millions. Presswork, together with the printing presses needed for it, is therefore that phase of printing which reflects most of all of our contemporary mass-production techniques.

In Chapter VI, "Printing Presses," the main units of presses are discussed for each process family and its different methods. In the present chapter these units are shown in their interaction as co-ordinated parts of presses, each having its share in the production of printed images which are the final results of printing proper, disregarding for the moment binding or other finishing operations by which printed sheets or webs are converted into the shape needed for their end use.

This chapter is divided into five sections. Section 1 is a preface to presswork; Section 2 discusses presswork in relief printing; Section 3, presswork in intaglio printing; Section 4, presswork in planographic printing; and Section 5, presswork in screen-process, or porous printing.

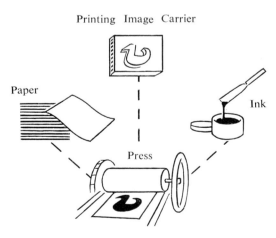

Paper, image carrier, ink, and press are the four members of the printing quartet. They all must be in tune.

Section 1:   A Preface to Presswork

Many buyers and users of printing, and also craftsmen active in other phases of the industry, have rather inadequate notions of the nature of presswork and the skills it demands. A widespread idea is that presswork takes place automatically, anyhow: "You simply press a button and the machine does the rest." Variations of this opinion are, unfortunately, rather frequent; they are completely incorrect, as everybody who is informed on, and interested in, presswork will confirm. It is true that mass-production equipment is highly mechanized and that much of it is provided with automatic controls. Without such controls the high speeds at which mass-production presses run would simply be out of the question. These more or less automatic controls are probably the factual basis on which current misconceptions of presswork rest. But the result produced by the existence of such controls is far from making presswork more simple. Quite the contrary! The more complex our presses become, the higher are the demands made on skills, knowledge, and resourcefulness of operating personnel. The horse-and-buggy of bygone times was certainly an incomparably simpler means of locomotion than contemporary equipment for transportation. But can there be any doubt where higher operating skills are needed—on the coachman's seat or in the pilot's cabin of a plane?

Another point seems to be worth mentioning. Presswork is, generally speaking, less represented in the literature than other subjects of printing production, composition, for example. There are several books in print that discuss presswork either as one of several subjects or as their main theme. Some of these books are written for the purpose of instructing high-school students who take a course in printing, others are for the training of plant personnel. Many good books are available for this purpose, especially the texts published by the Graphic Arts Technical Foundation, but in keeping with their purpose such books are devoted to presswork in a single printing method or with a certain kind of presses. The enormous proliferation and specialization of presses and presswork so far has not been reflected in the literature.

For all these reasons, presswork is described more extensively in this manual than might be expected. To avoid misunderstandings, it is added that the discussions of presswork have, as all other explanations found in this manual, the purpose of generating understanding and not that of teaching operational skills. We are, consequently, not concerned with describing each and every one of the many presses that can be found in the pressrooms of different plants and in the catalogs of press manufacturers.

On the other hand, we cannot restrict ourselves to highly generalized discussions, since such discussions are completely meaningless to the uninformed reader for whom this book is written. Consequently, wherever it was thought necessary, step-by-step descriptions of various kinds of presswork were prepared. The coverage is broad; it includes presswork on more than twenty different kinds of presses used for the printing of a great variety of products. Some of the following descriptions, which pertain to typical kinds of presses, can be made generically, without mentioning specific makes of equipment. Wherever this approach is practicable it is used, in the discussion of presswork on flatbed-cylinder presses and single-color offset lithographic presses, to mention two examples. But in many other instances this approach is not open because each make of equipment has its own distinctive characteristics and must therefore be identified in the interest of clarity and consistency of description.

Whenever the writer could not find sufficient information in the literature on subjects which seemed of importance to him, he tried to get the information by making visits to plants where the kind of presswork to be described is practiced. Much of this and the next four sections were thus developed. The reader is informed in each case in which plant this work was done and which equipment is described. This method of gathering firsthand information has great advantages; unfortunately it has, like any other method, also some drawbacks. It could appear to readers that some printing plants and some makes of equipment were singled out as the most outstanding ones, thereby reflecting on competitive plants and competitive machines. This is certainly not intended and would be an unwarranted deduction, since value judgments of competitive machinery are not a proper subject for this manual. The considerations governing field work were quite different ones. Whenever possible, plant visits were arranged near the writer's own location, which is Philadelphia. To find the right plant within a short traveling distance was not always easy. The second and even more difficult problem was to find the right plants which were also in a position to co-operate. Management had to be willing to permit their technical key personnel to take the time necessary for demonstration of the equipment, and management had to permit discussion of the methods used in their company. Technical key personnel sacrificed free time such as evenings and Saturdays for working with the writer. Usually three to five meetings were needed for collecting the information needed for description; in some cases of complex manufacturing processes, it took even longer. Finally, it is explicitly mentioned that the equipment here described by name is usually not the only one of its kind. But the described equipment is always of generally recognized merit, suitable to serve as a representative example.

After this space-consuming but inevitable explanation of the reasons for selecting some presses for description we can turn at last to the subject itself. This preface contains two units: one is concerned with a clarification of several terms which are widely used in discussing presswork, though unfortunately not always with the same meaning; the other unit is an exposition of the main operational tasks of which presswork consists.

Makeready, Packing, and Register

The terms "makeready," "packing," and "register" are by no means the only technical expressions heard in pressrooms, but they are of general importance because they are also used outside the pressroom by many people whose primary interest is not presswork itself but only related to it. Among those are artists who prepare art-and-copy, printing buyers, production men in advertising agencies and publishers' offices, people who sell printing, and many others. An explanation of pressroom terms and their different meanings is therefore generally desirable.

As said repeatedly in this manual, letterpress was the oldest printing process and for centuries also the only printing process. From the fifteenth to the nineteenth century, printing was identical with letterpress and letterpress with printing. As a result of this historical condition, letterpress terminology was naturally transferred to later developed printing methods. And this transfer of terms often made little sense, if we assume that terms should be descriptive and not puzzling.

Some examples will illustrate this point. Offset lithography cannot use type forms as printing-image carriers but needs single-unit, or integral, plates. Single-unit plates differ essentially from assembled printing-image carriers, particularly from type forms which are not curvable and almost an inch thick. Yet the word "form" is widely used, not only in the offset industry but in other branches of printing as well. Few people not conversant with letterpress are conscious that form is merely an abbreviation of type form, and the word "form" has acquired an additional meaning; at present form may mean both a type form or the assembly of pages and other images which are combined for common presswork. (With the exception of split-fountain printing, a form is printed in the same color.) Another puzzle is "type cylinder," a term still used in some branches of relief printing. This term means the plate cylinder of rotary relief presses, even though it is not possible to attach type to contemporary plate cylinders. Such cylinders are designed for various methods of attaching plates of different kinds but never for type. (In a brief period before the perfection of curved stereotypes during the nineteenth century, some rotary newspaper presses had cylinders slotted for the insertion of especially cast type. These cylinders were correctly named type cylinders. The principle of the slotted type cylinder is still used in the Multigraph, a contemporary machine for the production of direct-mail material.)

These and other instances of confusing terminology are pointed out in this manual for two reasons: one is to show that some terms have either completely lost their original meaning or that this meaning has changed, expanded, or contracted, in the course of printing history; the other reason is the hope that some of those who use ambiguous terms as a matter of course may be made aware of the difficulties in communication between themselves and uninformed people due to terminology. Some such difficulties are demonstrated in the following explanation of makeready.

Three meanings of makeready. The word "makeready" has at least three different meanings which can be compared with concentric circles of strongly diminishing diameters. The broadest meaning of makeready includes all work done on the press prior to running. "Each complete makeready cycle consists of a large number of elemental operations which may vary greatly from one job

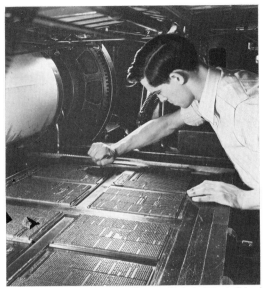

Pressman inspecting and leveling a large type form on the bed of a flatbed-cylinder press. With his right hand he is tightening a quoin, thereby securing a type page in the chase.

to another, from one form to another, and, indeed, from one plant to another doing similar work. All of these many and variable elements, however, may be related to one of four major makeready components: (1) operations concerning the handling of paper, (2) operations concerning the type form and its position, (3) operations concerning the color and inking system, and (4) operations concerning impression."[1] This quotation shows that makeready can signify all preparatory operations on the press. It further shows that the term makeready can be applied to all printing processes and methods by replacing the word "form," which stands for type form, with the more general term printing-image carrier and the word "paper" with the more general expression printing stock. *In this manual, the words "press preparation" are used in replacement of makeready in its broadest sense.* Presswork in all printing methods needs press preparation of some kind or other.

Makeready in the second meaning may be included in our largest circle but it is also used independently, by itself. Makeready in its second meaning is not applicable to all printing methods but it is a typical letterpress term. It comprises operations performed on the printing units of

most presses for letterpress. (These operations will be extensively described in the following section.) *In this manual, makeready in its second sense is called "letterpress makeready."*

The third and most restricted meaning of makeready is often included in the first and second meanings of the term, but it is also used independently in this restrictive sense alone. Operationally this kind of makeready is performed on only one element of a letterpress printing unit, either the platen or the impression cylinder. This operation consists in "overlaying" and is described under the head "Introduction to letterpress makeready" in the following section. *In this manual, makeready in its third sense is avoided as a term in favor of "overlaying," or "overlay," or "overlay sheet."*

Makeready is used with other meanings in various branches of the printing industry, for example, in newspaper relief printing. There the term is indicative of color printing in some plants at least, as distinguished from printing with black ink only, which does not require makeready in newspaper printing.

The competitive use of makeready. The meaning of makeready became competitively important, and therewith emotionally charged during the period of process competition which has in the opinion of many run its course. Some aggressive partisans and promoters of offset lithography (a printing method which was developed during the first quarter of our century and attained competitive maturity in its second quarter) made makeready a pivotal argument in their competition with letterpress. They emphasized to customers the great money savings possible in offset lithography because offset did not need makeready whereas letterpress did, as every printing buyer knew. This line of argument is true or false depending on the meaning attributed to makeready. If makeready is meant in our first sense, namely press preparation, the statement is false, because press preparation is needed in offset lithography not less than in letterpress; but if the meaning is in our second sense, which is letterpress makeready, the statement is true. You read often in this manual that the competitive advantage of one printing method over another printing method cannot be established without considering all relevant points; statements attributing decisiveness to a single point should be taken with a good grain of salt because they are usually not correct. This cautioning seems especially needed in the present time which abounds with new developments in printing technology.

Different kinds and purposes of packing. Not all printing presses need packing. Those that do may require packings different in kind and purpose, depending on the printing method and on the design of a press. The packing consists of papers varying in thickness and compressibility. On presses designed for printing with assembled printing-image carriers such as type forms or curved duplicate plates, the packing is put on the impression cylinder and enables the pressman to make adjustments for changes in the nature and thickness of the stock; the packing is also related to letterpress makeready as will be described in the next section. On presses designed for printing with integral or single-unit plates, such as used in offset lithography and in indirect relief printing, the packing serves not only to influence the printing pressure but also to control the length of the printed images. On such presses adjustments for the thickness of different stocks are made by moving the impression cylinder. The packing is done under the plate on the plate cylinder and under the blanket on the blanket cylinder; the impression cylinder is not packed. Direct printing presses for wrap-around plates can have fixed cylinders, and on such presses the packing must provide adjustments for varying thickness and compressibility of different printing stocks as well as the necessary adjustments in the length of printed images. Such presses are packed under the plate on the plate cylinder and under the stock on the impression cylinder. Harris wrap-around presses which have a blanket for applying ink to the plate can also be packed under the blanket to control the transfer of printing ink to the plate. (Different packing techniques are discussed in the following sections devoted to various kinds of presswork.)

The meaning of register. Originally the word "register" referred in printing to the position of printed images on both sides of the printed sheet. Pages printed on both sides of the sheet were considered in register when the positions of printed images and that of the unprinted areas, called margins, were the same on both sides. The meaning of register expanded first with the growth of color printing and again with the more general use of web printing. At present, register refers to the correspondence of a number of points which depend in their nature on the detail of specific printing tasks. Register in its original meaning

is often called back-up register, and other adjectives are used to identify other kinds of register. In sheet-fed presswork two kinds of register are important; one is *back-up register*, and the other is *color register*. Sheet-fed jobs printed in color are often classified according to the degree of intricacy required in color register as *no-register*, *loose-register*, and *close-register* jobs. (These distinctions are explained in Chapter XI, Section 3.) In web printing several additional kinds of register are recognized. These are related to the fact that the stock is a web rather than sheets. In addition to back-up and color register, web printing recognizes *side margin register, cut-off register*, and *web-to-web register*. (Various kinds of register in web printing are explained in Chapter VI, Section 5.) Not all mentioned kinds of web register are necessarily present in each web printed job. Newspaper printing in black ink only does not need to be concerned about color register, and web printing done on presses handling a single web only has no need for web-to-web register.

Four Main Groups of Operations in Presswork

For uniform treatment, presswork is divided into four main groups of operations. These are: (1) planning for presswork; (2) quality control of component elements, including equipment and materials for presswork; (3) preparation of the press equipment for running; and (4) running itself. Each of these four points is discussed in this preface to reduce, or possibly avoid completely, repetition in the following sections.

Planning for presswork. Planning for presswork is done in many different ways, depending on the printing method, the kinds of presses involved, the length of the press run, and on the nature of binding, finishing, or other operations which must be performed after presswork. These operations can be more or less complex depending on the end use of the printed product. Planning for presswork can be formal or informal. Formal planning is done in planning departments staffed with specialists. Such planning departments are in the minority, and most printers use informal planning. By informal planning is meant that planning for presswork is left to expert craftsmen who plan as they do the work, guided by highly experienced foremen or other supervisors. Planning of presswork is of course only one phase of planning among many needed in printing production. Presswork must dovetail with other produc-

Craftsman comparing the position of made-up type pages with the dummy of the job.

tion phases, particularly with those which are needed to convert the printed sheet or web for end use.

Quality control of all elements to be combined in presswork. Four elements must be combined in presswork: (1) a press, (2) a printing-image carrier, (3) a printing stock, and (4) a printing ink. The extent to which the quality of these elements is controlled varies greatly in the printing industry. Some large organizations have quality control departments, equipped with physical and chemical testing apparatus and staffed with chemists, physicists, electrical or mechanical engineers, depending on the needs of an organization. Such quality control departments are not often needed. Most printers rely for quality control of stocks and inks on their suppliers and concentrate on making sure that the image carrier will be of the proper quality. Quality control is, generally speaking, done by highly qualified craftsmen using precision instruments for inspection and measuring. Quality control of printing-image carriers, printing stocks, and inks is important and so is the state of the press. Quality control in its broadest sense includes therefore the maintenance of equipment.

Press preparation. All kinds of presswork require some preparation of the press prior to running. The extent of press preparation and its detail is far from uniform. Press preparation is not the same for all printing methods; it differs further in sheet-fed and in roll-fed, or web, printing. In multipurpose printing, press preparation at changeovers from one kind of job to another may be more extensive than in presswork on single-purpose equipment. In the first mentioned kind, which is practically synonymous with job-and-commercial printing, the time needed for press preparation depends on the nature of the change from job to job. In some jobs the printing stock, the ink, and the image carrier are completely different from those for the preceding job. In other jobs, the change may be limited to paper, or ink, or solely to the image carrier.

Essentially, press preparation consists in setting the feeding unit, the printing unit, the inking unit, and the delivery unit for the job in hand. In web printing several additional units must be added to this list. These vary for different kinds of web printing and may include roll-feeding machinery, driers, folders, or inline fabricating equipment. Press preparation is often called makeready in the trade. The reasons for replacing this word in the present book with press preparation are given in the preceding discussion of different meanings of makeready.

Running. After the press is prepared for the job and sample sheets are approved by those in authority, running, or continuous image transfer begins. The main duties of the personnel in charge of running can be identified as two: One group of tasks is constant quality control of the printed sheet or web and the making of such adjustments as may be needed for this purpose. The other task is not less important than the controlling of the quality of printed images; it is the maintenance of production efficiency. Controlling and insuring efficient production has the object of keeping running at the correct maximum speed, which varies of course for different kinds and classes of work. Ideally, running should proceed without any interruption whatever; where interruptions cannot be completely eliminated, they should be kept to a minimum.

In single-color and multicolor jobs on sheet-fed and on slow-running roll-fed presses, quality control of printed images can be done by visual inspection of printed samples taken for this purpose at certain intervals. In full-color printing, instruments such as reflection densitometers may be needed to supplement visual inspections. In high-speed web printing, the web moves much too fast for visual inspection by the unaided human eye and for manual adjustments of the press as practiced in sheet-fed printing. In high-speed web printing, some or all quality control functions during running are usually performed by automatic electronic equipment which continually makes the required press adjustments. In web printing with rewind deliveries, which are often needed in package printing, inspection of printed webs is made possible by installing web viewers at the delivery end of presses. (Web viewers are described in Chapter VI, Section 5.)

Ideally, presswork should not be interrupted at all, and all efforts are bent toward reducing interruptions to a minimum. Depending on the length of the press run, varying quantities of blank or partly printed stock, and also of printing ink, must be added and the printed stock must be removed from the press at certain intervals. These operations may coincide with the change-over from one job to another in press runs which do not exceed the capacity of the feeding unit, the ink fountain, and the delivery unit of the press. In long production runs on sheet-fed or roll-fed presses, the storage capacity of the press for stock and ink may not be sufficiently large, and blank or partly printed stock as well as printing ink must be added, just as the delivery must be emptied to make room for sheets to come. In sheet-fed presswork these chores are known as *maintaining the feeder, maintaining the inking unit* or *the fountain*, and *maintaining the delivery*. Whether these operations can be performed without interruption or not depends not only on the length of run but also on the kind of feeder and delivery with which a sheet-fed press is actually equipped.

Interruptions caused by the nature of the equipment are inevitable, and so are some interruptions caused by troubles during presswork. There is no trouble-free printing method; each method has troubles of its own as well as troubles that it may have in common with other printing methods, particularly those belonging to the same process group. Not all troubles can be predicted nor is this the place for an explanation of the methods whereby these troubles are diagnosed and remedied. (Some typical presswork problems and troubles will be explained in following sections on presswork in different printing processes and methods.)

Section 2:   Presswork in Relief Printing

In this manual relief printing is divided into four methods: letterpress, newspaper relief printing, flexography, and indirect relief printing. The general characteristics of relief printing and its several methods are set forth in Chapter I, "Printing Processes and Methods," and do not need to be repeated. We turn therefore immediately to presswork in letterpress, beginning with an explanation of letterpress makeready.

Introduction to Letterpress Makeready

The variety of presses and of printing-image carriers used in letterpress is the reason for differences in press preparation as well as in letterpress makeready. The subject is further complicated by the fact that the letterpress industry is at present in a period of transition with a large number of different kinds of presses existing side by side. Some older kinds of presses are, according to the opinion of some competent industry people, on the way out; other kinds, which were recently developed, are in the minds of the same experts the presses of the future. Though these recently developed presses differ from traditional presses for letterpress in many points (some are presses for direct printing whereas others are designed for indirect relief printing), all of them have nevertheless one characteristic in common: they cannot use assembled printing-image carriers but are built to print exclusively with integral or single-unit relief image carriers. These are called wrap-around plates in distinction from duplicate plates which are relief plates used in assembled image carriers. Wrap-around plates differ substantially from assembled image carriers in press preparation and letterpress makeready, our present subject. Wrap-around plates do not need letterpress makeready, and our discussion of the subject does not apply to them. Letterpress makeready is done on assembled image carriers, type forms, and assemblies of plates for printing on flatbed-cylinder, sheet-fed and roll-fed rotary presses. (It is possible under certain conditions to print with assembled image carriers without going through letterpress makeready. This method is known as "level impression" printing; it is discussed later in this unit, after the explanation of letterpress makeready has provided you with the knowledge without which level impression printing cannot be understood.)

Our discussion of letterpress makeready begins with type forms which are assembled image carriers consisting of metallic type and relief image carriers of pictures. Type forms can be printed in presses equipped with a flat bed. Such presses are either platen or flatbed-cylinder presses. Platen presses are widely used for short- and medium-length runs of smaller sheet sizes, whereas flatbed-cylinder presses are available in much larger sizes. Large flatbed-cylinder presses are primarily domestic machines, though they are no longer manufactured in the United States. Up to the middle of this century, large flatbed-cylinders were the typical presses of the job-and-commercial segment of the letterpress industry. The trend seems to be away from the use of large type forms, and letterpress makeready may be of a much less general interest in the future. But the future is always uncertain, and at present there are still thousands of flatbed-cylinder presses and platen presses in operation, and thousands of craftsmen perform letterpress makeready on type forms day by day in the United States. This existing condition makes a description of letterpress makeready for platen and flatbed-cylinder presses mandatory.

The two main purposes of letterpress makeready. Letterpress makeready has two main objects: one is compensating for imperfections in both the image carrier and the press itself; the other object is the adjusting of printing pressure for the job in hand. Compensating for imperfections in the image carrier is most often needed with type forms and less with duplicate plates. Makeready of type forms can be substantially reduced by quality control of the elements combined in type forms, a group of operations known in the letterpress industry as "pre-makeready." The second task of makeready is the adjusting of printing pressure for the job in hand; it can be performed in various ways depending on the kind of image carrier and equipment used in a specific case. Generally speaking, adjustments of printing pressure are made on presses having individual printing units (consisting either of a flatbed or of a plate cylinder for the image carrier, and of a platen or an impression cylinder) by overlay sheets placed in the *packing* of platens or impression cylinders. This method is not suitable for presses having a common impression cylinder for several plate cylinders. It is also possible to make adjustments in printing pressure during the preparation of the type form. Before we turn to the techniques used in letterpress makeready, an explanation of the packing is in order.

Functions of the packing in letterpress. Most presses for letterpress are multipurpose machines. They are built for the printing of a variety of stocks ranging from Bible paper to relatively thick paper boards. The impression must be made under controlled pressure, and the stock must be forced against the inked image carrier for image transfer. As there can be a difference of, say, 0.025 inch between the thinnest and the thickest stock to be printed on the same press, it must be adjustable for stocks of different thicknesses. Platen, flatbed-cylinder, and rotary presses are mainly adjusted for this purpose by changes in their packing.

The function of the packing is the same in platen presses and in presses equipped with impression cylinders, but the description of the packing can be better illustrated and easier understood by discussing presses having impression cylinders. As explained in Chapter VI, Section 2, "Printing Units," American presses are constructed with bearers. (Bearers are strips or rims of hard steel serving as riding surfaces during printing.) Each of the two elements of the printing unit has a pair of bearers; during the impression the bearers of both elements ride in contact with one another. The body of the impression cylinder has a smaller diameter than its bearers. The difference between the cylinder diameter and the diameter of its bearers is known as the "undercut" of the cylinder. (Plate cylinders, too, are undercut, but at this point our interest is absorbed by the undercut of impression cylinders.) The cylinder undercut provides the space needed for the packing of the impression cylinder. The packing ad-

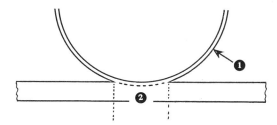

Diagram of impression squeeze in a flatbed-cylinder press. The packing with the paper (1) increases the diameter of the impression cylinder beyond that of the cylinder bearers which ride on the bearers of the flat bed. During the impression the rotating cylinder with the paper on its surface is brought into contact with the type form on the moving bed. At the constantly changing area of contact (2) the packing is compressed and supplies the requisite impression squeeze.

justs the impression cylinder for stocks of different thicknesses. The overlay sheet, which has the function of adjusting printing pressure for different areas of the image carrier, is part of the press packing.

The undercut of the impression cylinder. The undercut of impression cylinders is not standardized but differs for different models. For flatbed-cylinder presses, which are the subject of this discussion, the range is between 0.050 and 0.100 inch.[2] The total thickness of the packing and the sheet to be printed must at least be equal to the undercut of the impression cylinder. In actual practice the packing must be thicker because it must provide a certain amount of "impression squeeze."

The permanent and the temporary packing of flatbed-cylinder presses. The packing for impression cylinders of flatbed-cylinder presses consists of two kinds: the permanent and the temporary packing. The *permanent packing* usually remains on the press for many jobs, whereas the *temporary packing* is changed for each job requiring a letterpress makeready. The techniques used in the packing of presses are interesting examples of the ingenuity of printing craftsmen who can obtain relatively high precision almost without measuring instruments, simply by standardizing the materials for packing. These are papers of different compressibility and thickness which can be recognized by their different colors. With these papers the pressman adjusts the diameter of the impression cylinder as well as its degree of compressibility. This he does by assembling a number of papers of two kinds primarily. One kind is "manila" or "tympan" paper which has a yellowish color, is 0.006 inch thick, and rather hard. The other kind is sized and supercalendered paper (abbreviated as S&SC) which is white and 0.003 inch thick. The permanent and the temporary packing is each covered with a sheet of tympan which is known as the "drawsheet." "The packing is attached to the impression cylinder with a series of pins spaced across the cylinder. There the packing is held in place with packing clamps. The back or tail end of the top sheet of the permanent and of the temporary packing is each held by a different reel. The tail end of the top sheet is wound on the reel and pulled tight with the pin wrench. The reel is held in place by means of a ratchet on its end and a dog on the cylinder."[3]

At this point it might also be mentioned that the 3M Company has developed a line of materials which can be used instead of tympan papers and drawsheets. These products are sold under the trade name Spherekote. *Spherekote* brand products are coated with "millions of tiny precision made glass beads—as many as 120,000 of them to the square inch."[4] They are supplied as papers, as lightweight boards, and also as a double lamination of firm but resilient glass-beaded rubber and cloth in a number of different thicknesses. Spherekote tympans and drawsheets are used in letterpress printing and for the proofing of photoengravings, whereas the cloth and rubber laminations are used in newspaper printing primarily. The glass coating "reduces problems caused by static, resists impression matrix from rules, edges, and type, reduces ink transfer too because glass is a poor ink receptor."[5]

All three functions of the packing, namely, (1) adjustment for stocks of different thicknesses, (2) adjustment in the resiliency of the packing, or in its degree of hardness or softness, and (3) adjustment of the printing pressure for different areas by means of overlay sheets, are performed by the temporary packing which changes from job to job. The temporary packing is therefore also called "makeready packing" or "working packing." The permanent packing consists usually of hard papers; the temporary packing combines hard and soft papers depending on the job. Most high-quality jobs need hard packing, but there are also jobs that are best printed with soft packings.

Some reasons for lack of uniformity in type forms. Type forms may contain a number of different elements such as foundry type, Monotype, slugs of type, wood engravings, photoengravings, and duplicate plates. These materials may come from different sources with different quality standards. There may be differences of height and imperfections which were not corrected before the final assembly of the material for any reason imaginable. Makeready must now take care of all these deficiencies in order to produce a job of the required quality. Therefore, letterpress makeready is often described as "an operation of perfecting imperfections."[6] Much of the work done during makeready on the press can be, and frequently is, eliminated by quality control of component elements prior to assembly. But it is not possible for each and every printer to achieve a perfect assembly for each and every job.

It must be remembered that printing is a highly

competitive business, that it is a business which is under constant time pressure, and that it is a business where last minute changes—be they now inevitable or merely caused by whim—are considered an established prerogative of the customer. These conditions are less grave in mass-production printing but they are characteristic for small business job-and-commercial printing and therefore relevant to the present discussion. The material to be used for specific jobs is not entirely in the printer's choice. He is more or less frequently instructed by his customer to use printing elements which are less than perfect in his own opinion but are nevertheless still usable in that of the customer. This can often be observed in discussions of engravings, electrotypes, and standing matter. (Standing matter, or standing forms, are type forms held for reprinting by the printer.) Nor are imperfections of the equipment to be forgotten. These may be mechanical inaccuracies resulting from wear, abuse, accidental jam-ups, or simply due to old age. Many of the large size flatbed-cylinder presses still in operation are rather old models, and not all of them are kept in perfect condition.

Techniques of letterpress makeready. Letterpress makeready uses three different techniques, singly and in combination. These are underlaying, interlaying, and overlaying. Underlaying and interlaying are done on the bed of flatbed-cylinder presses (underlaying can also be done on the plate cylinder of rotary presses), whereas overlaying is done on the platen or on the impression cylinder of the press. A brief explanation of these three techniques follows.

The first is *underlaying*, which consists in the "measuring of the height of cuts, or photoengravings, in a form, the placing of sheets of paper under low cuts and reducing the height of high cuts so as to make all cuts as nearly the correct height as possible. On low cuts mounted on wood bases the sheets of paper are pasted on the bottom of the wood base. On duplicate plates mounted on patent bases the sheets of paper are placed loose between the plate and the base."[7] Underlaying is rarely used for body type, but may be found practical for large type, in display composition, for example. Modern pre-makeready methods use more sophisticated techniques. Some of them, including the "Vandercook Minimum Makeready System," are described later in this unit.

The technique of *interlaying* has the purpose of "leveling the surface of individual photoengravings by marking out and spotting up an impression of the engraving and by then placing this spot sheet between the printing plate and the base upon which it is mounted. [The meaning of spotting up and of spot sheet is explained in the following.] With most plates mounted on patent base it is the correct method and the general practice to use interlays. With engravings mounted on wood bases, however, interlaying is practical only when cuts are so badly warped that satisfactory inking and printing is impossible without interlays."[8] In actual practice printers try to avoid the use of such engravings as much as possible. But worn engravings of low quality must sometimes be accepted, for example by publication printers of short-run magazines. Such materials are often supplied by their advertisers to the publishers of various magazines who may not feel in a position to refuse the questionable material and simply pass it, and the buck with it, to the printer. Advertisers who provide defective engravings may often neither be able to judge their quality nor care too much for the trouble caused the printer.

The last of the three letterpress makeready techniques is *overlaying*. It "refers to the preparation and placing in the packing of spot sheets, hand cut or mechanical overlays, or anything else used in an attempt to obtain the correct impressional contact."[9] This technique has remained of great importance and is therefore more extensively discussed than underlaying and interlaying. As overlaying is done in order to adapt the actual printing pressure to various areas of the image carrier, overlaying leads us directly to the problem of printing pressure in letterpress printing, a rather controversial subject. But first an explanation of overlaying is in order.

Overlaying and overlay sheets. As mentioned in the preceding paragraph, overlaying has the purpose of adjusting the printing pressure, or as the pressman says, the impression, for various areas of the image carrier. "The purpose of an overlay is to increase the impression in the dark portions of a halftone print, and reduce impression in the highlight areas. To make an overlay more clearly understood: an overlay is thick where the picture is darkest (solid), thin where there is little or no color, and varies in thickness as the tone of the subject is lighter or darker."[10] The layman who sees overlaying done by expert craftsmen for the first time is usually strongly impressed by the difference in the appearance of the printed image before and after overlaying. Considering the primitive means with which overlaying is done, particularly when the method is "spotting up," overlaying is certainly a feat of craftsmanship. It is difficult to realize what difference the local adding (or removing) of a few thousandths of an inch to the diameter of the impression cylinder can make if one looks at a cylinder having a diameter of two dozen inches or more. The whole thing is somewhat incongruous. The equipment is big and cumbersome, the procedure of making an overlay sheet and of spotting is primitive, and the result is completely unexpected.

The following description of overlaying and spotting is restricted to the most important points of this operation. After the press is properly adjusted for printing, an overlay sheet is pulled. Depending on the size of the sheet and the nature of the job, the overlay sheet may or may not be divided into several units. The completed overlay sheet must be put into the packing in its correct position relative to the type form, otherwise it would not add or reduce pressure where it should. The guide for proper positioning of overlay sheets is obtained by "stabbing" through the sheet and into the temporary packing with an overlay knife. "The sheet is stabbed so that it may be cut into convenient sections and that there will be two *stab marks* on the front edge of each section. The sections are then marked with the numerals 1, 2, 3, 4, etc., so that their position on the cylinder will be known when they are hung in the packing."[11]

Marking out and spotting. Next the sheet is "marked out" from the back. "An inspection of the back of the sheet will disclose any variations of the pressure of the form. As the sheet is marked out from the back, the impression should be sufficient to give a clear idea of high and low areas. It is usual to select an area with the correct amount of impression as a guide and to build up the low areas accordingly."[12] Different pressrooms have different marking systems and codes. "One of the most used forms of marking the spots is as follows: On spots to be spotted up with tissue no mark is made, where folio is to be used the spot is marked with "F" and where book paper, with "B." The word "own" designates the stock on which the job is printed. A part to be cut or torn out is marked "X" and a spot to be scraped or peeled off is marked "XX."[13] It is to

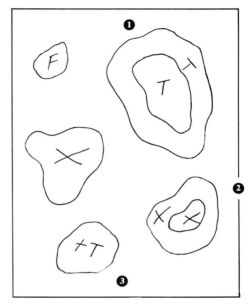

Some marks used by pressmen on makeready sheets. In this code, letters indicate which paper (folio or tissue) must be added to increase pressure; X means that pressure must be relieved by cutting out folio paper in the temporary packing; (1) means add tissue first in larger area and add another tissue in the enclosed area; (2) cut out folio in larger area and another folio in the enclosed area, and (3) means cut out folio first and then add tissue.

be added that tissue is usually 0.001 inch thick; folio in the pressroom means manifold paper 0.002 inch thick (and must not be confused with the meaning of folio as page number); and book paper for spotting is approximately 0.003 inch thick. You can see the same approach here as in determining the thickness of the packing. Different papers of different thicknesses make exact measuring with instruments unnecessary.

The overlay sheet which is already marked on the back is next turned face up, where the pressman can see the image of the print, for marking the engravings. Before he begins marking he puts a sheet of carbon paper under the overlay sheet with the carbon side up in order to transfer the identical markings made on the face of the overlay sheet to its back at the same time. The marking of the sheet is, of course, only the preliminary operation which must be followed by the actual adding of thickness to the sheet or by removing thickness from it in the required places and shapes. This step is known as *spotting up* or *patching*. "A thin film of adhesive paste is rubbed or daubed on the inside of the marked area and the spot of paper must be cut exactly on the mark. After spotting is completed, the sections of the sheet are prepared to be hung in the packing. The prepared overlay sheet is then placed in the packing often under four or five white sheets and the drawsheet of the makeready packing."[14]

After the overlay is hung, the packing is closed and another sheet is printed and closely examined. If it is decided that an additional overlay sheet is necessary, the same procedure is repeated. This decision depends on the standards and quality requirements of individual plants and jobs.

Mechanical overlays. Pressmen make a distinction between spotted overlays and mechanical overlays. *Mechanical overlays* are made faster than spotted ones as the whole area is treated at the same time, and differences in printing pressure are produced "mechanically" rather than by individual treatments of different printing areas. In the past a number of mechanical overlays such as wheat flour and chalk overlays were rather popular. There are also some proprietary methods, among them the Bierbauer press makeready method, also known as the Bierbauer overlay,[15] the Primaton mechanical makeready system, otherwise referred to as "a thermosetting mechanical overlay,"[16] and the Perfex top sheet.[17] The most widely used proprietary makeready system is, at present, the 3M Brand makeready system, described in the next paragraph.

The 3M Brand makeready system. This system "consists of two elements, the 3M Brand makeready exposure unit and a plastic coated, heat-activated material called 3M Brand makeready. The latter is furnished in thicknesses of 0.007 and 0.010 inch. When processed in the exposure unit, the 0.007 material expands approximately 0.004 inch and the 0.010 inch material expands approximately 0.0065 inch depending upon the amount of heat absorbed. In the 3M makeready system the form is leveled in the press, a print is made directly on 3M makeready material and stabbed for register while it is held by the cylinder grippers. This printed material is processed in the exposure unit. The carbon black in the ink absorbs the infrared from the exposure unit transforming it into heat energy which expands the 3M makeready. The heat energy causes the 3M makeready to expand according to the amount of heat absorbed which is determined by the amount of carbon black in the ink. Since there is more carbon black in the solid areas and less in the light tones, the 3M makeready expands proportionately,

Courtesy 3M Printing Products Division

Operator inserts a proof printed on 3M Brand makeready material into the exposure unit.

most in the solids and less in different tones. The exposed 3M makeready is hung in the packing of the press as an overlay in register with the form."[18]

This concludes our discussion of letterpress makeready for differential printing pressure depending on the size of individual printing area elements. Our next subject is an explanation of the differences between level impression printing and printing with differential printing pressure.

Level impression printing and printing with overlays. Letterpress makeready in the sense of providing differential printing pressure for highlights, middletones, and solids can become a controversial subject. Some experts are convinced that various areas of image carriers must be printed with different pressures, other experts maintain that this is not so. The position of those in favor of differential printing pressure is well expressed in the statement that "a hairline rule or pin point dot and a 7 by 10 inch solid requires different amounts of pressure. The actual amount varies with the kind of stock being printed and the relative position of dots and solids to each other on the press."[19] This school of differential printing pressure is opposed by the school of uniform printing pressure, or of level impression printing. In the United States the pioneer of this school of letterpress printing was the late Lex Claybourn. "The Claybourn process is a method of making precision flat or curved plates with the aid of special platemaking machinery. These machines are all built by C. B. Cottrell & Sons Company."[20] It was only natural that Cottrell should build equipment for the making of level impression printing-image carriers as this company manufactured common impression cylinder presses where one impression cylinder is used for a number of plate cylinders. As each of the plate cylinders makes an impression on the same area of the impression cylinder, overlay sheets cannot be used on these presses.

The Curtis Publishing Company of Philadelphia, which publishes and produces among other magazines the *Saturday Evening Post*, a general-interest magazine printed in millions of copies, was probably the first company to develop level impression printing for long-run magazine production on common impression cylinder presses. Mr. W. H. Ticehurst, Manager of the Curtis Plate Department, defined "level impression printing simply as the process of printing on flat, hard packing using a plate, flat or curved, with all elements in exactly the same plane. It precludes the use of makeready in the accepted sense, both pre-makeready of the plate and press and makeready of plate and packing."[21]

These two approaches to printing seem to be diametrically opposed. But the discrepancy is in truth much smaller than it appears to be if the two methods are considered in their proper context. Lex Claybourn, the most consistent advocate of level impression printing, supposedly once said: "Give me a perfect plate, perfect paper and a perfect press and I will give you a perfect printing job."[22] Level impression printing was developed for high-speed rotary magazine printing. Mr. Ticehurst of Curtis reported that it was used for press runs of seven million impressions at speeds of 1,400 to 1,500 f.p.m.[23] This result was the culmination of decades of development work on presses, papers, ink, and electrotypes not less than press preparation methods.[24]

How different are the conditions in job-and-commercial printing with flatbed-cylinder presses where printing with overlays is commonly practiced! These are well summed up in the following quotation from *Training Manual of the U. S. Government Printing Office:* "Four main factors necessitate the regulation of the pressure in the packing thickness of form height for printing. First, paper surfaces, as different stocks require various amounts of pressure to print the same form; second, the nature of the job as each job is made to order and uses a different form; third, the form to be printed, since it may be composed from any of the materials from which prints can be made; fourth, the necessity to compensate for compression and stretch, since these strains affect the press parts, packing, form, and the sheet being printed. These are the four main factors which necessitate makeready."[25]

Printing with differential printing pressure, done with overlays, is necessary under certain conditions. It is practiced not only on platen and flatbed-cylinder presses but also on rotary presses with individual printing units which have an impression cylinder for each plate cylinder. In job printing, no matter on what kind of press printing is done, it is simply either not possible or not practical to attain the same degree of perfection of all component elements that can be achieved in long-run high-speed magazine printing. It should also be remembered that magazine web printing can be standardized to a much greater extent than is possible in general job-and-commercial printing. The differences between those who are in favor of level impression printing and those who insist on the necessity of differential printing pressure are, consequently, much less strong than they appear in emotionally charged discussions. It seems to the present writer that these differences are more due to unqualified and absolute value judgments of what is right than to anything else. But right and wrong cannot be established without the proper understanding and consideration of all factors that are relevant in each specific situation.[26]

Pre-makeready. Pre-makeready is, generally speaking, that part of quality control in letterpress which deals with the printing-image carrier and has the purpose of reducing to a minimum the time spent for makeready of type forms on the press. For this reason printers also speak of minimum makeready methods. *Minimum makeready* can be done in a number of different ways, depending on the requirements of a specific plant. There exist several tools and instruments to be used for this purpose. In the United States the Vandercook minimum makeready system is widely used because it includes all equipment needed for pre-makeready of elements to be used in type forms as well as for adjusting the assembled type form itself. This system provides not only precision measuring instruments for the checking of plates, mounting bases, and cylinder packing, as well as for all dimensions of type and type slugs, but also comprises casting equipment for lightweight metal bases, machinery for planing of metal bases, and equipment for bonding the engravings to the prepared bases. In addition, the Vandercook system includes gauges for the exact positioning of plates and for the makeup of pages. The assembled type form is placed in a test press which is "used to check printing surfaces, register and lineup. Carbon paper impressions can be made on impression leveling sheets that may be transferred to the production press in exact register."[27] The carbon paper impression is used as a guide for the overlay sheet which merely has the function of leveling the impression.

Presswork in Letterpress Printing

The letterpress industry has a larger number of different kinds of presses at its disposal than any other branch of the printing industry. Many of these presses can be discussed generically, but some must be named because they are known by their names in the industry. In this section you find descriptions of presswork as it is practiced on ten kinds of presses: (1) platen presses, (2) two-revolution, single-color flatbed-cylinder presses, (3) two-revolution, two-color flatbed cylinder presses, (4) perfecting flatbed-cylinder presses, (5) Miehle vertical presses, (6) single-revolution, single-color flatbed-cylinder presses, (7) Heidelberg two-color, flatbed-rotary combination presses, (8) sheet-fed rotary presses, (9) Harris wrap-around presses, and (10) magazine presses. As more than a single make of presses is discussed in some of the listed groups the total number of presses described is more than a dozen.

Presswork on Platen Presses

Platen presses can be either open presses, which are hand-fed, or job automatics which have mechanical feeding and delivery equipment. Open platen presses are used for short-run work and for teaching of printing in schools; job automatics serve for the printing of medium-length runs and for a number of special purposes, the printing of envelopes, for example. The printing unit of platen presses consist of two plane surfaces: the bed where the type form is put and the platen which carries the printing stock. As explained elsewhere, the bed is stationary, whereas the platen opens and closes for each printing cycle.

Planning for presswork on platen presses. Formal planning is not common in platen press printing. The pressman may be provided with the locked-up type form and a job ticket. In school, the student is usually taught imposition and lockup as well as the operation of platen presses. In small print shops the pressman himself may take care of these operations; in larger shops imposition and lockup are usually handled in the composing room.

Pre-makeready and quality control of type forms for platen presses. Pre-makeready consists primarily of the visual inspection of printing elements and of measuring the height of photoengravings or other plates. Measuring can be done "with an inexpensive horseshoe gauge, a one inch friction thimble micrometer, or a Vandercook plate gauge."[28] Lockup includes not only the correct positioning of printing elements within the chase, but also the application of the correct pressure to the material and the leveling of the type form.

Press preparation of platen presses. In this manual the heading of press preparation comprises all steps which are needed prior to the actual running of a job. There is ample literature on platen press printing but most of it has the purpose of teaching the subject to students of printing.[29] As the purpose of this manual is not the teaching of operational skills but solely that of providing general information, the subject must be presented in much less detail than in instructional books. For our purpose it seems adequate to recognize the following 12 operations: (1) removal of the old packing, (2) packing of the platen, (3) inking the press, (4) adjusting the height of rollers, (5) placing the image carrier on the bed, (6) pulling an impression on the top sheet, (7) determining correct margins, (8) placing of guides, (9) adjusting of grippers, (10) preparing and hanging the overlay sheet, (11) adjusting the ink fountain, and (12) printing a sheet for approval. Each of these steps is now briefly explained.

As the packing changes from job to job, *removing the old packing* needs no further explanation. In addition to manila or tympan paper, *the packing of platen presses* usually has a compressed fiber board 0.018 inch thick, known as pressboard. Pressboard can be used on the flat platen but not on impression cylinders for which it is too rigid. "The amount of packing depends upon six conditions: (1) The density of the printing surface; heavy solids need more packing than light lines. (2) The size of the printing surface; large forms use more packing than small forms of similar nature. (3) The thickness of the paper to be printed; a sheet of thin book paper needs much more packing than a sheet of poster board. (4) The paper surface; a rough surface like a leatherette cover needs more packing than a smooth surface of the same thickness like a plate finish cover. (5) The condition of the form; worn forms require slightly more packing than they needed originally. (6) The adjustment of the platen screws. As the platen is set farther away from the bed more packing is needed."[30] The next step is *inking the press* with a spatula. The ink is applied by hand to the ink disk for the preparation of the job. Then the *height of the rollers* is checked, usually with a type-high roller gauge, on the bed. If changes are required they must be made now. Thereafter the *chase with the type form is put on the bed* of the press and secured in its position.

Now the press is packed, inked, has its rollers adjusted, and the type form in place; everything should be ready to *pull an impression on the top sheet of the packing.* This is usually done by turning the flywheel with the hand. The impression on the top sheet is needed to *determine the correct margins* of the printed image on the stock on which the job is to be printed. This step includes the marking of the position for the guides. After the impression has been taken, the *guides are placed* on the top sheet of the tympan. Before the guides are attached, the top sheet is cleaned with a solvent whereby the impression is removed. Usually three guides are used; two of them are bottom guides, one is a side guide. The *side guide* is normally put in the lower left-hand corner; the location of the *bottom guides* is indicated by their name. The guides must be so arranged that they will not be touched by the printing surface of the type form. Next, *the grippers must be adjusted.* Grippers on platen presses must not be confused with those used on impression cylinders. Grippers of the latter kind have a clamping action which pinches the sheet and holds it during the impression, as long as the grippers remain closed. Grippers on platen presses are narrow strips of metal, attached to the bottom of the platen. The grippers can be moved to suit the job in hand. They have the purpose of preventing the printed sheet from sticking to the type form after the impression was made. The grippers of platen presses help to release the printed sheet either by touching the paper directly or by touching it with *gripper fingers,* which are small metal tabs attached to the grippers.

The next steps are devoted to letterpress makeready in the sense of adjusting the printing pressure for different areas of the form. Pressure adjustments "may be necessary in different areas of the packing to correct one or more of the following conditions: (1) the platen surface may not be uniform for various reasons, (2) heavy solids need more pressure than light lines or halftone highlight dots, (3) that various elements in the form and the parts of the press which apply pressure yield when a heavy impression is made."[31] *Pulling a sheet for overlay* is the first step in the adjusting of printing pressure. It takes experience to interpret the sheet properly and to mark it for the necessary adjustments. These are made by adding more or less thickness to the final overlay sheet in the marked areas. Several techniques can be used for preparing overlays. Among them is the traditional spotting up which consists in pasting cutouts of paper of varying shapes and thicknesses in such areas as need more printing pressure. Some areas may require the adding of five or six spots, others fewer, and some may print too heavy, and the pressure must be relieved by reducing the thickness of the corresponding areas in the overlay sheet. The completed overlay sheet must be placed in the packing of the platen. This step is called *hanging the overlay* by printers.

The hanging of the overlay completes makeready in its specific letterpress meaning. The next step "is to adjust the ink fountain so that adequate, uniform inking will be maintained throughout the run."[32] This step is omitted in very short runs for which the ink is put directly on the ink disk with a spatula. After the fountain is completely adjusted, the pressman prints a few sheets for approval by those who have the authority to do so. If this okay sheet is approved, press preparation is ended and running can begin.

Running of hand-fed platen presses. The operator stands in front of the press; he has the feed board to his right, and the delivery board where he puts the printed sheets is usually directly before him—between him and the press. The blank stock (or the stock printed on the other side or in another color, in multicolor work) is put on the feedboard in a pile, approximately 2 inches high. The operator uses both hands during feeding. His right hand does the feeding and his left hand delivers the printed sheet. Both feeding and removal of the stock are done almost simultaneously. "Feeding is accomplished by an uninterrupted sweeping motion co-ordinated with the

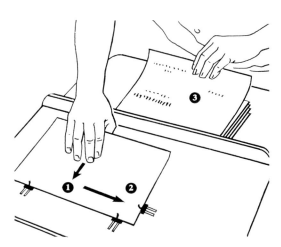

Feeding and delivery on an open platen press. His right hand feeds the paper to the front guides (1) and then to the side guide (2); his left hand delivers (3) the printed paper at the same time.

movement of the press. By the time the platen comes into position to receive the sheet to be printed, the right hand of the feeder has the sheet ready to place to the guides. Just as the platen opens, the left hand is ready to remove the printed sheet. Since the printed sheet can easily be damaged by removal, the feeder takes care not to touch the wet ink on the sheet during removal. It is helpful to use a 'fingerstall' made from sandpaper or emery cloth, on the index finger of the left hand."[33]

The pressman inspects a printed sheet from time to time. He checks not only the quality of the ink image on the stock, but is also concerned with the proper positioning, or register, of the paper and he "must watch for work-ups, pullouts, slurs, and wrinkles."[34] These points are explained in the discussion of running of flatbed-cylinder presses. Here it is merely mentioned that work-ups and pullouts are due to defects in the lockup of the type form; slurs are blurred impressions, and wrinkles are creaselike damages done to the stock during the making of the impression.

This description of presswork on hand-fed platen presses is by necessity far from comprehensive. Nor are modern job automatics included because the discussion of mechanical feeders and deliveries would complicate the matter beyond need. Our next subject is presswork on flatbed-cylinder presses which includes mechanical equipment for feeding and delivery.

Presswork on Two-Revolution Flatbed-Cylinder Presses

During the last seventy-five years, approximately, flatbed-cylinder presses dominated job-and-commercial letterpress printing. But after the end of World War II the trend changed in the United States away from flatbed-cylinder presses. The new trend reached its climax in 1961–62 when American press manufacturers decided to discontinue the building of flatbed-cylinder presses with the exception of the Miehle Vertical. Several makes of flatbed-cylinder presses are imported from Europe and sold in the United States. Some models were originally designed and manufactured in this country, others originated in Germany, Italy, and Sweden.

As set forth in Chapter VI, Section 2, flatbed-cylinder presses can be based on several construction principles. In the United States horizontal flatbed-cylinder presses were built as two-revolution presses because they lend themselves best to longer printing runs, say up to 50,000 impressions. Two-revolution presses exist in three different versions as single-color, two-color, and perfecting presses. In Europe other basic designs of flatbed-cylinder presses were preferred by many printers over American long-run cylinder presses. But it is also true that many European printers use two-revolution presses, and that such presses are manufactured in Germany and in Sweden, not to forget the United Kingdom. It is equally a fact that single-revolution flatbed-cylinder presses have been imported into the United States during the recent past and that many American printers, particularly those engaged in the production of relatively short runs in smaller sizes, have become warm advocates of these presses. The Miehle Vertical, which is a stop-cylinder press, and Heidelberg single-revolution presses are each the subject matter of a later unit. In this unit we concentrate on two-revolution flatbed-cylinder presses which are still running in ever so many American printing shops and plants.

The following description of presswork with horizontal two-revolution presses includes discussions of presswork on single-color, two-color, and perfecting presses. The bulk of the description is devoted to single-color presswork. The operational features of two-color and perfecting presses are but briefly explained because the general lines which must be followed in their operations are essentially the same as those described for presswork on single-color two-revolution presses.

Courtesy Electrotypers and Stereotypers Handbook

Bed of a flatbed-cylinder press equipped with a honey-combed patent base for printing from unmounted flat plates. The plates are attached to the patent base with hooks that engage the beveled plate edges.

In every discussion of flatbed-cylinder press-work it must be kept in mind that these presses can print from type forms and that they were, and often still are, available for the printing of rather large sheets. These two characteristics explain the wide use of two-revolution presses for the printing of books and for that of limited-interest magazines which are produced in relatively short runs. General-interest magazines completely outgrew the capacity of flatbed-cylinder presses in the first quarter of this century. Such magazines are at present produced by web printing in letterpress, rotogravure, or offset lithography. As to the kind of image carrier suitable for flatbed-cylinder presses, it is to be mentioned that type forms are only one of several kinds that can be used on this kind of equipment. With plate bases the bed of the press can be adapted for printing with duplicate plates (stereo-types, electrotypes, rubber, and plastic plates) as well as for the use of photopolymer plates as printing-image carriers.

Planning for presswork on flatbed-cylinder presses. Even though relatively little formal planning is done for printing on flatbed-cylinder presses, there are nevertheless many details that must be considered by those in charge of planning. Planning differs for advertising and promotional printing and for book and periodical work. In book and periodical printing impositions are well established, and the stone man (a compositor who assembles the type form) plans his work as he actually does it. There are also a number of larger companies that have formal planning departments which provide exact and detailed instructions for craftsmen engaged in the imposing, positioning, and lockup of forms as well as for those who do presswork.[35] The printing of advertising material is much less standardized and requires a kind of planning differing considerably from that for routine jobs. Usually more difficult jobs are planned by discussions of supervisory personnel rather than by more formal methods.

Most printing companies have well-staffed production departments which take care of scheduling of jobs, procurement or dispatching of materials and services, and—generally speaking—of linking manufacturing departments to sales people and to customers. Such departments are sometimes also called planning departments, but their work differs from formal planning in which all manufacturing details of a job are worked out on paper before manufacturing begins.

Quality control for presswork. Most small and medium-size companies operate pre-makeready departments where elements of the printing-image carrier are inspected and measured before they may be used for assembly in the type form or on plate bases. Only the largest companies have laboratories staffed with graduate personnel for testing of papers and inks.

Press preparation and running. Each job may need different press preparation, but it is nevertheless possible to arrive at a more or less generally valid listing of the steps whereby a flatbed-cylinder press is prepared for running. The basic assumption is for this purpose "an average job requiring a change of color and a change of rollers on a single-color flatbed-cylinder press. The total work required to get the run started can be broken down into 23 operations."[36] Rather than merely listing each of these 23 different steps, they are briefly explained in the following.

Washup and packing. The first step is press washup, since a change in color was assumed; the next step, roller changes is also part of the original assumption. *Roller changes* may be necessary for several reasons; one of them may be lack of compatibility of the ink to be next used with the rollers on the press; another may be that the rollers are damaged and must therefore be replaced. The next step consists in *packing the press*. "Where little or no overlaying is required on short runs using a soft packing, multiple jobs are frequently run with the same packing. However, for most jobs on flatbed presses the packing is changed for each job and the packing on all presses must be changed occasionally. The packing is best done while the bed is empty to prevent damage to the form." After the press is packed the *press bed must be cleaned* before the new form is put on it.

Placing the type form on the press bed and related operations. The next group of operations is related to the printing-image carrier, or type form. First it is necessary *to get the next form and the instructions* pertaining to it. Then the "new form must be cleaned front and back. A bristle brush and a piece of rule is commonly employed for *cleaning the form*. The face of the form is brushed to remove any metal slivers or dirt particles. The backs of machine-set slugs are scraped with the rule to remove metal slivers and then the whole back of the form is brushed to remove any other dirt." Now we are ready for *positioning the form on the press bed*. Positioning the form requires a number of technical considerations, obtaining the correct gripper bite and margin among them. (The gripper bite refers to the space needed for the cylinder grippers which hold the sheet during printing.) The next two steps consist in *unlocking the form* and in *clamping the form on the press bed*. These two operations are necessary before the form can be inspected and, where needed, adjusted. The unlocked form permits the *checking of cuts for height*. This step is particularly important in jobs where cuts are included in the type form without their prior inspection. At this point, cuts are measured for their height by the pressman, and the measured cuts are adjusted if they need adjustment. "Cuts that are too high must be planed or sanded down to the correct or below the correct height. Cuts that are low must be built up to the correct height with pieces of paper of the required thickness. When one end or corner of a cut is low, it is built up with strips or pieces of paper so as to eliminate any possibility of the cut's rocking on its base." The next step is the last in this group of operations. It consists in *locking and planing of the form*. This step is highly technical and must be done with great care. It has a decisive influence on page alignment, on forcing high slugs of type down the form, on color register in multicolor jobs, and on backup register, meaning the proper position of printed images on the other side of the sheet. "When part of the form is not properly planed,

this part will sink under printing pressure or drop when the form is again opened, causing additional delay during the run."

This step completes the first dozen of operations by which a flatbed-cylinder press is prepared for running.

Setting of guides and other operations related to proper positioning of the sheet. Now the pressman is ready to turn his attention to the press itself and to proper feeding. His next task is the *setting of press guides*. These are set "to produce a gripper bite parallel to the front edge of the cylinder and place the front edge in correct relation to the packing." The next step is *inking the press*. Stock and ink must be well suited to one another, and the amount of ink must be carefully regulated. After inking, the first sheet is printed and serves as a guide for the positioning of the form on the sheet. If adjustments are needed they must be made with precision. The first sheet also serves for other purposes. It will show how the form is printing, and in some instances this sheet will indicate that *interlaying of cuts* is needed. (As explained in the discussion of letterpress makeready, interlaying consists in placing paper sheets between the engraving and the base on which it is mounted.) This is also the time for *preliminary registration*. "Unsatisfactory back up registration must at this time be corrected, and color registration put into nearly correct position prior to overlaying." Before the pressman begins with overlaying, he may ask for *reader and position okay*. "Before proceeding with the overlaying, it is necessary to make sure that nothing will be changed in the form; therefore it is customary in most plants to obtain a reader and position okay before proceeding with the overlaying."

Overlaying. As explained in the introduction to letterpress printing, overlaying serves two purposes: one is to level the impression and the other to provide varying pressure for light and heavy tones in a halftone and for large and small solids. A large portion of all overlaying is done to simply *level the impression cylinder* in order to compensate for deficient areas in the impression cylinder, the packing, the press bed, and the type form. Leveling the impression cylinder has the additional purpose to obtain a balance of pressure when bed and cylinder are forced apart due to lack of rigidity in the press. The degree to which a press may be lacking in rigidity depends on a number of factors; its construction, age,

American-built presses handle sheets that have several times the area of those built at present by Heidelberg.

Press down-time caused by lockup of curved plates. Lockup and registering of curved plates on sheet-fed rotary letterpress equipment is rather time-consuming, as can be seen from the following data. These are provided to give the reader an approximate idea of the nature of the work, assuming normal conditions. For demonstration a press is selected that can print 32 pages, size 8½ by 11 inches, on one side of the sheet in four colors. If each of these 32 pages is printed in full color, and if each of the four plates needed per page in full-color printing is a single plate, 128 plates, which are curved electrotypes, must be positioned and locked up in register. The time needed for positioning, lockup, and for letterpress makeready can vary between 25 and 55 hours, depending on the particular job. (It should be mentioned that often there are two, or three, or more color plates to be locked up and registered for each color per page.) Lockup and makeready is usually continued throughout the shifts which are operated in a particular plant, but even with three shifts, press preparation and makeready

Courtesy Electrotypers and Stereotypers Handbook

Pressman attaching curved electrotypes to a plate cylinder of a multicolor rotary letterpress for publication printing. The plate hooks, or catches, engage the plates on their beveled edges. These hooks ride in the spiral grooves of the plate cylinder.

Ideally each color plate of a set for full-color printing should be a single, undivided plate. Unfortunately this condition is rather rare in sheet-fed rotary printing, and color plates may consist of a number of different pieces for each page, sometimes as many pieces as there are color illustrations on the page. Consequently many color plates need lockup of more than one plate per page in actual practice. This condition in combination with the necessity of exact color register adds substantially to the time needed for lockup of color plates.

Techniques for positioning of color plates are not uniform, but many of them are based on a printed sheet of the key plate assembly. If the Rotary Registerscope is used, the printed sheet of key plates replaces the layout sheet which was prepared to find the exact location of key plates. This printed sheet is now placed on the impression cylinder and is mirrored back to the plate cylinder for accurate color position. This operation is of course required for each color. In another technique the printed sheet of the key plate assembly is made translucent with a suitable liquid, glycerin, for example. Such translucent guide sheets are positioned face down on the plate cylinder for each color. The individual color plates are then placed on this sheet which may or may not remain on the plate cylinder during the run. In a variation of this method a printed sheet of the key plate assembly is put face down on the plate cylinder for each color, folded back as necessary, and the individual plates are positioned under it on the plate cylinder. This printed sheet is not made translucent.

An interesting method is used on unit-type rotary presses manufactured by Heidelberg. The plate cylinders of these presses consist of a core that remains on the press and of a shell that can be separated from the core and removed from the press. The plates are locked up on a shell which is placed on a matching core in a premakeready unit. A print of the key color is made on a transparent plastic sheet which serves together with other devices for finding the precise position of color plates. After lockup, the shell with the attached plates is put on the core of the impression cylinder on the press. The Heidelberg system is described in the preceding unit on two-color Heidelberg presses. It should be mentioned that Heidelberg presses are made for sheet sizes which are small if compared with the sheet sizes that can be printed with domestic presses.

Sheet Flow of a HEIDELBERG Two-Color Sheet-Fed Rotary Letterpress

A sheet feeder, two individual printing units, and a delivery comprise the basic units of this press. Each printing unit prints one color, one side, directly on the sheet.

In each printing unit letterpress plates are mounted on removable plate shells instead of solid plate cylinders. This system of removable or interchangeable plate shells permits the utilization of a wide variety of plates—from the one piece wrap-around plate to precurved segment plates.

The illustrations depict the progress of the sheet through the press; the all-over diagram shows all sheets in motion at one time.

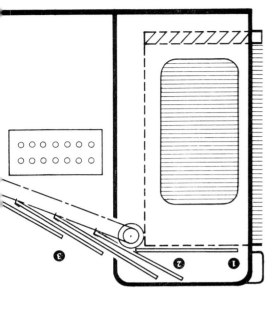

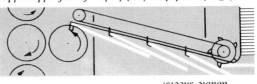

4 Registered sheet is picked up from feed board by the swing gripper of the ranger drum.

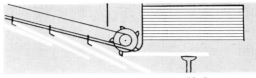

3 Remaining sheets are forwarded in a stream while on the feed board the first and successive sheets are registered by front and side guides. The sheet is also detected for alignment and double sheets.

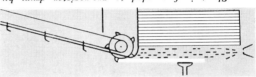

2 Sheet is forwarded to pre-register drum by forwarding sucker over a cushion of air where it is pre-registered and placed in the open feed table grippers.

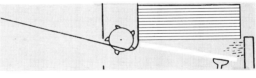

1 Top sheet is picked up by pick-up suckers. Separation is effected by blast of air at tail of sheet.

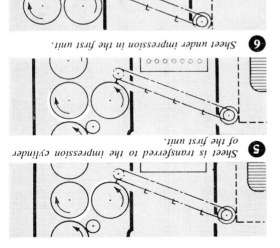

5 Sheet is transferred to the impression cylinder of the first unit.

6 Sheet under impression in the first unit.

7 Sheet has been transferred to transfer drum.

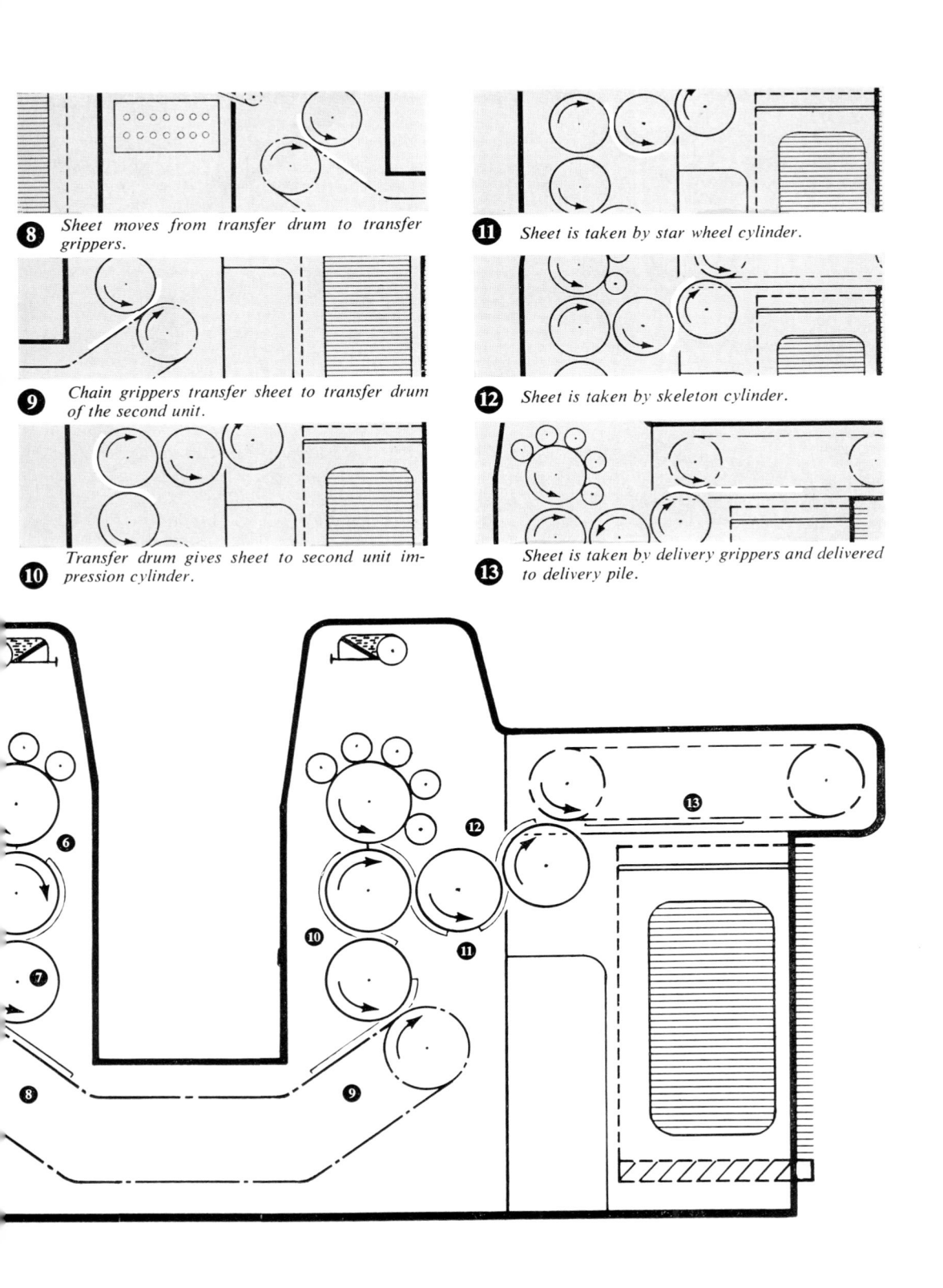

8 Sheet moves from transfer drum to transfer grippers.

9 Chain grippers transfer sheet to transfer drum of the second unit.

10 Transfer drum gives sheet to second unit impression cylinder.

11 Sheet is taken by star wheel cylinder.

12 Sheet is taken by skeleton cylinder.

13 Sheet is taken by delivery grippers and delivered to delivery pile.

requires more than a calendar day, and possibly more than two days. If such a press was operated on a single-shift basis, press preparation would need between four and eight calendar days. This long delay would not be acceptable for the delivery requirements of most customers.

The expense of press preparation and make-ready is not the same in all plants and therefore not expressed in figures in this manual. But there can be no doubt that this cost is considerable. For this reason it is quite understandable that letter-press printers are eagerly looking for different ways of doing presswork whereby press down-time can be substantially reduced. Printing with wrap-around plates seems to meet this require-ment though it is not yet possible to match highest quality electrotypes with the relatively new wrap-around plates.

Adjustment of printing pressure on sheet-fed rotaries. Printing pressure is adjusted by the same techniques which are discussed in this chapter under the head "Introduction to Letterpress Makeready." It is merely repeated that on com-mon impression cylinder presses, pressure adjust-ments must be made either under the plates or not at all. On unit-type presses, pressure adjustments can be made under the plates as well as on the impression cylinder.

Setting of the feeding, inking, and delivery units. The remaining three press units are set simul-taneously with lockup of plates. A large press is operated by several men who divide the work among themselves. For sheet-fed rotary letter-press printing, the feeder may be a conventional pile-feeder, or a sheeter feeder that converts rolls of paper into sheets of the required size as press-work progresses. The printed sheets may be delivered to a single or a double delivery; single deliveries may or may not be equipped for con-tinuous operation. Feeders and deliveries are described in Chapter VI, Sections 4 and 6, respec-tively and do not need further discussions at this point. A few words on rollers are added never-theless, even though this subject is extensively discussed in Chapter VI, Section 3. Sheet-fed rotary printing is done at high speeds, and com-position rollers including those of the non-malleable variety do not hold up very long at such speeds. They are therefore often replaced with heat-resistant, high-speed rollers which are usually made of synthetic rubber. Inspection, care, and setting of rollers is an important part of press preparation.

Courtesy 3M Company

Static electricity can be a problem in high-speed handling of sheets, during feeding, delivery, jogging, or folding. Static eliminators are useful accessories to presses and binding machinery.

After all plates are in register and the press sheet is approved for margin, reading, levelness, color, and register, the press is ready for running.

Accessories for sheet-fed rotary letterpresses. A number of different accessories are more or less widely used on sheet-fed rotary presses. Many plants put banks of infrared lamps across the feeder, and sometimes at the sides of the pile of paper in the feeder, which help in the reduction of static electricity and also improve the recep-tivity of sheets for printing. The sheets move rather fast in high-speed printing and thereby generate friction which may result in static elec-tricity. Static electricity on its part may cause the sheets to cling to one another which is not de-sirable. Many companies use equipment for elimination or reduction of static electricity on the feeder as well as on the delivery. Other acces-sories are antioffset sprays, open flame (gas burning) heaters for the setting of inks, as well as ink agitators, washup machines, and fountain separators which make it possible to do split-fountain work.

Running on sheet-fed letterpress rotaries. The main effort in presswork on sheet-fed rotaries is press preparation; running itself does not present a big problem. The pressman must see to it that each printing unit remains at its proper quality setting, that the feeder and delivery are main-tained, meaning that stock to be printed is added and printed stock is removed as presswork progresses, and that printing ink of the correct color is added when necessary. Troubles en-countered during running are more due to the jamming of paper, called jam-ups in the press-room, than to other causes. If a *paper jam-up* occurs the pressman must immediately attend to it in order to keep the press running and to pre-vent damage to plates or, possibly, to the press. Among other press troubles are plate batters and plate cracks. *Plate batters* mean damages to plates caused by extraneous matter. *Plate cracks* have, fortunately, become rare as methods for attaching the plates to the plate cylinder were improved. The pressman and his assistant see to it that the plates are kept clean and that there are no ''fill-ins'' of dried ink between halftone dots since such fill-ins are injurious to the quality of printed images.

Presswork on Harris Wrap-Around Presses

Harris wrap-around presses are sheet-fed rotary presses designed for printing with single-unit low-relief plates. These presses transfer the ink image from the plate to the stock, or by direct printing, and must not be confused with presses for in-direct relief printing. Harris wrap-around presses cannot take other image carriers, such as electro-types or rubber plates, but are designed for the printing with wrap-around plates only.

Some reasons for the development of low-relief plates. Low-relief plates can be made with vary-ing differentials between the printing areas and the non-printing areas of the plate. At the time of writing this differential is at the maximum depth frequently 0.016 inch. In traditional high-relief image carriers the distance between print-ing and non-printing areas of reading matter or line engravings is a multiple of this figure. The extent of this difference has a controlling influence on the production cost of relief printing-image carriers. Low-relief plates can be made of thinner base materials and much more simply than high-relief plates. In the opinion of Mr. Robert H. Downie, a pioneer in printing with low-relief plates, ''the development of powderless etching systems that will deliver 0.003 inch relief, should be a comparatively easy thing. The problems of powderless etching develop in severity as you push beyond 0.010, 0.015, and 0.020 inch reliefs. Shallow relief of 0.003 inch would open up the possibilities of other plate materials—to mention one, steel—and the cost may be even further reduced. In the Dycril system, 0.003 inch would mean faster plates. [A relief of 0.003 inch is not considered practical by other experts for line work in Dycril and other low-relief plates at the time of writing.] If you have got less photopoly-mer you are going to have a faster plate.''[63] Wrap-around plates can be put on the press in a much shorter time than individual electrotypes and are for this reason instrumental in the saving of down-time during press preparation. But it is not possible to simply put wrap-around plates on equipment not built for them, as already explained.

The most critical point in the printing of shal-low-etched relief plates is the inking system of the press. The form rollers, or plate rollers, of tradi-tional letterpress printing machines were designed for the inking of traditional, high-relief letterpress image carriers. The printing system of such presses is not suitable for the use of low-relief printing plates. The Harris wrap-around press embodies a novel approach to the inking of low-relief image carriers; other builders of presses for wrap-around printing attack the inking problem in different ways.

The construction of Harris wrap-around presses. As mentioned in Chapter VI, Section 3, ''The Ink-ing Unit,'' Harris wrap-around presses use a single large drum for the inking of the plate. ''Harris wrap-around presses are mechanically quite similar to Harris offset lithographic presses except that for the wrap-around design the im-pression cylinder has been equipped with bearers, a tympan clamp, and reel rod; and the cylinder adjacent to the ink distribution system carries an inking blanket, thereby becoming part of the inking unit. The inking cylinder is inked solid, and it transfers ink only to the printing surface of the shallow-relief plate. The plate, in turn, prints directly to the paper. The rigidity achieved by using an inking cylinder that rides in bearer-to-bearer contact with the plate cylinder permits the efficient use of plates with as little relief as 0.008 inch without putting ink on the non-image or dead metal areas. In fact, Harris have run plates with 0.004 inch relief.''[64]

To summarize, Harris wrap-around presses are built like Harris offset lithographic presses. But in Harris offset presses the topmost cylinder is the plate cylinder; it is followed by the blanket cylinder and this cylinder transfers its images to the stock which is carried on the last cylinder, the impression cylinder. In offset presses plate cylin-der and blanket cylinder have bearers (rims of hard steel on either end of each cylinder), whereas the impression cylinder is not equipped with bearers. In the Harris wrap-around press, the plate cylinder becomes the inking cylinder, the blanket cylinder becomes the plate cylinder, and only the impression cylinder retains its function. All three cylinders now have bearers.

In actual practice Harris wrap-around presses have many advantages. ''The inking mechanism will not 'ghost' due to the one-to-one ratio of ink transfer. Fidelity of color and coverage can easily be retained throughout the run making it ideal for quality color work on labels, etc. Sections of print can be removed by cutting the six point manila under the inking blanket. This can also be applied to scoring by including the scoring rule on the form and cutting out beneath the blanket and adding to the impression cylinder. When the blanket is tightened it will not ink the area."[65]

Uses for Harris wrap-around presses. Harris wrap-around presses are used for a number of different purposes. These include job-and-commercial printing, publication printing, label printing, and the printing of folding paper boxes. In the following you find a brief description of the printing of folding paper boxes as practiced at the Downingtown Paper Company. This company uses two Harris 49 two-color wrap-around presses for the printing of folding cartons. As always when specific practices of specific companies are discussed in this manual, it is mentioned that these are not necessarily followed by other printers. Nor should it be inferred by the reader that cartons cannot be printed, economically and in good quality, by other press equipment.

Planning for presswork on Harris wrap-around presses. At the Downingtown Paper Company, Dycril plates are used. These are not made by Downingtown but purchased from a photo-engraving concern. The letterpress department provides the engraver with art work and all instructions needed for the making of the Dycril wrap-around plates. The engraver supplies proofs which are checked by the staff of the letter-press department and submitted to the customer. After approval the plates are passed for production.

Press preparation of Harris wrap-around presses for carton printing. Press preparation of Harris wrap-around presses comprises—like that for other sheet-fed presses—the setting of the four main units, the feeder, the printing unit, the inking unit, and the delivery unit. On two-color presses there are of course two printing units and two inking units to be prepared, not to forget the transfer mechanism by which the sheet is transferred from the first to the second printing unit. Carton printing is done on paper board which is approximately eight to ten times as thick as the usual printing papers. For this reason the feeder holds not more than one-eighth or one-tenth of the number of sheets which it can hold if the printing stock is paper. A continuous feeder is therefore a necessity for the efficient production of longer printing runs. In order to increase

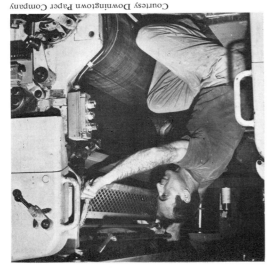

Pressman at work on a Harris Wrap-around press for carton printing on paper board.

Courtesy Downingtown Paper Company

feeder and delivery capacity, the wrap-around presses are on a raised concrete foundation.

Setting of the printing and inking units on Harris wrap-around presses. The setting of the printing unit and of the inking unit must be done with care and precision. All three cylinders have fixed positions in the press and must be adjusted by changes in the packing for the needs of the job in hand. Every new job may require a different packing of all three cylinders. Changes in the packings are more critical in jobs requiring precision registration than in jobs with loose register. In more critical register jobs the shortening or lengthening of the impression may be needed, an effect that can be obtained by changing the thickness of the packing under the plate. Paper board is much more compressible than many kinds of printing paper and therefore needs more squeeze pressure. Downingtown has developed a table which indicates the correct packing of each cylinder for boards of different calipers. This table guides pressmen in the packing of presses.

The preparation of the inking cylinder is of particular importance. At Downingtown this cylinder has a blanket of a durometer reading between 80 and 85. (In other applications somewhat softer blankets seem to be preferred.) The inking cylinder should be set for a "kiss impression," a term indicating that the least pressure compatible with proper image transfer is to be used. Too much pressure between the inking cylinder and the plate squashes the ink, resulting in unsharp, muddy printing. Excessive pressure may even cause unwanted ink deposits in the non-image areas of the low-relief plate. The ink should be metered in such a manner that the inking blanket is practically clean in the image areas of the plate after the impression. (In the non-image areas this cannot be expected and some ink will always be left on the blanket.) The setting of the ink fountain is therefore rather critical for high-quality printing.

Printing of heavy solids in glossy ink. Carton printing often needs printing of heavy solids in glossy ink or in gold. The Harris wrap-around press is particularly good in this respect. Carton printing is, of course, not the only field which has need for heavy solids, and several companies using these presses for other purposes found their ability to print heavy solids of considerable interest.[66] Harris wrap-around presses produce good solids for two reasons. One is that practically the whole ink film is transferred from the plate to the blanket, the other is that Dycril plates are somewhat resilient and have high ink release.

Running. The running of Harris wrap-around presses is concerned with maintaining the approved job quality and with producing as many sheets per hour as can be printed, keeping the quality of the job in mind. The great bulk of folding paper board does not contribute to speed of operation, nor does the printing of heavy solids. Paper boards printed with heavy solids cannot be stacked to the full height of the delivery pile. To keep the press running, dividers are placed at certain distances in the delivery, thereby reducing the height of each individual printed pile. The number of sheets per pile depends upon the job.

Presswork on Magazine Presses

Large presses for roll-fed letterpress printing are traditionally designated magazine presses because they are designed for the production of national general-interest magazines, *McCall's*, *Time*, or the *Saturday Evening Post*, to mention a few names. Such magazines are printed by the millions, and magazine presses are among the giants of printing presses. Since magazine presses are custom built and concentrated in a relatively small number of plants, a detailed description of the equipment—and of presswork done with it—is outside the frame of this manual. (The term "magazine presses" may imply to some readers that national

magazines cannot be printed by other processes than letterpress. Even though it is correct that letterpress dominates this field, gravure and possibly web offset are being used in the production of nationally distributed magazines.) The following paragraphs are limited to a brief survey of the most significant points.

The two basic kinds of magazine presses. Like sheet-fed rotary presses for letterpress printing, magazine presses are manufactured in two basic designs. One is the *common impression cylinder* design which was pioneered in the United States by the Cottrell Company, the other is the *individual impression cylinder* design which often resembles the general design of newspaper presses. Both kinds of presses are successfully operated in magazine printing plants, and both have an important place in letterpress web printing.

In common impression cylinder presses a number of plate cylinders, usually five, are arranged around the perimeter of the impression cylinder. The web is printed in all colors on one side, then passed through a drier and thereafter printed by a similar unit, or by the same one, on the second

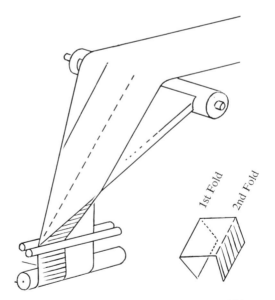

Making a gate fold on former folders. Gate folds are often desired, in magazine covers, for example, One technique uses two former folders in sequence. You see the web as it enters the first former folder. The solid line indicates the center fold; the broken line is the gate fold. The first former makes the gate fold, the second former (not shown), which is at a 90° angle to the first, makes the center fold.

side. After perfecting, the web is dried again and then either sheeted or folded depending on the nature of the work. Covers for magazines are often printed on heavier stock than their inside sections, and the covers are usually delivered sheeted whereas inside sections are delivered as folded signatures.

Printing by double-ending. It may be puzzling to some readers that the web can be perfected on the same printing unit on which the first side is printed. This result is obtained by the *double-ender* design, which uses webs of a width less than half the width of the impression cylinder. After the web comes out of the drier where its first-side impression is dried, it is directed by turning bars back to the printing unit, but now with its already printed side against the surface of the impression cylinder and with its unprinted blank side in contact with the plates. Double-ending can also be done on presses having individual impression cylinders. Arrangement may differ in detail but the principle remains the same: a web, half or less the width of the impression cylinder is printed on one side, dried, and turned for

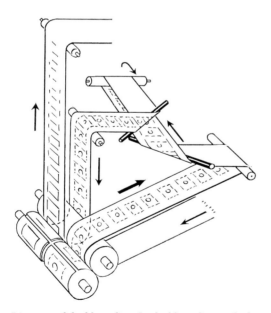

Diagram of double ending. In double ending, webs having half of the press width are printed on both sides in one pass through the press. The printing units are also divided in half, one for each side. You see the one-side printed web as it emerges from the printing unit. This web is turned and reversed in its path for printing the second side. Then it is either sheeted, rewound, or folded.

printing on the other side, dried again and finally either sheeted or folded. In actual practice both sides of the web run side by side on the press.

Feeding, web-control, and folding on magazine presses. Like all mass-production web presses, magazine presses are equipped with reels that hold several rolls of paper and are capable of automatic or semiautomatic connecting of the new roll to the expiring one. Web presses for magazine printing are provided with all control mechanisms and safety devices found on other high-speed web presses, even though the detail of the equipment may differ. The same holds true for the deliveries of magazine presses which are either ribbon folders or combinations of former plates and jaw folders. But essentially roll feeding, web control, and folding are the same as described in Chapter VI, "Printing Presses."

Press preparation and running. Press preparation includes the setting of web controls, of the folder, of all safety devices, and the drying equipment. But the most important part of press preparation is here, as in sheet-fed rotary printing, the positioning and lockup of curved electrotypes. This phase of press preparation is very similar to that described in the preceding unit on presswork in sheet-fed rotary letterpress printing. There are also some differences which are worth mentioning. These differences are related to the quality requirements of electrotypes and to letterpress makeready. In the long production runs which are typical for magazine printing (a term that includes other printed products which are also produced in huge quantities, mail order catalogs, for example) all component elements must be of highest precision. In the printing with unit-type presses, letterpress makeready and overlays are avoided as much as possible; in printing with common impression cylinder presses, level impression printing is practiced.

Another difference between plate lockup on sheet-fed rotaries and on magazine presses is the kind of attachment by which the plates are fastened to the plate cylinder. On sheet-fed rotaries, compression lockup by means of plate hooks, or catches, which engage the beveled edges of plates is prevalent. Lockup on magazine presses is usually tension lockup, also called internal lockup, which fastens the plates with their back to the plate cylinder.

Running, finally, has as always the two tasks

of producing the printed product at its predetermined quality level and of producing it as fast and efficiently as possible. National general-interest magazines must be distributed throughout the United States, Canada, and foreign countries. For this reason they have exceptionally tight production schedules which must be met precisely.

Presswork in Newspaper Relief Printing

Newspapers are beyond doubt the main staple of America's printed fare. Thousands of newspaper presses run day and night throughout the country, millions of printed papers are rapidly distributed, read, and discarded almost as fast as they are produced. American newspapers are an inexpensive commodity. Considering their low price, American newspapers are among the most significant examples of mass-production printing.

Not all American newspapers are printed in large quantities, and not all of them are printed in relief printing. Some daily papers and many weekly papers, which are published for rural or suburban areas and for small towns, are printed in relatively short runs and have not nearly as many pages as our metropolitan papers. In this field web-offset printing is making substantial inroads, replacing the customary relief printing methods. Rotogravure too has become important in newspaper printing as most larger papers have rotogravure magazine sections on Sundays and possibly gravure printed inserts during the week as well; however, only a few newspapers produce their own rotogravure supplements. But relief-printed metropolitan newspapers have remained the pacemakers of the newspaper industry; the present unit describes presswork as practiced by such a newspaper.

Three points must be kept in mind for every understanding of the problems existing in the production of contemporary metropolitan newspapers. These are time pressure, the role of advertising, and the growth of suburbia. Time pressure is constantly increasing and necessitates ever faster press equipment. Advertising is a crucial economic element in the newspaper business. Advertising is part of the information, expected by the reader and his family. Without advertising the low sales price of American newspapers would be simply impossible and advertising has become not only a financial but also an important technical consideration.

The growth of suburbia, finally, has removed many readers of metropolitan newspapers to new communities with their own problems and interests. These have become a new field for editorial coverage for many newspapers. Suburbia has its characteristic shopping centers and other local stores. Advertisements of these shopping centers and stores may not be interesting to people of other areas, and local advertisers may not want to bear the cost of advertisements printed in the complete edition of a paper which is read by a vast number of people who are not potential customers. Many newspapers meet these new conditions by individual sections devoted in their editorial and advertising matter to a given locality. These sections are inserted in such papers only as will be sold in the particular locality for which they are intended. A large metropolitan newspaper adopting this policy may therefore have a different composition for the city itself, supplemented by several local editions which carry different local sections for different geographical areas. But not all newspapers divide their weekday editions into sections devoted to particular interests and especially to local areas. Some newspapers prefer the continuous style and do not publish suburban sections; the *New York Times* is perhaps the most important example of papers preferring a continuous arrangement.

The following description of newspaper relief printing does not include the production of tabloids but concentrates on standard, or full-size, newspapers. The subject was developed at the *Philadelphia Bulletin*, an evening paper which also publishes a Sunday edition. On weekdays the *Bulletin* prints approximately 800,000 papers divided in ten editions. The methods described in the course of this unit are those used by the *Bulletin*. Other newspapers may follow different procedures, depending on their needs and equipment. But it can be said that experts in newspaper printing consider the methods of the *Bulletin* at least representative, and possibly in advance, of those practiced by many other large metropolitan newspapers.

Our discussion of presswork for newspaper printing is divided into the usual four major points: (1) planning, (2) quality control of component elements, (3) press preparation, and (4) running. Each of these four phases of presswork has its own characteristics which differ more or less from those met in other branches of the printing industry. The problems with which newspaper production must cope are in many respects unique in the graphic arts industry.

Planning for Newspaper Printing

The first consideration of contemporary American newspapers is, of course, their editorial content. The *Bulletin* has several rules for the placement of editorial material that will be discussed later in this unit. The amount of editorial space, however, fluctuates much less than the space needed for the printing of advertisements. Advertising is, consequently, an important factor in the planning of newspaper production. The number of pages which comprise a newspaper on a given day varies substantially during different seasons of the year and also for different days of the week within a season. These variations are in direct relationship to the fluctuations of advertising volume.

In the newspaper industry the number of pages is in a general way designated as "the size of the paper": papers having more pages than others are often called "bigger papers" and those having fewer pages, "smaller papers." This designation should not be confused with the page size or the dimensions of the page itself. The page dimensions are for long periods of time practically the same for a newspaper and are not influenced by the size of the paper which means merely the number of pages of which a newspaper consists on a specific day.

Relation between advertising and planning of newspaper production. Advertising has not only an influence on the number of pages to be produced, but poses many other significant production problems. There is first the position of advertisements which must be determined by considering both an advertiser's preferences and the editorial or manufacturing needs of the paper. Often advertisers desire to be either on the first or on the last page of a section which is, in trade terminology, known as the "break page." Other points that are related to advertising are the placement of the advertisement on the first printed or on the second printed side of the web, the printing of full-color advertisements, or ROP newspaper printing (ROP stands for run-of-paper) and, finally, the inserting of preprinted advertising material into a newspaper before it is folded. The last technique is rather novel at the time of writing, and it is not yet clear to what extent it will establish itself in the newspaper industry.

Planning as a co-operative effort between makeup and mechanical departments. Production planning for newspaper presswork requires close co-operation between the makeup department and the mechanical department. The mechanical superintendent is in charge of scheduling and also controls the handling of technical detail. At the *Bulletin* the established procedure is that the makeup department decides on the preceding day how many pages the next day's paper should have, and it transmits this decision to the mechanical superintendent for his comments. The mechanical superintendent analyzes the request of the makeup department from the viewpoint of production, identifying various points that could cause trouble. The troublesome problems may lie in the positioning of ads, in section breaks, or in the use of color, to mention some. The mechanical superintendent discusses such problems with the makeup department and in a friendly give-and-take between these two departments, the final decision on the next day's paper is established.

The role of the pressroom foreman and his staff in the planning of presswork. The decision on the next day's paper is immediately conveyed to the pressroom foreman in a kind of technical shorthand language by the mechanical department. Now the pressroom foreman knows where section breaks will occur and whether the paper will be produced by a straight run or by a collect run; he is also aware of many other details which do not need to be mentioned for our purpose. The next step is that the staff of the pressroom foreman prepares a layout in triplicate. This layout indicates the number of printing units and the position of each page on each of the plate cylinders of the printing units, as well as the number of presses on which tomorrow's paper will be printed. One copy of this layout is transmitted to the foreman of the night crew, one to the foreman of the electrical crew working at the same time, and one to the office of the mechanical superintendent. The foreman of the mailroom, where printed papers are bundled and dispatched, is advised by the pressroom foreman on the telephone as to the number of pages in the paper and which presses will be running. The manpower requirements of the mailroom depend on these factors.

The manning schedule and its revision. After the

layout for the next paper is made, one of the assistants of the pressroom foreman goes over the actual manning needs for the next day and compares them with the manning schedule, which he revises if necessary according to actual requirements. The manning of presses is outside our interest as much too technical, but a few words on the preparation of the manning schedule and on various causes for its possible revision will not be amiss since they give a better idea of the whole operation. A week ahead, actually on every Friday, the makeup department tries to determine the size of the paper for each day in the following week. On the basis of this forecast, manning is scheduled and the assistant of the pressroom foreman makes the necessary arrangements. But these schedules are by the very nature of the newspaper business only tentative ones and often require adjustments as the week progresses. Certain advertisers may want to increase or decrease their space for advertisements depending on a number of foreseeable, and often unforeseeable factors. A snowstorm, for example, may deter many shoppers from going to the store on the following day—advertisers tend to cancel already scheduled advertisements. On the other hand, unforeseeable political events such as, for example, the sudden death of a President of the United States, may make an expansion of the editorial part of the paper mandatory. In either case, decrease or increase of the estimated paper size, the number of craftsmen and other workers needed for the production of the paper changes accordingly. Once the final size of the paper is determined the assistant of the pressroom foreman must implement this decision in terms of manning by securing the necessary manpower and by the exact scheduling of pressmen and their assistants. Such implementation is done in cooperation with individual pressmen and their union. Craftsmen and workers employed in the pressroom understand that the necessities of the newspaper business are such that changes in the hours and days of work are often inevitable.

The equipment for newspaper printing. The *Bulletin*, like most other metropolitan full-size newspapers, is printed on double-width, unit-style, semicylindrical presses. These terms mean, as explained in Chapter VI, that each unit is a perfecting unit consisting of two printing couples (a plate cylinder and an impression cylinder forming a printing couple). Each of the two plate cylinders can take four plates across its length

Courtesy Electrotypers and Stereotypers Handbook

Curved cast stereotype plates ready for use on plate cylinders of a semi-cylindrical newspaper relief printing press.

and two plates around its circumference, amounting to eight standard pages. The two printing couples of each printing unit are capable of printing a web of paper with 16 pages, eight on one side and eight on the other.

The *Bulletin* has two lines of presses. A newspaper press needs not only printing units but also folders and reel stands for the feeding of rolls of paper. In the *Bulletin* the reel stands are on the floor below the pressroom as will be later more fully described. The folders are of course on the pressroom floor, one folder each after four or five printing units. Printing units and folders can be connected as required; if necessary, folders may also be disconnected. Collect and straight runs require different press arrangements. (To refresh your memory it is repeated that a collect run means that each of the 16 plates present on a printing unit is different, whereas in a straight run there are two sets of the same 8 pages.) In some instances it is preferable to produce a paper by a straight run, in others by a collect run. Some of the reasons for alternative selection of the kind of run follow.

Reasons for deciding to run a given day's paper straight or collect. The decision whether a paper should be produced straight or collect is a highly technical one depending on a great number of different items. (The difference between "straight" and "collect" runs is explained in Chapter VI, Section 5, under the head "Folder Deliveries of Newspaper Presses.")

Generally speaking, a straight run produces on weekdays a two-section paper and a collect run produces a four-section paper. One item which enters importantly in the decision of straight or collect running is the labor contract agreement concerning the manning of presses. Another point is that collect runs require multiples of 4 pages and cannot be increased by 2 pages. This means that a paper may have, for example, 40 or 44 pages in a collect run, but it cannot have 42 pages. If the paper needs only 42 pages, and if there are no commitments made to advertisers which necessitate a collect run, the mechanical production department may prefer to run this job straight because running it straight would save 2 pages or, in our example, approximately 5 per cent of paper. Since paper is the biggest single cost item on the material side, this saving is worthwhile. On the other hand, it must be considered that in straight running a single web is needed for each 8 pages, whereas in collect running a single web accommodates 16 different pages. This means that fewer printing units are needed per press for printing in collect running than in straight running, though, of course, more presses. For a 48-page paper which is run straight, six printing units are needed, and six webs must be associated at the roller-top-of-former before the paper can be folded. If a paper of the same size is run collect, three printing units are sufficient and only three webs are to be associated. In addition, the lengths of the web leads is much shorter in collect runs than in straight runs, and this item is an important consideration during presswork. For one, it takes much longer to relead a press of six units than one of three units. It is also a fact, statistically proven by the *Bulletin*, that long web leads have a greater tendency to break than short web leads. The problem of re-leading can also occur when a paster (meaning the connection between the expiring roll and a new roll) is missed at the feeding end of the press. In this case too, the press must be rethreaded, or releaded, and it will not be producing for the time which this operation takes. As time is quite scarce in newspaper printing, press down-time is, naturally, to be avoided whenever possible.

Another point that may first sound paradoxical is the fact that every straight running press loses production equivalent to two collect running presses when it is down. Each press, be it now operated as a straight running press or as a collect running press, produces of course the same number of impressions assuming that the two presses are running at the same speeds (which they actually are), but the press producing a straight run will wind up with twice the number of prod-

ucts, each having half the number of pages if compared with the product of the collect running press. (It must not be forgotten that two collect running presses are needed to print and fold the same quantity of papers as can be produced by one straight running press.) But the number of printing units is twice as much in a straight running press than in a collect running press; therefore, if a straight running press is down, it loses the production of two collect presses.

Finally, it should be said that just as there are advantages to collect running, so there are also advantages to straight running. The *Bulletin* keeps accurate statistics on press performance in straight and in collect runs, related to the size of papers. Based on these statistics, it is decided which type of run is the most desirable in a given case.

The meaning of first and second impression. There is a rather strong quality difference between printed images on first and on second impression. *First impression* is also called first-side printed, *second impression* is printed on the other side of the web, after the first side is printed. For reasons to be explained presently, the second impression produces somewhat more attractive printed images and may be preferable for some kinds of advertising copy. The placement of advertisement on first-impression or on second-impression pages are considerations in the planning of the paper and therefore discussed here.

Since it is not self-evident that second impression is preferable to first impression, this point needs a brief explanation. In Chapter VI it is explained that newspaper printing differs significantly from other forms of relief printing, particularly by the manner in which the printing-image carrier and the printing stock interact during the making of the impression. Newspaper presses produce the impression by forcing the ink into the fibers of newsprint. News ink, the ink used for the printing of newspapers, does not form a dry film but is more or less completely absorbed by the fibers of the paper. (All these points are discussed in Chapters VI, VIII, and IX.) Now it must be added that the time which it takes to achieve satisfactory absorption of the ink by the fibers of the newsprint is somewhat longer than the time elapsed between the printing of the first side of the web, or between making the first-side impression, and the making of the impression on the second side. This fact leads to quality differences between first-side and second-side impressions. The still wet first-printed side moves over the impression cylinder of the second printing couple for the printing of the second side. This impression cylinder is packed with a rubber blanket. Since the ink deposited on the first-printed side of the web is not yet completely absorbed by the paper, the images printed on the first side have a tendency of releasing some of the ink vehicle onto the blanket of the impression cylinder when the second side of the paper is printed. This involuntary and, unfortunately, inevitable ink transfer—known as second impression "offset," or more recently "set-off"—is part of each and every impression. Therefore, the first-side impression is generally considered somewhat inferior to the second-side impression. The outside sections of newspapers are always second-side impressions, just as the makeup department tries to position images that would especially be impaired by unintended ink vehicle transfer on second-side impression pages. The smudges caused by offsetting of wet ink are particularly disagreeable in the reproduction of halftones. When the image carrier for the second-side impression contains large type, the pickup of ink vehicle from the second impression cylinder is increased on the first impression side because of the strong pressure exerted by large-type areas. In some cases first impression offsetting, or set-off, has been effectively counteracted by the use of 3M Spherekote on the impression cylinder.

Strike-through and show-through. There are two other undesirable effects which are caused by the ink and by the paper used in newspaper printing. One is strike-through, the other is show-through. *Strike-through* is the term normally used to describe penetration of the ink from one side of the paper to the other; and *show-through* means that a particular batch of paper is too translucent for printing of good quality newspapers. In this defect the printed matter shows through the paper from one side to the other, thereby giving a visual disturbance to the reader.

General rules to be considered in the planning of newspaper production. Every paper has certain rules for the positioning of certain kinds of reading matter. In the *Bulletin*, for example, pages 1, 2, and 3 are always completely reserved for news and editorial matter. No advertisements may appear on these pages. Comics and late news items are placed on the last page. The sports page should, if at all possible, lead off the fourth sec-

tion of the paper, if it is a four-section paper. It is also customary to rotate the advertisements of important advertisers, those placed by large department stores, in such a manner that each of them at some time has its advertisement printed on the first or last page of a section, which are the desired "break pages." These are some additional points which must be considered in the planning of the paper.

Our description of production planning has arrived at its end. It will convince the reader that long experience and a keen sense for detail, supplemented by a good nose for smelling possible trouble are among the personal attributes necessary to the people who are in charge of this production phase.

Quality Control of Component Elements for Presswork

The time pressure under which newspaper printing must be done does not permit extensive quality control of image carriers. As soon as a page is made up, the necessary number of stereotypes are cast without much time being given to check the correctness of composition. Careful proofreading is done during the interval between the first and the second edition which is usually almost completely pruned of typographic errors. Pictorial image carriers are made in a photoengraving shop located in the building of the newspaper. These must be made to specifications and carefully proofed on newsprint and with news ink equivalent to those actually used in production.

The preparation of photoengraving sets for ROP (run-of-paper) full-color printing is done in the same photoengraving shop and requires, as in all printing methods, much more complex techniques than the making of image carriers for single-color reproduction. Full-color engraving sets are needed editorially and for advertising. Their proofing is rather critical and must be done with a view to anticipate correctly the results obtainable on the press. By a continuing process of comparing and adjusting the quality of ROP is systematically improved. But it must be remembered that the final image carrier is two steps removed from the original sets of full-color engravings. These must first be subjected to the making of stereotyping mats in which the actual image carriers, curved stereotypes, are cast in a separate operation. Unfortunately the whole principle of newspaper printing with its making of deep impressions on the paper and the soft packing of the impression cylinder is far from ideal for full-color printing notwithstanding its proved efficiency in single-color printing with black ink only. The handicap of ROP is further increased by the color of newsprint and by its structure. But these difficulties are more or less successfully surmounted by patient attention to detail and by constantly improving each of the contributing elements. The result is surprising and would not be considered possible by those who know how much care is expended on color printing in other methods which do not need to contend with such adverse basic conditions.

Quality control of inks and papers relies more on performance data and statistics compiled from them than on laboratory methods. The *Bulletin* does not operate its own laboratory but submits samples of the materials to be tested to organizations specializing in this kind of activity.

Press Preparation for Newspaper Printing

Large metropolitan newspapers must be printed on a number of presses because of their large editions and of the short span of time during which presswork must be completed. The number of presses depends on the total number of papers but also on the kind of run selected for a particular day. The *Bulletin* has an approximate press run of 800,000 copies. It uses six or seven presses for straight runs, and eleven presses for collect ones. Depending on the size of a paper, or its number of pages, a varying number of units must be connected for each press. This number, and other pertinent detail as well, is indicated in the layout prepared by the staff of the pressroom foreman.

Basic and final press preparation for newspaper printing. At large metropolitan newspapers, press preparation is divided into two phases. The first phase is here designated as basic and the second as final press preparation. (These two terms are not commonly used in newspaper printing; they are here introduced to help the reader in understanding the subject.) The *Bulletin* is an evening paper and therefore printed during the day. Basic press preparation is at the *Bulletin*, as in other evening papers, the task of the night crew. (In morning papers, which are printed during the evening and night hours, conditions differ somewhat.) Final press preparation is the task of the day crew and takes place prior to running as well as prior to every changing edition.

The main tasks of basic press preparation. The night crew consists of two different groups of workers: pressmen and their assistants are the personnel of one group, electricians and mechanics make up the other. Each group has its own foreman who must be an experienced, responsible craftsman. Both foremen receive the layout for the next day's paper and are guided by it in their work. The crew of craftsmen working on the press has a number of different but, naturally, closely related operations to perform. These can be classified in five groups: (1) the mechanical hookup of the required number of presses according to the new press layout, (2) tasks related to color printing, (3) the webbing of all presses, (4) indicating the position of each page on each plate cylinder of each unit and each press, and (5) general maintenance work. A few words on the manner in which these tasks are performed follow.

The job of *hooking up* various units according to the new layout is partly done by the electrician's mechanics and partly by the crew of craftsmen working on the press. Their work is both mechanical and electrical; it consists in connecting the required number of printing units to the folder and in disconnecting those not needed. The connecting of units is technically known as "clutching in," disconnecting of units as "clutching out." The tasks related to color printing are immediately tackled by a number of experienced pressmen and their helpers. The color units are stripped of their old plates, if changeovers in color are made the ink fountains are emptied, cleaned, and charged with the new color inks, or replaced with clean fountains, and the inking rollers are thoroughly cleaned. The new color plates are put on their plate cylinders, carefully registered and finally locked up. The operations related to color printing differ for spots or solid areas of a single color and for full-color printing. Since it is impossible to achieve fine adjustments when the press is down, the registering of sets of color plates is at this stage only approximate. The webbing of the press must follow the new layout and as a number of presses must be threaded with paper this operation is time consuming. During the time when some people work on the webbing of the press, other craftsmen may indicate the position of pages according to the new layout. This indication is made by writing the page folios with chalk on the press frame near each plate cylinder. The general maintenance work done by the night crew includes oiling and

Pressman attaches semi-cylindrical stereotype plates to the plate cylinder of the press.

lubrication of the press, replacement of worn blankets on impression cylinders, and the like.

Maintenance does not comprise repair work which is done by the staff of the machine shop. The *Bulletin* has four repair departments. One is attached to the composing room and keeps line-casting equipment in good order. Another repair department is responsible for the mechanical functioning of presses and stereotyping equipment. The third repair department is concerned with the mailroom, and the fourth repairs all electrical equipment.

In conclusion of this brief description of basic press preparation it must be made clear that all preparatory work done in this phase is in the nature of first, or approximate, adjustments. This point was made at the discussion of registration of color plates, it is equally valid for other operations and for the same reason—fine adjustments must be made when the press is running.

Attentive readers may have the impression that the preparation of the folder was forgotten in this listing of basic press preparation steps. But the folder was not mentioned because the *Bulletin* keeps one of the two folders with which each of the presses is equipped always ready for straight runs and the other for collect runs. This arrangement saves time and also provides a spare folder in the event of severe damage to a folder which can occur under high-speed operating conditions.

Final press preparation. Final press preparation is a major step before the press is ready for the first edition; thereafter it becomes a brief interruption of running, made necessary for producing later editions of the paper. The reason for separating final press preparation from running is simplicity of explanation; in the pressroom this distinction is not made. Final press preparation can be divided into the following four points: (1) removal of plates from their plate cylinders, (2) putting new plates on the plate cylinder, or lockup, (3) fine adjustment of the folder, and (4) work on color plates.

Final press preparation is done by the day crew, or more generally, by the crew which takes care of running itself. (In morning papers running is done by the night crew, since morning papers are printed during the night.) When the running crew reports for work it is divided into several groups which work simultaneously on the several units which combined are a newspaper press. Some men work in the reel room (which will be separately described), some on the folder, and some on the several printing units. The first task of these craftsmen is to remove the old plates from the press and to put them on the conveyor system which carries them back to the stereotyping foundry. The conveyor system is recessed in the pressroom floor. It has two tracks in which the curved plates travel, one end in either track. The same conveyor system that returns the used plates to the foundry brings the new plates from the foundry to the presses. New plates are put on the plate cylinder in accordance with the instructions concerning their position chalked on the press frame. (Noting the arrangement of pages on the press frame is merely a safety measure; most experienced pressmen can tell the position of a plate without looking at the notations.) The plates are locked up on the plate cylinder by compression lockup for which the presses of the *Bulletin* are equipped. During the time when the press is plated another pressman takes care of the *fine adjustment of the folder*. He has the job of adjusting both nipping and folding rollers for trouble-free running. Additional adjustments may be needed during running itself, when the press reaches cruising speed. The most difficult adjustments are those needed for full-color printing. In addition to regulating the feeding of paper in its length, which will be explained under the head of running, there may be a necessity for doing work on the plates themselves. This work

The HOE *Colormatic Printing Unit*

The Hoe newspaper printing system utilizes the Colormatic perfecting unit. Each Colormatic unit has two plate cylinders and two impression cylinders. As each plate cylinder can take eight plates, each unit can produce 16 printed pages on a web of paper up to 70 inches wide. The cylinders are arranged in an arch which facilitates the putting of plates on the plate cylinders and also makes the mounting of color cylinders and color units practical. The press is designed for a production of 70,000 newspapers per hour if the plates are attached by underside lockup.

The diagram and pictures on this spread show some of the features of the Hoe newspaper printing system, notably the fully automatic web tension and roll changing mechanisms which splices rolls of newsprint at full operating speed, the Hoe Colormatic unit with ink controlled from the outside of the press by individual push buttons for each newspaper column, and the Hoe folder which delivers papers having up to 128 folded pages.

2 *Photo showing a Colormatic press unit. The two printing couples (plate cylinders and impression cylinders) are inside the housing. Some of the printed web can be seen at the top. Note the push button controls and dial speed indicator at the right.*

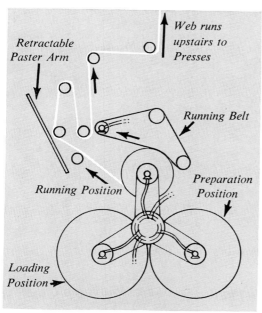

1 *Diagram of the Hoe three roll reel. The running roll is in the center, above the loading roll which is next. Running belts, in contact with the running roll, control the tension of the paper web.*

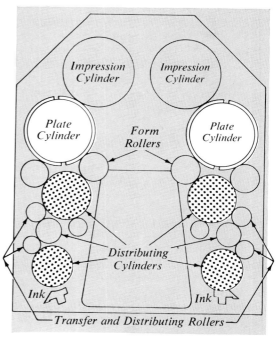

3 *Diagram of Colormatic ink motion. Path of ink is shown from the ink rail (on the bottom) to the two form rollers which ink the plates on the plate cylinders of each of the two printing couples. White circles indicate metal distributors, tinted circles rubber covered rollers. The ink rail on the left is open, that on the right is closed.*

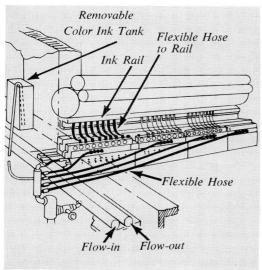

4 *Photo of ink pumps and ink rail. Each page has its own ink pump, four such pumps are shown in this picture. Each newspaper column has its own metering pump; in this picture you see 8 such pumps per page. The amount of ink fed in each column is independently controllable from the outside of the press.*

6 *Photo showing the impression cylinder with the just printed web, the plate cylinder and plates, as well as some inking rollers. All controls are placed on the outside thereby enabling the pressman to adjust the press fast and simply.*

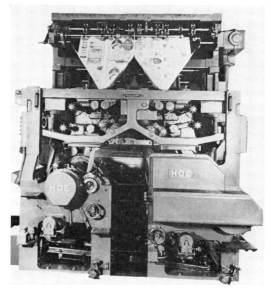

5 *Diagram of Hoe inking system. Black ink is force-fed from large storage tanks and continuously circulated through the closed loop piping system. Diagram shows two pipes; flow-in pipe is connected to page pumps, flow-out pipe returns overflow of ink to the tank. Removable color tanks can be easily attached to press housing and connected to inking system with flexible hoses.*

7 *Photo of the Hoe combination 3:2 and 2:1 folder. You see two former plates side by side. After passing the former the web can enter either a 3:2 or a 2:1 folder. The basic principle of the Hoe 3:2 folder involves a folding cylinder one and one-half times the diameter of the plate cylinder and a cutting cylinder approximately equal to the diameter of the plate cylinder. The cutting cylinder has two sets of cutting knives. A Hoe 2:3 folder can deliver newspapers having up to 128 folded pages.*

may include changing the position of plates, either sideways or around the cylinder, or in both directions, and shimming of plates in certain places with card stock of varying thicknesses. These operations are usually performed in the intervals between editions, primarily between the rather short first and the second edition.

Some reasons for different newspaper editions. Editions change because some of the editorial or advertising matter needs changing. As the day progresses news items continue to arrive at the editorial department, mainly from local reporters and over teletypes connected to the news services. These incoming news items are edited and change the contents of various pages. Before the new stereotypes can be cast, type must be set and the pages to be changed must be made up again. Editorial changes may be necessary in practically every field that is covered by a newspaper. These include international, national, and local items, sports, quotations on the two New York stock exchanges, and others. But it may also be necessary to change some of the advertising matter, to correct mistakes. In actual practice almost all plates containing editorial copy are changed during running. Some pages, or to be more precise, the plates for some pages, are changed more often and others fewer times. Plates for full-page advertisements, which do not have any editorial matter, do not need changing during the run. But such plates are relatively rare on an average weekday. Each change of edition is also used to correct typographic errors made in the composition for a preceding edition which are due to the lack of time for adequate proofreading. Often, in the case of last minute news items, composition is done in great haste without proofreading before page makeup and stereotyping; proofreading and correcting of typographic mistakes is done later when the respective edition is already running.

Running of Newspaper Presses

Running of newspaper presses is the final phase of newspaper production if we include the work done in the mailroom under this heading. Running takes place on three different levels of a newspaper plant. The pressroom is in the middle between the other two floors which are needed for running. Below the pressroom is the reel room where rolls of newsprint are loaded on reel stands; above the pressroom is the mailroom where the printed papers arrive from the pressroom on vertical conveyors and where they are

made ready for distribution to different points in the area. Each of these three levels is organically connected. The following description will be made from the bottom up. A strictly technical discussion would not convey one of the essential points of newspaper printing, namely, the great importance of communications, timing, and controls, or in one word, the organization which makes it possible to produce a modern newspaper in quantity and to do so efficiently and on time. For this reason descriptions of organizational features are included in each of the following descriptions which cover the three related stages of presswork.

The reel room. The reel room, sometimes also known as the substructure of the pressroom, is a large hall directly underneath the pressroom. The whole large hall is needed for the feeding of rolls of newsprint. All reels are located here, one for each printing unit. As the *Bulletin* has 36 printing units in each line, there are 72 reels on this floor. (The presence of the reels explains why this hall is called the reel room.) The *Bulletin* uses semi-automatic pasters; each reel has two three-arm spiders and can therefore hold three double-width rolls of newsprint. In addition to the reels, the reel room houses the storage tanks for black newsink.

Paper and ink consumption in newspaper printing. Both paper and ink are consumed in huge quantities by large metropolitan newspapers. The *Bulletin* consumes 95 rolls of paper per printing unit, assuming a collect run. If a paper is produced with four collect-running printing units the paper has 64 pages, assuming that it is printed from 4-page wide rolls throughout. For such a paper the total number of required rolls of newsprint is 380. If a paper is to be printed on seven units, collect, its size amounts to a total of 112 pages, and 665 rolls of newsprint are needed for the production of a run of approximately 800,000 papers. The number of 665 rolls of paper is equivalent to approximately 22 freight car loads. Ink consumption of black newsink is roughly 1.6 pounds for every 8,000 pages. As the total run is a hundred times as big we arrive at a figure of 160 pounds of ink per page on the whole run. Repeating our two examples of a paper having 64 and another having 112 pages, we arrive at a total ink consumption of 10,240 pounds for the 64-page paper and of 17,920 pounds for the 112-page paper.

The planning of paper and ink supply must be

Paper handling in a newspaper plant.

done rather carefully, and the dispatching of paper rolls, which can be 4-page wide, 3-page wide, or 2-page wide, depending on the size of a particular paper and the kind of run, requires good planning, just as the handling of the rolls needs sufficient space.

Storage and handling of newsprint. A large number of rolls of newsprint are stored in a warehouse located within the *Bulletin* building. This warehouse is connected to the reel room with a 2,000 foot conveyor. Rolls of newsprint are brought by this conveyor to a "stripping platform" where paper handlers take the wrapping off the roll, record its number and the name of the manufacturer on a card which they insert into the core of the roll. Then the roll goes back on the conveyor and is transported to the general area where it is to be used. A paper handler brings the roll near the reel where it is needed by putting it on a dolly whose casters run in a track leading directly into a reel. From here on the pressman takes over.

Roll preparation and making of changes. Each reel is assigned to a pressman. He removes the roll-card, on which each roll of newsprint is identified by number and source, and puts this card into a rack provided for this purpose. Then he pushes the dolly with the roll into the reel, locks the roll in position, and prepares the roll for making the paster. As the *Bulletin* has semi-automatic pasters, the pressman must energize the equipment for making the paster. To give the

reader an idea of the rate of paper consumption, it is mentioned that a 40-inch diameter roll will last for approximately 20 minutes at a normal running speed, producing 45,000 papers per hour. The pressman at the reel must, therefore, prepare about three rolls per hour and must make three changes within this time. If he misses a change, or as pressmen say, a paster, or if he has a web break, the web is automatically severed and the press is stopped for re-webbing. The pressman at the reel must re-web the press up to the pressroom floor. There the pressroom crew takes over.

Report cards on rolls of newsprint and their purposes. An important part of the pressman's job in the reel room is the filling in of a report card which indicates how many pages were printed from each roll. This report enables the mechanical department to check the basis weight of the paper. (Basis weight relates two factors, the weight and the area of paper. Since paper is charged by its tonnage, or weight, but consumed and sold to the advertiser by its area, it is important that the supplied rolls actually yield the calculated number of pages.) The pressman's report must also include missed changes and web breaks, as well as the time lost by such mishaps. Web breaks may be due to imperfections in the roll of newsprint or to other causes. If the pressman can ascertain the cause of a web break he mentions it on the roll-card if he cannot establish the cause he mentions this fact too. These reports are tabulated and carefully studied by the staff of the mechanical department. They are a most valued source of information for future planning.

Press operation during running. Once the last plate for an edition has been received, the press is started to run. For this reason the last plate is known in the pressroom as the "starter plate." When the press is completely plated, running begins, and within approximately 15 seconds the press speed is up to 10,000 revolutions per hour or, since every revolution produces two impressions, up to 20,000 i.p.h. At this time, the pressman in charge of a press does paging-up. *Paging-up* is another trade term which simply means that the pressman takes a folded paper and checks it for correct sequence of pages. If everything is in order the speed is increased until the press runs at normal operating speed. It takes about 45 seconds to get the speed up to approximately 45,000 newspapers per hour, a speed which is retained throughout running. When the pressman does paging-up some of his crew members are charged with *coloring-up*, meaning that they adjust the amount of ink fed for each column of the paper. If color printing units are operated, other craftsmen check these for color and for register.

Adjusting color register on the press. Color work requires finer adjustments than printing in a single color, or in black only. Apart from adjusting of plates, register is the main problem of color work. Register adjustment is done at present by regulating the length of paper fed between color units, an operation called *web compensation* and performed during running by simply turning a handwheel either clockwise or counterclockwise. The direction of turning determines whether the length of the paper web between color units is increased or decreased and the amount of turning influences the amount of paper fed. But this method is not really satisfactory as adjustments of this nature should be made continually which is, of course, not possible by manual turning of handwheels. For this reason, the *Bulletin* has decided to add electronic web control equipment for its color printing. This equipment is on order and will soon be installed.

Adjusting of impression and cut-off register. Another task of the pressman is to adjust the impression of each printing couple, meaning the extent to which the plates press into the paper. This adjustment is made by moving the plate cylinder either closer to the blanket of the impression cylinder or further away from it. Another point is the adjustment of the cut-off register, which determines the length of the newspaper page and cannot be made accurately by the night crew. Adjustment of impression and adjustment of cut-off register are fine adjustments of the press which must be done when the press is running. Generally speaking, the night crew works at all these tasks but can do them only up to a point. The definite fine adjustment must be made by the day crew under actual press operating conditions.

Folding. It is already mentioned that the *Bulletin* has one of the two folders (which are on each press side by side) constantly set for straight runs and the other for collect runs. The *Bulletin* uses upper, or balloon, formers, which double the number of sections possible with a lower former folder. The printed 4-page wide web is split into two 2-page wide webs just before the webs go over the former plates; with balloon formers the total number of web assemblies is, of course, four. These web assemblies receive their center folds by the four former plates which fold the web in its running direction, or lengthwise.

After the webs leave the former plates they are combined, and put through the folding and cutting cylinders. There the webs are divided into individual papers and folded as required, either collect or in straight runs. At the *Bulletin* the folders are named inside folders and outside folders. One is always used in straight runs, the other in collect ones. If the inside folder (which is reserved for straight runs) is in operation, the folded newspapers are delivered by a so-called "subway delivery" to the vertical conveyor which transports the papers upward to the next higher floor where the mailroom is. But before we follow the printed papers to the mailroom, some aspects of communications and controls during presswork must be explained.

Several kinds of information needed for running. As you may remember from the discussion of planning for presswork, the pressroom foreman provides a general layout for the next day's paper. You may also remember that the night crew marks the position of each page with chalk on the press frame for each plate cylinder. Each pressman in charge of a press needs two additional

Courtesy *The Bulletin*, Philadelphia

Two pressmen inspect the paper at the beginning of a run.

items of information. He must be told which plates are to be changed for different editions and how many papers his press must produce for each edition. The pressroom foreman in turn receives his information from two different sources. The composing room foreman advises him on plate changes, and the circulation department, located in the mailroom, tells him the number of papers wanted of each different edition. The pressroom foreman must on his part convey this information to the operating personnel. Either kind of information is communicated differently.

Procedure for keeping track of plate changes for different editions. The required plate changes, which are not the same for each of the ten editions printed at the *Bulletin*, cannot be left to the memory of the pressman but must be recorded in a practical manner. In the *Bulletin* required plate changes are written with chalk on blackboards. Each press has its own blackboard close by. The noise level in the pressroom is rather high. If people want to talk to each other they can best do this by speaking directly into one another's ears. Communication is safest either by writing or by signaling, even though pressmen are much more used to the whirring noises of their machines than outsiders and can understand the spoken word better.

But we have left our subject, namely, how pressmen keep track of plate changes. The office of the pressroom foreman sends slips of paper to each pressman immediately after it is informed by the makeup department of plate changes. This information is put on the blackboard and can be read by every person who must take a part in plate changes. In a collect run requiring five printing units there are ten plate cylinders with 80 plates on each press, for example. For fast change of plates, a number of people must perform this step at the same time. The workmen assigned to certain plate cylinders can take the necessary instructions from the blackboard.

Signaling to individual presses that their quota is printed. The next point concerns the number of papers to be printed by each press for each edition. It was already said that large metropolitan newspapers must be printed simultaneously on several presses. At the *Bulletin* the number of presses varies for different times of the day, and presses are staggered in order to achieve best efficiency. For the first two early editions only four presses may be used; then at the peak load of

production, the number of presses may be increased to eleven for the printing of the next four editions; the later editions are again smaller, and four to six presses may suffice. The production of these presses must be controlled, and this controlling is done in the office of the pressroom foreman.

The office of the pressroom foreman is a little house, complete with its own roof, on the pressroom floor. It is a rather large office with many desks and would not be considered small in another setting, but here in the pressroom, which is one immense hall several stories high, this office appears to be just a little wooden house. One wall is completely occupied by control equipment of two different types. We are interested mainly in the totalizer. The *totalizer* is electrical counting machinery which indicates in figures the production of each press as well as their total for each edition, and also the total of all editions, as printing progresses. The totalizer is carefully watched by an assistant of the pressroom foreman who is assigned to this job. When production of an edition approaches the requested figure, the assistant in charge of production control signals to the pressman at the folder of a press that his quota is printed. This he does by switching on a signal light. As soon as the pressman receives this signal he stops the press. The press crew begins immediately to replate the press for the next edition.

Records kept in the pressroom. Not the least important duty of a pressman is the keeping of records of troubles and of the time it took to take care of them. Among the troubles to be reported are web breaks; blanket failures, roller failures, and mechanical failures; missed changes of rolls; folder jams and conveyor jams; shutdowns due to troubles in the mailroom. Troubles in the mailroom cannot be seen from the pressroom floor and press shut-downs due to them must be ordered from the mailroom.

The office of the pressroom foreman has electrical equipment connected to each press, tracing a continuous graph of press speeds in increments of 15 seconds. But these graphs do not give the reasons for slowdown and stoppage of running, and these reasons must be listed in the written reports of pressmen. Graphs and reports are consolidated in the mechanical department; the knowledge gained is used for improving efficiency of presswork in the future.

By studying the consolidated pressroom reports, it can be determined which kinds of web-leads are most troublesome; such web-leads are of course eliminated if this is practical, which is not always so. (Often eliminating one source of trouble can result in other, and sometimes even more undesirable, difficulties.) The pressroom reports have an additional purpose of great value. They enable the mechanical department to evaluate the performance of newsprint supplied by different paper mills. On the basis of past performance, the mechanical department decides which make of paper is best suited for a selected kind of web-lead and for color printing.

The mailroom. The folded printed papers are moved by vertical conveyors, in which they are held between continuous wires, to the floor above the pressroom where the mailroom is located. First the papers pass through a machine which is called "counter-stacker". The counter-stacker counts a predetermined number of papers and produces a stack of them. (The number of papers to be put in a stack can of course be changed as the needs may require. The machine can simply be adjusted for the necessary changes.) The stack of papers is ejected by the counter-stacker onto a roller conveyor which brings it to a pacing device.

The pacing device straightens the stack and positions it for the next operation, wrapping with wrapping paper. At the *Bulletin* the pacing device was developed by the assistant mechanical superintendent. The pre-cut wrapping paper is automatically put beneath the stack of papers, the bottom wrapping machine pushes the wrapped stack into the tying machine where the bundle of newspapers is automatically tied with wire. After this operation is completed, the bundle is ready for shipment. It is ejected to the loading platform where it is loaded into the waiting delivery trucks. If sections of newspapers are to be hand inserted, this operation is also done on the mailroom floor where it is at present performed by hand rather than by mechanical equipment.

Like the pressroom and the reel room, the mailroom is a huge hall. The described handling of papers takes place in many assembly lines, one for each press. Various editions must be timed for

Courtesy *The Bulletin*, Philadelphia

The printed and folded newspapers are automatically conveyed from the pressroom to the mail room by vertical conveyors.

delivery to different parts of Philadelphia and its suburbs, including Camden and other places in New Jersey. A fleet of trucks is constantly being loaded to deliver the huge quantity of printed papers to the thousands of places where the readers of the *Bulletin* expect to find their newspapers at the accustomed time. The making of a big newspaper is not only an exercise in the art of communications but also an example of applied logistics.

Presswork on Flexographic Presses

Flexographic printing has grown rapidly since the end of World War II. It is widely used for printing and converting of package material and shares in the growth of the prosperous package

industry. Flexography can process a variety of stocks including paper, paper boards, aluminum foil (laminated either to paper or paper boards), and plastic films. Like other package printing, flexographic printing can be done inline with converting machinery that produces a completed product in one pass through the equipment, paper bags or folding cartons to mention two examples. But it is also often found practical to sheet the printed web or to rewind it and to process it further on independent fabricating equipment. This method of manufacturing is preferred when the fabricating machinery must be operated at a lower speed than the printing equipment.

Those active in the flexographic industry think of themselves less as of printers than as of manufacturers of package material, and they are usually called converters rather than printers. Flexographic printing may be only one of several stages through which the conversion of stock may pass on its way to becoming package material. The same holds true in other branches of package production; printing is always an important operation but it may need to be subordinated to others which are decisive for the required end product.

The present unit discusses the flexographic printing of stretchable films which have acquired a key position in certain kinds of packaging. Flexographic printing of stretchable films was selected to give the reader a well-rounded picture of package printing. In a preceding unit of this section the printing of sheets of stock for folding cartons is described under the side head of the Harris wrap-around press. In the following section, which covers intaglio printing, you find a description of inline production of die-cut folding cartons on a rotogravure installation equipped for color printing which may be preceded by laminating aluminum foil to the printing stock. The present unit adds a description of printing of flexible films and informs you about a branch of package printing which is of consistently growing importance.

Planning for Flexographic Printing

Flexographic printing of plastic films must be carefully planned from its inception, beginning with the preparation of art-and-copy. "Rubber plates, if made without any control fabric, metal or other means of controlling size, will shrink when they are taken from the mold and cooled. This shrinkage takes place in both a horizontal and a vertical direction. If the rubber is molded directly to a sheet of brass, or other metal, or if fabric control cloth or plies are molded

into the plate, the shrinkage can be completely eliminated or drastically reduced."[67] It is not always desirable—nor always possible for cost reasons—to mold directly to metal, and shrinkage is therefore often a factor to be considered in art-and-copy preparation. Another kind of distortion is practically inevitable, namely the elongation of a rubber plate when it is put around the plate cylinder. The extent of this elongation is determined by a number of variables of which the cylinder diameter is usually considered the most important. Flexographic printers guide those who prepare art-and-copy by indicating the extent to which distortion is to be expected on a specific job and under actual manufacturing conditions.

Other points to be considered in the planning of flexographic printing of plastic films are the interrelations between specific films with the printing inks that must be used for them and with the material of which the plates must be molded. The selection of the kind of film which is to serve for a given packaging task depends

Courtesy Flexography Magazine

A common impression cylinder, multicolor flexographic press is adjusted for running a new job.

primarily on the end use of the printed product. Another point that must be decided in the planning stage is the diameter of the plate cylinder which determines how many units of the final product are printed at each cylinder revolution. Since the nature of plastic films has a controlling position, we turn first to a brief description of these materials.

Classification of films for package printing. The flexographic industry divides films into three groups. One consists of non-stretch-non-melt films, the other of non-stretch-melteasy films, and the third of stretchable films. The first group of *non-stretch-non-melt* films is made up of variously coated cellophane. In the second group of *non-stretch-melteasy* films are cellulose acetate, polystyrene, polyesters and polyvinylidene chloride. The third group of *stretchable* films includes polyethylene, polypropylene, polyvinyl chloride, and rubber hydrochloride. Most plastic films are better known to non-technical people under their various trade names.[68] Different plastic films are printed with different inks, some of which may contain solvents that attack plates made of natural rubber. For jobs where such inks must be used, plates are often made of Buna, a synthetic rubber.[69]

End use specifications. The end use specifications are usually conveyed in the planning stage to the supplier of printing inks. He will want to know the answers to such questions as: "Is heat resistance, gloss, alkali proofness, or acid resistance a factor? Will bleed resistance, boilability, grease proofness, permanency, or water resistance be required?"[70] Many of these points are self-explanatory if you consider the final uses of films as packaging materials and the chemical characteristics of the products packaged with them. Package material for soaps and soap powders must obviously be alkali resistant, and pouches holding prepared frozen food which are boiled in the plastic pouch, must be boilable, to give merely two examples. (The relations of end use specifications to printing ink properties are discussed in some detail in Chapter IX, "Printing Inks." In this chapter you also find descriptions of some standard tests for end use requirements.)

Selecting the diameter of the plate cylinder. The diameter of the plate cylinder is determined by the size of the unit to be produced and by the number of units combined around the cylinder. Since plate elongation is worst at very small diameters, many jobs requiring close register are not put on cylinders having the smallest possible diameter for the job in question. The minimum diameter varies for different jobs; it is the cylinder diameter needed for attachment of a single set of plates around the cylinder. In long-run jobs two or more plates around the cylinder are preferred, resulting in larger cylinder diameters and higher production. But in short-run jobs, the cost of molding more plates than absolutely necessary can be prohibitive.

Sandwiching of printed images between two layers of film. Another point that influences planning of film conversion by flexography is worth mentioning, if ever so briefly. Converters are providing package material to their customers by laminating two films with printed images sandwiched between them. Such laminations can have most desirable characteristics which cannot be produced by using a single film. Lamination is done roll-to-roll on special equipment with adhesives suitable for bonding the two kinds of films in question.

The preceding discussion of planning for flexographic presswork is far from comprehensive and solely intended to give the reader an idea of some of its more important points. It might be added that planning includes selecting the most economical width of the plastic film to be converted, determining the sequence in which various colors are to be printed, and other highly technical items, depending on the nature of a job.

Quality Control of Plates, Films, and Inks

Quality control of all component elements needed in the production of a specific job can be done in flexography (as in all other branches of printing) on different levels of technology. Large converting plants have their own laboratories, staffed with graduate personnel, for testing the qualities of printing stocks and inks; in smaller companies such facilities are unavailable and testing is done by craftsmen in a more simple manner.[71] Our discussion is limited to two points which are decisive for efficiency of printing and quality of printed images. One is the checking of plate cylinders for concentricity, the other is quality control of molded plates.

Checking the concentricity of plate cylinders. The plate cylinder selected for the mounting of plates must be checked for its concentricity prior to plate mounting. This step of quality control is done with a simple instrument, called a dial indicator. "The tip of the indicator is applied against the surface of the cylinder as it is rotated 360°. The resultant reading is measured in thousandths of an inch TIR (Total Indicator Runout)."[72] *Runout* means the extent to which a cylinder differs in concentricity in various areas, or said in plainer words, the extent of its out-of-roundness. Tolerances in concentricity are narrow, particularly in high-quality color printing.

Quality control of molded plates. Molded plates are carefully inspected and checked for their correctness both as to the height of the relief printing areas and to their size. "The rubber plate should be checked for dimension in accordance with the layout of the design supplied. This can be done in a flat state by a man who knows what the reaction after mounting is going to be, but a more thorough check is to take the key color, put it on backing, and lay it on the cylinder prescribed in the correct direction, and measure for proper dimensional layout."[73] The checking of rubber plates for their correct height is done with another instrument, standardized by the Flexographic Technical Association under the name "FTA Rubber Printing Plate Micrometer."

After completion of the press run, all plates are again carefully cleaned, inspected and stored to make sure that they are in perfect condition when the job will be repeated. Most jobs in package printing are produced many times from the same plates, sometimes over a span of years. Quality control of plates is therefore necessary before the beginning of the run and after the run is finished.

Press Preparation and Running for Flexographic Printing

Flexographic printing can be done on three different kinds of presses, as explained in Chapter VI, Section 1. Since press preparation varies to some extent for each of these three basic kinds, not to speak of different makes, it is necessary to select one type for our description of this phase of presswork. As stack-type presses are probably the kind of presses most widely used in this industry, the following description of presswork refers to stack-type presses.

Brief description of stack-type presses. Stack-type presses have individual printing units, usually arranged in two parallel vertical columns. Each of these two columns, or stacks, has two or three (and possibly more) printing units including the necessary ink reservoirs and rollers. On a typical stack-type press the web of material enters the first column at the top, goes down as it is

printed, is led into the second stack from the bottom, passes through the second stack on its way up and leaves the printing stations at the top of this column. Drying units are placed after each printing unit; wet-on-wet printing is not possible without forced drying at the speed at which modern flexographic presses operate.

Some flexographic presses are equipped with roll stands, others have reels which permit either semiautomatic or fully automatic connecting of the expiring roll of material to the next roll. The running roll at this end of the press is usually called the "unwind" roll. At the other end of the press is the delivery which can be either inline, or a sheeter, or machinery for rewinding. Because many flexographic installations for the printing of stretchable films have rewinding facilities, these are selected as the delivery for the present description of presswork. The roll at the delivery is called the "rewind" roll, parallel with "unwind" roll, the term used for the roll at the feeder end of the press. The printing units together with their inking equipment and the driers are between unwind and rewind.

The main differences between press preparation for flexography and for other relief printing methods. Press preparation for flexography differs in two essential points from press preparation for all other relief printing methods. The first point is that flexography can use plate cylinders of varying diameters on the same press and that plates are mounted on the plate cylinder away from the press. The cylinder with the plates mounted on it is then inserted into the press. The second point is that the impression cylinder does not receive any packing at all in flexography; in this relief method the web rides directly on the base metal surface of the impression cylinder during the making of the impression. Adjustments between cylinders are made by mechanically changing their location. Local pressure adjustments such as overlays are not used in flexography. Even though this term is not part of the flexographic vocabulary, flexography is a level impression printing method, if we may use a term of letterpress printing.

A brief comparison of the capabilities and techniques of flexographic printing with those of other processes and methods might be interesting to some readers. As mentioned, cylinder diameters can be changed within the limits for which a specific press is built. This condition does not exist in other relief printing methods nor in

Courtesy Mosstype Corporation

Flexographic plates are attached to the plate cylinder of the press on a Mounter-Proofer. The same equipment is also used for proofing. After proofing the plate cylinder is removed from the Mounter-Proofer and put back on the press for presswork.

planographic printing, but does in rotogravure for package printing. Flexography resembles rotogravure also in another point: in both methods the cylinders bearing the printing images are completely prepared away from the press. The difference between gravure cylinders and flexographic plate cylinders is that in rotogravure, cylinder and printing-image carriers are one and the same whereas in flexography the image carriers are removable without physical change of the plate cylinder itself.

Finally, it should be mentioned that the plate cylinders on Heidelberg presses, which are used in letterpress, are constructed in such a manner that the plates can be attached away from the press. As described under the side heading "The Heidelberg Two-Color Flatbed-Rotary Combination Press," the plate cylinder consists of two parts. One is a core which is a permanent part of the press and cannot be removed, the other part is a removable shell for curved electrotypes, or another kind of shell for attaching rubber or plastic plates. This shell can be equipped with plates away from the press and put back on its core after plating. This system is used on all Heidelberg plate cylinders and provides some of the advantages of flexographic techniques. But so equipped presses are neither manufactured for web printing nor for large size sheet-fed letterpress printing. (To avoid misunderstandings: Heidelberg presses are not used for flexographic printing.)

The scope of press preparation on flexographic presses. Press preparation includes as always the setting of the four major press units, or press sections. In the following description we are limited to those operations which are typical for flexography, and must exclude detailed discussions of various techniques. The points to be covered are six: (1) selection and setting of Anilox and fountain rollers, (2) adjustment of ink viscosity, (3) registering of plate cylinders, (4) control of web tension, (5) the rewind unit, and (6) accessory equipment. These items are far from a complete listing of all steps needed in the preparation of flexographic presses for running. In the flexographic industry press preparation is usually called "mechanical makeready" to distinguish it from the adjustment of molded plates, an operation customarily known in converting plants as "plate makeready."

Selection and setting of Anilox and fountain rollers. The selection and adjustment of Anilox rollers depends on the nature of the job in hand. "For normal purposes Anilox rollers with 165 lines per inch are used, for fine type 180 and possibly 200 lines."[74] Not only the Anilox roller must be selected to suit the job in hand, the fountain roller, too, must be covered either with natural or with synthetic rubber depending on the kind of ink to be used. This requirement may cause changes of the fountain roller in changeovers from one material to another. The setting of the rubber fountain roller to the Anilox, or metering roller, and that of the Anilox roller to the plate cylinder, as well as the setting of the plate cylinder to the impression cylinder must be done carefully. "Depending on the press, pressure between the fountain rollers is set either hydraulically or manually. In film printing of quality work, the forward movement of the plate cylinder from 'kiss' contact to full impression cannot be more than 0.0035 to 0.0045 inches. In some finer types of work this tolerance is even tighter."[75]

Adjustment of ink viscosity. The adjustment of ink viscosity is an important part of press preparation. Flexographic inks are usually supplied to the converter as concentrates requiring adding of solvents for presswork. Various types of inks must be adjusted with different solvents. Adding of solvents incompatible with the film-formers used in a particular ink formulation can precipitate these, an effect called "souring of inks" in this industry. (Soured inks may or may not be salvageable.) The correct viscosity to which the ink should be adjusted differs for different inks and applications. The pressman is instructed on this point by supervisory personnel, and he controls the amount of solvent added by making certain tests. Viscosity of ink can also be controlled by automatically operated press equipment which adds solvent as the run progresses.[76]

Registering of plate cylinders. From the department in charge of the mounting and proofing of plates, the completely prepared cylinders come to the pressroom ready for presswork. They are put in the press on their respective printing stations and must then be brought into register. This is achieved by first properly positioning the key color and by making prints of it. Then every other cylinder is "rotated to a position where the plate cylinder registers with the print copy of the first-down color."[77] The detail of this operation is highly technical; it is well described in the last quoted article and also in others published in the trade press.

Control of web tension. Tension control of the moving web is important in all kinds of web printing but it is nowhere as critical as in the printing of stretchable plastic films. If tension of such materials is not maintained accurately, the printed product may be more or less unusable. "Three basic areas of tension control are important: infeed tension, outfeed tension, and wind-up tension."[78] The methods and equipment for tension control vary; some of them are described in Chapter VI, Section 5. Merely to give the reader an idea of the precision with which web tension must be regulated in the printing of stretchable films, it is mentioned that polyethylene, a widely processed stretchable film, used in a thickness range of 0.0005 to 0.010 inches, must have a tension of 2 ounces per inch of web width per mil, or 0.001 inch, film thickness.[79] An example will clarify the meaning of these figures for those not conversant with flexographic printing of stretchable films. Assume a web width of 20 inches and a thickness of 5 mils (0.005 inch), and the total web tension will be 200 ounces across the whole press.

The rewind. A few words on the rewind, which is usually the delivery in the processing of plastic films. The rewind must be perfectly synchronized with the unwind and the printing stations. Since the roll increases in its diameter as rewinding progresses, special equipment is necessary to keep the rewind in perfect balance without increasing web tension. Often rewinding is preceded by slitting which is done with slitters. Slitters are fixed or rotary knives that cut the running web into several narrower webs; they can also be used to trim edges on either side of the web, if this is wanted. All webs slit from a master web are rewound on individual cores on a single shaft. One of the problems that had to be solved in flexographic printing is the "blocking" of the printed and rewound web. *Blocking* means that successive layers of the printed material adhere to such an extent that they cannot be separated from one another without some damage.[80]

Accessory equipment. The subject of blocking leads straight into a brief discussion of accessories for flexographic printing. Blocking is prevented by thorough drying which is sometimes followed by applying a powder to the dry web before rewinding. Both drying equipment and sprayers must be properly adjusted during press preparation. Other accessories include scanners, which serve to maintain proper register and web viewers which make it possible for operating personnel to view the running web, something impossible for the unaided eye because of the speeds with which printing is done.

Running of flexographic presses. The main tasks of running were aptly expressed by a participant in the Third Annual Meeting and Technical Forum of the Flexographic Technical Association as "(1) to maintain a consistently satisfactory quality level throughout the run, and (2) to convert the largest amount of material in the least amount of time—in short to develop peak productivity."[81]

All press units, or sections, from the unwind to the rewind must be maintained in their proper settings, and printing stock as well as printing inks must be added as the work progresses. Running can pose many problems, but these are more of interest to operating personnel than to the readers of this manual.[82]

Presswork on Indirect Relief Printing Presses

Presses for indirect relief printing are modified offset lithographic presses. In the past, the plate cylinders of most if not all offset presses intended for indirect relief printing needed adapting by grinding down because the undercut of plate cylinders for offset printing is too low for indirect relief printing. More recently, dual purpose machines suitable for both offset lithography and indirect relief printing are supplied by press manufacturers.

Since presses for indirect relief are offset lithographic presses, and since the operation of such presses is discussed in detail in Section 4, we can limit the description of presswork in indirect relief printing to a few points of difference between these two printing methods. The most important difference is the elimination of dampening in indirect relief printing. If a dual purpose press is frequently used for both offset lithography and indirect relief printing, the dampening plate rollers remain on the press and are merely disconnected for indirect relief printing. If a dual purpose press is operated most of the time for indirect relief and rarely for offset lithography, the dampening plate rollers are usually removed from the press and put back on it only when it is operated as an offset lithographic press. If a press is intended to be used exclusively for indirect relief printing it can be bought without dampening units. And if a press already has dampening units, these can be completely removed if such a press will not be used for offset lithography.

The packing under the plate and blanket is the same as that for good quality offset lithography. But excess pressure is more harmful in letterset than in lithography because the blanket wraps around relief halftone dots and fine line detail, thereby thickening and distorting their printing values. Pressure adjustments for different stocks are made between the blanket and the impression cylinder, usually by moving the latter. Modern offset presses have usually four plate inking rollers; for indirect relief printing these plate rollers must be set to exert the least pressure on the plate that will still produce sufficient inking.

In all other points, the operation of presses for indirect relief printing is so similar to that of corresponding offset lithographic presses that a detailed description would merely anticipate the discussion presented in Section 4. Letterset printing is done on both sheet-fed and web presses. In those applications for which it has been found suitable, letterset proves itself an efficient printing method. Compared with rotary letterpress from curved electrotypes, it saves costs in the making of plates and avoids practically all press down-time needed for letterpress makeready and overlaying. Compared with offset lithography, the absence of dampening makes running easier, particularly for craftsmen who lack experience in offset lithographic presswork. Other advantages of indirect relief printing are uniformity of printed images in long-run jobs and ability to print stocks and inks which are difficult to use in offset lithography because they are incompatible with the fountain solution. (Examples include the printing of gummed papers, bronzes, and varnishes in good quality.)

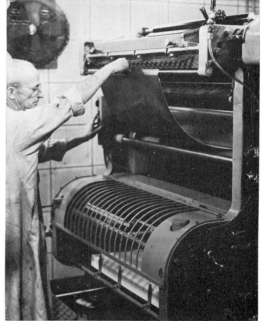

Courtesy duPont Company

Pressman attaches a Dycril plate to the plate cylinder of an offset press for indirect relief printing.

Even though a discussion of presswork for indirect relief printing is omitted for the already mentioned reasons, the following description of indirect relief printing on standard web-offset equipment might be interesting to many readers.

*Bible Printing by Multi-Web Indirect
Relief Printing*

In this unit it will be described how indirect relief printing on web-offset equipment was introduced to cope with steadily rising manufacturing costs of Bibles, which are consumer goods completely manufactured by printing and binding. The Holy Bible has been for centuries the book printed in the largest quantity, year in and year out, in the United States and several other countries.

Some technical problems of Bible printing. Bible manufacturing faces a number of problems of its own. Since the Bible is a voluminous book, it is usually printed on Bible paper which is exceptionally thin. Bible papers are made in different qualities and different basis weights. Since all basis weights of book papers express the weight of 500 sheets of paper having an area of 25 by 38 inches we can give you an approximate idea of the thinness of Bible paper by mentioning that such paper has a basis weight of, say, 20 pounds, whereas that of other book papers ranges most commonly from 50 to 70 pounds. But the basis weight is by itself not a complete indicator of the thickness of a given paper. Some papers are manufactured to "bulk high," or to make a thick book with relatively few sheets, whereas others are purposely made to bulk extremely low, or to result in a comparatively thin book, assuming the same number of pages. Bible papers are of the latter kind. They are not only used for the printing of Bibles but also for other books which consist of a great number of pages that could not be practically combined in a single volume if printed on thicker papers. To give some examples of other uses of Bible papers it is mentioned that they are often selected for the printing of unabridged dictionaries and one-volume encyclopedias, as well as for rate books of insurance companies.

It might be worth adding that our rapidly advancing technology makes it necessary to print many different reference books that must contain a constantly increasing volume of information, and that this condition is bound to lead to an increasing substitution of thinner papers for the heavier and thicker ones which are traditionally used for the printing of books. Bible papers pose many problems in printing and folding not encountered with heavier papers because their extreme thinness makes them difficult to handle. This thinness is the reason why books printed on Bible paper have a certain amount of show-through. (Show-through means that the printing of one side can be more or less strongly noticed on the other side, thereby distracting the reader.) Bible papers have also a greater tendency to stick to the offset blanket in lithographic printing than heavier papers. Even though Bible papers are successfully run in lithography, the speed with which a press can be operated is less for Bible paper than for the heavier offset or book papers. This brief explanation of the role played by Bible papers is merely an introduction to the problem of processing Bible papers. Readers interested in more information on paper, its basis weight, bulk and opacity should consult Chapter VIII.

Some economic problems of Bible printing and publishing. The publishers of Bibles have business problems peculiar to this kind of business. Bibles are consumer goods and like all other consumer goods subject to the price pressure of the marketplace. Even though Bibles are made in a wide range of quality, differing in sizes, binding, color printing, illustrations, and annotations, each different quality must nevertheless be competitively priced.

Not only are there several domestic competitors active in this field, but as Bibles can be imported into the United States free from duty, a number of companies which manufacture Bibles in different areas of the globe are also serious competitors for the domestic market. The wages paid abroad to workers in the printing industry have risen strongly in the more recent past, but even the increased wages paid overseas are still much lower than wages paid in the United States. It is of course true that importers of Bibles have considerable shipping expenses, but these do not compensate for their great advantages in wages and working conditions.

Traditional manufacturing methods in Bible printing. Traditionally, Bibles are printed from flat electrotypes on flatbed-cylinder perfecting presses. The preparation of these presses which print large sheets with either one or two 64-page signatures, depending on the final size of the printed product, is tedious and causes long press down-times. Large size perfectors are relatively slow machines and their speed is cut down to a certain extent when the stock is Bible paper. A two-up 64-page form may take approximately six hours for press preparation, and the running speed of a press printing a sheet of a maximum size 45 by 68½ inches is less than 1,500 impressions per hour. After printing, the sheets must be folded on large knife-folders, producing approximately 2,000 two-up 64-page signatures per hour. In this manner Bibles are still printed in many instances even though some companies have changed from flatbed-cylinder presses to sheet-fed rotaries and the use of curved electrotypes. Such presses are operated at a running speed of approximately 3,500 impressions per hour when they print on Bible paper.

Multi-web indirect relief printing of Bibles. One publisher of Bibles, the National Publishing Company, Philadelphia, approached increased efficiency in Bible printing along different and rather novel lines. It was decided to adapt existing web-offset equipment in combination with wrap-around letterpress plates—which were originally duPont Dycril plates and later also Kodak Relief Plates—to the exigencies of Bible printing. After a thorough analysis of the problem a four perfecting unit blanket-to-blanket web-offset press was selected. This press has a maximum web width of 38 inches and a cut-off of 22¾ inches. The eight plate cylinders of this press were each undercut 0.035 inches thereby making them suitable for Dycril plates. Different from other web-offset presses used for job-and-commercial printing, this press was equipped to print four rolls simultaneously, one on each perfecting unit. The press has four duplexed roll stands. Two of them are at the feeder end of the press in a straight line with printing units and other equipment, one behind the other. The other two duplexed roll stands are approximately in the middle of the four printing units, at the non-operating side of the press. They feed the paper into the remaining two printing units after the web is turned 90 degrees by angle bars.

The term *duplexed* means in this case that each roll stand holds two rolls of paper, one above the other. The web is connected by pasting the beginning of the ready roll to the end of the expiring roll. Each roll can hold a rather large quantity of Bible paper, varying of course with its basis weight, generally speaking approximately 50,000 feet.

Four-level drying and various kinds of deliveries. After the four webs are printed on both sides they are put through a four-level Offen two-stage drier which was especially designed for this press. The dried webs are associated for common folding. The press is equipped with two sets of folders; folding can be done either with a former folder or as ribbon folding. Folder No. 1 has a former

folder, two parallel jaw folders, and a chopper folder. It can deliver signatures of various kinds, including tabloid, double digest, and catalog sizes. The folded signatures are delivered to a Stobb bundler by a belt delivery. Folder No. 2 is also equipped with a former, and has three parallel jaw folding units. It can produce either double digest or triple parallel signatures. Triple parallel signatures are needed for Bibles in a vest-pocket format. This folder delivers the folded signatures in two packer boxes before they are put in the Stobb bundler.

The main advantages of multi-web indirect relief printing. The main advantages of this equipment are the following: (1) The equipment is quite flexible and can be operated either with four webs for black-and-white printing, or with two webs for two-color printing, or with a single web for full-color printing. If the press is used for black-and-white printing all four webs, which are printed simultaneously, are automatically run through a four-level drier and then associated for folding. The folded product consists, in many cases, of two-up 64-page signatures. (2) The matching of color, or of values, in black-and-white printing is rather simple, resulting nevertheless in uniform values throughout. (It took not more than five signatures for "coloring up" after a web break when the writer visited the plant of National Publishing.) (3) Since heat-set inks printed from offset blankets are not forced into the fibers of the paper, show-through on Bibles produced by indirect relief printing is substantially less than on direct printed ones. (4) Changeover restricted to plates is rather fast and can be accomplished in 60 minutes for all eight plates.

The press can be operated either for indirect relief or for offset lithography. Since it has four perfecting units a number of combinations using color to a varying degree can be of advantage in other printing tasks and in developing new kinds of the main product published by National. Switching from indirect relief to offset lithography is, as explained in the preceding general discussion of indirect relief printing, rather easy. The press has, like all web-offset presses, dampening units which are disconnected for indirect relief printing but must be activated for web offset.

Production efficiency in multi-web indirect relief printing. Last but not least, the high production of this press must be mentioned. If run at its maximum rated speed, which is not always practical, the press produces 25,000 two-up 64-page signatures per hour. Even if run at 80 per cent of top speed, this means a production of 20,000 printed and folded signatures as compared with 1,400 printed sheets per hour on perfecting presses and of 2,000 folded signatures per hour by knife folding. The application of modern printing technology to the perennial problems of rising costs and keener competition was, in the experience of National Publishing, a full success.

Section 3: Presswork in Intaglio Printing

In the preceding section on relief printing you have seen that this process family is particularly diversified. Relief printing is practical for extremely short runs but also for extremely long ones, not to speak of those between these two extremes. Relief printing can be used for multiple-purpose as well as for single-purpose production; finally, image transfer may be either direct or indirect in relief printing. The equipment for relief printing varies accordingly and so do stocks and inks handled in the four methods into which relief printing is divided in this manual. Intaglio printing differs strongly from relief printing in most of these points. If we disregard specialty printing, a subject excluded from this manual, contemporary American intaglio printing is a mass-production method used for two kinds of printing in the main. One is publication printing, the other package printing. A small number of companies applies the intaglio process to job-and-commercial printing, but the volume of this kind of intaglio production is minute in comparison with publication and package printing done by rotogravure.

The following discussion of presswork in gravure is divided into three units: (1) sheet-fed gravure, (2) rotogravure for publication printing, and (3) rotogravure for inline package printing. Those interested in the subject should consult in particular Chapter V, "Printing-Image Carriers," where the gravure principle and the making of plates and cylinders for gravure are extensively discussed. Other chapters of interest in this context are VIII, for papers and other stocks, and IX, for gravure inks.

Presswork in Sheet-Fed Gravure Printing

Sheet-fed gravure is a high-quality reproduction method for pictures, alone or in combination with type, in medium-length press runs. Even though as many as 250,000 sheets are sometimes printed in sheet-fed gravure, a typical gravure job is run in several ten-thousands. If the quality peculiar to gravure is decisive and the required quantity is small, this method is often used for printing a few thousand sheets. Sheet-fed gravure is practiced in the United States by a small number of firms; some use it for package printing in quantities too small for rotogravure, others use sheet-fed gravure presses for the proofing of intermediates prior to the making of cylinders for rotogravure, and only a few companies are in the business of commercial sheet-fed gravure printing. It is therefore not surprising that the subject is not too well represented in our literature on presswork. But sheet-fed gravure printing is nevertheless a basic printing method and cannot be omitted in this manual. This unit was developed in co-operation with the Beck Engraving Company in Philadelphia. This company makes photoengravings and other relief printing-image carriers, offset plates, and color separations for all printing methods, and it manufactures etched cylinders for rotogravure. At the time of writing Beck also operated a sheet-fed gravure department which was later discontinued. The practices described in the following may not be the same as followed by other printers of sheet-fed gravure.

Planning for Presswork in Sheet-Fed Gravure

Planning for sheet-fed gravure must consider three basic points to begin with: the available equipment, the relatively high cost of gravure plates, and a number of other points related to the nature of a job and to the desired quality level of the printed product.

Presses for sheet-fed gravure. In the United States sheet-fed gravure presses are built by a single manufacturer, the Miehle Division of Miehle-Goss-Dexter. The maximum sheet size of these Miehle presses is 29 by 43 inches and they are available as single-color, two-color, three-color, and four-color models. Imported sheet-fed gravure presses are available in a variety of sizes. Some of them can print sheets

Courtesy The Beck Engraving Company

Finisher at work on an etched rotogravure cylinder. Minor flaws can be corrected by hand tooling or etching; skill of a high order and long experience are needed for this work.

that are too small for the Miehle presses which have a minimum sheet size of 17 by 22 inches. Smaller presses are more important for the proofing of four-color separation sets which will be finally used in the making of rotogravure cylinders than for the production of sheet-fed gravure jobs. The Beck sheet-fed gravure department used Miehle presses primarily and considered it an advantage that all Miehle presses have the same sheet sizes thereby permitting standardization with its advantages in planning and production.

The importance of plate costs in planning. Sheet-fed gravure is used for high-quality work, often for full-color facsimile reproductions. (The word "facsimile" means in contemporary printing language highest fidelity of reproduction.) Such jobs are usually made by conventional or straight gravure, a method which uses cells of uniform areas and varying depths. Etching of plates is done by hand in several stages, and it is not easy to etch the same color images uniformly several times on the same plate. (Conventional gravure is explained in Chapter V, Section 4.)

The making of plates for single-color jobs and the making of sets of plates for full-color printing are usually planned and handled differently. While plates for single-color jobs may contain multiples of the same images, repetition of the same images on the same plates is not considered

desirable in full-color printing. In short-run jobs (a vague expression as even the printing of a relatively high number of sheets—several ten-thousands, for example—may be considered a short run in gravure) it is most economical and expedient to plan the plates for full-color jobs without duplication of the same images. It is often more satisfactory to use plates bearing only single images of full-color pages rather than going through the time-consuming process of trying to match duplicate images on the same plate. The expenses that may be incurred in such an effort are unknown whereas those of making the added number of impressions from already approved plates are predictable. Putting a full-color job twice through the press is therefore less expensive and less risky than etching plates with duplicate images.

This general situation in sheet-fed gravure has a decisive influence on the selection of the imposition for different jobs.

Impositions for sheet-fed gravure. The term "imposition" refers to the arrangement of pages on the sheet or web. Since impositions are closely related to the available folding equipment they are discussed in Chapter X, Section 2. As a rule, work-and-turn impositions are preferred to sheetwise impositions for sheet-fed gravure. The reason is simple. In full-color jobs, work-and-turn impositions require a single set of plates, one each for the yellow, magenta, cyan, and black ink. In sheetwise printing, two such sets would be needed. Since the cost of running may be substantially less than that of the plates, and considering the practically unlimited life expectance of a chromium-plated gravure plate, Beck planners try to save customers the expenses of a second set of plates. There are, nevertheless, situations where sheetwise printing is more economical than work-and-turn, and then a job is planned with two sets of plates. Not all color jobs are printed in full color; many are done in multicolor and in such jobs it may well happen that the colors printed on one side of the sheet differ from those printed on the other side. Such jobs are, naturally, printed sheetwise.

Some other considerations in planning sheet-fed gravure. Plates and impositions are foremost but other points must also not be overlooked. Among them is the paper (which is selected to suit customers' preferences) and the direction of paper grain, the kind of inks and their overprinting, and possibly varnishing to be done directly on the press. Gravure can produce better press-varnishing than other methods and ranks in this respect between varnishing done on independent equipment and varnishing done by letterpress or on lithographic presses. (A limitation of gravure in comparison with other printing methods is, on the other hand, that gravure cannot do split-fountain printing.)

Ink trapping, or the proper overprinting of successive inks, can be important, especially in package printing with daylight fluorescent inks. Planning includes correct anticipation of production time on which delivery promises are based. Unlike other methods for facsimile reproductions, sheet-fed gravure knows no waiting time for backups. The sheets arrive dry at the delivery of gravure presses and can be backed up immediately.

Last but not least a good planner keeps in mind that proofing is not done in sheet-fed gravure on proof presses but on production equipment. This leads into our next subject, quality control.

Quality Control in Sheet-Fed Gravure

The crucial item in quality control for sheet-fed gravure is the plate, and the plate cannot be evaluated before proofing. Proofing is of course not possible without press preparation and therefore not discussed at this point. But a few words on papers and inks for sheet-fed gravure might be interesting.

Papers for sheet-fed gravure. Sheet-fed gravure is done on a wide range of papers. This range goes from coated papers to uncoated sheets which may have an antique finish. (Papers that were embossed in order to give them a specific texture are, as a rule, not suitable for sheet-fed gravure, especially not for full-color jobs. Nor can certain cast-coated papers be used, since their coatings do not absorb the ink whereas gravure needs an absorbent sheet for good production and high quality.) A smooth paper surface is more conducive to the printing of fine detail than a coarse one, and coated papers that have good ink absorption are widely used. But sheet-fed gravure is also done on cover stocks, English or eggshell finished papers, and on vellums. If the final appearance of a printed job makes a deeper paper structure desirable, pebbling subsequent to printing can provide such effects. Often a job is proofed on a number of different papers, and the customer makes his final choice after comparing variously proofed samples. To avoid misunderstandings it is added that gravure can handle many other stocks besides paper. These include foils and plastics, but such stocks are more processed in rotogravure than in sheet-fed gravure which is usually selected for high-quality book work and advertising material, even though some producers of package material use sheet-fed gravure for runs too small for rotogravure.

Inks for sheet-fed gravure. Printing inks for sheet-fed gravure can be more viscous than those for rotogravure. This feature combined with the slower running speed of sheet-fed gravure presses in comparison with rotogravure presses is very beneficial to the appearance of images printed by sheet-fed gravure. Images produced by sheet-fed gravure have a distinctive richness and depth of their own. For full-color printing the three standard color inks (yellow, magenta, and cyan) are needed, usually supplemented with black as a fourth color. Monotone jobs are often printed either in black, or in a deep brown, or in a dark green; multicolor jobs may need special ink matches. Quality control of inks is important. Their hue must be correct and they must be of the right intensity and viscosity.

Press Preparation in Sheet-Fed Gravure

Press preparation of sheet-fed gravure presses resembles that of other sheet-fed presses because it, too, requires the setting of the feeder, of the printing and inking units, and of the delivery. Sheet-fed gravure presses have in addition some facilities for drying which may need adjustment from job to job. The feeder and the delivery of domestic sheet-fed gravure presses are the same as those of other domestic presses built by Miehle but they are not arranged in the same way. In sheet-fed letterpress and offset lithographic presses, the feeder is at one end of the press and the delivery is at the other; between feeder and delivery are the several printing units and their inking units. Printing takes place, in letterpress and offset, in a straight line, beginning with the feeding and ending with the delivery of the printed sheet. In sheet-fed gravure presses built by Miehle, the delivery is at one end of the press. After the delivery comes the feeder which is followed by one or several printing and inking units. From the last printing unit the sheet is delivered by traveling above the printing unit, or printing units, and above the feeder to the delivery. This arrangement has the purpose of drying the sheet thoroughly before it is piled in the delivery.

Miehle sheet-fed gravure presses have another feature which we have met on sheet-fed common impression cylinder presses. On such presses, the sheet is turned prior to being impressed and not printed on the side which is on top in the feeder but on its other side. This construction saves repiling or turning skids of one-side printed sheets before backup.

The following discussion is limited to the printing and inking units and a few remarks on drying. Feeder and delivery do not need description as they are the same on all sheet-fed presses.

Preparing the printing unit of sheet-fed gravure presses. The printing unit of presses for sheet-fed gravure consists of a plate cylinder and of an impression cylinder. The plate is put on the plate cylinder, an operation that must be done with care. The surface of the plate cylinder and the back of the plate must be immaculately clean and free of any foreign matter. Even small particles of foreign matter between plate cylinder and plate will manifest themselves as distortion of the plate and, consequently, as printing defects. If such defects occur they must be eliminated by taking the plate off the cylinder and by hand tooling, a time-consuming operation which also raises production costs and is therefore best avoided. After the plate is mounted, the cylinder gap of the plate cylinder, in which the plate is clamped with both ends, is completely covered with a metal cap thereby shielding the cylinder gap from the fluid gravure ink.

The impression cylinder is one of the differences between sheet-fed and rotogravure presses. Rotogravure presses have no impression cylinders but are constructed with a rubber-covered impression roll and a bare steel back-up roll. The impression cylinder of sheet-fed gravure presses has the same diameter as the plate cylinder. The impression cylinder is packed like that of other sheet-fed presses, and it carries the gripper mechanism whereby the printing stock is held during the impression.

The packing of the impression cylinder has two functions which are well known to you from descriptions of letterpresses. One function of packing is the adjustment of the cylinder diameter for stocks of varying thickness. The other function is differentiation of local printing pressures; this result is accomplished with overlay sheets placed in the packing.

The setting of the inking unit. As you know, presses in all gravure methods are inked by flooding the whole image carrier, plate or etched cylinder, with ink and by removing most of the ink deposited on the non-printing areas in the course of inking. In sheet-fed gravure the means for flooding the plate is a steel fountain roller which acts as ink applicator and rotates in the open, unenclosed, fountain. The plate is not touched by the fountain roller but sufficiently close to it to be flooded with ink. After leaving the fountain area the plate is doctored by a metal doctor blade in such a way that the ink removed from the non-image areas can flow back into the fountain. The setting of the inking unit, and especially that of the doctor blade, requires skill and exactitude.

Drying on sheet-fed gravure presses. On multicolor presses the sheet is dried after each color to the extent that good ink trapping (meaning correct overprinting of successive inks), can be accomplished. After the sheet leaves the last printing unit it is dried with fans which apply a big volume of air to the printed surface before the sheet is stacked in the delivery. The solvent-air mixture is removed from the pressroom by an exhaust system. The drying equipment of sheet-fed gravure presses is rather simple in comparison with the driers needed in rotogravure. If heaters or fans need adjustments for a new job these can be easily made during press preparation.

Proofing and Running in Sheet-Fed Gravure

The most intricate kind of work in sheet-fed gravure, as in all other branches of the printing industry, is full-color printing. Proofing of full-color jobs requires skill and experience. Proofing is done on the press and by using the stock on which the job will be printed.

First the pressman tries to obtain prints of a satisfactory quality by getting all units into perfect working order. Next he resorts to adjusting of inks if he believes that such adjustments are needed. He can intensify printed color images by adding toners to the respective ink, or he can add extenders if he wants the opposite result. He can also adjust the viscosity of ink by adding solvents.

If the pressman finds that he cannot achieve the required result after having made all possible adjustments, he may ask for corrections on the plates. These corrections are made directly on the press, possibly causing considerable press downtime. The actual time needed for proofing and corrections depends on a number of points, including the nature of the original art work or color photos, the purpose of the job, and the wishes of the customer. Customer satisfaction is as necessary as it is personal. It is rather subjective and not always predictable, requiring in certain instances repeated proofings. After the proofs are finally accepted by the customer, the etched copper plates are chromium plated at Beck to protect them and to lengthen their life expectance. It is also possible to print with unplated etched copper plates, particularly if the press run is relatively short and the nature of a job precludes reruns. (Annual reports to stockholders can serve as an example of jobs that are printed only once.)

Finally comes running. The main task of running is maintaining of the approved job quality at maximum efficiency. The pressman must keep all printing units functioning and must make all necessary adjustments during the course of running. Every so often the pressman takes a sheet from the delivery and compares its appearance with the okay sheet which guides him in the quality requirement of the job. From time to time the superintendent of the pressroom department will check the sheets himself, thereby making sure that the pressman maintains job quality. After the job is completed, the plates are taken off the plate cylinder and are protected for storage. The ink fountains are either thoroughly washed or, if the same inks or inks very near in color will be printed next, washing may be omitted. But when a pastel or white ink is to be printed after a dark one washup is a real chore.

Presswork for Publication Printing in Rotogravure

Rotogravure is used for various kinds of publication printing. One of them is the production of newspaper supplements which are gravure-printed magazines added to the Sunday editions of many daily newspapers. Another branch of rotogravure publication printing is the manufacturing of high-quality magazines in which gravure can be used for a number of signatures which are combined with signatures produced in other printing methods or for the complete printing of magazines. Gravure publication printing includes catalogs for mail order houses as well as gravure-printed inserts that are combined with webs of newspaper printing prior to the folding of newspapers. Each of these different kinds of products has manufacturing problems of its own. Gravure supplements are printed on uncoated, less expensive paper than high-class magazines or mail order catalogs; the production of gravure inserts for newspapers differs from that of other gravure printed items inasmuch as such inserts are not folded on the press but are rewound.

The present subject was developed at Triangle Publications in Philadelphia which publishes several gravure-printed magazines, among them the *TV Guide*, a digest format publication appearing every week and printed in editions exceeding eleven million copies. The magazine selected for this unit is *Seventeen*. The reasons for choosing *Seventeen* are that *Seventeen* is a completely rotogravure-printed magazine of a large page size, that it has a large circulation, and last but not least, that it contains a substantial volume of high-quality color work. When the unit on rotogravure publication printing was prepared, the August, 1964, issue of *Seventeen* was on the presses. This issue consists of more pages than most other gravure-printed magazines; it also has an exceptionally large number of color pages, and is therefore well suited to give the reader a good idea of the complexities encountered in the production of a gravure-printed high-quality magazine. It is added that this unit reflects the methods and procedures in practice at the company where the subject was developed. Other concerns may use different methods or procedures.

Summary of rotogravure facilities at Triangle Publications. The pressroom of the Triangle Rotogravure Division is one of the largest of its kind in the United States. It has ten different rotogravure presses, comprising a total of 82 printing units, 20 reels for semiautomatic pasting, and 23 folders. In addition there is a five-unit proof press for the proofing of gravure cylinders, and also all equipment needed for the binding of magazines. The pressroom is on the street floor of the Triangle plant, underneath is the reel room and above the pressroom is the bindery. Unlike newspaper relief printing or blanket-to-blanket web offset, rotogravure printing is done by printing first one side of the web in all colors and then the other side. Printing units in rotogravure are therefore not perfecting units. In rotogravure, drying follows the printing of every color and the one-side printed web must be dry before it can be printed on the other side.

Triangle is equipped to make color separations and has a large cylinder-making department on the same floor adjacent to the pressroom. Color separations are, as usual, proofed on sheet-fed presses from etched plates for submission to advertisers or to the editorial department. The reason for mentioning cylinder making at all in the context of presswork is that the proximity of the cylinder-making department to the pressroom is of great value in presswork, saving irreplaceable production time.

Paper and ink consumption. To give the reader an idea of the amounts of paper and ink consumed by this plant, it is mentioned that the average daily paper consumption is in the order of more than one thousand 40-inch diameter rolls, and amounts to 70,000 tons of paper per year. The average weekly ink consumption is approximately 115,000 pounds. Ink is supplied in tank cars and stored in 16 tanks, each tank having a capacity of 4,000 gallons. Solvent for the dilution of gravure inks is stored in 14 tanks, each with a capacity of 15,500 gallons. Ten of these tanks are active; the remaining four are either being filled or ready for filling. Triangle has also a large solvent recovery installation which will be described later in this unit.

An appreciation of presswork is almost impossible without knowing something about the magnitude of the job to be done, and our next subject is a brief, almost statistical, description of the August, 1964, *Seventeen* issue. This magazine has a trimmed page size of 13⅛ by 10⅜ inches. The inside pages are printed on 43-pound coated paper, the cover is printed on paper of an 80-pound basis weight, approximately twice the basis weight of the paper for inside signatures. Since the cover is on different paper, it cannot be printed together with the inside signatures but must be printed separately. The August, 1964, issue of *Seventeen* had a press run of 1,339,000 copies. The number of pages varied for different geographical areas. Apart from the outside of the cover, there were 3 pages of 4-color cover ads, 159 pages of 4-color inside ads, 51 pages of editorial matter in 4-color, 13 pages of 2-color ads, 8 pages of a 4-color retail section, 8 pages of a monotone retail section, and 131 pages of monotone editorial matter and monotone advertisements. (In gravure, the term "monotone" means single-color, as you may remember.) The total number of pages was 362, more or less, depending on the geographical area of distribution. This issue entailed the preparation of not less than 244 pages in full color, an exceptionally large and difficult task. (All pages identified in this description as 4-color ones, are in the terminology of this manual full-color pages.) It took 1,800 tons of paper and 115,000 pounds of ink to produce this issue of the magazine.

Planning for Rotogravure Publication Printing

Magazine production requires several different, though related, forms of planning. Like all other mass-produced magazines, *Seventeen* contains two kinds of copy, editorial material and advertisements. Since *Seventeen* is owned by Triangle Publications, there is close co-operation between the departments in charge of editorial material and those in charge of cylinder making and presswork. The editorial and advertising sales offices are in New York City whereas the manufacturing departments have their seat in Philadelphia, 90 miles away.

The purpose of an editorial and sales production office. In addition to editorial and advertising departments the New York office of *Seventeen* has its own production department which renders service to, and solves problems for, the editorial and the advertising staff. Among other tasks, this production department assists advertisers in the preparation and evaluation of material to be used for advertisements, makes suggestions for the improvement of art-and-copy if such suggestions are needed, and develops the dummy of the magazine. This dummy indicates the position of each page in the magazine and serves as a guide for the arrangement of pages for cylinder making and presswork.

Co-operation between the two production departments. The production department in New York and the one in Philadelphia co-operate in the development of the layout for the next magazine. Like other magazines deriving substantial proportions of their revenue from advertising, *Seventeen*, which is published monthly, has strong fluctuations in the volume of advertising and editorial pages, depending on the change of seasons. Every issue of the magazine must therefore be carefully planned. The Philadelphia production department, which is part of manufacturing, provides the imposition diagrams which were developed for utmost economy in cylinder making and in presswork. The selected imposition must be suitable for the needs of manufacturing as well as for editorial and advertising requirements.

Some give-and-take between New York and Philadelphia is a necessity for this result. After agreement on the layout for the next magazine is reached, one copy of the layout is transmitted to the cylinder-engraving department and one to the pressroom.

Characteristic points of gravure presses for publication printing. In comparing publication presses for rotogravure with equipment for web printing by other methods we find many resemblances but also many differences. Roll feeding is perhaps the only operation done with the same kinds of equipment in all forms of mass-production printing. The delivery of gravure publication presses differs for rotogravure newspaper supplements which are folded on newspaper folders and for rotogravure magazines which are folded by magazine folders. *Seventeen* is folded by ribbon folding, a folding method briefly characterized in Chapter VI, Section 6. (Ribbon folding will be described in some detail in the course of the present unit.)

One significant difference between rotogravure and all other printing methods is the previously mentioned fact that each color must be dried before the next color can be printed. Wet-on-wet printing is not feasible in rotogravure, nor can the web be printed on both sides at the same time as in blanket-to-blanket web-offset printing. In rotogravure one side of the web is printed first and then the other. A printing station has, hence, in rotogravure only a single gravure cylinder. After all colors are printed on both sides of the web, the web passes through the folder. The products of the folder are folded signatures which are carried automatically by a vertical conveyor to the bindery floor above the pressroom where the printed signatures are gathered, side-stitched, covered, and trimmed.

The printing of inside signatures. To return to the printing of *Seventeen*, it must be remembered that this product consists of inside signatures printed on a thinner paper than the cover. Inside signatures and covers must therefore be printed separately. The presses used for the printing of inside signatures have ten printing units, the necessary number of paper reels, turning bars, and two folders—one at each end of the press. The ten printing units can be combined in different ways, depending on the nature of the work to be done. *Seventeen* is run either on full-width webs of 54 inches or on three-quarter width webs, which are 40½ inches wide. A full-width web can produce three different kinds of signatures: (1) four signatures of 8 pages each, (2) two signatures of 16 pages each, and (3) one signature of 32 pages. The three-quarter wide web can produce either two signatures of 12 pages, or one signature of 24 pages.

The printing of covers. Cover printing is done on 22-inch wide webs by double-ending. Double-ending means, as you may remember, that the press has at least twice the width of the web to be double-ended. First one side of the web is printed, then the web is turned by means of angle bars and perfected on the same press. Both sides of the web run next to one another as if they were two different webs. The cylinders for the printing of the two sides are of course not the same, nor are they of full length. They are two different sets of gravure cylinders, each having the width required for printing the narrow web. After printing, the web for the covers of the magazine is sheeted on the press. Each sheet has three covers, one above the other. These sheets are transferred to the bindery and are there separated on guillotine cutters before they are used for covering the assembled and side-wire stitched inside signature of the magazine.

Relation between ribbon folding and page layout. *Seventeen* is folded by ribbon folding, a method that omits former plates and combines slitting the printed web into narrower webs, associating them, and folding them with jaw folders, to in-

Courtesy Triangle Publications, Philadelphia

Sheeter delivery of a rotogravure press. Covers for magazines are web printed and then sheeted by an inline sheeter. The covers are combined with the inside signatures in the bindery.

dicate the main steps only. This technique produces more precise folds than folding equipment for newspaper printing and is therefore often used in magazine printing. Since the finally associated narrow ribbons of paper have a width equivalent to the untrimmed height of a single page, the layout for the cylinder provides for positioning of pages from head-to-foot across the cylinder and from left-to-right around it. (The head-to-foot dimension is in *Seventeen* the longer one, but ribbon folding can also be used for landscaped layouts where the head-to-foot dimension is shorter than the left-to-right dimension.) A cylinder bearing 16 pages for *Seventeen* needs consequently a circumference corresponding to the width of 4 pages, and a length equivalent to the height of 4 pages. As mentioned, the final trimmed size of the magazine is 13⅛ by 10⅜ inches. The cylinder has an active length of 54 inches (4 by 13⅛ inches, plus trim) and a circumference of approximately 43½ inches, (4 by 10⅜ inches plus trim). The term active indicates the actually etched cylinder area; it is less than the maximum usable cylinder length which is standardized by Triangle at 67 inches. (The exact figure for the cylinder circumference is 43.379 inches.)

The kind of signatures wanted is an essential consideration in the planning of cylinder layouts. The sequence of pages differs in different layouts. It must always be remembered that rotogravure cylinders are integral, or single-unit, printing-image carriers on which the sequence of pages cannot be changed without remaking the whole cylinder.

Summary of planning for gravure publication printing. Planning for gravure printed magazines includes the positioning of advertisements and of editorial matter according to the wishes of advertisers and the editorial layout staff. Planning must of course also keep in mind that presswork should be done as efficiently as possible, and that compromises between requests made by advertisers, the editorial department, and the needs of manufacturing must be made in certain cases. Planning includes not only cylinder layouts but many other points. Of these we mention but one which can be troublesome: positioning of bleed pages interfering with the space needed for electric-eye targets. Since these targets are best placed in the center of the web, bleed pages cannot extend into this area because the bleed would use up the space needed for printing of electric-eye targets. (Electric-eye targets are indispensable because automatic electronic register control is based on them.) This is one of the points where editorial or advertiser requests may conflict with manufacturing necessities, and it is a point that must be carefully considered in planning.

Quality Control of Component Elements

As in all other mass-production printing methods each of the component elements—ink, paper, and image carriers—must be of the proper quality. The quality control of etched cylinders is the main item in every discussion of quality control for rotogravure in full color, but paper and inks must also have the required quality levels. Paper is especially manufactured for *Seventeen* according to specifications developed by the research and development department of Triangle Publications. This department is in charge of quality control of cylinder making as well as that for paper and inks. The research and development department has at its disposal a fully equipped laboratory, staffed with graduate chemists and engineers. The inks for the printing of *Seventeen* are the standard inks for full-color printing: yellow, magenta, cyan, and black. If other colors are wanted for spot-color printing, the advertising and the editorial departments can choose from a sample book which shows prints of inks carried by Triangle for this purpose. Should an advertiser want colors not offered in this sample book, inks are made to order.

Quality control of gravure cylinders. Quality control of etched cylinders is the most exacting item in publication printing done in full color. All full-color images must be proofed several times. Of full-color advertisements, Triangle makes first plates for individual proofing on sheet-fed gravure presses. (Triangle has two such presses in the proofing department.) When a sufficient number of proofs has been accepted the actual cylinders are made. The etched cylinders may need again a number of proofings, depending on the detail of the job and the request made by an advertiser. As in other branches of printing, customers often want to make last-minute changes. Since the manufacturing departments of Triangle co-operate to the limit with advertisers, such changes are faithfully executed as long as time permits.

Gravure cylinders are proofed at Triangle on a specially built web proof press which has five printing stations, drying equipment, and a rewind.

Courtesy Triangle Publications, Philadelphia

Proofing of rotogravure cylinders on a specially constructed five-color web proof press.

Depending on the time element, and on the kind of images borne by a cylinder, these are chromium plated either before or after they are finally proofed on the actual production press. In some instances it may be necessary to submit not only proofs taken on the proof press from the etched cylinder but also to show proofs of the job as it is actually printed.

The yield of chromium-plated cylinders. A chromium-plated cylinder which is properly handled on the press yields an extremely large number of impressions, far beyond the 1,400,000 needed for *Seventeen*. In some cases there were more than five millions of impressions printed from chromium-plated cylinders at Triangle; normally the figure of impressions wanted for a job is well below the number of impressions obtainable from a chromium-plated gravure cylinder. It might be interesting that *TV-Guide* is produced in more than eleven million copies every week. (The printing of this magazine requires only 2,750,000 impressions since each revolution of the press produces four signatures of this digest-format magazine.)

*Press Preparation for Rotogravure
Publication Printing*

Press preparation for rotogravure consists of many operations. Some can be performed simultaneously on different parts of the equipment, others follow preceding steps. It is practical to divide the subject into ten points: (1) connecting of different units for color printing, (2) preparing of printing and inking units, (3) washup of the press, (4) preparation of rolls for automatic or semiautomatic pasting and setting of reels when required, (5) webbing the press, (6) registering of cylinders, (7) setting of ink reservoir, (8) setting of the doctor blade, (9) adjusting of drying and chilling equipment, and (10) setting the folder. The above-listed groups of operations do not necessarily follow in the order given; some of them will be more extensively discussed than others in the following.

Connecting of different press units. Different color printing units must be connected according to the general layout of the job. As already mentioned, the presses for *Seventeen* have ten printing stations, and can consequently print up to ten colors. A press has two folders, one on each end, and it is therefore possible to connect the several units in such a way that the press delivers two signatures at the same time. Signatures to be printed on both sides in full-color need eight printing stations. The remaining two printing stations can be utilized for producing signatures in monotone on both sides of the web. This example is a simple one; in many instances it may take experience and ingenuity to arrange the press for maximum efficiency.

Preparing the printing and inking units in rotogravure printing. Both of these units, the printing unit and the inking mechanism, are so closely related that they must be discussed together. First the gravure cylinder of the last job must be removed from the press to make room for the cylinder of the next job. For this purpose the rubber pressure rollers which force the paper against the gravure cylinders are raised and the doctor blade mechanisms are moved away from the cylinders. Now the cylinders used on the last job can be taken out of the press. Since a cylinder of the size needed for the printing of *Seventeen* weighs approximately 1,600 pounds, this operation is done by mechanical means. All cylinders are removed and inserted at Triangle by a Monorail system and hoists with which the pressroom is equipped.

Washup. The next operation is the washup of the press. The extent of this operation depends on the difference in hues between the ink printed in the last job and in the new job. Washup includes the fountain, the doctor blade assembly, the rubber pressure roller, and pipe rollers. Whenever possible and practical, the same ink hue is used

Rotogravure cylinders are both heavy and delicate. Here you see a cylinder weighing approximately 1,600 lb. as it is detached from the hoist of the Monorail for placement in the press.

for printing on the same printing unit. After washup, the new gravure cylinder is put in the press. Then the press is webbed, and thereafter the pressure roller is adjusted for the job in hand. Rotogravure publication presses have in addition to the rubber-covered pressure roller a heavy solid steel roller, either called *backer roller* or *rider roller* at Triangle, which may weigh approximately 2 tons and is equipped with heavy springs whereby its pressure on the rubber pressure roller can be regulated.

The webbing of the press. The webbing of the press depends on several items, such as the number of active printing units, angle barring, and others. The web lead is prepared as a long taper because long tapers facilitate the moving of the web lead through the press. Webbing the press is not only necessary at the beginning of a run but also after every web break. The pressman working at the paper reel, which is in the reel room underneath the pressroom, must web the press until the web reaches the pressroom itself. There the web is put in the first impression unit between the rubber pressure roller and the etched cylinder. From here the web enters the drying unit, passes through it, and is then wrapped over a chill-roller which is usually chromium plated to keep friction between web and chill-roller at a minimum. Then the web

is threaded through some pipe rollers into the next printing unit. The same kind of webbing is repeated for each printing unit.

For the printing of the second side, the web is guided through two angle bars which turn it, thereby offering its unprinted side to the requisite number of gravure cylinders for printing. The turned web is again threaded, as already described, through as many printing units as are needed for printing the second side of the web. Each printing unit is, of course, followed by drying equipment and by a chill-roller. After the web has been threaded through the last drying and chilling units, it must be slit in preparation for folding.

Webbing of an eight- or ten-unit publication press is not a simple job. Such a press may have 300 to 350 feet of web running in the press. The web must be of proper tension throughout; web tension is controlled and maintained by equipment especially designed for this purpose.

When the press is webbed and the folder is set, the cylinders must be registered; for this purpose the press is put in operation.

Registering of gravure cylinders. For registering of cylinders, the press is slowly run and the printed product is carefully inspected to determine the needed adjustments. At Triangle, yellow is printed first, and all other cylinders are registered to the yellow cylinder. Rotogravure cylinders can be moved in two directions: axially, or lengthwise, and radially, or around their etched surface. The lengthwise adjustment is done manually with a hand wheel. The other adjustment is not done by hand but by auxiliary equipment which is electrically controlled. Each printing unit has two push buttons for this purpose. If the pressman pushes one button, the *cylinder is advanced*, or rotated clockwise; if he pushes the other button the *cylinder is retarded*, or rotated counterclockwise. (Advancing and retarding of cylinders are terms used in the pressroom.) All adjustments of cylinder register are made in small increments.

The ink reservoir of publication presses. The inking unit on gravure presses is much simpler than inking units of letterpresses or offset lithographic presses. Gravure ink, which is of rather low viscosity, if compared with letterpress or lithographic inks, is pumped from storage tanks at a speed varying between 20 and 50 gallons per minute into the fountain. Since it is necessary to hold the level of the ink in the fountain as high as possible, though not higher than the bottom of

A rotogravure cylinder in the press during adjustment of the doctor blade. The holder of the blade and the blade can be seen at the apex of the cylinder.

the cylinder bearing which must be kept free from ink, the ink level in the fountain must be controlled. Ink level control is usually done by means of valves which regulate the return of the ink by gravity through overflow piping into the ink tank. The ink passing through overflow pipes is filtered to remove extraneous matter which can get into the ink from the surface of the paper web.

The setting of the doctor blade. The setting of the doctor blade is an essential job in preparing the inking unit of rotogravure presses. The doctor blade is approximately 0.006 inch thick; it is made of steel and clamped between two bars acting as a holder. The doctor blade must be carefully set to the cylinder to assure wiping of its surface without affecting the etched cylinder surface injuriously by scraping or scratching. The angle of the doctor blade is determined by the construction of the doctor blade mechanism; this angle is always 14 degrees at Triangle. The doctor blade cleans the "lands" of the cells (meaning the surfaces of the cell walls), leaving the ink in the cells undisturbed. During the impression, ink is transferred from the cells to the stock, due to the heavy pressure exerted by the rubber pressure roller on the paper when it is in contact with the etched cylinder.

Drying and solvent recovery. As already explained, each printing station in rotogravure is followed by drying and chilling equipment. Driers for rotogravure are tunnels, or ovens, where two kinds of action take place. At the entry of the web, it passes an exhaust unit which removes some of the solvents. Then the printed web goes through a zone in which hot air is blown on its surface at high velocity. Finally, before the web leaves the drier, solvent fumes on the surface of the web are sucked off in a second exhaust section, similar to that through which the web passed when entering

the drier. Air temperature and volume are controlled, and driers may or may not need adjustments when different cylinders are put on the press for printing.

The expenditure for solvents is an important cost element in all mass-production rotogravure printing. Solvents are needed to thin the ink concentrate to its proper viscosity. After the ink image is transferred to the paper or other printing stock, the solvents must be removed from the stock by forced drying. In many instances, practically in all smaller installations, the solvent vapors are exhausted and not recovered. Triangle is one of the companies that have solvent recovery equipment whereby the solvent vapors are changed into liquids, and thereby become usable again. Solvent recovery is of course not possible without operational expenses and other costs, but the high percentage of solvent recovered represents a substantial saving of money, nevertheless.

Solvent recovery is a highly technical subject, but without going into its details the process can be understandably explained in its essential features. The solvent-laden air is removed from all driers by exhaust fans, passed in ducts through filters and blown over "carbon beds" which are

A technician adjusts a valve on the solvent recovery unit.

receptacles in which carbon pellets are placed. These carbon pellets absorb the solvent from the solvent-air mixture. When such a bed has absorbed all solvent it can, the solvent is driven out of it by live steam passed through it from the bottom. The mixture of steam and solvent vapors enters a cooling unit through which it flows down. During cooling the vapors are changed from the gaseous to the liquid state. The now liquid mixture of water and solvent arrives at a decanter, where the two liquids separate due to their difference in specific gravity. Water has a higher specific gravity than the solvent, and for this reason the solvent rises to the top. It is separated from the water, but since the decanted solvent still contains some water—and is therefore called the "wet-oil"—it must be purified by distillation. The final product is completely water free and flows by gravity back into the solvent tanks.

You may remember from the description of the facilities at Triangle that there are ten active solvent tanks, each with a capacity of 15,500 gallons amounting to a total of 155,000 gallons of solvent. The recovery unit was designed to produce 500 gallons per hour; it is operated 24 hours, every day.

Ribbon folding and setting the folder for it. In ribbon folding the completely printed web is slit into several narrow webs, or paper ribbons. *Seventeen* has 4 pages across the web, arranged head-to-foot, and is therefore slit three times, resulting in four ribbons. Each of these four ribbons has a width corresponding to the height of the untrimmed magazine page. These four webs must be associated in such a manner that they will produce the intended kind of signatures. For this purpose the narrow webs are angle-barred whereby their direction is changed 90 degrees. Then these printed paper ribbons come down into the folder, pass through a pair of pinch rollers which press them together, and travel into the equipment for collecting and cutting. If you keep in mind that the assembled webs have 4 pages in their running direction, you will understand that the webs must be cut after each 2 pages and that each assembly of 2-page long webs has 16 pages, namely four units, each having 4 printed pages. Since 32-page signatures are wanted, two such 16-page assemblies must be combined. This is done in principle like the folding of a collect newspaper run, though with equipment differing in detail.

The setting of the folder includes the setting of slitting knives, angle bars, pinch rollers, cutting cylinder, collect cylinder, and jaw cylinder which is needed in jaw folding. If *Seventeen* is run on presses equipped with former plates, these are not activated. The completely folded signatures are transported automatically by a vertical conveyor to the floor above where the bindery is located.

Running in Rotogravure Publication Printing

Presswork has, as always, the two tasks of producing the printed product as efficiently as possible and of making sure that its quality is maintained. Chromium-plated cylinders are capable of much longer runs than those needed for *Seventeen* without showing signs of wearing—under competent handling, to be sure. The main concern of those supervising presswork is the control of register and the adjustment of inks during the run. The pressman can regulate the concentration of his inks by varying the amount of solvent; he can also influence hue or intensity of inks by adding toners or extenders.

Quality control is exercised by pressroom personnel, pressmen, and foremen, directly on the press. In addition to this first line of quality control, Triangle has a special department for quality control which takes sample signatures in certain intervals and subjects them to such tests as are needed for proper evaluation. This department makes also statistical quality control studies.

The efficiency of running depends on its uninterrupted flow. The presses are equipped with all modern devices, such as tension controls, web-break detectors, automatic web severing, and of course electronic register controls, for speedy and

Courtesy Triangle Publications, Philadelphia

A gravure finisher corrects a rotogravure cylinder, used for the printing of a full-color cover, working directly on the press.

trouble-free production. The task of producing a 362-page magazine with so many full-color and multicolor pages is not a simple one. The magazine is printed simultaneously on three presses operated by three shifts. Each of the three presses produces 32-page signatures, and each shift can print about 100,000 signatures per press. The total number of signatures needed for the August, 1964, issue of *Seventeen* was approximately seventeen millions, and it took 160 shifts to produce them.

These figures do not include the separately printed covers.

After printing, the magazine must be bound. Binding of magazines requires such steps as guillotine cutting of covers, gathering and stitching of signatures, and covering the magazine prior to giving it the final trim. All these operations are described in Chapter X, "Binding and Finishing," and need no further discussion at this point.

Rotogravure Inline Production of Folding Cartons

One important application of rotogravure inline production is the printing, cutting-and-creasing of folding paper boxes in a single continuous operation. The subject was developed at the printing plant of the Downingtown Paper Company, Downingtown, Pa. The equipment described is a Champlain rotogravure press with four printing units, a laminating unit for combining of metal foil with the board, and a wash coater. The printed web passes immediately into an inline cutter-creaser which automatically strips the waste after cutting-and-creasing is completed. The methods described in the following are of course those adopted by the company where the subject was developed. Other manufacturers of die-cut and creased folding cartons may use different methods and procedures, depending on their equipment and other factors.

Planning and Quality Control

Rotogravure inline equipment is high-speed mass-production machinery; it is not used for short-run jobs, and each job requires careful planning for maximum efficiency. Planning must consider not only the shape of the carton and its printing but also various characteristics of the available equipment. Among these characteristics are (1) the maximum width of the board suitable for a particular press, (2) the range of cut-offs, meaning the second dimension of the printed stock, (3) the number of printing units available, (4) the tolerances permissible in the cutting and creasing of multiple-unit jobs, and (5) the thickness and surface characteristics of the board to be converted into folding cartons. These five points are the generally most important ones; individual jobs may need consideration of additional points.

The decisive role of cutting-and-creasing in folding paper box production. The folding box industry differs from most other branches of the graphic arts industry in one essential point: in most other branches of printing, the quality of printed images is the main concern of those in charge of production. In the folding paper box industry the situation is somewhat different. Printing quality is of course an important point, but the emphasis in manufacturing is on the cutting, creasing, and stripping of cartons. Rotogravure cylinders do not cause problems once they are approved, and they are relatively trouble free in operation. Therefore image transfer needs less attention than other phases of production.

Procedure for planning a new job. At Downingtown, formal planning is practiced. The planning department for gravure printing is headed by the gravure superintendent who receives for planning all information pertinent to a new job. This information includes a production order as well as dummies and artwork. The artwork for a job may have been created either in the art department of Downingtown or it may have been prepared elsewhere—by an independent art studio or in the art department of the customer. Artwork for the new job is usually supplemented by color swatches which are needed for several purposes. If the job has been produced before by a different company, printed and die-cut specimens are part of the basic material turned over to the planning department.

Planning for the end use of folding cartons. Not the least important part of the basic information needed for planning is related to the end use of cartons. Practically all mass-produced folding boxes are intended for packaging on high-speed, automatic machinery. The end product of this operation is a completely packaged item, for example, a box of frozen vegetables, as it will be sold to the consumer. Package machines cannot process cartons that vary substantially in their dimensions but require that the die-cut cartons stay within close tolerance limits. These tolerance limits are consequently essential information for planning.

The basic layout. After receipt and study of the material for a new job, the planning department prepares a basic layout which is needed for determining the diameter of printing cylinders and also for deciding on which press a job is best produced. Downingtown has two gravure inline presses; one can print a 26-inch web in four colors, the other, which is selected for description in this unit, can handle a 36-inch web, print it in five colors, is equipped with laminating facilities and also for wash-coating. The inline cutter-creaser can handle sheets of the maximum size that can be printed on the press to which it is connected. The cut-off on either press is variable between 17 and 36 inches. This means that the larger press can produce sheets of a maximum size of 36 by 36 inches. The actual cut-off and web width is determined by the nature of the job, and the layout is made for most economical production.

Ordering of base cylinders, engravings, ink, and stock. Since Downingtown buys base cylinders as well as their etching from companies specializing in these fields, the layout is immediately used for ordering base cylinders of the needed dimensions. These base cylinders will later be copper plated by the trade engraving plant, which will also etch them and therewith convert them into printing-image carriers. When base cylinders are ordered, the planning department advises the engraver selected for making the final engravings that a job is coming. (The terms "etching" and "engraving" are synonymously used in this industry; both have the meaning of making a roto-gravure image carrier.) It is also necessary that color swatches are transmitted to the supplier of gravure ink if special color matches are part of the job, and that the required quantity of board be ordered. After all this has been done, the attention of the planning department is focused on the making of cutting-and-creasing dies.

Several stages in the development of cutting-and-creasing dies. As mentioned in the introduction, cutting and creasing of the printed stock are critical operations. The first step in the development of cutting-and-creasing dies is the making of a single-unit die. The die is proofed by inking the cutting-and-creasing rules with an inked hand roller, or brayer; another method is to impress it on the stock by putting a sheet of carbon paper

between die and stock. The result of proofing is called a "one-up strike sheet." This *strike sheet* serves as a means of communication between carton manufacturer and customer. Depending on individual conditions it may be sufficient to supply the customer with a few die-cut samples, or it may be necessary to provide a larger number of them, sometimes several thousand.

On the basis of the one-up strike sheet the final die is developed. The one-up die may or may not need adjustments, alterations, or changes requested by the customer. When the one-up strike sheet is finally approved, the planning department can take the next step which consists in developing a layout for the jig die. *Jig dies* are single-unit dies and distinguished from *block dies* which are assemblies of individual dies. Even though both types of dies can be used for inline cutting-and-creasing of cartons, Downingtown prefers jig dies. (A brief discussion on jig dies will be found under the head of steel-rule dies in Chapter X.)

The layout for the jig die is turned over to a company specializing in steel-rule die making. When the die is delivered samples are cut and supplied to the customer. Should the job contain many duplicates of the same die, which is usually the case when folding cartons are needed in large quantities, and should the cartons be processed on equipment with critical tolerances, each of the several dies is identified as to its position on the jig die. The samples submitted to the customer for testing in the processing equipment are correspondingly marked. This procedure makes it possible to make sure that each die is correct and that all cartons will be suitable for further use. Should the tests show that one or the other of the duplicate dies needs correction, these are made immediately by the supplier of the die.

Preparation and proofing of cylinders. At the same time when the die is made, sampled, and possibly corrected, work continues in other fields, particularly in the preparation of gravure cylinders. The base cylinders were made and shipped by their manufacturer to the engraver, and the engraver has not been idle on his part either. He used the time needed for manufacturing of base cylinders to prepare for the etching of cylinders. If the original artwork calls for full-color printing, the necessary color separations were made; if the job is done in multicolor, gravure positives are made from pre-separated art in black and white. When the base cylinder is delivered to the engraver, it can be almost immediately copper plated and prepared for etching. Nor have the suppliers of inks and stocks wasted time: samples of these materials have usually also been delivered to the engraver's plant in the meantime. (If the job has special end use requirements to which the printing ink must conform, these were of course transmitted to the ink supplier and considered by his technical staff in formulating the inks for the job in hand.) The engraver who received a copy of the basic layout etches the printing cylinders accordingly. Then the etched cylinders are proofed by the engraver, and the proofs are submitted to the customer; where corrections and re-proofing are requested, these must be made until the customer approves the job for production.

Courtesy The Beck Engraving Company

Retouching of photographic transparencies requires close study of both the original art and the transparencies. These are on a tilted light table; the art is on an easel at the right of the retoucher.

Specification of the printing stock. It should be added that the stock needed for printing must be ordered in the required quantity as well as quality. Paper board of different thickness is specified as to caliper, surface, roll diameter, and roll width, not to forget the diameter of the core on which the stock is wound. (Lightweight boards can be wound on cores of a smaller diameter than boards of heavier basis weights.) If the job includes lamination of aluminum to the board, this material must also be ordered in the correct thickness, roll width, and quantity.

When the die-cut samples and the proofs taken from the cylinder are approved by the customer, and after firm commitments for the delivery of materials are received from reliable suppliers, the job can be scheduled for production.

Press Preparation

The 36 inch Champlain five-color press, equipped for laminating and inline cutting-and-creasing, is operated at Downingtown by a crew of four workers. This crew consists of a pressman, an assistant pressman, an inspector, and a helper who is also called an off-bearer or carton handler. The pressman heads the crew, other workers take orders from him. The most important and also the most time-consuming part of press preparation is the setting of the cutter-creaser. This task is the job of the pressman and his assistant. The other two crew members work simultaneously on the washup of the past job and take care of the exchange of gravure cylinders.

Preparation of the cutter-creaser. After the jig die which was used for the preceding job, is taken off the cutter-creaser, the new jig die is put in the chase, a sturdy metal frame similar to chases used in the lockup of type forms. This chase, with the jig dies securely fastened within it, is locked up on the upper bolster of the cutter-creaser, the cutting and the creasing rules facing down. As already explained, the Champlain inline cutter-creaser has two bolsters, the upper where the die is placed and the lower on which the stock is positioned for cutting and creasing. The lower bolster is stationary, whereas the upper bolster makes a brief downward motion for cutting and returns to its original position after cutting.

Preparation for cutting and creasing is done in two areas. One is the back of the jig die, the other is the surface of the cutting jacket on the lower bolster. If certain cutting or creasing rules need more pressure, thickness is added in these areas on the back of the jig die. The technique used is the pasting of one or several strips of gummed tape behind the cutting or creasing rules that do not have sufficient pressure. The pressure of cutting rules is tested by trial cutting of a sheet. The correct location of creasing rules can be verified by making trial impressions with carbon paper.

The two operations of preparing the die and the cutting jacket go hand in hand. The lower bolster or, more precisely, the cutting jacket resting on the cutting plate on the lower bolster must be equipped with a female counter sheet which is needed for the proper creasing depth. The sequence of operations is the following: First, the *counter sheet*, which is made of sturdy fiber board, is cemented to the cutting jacket. Then a carbon paper impression of the creasing rule is taken. The creasing rule is somewhat lower than the cutting

Web Flow Chart of the CHAMPLAIN *Model D-42 Reciprocating Carton Cutter-Creaser*

The Champlain D-42 Cutter-Creaser, manufactured by Bobst Champlain, Inc., is a heavy duty machine for producing folding carton blanks of a thickness up to .036 inches. This cutter-creaser can be operated either inline, following a web-fed printing press, or independently. Inline production results in printed, cut, creased, and stripped-of-the-waste blanks, ready for gluing or packaging. Independent operation produces the same result from preprinted rolls of board. Independently operated cutter-creasers are normally equipped

with a turnover unwind because this kind of unwind can be loaded from the floor without need for overhead material handling.

The processing of the web is shown in several detailed illustrations and in an overall diagram. Beginning at the left of this diagram you see the web, as it comes either from the press or from a turnover unwind, entering the *web-pull section* which conveys it at a constant speed to the *intermittent web-feed*, a set of driven feed wheels which, operating stop-and-go, feed the web into the *cutting section* of the cutter-creaser in perfect timing with its cycle. For cutting, the upper

❶ *The intermittent web-feed section. Upper feed wheels together with lower feed wheels (not visible) maintain constant contact with web. Web is guided between side guiding bars for precise alignment.*

❷ *Upper and lower chases are shown withdrawn from the press. The die is locked up, face down, in the upper chase; you see the makeready behind the die. The lower chase has the cutting jacket and the makeready for cutting and creasing.*

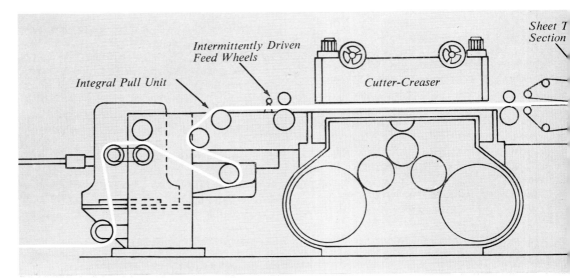

Sheet T Section

Intermittently Driven Feed Wheels

Integral Pull Unit

Cutter-Creaser

bolster, which has a steel-rule die attached in a chase, moves down and the die cuts and creases the stock against a hardened steel plate mounted to the lower bolster, under the stock. After cutting the upper bolster moves up again; the processed stock makes room for the next unit of the web. Printed webs are controlled in their cut-to-print register by automatic electronic equipment.

The die-cut sheet, held together by small tabs, is transferred by a *kicker roller* to the *sheet transfer section*, a moving belt which conveys it to the *universal waste extractor*. Emerging from the waste extractor the stripped-of-the-waste sheet is still held together by the small tabs; these are next broken by the *tab breaker*, thereby

freeing the cut-and-creased carton blanks. The individual blanks are finally delivered in an overlapped stream on a conveyor belt. If delivery on two belts is desired, an *alternator* divides the blanks equally between both belts.

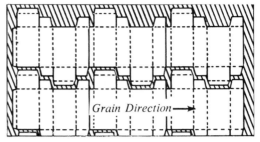

4 *A die cut sheet of folding cartons. Solid lines indicate cutting rules, dotted lines creasing rules. The shaded areas represent the waste to be stripped. (Steel-rule dies are described in Chapter X, Section 8 of this manual.)*

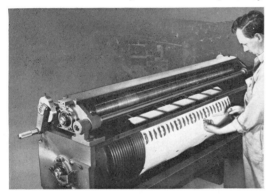

3 *Operator setting the pin clusters on the stripping cylinder, following a sample die cut sheet. The universal rotary waste extractor permits stripping of the most minute waste areas, disregarding their location.*

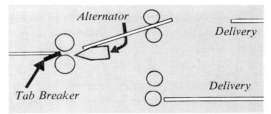

5 *Tab breaker and alternator for double delivery. Small tabs hold the sheet together during stripping. These tabs must be broken thereby separating the cartons for delivery. Alternator distributes cartons equally for double delivery.*

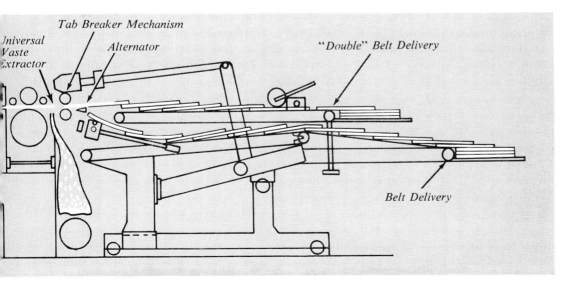

rule and has a rounded working surface. The crease comes about by cutting a channel of the proper width and depth into the counter sheet wherever the board is to be creased. During the impression, the creasing rule forces the board into these channels thereby creasing it. In the cutting areas, the counter sheet is prepared by cutting it away and thereby removing it where it is in the way of cutting rules. After these preparations are made, the draw rollers are adjusted.

Adjustment of pull or draw rollers. One of the great advantages of rotogravure is the possibility of using cylinders of differing diameters resulting in products of different cut-offs. The pull or draw rollers have the function to feed stock of different lengths at the correct speed to the cutting-and-creasing unit and are essentially a metering device. The adjustment for metering of different stock lengths is made in two steps. First several gears must be exchanged when the cut-off changes. After these gears are exchanged, the pressman can use a micrometer adjustment which permits him to achieve a fine adjustment of the stock feed to actual running conditions. The change of gears is part of press preparation whereas the micrometer adjustment comes into play only when the press run begins.

Preparing the stripping cylinder. The stripping cylinder must be individually prepared for each job. The preparation of the stripping is done either before or after adjustment of draw rolls. Stripping has the purpose of removing the waste from the die-cut sheet: it is an important step in carton production. The waste stripping system used by Downingtown can be prepared in two ways. For relatively simple jobs, a sample die-cut sheet is clamped to the stripping cylinder, for more complicated jobs a layout board is preferred for locating of the stripping pins which pierce the waste for removal. The cutter-creasers used by Downingtown operate up to 175 strokes per minute, cutting up to three sheets per second. Waste can be pierced in increments of ½ inch across the web and in increments of approximately ⅛ inch around the stripping cylinder. The "stripping pins" used on the described equipment have, as mentioned, the function of piercing and removing the waste. They are in "pin blocks" which can slide in the grooves of the stripping cylinder and can be fastened at any point on the perimeter of the cylinder. Stripping blocks are made with different pins for different stocks. At Downingtown each stripping block has two pins.

It is not possible to state an average number of stripping pins since every job is different; but for the purpose of illustration it is mentioned that few jobs require less than 20 settings of stripping blocks. This number may go up to, say, 100 settings on jobs combining many small units for common cutting and creasing.

If the adjustment of the stock feed and the draw rolls is done before the setting of the stripping blocks, the preparation of the stripping cylinder is the final step in getting the inline end of the press ready for running. The preparation of the inline machinery is the most intricate part of press preparation and requires a concentrated effort. Once this phase of press preparation is completed, the pressman and his assistant turn to the preparation of the several printing stations.

Preparing of printing units in rotogravure for package printing. The preparation of rotogravure printing units is not the same on presses built for publication printing and those built for package printing. Presses for package printing have facilities for using rotogravure cylinders of varying diameters whereas cylinders of invariable diameters are used in publication printing. Another difference is that package printing is, generally speaking, done on one side only of the web; in publication printing the web is printed on both sides, or perfected, though not at the same time when its first side is printed.

Washup. The preparation of printing units begins with the washup of the press. Press washup includes the cleaning of the cylinders used for the preceding run as well as the cleaning of the ink reservoir and all other equipment connected with it. The thoroughness with which washup must be done depends on the extent to which the new job differs in its colors from the preceding one. If the same color ink as before can be used for the new job, washup is rather simple. But if a light color follows a dark one, and especially if white ink must be printed, washup must be done most thoroughly. White ink is often needed on stocks which have aluminum foil as their printing surface. White can be part of the general design or it may be needed as a basis for successive colors.

Inserting and removal of cylinders. After washup, the old cylinders must be removed from the press and stored for future reruns. Removal of cylinders is a relatively simple and fast operation on the press under discussion. At the beginning of washup the ink applicator and the doctor blade are put in the cylinder removal position thereby freeing the cylinder. The cylinder itself is in a cylinder carriage which has rollers and rides in a track built into the printing unit. For removal and insertion of cylinders, a carriage extension is temporarily attached to the side frame of the printing unit and the cylinder is slid out of the press on this extension carriage. The new cylinder is slid into the press after the old cylinder is removed for storage. When the cylinders of one station are exchanged, the same extension carriage is used for the next printing unit.

Setting of ink applicator and of doctor blade. After the new cylinder is inserted and ink is put in the tank, the ink applicator and the doctor blade must be set. If the new job uses cylinders different in their diameter from those for the preceding job, ink applicator and doctor blade must be adjusted. These adjustments are made with hand wheels from the outside of the press. The equipment used by Downingtown has an ink applicator of the pressure type. A centrifugal pump circulates the ink continuously and forces it into the cells of the intaglio cylinder. The doctor blade wipes the surface of the cylinder and removes the ink from the non-image areas, or the lands, separating gravure cells. The doctor blade is adjustable in its angle; different jobs may require somewhat different angles.

The operations described for one printing unit are of course repeated for each unit that will be active in the production of the new job. The equipment here described can print five colors; but this does not mean that every job must be printed in five colors. If fewer colors are wanted, one or more printing units are simply by-passed.

Laminating of aluminum foil to board on the press. The inline package gravure press at Downingtown has a laminating section suitable for laminating aluminum foil to the surface of the board prior to its printing. The foil is extremely thin, 0.0003 inch in thickness; like the board to which it is laminated, it is put in rolls on the press. The foil travels from the laminator roll stand over a tension roll to an adjustable herringbone roller where it is smoothened. Then it progresses to a station where the adhesive is applied to its back. Immediately after receiving a coating of adhesive, the combining of board and foil takes place. The combining-roll assembly "consists of a steel combining roll and a rubber-covered pressure roller."[83] The combined board is then passed through the wash-coating station which degreases

the foil and makes it ink receptive. After passing a drying unit, the laminated stock is guided into the first printing unit.

Loading of rolls of board on the turn-over roll stand. The turn-over roll stand can hold two rolls of stock. The maximum roll diameter is 60 inches, the roll width is 36 inches maximum on the press here described. The weight of a 60-inch diameter and 36-inch wide roll of paper board is approximately a ton and a half. (It is here assumed that the job is started with a full-size new roll of board; roll splicing will be included in the discussion of running.) The assistant pressman is in charge of roll feeding. He or some other member of the press crew unwraps the roll and then puts it on the reel where it is attached with two plugs. After the roll is in position the press can be webbed. The leading edge of the stock is prepared for this purpose, and the web is threaded through the press, an operation requiring a good understanding of the equipment by those doing the work. The press is webbed through all units that are operating during the new run. Units that are not operating are simply by-passed. If all units are needed, webbing begins with the laminating section, includes the five rotogravure stations and of course also the inline cutting and creasing end of the press. In addition to the webbing of the press with paper board it must also be webbed with aluminum foil in jobs that require lamination of foil to the board.

Setting of electric-eye register controls. Color register, or the relative position of successive color images on the web, is controlled by an electronic unit for each printing station. The web is scanned by an electric eye. Correction is made by feeding either a longer or a shorter amount of stock to the following unit. The press member that changes the amount of stock is a compensating roller, similar to that described under the head of newspaper relief printing. But in carton printing the action of the compensating roller does not depend on manual adjustment; here the adjustment is continually performed by the register control equipment. "A hydraulic correction motor is employed because it has the ability to respond instantaneously to start, stop, and reverse commands. The correction signals energize solenoids which activate a four-way hydraulic valve mounted on the hydraulic motor. This motor makes the actual correction of register by acting, through intermediate gears, on the compensating roller. The amount of correction is controlled by a flow valve in the hydraulic line feeding the correction motor."[84]

If the register control equipment is set for very narrow differences between the upper and the lower limit, corrections are of course much more frequently made than if these limits are wider apart. To give the reader an idea of the frequency in which adjustments are made, it is mentioned that non-critical jobs may require ten moves of the compensator roller of each printing station per minute; jobs with very close register control settings need more frequent adjustments.

The setting of drying units. The deposited ink film is much too thick in gravure to permit wet-on-wet printing. The web must therefore pass through a dryer after each printing station and also after wash-coating. As conditions do not radically change from job to job, the drying units can be simply adjusted from the outside of the press. The drying system on Champlain presses is a hot air blowing system. The air is partly recirculated and partly exhausted together with the solvent fumes mixed with it.

Running of Inline Rotogravure Equipment

The running of rotogravure inline equipment for folding cartons is primarily concerned with keeping all press units in perfect and, ideally, uninterrupted operating condition and with maintaining the quality of the printed products at the proper quality level. Cutting and creasing is here as in other production phases the most important item. The pressman concentrates his attention on the inline end of the press and frequently checks the quality of the final product as to cutting, creasing, and cut-to-print register. The die-cut cartons are removed from the delivery

Courtesy Downingtown Paper Company

A four-color Champlain *rotogravure printing press with inline cutting and creasing equipment. In the foreground you see the delivery of the die-cut and stripped sheets; the four printing units are in the rear.*

end of the press by the off-bearer who stacks them on skids either for further processing on carton-making equipment or for bundling if they are to be shipped without additional fabricating.

Roll splicing. Roll splicing is another job that must be performed in intervals depending on the thickness of the board and the length of cut-off. Merely to give the reader some idea of the frequency with which splicing must be done, it is mentioned that a 60-inch diameter roll may last for half an hour to one hour; this means that one or two splices must be made hourly during running. Splicing is done semi-automatically. (The difference between semiautomatic and fully automatic roll splicing is explained in Chapter VI, Section 5, "Roll Feeding and Web Control.") The splicing unit is prepared for splicing by attaching splicing tape to the splicing cylinder. When the time for splicing arrives, splicing, or the joining of the new web to the expiring web, is done by the equipment after the worker in charge of roll feeding pushes a control button. The new roll is, of course, already in the feeding position of the turn-over reel.

Maintaining and adjusting the ink supply. In longer runs it may be necessary to add ink as the run progresses. Various units may require adjustments of printing ink in its intensity and color. These adjustments are made at Downingtown according to instructions given by the pressman, a craftsman with long experience. In some cases such adjustments consist in the adding of solvents, or of extenders, or of other items, depending on the job in hand.

Keeping of records pertaining to presswork. Since cartons are usually repeat jobs, all knowledge gained during the first run is put on record in order to shorten the preparatory time of reruns. Among the items recorded are the positions of various printing cylinders; the positions of pin blocks on the stripping cylinder; the position of the jig die on the upper bolster, the tolerances—upper and lower limits—used in the setting of the electric-eye register control system; the number of teeth of the gears used in the change box of the feed system for compensating of differences in cut-offs; the kind and proportion of ingredients added to each color ink; the setting of the doctor blade; the pressure setting of the impression roller of each printing unit; and the temperature settings of each drying unit. This non-exhaustive listing shows that many items must be co-ordinated for efficient inline carton production.

Finally, a few words on the production capacity of this equipment. The described installation can produce between 7,000 and 10,000 sheets of a maximum size of 36 by 36 inches per hour. These may contain a quantity of 20,000 to 100,000 die-cut and creased folding cartons, depending on their individual size. A sheet has rarely less than two and more than twenty units.

Section 4:   Presswork in Planographic Printing

In this manual the process family of planographic printing is divided into four methods. These are: (1) stone lithography, (2) direct lithography, (3) offset lithography, and (4) collotype or photo-gelatin. Stone lithography, the original litho-graphic method, is not practiced anymore as a printing business but has become the preserve of artist printmakers. Presswork for stone lithog-raphy and presswork for the rarely used direct lithography are not discussed in this section which is primarily devoted to presswork in offset lithography. This is necessary because of the posi-tion offset lithography has achieved in contempo-rary printing. Offset printing is done by a vast number of printing businesses ranging over the whole gamut of organizations, from small shops up to and including some of the largest corpora-tions that can be found in the printing industry. Offset printing parallels letterpress printing in its scope and diffusion, especially since the perfection of web-offset printing. Many job-and-commercial printers practice both letterpress and offset lithography. Such printers are said to operate "combination plants."

The needs of supervising and operating person-nel for information on offset presswork can be satisfied by the excellent publications of the Graphic Arts Technical Foundation, by literature published by press manufacturers, and by the trade press. Those needing general information can find much less in the literature. The present section is planned to fill this gap. This section is divided into five units. First, the three distinctive features of offset lithography are explained. In the second unit you find a general exposition of press preparation which is intended as basis for the understanding of all kinds of offset printing. The third unit is devoted to offset lithography on sheet-fed presses, the fourth unit discusses web-offset printing, and the fifth and last unit of this section contains a brief description of presswork in collotype printing.

The Three Distinctive Features of Offset Lithography

Three features distinguish offset lithography which is for all practical purposes synonymous with planographic printing in the present. The original two characteristic features of lithography are the distinctive selection of printing and non-printing areas by the lithographic principle and the use of integral or single-unit image carriers. These two features date back to the invention of lithography by Aloys Senefelder of Bavaria at the end of the eighteenth century, approximately 160 years ago. The third, more recent feature, is the introduction of indirect printing by inter-position of a rubber blanket between the printing-image carrier and the printing stock. This feature is the reason for the name "offset" lithography. The application of the offset principle to the lithographic printing of paper and paper board can be credited to Ira Rubel of Nutley, N. J. Indirect lithographing of sheet metal, or tin print-ing, was practiced several decades before Ira Rubel introduced offset printing of paper, in 1904 or 1905. Even though our knowledge of the invention and introduction of offset printing on paper is scanty, the present writer believes that Ira Rubel may have invented this form of offset printing independently, not knowing of its exist-ence in tin printing.[85] The offset principle was in-troduced at the right time. Together with photog-raphy and photomechanics it gave the litho-graphic industry a strong impulse. We are witness-ing the application of this principle to letterpress and only the future can tell what the result will be.

In the following you find first a discussion of the lithographic principle, then one of single-unit image carriers, and last one of indirect image transfer, all of them seen in their relation to press-work.

The Lithographic Principle in Its Relation to Presswork

All printing processes must distinguish between the printing areas and the non-printing areas of

Sheet Handling Chart of a HARRIS *4-color Offset Press*

A four-color sheet-fed offset press consists of four individual printing units, each of which prints one color on one side of a sheet as it passes through the press. The usual color progression is first unit yellow, second unit red, third unit blue, fourth unit black.

The inker places a film of ink on the printing areas of the plate which has already been moistened in the non-printing areas by the dampening unit. The ink is then transferred to the blanket which prints the form on the paper, passing between the blanket and impression cylinders. Since the ink requires some time to dry, a portion of the yellow ink (first unit) will be transferred from the paper to the second, third, and fourth blankets. Similarly, the rest of the colors will appear on each succeeding blanket. This is called "wet" printing and it can be seen that the sheet must be in perfect register through all color units if the desired results are to be achieved.

Depending on the size of the press, there are between fifteen and twenty sheets in motion at all times. The eleven drawings on the right describe in a step-by-step manner the progress of a sheet passing through the schematic press shown in Drawing No. 12 below.

1 Four sheets have been separated from the pile as the vacuum suckers seal to the next sheet.

2 Suckers raise the top sheet as the preceding sheets are being moved forward in a "stream".

3 A blast of compressed air raises the top sheet against the bottom of the preceding sheet.

4 The first sheet in the stream has come to rest at front guides (A) and is being side-guided.

5 Feed rolls (B) grip sheet, front guides (A) drop. Feed rolls accelerate the sheet to press speed.

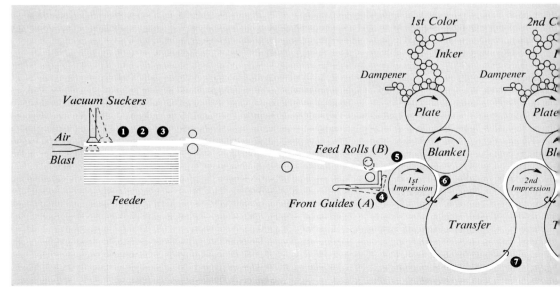

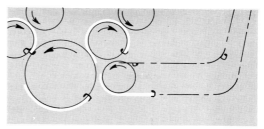

6 Guides rise, 1st sheet is printed with 1st color and is transferred to first transfer cylinder.

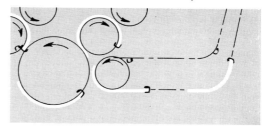

9 1st sheet is taken from 4th impression cylinder by gripper bar attached to delivery chains.

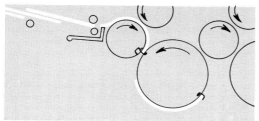

7 The first sheet is on the double-size transfer cylinder, and the second sheet is in position 6.

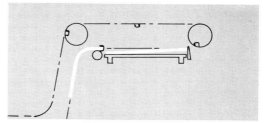

10 First sheet continues on toward the delivery pile while the other sheets are being printed.

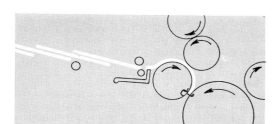

8 1st sheet receives 2nd color, proceeds through 3rd and 4th colors similarly to steps 6 and 7.

11 Delivery bar grippers open and the 1st finished four-color sheet is dropped on delivery pile.

12 Schematic diagram of the entire sheet-handling sequence on large Harris 4-color offset press.

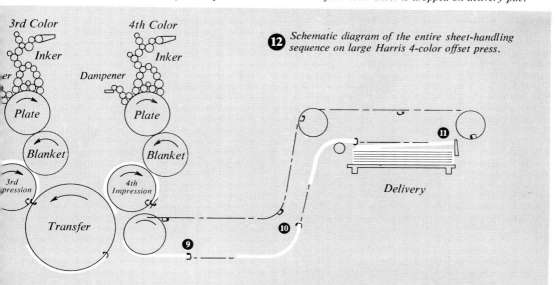

printing-image carriers in one way or another. (Printing areas are often called *image areas*, and non-printing areas *non-image areas;* both pairs of terms are used interchangeably in the literature.) In relief printing, the printing areas are on the surface of the image carrier; intaglio printing uses cells of different kinds which are below the surface of plates or cylinders; offset lithography has both kinds of areas practically on the same plane. For this reason all lithographic methods are technically classified as planographic ones. The invention of lithography added the lithographic principle to printing technology and made it possible to achieve selective area distinction by physicochemical treatments. Said in other words, *the lithographic principle enables us to treat the printing areas of the plate to be ink receptive and water repellent and to treat the non-printing areas to be ink repellent and water receptive*, all this in such a manner that both kinds of treatments can coexist without serious harm to one another. It will be seen that the words "coexist" and "without serious harm to one another" are the decisive operating terms.

A basic limitation in platemaking for lithography. The main point to be understood in this context is a basic limitation in the art of making lithographic plates. In spite of all progress made during, say, the last 30 years, in spite of applying science at a previously undreamed of rate to platemaking, we have nevertheless not learned to endow the non-printing areas of lithographic plates with permanent ink repellence. As of yore, the ink repellence of non-printing areas must still be renewed, or if you prefer, refreshed, during each and every printing cycle. Consequently, the lithographic printing cycle consists in the application of two different materials to the plate. First, fountain solution is applied to the plate for maintaining the ink repellence of the non-printing areas; immediately thereafter the plate is inked, and if the plate is well made and correctly handled on the press, ink will be accepted by the printing areas only and not by the non-printing ones. The fountain solution, which consists mainly of water, is known in the pressroom as "the water," and its application to the plate is called "dampening"; the correct combination of inking and dampening is often discussed as "ink-water balance." There are a number of different dampening systems in use, eight of them are characterized in Chapter VI, Section 3, under the side head "The Dampening Unit."

Moisture and ink are applied to the whole plate surface in lithography. Most dampening systems apply the fountain solution direct to the plate surface, immediately before the plate is inked. (In some dampening systems the fountain solution is not applied to the plate but to inking rollers which in turn apply it to the plate as part of inking.) The printing areas and the non-printing areas of lithographic plates are practically in the same plane and *both kinds of areas are subject to dampening and to inking during each press cycle.* This operational condition must be firmly grasped for a good understanding of the problems with which lithographic presswork must cope.

Some consequences of plate dampening and inking. When the dampening rollers pass over the printing areas of the plate they deposit a minute quantity of fountain solution on them. It can also happen that the inking rollers leave minute quantities of ink on non-printing areas where ink must not be put. And it also happens that the dampening rollers pick up some ink from the printing areas and that the inking rollers pick up some fountain solution from the non-printing areas. Consider that dampening and inking take place between 70 and 150 times per minute and you will agree that the undesired transfer of fountain solution and of printing ink can have a substantial cumulative effect. The setting of the dampening and of the inking unit must be done with care and skill if offset printing is to progress smoothly. Establishing the correct ink-water balance is, hence, a prerequisite for high-quality offset lithographic presswork.

These are by no means all consequences of the lithographic principle for presswork. Additional

Courtesy Graphic Arts Technical Foundation

A technician using the GATF *Press Inkometer to monitor the ink-water balance on a press.*

problems are caused by getting fountain solution on blankets and inking rollers. Fortunately lithographic inks are so formulated that they can absorb a certain amount of water and still print well. (This subject is discussed in Chapter IX, "Printing Inks.")

The lithographic principle requires precision control of inking and dampening. The Graphic Arts Technical Foundation has developed many methods for trouble-free lithographic presswork. In addition, the Foundation has identified most, if not all, troubles encountered in offset printing due to the lithographic principle.[86] To summarize: excessive, insufficient, and uneven dampening are all harmful and must be avoided; the same holds true of inking. It is not possible to produce high-quality and trouble-free jobs without well-made plates and without the correct ink-water balance.

Single-Unit Plates in Their Relation to Presswork

The assembly of all images or all image carriers that will be printed together are called a "form" in the printer's vernacular. (The word *form* meant originally a *type form* but is now generally used in the printing industry—in letterpress, lithography, and other methods—to indicate the assembly of all images or image carriers to be combined for the same press run, usually but not necessarily in the same color.) The image carriers for offset lithography are relatively thin metal plates, one for every form. In this manual such image carriers are classified as single-unit or integral image carriers as opposed to the class of multiple-unit or assembled image carriers. Next we will discuss the main advantage and some drawbacks of single-unit plates.

The main advantage of single-unit plates. Single-unit image carriers are used in many printing methods. Their greatest advantage is the speed with which such plates can be put on the plate cylinder of the press. In consequence of this feature, presses printing with single-unit plates have much shorter down-times than presses printing with assembled or multiple-unit image carriers. As explained in Section 2, the sustained interest in wrap-around plates and in presses for wrap-around plates is primarily due to the great reduction in press down-times in wrap-around or letterset printing, compared with the press down-times encountered in presswork with multiple-unit or assembled image carriers.

To avoid misunderstandings it is perhaps best to also say here explicitly that the operation of assembling is inevitable in the making of most single-unit image carriers, not less than in printing with multiple-unit image carriers. *The difference between these two classes of image carriers is not that one needs assembling and the other does not* but that (1) different physical objects are assembled in either class and that (2) assembling takes place at a different production stage.

Single-unit image carriers require the assembling of photographic transparencies prior to the exposure of the plate during platemaking. The units to be assembled can be different pages, labels, displays, cartons, and so forth. The assembly can be performed in lithography either by stripping or by photocomposing. Both are done away from the press. Multiple-unit image carriers for letterpress are either type forms or duplicate plates. Type forms are assembled away from the press; rotary letterpress is done with curved plates which must be assembled on the press on all large-size presses. (The detail of press preparation in letterpress printing is extensively discussed in Section 2.) Single-unit plates are typical for lithography, which was originally based on a single stone and was therefore in the true sense of the word using a monolithic image carrier. Offset lithography is based on lightweight thin metal plates, and the platemaking methods practiced in offset lithography are now used, with the necessary adaptations to be sure, in the making of plates for wrap-around and letterset relief printing.

Some drawbacks of single-unit plates. Like everything else, single-unit plates have certain drawbacks or limitations. If a set of single-unit plates for full-color printing is not made perfectly, these plates may not be usable at all. (Everything depends on the degree of perfection required in a specific job.) Multiple-unit image carriers for letterpress printing are assembled page by page, or plate for plate, on the plate cylinder of the press. This procedure is explained in Section 2 under the head "Presswork on Sheet-Fed Rotary Letterpresses." There you find that each page can be individually adjusted for position, and that the image carrier for a single page may be divided into several units, which facilitates its correct positioning. This flexibility of multiple-unit assembling has many advantages, but it must be dearly paid for by long press down-time. With single-unit plates press down-time is short but the pressman is not in a position to make changes in the spatial relation of assembled images. If an offset plate is not made correctly, it must simply be made over. The offset lithographic industry has learned to assemble images for platemaking with precision and the techniques developed for this purpose are now adapted to the making of single-unit relief plates which are either shallow-etched metal, photopolymer or other photomechanically made plates that can be used either for direct or for indirect letterpress printing. The great savings in press down-time are in the eyes of most experts decisive, and the limitations of single-unit plates do not count enough to offset these savings.

Indirect Image Transfer in Its Relation to Presswork

As you know, indirect image transfer is accomplished by transferring the ink image from the plate to the blanket on the blanket cylinder. From here the ink image is transferred again to the stock which, in sheet-fed presses, is carried or supported by the impression cylinder. The introduction of the blanket presented a number of operational problems. Since offset printing had no precedent, it was necessary to develop techniques for the making and the handling of the rubber blanket. The making of blankets of varying hardness and composition was learned, methods for preparing the blanket for mounting were devised, the proper stretching and the calibrating of blankets were studied, and instruments for calibrating of blankets were introduced into shop practice. In the course of time it was found that certain solvents affect rubber blankets injuriously and natural rubber was largely replaced by synthetic rubbers. It was also learned that certain inks are not compatible with blankets of some composition. A few of these points are further developed in the following discussion of presswork on single-color sheet-fed offset lithographic presses. The knowledge gained in more than fifty years of indirect lithographic printing is at present applied to indirect relief printing.

The role of the lithographic principle in indirect image transfer. An explanation of indirect lithographic printing cannot be limited to the blanket but must include some points related to the lithographic principle. The quality of the ink image transferred from the plate to the blanket depends

Small batches of fountain solution, with or without alcohol, of prescribed pH can be mixed uniformly with the Baldwin Automix.

to a large measure on correct ink-water balance. If this balance is not achieved, or if it is upset during the run, the ink image will reflect this disturbance and will be more or less defective. It must be kept in mind that the blanket is in contact with both the plate and the printing stock. If the plate is too much dampened, excess moisture is transferred from the plate to the blanket and from the blanket to the paper. Papers, and some kinds of coated papers in particular, are more hydrophylic than blankets, and excess moisture can become troublesome. Chemicals contained in paper coatings may cause trouble, and the paper itself can contribute to defects if the sheets are not clean. Dust or lint on the surface of papers will be transferred to the blanket and from it to the plate where it may disturb the image areas. Finally, the printed paper has a tendency to stick to the blanket, a fact that influences speed and delivery of the press. These few points indicate the relatedness of plate, ink, blanket, stock, and not least ink-water balance. Defects spread fast and must therefore be corrected as soon as possible.

After this explanation of the three distinctive features of offset lithography we turn to a general exposition of presswork on sheet-fed offset presses.

Introduction to Presswork on Offset Lithographic Presses

Presswork on sheet-fed offset lithographic presses depends in its detail on the nature of the equipment and of the work to be done. Fortunately, the subject was extensively studied by the Graphic Arts Technical Foundation which developed a number of basic procedures and tests to guide operating personnel in their work. In this unit you find brief identifications of some points which are indispensable for a good understanding of presswork. These points are here grouped under the following four headings: (1) the blanket, its selection and care, (2) soft-covered inking rollers, (3) the relation between plate cylinder and blanket cylinder, and (4) the fountain solution and its handling.

The Offset Blanket and Its Care

The blanket is the most characteristic element in offset printing. Even though indirect lithographic and indirect relief printing have somewhat different problems and use somewhat different techniques, they have nevertheless one common point which is, of course, the blanket. We divide our discussion of the blanket into three points; (1) selecting the proper blanket, (2) preparing and mounting of blankets, and (3) blanket care.

Selecting the proper blanket. As mentioned in Chapter VI, Section 2, contemporary offset printing has a considerable choice of blankets. "We now have soft, medium and hard blankets. We have blankets that are especially formulated for linseed oil inks, fast drying inks, heat-set inks, and glossy inks. Some of our present day inks would quickly ruin one of the old natural rubber blankets."[87] Blankets of different hardness have different operational characteristics; blankets of different composition are made to be used with inks formulated with different types of vehicles. But it is not practical for lithographic plants using a variety of inks and papers to change blankets with every change in ink or stock. Most lithographic shops "look for an all purpose blanket unless a plant has specific types of work where ink and paper can be standardized."[88] It is obviously not possible to make generalizations concerning the hardness and composition of blankets selected by various plants as their all-purpose blankets. This decision depends entirely on the actual conditions of operation and on the judgment of the people who make it.

Preparing the blanket for mounting. After the proper kind of blanket is selected it must be prepared for mounting on the blanket cylinder. The first step of blanket preparation consists in the measuring of its thickness. The thickness of the blanket is expressed in thousandths of an inch, and the correct thickness figure is the basis of calculating of the blanket packing. Measuring of blankets for their thickness used to be done with machinists' micrometers, but the blanket is compressible and the pressure exerted by the measuring craftsmen was far from uniform, resulting in inconsistent readings. "The GATF Blanket Thickness Gauge was designed to overcome these difficulties. This instrument is distinguished by two features: (1) pressure is applied by means of a dead weight, and (2) the gauge has a 4-inch throat in which the blankets can be rolled so that accurate measurements can be made at every point of their surface."[89] For uniform punching of holes, templates are usually prepared. It is not always necessary to punch holes in the blanket; already punched blankets are also supplied. (It might be mentioned that not all blankets are punched for attachment to the blanket cylinder; some presses use different fastening methods.) The next step is to screw or rivet bars on the ends of the blanket for attachment to the blanket cylinder. After the blanket is properly attached, the new blanket is prepared by thorough scrubbing of its printing surface with pumice, blanket solvent, and water.

Blanket care. Blankets are not only carefully selected and equally carefully prepared for mounting, they must also be treated with consideration after they are put on the press. "When a blanket finishes a long run, it has areas of concentrated, absorbed oils, and driers. These areas are slightly raised, and pressmen speak of them as *embossed* ones. This is especially true after running black type. If a blanket is then scrubbed thoroughly and rested, these oils disperse throughout the blanket surface and the slight embossing effect disappears. Blankets will last longer and do a better job when used intermittently."[90] The development of blankets with a surface of synthetic rubber has resulted in great improvements. Synthetic rubber blankets emboss much less than natural rubber blankets and are therefore preferred by many plants, particularly those engaged in long-run printing. Embossing is not the only problem encountered with blankets. Others are loss of sharpness in the printed image, the tendency of the paper to stick to the non-printing areas of the blanket, the mechanical impairment of the blanket surface by cutting, smashing, or indentation, not to speak of low spots.

Soft-Covered Inking Rollers

There is a basic similarity in the considerations governing the selection of blankets and of soft-covered printing rollers. For this reason their discussion immediately follows that of blankets.

Selecting of soft-covered inking rollers. Like offset blankets, soft-covered inking rollers must be compatible with the kind of ink which will be used for printing. Just as lithographers tend to select all-around usable blankets, so they tend to select all-around rollers. Without going into too much detail it is pointed out that there is a telling difference between the kinds of inks used in sheet-fed printing and the kind of inks needed for web offset. Most inks for sheet-fed presses dry by oxidation and polymerization, whereas inks for web offset contain solvents which must be removed by forced drying. Such inks are generally classified as heat-set inks. Sheet-fed offset lithographic presses are usually equipped with synthetic rubber rollers; sometimes vulcanized oil rollers are used on slower sheet-fed presses; more recently PVC rollers have been developed which have proved satisfactory on sheet-fed presses. Rollers for web offset are usually made of synthetic rubber. These proved to be most suitable for high-speed printing with heat-set inks. (For a discussion of rollers, see Chapter VI, Section 3.)

The setting of soft-covered rollers. The inking system of offset lithographic presses contains many soft-covered rollers; for our discussion we can omit all of them with the exception of those that have the function of inking the plate. These rollers are either called "plate rollers" or "form rollers." Form rollers meant originally rollers that inked a type form; like the word form, form roller has expanded its meaning and is used for soft-covered rollers that ink any printing-image carrier. Modern offset presses have usually four plate rollers. These must be in perfect condition and well set to produce good inking of the plate at the lowest possible pressure. "A roller that will print a line ⅛ inch wide on the plate, when inked up and lowered carefully to the plate with the press standing still, is properly set. On very large presses this line may be increased to 3/16 inch in width. On a small press a line width of even less than

⅛ inch may be used."[91] The Graphic Arts Technical Foundation has devised a test which indicates whether the plate rollers are properly set in relation to the plate as well as to the ink drum from which they take the ink film prior to its application to the plate. This test can be simply made and is described in the literature under the name, "Picture Test."[92]

The Relation between Plate Cylinder and Blanket Cylinder

As explained in Chapter VI, Section 2, the printing unit of offset lithographic presses consists of three cylinders: the plate cylinder, the blanket cylinder, and the impression cylinder. These three cylinders must be carefully adjusted in their relations. The plate cylinder and the impression cylinder each make contact with the blanket cylinder and must be adjusted accordingly. Some of the necessary adjustments between plate cylinder and blanket cylinder are now explained.

Testing the bearers for contact. American presses have bearers on both ends of the plate cylinder and the blanket cylinder. These bearers are rims of hardened steel that have several functions. "One of the most important functions of bearers is to smooth out the transmission of power from one cylinder to the other. To make bearers really effective it is necessary that they be forced together under pressure by the bearings. Bearer traction must be greater than the traction between blanket and plate."[93] Offset pressmen can ascertain the contact of bearers with the *thumbprint test.* They make a few thumbprints with ink on the bearers of the blanket cylinder. Then the plate cylinder with a properly packed plate and the properly packed blanket cylinder on which a sheet of stock is put for the test are put through a single revolution. If bearers have the proper contact a clear set of prints will be transferred from the bearers of the blanket cylinder to the bearers of the plate cylinder.[94] If the thumbprint test shows that bearer contact is insufficient, this condition is corrected by adjusting the blanket cylinder according to the instructions which are provided by press manufacturers in their operating manuals.

Comparison between press packing in offset and in letterpress printing. Offset presses are packed on the plate cylinder and on the blanket cylinder. The impression cylinder is not packed on most presses; there are, though, some presses which have a packing on the impression cylinder. Offset presses differ in this respect from presses for letterpress. In letterpress, the packing serves two purposes; one is the adjustment of the press for stocks of differing thickness and compressibility, the other is the local adjusting of printing pressure. In offset lithography the first purpose is accomplished not by packing but by changing the position of the impression cylinder or of the blanket cylinder. (Which cylinder is moved depends on the construction of a particular press.) The impression cylinder is, as mentioned before, not packed at all. Local pressure adjustments serving the same purpose as in letterpress, namely to differentiate printing pressure for different kinds of images, is not practiced in lithography. Sometimes local pressure adjustments may be necessary, though, to level low places in the blanket.

The two purposes of packing in offset printing. Offset lithographic presses are packed for two purposes. One reason for packing is to provide the required *squeeze pressure*. The second reason is related to the *length of the printed image*. Packing is done under the plate and under the blanket. "The packing of a press has become a controversial subject on which pressmen and even press manufacturers do not agree. One builder recommends that the plate be packed just to bearer height, and all squeeze pressure build-up be put under the blanket. Another builder recommends that the plate and blanket be packed to about equal height. A third American builder instructs the pressman to pack blankets below bearers and plates quite high."[95] The detail of packing depends on the kind of press to be packed as well as on standards and rules established in different pressrooms.

The second purpose of packing is to influence, or control, the length of printed images. "In connection with change in image size it is important to understand that the printed lithographic image tends to be longer than the image on the plate. This is due to the stretch of plate when the plate is bent around the cylinder, possibly to excessive pulling when the plate clamps are tightened; to stretching the sheet during printing; and to moisture pickup by the sheet from the blanket."[96] After the plate cylinder and the blanket cylinder are properly packed and have the correct squeeze pressure, changes in the packing are made by transferring some of it from one cylinder to the other (meaning the plate cylinder and the blanket cylinder) but not by adding or removing packing to or from one cylinder only.

The correct squeeze pressure must be maintained, and *changes in the packing made on a single cylinder will either decrease or increase this pressure whereas transferring packing from one cylinder to the other does not change the squeeze pressure but merely affects the length of printed images.*

Checking the completely packed press with a packing gauge. Both ends of the plate cylinder and the blanket cylinder are checked with a packing gauge after they are packed. Several types of packing gauges are in use. Some of them are shop-made, others are commercially available instruments. The essential function of packing gauges is to determine the relation between the height of the plate, or of the blanket, and the cylinder bearers. For this purpose packing gauges have dial indicators connected to an extended member such as a bar, with which the indicator gauge is aligned. "A packing gauge enables the pressman to make exact relative measurements of plate and blanket heights under actual printing conditions."[97] Since the packing is closely related to the length of the printed image, our next point is a brief discussion of the GATF Register Rule which is widely used for measuring image length.

Checking the length of the printed image. The GATF Register Rule is a precision instrument that serves for three related purposes. One is to measure accurately the dimensions of images on the plate, another is to do the same with images printed on paper, and the third is to measure dimensional changes in the paper or other printing stock "occurring during the printing operation.

Courtesy Graphic Arts Technical Foundation

The Colite Magnetic Packing Gage *guides the pressman in packing the plate and the blanket cylinder. The base of the instrument is held by powerful magnets to the cylinder; the slideable bar has a micrometer dial, calibrated in thousandths of an inch. You see the pressman zeroing the dial on the press bearer. When the bar is slid back, the dial indicates how much above or below bearers the plate or the blanket is.*

The Register Rule is an essential tool in preventing misregister, and in analyzing and correcting register troubles. It consists of an aluminum alloy bar graduated throughout its length in inches. At the right-hand end, 1 inch is graduated in tenths of an inch and is movable by means of a knurled head carrying a dial graduated in thousandths of an inch. With it measurements can be reproduced within plus or minus of 0.001 inch."[98] After this brief discussion of packing we turn to the final point of this introduction, the fountain solution and its control.

The Fountain Solution

From the discussion of the lithographic principle you know that the non-printing areas of the plate must be dampened during each printing cycle to keep them properly ink repellent. The fountain solution, or dampening solution, is called "the water" in the pressroom, a designation that is almost, though not quite, correct. The main component of the fountain solution is indeed water, but the solution also contains other ingredients which are essential for dampening.

Among them are various gums, phosphoric acid or acid phosphate salts, and ammonium bichromate alone or in combination with a nitrate salt. The solution should be mildly acid.[99]

The pH scale. The acidity and alkalinity of solutions is by chemists expressed in a scale which permits electrochemical measurements in units designated pH by the inventor of this scale. The use and application of pH measurements was introduced into lithography many years ago by GATF. The pH scale goes from zero to fourteen; zero indicates strongest acids, fourteen strongest bases or alkalies and seven is neutral. The pH of the fountain solution can be measured in many ways, with specially prepared paper strips, or preferably with a pH meter.[100]

The pH of the fountain solution depends not only on its composition but is also influenced by other factors. These may include the pH of coated and uncoated papers, plate metals, and printing inks. All items combined for printing must be carefully controlled in their quality. Fountain solutions that are defective can cause serious troubles during printing.

Presswork on Single-Color Sheet-Fed Offset Presses

No other branch of the printing industry has a literature on presswork comparable with that existing for offset lithography. This fortunate condition is due to the work done by the Graphic Arts Technical Foundation whose original name was Lithographic Technical Foundation, abbreviated LTF. The manuals published by the Foundation are written for operating personnel; they are periodically revised and brought up-to-date. These publications can be of great value also to those not directly concerned with the operating of presses since they are well written and discuss problems and tasks generally encountered during presswork. The following description of presswork on single-color presses draws freely on literature published by GATF.

It should perhaps be explained why this discussion of sheet-fed offset presswork is limited to single-color presses, even though many multicolor presses, and more recently also perfecting presses, are in actual operation in a large number of lithographic plants. Single-color presses are obviously the least complex ones and lend themselves better to basic explanations, particularly for readers who are not interested in acquiring operating skills. The various points discussed for single-color presswork are not less valid in presswork done with more complex equipment. There, additional operations must be performed which are in principle the same as those needed in presswork on single-color presses.

Planning for Presswork on Single-Color Offset Presses

Planning for presswork on single-color sheet-fed presses is less complex than planning for presswork on multicolor sheet-fed presses or planning for web-offset printing; but planning for single-color offset presswork contains nevertheless many basic points which obtain equally in the planning for more complex equipment, even though additional points must be included in the latter kind of planning. Printing on single-color presses is not restricted to the printing of jobs requiring a single color. Multicolor and full-color jobs may be produced on single-color presses if these are the only kind of presses available or if the press run is too short or the sheet size not suitable for available multicolor presses.

Relation between planning and platemaking. All planning for offset printing must be done either before or during platemaking. Offset printing is based on single-unit printing-image carriers; in such image carriers, the arrangement of pages or of other units to be combined on the same plate must be determined before the plate is made. In large plants which use formal planning, the layout is developed by planning departments; in smaller plants the plate layout is usually made by craftsmen working in the stripping department who are provided with the necessary information by their supervisors.

Various points to be considered in planning. Planning includes such items as the kind of imposition, which may be sheetwise, work-and-turn, or work-and-tumble. (Various impositions are described in Chapter X, "Binding and Finishing" because the available binding equipment is a controlling factor in the selection of impositions.) In addition to these basic considerations there are many others directly related to the nature of the job in hand and to the required quality level. After the layout is made, photographic intermediates, which are for single-color presswork more often negatives than positives, are assembled as a flat for common exposure. The completed plate must contain all images in their correct position, and it must be made to permit its correct placement on the plate cylinder of the press.

Quality Control of Component Elements

All elements which are combined in presswork must have the required quality level. In single-color presswork, quality control concentrates on the plate and the press. Ink and paper are usually purchased from reliable suppliers, and in smaller plants quality control of ink and paper is limited to inspection. Some large plants have laboratories equipped with testing facilities. There ink and paper may be subjected to a number of laboratory tests. Some of these are described in Chapters VIII and IX which deal with printing stocks and printing inks.[101] Most plants do not have formal quality control departments and are more concerned with inspection of plates and the state of the press than with other items.

Before the plate is turned over to the pressroom it is thoroughly inspected for both contents and image quality. Single-color and multicolor jobs are often proofed photomechanically, by the making of blueprints or diazos from the assembled flat. Such proofs may or may not be submitted to the customer depending on the nature of the job, the practices adopted by a lithographic company, and the demands of the customer. Full-color jobs, which are less frequently produced on single-color equipment than on two- or four-color presses, are either proofed photomechanically or on proof presses. Photomechanical proofs are not proofs of the plate itself but of the photographic intermediates from which the plate will be made; they are nevertheless highly useful. Since such proofs do not indicate the image quality of the plate, the plate itself must be carefully inspected before it is put on the press.

Press Preparation of Single-Color Offset Presses

Press preparation includes in this manual all steps taken on the press from the end of running the last job until the new job is ready for running. Press preparation is, therefore, closely related to job changeovers. In lithographic plants and shops, and consequently also in the literature published by GATF, the term makeready is still generally used. "When a lithographer refers to makeready he means the preparatory steps taken by the pressman in preparing his press for running. Offset makereadies may be divided into three general classes. They are: (1) the makeready that just involves a change of plates; (2) the partial makeready; and (3) full makeready."[102] Makeready, or press preparation, involving merely a change of plates, is less time consuming than partial makeready which is needed in multicolor or full-color jobs to be printed on a single-color or on a two-color press. Such makereadies require not only change of the plate but also changes of the packing and changes of inks. The full makeready is the most extensive of the three classes into which the GATF divides press preparation.

Characterization of press preparation for single-color offset. The detail of press preparation depends not only on the job in hand but also on the make of the press. The full preparation of a single-color offset press may require 48 different operations.[103] For our purposes it is neither necessary nor desirable to describe all these steps which are of importance to operating personnel but would be mere ballast for those not so employed. Press preparation in the sense in which the GATF and the lithographic industry use the term "full makeready" consists in the setting of the four main press units: (1) the feeder, (2) the printing unit, (3) the inking and dampening unit, and (4) the delivery. Feeder and delivery are extensively discussed in Sections 4 and 6 of Chapter VI and do not need further explanation. But there are

Ink agitators are valuable press accessories. Baldwin Ink Agitators *are independently driven rotating cone mixers. Their independent drive makes it possible to continue mixing during press shutdowns. For split-fountain jobs separate agitators are used for each different color ink.*

several points related to other press units and to the plate that seem worth mentioning. These are: (1) examining of the plate before attaching it to the plate cylinder, (2) attaching the plate to the plate cylinder, (3) preparing the inking and dampening units, (4) running the press to establish ink-water balance, and (5) the purposes of color patches, the GATF Star Target, and other controls.

Examining the plate prior to putting it on the press. Before the pressman puts a new plate on the press, he examines both its face, or printing surface, and its back which bears no printing images. Examination of the face does not need justification, its purpose is self-evident. But the back is also quite important. Often the plate is not completely clean on its back when it reaches the pressroom. Therefore the back is usually carefully cleansed during plate inspection. Sometimes plates have kinks or dents; these must be straightened and remedied before the plate may be put on the press. A plate with a dirty back or with mechanical defects will cause trouble during printing. The plate is measured with a micrometer, then the sheets needed for packing are selected. These steps are called "premakeready" since they are taken away from the press.

Attaching the plate to the plate cylinder. The plate cylinder has sets of adjustable plate clamps

which are needed for attaching and stretching the plate tightly to the body of the plate cylinder. The clamps themselves are positioned in the cylinder gap. The leading edge of the plate is first slipped into the front clamps, and the jaws of the clamps are tightened after the plate has been centered sideways. A center mark on the plate and a mark on the cylinder determine this. Next, the clamps and the plate are moved up or down to get front register. This may be determined by marks on the plate and cylinder marks. Before the other end of the plate is clamped by the back clamps, the prepared packing is inserted. The squeeze pressure is predetermined; it is the combined effect of packing the plate cylinder and the blanket cylinder. As explained, packing an offset press is a critical operation. Many pressrooms have the rule that both cylinders must be checked with a packing gauge at every changeover.

Speaking of the blanket, it might be added that it must not only be properly packed but also cleansed. A thorough scrubbing and cleaning is indispensable whenever a light color follows a dark one. Light colors are often printed first; dark ones—black in particular—last.

Some points related to preparing the inking and dampening units. As already explained, all plate rollers pass over both kinds of plate areas, the image areas as well as the non-image areas. Since the ink repellence of dampening rollers is not absolute, the dampening rollers are bound to become dirty in the course of time. Molleton rollers that have become too dirty for running are exchanged for clean ones when the press is prepared for a new job; the dirty molleton rollers are washed and kept ready for future use. The setting of the inking unit does not need to be described in detail. Some aspects of the subject are explained in the introduction; generally speaking, inking units on single-color offset presses are regulated, just like other inking units for highly viscous inks, by the setting of fountain keys which control the amount of ink applied around the plate. The most important task in the adjusting of inking and dampening units is the establishing of the correct ink-water balance.

Establishing the correct ink-water balance. On presses using conventional dampening systems it takes a number of sheets until the ink-water balance is established and the blanket is well worked in. The number of sheets needed for the running in of the job varies. To give the reader an indication it is mentioned that it often takes between 300 and 500 sheets before this result is accomplished. It would be quite expensive to waste 300 to 500 sheets of paper, and this expense is avoided by combining waste sheets of the correct size with new sheets which are interspersed in various ratios, say, one new sheet for every ten waste sheets. The new sheets are carefully examined and the press is adjusted in order to obtain the best result.

As you see it takes some time and paper to arrive at the right ink-water balance on presses having conventional dampening systems. Such systems are also not entirely satisfactory in maintaining the ink-water balance during running. Both establishing and maintaining this crucial balance is substantially improved with some other dampening systems. Some proprietary dampening systems enable the pressman to arrive at the right ink-water balance by printing not more than a few trial sheets. (Different dampening systems are described in Chapter VI, Section 3.)

A pressman puts a container with fountain solution on the press. Baldwin Gravity Feed Water Levels *provide a visible check on the supply and automatically maintain the predetermined level of the fountain solution in the fountain pan.*

When the pressman feels that the job is printing right, he submits a sheet for approval to the person or department in which the authority for giving approval is vested. The approved sheet serves as the standard for quality during running. A number of instruments and devices can be used for analyzing and adjusting of printed quality. Three simple aids are our next subjects. These are color blocks or patches, the GATF Star Target, and "Signalstrip".[104]

Color blocks. A thorough inspection of each and every smallest area of a large sheet for the quality of printed images is, if not completely im-

The densitometer is an important instrument for quality control. Here it is used to check color control patches in full-color printing or proofing.

possible, then certainly much too costly and time consuming. The graphic arts industry has developed different techniques which make it possible to analyze and adjust press conditions without resorting to minute inspection of the total printed area. Color blocks, or color patches, are widely used in full-color printing; they serve as guides to color balance. Color patches are narrow strips of solids and halftones printed in the waste of the sheet and trimmed off before the job is delivered. These patches are analyzed with a reflection densitometer by craftsmen or printing technicians.[105]

The GATF Star Target and Signalstrip. The GATF Star Target is a more recent addition to lithographic printing technology. "This target is smaller than a dime. It consists of pie-shaped wedges of lines that converge to the center. Targets do not take the place of color bands or dots on the sheets. These bands are used to detect variations in color strength from sheet to sheet. The Star Target is used to detect slurs or doubles or squash."[106] The quality of printed images depends on a number of variables. Each defect is due to one or several of these variables, and it is often not easy to identify these defects correctly and to change their causes. The Target is an aid in diagnosing, not the least because it magnifies defects very strongly. "One of the main advantages of the Star Target is that a spread, slur, or double which lengthens a halftone dot 0.001 inch will cause a spot 0.023 inch to appear in the center of the target."[107] Targets are printed in several places on the sheet; they can be examined either by eye or

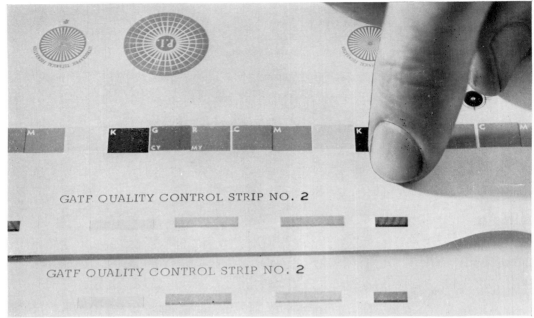

Courtesy Graphic Arts Technical Foundation

Color patches, the GATF Star Target, *the* GATF Dot Grain Scale, *and other aids permit improved quality control of lithographic presswork. In this picture you see a* GATF *reproduction technician pointing to differences in the* GATF Quality Control Strip No. 2 *on two different sheets.*

with a magnifier, and are trimmed off before the job is delivered. Another aid for evaluating print quality is "Signalstrip," manufactured by Lithos, Inc., Chicago. This strip is incorporated in the flat during stripping and appears on the plate, printing in the waste of the stock. Signalstrip is "made up of fine dot and line patterns, extremely sensitive to image size change. Such a change causes a Signalstrip pattern to appear, quickly signaling any deviation from 'normal' dot image on the plate or press sheet."[108] The GATF Star Target and Signalstrip are valuable guides to high printing quality in the hands of experienced offset pressmen.

The Running of Single-Color Offset Presses

Running of single-color offset presses must maintain the approved quality of the job, and it must proceed with maximum efficiency. The approved press sheet serves the pressman as his guide for the quality of production. The pressman inspects printed sheets periodically, particularly often if something goes out of order. The maintaining and adjusting of the correct ink-water balance during running is among the main concerns of the press-

man. In addition to watching the quality of printed sheets, he must also add stock, ink, and fountain solution as running progresses and he must remove the printed sheets from the delivery or see to it that his assistant takes care of this task, whenever the length of run exceeds the capacity of the delivery. (The manning of presses depends on a number of factors. Large size multicolor presses are operated by larger press crews than small size single-color presses.)

Protection of plates for reruns and during interruptions of presswork. Many plates are not just used for a single press run but for repeated printing. Such plates must be carefully protected and preserved in order to retain their usability. If a run spreads over more than a single day, certain precautionary measures are needed for the interval between the end of one day and the beginning of the next working day. In both instances the plate is carefully gummed, then washed out and covered with asphaltum. The blanket is scrubbed and the press is washed up. If the blanket has been in use for a long time it may be removed and prepared for a period of rest. Plates that are expected to be rerun are carefully stored after they are taken off the press and have been treated for storage.

Washing up the press. The latest designs of presses are equipped with automatic washup facilities. Older presses do not have automatic washup but must be washed up by the press crew either with or without a washup machine. The detail of washup "was studied by a group of physical chemists headed by John A. Hinckley. The results of this group's work on the problem were summarized in a technical paper that Hinckley presented before the 1952 annual meeting of TAGA, Technical Association of the Graphic Arts."[109]

Three-solution roller cleaning. In the past, roller cleaning was done with a single solvent. "Common solvents include gasoline, V.M. & P. naphtha, mineral spirits and kerosene. One roller manufacturer recommends a mixture of 2 quarts of high test gasoline, 2 quarts kerosene, and half a pint of light machine oil."[110] But single-solution washup was not entirely satisfactory. Three-solution washup proved highly superior. The first solution removes the ink largely by a dilution process, but some ink always remains on the rollers. The second solution is applied after most of the ink has been removed by the first solution. This solution acts quite differently. It tends to emulsify the remaining ink. In this way the remaining ink is removed from the rollers almost completely. If the second solution is left on the rollers they will not accept ink when the press is rolled up with ink for the next run. One of the purposes of the third solution is to remove the second solution from the rollers; it also removes the last traces of color. Three-solution washup makes it possible to go from black to yellow

Pressman operating a Baldwin Press Washer. *The whole roller train of the press is cleaned by bringing the washup blade into contact with the vibrating roller. You see the mixture of washup solvent and ink as it comes off the roller. This waste is drained off into a removable drip pan.*

without losing nearly as much time as in conventional single-solution washup.[111]

Presswork on single-color perfectors and multicolor offset presses. Presses having several printing units may pose additional problems, since the equipment is more complex than single-color presses. But essentially each unit must be handled as if it were a single-color press. The additional press preparation and care in running is primarily a task of co-ordinating the flow of paper from unit to unit and of maintaining proper register. The detail of these operations depends on the construction of a multicolor or perfector press. Some presses have individual impression cylinders for each unit, others may combine common impression-cylinders for two, and possibly more, plate and blanket cylinders.

Presswork on Web-Offset Presses

Web-offset printing came into its own in the nineteen fifties. It had a consistent growth since that time, and many hundred web-offset installations are in operation in the United States. The growth of web-offset printing can be attributed to several causes. Web printing is by its very nature much more productive than sheet-fed printing. The two printing methods where web printing was well established before web offset entered the lists are rotary letterpress and rotogravure. At the time when web offset began to become popular, both of these methods needed image carriers that

were much more expensive than offset plates. A large number of lithographers and many trade shops were in a position to make good lithographic plates, and these are more or less the same for sheet-fed and for web-offset printing. Many lithographers felt that they had mastered presswork on sheet-fed presses, and the step from sheet-fed to web offset was for them not a radical innovation but rather part of an evolutionary process. The trend toward web offset was supported by growing competition and by the fact that many customers were looking for a printing

Web Handling Chart
of a HARRIS-COTTRELL
Model 1000 Web-Offset Press

Of unit construction and blanket-to-blanket in design, the Model 1000 is available in one to five perfecting units complete with combination or two-former folder. Its size of 22¾ and 23½" x 38", plus operating speeds of 1000 feet per minute, make it suitable for in-line production of catalogs, tabloids, newspapers, digests and a wide variety of folded commercial work.

As the web leaves the unwind device (roll stand), it is threaded through a variable speed controlled infeed mechanism maintaining constant tension at all speeds.

Each perfecting unit on the Model 1000 will simultaneously print one color on each side of the web as it travels through the press horizontally at speeds up to 1000 feet per minute. Plate and blanket cylinders on the Model 1000 are staggered in a slight reverse "S" fashion, with the blanket cylinders being double the circumference of the plate cylinders. For uniform web tension, centers of the blanket cylinders are offset from each other to produce a slight wrap of the web around them before and after printing. As a further aid to web tension, blanket cylinder gaps have been rotated a full 180°. With gaps never meeting, constant blanket contact with the web is maintained. (See drawing 2)

After the printing operation, the web (or webs) enters a tunnel-type gas dryer, is wrapped around three 12 inch chill rolls to set the ink, and is forwarded to either a Model 1000 combination or a two-former folder.

The combination folder offers the maximum in product flexibility for production of catalogs, tabloids, newspapers, digests and a wide variety of folded commercial work. The two-former folder was designed for versatility in paging and highspeed production of catalog size products—inserts and covers—at full press speeds. With use of one or two webs, the two-former folder will deliver a wide range of paging including 4-8-12 or 16-page signatures (all products can be different) at speeds up to 64,000 folded signatures an hour. The use of two folders on the Model 1000, alike or different, will provide even greater paging versatility and/or product size.

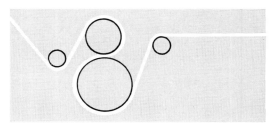

1 *At the infeed the web is directed into contact with, and wrapped around, controlled speed rollers which meter paper to the printing unit.*

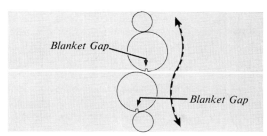

2 *Blanket cylinders twice the size of the plate cylinders, with blanket gaps rotated 180°, assure more uniform web tension.*

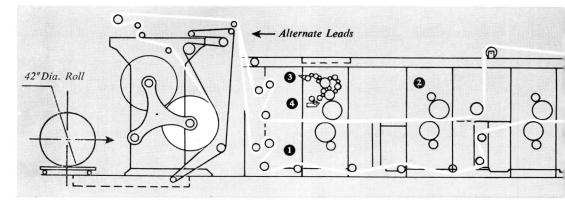

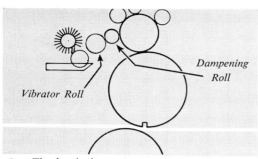

3 The brush dampening system provides a continuous finely metered supply of water to the plate cylinder. No fountain additives are required.

4 13 rollers break up, distribute and apply ink to the plate. Ink break-up is further improved by oscillation of 4 steel vibrator rollers. Ink adjustment keys span the full width of the web.

5 By using a pre-press registering system, plates are pre-registered on a plate bending fixture in relation to the cylinder and in register with each other. When plates are locked on press, operator is assured of a minimum of registered problems.

6 Lateral and circumferential running register of both cylinders can be made at the printing unit or by remote control from the electronic console.

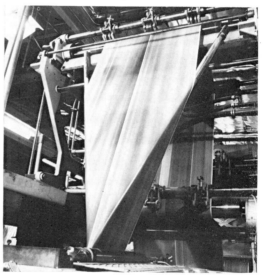

7 Two different folders are offered as standard on the Model 1000. A combination (former-jaw-chopper) folder or a two-former four-delivery folder is available in both the 22¾ and 23½ x 38" sizes.

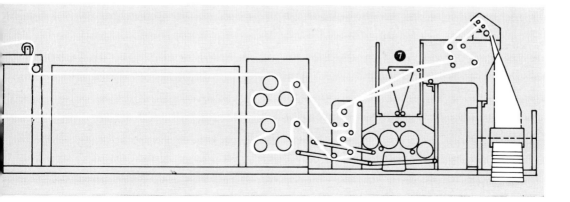

method that could produce medium-length runs cheaper than sheet-fed printing or letterpress web printing.

In addition, web-offset presses had become much more practical and reliable than they were when this kind of equipment was first introduced in the graphic arts industry in 1914. Heat-set inks had come into existence and so did new kinds of plate rollers and blankets without which these inks could not be utilized. Techniques and equipment for the forced drying of paper webs, printed with heat-set inks, were developed which could never have been used with traditional lithographic inks based on linseed oil vehicles.

Roll feeding and the delivery of folded signatures had been pioneered by newspaper printing and adapted to higher precision by web printing in letterpress for the production of mass-produced general-interest magazines and other high-quality products. The handling of webs of paper from the roll to the completely and precisely folded signature at the delivery end had become a highly developed art, applicable to web offset with the necessary adaptations and modifications. Finally, and by no means least important, the blanket-to-blanket design gave the web-offset industry presses that were relatively inexpensive, permitted the perfecting of the web on each printing unit, lending themselves to a straightforward operation and eliminating the need for intermediate drying of the web prior to the printing of its second side.

Seen from the comfortable cockpit of hindsight, most if not all prerequisites for a success of web-offset printing existed when this method was recognized by a few pioneers as a promising one. But like everything that is new, web offset had to fight for its acceptance and to prove its value before it became generally admitted. The trade press and various trade associations kept the industry informed about web offset by publishing instructive articles and by organizing forums devoted to web offset and its progress.

Web offset can be used for a wide variety of purposes. These may perhaps best be classified under three heads: (1) web offset for job-and-commercial printing, (2) newspaper printing by web offset, and (3) specialty printing, our vague catchall. The equipment is not the same for each of these three classifications. Since specialty printing is not discussed in this manual, we can concentrate on the differences between presses designed for job-and-commercial work and those for

newspaper printing by web offset. Web-offset presses for job-and-commercial printing are designed for high-quality full-color printing. Such presses have usually four (and sometimes eight) perfecting units, one each for the three full-color inks and one for black. Web-offset presses of this classification are equipped for the processing of a single web or of several webs. Web-offset presses for newspaper printing may be designed to handle one or several webs, and the product may be printed in black ink only or in black ink and colors. Usually, web-offset presses for newspaper printing are not equipped with driers. Installations for smaller papers have roll stands; the delivery of web-offset presses for newspaper printing is a typical newspaper folder, as described in Chapter VI, Section 7.

After this introduction to web offset we turn to a description of an installation for high-quality job-and-commercial web-offset printing. This branch of web offset is selected because it is of greatest general interest. The subject was developed at the Fawcett-Haynes Printing Corporation in Rockwell, Maryland. The installation described is an eight-unit Harris-Cottrell 1,000 Web-Offset Press.

An Eight-Unit Blanket-to-Blanket Press

The web-offset installation at the Fawcett-Haynes Rockwell plant selected for description consists of eight blanket-to-blanket perfecting units, capable of processing two webs at the same time. It has two fully automatic pasters, two sets of driers and chilling rollers, two folders, and push button controls for many operations. The press can take webs of different width up to 38 inches, and has a cut-off of 23½ inches. Since it can handle two webs concurrently, every revolution of the press produces two units, each having a maximum size of 23½ by 38 inches, printed in eight colors, four on each side, thereby producing a total of sixteen colors. The maximum rated speed is 1,000 f.p.m., and at this speed the press produces the equivalent of more than 60,000 sheets of the mentioned maximum size per hour, each printed in eight colors. The maximum rated speed is not always the best operational speed, but assuming an operational speed of 80 per cent of maximum speed, the output of this press is in the order of 50,000 units. The product of the press consists of folded signatures.

On a web press the number of delivered signatures is the same as the number of cutoffs made by the press. The number of pages of which a signature consists depends on the number of folds to which the cut-off is subjected. In the next unit on planning for web offset you find an explanation of the range of signatures and page sizes obtainable with the described equipment.

The arrangement of web-offset press equipment. The whole machinery comprising this installation is arranged in a straight line on the pressroom floor. At the feeder end there are two three-roll reels, one for each of the two webs that can be printed by the press. There are two fully automatic pasters that can also be operated semiautomatically if preferred. The two reels are followed by four blanket-to-blanket perfecting units. After the web leaves the last perfecting unit it moves into a two-stage high-velocity drier where it is dried on both sides, passes then into the chilling equipment, and is there cooled for further processing. Following the presses for the first web, the same equipment, namely, printing units, drier, and chilling rollers, is duplicated for the second web as shown on pages 508–509.

The delivery end of the press has two folders. One folder is a combination folder comprising a former folder, a jaw folder, and a chopper folder; it is in a straight line with the rest of the equipment. (The length of the assembled units is approximately 130 feet.) The other folder has two former folders and is designated as a two-former folder. It is at a 90 degree angle to the main assembly. The Harris-Cottrell Model 1000 Offset Press has many interesting features. Among them is the double-size blanket cylinder which "reduces the number of stops for blanket washups, and thereby results in greater net production," and the brush dampening system that "provides a continuous finely metered supply of water to the plate cylinder."[112] At Fawcett-Haynes, four of the eight printing units have the Harris Cottrell Brush Dampening System, the other four units are equipped with the Dahlgren dampening system.

Various kinds of press controls. A high-speed web-offset press needs many different controls. Some of them are mounted on one side of each printing unit, others are in consoles placed independently on the floor. Controls for inking and drying are at Fawcett-Haynes approximately in the center of the installation, the console housing the controls needed for folding and register is near the folders. The controls on the side of each printing unit are used by craftsmen working on

these units; colored signal lights indicate whether units are operative or not and that a unit is or is not ready and safe. The speed of the press is determined from a central position.

This brief description of the Model 1000 Web-Offset Press must suffice though it covers merely a few points, and these without going into any detail. But you can see even from this cursory description that this equipment is complex and on a high technological level. Operating personnel must understand the working of the many different units and co-ordinate them properly.

Planning for Presswork on Web-Offset Presses

All job planning must consider every pertinent detail, a point repeatedly emphasized in this chapter. Planning for web-offset printing differs from that for sheet-fed printing in one essential respect: it includes the planning of folding as well, since folding is done as part of presswork and not in the bindery. Another difference between planning for sheet-fed and planning for web offset is that the cut-off cannot be changed and that jobs must fit the cut-off of the press. The width of the web can be changed within the limits set by the design of the press. (On the Model 1000 press the cut-off is 23½ inches, the minimum web width is 26 inches and the maximum web width is 38 inches.) Folded signatures of different kinds have therefore one fixed dimension, related to the fixed cut-off of the press, whereas the second dimension is variable, depending on the width of paper chosen for a job. It can, of course, happen that a given layout does not use the full cut-off. But such layouts are shunned since they cause expensive waste of paper. For this reason the development of the format for web printed products is always done in close co-operation between the customer and the technical staff of a web-offset printer.

Standard folds and signatures produced on web-offset folders. A number of different folds are identified by generally accepted terms in the industry. These are now briefly described. The dimensions of pages given in the following are based on a 23½ inch cut-off and a web width of a 26 inch minimum and a 38 inch maximum. For this reason the dimension derived from the cut-off is always a single figure whereas the second dimension is expressed as a range from the 26 inch minimum web width to the 38 inch maximum web width. All figures refer to untrimmed signatures as they come off the folder. The most com-

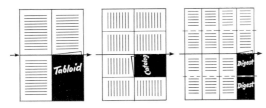

Three standard folds made in commercial web offset. In the tabloid fold each cut-off of a single web produces 8 pages; in the catalog fold, 16 pages, and in the double-digest two units of 16 pages each.

mon folds that can be made by combination folders (having a former folder, a jaw folder, and a chopper folder), are in the order of descending page sizes the following three: (1) the tabloid fold, (2) the catalog fold, and (3) the double-digest fold. The *tabloid fold* has a page width of 11¾ inches, arrived at by dividing the cut-off in half. The height of the page can vary between 13 and 19 inches, depending on the width of the web. One web produces 8-page signatures. If two webs are associated the products are 16-page signatures. The *catalog fold* has a page width between 6½ and 9½ inches depending on the web width, which is divided into four, and a page height of 11¾ inches in the cut-off direction. One web results in 16-page signatures, two webs in 32-page signatures. The *double digest* fold has a fixed page width of 5⅞ inches, which is one-quarter of the 23½ cut-off. The height of the signature can vary between 13 and 19 inches depending on the width of the web. In the double-digest fold two 16-page units are vertically arranged, one above the other. The actual page size is 5⅞ inches in width and varies between 6½ and 9½ inches in its height. One web produces, after trimming, two

16-page signatures, two webs result in two trimmed signatures of 32-pages each.

The *two-former folder* has neither jaw nor chopper folding equipment. It consists of two former folders and has the purpose of producing 4-page catalog size signatures which are used as inserts of advertisements into magazines. The web is slit into half, "led around turner bars and over ribbon compensators, super-imposed over formers, led through pinch rolls into folder cylinders for cut-off, transferred to slowdown delivery cylinders and delivered onto two creeping belt conveyor systems."[113]

The above-described folds show the range of signatures that can be produced by folders connected to web presses. Depending on the nature of a business and its needs, folders can be developed to suit particular cases. In Section 2, you saw that Bibles, printed by indirect relief methods on web presses can be folded to a vest pocket format by triple parallel folding, and in Section 3, there is a description of ribbon folding under the head of "Presswork for Publication Printing in Rotogravure." The elements of angle bars, former folders, jaw folders, and chopper folders can be combined to produce folders that can cope with practically any requirement. (Ribbon folding, jaw folders, and chopper folders are explained and illustrated in Chapter VI, Section 6.)

Finally a few words on the relation between folds and plate layout. The arrangement of printing images must correspond to the sequence of pages determined by folding. In tabloids and double-digest folds the pages are usually positioned with their width in the running direction of the web and their length across it, or with their

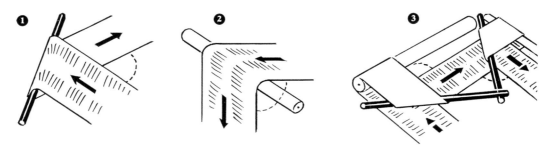

The path of the running web is controlled with angle bars and guide rollers. Diagram (1) shows how an angle bar changes the web direction 90° horizontally; (2) how the web is guided 90° vertically by a guide roller; (3) shows reversal of the web path by means of two angle bars and two guide rollers.

length across the longer plate dimension. Catalog folds are usually positioned with their width across the web and with their length in the direction of the web travel, or with their length in the shorter plate dimension. At Fawcett-Haynes as in many other planning departments of web-offset printers various imposition layouts are on file; if a job needs a special layout the required imposition is developed for it.

Quality Control of Component Elements for Presswork in Web Offset

All elements needed for web-offset printing at high speed in full color must have the required quality level if presswork is to be done efficiently. The three full-color inks must have the correct absorption and reflection ranges, and since color correction is based on these properties, they must be carefully controlled. The same holds true of the visual qualities of the paper which are, just like those of color inks, included in the calculations on which color correcting is based.

Some points concerning the quality of inks and papers. Apart from their visual qualities inks and papers must have the right working properties. It must be kept in mind that high-speed web-offset deposits ink images at the same time on both sides of the web, and that the web is not dried between colors. Printing is therefore done wet-on-wet with extremely small intervals between the image transfer of successive colors. The perfected web, printed in four colors on each side, is then dried. The web is moving at the same speed at which it is printed through driers, where it is exposed to heat and air for seconds only. Deviation of inks from approved standards can have very serious consequences impairing production speed, affecting color combinations by over-printing, and increasing production costs. The drying properties of the ink must be carefully balanced with the drying equipment of the press.

The working properties of the paper are not much less critical. For high-fidelity full-color reproductions, coated papers are commonly used. The coating must be suitable for offset printing and have uniformity of color. Other requirements are that the paper must arrive in well-protected rolls without any splices, that the stock must present a perfectly clean surface to the blankets for image transfer on both sides of the web, and that it must be wound at the correct tension on cores of specified diameter. These scanty remarks on the two most important materials consumed in web-offset printing must suffice at this point.

Quality control of inks and papers poses less of a task for the printer than for the manufacturers of these products. Paper mills and ink mills have well-appointed and well-staffed quality control laboratories and are organized to maintain their products at the correct quality levels. The main concern of quality control exercised by the printer in web offset is the plate. Paper and ink may remain the same for protracted periods of time, not so the plates. Each job to be printed on both sides of the web in full color requires two sets of four plates, or a total of eight. Since the press discussed has eight perfecting units, not eight but sixteen plates, or four sets of full-color plates are needed for presswork.

The Harris-Cottrell Key Register System. Quality control of plates has many highly technical aspects. We must limit the subject to one feature of particular importance in web offset— the registering of plates for common presswork. Offset plates are single-unit plates that cannot be rearranged like letterpress plates on the plate cylinder but must be made to perfection. There are some adjustments possible of plates already on the press since plate cylinders can be adjusted circumferentially and laterally up to $\frac{1}{8}$ inch in each direction from dead center, and plate cylinders can be cocked plus or minus 0.020 inch from dead cylinder on one end. But it must be understood that these adjustments affect the whole plate and not the position of individual pages relative to other pages on the same plate. The position of pages depends entirely on the precision with which plates are made.

The Harris-Cottrell Key Register System combines precision in the making of individual plates and positioning of images on the plates with facilities for bending of plates as needed for their attaching to the plate cylinder. This system uses a 3-hole key register punch for the assembling of individual images, for the making of the plate itself, and finally for the bending of the plate. "The rear end of the punched plate is positioned to mate with the three Key Register pins on the plate bender, locked in place and the bend is made. Each plate is then bent to the same alignment."[114] The bends of the head and tail of the plate must be made exactly since the cylinder gap is extremely small. The correctly bent plates are attached to the plate cylinder during press preparation, which is our next subject.

Press Preparation of a Web-Offset Press

Press preparation for web-offset printing combines two different kinds of operation. One group comprises preparative steps essential for high-speed web printing, whereas the other group consists of steps essential in offset lithographic presswork. To begin with, the plates of the last job must be removed and the press washed up. All component elements necessary for presswork must be dispatched to the press. These include rolls of paper, inks, plates, and precise instructions for the new job. The installation at Fawcett-Haynes is operated by a crew of six men. These tackle press preparation simultaneously at different points. Essentially, the preparatory steps for web printing consist in roll preparation, putting of rolls into each of the two reels, webbing the press, and guiding the web through the drier into the folder, which must be properly set. The operations related to offset lithography include putting the plates on the several plate cylinders, packing plate cylinders and blankets, checking the squeeze pressure with the usual instruments, and adjusting the inking and the dampening units. This is a summary description omitting all detail, but together with the description of sheet-fed offset printing, the task of press preparation for web offset will be understood by the reader.

Running a Web-Offset Press

Functionally, running of web-offset presses does not differ from the running of sheet-fed offset presses, but operationally it certainly does. The high speed with which web-offset presses operate makes correct timing imperative. If it is undesirable to interrupt the running of sheet-fed presses, it is many times more expensive and annoying to do so on web-offset presses. Web offset presses are expensive equipment. The installation described in this unit costs approximately three-quarters of a million dollars. It needs no further explanation that such a press with a crew of six men costs a substantial amount of money per hour. The investment must be amortized, expenses for the space occupied must be met, and the wages of six men must be earned. For all

Two turning bars and a guide roller are needed for turning a web, yet maintaining its running direction.

these reasons, down-time must be reduced to the barest minimum.

Unfortunately the cost of down-time is not limited to the type of expenses mentioned. Interruptions cause other, not less burdensome costs. As you may remember from our discussion of sheet-fed offset printing, it takes a certain time before the press produces at the required quality level. If you run a press at 1,000 f.p.m. (or at 80 per cent of its maximum speed) a few minutes of running to get quality up to standard mean an enormous waste of paper. During every minute, such a press consumes at full speed, roughly speaking, the equivalent of a ream of sheeted paper of a comparable maximum sheet size. If such losses occur frequently they can become quite expensive; interruptions causing them must be kept as rare and short as possible.

The basic rules applicable to all high-speed manufacturing remain valid in high-speed printing of any kind. These rules are simply that every detail must be most carefully planned, all component elements must be in perfect condition, and preparation of the equipment must be done with the highest precision. Semiautomatic or fully automatic pasting of new webs to the expiring one, web-break detectors, electronic register controls, push-button adjustment of all units on the press from the plate cylinder to the folder, enable operating personnel to attain this precision in a minimum of time. It is understood that each man who participates in operating the equipment must have a thorough grasp of its functional features, and must know his own job well.

Presswork for Collotype Printing

Collotype differs in many ways from other planographic printing methods. It is a direct printing method, and image transfer is made by bringing the inked plate directly into contact with the printing stock; collotype presses are usually rebuilt direct lithographic presses which have, consequently, no blanket cylinders. Another difference between contemporary offset lithography and collotype is the fact that collotype is not capable of long-run printing which is possible and often practiced in offset lithography, where runs of several hundreds of thousand and even millions of impressions can be made from the same plate. Collotype is a short-run method for several reasons. One of them is the comparatively brief life expectancy of the plate, another is that it is a slow printing method. Collotype presses are still hand-fed, whereas all modern high-speed printing is done with automatic feeders. Yet collotype has retained its position of prominence for high-quality reproductions in spite of all its handicaps. Collotype is still the only method which can produce continuous-tone images without disintegrating them into halftones, and direct image transfer has the great advantage of making exceptionally strong ink deposits possible. This feature compensates often for the short plate life which is mostly due to abrasion by the printing stock.

Collotype is used at the two ends of the quality scale: for large size short-run utility printing of low quality, posters for motion pictures and the like, but also for fine art reproductions of paintings and other art subjects. (This is not to say that collotype has no place in promotional and advertising printing; here too it is selected for high-quality jobs in short runs.) The use of collotype for large size low-quality work is decreasing, whereas that for high-quality reproductions in the art field is increasing, in keeping with the steadily growing interest in the visual arts in this country. The following description of presswork for collotype was developed at the plant of Triton Press in New York City, a company specializing in full-color reproductions of fine-art subjects and in high-quality work for advertising and promotional purposes. The methods set forth in the following are those practiced by Triton Press. Other collotype printers may follow different procedures depending on their particular conditions and needs.

Planning and quality control for collotype presswork. Planning for collotype printing is essentially the same as that for other sheet-fed planographic printing. The elements which are to be present on the same plate must be assembled prior to platemaking since collotype plates are single-unit, or integral, printing-image carriers. Full-color jobs are usually proofed on the production press prior to presswork; in repeat runs separate proofing may not be needed since approved prints from past runs are usually kept in the files of the production department. Simple jobs in a single color or in multicolor are often printed without submitting proofs to customers.

Preparation of collotype plates for running. The already made collotype plate must be prepared for running. The pressman takes the plate from its storage place to a tank which is filled with a mixture of glycerin and water of prescribed proportions. The quality of this mixture is checked with a hydrometer, a simple instrument indicating the specific gravity of the solution. The plate is put on hooks and immersed in the tank for a period of 15 to 30 minutes. Then the plate is lifted and drained for a few minutes. Next the drained plate is placed with its face, or printing surface, down on a flat work table on which clean stock was put for this purpose. The pressman faces the back of the plate, and he cleans this back of residual solution by wiping it dry. The plate hooks were of course removed before it was laid down on the table for cleaning.

Putting the collotype plate on the press. After the back of the plate is dried, the plate is ready for putting on the press. For this purpose the plate (which is still protected on its face by the stock on which it was put face-down for wiping of the back) is positioned on the plate cylinder of the press. Its location is determined by scribed marks on the cylinder and corresponding notches in the plate. The plate cylinder has a cylinder gap in which the clamping mechanisms for the head and for the tail of the plate are housed. After the plate is correctly positioned and clamped on both ends, the pressman takes the protective paper off and dampens the plate with a solution of glycerin and water. Then he jogs the plate cylinder, meaning that he moves it little by little, and blots off the excess solution from the plate surface with newsprint.

Setting of fountain, guide, and grippers. The following preparatory steps consist of setting the ink fountain, setting the side guide, and setting the cylinder grippers. All these steps do not differ in principle from those described for sheet-fed offset lithographic presses. The ink fountain has the customary fountain roller, fountain blade, keys, and, of course, a ductor roller which connects the fountain with the ink distributing system. Where more ink is needed on the plate, the fountain blade is moved a little away from the fountain roller; where less ink is wanted the fountain blade is pressed closer to the roller; all of this is accomplished by adjusting the fountain keys, as in all other roller-operated inking systems for lithographic and letterpress printing. Compared with other planographic presses, those for collotype differ in one significant point: collotype presses do not have a dampening system, whereas off-set and direct lithographic presses must be dampened in every printing cycle to keep the non-printing areas ink repellent. This kind of dampening is not needed in collotype.

Printing-pressure adjustments. The presses used by Triton for collotype printing are not equipped with bearers. Adjustments for differences in the thickness of printing stocks are made by moving the impression cylinder either toward the plate cylinder or away from it, depending on the change in thickness of the stock to be used for the job in hand. Neither the plate nor the impression cylinder is packed at Triton. If very heavy solids are to be printed, the corresponding areas under the blanket of the impression cylinder may be built up by underlaying with paper of varying thickness. Adjustments in printing pressure are made during press preparation. As trial sheets are printed, the pressure is regulated to the point where the lowest pressure will still produce an acceptable impression. In collotype, as in other printing methods, this pressure is called by the trade a "kiss impression."

Treatments of collotype plates as part of press preparation. Not the least important phase of preparation for presswork consists in local chemical treatments of the collotype plate. A collotype plate can be chemically influenced in its ink receptivity. If the pressman wants to increase ink receptivity, or to "bring up" a given area, he hardens this area; and if he wants to decrease ink receptivity, or to "take down" the plate, he uses chemical swelling agents. (Solutions containing formaldehyde, chrome alum, or tannic acid are used for hardening; solutions of sodium sulfite or of oxgall are examples of hydrophylic agents which swell plate areas.) These techniques are extremely valuable in preparing the plate for printing; they are one of the distinguishing features of collotype printing.

Fountain and plate adjustments are made until a printed sheet shows the required quality. This sheet is submitted by the pressman to the head of the preparatory department for approval. If the sheet is approved, running can begin.

Running in collotype. Collotype presses are, as already mentioned, hand-fed. The feeder, in this case a workman and not a machine, puts small lifts of paper on the feed board of the press and feeds them as described in Chapter VI, Section 4. The delivery, too, is of an antiquated construction. After the sheet is printed, it is removed by fly sticks, which are interspersed with running cords, face-down and turned over by the sticks face-up into a delivery box. When the delivered pile, which is stationary and not receding as in deliveries of contemporary designs, reaches a height of five or six inches, it is removed from the delivery and piled on nearby placed skids. As the ink deposit of collotype is rather heavy, ink sprays are used at the delivery end of the press. These give the ink a little more time to set and thereby prevent transfer of wet ink from the face of a printed sheet to the back of the following sheet. In two-side printing which is often needed for bookwork and for advertising material, it may be necessary to "slip-sheet" the job. (Slip-sheeting means that a sheet of waste paper is inserted after each printed sheet. When the ink is dry the slip sheets are removed.) The pressman must see to it that all settings remain correct during the course of the run, and that the quality is maintained at its proper level.

Humidity control and replacement of glycerin in collotype printing. These two items are most important in collotype presswork. You are already aware that collotype plates are not dampened during each printing cycle, and that collotype differs in this point from lithography where dampening precedes inking in every printing cycle. The collotype plate is rather *hygroscopic*, meaning that it can attract and absorb moisture from the air. Since collotype is a direct-printing method in which the plate is in contact with the paper during each impression, and since paper has a tendency of absorbing moisture, the plate loses moisture to the paper and also to the room air. This moisture must be replaced; otherwise printing becomes flatter, meaning that differences between tones (or, to say it more technically, differences in values of the printed ink) are reduced. Humidity control is provided at Triton Press by air conditioning. Each press is in a separate room. This arrangement makes it possible to regulate humidity for the jobs to be printed on different presses. Humidifiers spray a mist of water into the room air which is usually kept at a relative humidity of 55 to 60 per cent but may mount to 65 or 70 per cent at the end of a working day.

In addition to controlling the relative humidity of the air the pressman sponges the plate with a solution of glycerin in water whenever he considers this treatment necessary, usually every 1,000 to 2,000 impressions. (Should the press be stopped for some reason or other, the plate may or may not be sponged, depending on actual conditions.) Prior to resuming running, the plate is blotted to remove excess solution. The reason for sponging the plate is that the plate loses during running not only moisture but also glycerin, which is an important ingredient of the plate. The moisture can be replaced by controlling the moisture content of the air, but the lost glycerin must be put back into the plate by sponging.

Washup. At the end of a press run or at the end of the working day the rollers are washed by hand. If the run is continued on the next day, the ink is left in the fountain and the plate is left on the press. When the run is completed, the ink fountain is emptied and the plate is taken off the press.

Production in collotype. Production in collotype is like that in other printing methods not uniform; everything depends on the nature of the job in question. By way of example it is mentioned that at Triton Press a run of 5,000 sheets is considered average production for a full working day. Approximately one-third of this time is needed for press preparation, running itself occupies two-thirds of the day. This low production figure (low in comparison with other methods but not for collotype), is somewhat counterbalanced by the fact that the presses used by Triton, and also by some other collotype companies, can take a sheet of 44 by 64 inches.

Section 5: Presswork for Porous or Screen-Process Printing

Screen process is the youngest of our four process families, having matured in its contemporary form in the second quarter of our century. Whether this method has its roots in techniques used hundreds and possibly more than a thousand years ago in the Orient, as some writers assert, will not be discussed here. But screen process in its contemporary form was unquestionably developed in the United States whence it traveled east and west, first to Europe and later to Asia. Since all other printing processes are designated in this manual by the main characteristics of their image carriers, the term "porous" was selected as a generic one, because it characterizes the essential feature of image carriers for screen process. In this printing process the image carrier is a frame with porous stencil cloth stretched on its bottom. Stencil cloth is a version of bolting cloth which was made for the sifting of flour and milled powders before it was used for screen process. Such cloth can be woven of silk, synthetic fibers, and thin metal wire in different kinds of weaves and with different numbers of pores per linear inch. The image carrier, called "screen" by the trade, is brought about by blocking all pores in the non-printing areas and by leaving the pores in the printing areas open. Image transfer takes place by pressing a more or less fluid ink through the open pores onto the stock which is positioned underneath the image carrier. The tool with which the printing ink is forced through the open pores is a rubber squeegee. Squeegeeing does not need the high pressures under which image transfer is accomplished in other printing methods. The low printing pressure explains that large posters printed on sheets 44 by 64 inches, to mention a frequently used large size, can be produced by hand printing in screen process.

The screen-process industry utilizes a variety of equipment for presswork which is discussed under the three heads of presswork on hand presses, on flatbed presses, and on cylinder presses. These descriptions of presswork are prefaced by brief explanations of the adaptability of screen process, effects of mechanization on the industry, and of the contemporary role of hand printing in the screen-process business.

Some reasons for the adaptability of screen-process printing. Screen process owes its remarkable adaptability to several intrinsic features. One is the ability of screen process to deposit ink films varying in their thickness over a wide range; another is the fact that image transfer needs exceptionally low pressure, and a third the simplicity of this printing method. The printed ink films range from transparent to quite opaque. If it is desired to obtain additional colors by overprinting, say, of a transparent blue over a yellow, resulting in a green, this is possible in screen process as in other printing methods. But screen process can also surprint pastel colors, and even white ink, on dark colors. The wide range of printing media usable in screen process can be exemplified by high-gloss enamels, which endow the printed product with an apparently embossed quality, by pastes of various kinds needed for spot pasting, by clear overprint varnishes or lacquers for spot varnishing, and by ink formulations for the printing of electric circuits. Low printing pressure comes into play at the printing of fragile material such as glass and objects made of fragile materials. The simplicity of the process accounts for its adaptability to a variety of printing tasks including the decorating of formed objects such as glass or plastic bottles, ash trays, crockery, and many others.

The absence of mechanical power-operated presses during the formative years of screen process, and the execution of presswork by hand printing resulted in a great variety of screen-printed jobs. It was possible to switch from printing of book paper, for example, to that of dials or panels of glass without expensive preparation and tooling up. Most screen-process shops, though not all, were originally all-around service shops, supplying printing and decorating that could not be done by job-and-commercial printers in letterpress and offset lithography.

In the 1940's and 50's a visitor to a screen printing shop could see an amazing variety of work in process. Point-of-purchase displays, glass bottles, metal dials for machinery, plastics, paper streamers, fabrics, and many other diverse items were handled as a matter of routine by most screen-process printers. Each of these different jobs had some problems of its own, particularly as to the kind of ink required to satisfy process and product specifications. Product specifications in particular changed for different stocks and different end uses of the printed objects. Since screen process is mainly used for color printing, most screen-process shops do their own color matching and employ skilled craftsmen for this work. In the past, full-color printing was done but rarely in screen process. Most of the work was then in multicolor. But at present, full-color printing is regularly done by leading screen-process shops in most parts of the United States.

Some effects of mechanization in screen process. Mechanization of printing and drying equipment changed the conditions materially; mechanical printing and drying increased production substantially. In all mechanization, speed can be increased only by introducing some measure of standardization. The practically unlimited scope

of hand printing must yield to selectivity, and selectivity becomes, or has the tendency to become, specialization.

The mere presence of mechanical equipment exerts pressure in the direction of specialization. The equipment is expensive, it must be amortized, and it must be put to work. Sales efforts must be directed toward jobs that can be most efficiently produced with the new equipment. The emphasis

Courtesy M & M Displays, Philadelphia

Hand feeding a screen process cylinder press. The operator starts and stops the press by stepping on and off a switch.

on mechanical operation makes itself also felt in the selection of the work force. Craftsmen with ingenuity and versatility are a great asset in all-around service shops that handle a wide range of different jobs, but these abilities become less important and also less desirable in more specialized organizations. Now craftsmen who can operate the equipment with high efficiency are needed and preferred. The screen-process industry is like other branches of printing in a phase of transition. Specialization is neither general nor uniform throughout the whole industry and varies in its degree from shop to shop. Few screen-process printers specialize in a single kind of product or service to the exclusion of all others. Many shops equipped with mechanical presses and forced drying installations still maintain smaller or larger hand-printing departments.

The role of hand printing in contemporary screen-process printing. Hand printing is used for two different kinds of jobs: those for which mechanical equipment either does not exist or is not available when a job must be produced, and for jobs that could be printed on available mechanical equipment but are more economically produced by hand printing because the quantity in which they are to be printed is too small. Short-run printing is required in many instances. The need for short-run printing is a by-product of mass production. One of the consequences of our mass-production society is a strong desire of people and businesses to emphasize that they are different, that they are not like everybody else in every point, that the products they make or the services they render have some distinctive or unique features.

Screen process can effectively produce a variety of items in small quantities. Among them are posters, window and counter displays, presentations, greeting cards, gift wrapping, and many others. An interesting use of screen-process printing is for test runs of advertising and of package materials which will ultimately be produced in large quantities by other methods better suited to mass-production printing. There is obviously always a point where hand printing becomes less efficient than mechanical screen printing, just as there is always a point where mechanical screen printing gets less efficient than faster methods.

Planning and Preparation for Presswork by Screen Process

Planning for presswork in screen process depends in its detail on the nature of the work handled by a shop. The more diversified the work, the stronger planning relies on the judgment of those in charge, on their experience and ability to solve new problems effectively. Few screen-process businesses are large enough for formal planning departments, and most screen-process shops resemble in this point letterpress and lithographic businesses that do job-and-commercial printing.

Some considerations in planning for screen process. As already mentioned, screen process is mainly a method of picture printing and decorating, but not suitable for printing reading matter in bulk. For this reason bindery impositions are much less important in the planning of screen process jobs than in letterpress or offset lithography. But many jobs are printed work-and-turn or work-and-tumble, and back-up register is an important point in the planning of jobs which are either printed on both sides or when lightweight sheets of stock, printed on one side only, are scored and then pasted back-to-back for final use as display items.

Another point peculiar to screen process is the proper mating of printing inks and stencil materials. Inks must, of course, be selected in accordance with product specifications, or the end use of the job. Not all inks are compatible with each material usable for making screen process stencils, a point that is not overlooked in job planning. Planning comprises selecting the most efficient printing equipment, ordering of printing stock and, possibly, specially made inks in the proper quantities. Planning may also include subsidiary operations such as mounting, die-cutting, or laminating with clear plastics, to mention some.

Quality control of component elements. Quality control of component elements needed for presswork in screen process again resembles that practiced by other job-and-commercial printers. In screen process too, quality control concentrates on the control of the image carrier and the matching of colors. Some jobs may require proofing and the submission of proofs to the customer for his okay, others are produced without proofing. If a printing stock that was not handled previously by a screen-process printer is to be processed, the supplier of the stock and the supplier of printing ink are consulted to insure proper co-ordination. The constantly increasing number of different plastics, and of papers coated with new materials, require close co-operation between the printer and his suppliers. When such new materials are to be printed, it is customary to submit samples to the ink supplier, and to make trial printings before beginning the press run. Testing is done informally in most screen shops. The printer relies on the knowledge and experience of the technical staff employed by the supplier of his inks for more formal testing. The printer may also submit samples of trial printing to his customers for approval.

Relations between screens and presses in screen process. In most printing processes and methods the image carrier is prepared independently of the printing equipment to which it is attached for presswork. Not so in screen process. The screen has three functions which are in other processes and methods discharged by separate and different component parts. The three functions of the screen are: (1) to serve as the carrier for the stencil, (2) to act as an ink reservoir for the ink needed in printing, and (3) to be a part of the printing unit of the press. All printing methods with the exception of rotogravure use independent image carriers which are either positioned on a press bed (in platen and flatbed-cylinder presses) or attached to a plate cylinder. Rotogravure cylinders and screens for screen process are the only two exceptions: both are parts of the press in addition to being image carriers. But the function of the screen to serve, in addition, as an ink reservoir is unique. This triple function of screens must be kept in mind when they are prepared.

Preparing a screen-process screen consists in blocking its pores in the non-printing areas and leaving them open in the printing areas. Several methods of making screen-process screens are discussed in Chapter V, Section 6. At this point we are not interested in the detail whereby various kinds of stencils for screen process are made but solely in the transfer of stencils to the screen which thereby becomes the printing-image carrier. Since different transfer techniques are used for hand printing and for mechanical printing, the subject is discussed under the heads "Presswork on Hand Presses" and "Presswork on Flatbed and on Cylinder Presses."

Screen-Process Printing with Hand Presses

The first point to be explained is the technique whereby stencils are transferred to the screen for hand printing.

Stencil transfer for hand printing. The basis for stencil transfer to the screen is a layout, lineup sheet, or, as it is often called in screen printing shops, a set-up sheet. The *set-up sheet* has the dimensions of the stock to be printed and is best made on a sheet of the actual stock. On the set-up sheet, crosses in several places indicate the precise position of stencils. Corresponding crosses are put on knife-cut stencils during cutting, or on the positives with which photomechanically made stencils are exposed. A frequently met technique is the taping of finished artwork to a sheet of stock of running (or untrimmed) size in the position in which the printed images will finally appear on the stock. Since customers' artwork must not be damaged, it is often protected with a sheet of clear plastic. Register marks, such as crosses, are either made directly on this protective sheet of

plastic or on pressure sensitive tape. These register marks serve as guides for stencil transfer to the screen as well as for checking internal register, or fit, of images.

Positioning of the set-up sheet for hand printing. The preparation department where the stencils are made usually also provides the set-up sheet. In larger shops, stencil transfer to the screen is the duty of *set-up men*, as craftsmen specializing in this work are often called. In smaller shops stencil transfer is done either by a craftsman who has the skill of preparing stencils or by an experienced printer. Be this as it may, the actual procedure of stencil transfer remains the same. The set-up sheet, with the first stencil taped to it in correct position, is turned over to the set-up man. He selects a screen of fitting size and inspects the stencil cloth, which must be unobstructed in the image areas. After he has satisfied himself on the suitability of the selected screen, the set-up man proceeds with making the set-up by hinging the screen to a baseboard of corresponding dimensions. This baseboard may or may not serve for the actual running of the job. A bed for set-up can be as simple as a piece of heavy plywood equipped with two halves of common door hinges. The other two halves are screwed to that side of the screen frame which will be attached to the baseboard for a particular run. Both halves of the hinges are connected by inserting a metal pin. Set-ups can also be made with special clamping mechanisms that save time in changeovers, and with vacuum bases.

After the screen is fastened to the bed in such a way that it will not budge during stencil transfer, the screen is raised, the set-up man maneuvers the set-up sheet until he finds a place on the screen that is perfectly clean and without defects—continued use of screens results inevitably in some defective areas—and that provides sufficient space for the fountain areas. When a satisfactory space is located, the screen is lifted without disturbing the position of the set-up sheet and suspended or supported at a distance above the bed, giving the set-up man enough room for the job in hand. Before he sets guides, he tapes or tacks the set-up sheet to the base because both set-up sheet and screen must not change position from now on. After screen and set-up sheet are securely positioned, guides can be set and the stencil can be transferred to the screen.

Setting of guides and stencil transfer in hand printing. Three guides are commonly used for sheet-fed screen-process printing as in other kinds of sheet-fed printing. Two of these guides can be called front guides since they are near the front edge of the baseboard, the third is a side guide. On wooden bases, the guides—which are small strips of cardboard, or of plastics, or of printers' leads—are nailed to the base with thin and relatively long nails. On vacuum beds, guides cannot be nailed but must be cemented to the surface of the bed which consists usually of Formica. After the guides are set the stencil can be transferred to the screen. (Stencil transfer, or adhering, is described in Chapter V, Section 6.) The next step is the sealing of all non-printing areas on the screen outside the adhered stencil. Since sealing is done with a fast-drying lacquer, this step is known as *lacquering a screen*. The lacquer is applied by scraping with a piece of cardboard. Register marks close to areas that need lacquering are first protected with pressure-sensitive tape.

Printing of register sheets. After the screen is ready, it may either be proofed or be used for running without proofing. In both cases, a certain number of sheets is printed with register marks. These are often called "register sheets," or if the stock is cardboard, "cross cards." *Register sheets* are kept separate and used for the setting up of successive colors and also for testing the register of successive color images. After a sufficient number of register sheets is run, register marks not placed in the waste are prevented from printing by blocking them either with pressure-sensitive tape or by lacquering. As in all other branches of the graphic arts industry, proofs must be submitted to those in charge and okayed by them before running can begin.

Hand presses for screen process are described in Chapter VI; at this point it is sufficient to remark that they are set-ups provided with simple mechanical devices for continuous operation. Our next subject is the printing cycle of such presses.

The printing cycle of hand presses for screen process. The actual printing cycle begins when the *squeegee man* feeds the stock to the guides on the base. Then he presses the screen down with his left hand and keeps it down during the impression which is made by pushing the squeegee across the screen with his right hand. After he completes pushing, he turns back to the stock table for feeding; the screen is lifted out of contact by contraction of the springs, and the *helper*, or *racker*, removes the printed sheet to the drying equipment. Removal of the printed sheet and

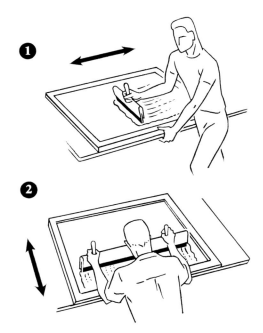

Single-handle squeegees (1) are used for pushing sideways; double-handle squeegees (2) or squeegees with a molding suitable for gripping are used for pushing front to back. Most flatbed presses use the latter kind of squeegee action.

feeding of the next sheet are timed to permit an uninterrupted flow of work. After the next sheet is in guides, the squeegee man depresses the screen again, but this time with his right hand. The left becomes now the hand that pushes the squeegee. Right and left alternate in pushing the squeegee and in holding the screen down. (This is but one technique of hand printing. In another, the squeegee is pulled from back to front and not pushed from side to side.) Three-men teams are at present rarely needed; the introduction of one-man squeegees and of large flatbed presses permits much more economical handling of large sheets.

In a not so distant past, each screen-printed sheet required air drying in racks for many hours, usually overnight. At present conditions are considerably improved by the development of fast-drying inks and by the introduction of modern drying equipment. Many cylinder-press installations comprise not only the press itself but also drying equipment designed to deliver dry sheets at press speed. Forced drying is also widely used for hand printing and for printing on flatbed presses. Each screen-process shop or plant selects the kind of printing and drying equipment that is most suitable for its kind of work. Two different driers are described later in this section. (Drying methods and equipment for all printing processes are the subject matter of Chapter VI, Section 7.)

Presswork on Flatbed and Cylinder Presses for Screen Process

The present unit was developed at the plant of M & M Displays, Philadelphia. The flatbed press and the cylinder press as well as the General tower drier connected to it, described in the following, are standard equipment, but the conveyor-belt drier was especially designed and built for M & M Displays. As in all other units based on field work it is added that the mentioning of proprietary equipment does not imply that other equipment for the same or similar purposes is not available.

As in the description of presswork on hand presses we begin with stencil transfer to the screen.

Stencil transfer for mechanical printing. The procedures for stencil transfer to the screen are essentially the same in mechanical and in hand printing. But in mechanical printing—with cylinder presses in particular—set-up must be rather precisely positioned with less latitude than in hand printing. Set-ups for printing on cylinder presses are usually made on "master bases" equipped for clamping the screen during adhering and ruled to indicate the correct feeding position of the sheet. The sheet must be placed within the narrow adjustment range of press grippers and guides.

Courtesy M & M Displays, Philadelphia

A screen-process craftsman making a new setup for a cylinder press. He matches the center mark of the setup with the center mark on the setup table.

Courtesy M & M Displays, Philadelphia

A sheet, screen printed on the adjacent flatbed press, is transferred to the infeed of a large conveyor belt drier.

Presswork on flatbed presses. Flatbed presses have, as explained in Chapter VI, Section 2, a flat surface, corresponding to the platen on platen presses, for positioning of the stock. The flatbed press used by M & M Displays can take a sheet of 50 by 80 inches and has a maximum rated speed of 500 impressions per hour; its motive power is compressed air. Printing is controlled in all its phases by the operator who must initiate each motion by a toggle switch. The first step is the lifting of the screen, controlled by an electric switch. Next the operator can either ink the screen or flood it with ink, depending on the switch he uses; third he feeds the sheet to guides; after the sheet is fed on the press bed the screen is brought down, as the fourth operation; fifth, the squeegee makes the impression by printing from the back to the front of the press. Then the screen is lifted, and the sheet is removed onto the adjacent conveyor belt of the drier. There are other flatbed presses on the market which can be "cycled" or continuously operated. When a press is *cycled* it makes one complete printing cycle every time the operator pushes the cycling button. A continuously operating press makes cycle after cycle without need for initiating each cycle. The plant where the described flatbed press is in operation prefers to control each step of the printing cycle separately; this method is best suited for producing the kind of work that is printed on a flatbed press at M & M Displays. Some flatbed presses come with a take-off mechanism that removes the printed sheet from the press bed to an adjacent conveyor mechanism as part of the printing cycle. Different manufacturers of flatbed presses offer independent take-offs which can be installed on their presses.

Description of a custom-made conveyor drier. The drier especially designed and built for M & M Displays is 40 feet long and has an inside working width of 80 inches. Oil burners are used for heating of air, and blowers apply the hot air to the printed surface of the job. The first half of the drier heats the sheet, the second half is used for cooling it to room temperature. The conveyor is made of wire and extends on both ends beyond the drier. At the delivery end the extension is much shorter than at the infeed; there the conveyor extends far enough to permit the laying on of the output of several presses for common drying. The dried sheets are removed by an operator and piled in stacks of varying height, depending on the nature of the job. The speed of the belt as well as the temperature of the air can be regulated to suit different jobs.

Description of presswork on a screen-process cylinder press. The M & M cylinder press installation consists of a General screen-process press and a General Tower Drier which is connected to the delivery of the General press. This press takes a maximum sheet of 35 by 45 inches and has a maximum rated speed of 1,600 im-

pressions per hour. At M & M the average running speed is approximately 75 per cent of the maximum rated speed. Transfer of stencils to the screen is done on a set-up table equipped with a master bar for positioning the screen. On this table scribed lines indicate the center of the screen, the gripper edge of the impression cylinder, and the position of the side guide. The stencil must be transferred to the screen within the adjustment range of guide and grippers. First the set-up sheet is lined up at its gripper edge, then with the side guide. The set-up sheet has crosses, guide lines, or guide arrows. The guide marks are incorporated in the stencil for makeready and must be matched by successive colors. After makeready is completed, the guide marks are

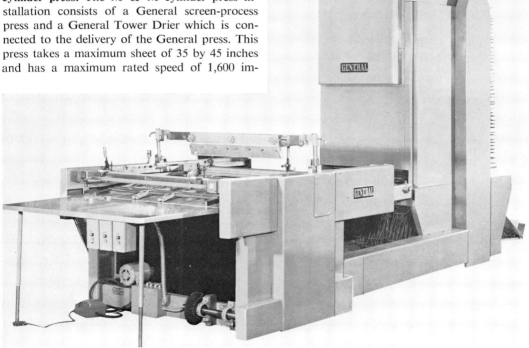

A General cylinder press for screen process, connected to a General tower drier. This installation is described in the text though with the difference that the drier shown in this photo is not equipped with tapes for delivery of the dried sheets whereas the described drier is.

blocked in the screen if they are within the final size of the printed product; if they are in the waste, they are left to print throughout the run.

Getting close register on General presses is less difficult than in hand printing with screens tacked to wooden frames. The General Press is equipped with the "Serachase," a patented screen frame that makes it possible to obtain register by locally adjusting the screen in its tautness or by making adjustments of larger screen areas. For this purpose the screen frame is provided with ten bolts on each of its four sides.

The printing cycle of a cylinder press. Cylinder presses can be either fed by hand or by sheet feeders. At M & M Displays the press is hand-fed since it is used for a wide variety of stocks. The sheet is held by the suction segment of the impression cylinder during the impression. The impression is made when the screen moves toward the feeding end of the press. The squeegee, which is adjustable in its pressure is, as mentioned, stationary. As in other presses having one curved member of the printing unit, the impression is made in a constantly shifting thin strip across the impression cylinder. At the end of the printing stroke, the stock is delivered and the screen returns with a reciprocating motion to the rear end of the press, ready for the next cycle.

The General Tower Drier. The printed sheet is automatically placed on one of the horizontal shelves, or wickets, of the General Tower Drier. This drier is approximately 12 feet high and has two stacks of shelves in sequence. After a shelf is loaded at the delivery of the press, it moves into a hot air zone. From the hot air zone, which holds 50 shelves, it moves into the cooling zone, which also holds 50 shelves. At the end of the cooling zone the printed stock is delivered on tapes. The space between the delivery and the infeed holds 20 shelves which return, of course, empty. The speed of the drier is automatically regulated to match the running speed of the press.

Chapter VIII

Paper and Other Printing Stocks

Functionally, paper and other printing stocks are the materials onto which the ink image is transferred during presswork and on which this ink image becomes the final printed image. Together with printing inks, papers and other stocks are the most important materials consumed in printing; but papers and other stocks exceed printing inks by far in weight and value, though probably not in variety. The most generally used and the most highly diversified printing stock is paper including paper board. The classic product of printing, the book, is printed on paper, and so are newspapers, magazines, and most products of job-and-commercial printing. In package printing, paper and paper boards are most widely used materials though plastic films and aluminum foils have found growing favor for many purposes.

Some knowledge of printing stocks is a necessity for everybody interested in some aspect of printing. This is so because printing stocks influence printed products in at least four respects: (1) cost, (2) printability, (3) end-use properties, and (4) appearance. Printing stocks are the biggest single cost item in all mass production printing, so the crucial role of cost and price needs no further explanation. Printability is of interest primarily to the printer but not much less to buyers of printed material. Next come end-use properties of printed products. Not all stocks are equally suitable for all kinds of printed products, a point of particular importance in package printing. And as there is a pronounced relation between the appearance of printed images and the nature of the stocks on which they are printed, appearance must also be considered when printing stocks are chosen.

The sum total of these four points can be expressed in one word: *compatibility*. Cost, end-use properties, and appearance must all be compatible with one another as well as with the printing method selected, which implies compatibility of image carrier, printing press, printing ink, and printing stock. Compatibility requirements are not terminated with presswork; printing stocks must also be compatible with the equipment on which the printed sheet or web must be processed for its end use. End use can be one of two kinds: by people and by machines. Newspapers, books, and persuasion printing have people as end users. Package printing and printing for electronic data processing are examples of end use by machines. Machine end use is much more exacting than end use by people. Each machine has its own requirements, and tolerances are often extremely critical.

Paper and paper boards are the most widely used printed stocks; they will therefore have the lion's share of this chapter. Plastic films, aluminum foils, and some other stocks are less generally used and, consequently, less extensively discussed. Paper and paper boards are the products of complex manufacturing processes which all have a bearing on cost, end-use properties, and appearance characteristics of the final paper. A brief characterization of the main stages of paper production will make it easier for you to find your bearings.

The first stage of papermaking is the making of pulp from wood or non-woody plants. The next stage is stock preparation; in this stage the pulp is mechanically treated and compounded with other ingredients as required for a specific kind of paper. The prepared stock is made into paper or paper board on a paper machine. The paper machine has a "wet end" and a "dry end." On the wet end the stock is evenly spread to form the paper, and much of the excess water is removed; on the dry end the remaining excess moisture is evaporated. If the surface of the paper is to be smoothed and coated, these and other operations can also be performed on the dry end. Many papers emerge in their final form from the paper machine, though some papers need coating and other treatments at a later stage, or off-machine.

Papermaking has a long history dating back to the invention of paper by the Chinese in the second century; slowly traveling westward, paper reached Europe in the thirteenth century and North America in the seventeenth. The European history of paper is approximately 150 years older than that of printing with movable types. During most of its history paper was made by hand. The two basic paper machines (the fourdrinier and the cylinder machine), which are still in use, were invented at the end of the eighteenth and the beginning of the nineteenth century. Paper machines were greatly improved and increasingly put into production in the first half of the nineteenth century; the main theme of paper technology in the second half of the same century was the introduction of pulps made from wood, and also from non-woody plants, decreasing the relative importance of rags. Groundwood and chemical pulps became widely used, and the transition from papermaking as a craft to an industry was spearheaded by the development of paper chemistry. During our own century, papermaking became a large scale, scientifically operated industry.

One aspect of this development is particularly worth noting. It is the transition from discontinuous to continuous manufacturing. Until the invention of the fourdrinier machine all paper was made in batches, a discontinuous manufacturing method. The fourdrinier introduced continuous manufacturing, but only in the stage of papermaking itself; pulpmaking and stock preparation remained on the level of batchwise production, even though the batches became increasingly larger and manufacturing more scientific. (Batchwise manufacturing has certain advantages and may remain in use for the making of certain kinds of paper.) Generally speaking, the trend is toward continuous manufacturing, away from batchwise production, especially since continuous digesters for pulpmaking have come into use.

Contemporary paper terminology and trade customs are a mixture of precise modern and less precise, or less rational, traditional terms and modes of doing business, as you will see in the following sections. This tracing of the main lines along which paper technology developed should prepare you for some of the rather puzzling words and things that you will soon encounter. It is interesting that none of our paper terms are derived from the Chinese. The word paper comes from the Latin *papyrus* (the latinized version of a Greek word); it meant to the Romans both a common reed, chiefly found in Egypt, and the writing material made of it. The word *ream* reminds us that the West received its knowledge of paper indirectly from the Arabs, and not directly from the Chinese. Two other writing materials used before paper are still alive in our vocabulary: parchment and vellum. Both are prepared skins of animals; *parchment* is usually sheepskin, and *vellum* that of calves. In our time neither of them is extensively used; contemporary parchment paper, called vegetable parchment, looks like parchment, and vellum is a name applied to a certain paper finish. These examples will suffice; you will meet others as the subject is unfolded.

This chapter consists of six sections: Section 1 discusses pulpmaking and bleaching; Section 2, stock preparation and furnishing; Section 3, the making of uncoated and coated papers; Section 4 is an introduction to paper properties and paper terminology; Section 5, a characterization of papers and other printing stock; Section 6, finally, deals with printability and paper testing.

Section 1: Pulping and Bleaching

Pulping has the purpose of providing fibers from woody and non-woody plants for papermaking; bleaching has the purpose of improving the whiteness of pulps and of removing substances detrimental to the permanence of papers and paper boards. As different as papers may be in their composition, they all have nevertheless one ingredient in common: fibers. Without fibers there can be no paper. Even though fibers do not account all by themselves for the strength and quality of papers they have a great influence in these and many other respects.

Wood Pulping, and Papermaking on the Fourdrinier Papermachine

1 The forests of the United States and Canada provide most of the wood for American paper.

2 Logs of pulpwood are stored, then put through barkers where their bark is removed.

3 The logs pass through chippers and after screening into a digester for chemical pulping.

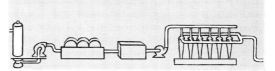

4 The wood pulp is blown into a blow tank; then it is washed, screened and cleaned.

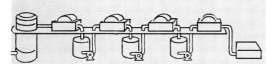

5 The cleaned pulp is bleached to improve its brightness, and screened.

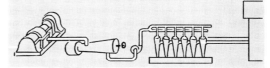

6 The pulp is now mixed with other ingredients, beaten in refiners and jordans, and cleaned.

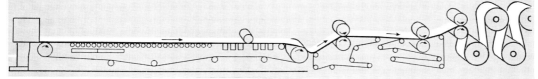

7 The "wet end" of a fourdrinier paper machine. The highly diluted stock is spread on an endless wire screen where the paper is formed. Some water is drained during this stage.

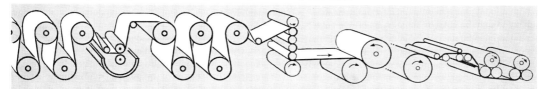

8 The "dry end" of the fourdrinier. Here the excess moisture is evaporated, the paper is sized and possibly coated. The completed paper can be smoothed on a calender stack and is wound into a master roll of machine width. This master roll is slit, rewound, and sheeted as required.

This is a broad outline of how paper is made on the fourdrinier machine. Other paper fibers, various pulping processes, papermaking on the cylinder machine, and several methods of pigment coating are explained and illustrated in the text.

Until a relatively recent time fibers for paper-making were only derived from four different kinds of sources: (1) wood, (2) non-woody plants, (3) used papers and paper boards, and (4) rags. Since the end of World War II the range of fibers available for papermaking has been considerably expanded by synthetic fibers of a great variety as well as by fibers made of glass, ceramics, and even metals. Among the achievements due to use of synthetic fibers are mentioned substantial improvements in foldability, tensile strength, tear resistance, wet strength, and life expectancy of papers; and even papers being completely impervious to acids and alkalis.[1] These new kinds of fibers are used primarily in industrial papers which are developed to cope with problems resulting from our rapidly growing technology, and also to take advantage of completely new possibilities offered by it. Since the first four kinds of sources of fibers are the only practical ones for the making of papers for writing, printing, and packaging, these are the subject of the following discussion.

Wood and non-woody fiber sources. Wood is the most important raw material for paper fibers. Wood is divided into softwood and hardwood. Softwood is also called "coniferous" wood because it has its origin in the cone-bearing trees such as spruce, pine, cedar, cypress, hemlock, and fir. Hardwood is also called "deciduous" wood because it has its origin in the trees which shed their leaves in the fall season, such as chestnut, maple, birch, beach, gum, water oak, and poplar. Many non-woody plants were and still are used for papermaking. Among them are cereal straws, hemp, jute, flax, cotton, bagasse (the fibers of sugar cane after extraction of sugar liquor), cornstalks, bamboo, and esparto or alfalfa grass.

Each of these kinds of vegetation has a different percentage of cellulose and fibers of different dimensions. Cotton consists of 98 per cent cellulose and ranks highest in this respect; woods, cornstalks, and wheat straw have between 41 and 44 per cent, jute has 58, and hemp 65 per cent cellulose.[2] Not only do various woods and plants differ in their cellulose content, they also differ in the size of their fibers. Of woods, the evergreens have relatively long fibers whereas the broadleaf trees have short fibers. Cotton and flax have very long and thin fibers, esparto, which is used in England and France, has short and relatively thin fibers. During pulping and stock preparation these fibers undergo certain changes. Combination of

different fibers is one way, but only one of many, by which paper properties can be influenced.

Used papers and rags. These two groups differ essentially from the preceding two. The former are part of nature before they enter into the process of pulping, the latter are either reclaimed papers or wearing apparel which may contain a number of different materials, not only linen but also cotton, wool, and artificial fibers. Being secondary or used fibers does not impair their suitability for papermaking. Some of the best papers are made from such fibers.

Wood Pulping Processes

Historically linen and cotton rags were the only source of fibers for Western papermaking. All European and North American paper was practically rag paper up to the nineteenth century, and rag paper still enjoys its traditional high prestige. But the need for paper increased much faster than the supply of rags, and additional materials were needed to satisfy the ever growing appetite of a civilization based on the printed word and picture. This demand could only be met when processes for converting wood into paper became practical. Even though other plants are still used for papermaking, the bulk of our printing and package papers is derived from wood. The growth of the paper industry was predicated upon the development of a pulping technology that made it possible to utilize all kinds of wood for pulping and to do so economically and efficiently.

Composition of wood. Even though the composition of wood varies considerably, "wood contains five principal materials: (1) cellulose, (2) hemicellulose, (3) lignin, (4) mineral matter, and (5) extractives."[3] Cellulose is the structural element of wood and other plant fibers; it is white, insoluble in most solvents, and resists the action of most chemicals except strong acids. Hemicelluloses are like cellulose carbohydrates but they are less polymerized than cellulose. They are soluble in diluted alkali, in which cellulose is insoluble, and they are chemically changed by diluted acids which, too, do not affect cellulose. Cellulose and hemicellulose together constitute the holocellulose of wood. "Lignin is not a single chemical but is a group of related materials, each of which has a very complex polymerized structure. Most lignins have a light yellow color as they occur in nature, but they quickly change to highly colored bodies when exposed to heat or chemical reaction. Lignin is insoluble in water and most common

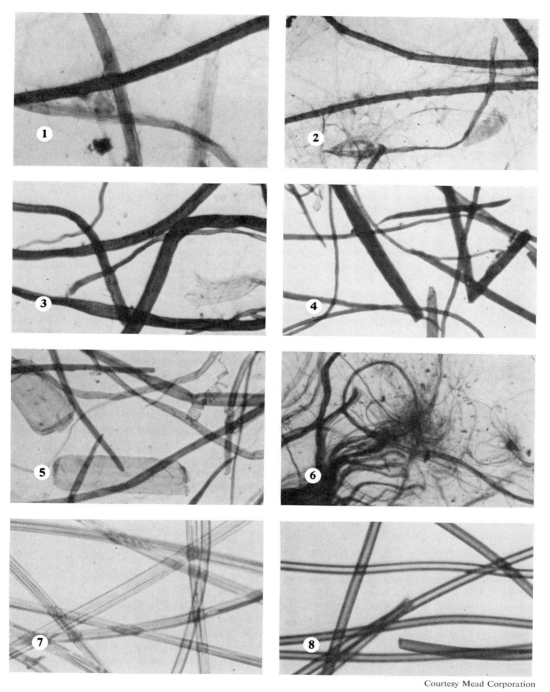

Eight microphotographs of non-woody fibers used in paper making. (1) is linen,
(2) is flax, (3) is cotton linters, (4) is bleached esparto, (5) is straw, (6) is asbestos,
(7) is rayon, and (8) is nylon.
Magnification of all is 150 times.

solvents but can be made soluble by chemical action."[4] Chemical pulping processes make lignin soluble and therewith removable. Unfortunately it is not possible to remove all lignin chemically during pulping, and as the remaining lignin gives the pulp a yellowish or brownish color, bleaching is needed for pulp to be used in white papers.

The remaining two main components of wood, mineral matter and extractives, pose no problem in pulping. The minerals are insignificant in quantity and the extractives comprise oils, waxes, resins, and other chemicals which are valuable by-products in some pulping processes. The following figures are mentioned to give you an idea of the relative proportions in which the five main components may be present in woods. Cellulose has the biggest share varying between 55 and 64 per cent; lignin comes next with 17 to 32 per cent; hemicelluloses range between 8 and 25 per cent; extractives between 3 and 8 per cent and mineral matter is 0.1 to 1.0 per cent of wood.[5]

The three principal kinds of pulping processes. It is customary to divide wood pulping processes into three major kinds: (1) mechanical pulping, (2) chemical pulping, and (3) combinations between mechanical and chemical pulping, called *semi*chemical and *chemi*mechanical. (The difference between these two methods is described at their discussion.) These terms can become confusing, to outsiders in particular. Like the graphic arts industry, and probably all modern industries, the pulp and paper industry suffers from unsystematic terminology. "Everyone agrees that there is need for a revised, standardized nomenclature, but no generally acceptable system has come forth."[6] It is worth noting that the term pulping, too, is not always used with the same meaning. As written at the beginning of this section, pulping has the purpose of providing fibers for paper-making from woody and non-woody plants. (It should be added that pulping also provides the raw material for a group of plastics known as cellulosics, cellulose acetate, for example; and also for rayon and cellophane.) This usage follows the definition of the official *Paper Dictionary.* Another authority writes: "Pulping may be defined as the process of re-suspending dried pulp or broke in water."[7] In the second definition pulping is used in a much more limited sense than in the first.

Mechanical Wood Pulping

Mechanical wood pulp is also known as ground-wood because this pulp is made by grinding peeled wood. Mechanical wood pulp is also known as ground-wood because this pulp is made by grinding peeled

and cleaned pulpwood logs with a grindstone. "Water is applied to the stone to maintain the proper temperature, and the pulp then goes from the grinder pit to the sliver or bull screens where pieces of wood and slivers are removed."[8] The

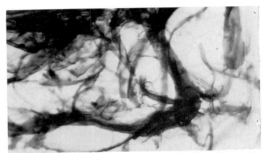

A microphotograph of groundwood, or mechanical pulp, magnification 160 times.

pulp is further diluted and screened again before it is prepared for use on the paper machine. Grinding wood with stones is not the only method whereby mechanical pulp is made. Another method for producing groundwood pulp consists in passing chips of the desired species of wood through refiners in either a single stage or in a double stage operation.

Continuous grinders and composition stones. Originally grinders were relatively simple machines. The great expansion of the paper industry stimulated the development of equipment of a higher technological level. Batchwise grinding was superseded by various methods of continuous grinding, and as the size of stones increased, natural grinder stones began to pose problems that were solved by changing the design of grinders and by replacing natural stones with man-made composition stones. Contemporary grinder stones are made in segments of varying hardness and grits; these segments are usually assembled on a concrete rather than steel core. "The development of artificial pulpstone has permitted closer control of pulp quality because of the highly uniform character of the stone. Moreover, the pulpstone cost per ton of pulp is much lower because artificial stones last two to three years whereas sandstones lasted only a few months."[9]

Power consumption in grinding of wood. The energy requirements for making groundwood depend on a number of factors, but the power needed for the making of one ton of groundwood is greater than that for any other method of pulping. According to Casey it takes 32,000 kw days to produce 500 tons of groundwood. "Since cheap power is essential to economical operation of a groundwood mill, much of the groundwood production is in Canada where there is abundant hydroelectric power."[10]

The main reasons for using groundwood pulp. Groundwood pulps are used in printing papers for several reasons. First comes economy. The groundwood process yields an extremely high fiber content varying between 90 and 95 per cent, more than twice as much as in chemical pulping. Another reason for the use of groundwood in newsprint and newsprint-like papers is that papers containing a high proportion of groundwood are highly absorbent. In newspaper relief printing, drying takes place by absorption only; in other high-speed printing methods using newsprint-like papers, fast absorption of the ink is also most desirable. Web-offset printing, for example, can be done on such papers without forced drying whereas less absorbent papers must be heat dried. But groundwood pulps are not limited to newsprint and newsprint-like papers. They are also used in papers for magazine printing and in other printing papers because they contribute opacity, compressibility, and bulk which are needed in printing papers.

Impermanence of groundwood. The high yield of mechanical pulping is due to the fact that groundwood pulps contain not only cellulose but also other components of wood, lignin in particular. Even though hardwoods, poplar in particular, are used for mechanical pulping, groundwood is usually made of softwoods which contain a higher percentage of lignin than hardwoods. And since the lignin is not removed in groundwood pulps, these have a rather high lignin content. Lignin is subject to oxidation, and after some time exposure to air and light becomes highly detrimental to papers made with high groundwood content. When groundwood was new, in the middle of the nineteenth century, the pernicious influence of lignin was not understood. The newspapers and books printed on such papers became brown and so brittle that the pages crumble when they are turned. The preservation of such printed material can be a serious problem for reference libraries. Groundwood pulps can be bleached, and for certain purposes they are mechanically treated in refiners. Under normal conditions groundwood

pulps are not the only pulp used in papers. Even newsprint contains chemical pulp.

Uses of groundwood pulps. Even though groundwood alone is rarely used in printing papers, combinations of groundwood and chemical pulps are useful in the compounding of many printing papers and paper boards, particularly when price is decisive and permanence is not a major factor. This situation exists in all mass-production printing that serves the needs of the day, in package printing not less than in that of newspapers. (Traditionally newspapers are printed by relief printing; the paper for this purpose is called "newsprint." Paper for rotogravure supplements is a newsprint-like paper; rotogravure paper differs from that for web-offset printed newspapers which is another variety of newsprint-like paper.) Groundwood is also present in many coated and uncoated papers for magazines and for impermanent, mainly paperbound, books; it is an important component of many sanitary papers.

Chemical Pulping Processes

The pulp and paper industry has a number of chemical pulping methods at its command. Each of these methods was developed because existing pulping methods were lacking in some way or other. Even though different pulping processes differ in their economics and resulting pulps, all chemical pulping processes of wood have nevertheless one common denominator: they remove more or less of the lignin contained in pulpwood, and chemical pulping has even been called delignification, which emphasizes the key function of all chemical pulping methods. The absence of lignin—together with other factors, to be sure—accounts for the greater permanence of chemical pulps; the process of removing lignin accounts for the higher cost of delignified pulps in comparison with groundwood where the lignin remains in the pulp.

Economical differences between chemical and mechanical pulping. The higher manufacturing cost of chemical pulps can be attributed to several reasons: the equipment and facilities for chemical pulping are more expensive than those needed for mechanical pulping; during chemical pulping certain chemicals are consumed whereas no chemicals are needed for mechanical pulping; and the yield of chemical pulping is considerably less than that of mechanical pulping, meaning that much more wood, roughly speaking about twice as much, is consumed in chemical pulping to obtain

Piles of wood chips. For chemical pulping, the logs of wood are first debarked and then chipped. The screened chips are blown into piles for storage.

the same amount of pulp as in mechanical pulping. On the other side of the ledger valuable by-products reduce the total cost of chemical pulping.

Batchwise and continuous pulping. Originally all chemical pulping was done in batches; more recently continuous pulping has been introduced. Different chemical pulping processes vary in their equipment. Cooking, the most characteristic stage of chemical pulping, is done in digesters, huge cylindrical vessels with a conical end, capable of producing in a single batch "12 to 35 tons of

The control board of a continuous flow Kamyr digester This digester cooks softwood pulp at temperatures up to 350°F.

pulp. A digester is usually made of mild steel and lined with a corrosion-resistant ceramic tile, but in some cases it may be constructed with a lining of an appropriate stainless steel."[11] The emptying of digesters is called "blowing." Washing and screening of the cooked pulp follows blowing. Other stages of chemical pulping are concerned with the recovery of chemicals, the disposal of waste liquor, the making of by-products either during cooking or by chemical treatments of the waste liquor, depending on a specific process.

Alkaline and acid pulping. Chemical pulping is divided into the two main groups of alkaline and of acid pulping. The earliest pulping process, called the soda process, is an alkaline process. It is of little importance in contemporary pulping and will therefore be only briefly characterized. The sulfate process, also an alkaline process, and the sulfite process, an acid process, are of great importance. These processes are therefore described in some detail.

At this point readers who are not chemists may need to be alerted because it is very easy to confuse the terms sulf*ate* and sulf*ite*, particularly when merely scanning a page. As most non-chemists have probably forgotten their inorganic chemistry, they may find it helpful to be reminded that chemicals whose name begins with *sulf* contain the element sulfur; sulf*ates* are salts of sulf*uric* acid, sulf*ites* are salts of sulf*urous* acid, and sulf*ides* are compounds of sulfur itself.

The soda process. The soda process derives its name from the caustic soda which is its delignifying agent. In this process the chipped wood is boiled with soda under pressure. The resulting pulp is of a brownish shade; even though soda pulp was originally not as well bleachable as sulfite pulp, modern bleaching methods have overcome this limitation. The soda process was the first that made it possible to make chemical pulp from hardwoods but it has lower yields than the sulfate process; hardwood soda pulp is of low strength, and the recovery of caustic soda is costly. For these and other reasons the soda process is losing ground fast to the sulfate process. After bleaching soda pulp is used in a variety of papers including bristols, book papers, blotting papers, cover papers, and writing papers.

The sulfate process. The sulfate process is the dominant pulping process in the United States and Canada, if not in Europe. The cooking liquor consists of two main ingredients: caustic soda and sodium sulfide. The presence of the latter distin-

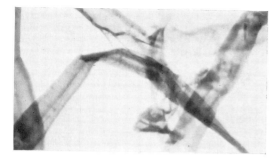

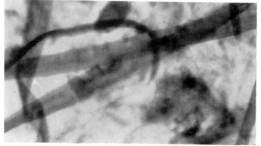

Courtesy Kimberly-Clark Corporation

Two microphotographs of softwood Kraft, or sulfate, pulp. The first picture shows the pulp before refining, the second shows the refined pulp. Magnification 160 times.

guishes the cooking liquor of the sulfate process from that of the soda process and accounts for the greater speed of cooking as well as for the greater strength of sulfate pulps.

The pulpwood logs are first cleaned of their bark and then reduced to chips. These and the cooking liquor are fed into the top of digesters under carefully controlled conditions for cooking under pressure. Cooking takes usually about two to four hours at 100 to 110 p.s.i. pressure. During cooking, turpentine and other volati'es are distilled. In the opinion of some, these are valuable by-products of pulping, others hold that their recovery is seldom economical. After completion of cooking the digester is emptied by blowing pulp and liquor with steam into the blow tank. Pulp and liquor are diluted, and the liquor is washed out of the pulp in the "brown-stock washers." The pulp can be bleached and the liquor is partly re-used and partly sent to a recovery unit for reclaiming of chemicals.[12]

The name sulfate process is misleading, as pointed out by several writers. The sulfur compound active in the cook is not sodium sulfate but sodium sulfide. For this reason Dr. Sutermeister proposed the more exact name sulfide process, but

he also expressed doubt that this suggestion would be accepted. He was right in both respects; it is extremely difficult to change technical terms that have become generally accepted.[13]

Advantages and disadvantages of the sulfate process. The main reason for the popularity of the sulfate process in the United States is its wide scope. The sulfate process can use a wide range of woods including hardwoods, and sulfate pulp can be used for a variety of products. One authority lists the following seven advantages of the sulfate process: "(1) maximum flexibility with regard to species, (2) cooking times are short, (3) the pulp can be bleached to high brightness levels (although at greater cost than with sulfite pulps), (4) no pitch problem, (5) high pulp strength, (6) valuable products are produced in the form of tall oil and turpentine, and (7) the recovery of the spent liquor is relatively easy."[14]

The sulfate process has, like everything else, also certain disadvantages, particularly that the decomposition of the black liquor is accompanied by unpleasant odors. Other disadvantages are the high cost of plant and the poor color of unbleached sulfate pulp.

Uses of sulfate pulps. Unbleached sulfate pulps are brown and are used for wrapping and bag papers. Container board is usually made of unbleached sulfate pulp. Lighter sulfate pulps are found in envelope papers, tag stock, and in toweling. A grade known as semi-bleached sulfate is still lighter and has several uses, mainly in newsprint and as a component of boards for the packaging of foods, called food board. Bleached sulfate pulp can be part of bristols, of papers for gummed tapes, and of sanitary tissue papers. The usability of bleached sulfate pulp is almost unlimited: it is present in many kinds of quality papers, from bonds to waxing papers, and in many grades of coated and uncoated printing papers. As sulfate pulp can be made in a wide range of fiber lengths long fibered and short fibered sulfate pulps can be combined depending on the purpose of specific papers.

The word Kraft is used interchangeably with unbleached sulfate pulp in the United States. One can also hear people saying that this word designates the inventor of the process, which is a mistake. The word Kraft is the German word for strength, the outstanding feature of sulfate papers. (Kraft, like all German nouns, is capitalized.) Carl F. Dahl received a German patent for sulfate pulping in 1884.

The sulfite pulping process. The sulfite process is the invention of the American chemist Benjamin Chew Tilghman, patented in the United States in 1867. In point of time the sulfite process comes after the soda process invented by the Englishman Hugh Burges, about 1851 and precedes the sulfate process by approximately 17 years, almost the same number of years that separate it from the invention of the soda process."[15]

The cooking agent of the original sulfite process is a solution of calcium bisulfite. This acid is made by burning sulfur and by putting the resulting gas through "limestone-packed towers down which water trickles, so forming a solution of calcium bisulphite. For practical usage in the pulp mill the strength of the acid solution used for pulping, called the cooking liquor, is expressed as percentage calcium oxide, and percentage total free and combined sulphur dioxide."[16]

The sulfite process is successful with woods containing relatively small amounts of resins but not with those having a large resin content. Among the resin-poor woods are spruce, hemlock, balsam, fir, and paper birch but hardwoods, which are resin-rich and more plentiful than the softwoods, are not suitable for the original sulfite

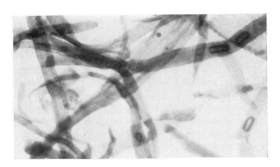

The upper picture is a microphotograph of hardwood sulfite pulp, the lower picture a microphotograph of softwood sulfite pulp, magnification 160 times.

process. Calcium sulfite pulping has, in addition, problems in the recovery of the chemicals used in the cooking liquor. But sulfite pulping has many good features and not only limitations. "The great advantages are bright color of the unbleached pulp for direct use and ease of bleaching. Particularly in Europe long experience in operation has resulted in high quality of sulfite pulps."[17] Another point worth remembering is that the Kraft, or sulfate, process was not too widely used for a long time because of its inherent difficulties in bleaching. For these and other reasons several variations and modifications of the sulfite process were developed.

Modified sulfite pulping. Modified sulfite processes can perhaps be best divided into those that retain calcium and those that replace calcium with another mineral. Among the first are the Mitscherlich and the Ritter-Kellner processes. The Mitscherlich process is known as "slow cook," the Ritter-Kellner process as "quick cook." Both methods were and still are used in the United States and in Canada, though the quick cook process is generally preferred in North America. In the more recent past a number of sulfite processes were developed which replace calcium with other natural or synthetic materials. Among those new processes are the ammonium-base acid sulfite, the magnesium-base acid sulfite, and the sodium-base acid sulfite process. A discussion of their detail is outside the frame of the present manual, but it might be mentioned that non-calcium sulfite processes have much better chemical recovery than calcium sulfite pulping.

Kinds of sulfite pulps and their uses. "Three more or less different types of sulfite pulps are manufactured. These products are called unbleached pulps, bleached pulps, and dissolving pulps or chemical celluloses."[18] Unbleached pulps are mainly used in newsprint and catalog papers, bleached sulfite pulps are divided into those for bond grade and for book grade papers; both are used in a variety of papers besides those indicated by their names, including cover stocks, sensitizing papers, waxing and wrapping papers, sanitary tissues, and others. Dissolving pulps, finally, are among the raw materials for cellulosic plastic films, cellophane, and rayon.

Waste liquor of sulfite pulping. As already mentioned, calcium sulfite pulping poses problems in conjunction with the waste liquor. Unfortunately efforts made to gain useful by-products, or to be more precise, to find by-products of economical significance have not been entirely successful. The waste liquor was and possibly still is simply discarded by most mills and this waste liquor "is a cause of serious stream pollution. For every ton of fiber produced, approximately a ton of material is contained in the waste liquor, and as this liquor is greatly diluted during blowing and washing any process of disposal which involves evaporation is necessarily an expensive one. Many efforts have been made to prepare useful by-products from the waste liquor, but none has developed to the point where it takes more than a small portion of the total waste. Among products made from waste sulfite liquor are road binders, adhesives for coal briquettes, and chemicals used in adhesives for linoleum and wall coverings. One mill is producing vanillin from the waste liquor, but it can supply enough vanillin to satisfy practically all the needs of this country."[19]

Semichemical and Chemimechanical Pulping

These two kinds of pulping, semichemical and chemimechanical, are recent developments that aim at high yields and at "making pulps from hardwoods with properties approaching those of softwood chemical or groundwood pulps."[20] The main difference between these two kinds is that no lignin is removed in chemimechanical pulp whereas semichemical pulp contains less lignin than the wood from which it is made.

Semichemical pulping. Semichemical pulping is the older of the two pulping methods. It was developed by the United States Forest Products Laboratory in 1926 and later modified. The main purpose of this process is the pulping of hardwoods with a higher yield than that obtainable in chemical pulping. "The conventional chemical pulping processes, Kraft and sulfite, produce pulps at a relatively low yield since most of the lignin is removed and this constitutes almost half the wood substance. Well-digested pulps are, however, easy to bleach since the amount of residual lignin to be removed is low. With the semichemical processes the yield is high and the pulp is accordingly difficult to bleach."[21] Even though semichemical indicates that this process is between chemical and mechanical pulping, this term "is not accurately descriptive, since the process is, generally speaking, more mechanical than chemical."[22]

The chemical treatments of the wood chips are much shorter than in chemical pulping processes; the chips are not fully pulped by these treatments, and chemical treatments are followed in semi-chemical processes by "mechanical disintegration and refining to separate the fibers of the softened chips. The chemicals for such processes may be any of those used in the regular cooking procedures, and quite a number of others have been proposed in addition."[23] The most widely used semichemical process is the *Neutral Sodium Sulfite Process*, abbreviated NSSC. "The NSSC process has the advantage of producing light-colored pulps, high yields for a given degree of delignification, high strength, and no offensive odor. The economy of wood and chemical consumption, plus the wide adaptability to different wood species, particularly those readily available but little used such as the oaks, gums, aspen, and birch has made this a very popular process."[24] Even though the neutral sulfite process is the most widely used semichemical process, it is not the only one. There is among others also "a Kraft process using continuous digesters. It is invariably found in connection with a Kraft mill to whose chemical recovery system the excess black liquor is fed."[25]

Chemimechanical pulping. The term chemimechanical is an example of terminological troubles now existing in the pulp and paper industry. Apparently this kind of pulping is considered by most though not all authorities a version of semichemical pulping. The term itself appears in some works of reference but not in others. Chemimechanical pulping is quite new and its technology is still in flux. The chemical agents used in this process may be caustic soda, or either neutral or acid sodium sulfite solutions. If caustic soda is used treatment takes place at room temperatures; for this reason this method is called the *cold soda process* which name distinguishes it from the original soda process in which cooking is done at elevated temperatures.

The cold soda process is also known as groundwood-from-chips process.[26] Like all semichemical pulps, cold soda pulp must be mechanically fiberized. The great advantages of this process are high yield, equal to that of groundwood, and reduced power consumption during fiberizing. At this point the *chemigroundwood process* can be mentioned which has similarities with chemimechanical pulping.

All these modern pulping methods are highly technical; they are mentioned to show the reader the complexity of contemporary pulping methods. Their differences cannot be discussed, and it must suffice to add that the more recent methods and pulping installations tend toward continuous pulping rather than batchwise operation.[27]

Reclaimed Waste Paper Pulps

Reclaimed papers and paper boards account for a substantial proportion of the fibers consumed by the paper industry. Even though waste papers are classified in many different groups, it is sufficient for our purposes to divide these materials into two broad classes: papers that can be re-used without de-inking and papers that must be de-inked.

Uses of not de-inked waste papers. Not de-inked waste papers cannot be used in the making of white papers. Their black ink content has the effect of turning the paper or board made with them gray. The main field for using reclaimed printed papers without de-inking is the paper board industry. One board grade, *news board*, points with its name to the origin of its most important fiber constituents, the newspapers. Other boards have inside plies, called "fillers" or "centers," made of reclaimed not de-inked papers and outside plies, called "liners," of different pulps. Such boards are made on the cylinder machine (described in Section 3) which can combine a number of different layers of board in the same web.

Not de-inked waste paper pulp is made mechanically, has a light gray color, and is normally of low strength. Some grades of paper board have a filler made from reclaimed pulp, sandwiched between two liners of Kraft board. The outside Kraft layers may be made from fresh pulp or they may contain admixtures of pulp made from Kraft waste. Such boards are called container boards. As the name indicates, they are used for cardboard containers and for similar purposes including the making of easels for window and counter displays. (To avoid misunderstandings it is added that container boards are made on fourdriniers as well as on cylinder machines.)

Uses of de-inked waste papers. De-inked papers are intended as admixtures in pulps of white papers. For de-inking the paper should be properly graded when it arrives at a paper or pulp mill. In the past, waste papers were graded in the mills by hand sorting; at present "the trend is away from hand sorting because of excessive labor costs, and toward the use of de-inking methods based upon the proper balance of chemical and mechanical operations to produce the desired end result from a variety of papers."[28] De-inking combines chemical and mechanical operations. The waste stock is mechanically disintegrated and cooked with such chemicals as will be most suitable for purification of the stock during the following washing. If the color of the stock needs improving, bleaching may follow washing. De-inked paper stocks are used for papers which possess good formation, opacity, bulk, greater dimensional stability, and better printability.

Rag Papers

Until the development of wood pulping practically all Western paper was made of linen and of cotton rags. The East, though, made paper directly from vegetable fibers and shortened the circuitous Western path of first spinning and weaving flax or cotton, then turning it into garments, and waiting until these garments had become rags before their fibers were made into paper.

During the nineteenth century the scarcity of rags presented a serious problem to the paper industry. More paper was needed than could be made of the available rag supply; paper was faster consumed than people's underwear, petticoats, and night-shirts wore out. The short supply of rags greatly stimulated the development of wood pulping which became the foundation of our present paper industry. But papermakers of the 1850's and 1860's needed readily available materials more than anything else, and at least one ingenious Yankee solved this problem in the most unlikely manner by importing several shiploads of mummies from Egypt, stripping them of their cloth wrappings and making paper from them.[29]

The printing of handmade papers. Handmade papers were far from ideal printing papers. They were much too hard and uneven to be printed dry and required wetting for presswork. Wetting made the papers limp and the pressman could force the relief image into them. The skill of a pressman showed itself in the amount of pressure applied to the paper in the press. Handmade papers were far from uniform in thickness and in color, not to forget composition of the paper. If you leaf through some old books you will often notice these differences. Another limitation of handmade paper is lack of smoothness. Historic paper was well suited for typographic printing of old style type; it was also usable for the printing of line engravings but not for such small image detail as is present in halftone reproductions of photographs. Last, but not least, the wet, printed paper required a lot of handling; it was dried in small

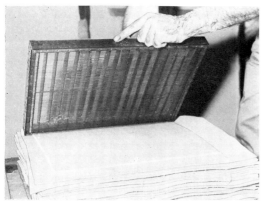

Courtesy Bird & Bull Press Philadelphia

Contemporary papermaking by hand, showing the hands of Henry Morris. In the first picture you see the laid mold with the deckle in position; in the second picture the sheet is formed on this mold, right above the tub with the paper furnish; in the last picture the newly made sheet is couched on the felt.

batches in the printer's warehouse which was equipped for this purpose with long strings or ropes under the ceiling. The warehouseman had the duty of putting the wet paper over these ropes and of taking the dry paper down, making room for the next batch. Handmade papers are certainly much more romantic to those who have neither experienced the backbreaking work that goes into their making nor the troubles caused by them during printing, than they were to papermakers and printers of the past.

Two outstanding qualities of handmade papers. The classic handmade papers have two outstanding attributes, texture and permanence. In a time when everything changes with incredible speed, in a time when cities deteriorate, are partly razed and rebuilt within decades, it seems somewhat miraculous that books printed three, four, and five hundred years ago are still in existence and may continue to exist indefinitely. The primitive methods whereby these papers were made increase our respect for this kind of paper just as the crumbling pages of newspapers, magazines, and books printed on machine-made papers in the nineteenth and early twentieth centuries make us distrust the permanence of machine-made papers. But these early machine-made papers are not representative of contemporary paper technology. Like all other aspects of paper, permanence has been extensively studied and papers of good permanence are made by many mills.[30]

Contemporary paper technology produces an enormous range of papers. Just as papers vary in many other characteristics, so do they vary in their permanence. Newspapers have an active life span of hours and possibly a day or two for anyone but historians. The paper for such products is not manufactured to last, and the same holds true for many other printed products, though in different degrees. Modern paper research has found the reason for the fast decay of certain papers and it has increased our knowledge of paper characteristics needed for long life expectance. (How the librarian of 500 years hence will judge our papers in comparison with those of Gutenberg's time, cannot be predicted. Nor can it be predicted that libraries, as we know them, will then still be the main repositories of knowledge.)

Raw materials for rag papers. In present American practice papers that contain at least 25 per cent cotton or linen fibers are classified as rag papers. Cotton and linen fibers can have different origins: (1) used textiles, or rags; (2) unused textile waste sold by textile mills and the needle trades; (3) non-woody plants such as cotton or flax; and (4) cotton linters, as the short fibers adhering to cottonseed after ginning are called.

The first two groups can be troublesome to the papermaker. The textile industry uses many different chemicals as dyes. Traditionally old rags were turned over to women for sorting and grading, removing of buttons, metal eyes and hooks, and most important because rubber is ruinous for paper, the detaching of elastic and other rubber-containing materials. During this process the rags were dusted, then they were chopped in heavy rag cutters, dusted again, boiled with chemicals, and further refined. This brief listing has merely the purpose to show how many manual operations, and rather unsanitary ones to boot, were needed in the processing of old rags.[31]

The sorting and grading of rags was simple before the epoch of synthetic fibers; the labor needed for the handling of rags was more available in the past than it is now, and it was also much less expensive. For these reasons old rags have become much less desirable to the papermaker than cotton and flax themselves. Cotton linters can be removed by passing the seed through a linter machine, which resembles the cotton gin, except for the closer setting of the saw blades. And due to modern methods of chlorination and bleaching, the flax obtained from plants grown for linseed oil production is now largely used as a substitute for linen fibers from rags. Flax fiber is extensively used in cigarette paper, in writing and ledger papers, in blottings, fiber board, and in roofing papers which are to be impregnated with asphalt. The amount used in these products far exceeds that used in high-grade papers.[32]

Bleaching of Pulps

Before pulp is passed on for the making of high quality white papers it is normally bleached. "It should be realized that the usual purpose of bleaching is to whiten the pulp. With most present methods the necessary high brightness can only be obtained by the extensive purification entailed in the removal of lignin."[33]

Brightness numbers. Brightness is a measure of the diffuse reflection of blue light. Brightness is tested by instruments which essentially relate the brightness of a paper or pulp sample to that of a carefully prepared standard. The result of testing is expressed in numbers; higher numbers indicate greater brightness than lower ones. This method

makes it very easy to rank different papers in their brightness and to establish the effect of bleaching on brightness. According to the U. S. Government Printing Office unbleached Kraft has a brightness between 45 to 50 per cent, unbleached sulfite one between 50 and 65 per cent, semibleached Kraft has between 60 and 75 per cent, bleached sulfite and bleached Kraft 75 to 85 per cent, and bleached and purified sulfite, Kraft and cotton content papers have a brightness from 85 to 90 per cent.[34] As you can see, bleaching of sulfite pulp can add up to 35 points, or 35 per cent, to its brightness. (Brightness tests are described in Section 6.)

Bleached and unbleached pulps. Not all pulp for white printing papers is subjected to bleaching; groundwood pulp for newsprint and newsprint-like papers as used for gravure supplements and web-offset printed newspapers is not bleached, and the same holds true for brown wrapping papers and for some paper boards. Bleaching is often characterized as an extension of the purification process of chemical pulping. "In some processes it is almost impossible to make a sharp distinction between cooking and bleaching."[35] Bleaching can be carried out as a batch and as a continuous process and the chemicals used in bleaching differ for various processes. One problem of bleaching was that in older methods pulps could not be bleached beyond a certain point without impairing fiber strength, those made by the sulfate or Kraft process in particular. But modern "bleaching methods have overcome these handicaps so that strong Kraft pulps, bleached to a beautiful white color without much loss of strength, now form one of the chief ingredients of many white papers.[36]

Bleaching chemicals and stages. Bleaching is done at lower temperatures than pulping. Different pulps have their own characteristics and requirements and bleaching is planned to suit them individually. By way of generalization it may be said that each of the main kinds of pulp requires different handling though not necessarily different bleaching agents. These are peroxides for groundwood pulps though peroxides are also used for semi-chemical pulps; chemical pulps are bleached with chlorine and with one or the other of its compounds, but chlorine compounds are also used for semi-chemical pulps and for groundwood pulps made of hardwoods. The subject is, like all chemistry, highly technical and need not be further pursued. It might be interesting, though, to the non-technical reader that paper chemists developed a number of tests that permit them to determine the bleachability of pulp and the amount of chemical agents needed to arrive at a standard brightness of a certain kind of pulp.

Depending on the bleaching process and the kind of pulp to be bleached, bleaching is carried out in a number of stages. Bleaching of very strong

pulp to the highest whiteness requires according to Dr. Sutermeister at least six different stages.[37] These stages can be controlled from central control stations in modern plants. The bleached pulp is passed on to stock preparation which is discussed in the next section.

Section 2: Stock Preparation and Furnishing

Just as fibers by themselves do not make plants, so do fibers alone not make paper. It is possible to form a web of pulp consisting only of fibers on a paper machine but such a web cannot be used as paper because it will disintegrate in water and become pulp again. For papermaking the fibers must be subjected to planned and differently executed mechanical treatments. Then the treated fibers must be compounded with other ingredients whose nature and proportions depend on the kind of paper to be made. The first operation, or operations, are called stock preparation. (Paper fibers are indiscriminately known as stock or pulp.) The compounding of the mixture needed for papermaking is called furnishing, the mixture itself is known as the furnish.

Stock Preparation

Pulping determines the chemical constituents of paper stock; stock preparation influences "the shape, size, distribution, and physical condition of the pulp fibers."[38] Whereas other pulping methods than grinding of wood consist mainly in chemical treatments, stock preparation is done mechanically. "The treatment may be applied in a number of different ways, but it ordinarily includes a bruising, rubbing, or crushing effect on the fibers."[39] Mechanical treatment of fibers is traditionally known as "beating" or as "refining." These two words mean the same when used as verbs though not as nouns. Beaters and refiners are two different kinds of machines for the mechanical treatment of stock; neither of them functions as one might assume from their names. Beaters do not beat the paper fibers and refiners do not refine them in the same sense in which crude oil, for example, is purified by refining.

Beaters. The verb "beating" may have been descriptive in early papermaking when the fibers were pounded with a hand tool. The *Hollander* is the traditional equipment for stock preparation. Dutch paper mills used Hollanders in the latter

seventeenth century, and Hollanders soon became widely used in other countries as well. Originally a Hollander "consisted of an oblong wooden tub, rounded at both ends, in which revolved a solid wooden roll made from the trunk of a tree and fitted with about 30 iron knives. The linen and cotton rags circulated about the tub and were macerated by the action of the metal bars of the roll revolving over a metal or stone bed-plate set in the bottom directly under the roll. The material was kept in constant motion by the impetus given by a backfall and by the rotation of the roll."[40] Beaters have, naturally, become much more capacious than they were in past centuries, and beaters of different makes are on the market, but "the basic design and principle of the ordinary beater has altered little since it was first introduced as the Hollander."[41] Even though, or possibly because, the Hollander has been in use for more than 250 years beating is controlled less scientifically than empirically, by the experience of beater men. "Indeed in the fine-paper mill, where

Courtesy S. D. Warren Company

A beater. Beaters are traditionally used for stock preparation in batches. The paper fibers are mechanically treated in beaters: various ingredients of the paper stock are here added to the fibers and mixed with them.

beating is of special importance (particularly with rag furnishes) the beaterman still prefers to feel 'the stuff' in the beater or to listen to the sound of his roll against the bedplate as a guide to how the beating is progressing."[42] This is not to say that beating has not been thoroughly studied; there is an extensive literature on this subject like on all other aspects of papermaking.

The purpose of beating. The purpose of beating is the formation of the desired paper quality; that means the endowing of the paper stock with such characteristics as are needed in the final paper. Beating together with pulp selection and combination is needed for this effect even though the result is not apparent until the stock is made into paper. "Mechanical action shortens, splits, and bruises the fiber. At the same time the ends of the fibers become frayed, fibrils are loosened on the surface, and the fiber becomes much more flexible."[43] Fibrils are small or fine fibers, and *fibrillation*, or the loosening of these small fibers from the larger ones of which the pulp consists, is one of the main functions of beating. Another important effect of beating is hydration. *Hydration* as used in the paper industry means an increased capacity of the fibers for holding water. "Beating is probably the most fundamentally important process in papermaking. Paper made from unbeaten stock is low in strength, fluffy, porous, and unfit for most uses, whereas paper made from well-beaten stock is strong, dense, and hard in texture."[44] The fundamental influence of beating is perhaps best illustrated by the fact that the same stock can be used for blotting paper or for hard bond, depending on its beating. There are many variables in beating, and variations in the mechanical treatment of stock rank high among the methods whereby paper properties can be influenced.

Refiners. Beating takes place in a large stationary vessel in which the stock circulates; in refiners the stock is mechanically treated as it passes through the equipment. Refiners are usually divided into conical and disk refiners. The oldest conical refiner is the jordan. "Originally the jordan supplemented the beater and was supposed to give the finishing touch to the stock and to even out inequalities in the stock from different beaters. Today some mills have completely eliminated beaters and depend entirely on jordans and other refiners for their fiber treatment. The jordan consists of a conical plug covered with longitudinal knives, which fits into a conical shell similarly lined with knives. Depending on the distance of the plug from the shell the treatment of stock can be varied from a light brushing action to one of sharp cutting."[45] Modern jordans can have fully automatic controls that regulate the clearance between the shell and the plug; automatic plug control is needed on high-speed conical refiners for product uniformity.

Another kind of high-speed refiner is based on two disks and known as disk refiner. In such machines "refining is accomplished by passing the stock between grooved plates located on two vertical disks. These refiners are being used to a considerable extent in mills making bag wrapping, Kraft boards, and similar grades; and to a lesser extent in high-grade mills."[46]

Non-fibrous Paper Components

The paper furnish of various papers contains not only fibers but also non-fibrous materials. These materials are quite numerous and can best be grouped, according to their different purposes, into the following four kinds: (1) materials for sizing, (2) materials for loading and filling, (3) coloring materials, and (4) additives for special paper characteristics or simply for general improvement of paper performance.

The main reason for the sizing of papers. Cellulose fibers take avidly to water and other liquids. Liquid writing inks consist mainly of water, and it is not possible to write with such inks on paper unless the paper is treated to resist rapid and excessive penetration which causes feathering or spreading of the written characters. Treatment for this and similar purposes is called "sizing." Sizing

Courtesy S. D. Warren Company

A battery of refiners. Refiners are used in continuous stock preparation for mechanical treatments of paper fibers. Pulps are refined before being blended in automatic, continuous-flow proportioners.

The upper picture is the core of a refiner, the lower picture is its plug. Refiners cut, fibrillate, and hydrate pulp in a continuous operation.

is an important part of papermaking; not only writing papers but also papers for printing and for packaging must be properly sized. Sizing can be done in different ways.

Methods and degrees of sizing. Traditionally sizing methods are divided into three: (1) engine sizing, (2) tub sizing, and (3) surface sizing. Engine sizing is at present usually called beater sizing; in this method the sizing materials are added to the furnish in the beater prior to papermaking. This kind of sizing is also classified "internal sizing" as opposed to "external sizing." Tub siz-

ing was done in the past off the paper machine as a subsidiary and consequently more expensive operation. In tub sizing the sheet or web of paper was dipped into the sizing liquid and then dried. When sizing on the dry end of the paper machine became practical this method of sizing was called surface sizing to distinguish it from the off-machine tub sizing. As a sizing tub is used in either case and as the size is applied to the paper surface in either case, these distinctions have become useless. Tub sizing like other forms of external sizing is performed on the paper machine in present practice. The tub and its content are placed midway between two drier sections of the paper machine. The moving web enters the tub and is totally submerged in the liquid sizing material. Then it continues its travel in the second drier section.

The paper industry classifies papers according to their sizing into three groups: unsized, weak-sized, and strong-sized papers. Unsized papers are called *waterleaf;* weak-sized papers, *slack sized;* and strong-sized papers are known as *hard sized.* Blotting paper is an example of waterleaf, sized newsprint is one of slack sized, and bond paper one of hard sized papers.

Many printing papers are internally and externally sized; rosin size is the most widely used internal sizing material. Rosin sizing is generally used for printing paper, w th the exception of those containing carbonates as part of their filling materials.[47] Such papers cannot use the acid rosin sizing but need alkaline sizing chemicals which are available as synthetic materials.

Filling and loading. Filling and loading are different names for the same operation. Either name emphasizes a different aspect or function: *filling* that non-fibrous, mineral materials plug "the spaces between fibers in a web of paper or board," *loading* that the same basis weight of a paper can be maintained by replacing some of its fiber content with non-fibrous materials that have a much higher specific gravity than cellulose fibers. (The specific gravity of fillers is between 2.6 and 4.5, that of cellulose fibers is 1.5.)[48] "Fillers, or loading materials, were originally considered adulterants used chiefly to cheapen the paper. It was not long, however, before they were recognized as serving perfectly legitimate purposes by increasing the opacity of the paper, aiding in obtaining a good finish on calendering, and improving printing qualities by reducing 'show-through' and 'strike-through' of the ink. Today fillers are used in the great majority of printing papers though there are some bulky papers and specialties that are made without fillers."[49] Mineral fillers also improve the smoothness and uniformity of printed images.

Fillers. Fillers are either natural or manufactured mineral materials which are used in a number of industries. In papermaking the same materials can be used as fillers in the compounding of the furnish and as pigments for the coating of papers. Some of these materials are also used as raw materials in the printing ink industry. When these materials are used for other purposes than filling, they are usually classified as pigments. White pigments are discussed in Chapter IX, Section 2. There they are divided into opaque and transparent ones. Interestingly, most pigments used in filling and coating of paper are much less transparent than when such pigments are used in printing inks. This is so because the degree of opacity or transparency does not depend on the properties of a pigment alone but also on those of the medium in which it is used.

Clay is probably the oldest paper filler; it is also used as a coating pigment. Other fillers include calcium carbonate, barium sulfate, talc, diatomaceous earth, and the most opaque white pigment, titanium dioxide. Calcium carbonate and barium sulfate can be either natural or manufactured pigments; manufactured barium sulfate is called blanc fixe; titanium dioxide is a pigment obtained by large scale manufacturing.

Fillers affect both the making and the properties of paper. The paper properties affected by fillers are opacity, brightness (or whiteness), smoothness and strength as well as ink receptivity. "Calcium carbonate fillers improve ink affinity and quick setting of the ink, which allows a speedup in letterpress and rotogravure printing. Papers for gloss ink printing or varnishing require the opposite of printing ink acceptance. Here a reduction in ink or varnish penetration is desired. Small clay or talc platelets in close packing between fiber and filler are preferable to a loading with calcium carbonate."[50]

Fillers can be added to the paper stock as dry powders or as water mixtures. It is also possible to precipitate calcium carbonate in the beater. Beating disperses the fillers, and in certain cases dispersing agents are used. The selection and amount of fillers vary for different papers. Titanium dioxide is particularly important in thin printing papers which are increasingly favored over heavy papers. A few examples will illustrate the wide range of filling as regards kinds and proportions of fillers. Most newsprint is made without fillers, but if fillers are used for newsprint these are usually clay or calcium carbonate; the fillers for offset papers are clay in combination with high opacity pigments, and Bible papers are filled with a mixture of clay, chalk, and titanium white. The proportion of fillers expressed in per cent of fiber weight is between 0 and 6 per cent in newsprint; in offset papers for job-and-commercial printing between 8 and 15 per cent, and in Bible papers from 20 to 30 per cent.[51]

Coloring materials. Papers are colored by dyes and by pigments. It is customary to speak of three groups of dyes: acid, basic, and direct dyes. "Acid dyes need to be applied on sized stock as they do not take well to unsized fibers; they are of good light fastness but not as brilliant as basic dyes which are less light fast and not used where permanence is wanted. Direct dyes take well on unsized fibers but are not of great brilliance and are used only where this property is unimportant.[52] Colored pigments are less used than dyes. Pigments can be divided into mineral or inorganic, and synthetic or organic, pigments. Inorganic colored pigments have low color strength in comparison with synthetic pigments of the same color. For this reason synthetic pigments are preferred to mineral pigments which are rarely used and then often as much as fillers as for coloring. Since colored pigments are discussed in Chapter IX, Section 2, this subject is here not further pursued, but a few words on methods of increasing brightness and optical whiteners seem appropriate.

Various ways of improving paper brightness. The brightness of paper may be increased during manufacture by: (1) degree of bleaching of the pulp; (2) the addition of white pigments, such as titanium dioxide; (3) the addition of tinting colors, such as certain violet and blue dyes; and (4) fluorescent whitening dyes, such as calcofluor whites.

The brightness of paper is, in large part, determined by the basic brightness of the pulps from which it is made. Unbleached fibers do not provide brightness, and bleaching is necessary to produce fibers for making white papers. Bleached pulps, depending upon the extent of bleaching and species of wood used, will vary in brightness. Often, tinting dyes are added to the bleached fibers in papermaking to produce brighter and more pleasing shades of white.

The brightness of paper is also generally increased by adding fillers, such as titanium dioxide.

This pigment increases the opacity as well as the brightness of paper.

During the past several years, fluorescent papers have become quite common. A specific dye, sometimes known as an *optical bleach*, is added either to the furnish (fiber stock) prior to papermaking, or applied to the surface of the paper at the sizing press in order to enhance its brightness. (Some papers may have fluorescent dyes applied at both production stages.) Fluorescent whiteners are also incorporated in the coatings of coated papers. These fluorescent dyes make paper whiter than white (as it has been referred to in sales promotional statements) due to the fact that they have the unique property of absorbing ultraviolet light existing in daylight and converting this invisible ultraviolet to a visible wavelength which is then reflected from the paper surface back to our eyes. Therefore, the total light reflected by a fluorescent paper is the sum of that which would be reflected by the paper without the fluorescent dye, plus the converted visible light from the existing ultraviolet portion of the surrounding light. Consequently, optical whiteners are only effective if the paper is viewed in natural daylight or in illumination rich in ultraviolet, but not with incandescent lamps.

It may be said that the addition of fluorescent brighteners has created some problems. By mistake, fluorescent and non-fluorescent sheets are sometimes packed in the same skid and sometimes mixed in the same ream. There is considerable variation in the shade of white between the fluorescent and non-fluorescent papers, which become parts of the same publication.

Variation often occurs in the shade of white between the wire and felt sides of the same sheet. Unlike the permanent brightness imparted by bleaching of the pulp, and the addition of white pigment fillers, and tinting dyes mentioned earlier, the brightness imparted by the fluorescent whitening dyes is of a temporary nature, fading upon exposure to light. The fluorescent dyes in paper can have a pronounced effect upon colors in full-color printing. The yellows may be weakened, whereas the blues may be strengthened.

Additives. The term additive is a catchall for a variety of non-fibrous and also non-traditional materials that were developed to improve paper characteristics and to endow papers with special features. Paper additives are products of chemical manufacturing and include chemically processed natural materials as well as synthetics. "Additives may be put into the paper stock either before the sheet is formed or later at the size press, calender stack, or a subsequent converting operation. Materials added before sheet formation are called beater, wet-end, fan-pump, or head box additives. The beater or wet-end method of incorporating additives is often preferred because of its simplicity and economy and because the additive is more or less uniformly distributed throughout the fibrous structure.[53] Wet-end additives that function as binders and those that improve the wet strength of papers are of general interest and therefore here briefly discussed.

Binders and their purposes. Binders and sizing agents have the purpose of bonding the paper fibers and thereby giving strength to the paper. "Other important functions are to lay surface fuzz, increase the hardness and durability, increase the stiffness and rattle, impart functional properties, and with some colloids, to improve the sizing and formation of the paper."[54] In printing papers, additives improve pick resistance and reduce the objectionable linting and dusting. The increasing use of additives for binding permits greater economy in stock preparation because less strongly beaten stocks can be used together with these additives. The power consumption of beating is high, and highly beaten paper has properties that are undesirable in printing papers. Reduction of beating in conjunction with the use of binding additives offers the papermaker many valuable possibilities.

Paper chemists can select their binding additives from a wide range of materials including corn, tapioca, and potato starches; various kinds of natural gums; synthetic materials such as methyl cellulose; water-soluble resins, various kinds of emulsions, and others. Each of the many existing additives has its own characteristics and effects. It is part of the art and science of papermaking to select, combine, and proportion additives for specific purposes and effects.

Wet-strength papers. Papers with a substantially improved wet-strength are one of the more recent developments. Whereas normal papers lose their strength almost completely when wet, wet-strength papers can be made to retain a varying proportion of their dry strength. According to the *Paper Dictionary*, "a paper which retains more than 15 per cent of its dry strength when completely wetted with water may properly be called a wet-strength paper."[55] As mentioned at the beginning of this chapter papers of a much higher wet-strength can also be made.

Wet-strength is needed in many papers, most

obviously in those that are exposed to weather, like papers for outdoor posters, but also in many others including papers for the packaging of moist materials, photographic papers, and papers for maps, to mention some.[56] Paper can be endowed with wet-strength in several ways. Vegetable parchment for example is a paper of high wet-strength made by treating the unsized fibers with dilute sulfuric acid. Ordinary papers have no-wet strength because the bonds between the fibers are easily broken by water. "True wet strength is produced upon the development of water-resistant bonds or bridges between adjacent fibers in the paper."[57] Contemporary paper chemistry achieves this result by treating the fibers with resins. These are various organic thermosetting compounds, either urea or melamine-formaldehyde. (Thermosetting means that a resin does not soften again

after having been exposed to heat.) Such resins can be either part of the furnish or they can be applied to the surface of the already formed paper. When the paper is dried (at the dry end of the paper machine), the necessary heat is applied and the result is a hydrophobic or water resistant bond between the fibers.

Wet-strength is sometimes confused with water repellence. The difference between water repellence and wet-strength is rather simple: Water repellent papers resist getting wet to some extent, but when they become wet they lose most of their dry strength. Wet-strength papers may or may not resist getting wet but when they are thoroughly wet they still retain part of their dry strength. Water repellence can be obtained by sizing, wet-strength cannot.

Section 3:   The Making of Uncoated and of Coated Papers and Paper Boards

Contemporary paper machines are such enormous and complex installations that it may appear grotesque to compare them with the primitive, tiny equipment whereby paper was made by hand. The basic functions of papermaking have nevertheless remained the same, and much of contemporary paper terminology goes back to the past and handmade paper. In the West paper was made by two workers. One, the *vatman*, dipped a mold into the vat of paper furnish and formed the sheet on the mold; the other, the *coucher* (often pronounced cootcher) removed the sheet from the paper mold after sufficient water had drained off and put it on a piece of felt, sandwiching paper between felt in a pile until the pile was high enough for pressing.

The Western paper mold consisted of two parts. One was a frame with metal wires in both directions. These wires formed a sieve permitting the draining of water back into the vat and retaining the paper fiber. To confine the paper stock during molding, the vatman used a fence called "deckle." Before he dipped the mold into the vat, he put this fence, a wooden frame, on it; after lifting the mold out of the vat and shaking it, he took the deckle off, and used a new mold with the same deckle for the next sheet. (Strung wire molds were not the only kind; in the middle of the nineteenth century paper molds were made with woven wire; these were called "wove" molds.)

In some Eastern countries sheets larger than possible by dipping were made by pouring the paper stock on large molds and letting the paper dry directly on the mold. Dard Hunter, who observed this kind of molding himself, suggests the term pouring mold to distinguish it from the Western mold for making paper by dipping.[58] Both principles, that of pouring or spreading paper stock on a wire surface and that of dipping a wire mold into a receptacle containing paper stock are still used. The fourdrinier machine is based on the principle of spreading the stock on the wire, and the cylinder machine is based on the principle of dipping a mold in a vat.

The Fourdrinier Paper Machine

The invention of the paper machine by the Frenchman Nicolas Louis Robert in 1798 and its improvement by Henry and Sealy Fourdrinier (after whom the machine was named) and by others in the early decades of the nineteenth century, introduced continuous manufacturing of paper and thereby in time revolutionized the paper industry.

Modern fourdrinier machines have the principle in common with the original invention but not much else. "Some idea of the complexity of modern paper machines can be gained from one such unit put recently in operation. This machine is 425 feet long and is operated by over 600 electric motors including those on control equipment. Its installation required 33 miles of electrical conduit and several hundred miles of electrical wiring. There are approximately 1,000 push buttons and over 450 pilot lights."[59]

A detailed description of a modern paper machine is completely outside the frame of this manual. Such a description would fill a volume by itself. As one authority wrote when paper machines were less complex than they are now, "to describe a fourdrinier paper machine is not to describe a single machine but dozens of them, each being designed for some particular purpose and all so coordinated and synchronized that they work together with a single objective—the production of a sheet of paper.[60] A fourdrinier machine, and a cylinder machine not less, is usually discussed under two heads: the wet end and the dry end of the machine. The wet end of the machine comprises the stock system and the wire on which the paper is formed. Before these two are briefly characterized a few words on the crucial role of water are in order.

The role of water in papermaking. Water is, quantitatively, the most important raw material of papermaking. (The qualities of water are of course also important, but here the emphasis is on quantity.) Before the stock is spread on the wire of the fourdrinier it is diluted, in several stages, until its fiber content is possibly as low as one tenth of a per cent. From this point on water removal becomes one of the decisive functions of the machine. The paper stock, which contains other solids in addition to fibers, has approximately 99.5 per cent water; the finished paper usually not more than 7 per cent moisture. This change from stock containing almost 10 tons of water per 100 lb. of dry matter to a sheet of paper which seldom has over 7 lb. of moisture in 100 lb. of paper, takes place in less than a minute, occasionally in 30 seconds, and is one of the most spectacular operations in papermaking.

The wet end of the fourdrinier. After the paper stock is compounded it is collected in a large tank which is not part of the fourdrinier itself. From here it is pumped into the *machine chest* where it is further diluted; this diluted stock is pumped to a *regulating box* which controls flow to the machine and thereby uniformity of basis weight. After further dilution with the *white water*, coming from the paper machine and containing some paper solids, the stock is passed through screens or other devices to remove lumps and coarse particles. The screened stock then enters a *flow* or *head box* that agitates it for spreading on the wire. The stock leaving the head box passes over an apron of some such material as rubberized cloth. In slower machines *slices*, meaning adjustable sheets of brass, provide uniform flow across the machine; in faster machines other arrangements may be used.

Now the stock is on the wire. The wire is the surface on which the paper is formed. It is a woven brass or bronze cloth that can vary in the number of openings per square inch. A coarser wire has,

Part view of the "wet end" of a fourdrinier paper machine. The mixture of wood pulp, fillers, dyes, sizing agents, heavily diluted with water, is spread evenly across the endless wire of the fourdrinier machine. The wire vibrates to mat the fibers. Some of the water is drained from the stock spread on the wire.

say, 2,300 orifices per square inch; a much finer wire, twice that number. Paper machines differ in their widths and speeds; modern machines may be more than 300 inches wide and can be operated at 3,000 feet per minute. (Certain tissue machines operate at speeds in excess of 5,000 f.p.m.) Closest to the head box the wire is supported by the *breast roll* which is followed by a series of *foils* or of *table rolls* having a smaller diameter than the breast roll. The endless wire band moves over several suction boxes and finally under the dandy roll before it returns over a *suction couch roll*. The breast roll and the suction couch roll are the two extremes of the wire's travel. On its return trip to the breast roll the wire is controlled in its tightness by a number of *stretch rolls*. The white water is collected in receptacles under the table rolls for reuse in stock dilution. "It is customary to trim a few inches off each edge of the sheet (paper people speak of sheets even though they may mean a web) as it leaves the forming wire. The edges are usually light in weight and contain weak points. The cutting is done by fine, high-pressure water jets located over the wire between the last suction box and the couch roll.[61] This waste is of course reused and not a complete loss.

The dandy roll. When the paper passes under the dandy roll it is still sufficiently wet to receive a lasting impression by contact with this roll. The dandy roll provides watermarks and such different finishes as *laid* or *wove*. If the dandy is covered with woven wire, the paper will have a wove finish, and if the dandy is covered with evenly spaced parallel wires, the result is a laid finish. *Watermark* designs are put in relief on the dandy. Since these designs add to the diameter of the dandy roll, the paper becomes somewhat thinner and more translucent where it is watermarked. Watermarks can best be seen by viewing the paper against a good light. The dandy roll need have no design or pattern; then it compresses the whole web uniformly.

The rest of the fourdrinier wet end is occupied by a series of two or three rotary presses. When the wire reaches the couch roll the paper web cannot support itself because it still contains 80 to 85 per cent water. The needed support is provided by woolen felts which carry the paper through the squeeze presses. Each press has its own felt, kept taut by stretch rolls; suction boxes are usually provided to remove the water from the felts. The rotary presses reduce the water content of the paper web to approximately 70 per cent, and the web

is self supporting in its travel through the dry end of the fourdrinier which it enters now.

As the dry end is more or less the same for fourdriniers and cylinder machines, the latter are described before we turn to the dry end of paper machines.

The Cylinder Machine

The same kind of paper machine that is called cylinder machine in the United States is called the board or vat machine in England. The name board machine puts the emphasis on the products for which this machine is widely used: paper board, and particularly thick, multi-ply or multi-layer boards. The other two names, vat machine and cylinder machine refer to the manner in which paper or paper board is formed on this machine. The difference between the fourdrinier and the cylinder machine can perhaps be best explained by repeating that in the fourdrinier the wire takes the place of the pouring mold whereas in the cylinder machine the cylinder acts similar to a dipping mold. Fourdriniers, on which the paper stock is spread, do not need vats; cylinder machines do need receptacles that hold the stock during molding. These receptacles are traditionally called vats, hence the name vat machine.

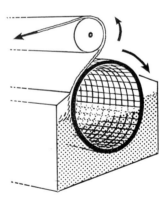

Schematic diagram of papermaking on a cylinder machine. The vat contains the suspended paper stock and a wire covered cylinder, open at the ends, which is the paper mold. That cylinder is so arranged that it rotates partly submerged in the stock and partly above the stock level. The paper is formed on the outside of the wire and drained back into the vat. When the cylinder reaches its topmost position the paper is lifted by an endless felt going over the couch roll. Even though felt and couch roll press against the paper and cylinder, the felt is not shown in this diagram and the couch roll is slightly above the cylinder to better convey the idea of papermaking in an endless web.

It is worth noting that the cylinder machine, too, is a continuous machine, like the fourdrinier. Continuity of operation results from the use of constantly moving cylindrical wire molds which replace the flat dipping molds of days gone by.

Fiber orientation in fourdrinier and cylinder machines. Papers and paper boards made on cylinder machines differ from those made on fourdriniers in several respects. One of them is the difference in the fiber orientation of the product. Papers and paper boards made on the fourdrinier have the greater proportion of their fibers with their longer dimension in the machine direction; but "when the sheet needs to be as bulky as possible in relation to its weight in order to provide 'cushion' to absorb shock or for economy in the use of furnish material the papermaker tries to assemble a large proportion of fibers with their axes perpendicular to the plane of the sheet. This is desirable in chipboard and some boxboard,"[62] and can be achieved on the cylinder machine.

Single-vat and multiple-vat cylinder machines. Cylinder machines can be single-vat or multiple-vat machines. Single-vat machines are used for the making of papers or paper boards that consist of a single layer whereas multiple-vat machines are used for the making of paper boards consisting of several layers, or plies. Among products made on single-vat machines are heavy paper boards, deckle-edge papers (called moldmade), and tissues. Deckle-edge papers and tissues are mainly made on fourdriniers whereas the typical products of multiple-vat machines are paper boards, which play such an important role as package materials. Therefore the following discussion concentrates on multiple-vat machines. Each vat has its own cylinder which is similar in construction to the dandy roll of the fourdrinier. It is open at the ends and covered with wire around its body, hollow in the center. "As the cylinder revolves about two-thirds immersed in the paper stock, the water in which the fibers are suspended rushes through the meshes of the wire in the same way as it runs through the wire on the wet end of a fourdrinier machine. As, however, the meshes are too fine to allow passage of the fibers, the latter cling to the surface of the wire drum, or cylinder, forming a film of fibers on it. As the drum moves round toward the top, the film of paper is lifted clear of the paper stock in the vat, and more water drains away."[63] The cylinder continues its rotation with the paper on its outside and above the level of the paper stock in the vat. When the cylinder, with

the paper on it, reaches its topmost position the paper is removed from the cylinder by a moving endless felt which is pressed against the wet paper by a felt covered roll, also known as the couch roll.

Making multi-ply board on a cylinder machine. Boards consisting of several layers are made by combining the products of different cylinders when they are still wet. The felt that carries the paper from the first cylinder travels with this paper on its surface to the next cylinder and picks up the paper formed on its surface. This process is repeated as often as needed, depending on the number of cylinders of a particular machine. "The reason paper can be picked up in this manner is that wet paper always adheres to the surface having the denser area, and since both the felt and paper surface are smoother and denser than the wire covering on the cylinder mold, the wet mat is readily induced to leave the wire."[64] The wet paper or paperboard is put through primary presses which may have suction rolls, and through a main press which usually has a rubber-covered suction roll. The main press is followed by a second press and possibly by a reverse press.[65]

Multi-ply boards are made in series of as many as ten different cylinders. Each of these cylinders has its own vat and may have a different paper stock. The final product can utilize many different combinations. In paper boards for package printing the outside is usually white; it may consist of white printing paper or it may be coated. The inside plies are usually reclaimed newsprint. It is also possible to produce boards with a colored printing surface on cylinder machines, mill bristols for example. Printing stocks made on cylinder machines can have greater strength in the machine direction than those made on fourdriniers, but they have less strength in the opposite, cross machine direction.

Several kinds of papers and boards can be made either on a fourdrinier or on a cylinder machine. Each of the two kinds has its own strong and weak points. These are highly technical and not discussed here.[66]

Finally, mention is made of the *Inverform* board machine. "The Inverform uses an endless wire similar to that in the fourdrinier machine but has mounted over the top of it a number of head boxes and forming wire units, each for a different type of stock. The advantages of this machine include high operating speed and a more economical manufacture of certain special boards."[67] The Inverform is only one of several new approaches to the design and construction of paper machines. Others are the Rotoformer, Stevensformer, Twinwire and Vertaformer. Only time will tell how successful these developments are.

The Dry End of Paper Machines

The wet end of the fourdrinier or of the cylinder machine has the tasks of forming paper or paper board of a given basis weight and quality, and of removing water until the paper is self-supporting. On the dry end of paper machines water content is further reduced until the paper has its correct moisture content. This much is common to all papermaking. Depending on the kind of paper to be made, sizing, various kinds of "proofing," and coating can be combined with drying. The dry paper web can further be processed for compacting, smoothing, and embossing. Compacting, smoothing, and embossing, whereby the paper is textured, can also be done after the paper has left the dry end of the machine. In the present unit drying and calendering are explained; paper coating is the subject of the next unit.

Machine drying. The web of paper is passed through the driers, cast iron drums of four to five feet in diameter arranged in two or more rows, the upper row staggered between the driers in the lower row. These drums are polished on the outside and steam heated. During the trip through these banks of driers which may be 20, for example, over 2 lb. of water must be evaporated for each pound of paper made. "The paper is held tightly against the drying rolls by a felt called a dryer felt, which also helps in threading of the paper through the drier bank."[68] Lightweight paper such as tissue "is pressed against and dried on a single 8- to 12-ft. diameter drier, called a Yankee. No felt is used on a *Yankee drier;* because the wet paper is pressed tightly to the highly polished drier surface, heat transfer is greatly improved. The paper may be creped as it is scraped off the drier. If it is not creped, it is called machine glazed (MG) having one glazed or shiny surface. Creped napkins and toweling are made on a Yankee machine using a special creping doctor blade. Heavy board is dried on standard-size steam driers but without drier felts. The web tension is great enough to hold the board tightly against the drier for good heat transfer."[69]

Depending upon the intended paper finish and compactness the paper may pass through stacks of calenders or it may be wound on a reel without calendering. (Antique papers are not calendered.) The reel provides for the uninterrupted winding of the paper as it comes off the paper machine.

Paper machines are usually equipped with one or more stacks of calenders. If a smooth paper surface is wanted, the paper is passed through them; calendered papers are machine finished papers. (There is also a grade known as Machine-Finish book paper, abbreviated MF. According to the *Dictionary of Paper*, this is a book paper of medium finish between vellum and English Finish, abbreviated EF.) As both coated and uncoated

Courtesy Oxford Paper Company

Rewinding of paper rolls. The paper coming off the machine is wound in master rolls that have the full machine width. These rolls must be rewound before the paper can be used on web presses. Rewinding results in tight neat rolls that are trimmed to customer specifications. The master roll is at the right, the rewind equipment with the rewound roll is at the left of the picture.

papers may be supercalendered, the difference between calendering and supercalendering is next briefly explained.

Calendering and supercalendering. Calendering is done as part of papermaking before the paper is wound on the reels; supercalendering is a subsidiary operation that takes place after the paper has been wound into rolls. Machine calenders are stacks of, say, ten cast iron rolls that are ground and polished on their surfaces. These rolls are arranged vertically, and adjustable as to their relative distance or nip pressure. The paper enters the calender stack at the top and is progressively compacted and smoothed on the way down. Supercalenders are also arranged in stacks of rolls, but these rolls are not all of cast iron, as in machine calenders. The rolls of supercalenders are either steel and cotton, or steel and paper in alternation. Both machine calenders and supercalenders are driven from the bottom by friction. The paper may be put through supercalenders as often as needed. Supercalenders are used for both coated and uncoated papers. Uncoated supercalendered papers are designated SC; S&SC is used for sized and supercalendered paper. The word sized means in this context surface sized.

Paper Coating

The difference between coated and uncoated papers can perhaps best be made clear in pointing out on which papers different kinds of original images are best reproduced. One group of original images, type and line drawings, can be perfectly printed on uncoated papers. The next group of original images, best exemplified by photographs, is reproduced as halftone images. These pose greater reproduction problems than type and line drawings. In printing methods using direct image transfer, uncoated papers are limited in the range of halftones to coarser and medium ones, say between 55 and 110 line screens, depending on the actual smoothness of a paper. (Relief printed newspapers use halftones from 55 to 85 lines, for example.) Offset lithography which uses indirect image transfer, and indirect relief too, can print fine halftones on uncoated paper, but letterpress requires coated paper for fine halftone reproduction. Full-color printing, finally, is done with much higher fidelity on coated papers than on uncoated ones. And the printing of glossy inks is greatly improved when coated papers are used.

Said more technically, coated papers are distinguished by a number of characteristics includ-

Courtesy West Virginia Pulp & Paper Company

A laboratory coating machine. This machine applies two coats of pigment coating in sequence and can be used for the testing of different coating methods as well as for that of different coating formulas.

ing greater affinity for printing inks, reduction of the lateral spread of printed images, greater smoothness, range of gloss from dull to very glossy, higher opacity, better ink holdout, and last but not least, much better whiteness than uncoated papers. As a result it is possible to produce printed images of an improved density, sharper definition, higher gloss, greater color fidelity, better contrast, and greater uniformity on coated papers than on uncoated ones.

The great popularity of black-and-white and of color photographs in general-interest magazines, catalogs, and high prestige persuasion printing, stimulated the demand for coated papers, just as the development of better coated papers resulted in an ever increasing use of color photographs as part of the art-and-copy to be reproduced by printing. Even though coated papers for general-interest magazines date back to the end of the nineteenth century, the greatest progress in paper coating has been made since World War II. Paper coating is far from being a closed subject; it is very much alive and will continue to be so in the near future.

Machine coating and off-machine coating. Coated printing papers are available as coated one side only (for labels, box tops, or covers) or coated two sides (for book and publication printing);

they may be glossy or dull, and embossed with different texture patterns. Different printing methods need coatings of different compositions. The base paper to be coated varies, but most of all do the methods by which coatings are applied to paper. The paper industry divides coating methods into those that are used as part of papermaking on the paper machine and into those that are done with subsidiary equipment after the paper has left the paper machine. Papers coated on the paper machine are called *machine coated* or *process coated*, those coated independent of the machine are said to be *off-machine coated* or *conversion coated*. Many coating methods can be used either way, though some cannot. Several major coating methods are now described.

Roll coating on the machine. Historically, independent or off-machine coating preceded coating on the paper machine. Of the several coating methods used in machine coating, roll coating was the most important. One of the best known roll coaters is the *Consolidated Coater* which coats both sides of the web in a single pass simultaneously at speeds up to 1,800 f.p.m. on lightweight publication papers. This coater has three kinds of

rubber covered rolls: a pair of metering rolls, several distributing rolls, and an applicator roll. The function of each of these three kinds of rolls is evident from its respective name. Metering and distributing rolls are usually 18 inches in diameter, applicator rolls have a much larger diameter, usually 48 inches. The hardness of the rubber covering differs for each of the three kinds of rolls.[70] The Consolidated Coater is used for coating both sides of the web simultaneously and has therefore two sets of coating rolls, one for each side.

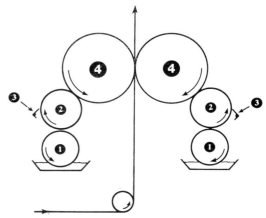

Schematic diagram of a two-side gravure coater. The gravure coater uses an intaglio metering roll that transfers the metered coating to a rubber-covered application roll. The coating material is in the furnish pan in which a rubber-covered furnish roll (1) rotates slowly. This furnish roll feeds the material to the engraved intaglio roll (2). The doctor blade (3) removes excess coating before the intaglio roll meets the rubber-covered application roll (4). This roll transfers the coating to the paper which is at the same time coated on the other side.

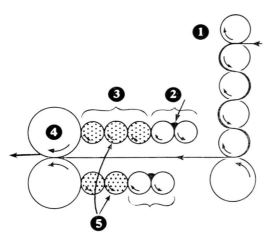

Schematic diagram of the Consolidated roll coater. The paper enters the calender stack (1) and is smoothed and compacted before coating. The first two rolls of the coater (2) are for metering, the arrow points to the coating reservoir; the next three rolls (3) are distributing rolls, the large roll (4) applies the coating to the paper. (5) indicates an oscillating roll in the distributor train. All rolls are rubber-covered. The rolls below the paper have the same functions as those above. The paper is coated on both sides in one pass through the equipment. (This and the following three diagrams of coating are adapted from TAPPI Monograph No. 28, Pigmented Coating Processes for Paper and Board.)

Roll coating can also be done by *gravure coaters* which are a more recent development. Such a coater uses an engraved intaglio roll as metering device. The coating material is applied to the intaglio roller in excess by a rubber-covered furnish roll which rotates partly in the furnish pan. The engraved intaglio roll is doctored by a blade whereby the excess furnish or coating is removed. The coating is then transferred to a large rubber-covered application roll and from it to the paper. If gravure coaters are built for the coating of one side only, the paper is backed by an impression roll. If both sides are coated at the same time the paper runs between the two application rolls. The design of the cells, which are often called "cups" in the coating industry, is usually hexagonal because "the hexagon is the one pattern in which the spreading action under pressure is equidistant in all directions with a uniform 'land area' around the cell." The depth of cells before chromium plating is between 0.003 and 0.004 in. and the number of cells per linear inch depends on the amount of coating to be applied. When the gravure roller contacts the application roll the contents of the individual cells form discrete deposits; these flow into each other and are a continuous film when the coating is transferred from the application roll to the paper.

The art of roll coating has been competitively stimulated by the success of blade coating. Even though not all experts are of the same opinion concerning the future of roll coating, some emphasize the great advantage of roll coaters which is primarily rugged simplicity resulting in trouble-free operation, especially when gravure coaters are used.[71]

The similarity between the described coating systems and printing presses is great. This becomes especially clear when you compare the gravure coater and the Anilox roller of flexographic presses. (See Chapter VI, Section 3, Inking Units.) There is also a similarity between roll coaters and web-offset presses. In blanket-to-blanket presses the blanket cylinder of one printing unit is the impression cylinder of the other, with the paper running in between. In simultaneous roll coating the two applicator rolls take the place of the two blanket cylinders; each applicator roll acts as back-up roll for the other. There are several roll-coating methods in use, differing in the number of rolls, the covering of rolls, and the rotational direction of the applicator roll relative to the running direction of the web. Usually these methods can be used for both simultaneous and successive coating of both sides of the web. In successive coating, called *tandem coating* in the paper industry, each applicator roll has its own back-up roll.

Blade coating of papers. "The most dramatic change in coated paper manufacture has been the conversion to blade coating. This change from roll to blade has taken place mostly in the last ten years with a phenomenal increase in the last five. Blade coating has given the printer the smoother printing surface necessary for the increased use of color and better copy reproduction. In the letterpress and rotogravure publication field there is very little roll coated paper sold any more. Blade coating has also allowed lower coat weights, which are necessary for the lighter weight pub-

lication grades."[72] Blade coating is done in a number of different ways, directly on the paper machine or off the paper machine by independent coating equipment. Two kinds of blade coating processes, the Champion coating process and the trailing blade process are next briefly characterized, beginning with the Champion process which was developed first, in the 1930's.

In the *Champion Coating Process* an applicator roll, which rotates partly in a pan with liquid coating, applies an excess of coating material to the running web of paper. (The applicator roll rotates in the opposite direction of the web travel.) "As the liquid portion of the coating layer adjacent to the surface of the web drains into the substrate, a semi-solid layer of filter cake is formed. Next a wiping blade, or doctor, removes the still-fluid portion of the coating from the web, leaving behind the smoothly coated surface. At one time steel doctors with a rounded wiping surface were used, and this wiping surface was chrome plated to resist abrasion and to prolong blade life. It was found, however, that foreign particles would catch on these blades, scratching the freshly coated surface. This serious problem was finally overcome by the invention of a coater blade which made use of a small-diameter, chrome-plated rod to doctor the coating. The rod diameter can vary, say, between little more than one eighth and three eighths of an inch. The rod rotates at a fixed speed on the order of 10 to 20 r.p.m. and is continually wiped clean by two thin spring-metal strips."

Two-side coating is done in two different locations separated from each other by six or eight drying drums. It is also possible to coat the paper twice on one side with two coaters, for high-quality label papers, for example, and to have a three coater installation, thereby coating one side once and the other two times. "In recent years four Champion coaters have been installed on some machines so both sides of the paper may be coated twice. On most board machines it is desirable to make two coating applications with Champion coaters. Single coated board, however, is frequently made as an intermediate quality between uncoated and double-coated grades." The main advantages of the Champion coater are low cost and simplicity of operation; the difficulties are due to the fact that coating takes place on a rough wet surface."[73] It should be mentioned that non-pigmented as well as pigmented materials can be applied by the Champion coater, which ex-

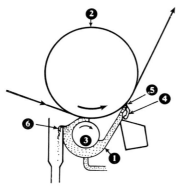

*Schematic diagram of a trailing blade flood coater.
(1) is the coating pan; the paper is flood coated between
(2) the back-up roll and (3) the applicator roll which
rotates in the coating pan. After the paper is flood
coated it moves on the back-up roll to (5) where a
doctor blade removes the excess coating. (4) is the jaw
that holds the doctor blade, (6) is the overflow of
the coater.*

tends the range of this equipment to grease proofing and to surface sizing.

The second blade coating process, or group of coating processes, to be described here is known as *trailing blade coating*. Trailing blade coating was first patented in 1945 and considerably modified thereafter. "Three types of trailing blade coaters have been used commercially on publication papers. Two, which are basically described in the 1945 patent, are the 'puddle' type and the 'inverted' type; the third is known as the Flexiblade coater." Much as these three types may differ in many points they have certain features in common. Essentially the coating is applied to the moving web in excess thereby covering the surface of the moving web more than amply. The excess is removed by a flexible steel blade. Blade thickness varies with the viscosity and solids content of the coating color, 0.020 inch blades being used at higher viscosities and lighter blades from 0.012 to 0.016 inch at lower ones. In puddle coaters the blade is usually at a 30° angle at the point of contact with the paper.

Trailing blade coaters operate best in a range of 1,500 to 3,000 f.p.m. They are widely used for coating publication grade papers on the paper machine. "The main advantage of trailing blade coaters is the levelness of the coating at any coat weight, with no undesirable pattern. The blade tends to leave a level surface with the 'valleys' filled in. This permits a superior printing surface without excessive crushing on the supercalenders,

resulting in a finished sheet with more resiliency and impression tolerance, and with better opacity and resistance to show-through of the ink. A further advantage is the low capital cost of the equipment. The trailing blade coater, however, requires very clean coating color, which must be carefully screened, in order to avoid scratches of the blade." The coating material can be of high viscosity and final coat weights can vary from 3 to 8 lb. per side per ream, basis weight 25 × 38 inches.[74]

Coating on the paper machine is very economical and results in papers of good printing quality, but "the highest quality coated papers are still produced by off-machine coating."[75] Two off-machine coating methods, the air doctor coater and cast coating are next briefly explained.

The air doctor coater. The name doctor coater is formed in analogy to the term doctor blade which you have met in the explanation of contemporary gravure printing. There, a sharpened steel blade is used to wipe the image carrier on its surface removing unwanted ink from the non-printing areas. In the air doctor the wiping function of the metal blade is performed by a jet of air with no metal blade used at all.

The air doctor, "a Warren development now generally used,"[76] is either installed on fourdrinier machines where the paper to be coated is made, or on the much slower cylinder machines on which paper boards are produced. The air doctor coater is composed of the following essential parts: (1) the dip roll, (2) the applicator roll and its coating

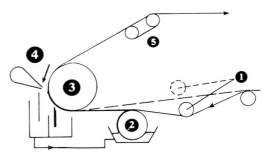

*Schematic diagram of the air doctor blade coater. For
coating, the dip roll (1) is lowered and the paper is
coated by the applicator roll (2) that rides in the coating pan. Then the paper goes over the breast roll (3)
and is exposed to the air doctor (4). The airjet acts like
a metal doctor blade, removing excess coating and
leaving a smooth uniform paper coat. The excess material is returned to the coating pan by a return system.
The suction apron (5) provides the driving force for this
kind of coater.*

pan, (3) the breast roll, (4) the air doctor itself, (5) a baffling and return system and (6) a suction apron. The position of the dip roll is decisive for bringing the web in contact with the applicator roll or for by-passing. The applicator roll is comparatively small; it may consist of rubber, steel, or brass; and it is controllable as to its speed and also as to its rotational direction. The main task of this roll is "to bring as uniform a film of coating as possible to the paper." The breast roll supports the paper during doctoring. The air doctor "consists essentially of a plenum chamber holding a reserve supply of air for forcing out through the lips which form the slot. These lips are carefully machined to give a smooth flow of air and are adjustable to regulate the thickness of the air jet." The excess coating is defoamed and returned to the pan by the baffling and return system. The suction apron, finally, supplies the driving force when coating paper. It is not required in air doctor installations for the coating of paper boards. The unique advantage of the air doctor is that a uniform weight of coating can be applied to all areas of the web. This feature distinguishes air doctors

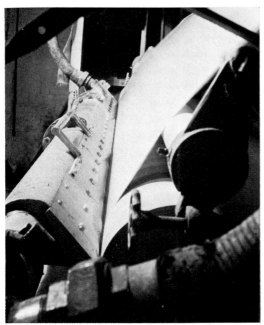

The air blade of an air-blade coater. In air blade coating the paper is first roll coated. Then it passes under the air blade which smooths the coating and blasts or shaves away excess coating material.

from fixed blade coaters which tend to scrape the hills and fill the valleys of the papers.

Common speeds of air doctors for pigment coated papers are between 400 and 1,000 f.p.m.; paper boards are air doctored at speeds between 200 and 800 f.p.m. Each side of the paper must be coated separately.

The main advantage of the air doctor coater is that it can be easily adjusted for different stocks and coating conditions. The main disadvantage is that air doctoring is limited to coatings of a low solids content or, in other words, to coatings having a relatively high percentage of water. High water content of the coating makes drying more difficult and expensive.[77]

Cast coating of papers. Cast-coated papers are the elite of pigment coated printing papers. This coating method can be simply described in its essentials. The paper is coated with a high solid content mixture on one side of the web. This side with the still wet coating is pressed against the surface of a heated metal drum. The working surface is chromium plated and highly polished, endowing the coated paper with a mirror-like quality. Donald Bradner, the original inventor of this process "coined the term 'cast coating' to define this process. 'Casting' is considered to be the process of hardening the pigment-coated surface against the polished metal drying drum to produce a surface corresponding to that of the drying drum. The drying drum surface is called the casting surface."[78] The same kind of coating is also named "molding." Cast coating is more practical with heavier papers than with lighter ones. The water of the wet coating is evaporated from the uncoated side of the web. Consequently, two-side cast coating presents certain manufacturing problems. Cast coating is slow, and cast coated papers are expensive. "The paper surface, however, is unmatched in gloss and smoothness."[79]

The drying of coated papers. As already explained paper coatings consist of two kinds of components: the coating solids and water. The coating solids remain on the paper and are the final coat; the water is needed for dispersing the solids and as a vehicle during the application of the coating. After coating the paper must be dried, meaning that now the water must be removed from the coated paper. Drying of coated paper is accomplished by exposing it to heat and air. The problem of heat drying is also present in printing and discussed in several places in this manual, particularly in Chapter VI, Section 7.

There it is mentioned that heat can be transferred to objects in three different ways, singly or in combination. The three methods of heat transfer are conduction, convection, and radiation. All of these methods are used in the drying of printing inks and all of them can be used in the drying of coated papers.

It is difficult to overrate the importance of water removal and drying in papermaking. As you may remember, the paper stock has a water content of 99 per cent, and even more, when it is spread on the wire of the paper machine whereas the final paper may not contain more than approximately 7 per cent moisture. A high proportion of the excess water is removed by suction on the wet end of the machine but when the paper enters the dry end it still contains a substantial amount of water. Coating on the paper machine adds to this amount, and drying must remove both unwanted water of the paper and the water functioning as a vehicle of the paper coating. Since the specific heat of water is higher than that of ink solvents, and since the total amount of water may be much larger than that contained in printing inks, the drying problem is much more severe in papermaking and in paper coating than is usually realized outside the paper industry.

With the exception of cast-coated papers in which coating and drying are done almost simultaneously, all coated papers must be dried following the operation of coating. Much off-machine coated paper is dried by convection, or hot-air drying. One-side coated papers are sometimes still festooned over sticks during air drying, though festooning is little used at present. In tunnel driers, which are used for the drying of papers coated by air doctors, the web is not festooned but supported by air jets or by a conveyor. Air is blown on the flat traveling web through nozzles. This arrangement permits control of drying and produces paper of a specified moisture content. Conveyor driers are built in various designs depending on the kind of paper wanted.

The paper industry uses several different kinds of driers for the drying of coated papers. Their detailed discussion would be too technical for readers interested in general information only. It might be mentioned that high-velocity air driers and driers using radiant energy are among them. The principles on which such driers are based are the same for driers of coated papers and of printing inks. These principles are explained in Chapter VI, Section 7, and need not be repeated at this point. After the completion of coating the paper is wound on the reels or rewound in off-machine coating. With the exception of cast-coated papers most coated papers are smoothed by supercalendering, an operation that may or may not be repeated depending on the grade of paper. Some dull-coated papers are supercalendered, others are not supercalendered.

The composition of paper coatings. Paper coatings are formulated with a great variety of materials. For a general discussion these can be grouped according to their state into liquid and solid substances. The most important, and practically the only liquid component of most paper coatings is water. The solids of paper coatings can be divided into three broad groups: (1) adhesives, sometimes called binders, (2) pigments, and (3) miscellaneous additives. The liquid component, water, does not remain on the dried coated paper, or perhaps more correctly, remains only to a small extent as part of the final coating. The solids, on the other hand, remain on the paper and form the actual coat. The ratio of solids to water is an important consideration of coatings, and it is customary to distinguish between high-solids and low-solids coating formulas. According to Casey, high-solids coating mixtures contain between 50 and 70 per cent solids whereas low-solids mixtures have 30 to 50 per cent solids.[80]

The difference in the solids contents percentage has a controlling influence on production speed, other conditions assumed equal. "A coating mixture of 40 per cent solids requires the evaporation of about 1.5 lb. of water for each pound of dry coating applied, whereas less than 0.5 lb. of water need be evaporated for a coating mixture of 70 per cent solids. Machine-coated papers must dry rapidly so that the coating will not be scratched by the drier surface."[81] It is therefore not surprising that the operating speed of the same paper machine drops sharply when coatings of a lower solid content are used.

The water content of a paper coating cannot be arbitrarily reduced but depends on the nature of the solid ingredients and also on the coating method selected. (Air doctor coating, for example, cannot be done with high-solids coating materials.) The flow characteristics of adhesives and of pigments differ, and so do other properties of these materials. Colloid chemistry, rheology (a branch of physics dealing with flow), the development of new processes and new raw materials have greatly advanced the science of coating, but it has remained an art to balance often conflicting requirements in the formulation of a coating for a particular purpose.

The solid materials constituting adhesives include casein, soybean protein, starches, animal glue, and also synthetic products like polyvinyl alcohol, water-soluble resins, and methyl cellulose, to mention the most commonly used ones. White pigments are inorganic and are practically identical with those enumerated under the head of loading and filling. If papers with a colored coating are wanted, colored pigments are incorporated in the coating mixture. Natural colored pigments have given way to synthetic ones which are superior to natural pigments.

Coat weight and basis weight. The final coat on the paper represents a different percentage of its basis weight depending on the kind or grade of paper wanted, the composition of the coating, and the coating method employed. (Basis weight is the weight of a ream, usually of 500 sheets, of a given standard size; coating is the liquid material to be applied to the paper, coat is the dry residue on the paper.) The following figures are given for the range of coat weights obtainable with four discussed coating methods: The Consolidated coater can produce coats ranging from 2 to 15 lb. per side and ream (ream means in this unit always 500 sheets, basic size 25 × 38 inches); the Champion machine coating process can make coats of as little as 2–3 lb., but the usual weight is 5–8 lb.

per side and ream in single coating and 7–14 lb. per side in double coating. The coat weight range of the air doctor coater is from 1 to 2 lb. up to 40–50 lb. per ream; and the coat weights obtained in cast coating are usually high, ranging between 10 and 25 lb. per side and ream.[82]

Generally speaking, machine coated papers have coats of lower weights than off-machine coated papers. In lightweight publication grades (basis weight 38–42 lb.) the coat weight must be kept to a minimum to leave enough fiber in the sheet for strength. Such papers are usually blade coated and have coats of 3 to 7 lb. per ream per side. "According to present practice, a 60 lb. litho coated one side generally contains about 15 to 16 lb. of coating per ream; a 70 lb. letterpress sheet coated both sides generally contains about 12 to 13 lb. per side; and a 50 to 55 lb. machine-coated magazine paper coated both sides generally contains about 7 to 10 lb. of coating per side."[83] Conversion of these figures into per cent of basis weight shows that the coat of 60 lb. one side coated offset runs between 25 and 27 per cent; the two coats of a 70 lb. two-side coated letterpress sheet are between 34 and 37 per cent of basis weight; and those of 50 to 55 lb. two-side coated magazine papers have approximately the same percentage. It might be added that "thickness of the dried coating film ordinarily varies from about 5 microns on machine-coated papers to about 12–15 microns on off-machine coated papers."[84]

Section 4:   Introduction to Paper Properties and Terminology

Everybody who becomes interested in printing papers faces two difficulties: paper terminology and the diversification of paper. Paper is made in an unbelievable variety. As new synthetic materials are constantly developed and applied to papermaking, the process of proliferation is a continuing one. The changing needs of society express themselves also in the paper industry which must meet some of the new demands with new products. It is only natural that such a large and diversified industry has its own peculiar vocabulary not known to outsiders. Similar situations exist in all industries, though the number of people who are marginally interested in paper is perhaps exceptionally large.

People of the most diversified occupations have to deal with paper, sporadically or more frequently, in the course of their work. Various oc-

cupational groups are evidently interested in different aspects of paper, and consequently in different paper terms. Designers and artists, to begin with, are most concerned with appearance; printers, binders, and those in charge of other phases of mechanical processing focus on performance characteristics; advertisers or users of package materials think of papers in terms of end use; and all occupational groups have a common interest in economy and price.

This section was written to explain some, and not more than some, of the many terms used in describing and specifying paper. These explanations precede the characterizations of papers and other printing stocks, in Section 5, because some of the terms explained here must be used there.

This section consists of three units: The first discusses paper terms and characteristics related to appearance. In the second unit the same is done for performance during printing and other processing. The theme of the third unit is terminology related to estimating and ordering of paper.

Terms Related to the Appearance of Paper

This unit begins with a suggestion. If you are really interested in appearance characteristics you will benefit most from the following discussion if you have some sample books of paper and a magnifying glass handy. Using them will supplement the written word with visual and tactile experience.

When you look at a sheet of paper you notice immediately that it has two sides and four edges. If these sides and these edges were always the same, mentioning the obvious would be pointless pedantry. But sides, and edges too, differ in different papers and need description and identification in relation to appearance as well as to performance of paper during printing and subsidiary processing.

In all discussions of papers, and particularly in a discussion of their appearance differences, papers are best divided into two groups: uncoated and coated papers.

Uncoated and coated papers. The difference between uncoated and coated papers is that the printing surfaces of uncoated papers consist of the paper stock itself (which may or may not be surface sized) whereas in coated papers the printing surface is a pigment coat, consisting of white mineral pigments in white papers and of synthetic organic pigments in colored papers. These pigments are held together and to the paper stock by adhesive materials which are combined with the pigments in the coating formula, as explained in the preceding section.

The surface characteristics of these two major groups of papers differ greatly, as will be shown presently. Surface characteristics are summarized by paper people with the word finish, which needs an explanation.

The meanings of finish. In the paper industry the term finish is applied to the texture or the "feel" of papers, and to other appearance characteristics. Finish "is a composite property and includes smoothness, softness, gloss, and other less definable properties. Because of its complexity, finish cannot be expressed by a single value, and is usually expressed as high, medium, or low in the opinion of the observer."[85] It is therefore always

best to explain what is meant by a certain finish. In uncoated papers finish refers to two differently produced surface characteristics.

Finishes indicative of paper smoothness. Uncoated papers are made in several degrees of smoothness. The smoothness of paper is an important consideration in its selection for different reproduction tasks. The general rule is simple: In all direct printing methods (letterpress, newspaper relief printing, flexography, gravure, collotype, and screen process) decreasing dot sizes of halftone images require paper of increasing smoothness. In offset lithography and other indirect printing methods, paper smoothness may be less important depending on the nature of art-and-copy, but here too it may matter, and even greatly. Paper can be used as it comes off the drying drums of the paper machine, or it can be passed after drying through stacks of calenders which are part of the paper machine, or it can be wound in rolls after machine calendering and later passed, once or several times, through independent supercalenders.

Uncalendered, machine-calendered, and super-

Courtesy S. D. Warren Company

A supercalender stack. The final glossy finish is obtained on supercalenders where alternate rolls of steel and cotton provide pressure and smooth the paper by polishing it.

calendered papers vary in their smoothness. The customary finishes of uncoated book papers are, from less to more smooth, *antique, eggshell, vellum, machine finish* (MF), and *English finish* (EF). All these finishes can be obtained on the paper machine without putting the paper through subsequent off-machine operations. For this reason these five finishes are classed together. Additional calendering on supercalenders further improve the smoothness of paper. A very frequently used grade of supercalendered paper is designated as *super* or *SC* (S & SC stands for surface sized and supercalendered), and uncoated papers including lightweight paper boards of still greater smoothness are called *plate finished*.

The two sides of uncoated papers have different surface characteristics. These are due to the way in which paper is made. The paper side directly in contact with the wire of the paper machine is called the *wire side*, the other side is the *top side* or the *felt side*. (Felt side dates back to the time when paper was handmade. Then the coucher peeled the wet paper off the wire where it was molded and put it between felts for pressing.) Paper is therefore considered a *two-sided* material, meaning that each of the two sides has different characteristics. "The wire side is more open, contains less size, filler, and short fibers, and has a more pronounced grain. The felt side, on the other hand, has a closer formation, and has less grain because of better crossing of the fibers. It is usually the better printing side."[86]

All uncoated papers are two-sided in consequence of papermaking, but some papers have in addition to their natural felt side also a *felt finish*. Felt finishes can be made in several ways. If they are made on the wet press by impressing the still wet paper with variously structured felts, they are akin to *linen finishes* made in the same way by using linen instead of felt. (Linen finishes and felt finishes can also be made by embossing the dry paper.) Two other frequently used finishes of uncoated papers are *laid* and *wove*, which are made by the dandy roll on the paper machine. The dandy roll is also used for watermarking, as explained in Section 3.

Paper finishes made by embossing. Some papers have a strongly pronounced finish which is not the result of progressive compacting and smoothing of paper but made by embossing the paper after it has left the paper machine. The difference between finishes made on the machine and those made by embossing is that practically any paper can be embossed with any conceivable pattern. The pattern is incorporated in a roll which is put into a rotary embosser, a machine similar to a mangle, and the paper is passed through this machine, dry under pressure, at the mill. Commonly used embossing patterns include linen, leather, skytogen, and tweed, to mention some. Just as paper mills give proprietary names to their papers they give also proprietary names to some of their finishes. Textured papers are not generally suitable for halftone printing by direct image transfer though they may be usable for halftone printing in offset lithography and other indirect printing methods. If fine halftones and strongly structured papers are wanted, smooth paper is used for printing, and embossing is done after printing. In large printing centers some finishers include rotary embossing, often called pebbling, in their services. It is also possible to emboss paper in vertical presses as used in binderies for stamping. The embossing dies are of course not rotary but flat for this purpose. And if necessary, structured papers can be smoothed in certain areas on vertical embossing presses, an operation called *debossing* or *blanking* in the trade.

Coated papers and their finishes. Coated papers are used where fine halftones are wanted for printing of books, magazines, catalogs, advertising, and other persuasion printing as well as for package printing. Even though typical non-package and typical package printing papers and paper boards can be rather different, it is not possible to draw a strict dividing line between the two. It happens frequently that papers made for package printing are used for advertising and other kinds of persuasion printing, and some papers originally developed as typical printing papers have been introduced with great success in the field of package printing.

Coated papers can be divided according to the composition of the adhesive ingredients of the coating: coatings with aqueous vehicles and coatings with non-aqueous, lacquer-like, vehicles. The first kind is overwhelmingly used in typical printing and also in typical package papers. The second kind is used to some extent in metallic papers and certain specialties which can be bypassed for the time being, so the discussion can concentrate on papers made with aqueous coatings.

Coated papers are identified by their proprietary brand names. Such brand names often contain the word enamel which has no precise technical meaning. Papers can be coated on one side only which is indicated by C1S or on two sides C2S; they can be coated once or several times, and some mills indicate double coats in their brand names. Coated papers are classified in three groups according to their relative gloss: dull,

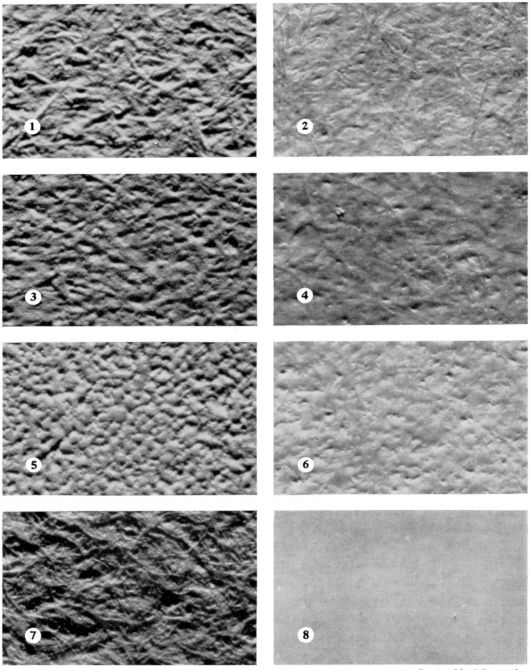

Courtesy Mead Corporation

Eight different paper surfaces: (1) is blade coated uncalendered, (2) is blade coated supercalendered, (3) is two-stage roll coated, uncalendered, (4) is two-stage roll coated, supercalendered, (5) is roll coated, uncalendered, (6) is roll coated, supercalendered, (7) is vellum, an uncoated paper finish, and (8) is finished cast coated. Magnification of all surfaces is 25 times.

semidull, and glossy. Dull coated papers are selected when ease of reading is the overriding consideration, glossy papers when the main emphasis is on fine halftone and full-color reproduction. Like uncoated papers, coated ones can also be embossed; such papers are used for indirect printing rather than for direct methods.

Papers for package printing are usually coated one side, and so are lightweight paper boards which are consumed in huge quantities for folding boxes. Coated boards are often described as *clay coated*, a term not in use with coated papers. Colored papers for package printing are often *flint glazed;* metallic papers are made either by coating or by metalizing; coated metallic papers contain bronzes of various colors as their pigments and the coating vehicle may be either aqueous or a lacquer; the latter kind is called *pyroxylin coated*. Metallized paper is made in a high vacuum by condensation of metal vapors on paper. Another kind of metallic paper, foil, is merely mentioned at this point. Foils and flint papers are discussed in Section 5, together with other stocks for package printing.

Deckle-edge papers. Handmade paper is made in the form of sheets in molds, whereas machine-made paper is made as a continuous, endless web. All four edges of handmade paper are somewhat irregular in outline, and the thickness of the paper decreases at the edges compared with the thickness of the sheet itself. These irregularities are due to the flowing out, or feathering out, of the paper as it approaches the deckle which is a wooden frame put on the mold to contain the paper stock.

Contemporary deckle-edge papers are made as webs either on fourdrinier or on cylinder machines. (Fourdrinier machines can be subdivided to make more than a single web at the same time.) On older machines, deckle straps were used on either side of the web. Deckles can also be made by jets of water or of air directed at the edges of the web. Each web can have two deckle edges, one on each side. If the final sheet has the full width of the web it has two deckle edges and two straight edges; the deckle edges are always grain long. If the final sheet has half the web width, it has one deckle edge and three straight edges. Deckle-edge papers made on cylinder machines are called moldmade papers. Since handmade papers are also made in molds this term can cause confusion. Many paper people prefer to call papers made in sheets handmade and to use moldmade for papers made as webs in molds of cylinder machines.[87]

Paper Terms Related to Printing and Subsidiary Operations

Even though all appearance characteristics have some bearing on printing, paper terminology includes a number of words that pertain primarily to printing and subsidiary production steps.

The meaning of paper grain. Paper grain is an important consideration for printing and binding. Even though this term is extensively used it is neither precise nor self-explanatory. Grain refers to the position of fibers in the paper. During papermaking the fibers are oriented with their longer dimension parallel to the length of the paper machine and with their much smaller dimension across the paper machine. The grain of a sheet indicates the machine direction; the other dimension of the sheet is sometimes called cross-grain.

Practical importance of paper grain. "The effects of grain on paper properties are shown in the following ways: (1) Paper tears more easily in the grain direction than across the grain. (2) Paper is stiffer in the grain direction. (3) When paper absorbs or gives off moisture with changes in atmospheric humidity, it expands or contracts more in the cross direction than in the grain or machine direction."[88]

Selecting paper grain. Grain selection can be rather technical. One well known writer on paper listed 12 different points that should be considered when specifying grain direction.[89] The grain direction is of particular importance in folding. Where paper made on a fourdrinier machine is folded with the grain and the fold runs parallel to the fibers these are not injured, but in the folds across the grain many of the fibers and fiber bonds must be broken. Paper boards made on cylinder ma-

In sheet-fed offset printing of register jobs the sheets are wanted grain long. Grain is equivalent to machine direction.

chines, on the other hand, are most successfully folded or bent across the grain.

In all books and periodicals grain direction and binding edge should be parallel. If paper with opposite grain is used the pages will turn less easily.

This is well known to some experienced advertising production men who like to print inserts for magazines with grain across the binding direction, knowing that the magazines will tend to open at their inserts, particularly if they are printed on a heavier paper than the magazine itself.

Paper grain for sheet-fed offset printing. Paper for sheet-fed offset printing is usually specified grain long. This means that the paper fibers are mostly parallel with the longer sheet dimension and also with the longer plate dimension. (Generally speaking, the plates of sheet-fed presses are longer across the cylinder and shorter around it.)

There are two reasons for specifying offset papers grain long. As mentioned above, changes in moisture affect paper more across the grain than with the grain. It is only sensible to select the more vulnerable dimension to be the short one and thereby to reduce register trouble. The second reason is that the sidewise position of printed images cannot be changed, or only very little changed, whereas the position of printed images can be much better controlled around the cylinder or in its short dimension. (Techniques for influencing the length of the impression are described in Chapter VII, Section 4, at the discussion of packing.) Paper with the grain long is more important in close register work than in loose or no register jobs. In single-color printing paper with the grain short may be used if grain short is desired for folding or end use. In web-offset printing, as in all other methods of web printing, the paper grain is always in the web direction.

Flatness and related terms. Ideally, printing papers should be absolutely flat. A sheet that has *wavy edges* is distorted, and this "distortion will result in *fanning in* or shortening of the back edges of the sheets laterally. If the condition is bad enough, wrinkles will be formed running from the center to the back edges. If a sheet has *tight edges*, indicated by the pile being bulgy or high in the center, the distortion during the offset impression will result in stretching or *fanning out* of the back edges."[90] Wavy edges can be attributed to the fact that during an increase in relative humidity the edges of the sheets absorb more moisture while the moisture content of the major portion of the paper remains unchanged. Tight edges are the result of conditions opposite to those causing wavy edges. When the surrounding pressroom atmosphere has a relative humidity lower than that represented by the moisture content of the paper in the pile, the edges dry out or shrink.

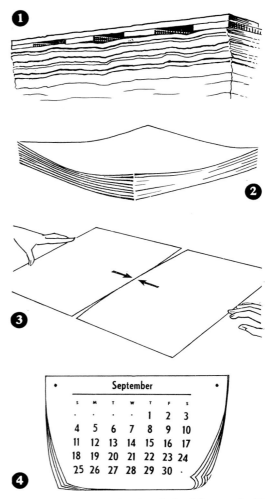

our paper troubles related to lack of flatness. In (1) you see paper with wavy edges; (2) shows paper with tight edges; (3) shows bowed edges and how they can be clearly seen, and (4) shows a calendar pad with paper curl. (All based on GATF Publication No. 308.)

Both wavy and tight edges can cause wrinkles during presswork.[91]

Slitting, sheeting, and trimming. These three terms refer to the edges of papers and to the squareness of sheets. As the paper comes off the machine, its two edges are removed by slitting. At a later stage the huge rolls that have the width of the paper machine are divided across the width by slitting. Sheeting divides the web in its length by use of rotary cutters. Sheeting can be done as a multiple or as a single-roll operation. In *multiple-roll sheeting* the webs of several rolls (3, 4, or more) are sheeted at the same time, and every cut

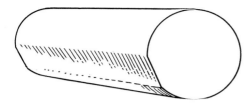

A deformed roll of paper. The flattening of the roll is due to storage on its side rather than on its end.

produces as many sheets of paper as there are webs. *Single-roll sheeting* results in a single sheet per cut. Papers cut with rotary cutters are said either to be *untrimmed* or to be *machine trimmed.* Such sheets may not be sufficiently square for presswork and are squared, either at the mill or at a printing plant, with guillotine cutters. Some mills use automatic finishing equipment which inspects, slits and sheets the paper, rejects bad sheets, and carries those that pass to paper skids for wrapping and shipping; such machines are also inserting ream markers automatically in the paper during piling.

Cores, splices, and flagging. These are some of the terms needed in describing paper in roll form as used in web printing. *Cores* are tubes on which the paper is wound; they can differ in diameter and in other respects. *Splices* join paper webs within a roll, *flagging* means that the location on the roll of a splice is indicated thereby enabling the pressman to remove a spliced signature or newspaper section from the delivery. Other terms used in conjunction with paper rolls refer to winding, slitter dust, width, and diameter.

Terms Related to Estimating and Ordering of Paper

The number of terms to be explained in this unit is much smaller than that needed for describing appearance or processing of paper. Unfortunately these few terms often pose more difficulties to the uninitiated than do all others together. The problem that causes this difficulty is in itself a simple one. It is the conversion of paper areas into paper weights and vice versa. This conversion must be made because paper is sold by its weight but used by its area.

Reasons for selling paper by weight and using it by area. The reason for selling paper by weight is that the cost of paper is determined by weight more than by any other factor. Even though variations in sheet size influence cost to some extent, these cost items are of much less importance than

weight. In use, the importance of weight and area is reversed. Weight still plays a role in material handling and the costs related to it, but paper area is now decisive. Paper area—in the form of either sheet size or web width and cut-off—is decisive in fitting paper to available press equipment. The total weight of paper does not even enter at this stage of printing production, though sheet thickness, or paper caliper, may. Advertising in newspapers and magazines is also sold by area; the publisher is said to sell "space" and the advertiser to buy it. The reason why paper is used by area is simply explained: Paper is only the substratum for printed images; the larger the area of this substratum is, the more images will be borne by it, other conditions assumed equal.

In the printer's office, areas of paper must be converted into weights and vice versa. Every estimate requires these calculations. It must be established how many sheets of a specified size, or how many rolls of a specified width and diameter, are needed for each particular job and to what weight, to how many pounds or tons, the wanted paper area amounts. For making these calculations two kinds of data are essential. They are technically known as the basic size and the basis weight of specific papers.

Basic size and basis weight. The official *Dictionary of Paper* has the following definition of basic size: "A certain sheet size recognized by buyers and sellers as the one from which its basis weight is determined." The same book defines basis weight as "the weight in pounds of a ream (usually 500 but sometimes 480 sheets) of paper cut to its basic size."[92] Basic size dates back to a time when printing was mainly done on sheet-fed presses and when web printing was only practiced in newspaper and magazine printing. In our own time web printing is constantly growing, and some people are confused by the expression basic *size* in its application to paper in roll form. A simple change in terminology can remove all doubts. You are invited to think of basic size, the established terms, as of *basic area.* Basic area is equally applicable to sheets and rolls of paper. In Table VI you find basic sizes expressed as basic areas. (Since basic size is the generally accepted terminology it is used in the following discussion, even though the writer is convinced that basic area would be preferable.)

Papers are made in many different sizes and different basis weights. The basic size may coincide with the actually needed size but it is essentially a standard to which any size and basis weight of paper of *its kind* must be referred for conversion of sizes or areas into weights. An example will make clear what this practically means. Bond paper, the kind of paper used for letterheads, has a basic size of 17 × 22 inches. It is usually made in basis weights ranging from 13 to 24 lb. This means that 500 sheets 17 × 22 inches weigh 13 lb. if the basis weight is 13, and correspondingly more if the basis weight is higher. Bond paper is commonly stocked in more than 15 different sizes. The weight of a ream of the selected size must be determined by relating the area of the selected size to that of the basic size and by multiplying or dividing the basis weight accordingly. Even though the catalogs of paper merchants contain this information for the standard sizes of papers stocked by them, the standard data are not always applicable. In situations where non-standard sizes are needed and in those where papers of *different* basic sizes though having *the same* basis weights must be compared and estimated, the necessary calculations must be made for the job in hand.

The variety of basic paper sizes. How considerable the variety of basic paper sizes is, can be seen from the following analysis of their listings in the *Paper Dictionary*. Under the head basic size there are 30 different kinds of paper enumerated with a total of 10 different basic size areas. These 30 kinds of paper are shown in Table VI, in ascending order of basic size areas. Two kinds of paper have two different basic sizes, and one kind of paper, box cover, has even three.

The smallest basic size you find in this listing is 17 by 22; the largest 25 by 38 inches. Many papers are made in several basis weights and some in a wide range of actual sheet sizes. The conversion of paper areas into paper weights can therefore become quite a chore. It is not surprising that repeated efforts were made to replace the variety of basic sizes and basis weights based on paper reams with a more simple system. Such a system is known in this country as the MM Paper System.

The MM Paper System. The MM Paper System means simply that the basic size of all papers should be 1,000 square inches and that the basis weight should be the weight of 1,000 such sheets. "Taking the place of all these useless and confusing basic sizes would be a standardized 1,000 square inches which is identified by the first M and the 1,000 sheet quantity is identified by the second M in the MM title."[93] During World War II a number of "national printing trade associations and many consumer groups endorsed the principle and a vigorous campaign was instituted to have it adopted as a wartime efficiency measure. The National Paperboard Association is the only organization which has actually put the reform into operation"[94]

Some advantages and some problems of the MM System. The change-over from a generally accepted counting, measuring, or weighing system is always expensive and troublesome. The benefits of the MM System are self-evident. Many computations could be avoided, which would save time and man hours. For this reason the Board of Directors of Printing Industries of America unanimously endorsed the MM System on October 25, 1961. The PIA Estimating Manual uses one of the two M's as a matter of course, eliminating basis weight per ream and replacing ream with 1,000 sheets, or M.[95]

The present system of using ten different basic

Table VI   TEN BASIC PAPER SIZES AND THEIR AREAS

KIND OF PAPER	Basic Size In Inches	Area In Square Inches
Bond, ledger, manifold, mimeo, railroad manila, writing	17 × 22	374
Blotting	19 × 24	456
Box cover, cover	20 × 26	520
Manuscript cover	18 × 31	558
Blanks, tough check	22 × 28	616
Mill bristol, postcard, tag, wedding bristol	22½ × 28½	641
Index bristol	25½ × 30½	778
Mill bristol	22½ × 35	786
Box cover, glassine, hanging, newsprint, poster, tag, tissues, waxing tissues, wrapping, wrapping tissues	24 × 36	864
Bible, book, box cover, gummed, offset	25 × 38	950

sizes has also its advantages. One of them is that basis weight is expressed in short, two-digit numbers that are easy to remember. But it is not possible to compare papers of the same basis weight unless they have also the same basic size. Both cover and offset papers are made in a 50-lb. basis weight, but they are far from equivalent as the first refers to an area of 520 and the second to an area of 950 square inches. A detailed comparison of the present system and the MM System is too technical for the purposes of this manual. It might be mentioned that apparently the users of paper would benefit more from MM than paper mills and merchants whose expenses would be considerable in a transition period.[96] This discussion cannot be ended without mentioning the method in which paper is specified in the metric system. In this system, which is used in many countries, basis weight is expressed in grams per square meter, abbreviated g/m^2. Both TAPPI and ASTM methods for testing basis weight contain methods and factors for conversion of basic paper sizes to grams per square meter.[97] If, as many believe, the United States will change to the metric system in the next decade or so, the gram per square meter specification method of paper may become in time generally used here too.

Specification of paper boards. Certain paper boards, used for package printing primarily, are specified by sheet size and by area. The area unit is 1,000 square feet. Paper boards made by the member firms of the National Paperboard Association are listed in three standard sizes, caliper of individual sheets, and weight in pounds per M square feet. Patent coated two sides for example, of .012 caliper, sheet size 24 × 36 inch, has a weight of 174 lb. per ream and of 58 lb. per M square feet.[98] Paper boards are further classified by finish in certain grades. "There are four standard finishes designated by numbers 1 to 4, the lowest to the highest. The degree of finish is regulated by the pressure exerted on the calenders under which the board passes. The pressure determines the density of the sheet. The resulting surface is incidental, but gains in smoothness as calender pressure is increased."[99] More than 10 gauge lists are published, covering all kinds of paper boards. Not all grades are made in all four different finishes; some are made in only two, and some only in a single finish. Non-bending boards, for example come in all four finishes, pasted chip boards come either in a rough or in a smooth finish, and test container boards are made only in a single finish.

Caliper, bulk, and substance. The correct term for the thickness of paper is caliper. The caliper of paper is expressed in thousandths of an inch. Each thousandth is called a point or, less commonly though preferably, a mil. (The term *mil* is preferable because the *caliper point* can be confused with the *typographic point*.) How paper is calipered is explained in the section on paper testing. *Bulk* is a function of caliper and expresses the number of paper sheets per inch.

Bulk is of great importance in book and publication printing; it is sometimes confused with basis weight. Papers of the same basis weight can be made to have widely different bulks. An example will illustrate this point: Depending on its construction 60 lb. basis weight book paper is available in a wide bulking gamut. High bulking paper may have as few as 320 pages per inch, low bulking paper of the same basis weight may have as many as 760 pages per inch. (High bulking papers are aptly called by some "whipped cream" papers since such papers contain a lot of air, just like whipped cream.) Intermediate bulking figures may be 390, 440, 550, 660, and 720 pages per inch. These figures are from the catalog of one mill, other mills may have different bulking data of a smaller or larger range.

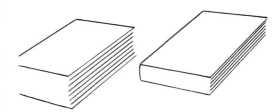

Illustration of high-bulk and low-bulk papers. The book at the left is printed on high-bulk paper and has 320 pages; the book at the right is printed on low-bulk paper and has also 320 pages. But the book at the left is twice as thick as the book at the right.

It remains to explain the meaning of substance. The explanation can be brief: *substance* is used by some as another word for basis weight. If paper is specified by *billing weight* (the weight of 1,000 sheets of actual size) substance or basis weight is sometimes added as a reference.

Section 5: Characterization of Papers and Other Printing Stocks

Papers and other printing stocks are best divided into the kinds of stocks typically used by three segments of the printing industry. These are (1) commercial, book, and publication printing, (2) the newspaper industry, and (3) package printing. Even though some printing stocks can be used in more than one segment, each of the three main industry segments has certain typical stocks which will be described now.

Papers for Commercial, Book, and Publication Printing

Paper and paper boards are the most important stocks of job-and-commercial printing. Book and publication printing uses fewer kinds of paper and paper boards than job-and-commercial printing, which is but another name for printing as a service business. As you know from the preceding section, there are more than two dozen different main groups of papers. Not all of them are typical printing papers, but it may happen that even some of those that are not are selected for printing.

Generically, papers are named by the main purpose for which they were originally made. But it should be kept in mind that these names are not precise and that papers intended for one purpose may be equally suitable for another. The generic classification of papers may need supplementing as to suitability for certain printing processes. Some papers are typical letterpress or typical offset lithographic papers, others can be used in any process and method of printing. As book papers are foremost among those used not only in book, but also in publication, and commercial printing, book papers will open the discussion.

Book papers. Book papers include papers made for publication printing; there is no grade "publication paper" as you can verify by looking at Table VI. Book papers comprise a large variety, possibly the largest class of all printing papers, differing as to colors, finishes, and basis weights.

Just as the book is the classic product of printing, so is book paper the classic paper. Traditionally, books were printed in letterpress on antique papers. Antique papers harmonize with classic printing types and are still widely used for books consisting either exclusively of reading matter or of reading matter and line illustrations. The development of halftone photography and photomechanics, and their successful application to intaglio and planographic printing make it possible to print text and halftone illustrations together in letterpress, or in gravure, or in offset lithography. Gravure is not generally used for the printing of books in this country, but gravure-printed art books are imported from Europe. Rotogravure is increasingly used in publication and commercial printing. Letterpress and offset lithography are widely used in book, commercial, and publication printing.

Halftone printing requires a smooth paper surface; more so in direct methods of image transfer, letterpress and gravure, than in indirect methods, such as offset lithography and letterset. This need can be met to a varying degree by compacting, machine calendering, supercalendering, surface sizing, and coating. The increasing use of full-color printing has added new demands on the quality of the paper surface. The better a paper reflects the whole gamut of light, the better will the final full-color reproduction be, other factors assumed equal. (These other factors are far from negligible; they include the quality of original images, color correcting, printing-image carriers, inks, and press work itself, which all affect reproduction fidelity.)

Factors causing diversification of book papers. Four factors account for the diversification of book papers: (1) *Process requirements.* Different printing processes and methods may vary in the specific properties of their papers. (2) *Requirements controlled by the smallness of image detail.* Image detail can refer to type design or pictures. Oldstyle type is more robust, modern-face designs are rather delicate. The detail of drawings and, perhaps most important, the fineness of screen number of halftones all influence paper selection. (3) *Color requirements.* Single color and multicolor jobs do not usually need papers of the same whiteness as are used for full-color printing. (4) *Cost requirements.* Economy is always a factor, but there is an essential difference in the role played by cost in persuasion printing and in printing as part of manufacturing. Persuasion printing is given away, and attractiveness is often more important than cost; cost is a much more critical item in printed products which are made for sale.

If you add differences in color and fancy finishes to these four main points, and then multiply all variables by different basis weights, the great diversification of book papers needs no further explanation.

Basic size and basis weights of book papers. The basic size of book papers is 25 × 38 inches. Offset papers and Bible papers, which are widely used as book papers, have the same basic size and are discussed together with book papers. Book papers and offset papers are made as uncoated and as coated grades; Bible papers are uncoated. The basis weight of uncoated book and offset papers is usually between 30 and 70 lb., that of coated ones ranges from 38, and even as low as 35, to 100 lb. and the basis weight of Bible papers is between 14 and 30 lb. Book and offset papers are stocked by paper merchants in a wide assortment of sizes from, say 17½ × 22½ inches up to 38 × 50 inches and even larger. Bible papers are stocked in fewer sizes, 25 × 38 and 35 × 45 inches, to mention some. Book, offset, and Bible papers are also supplied in rolls for web printing or for sheet-fed presses equipped with sheeter-feeders that sheet rolls of paper as part of feeding. Special sizes are supplied in the required basis weight as mill orders if the wanted quantity is large enough. As explained in the preceding section, uncoated and coated papers are made in different finishes which may be called by proprietary names.

Business papers. Business papers are those that

The surfaces of an uncoated and of a blade-coated off-set paper, 14 times magnified. Note that many hills and valleys of the uncoated paper are more leveled after coating.

are used for administrative purposes rather than for sales promotion and advertising. In this category are *bond* and *onion skin* papers which are used for stationery; *ledger* papers and *tabulating board* or papers and *punch card* stock, needed for accounting; *safety papers* for the printing of bank checks, money orders, travelers checks, and other valuable items; and also *mimeograph* and *duplicator* papers. Some kinds of business papers are for permanent records, others serve the fleeting needs of the moment. Consequently, ledger and bond papers, not to forget safety papers, are of higher quality than mimeo or duplicator papers, which are impermanent ones. Punch card papers, so widely used in machine accounting and data processing, are in a class by themselves because some of their properties must be exceptionally closely controlled.

All mentioned business papers, with the exception of punch card papers, are made in the same basic size: 17 × 22 inches. Manifold has a basis weight between 7 and 10 lb.; onion skin has the same basis weight range; bond paper is made in basis weights from 13 to 24 lb., mimeo has usually 20 lb.; and ledger papers come in basis weights between 24 and 36 lb. Bond papers are made in a wide assortment of sizes from 8½ × 11 to 35 × 45 inches; ledger papers are available in various sizes between 17 × 22 and 28 × 34 inches; and safety papers are stocked in several sizes beginning with 17 × 22 inches.

Now a few words on *tabulating board* or *punch card paper*. This kind of paper has the basic size of tag paper, 22½ × 28½ inches. It is a good example of the close tolerances that must be met in papers for machine processing. Punched cards are fed mechanically into machines. Unless these cards are relatively free from curl, feeding failures and damage to cards will result. To avoid curl, it is necessary to have uniform orientation of fibers on the two sides of the paper. It is also necessary to have uniform drying and uniform surface sizing on the top and wire sides of the paper.[100] Curl is only one of several possible troubles. Precise cutting, dimensional stability, friction control, tearing resistance, and many other points must be considered in punched card papers.

Bristols. Bristols are lightweight cardboards made either on a fourdrinier or on a cylinder machine. There are three kinds of bristols: (1) index bristols, (2) mill bristols, and (3) wedding bristols. *Index bristols* are usually made on a fourdrinier machine. They are writing papers, treated to accept writing ink and to permit erasure. The basic size of index bristols is 25½ × 30½ inches. Their basis weight is not given per ream but per M sheets and varies between 180 and 440 lb. Index bristols come in white and a number of pastel colors. *Mill bristols* are made on a cylinder machine; they are made principally for show cards and other advertising media that need a stiff sheet with a good printing surface.[101] Their basic size is 22½ × 28½ inches, their basis weight is specified per ream and varies between 90 and 200 lb. Mill bristols are made in white and in colors. Some mills make also duplexed mill bristols which have a different color on either side. *Wedding bristols* are white pasted boards with a vellum or antique plate finish. The basic size of wedding bristols is the same as that of mill bristols, 22½ × 28½ inches, their basis weight is between 120 and 240 lb. per 500 sheet ream. Wedding bristols come in different thicknesses indicated by the number of plies, from 2 to 4 ply. They are used for high prestige announcements and menu printing.

It is difficult to compare these three kinds of bristols in their areas and basis weights without calculation. The basic-size area of mill and wedding bristols is 641 square inches, that of index bristols 778 square inches. The basis weight of mill and wedding bristols is specified for 500-sheet reams, that of index bristols per M sheets. The difference between a 180 lb. index and a 90 lb. mill bristol is actually much less than the unqualified figures convey. A ream of either grade weighs 90 lb., and the main difference is in their basic sizes.

Cover papers. As the name implies, this group of papers serves for covering of printed materials. Cover stocks are widely used for soft-bound books, persuasion printing and catalogs. Considered functionally, cover stocks are to protect the covered material; this aspect of cover stocks is probably less important than appearance and attention-getting qualities. The great output of printed matter results in a keen competition for the reader's attention, and cover stocks are made in a wide variety to provide designers of printed products with the desirable choice. A line of cover papers may comprise eight to ten different colors, either strong hues or delicate pastels; different lines come in different embossed finishes, matte or high gloss, with or without deckle edges, and with different colors on either side.

Cover papers are used more for persuasion printing and for magazines that are printed in relatively small editions than for long run jobs.

General-interest magazines are either covered with the same paper on which the inside pages are printed or with a white paper that is heavier than these but not as heavy as a typical cover stock.

The basic size of cover paper is 20 × 26 inches; basis weights differ for uncoated and coated cover stocks; uncoated covers come in 50, 65, 80, and 130 lb.; coated covers in 60, 80, and 100 lb. The standard sheet sizes are 20 × 26, 23 × 35 and their doubles 26 × 40 and 35 × 46 inches.

Postcard and blotting papers. Papers for the printing of postcards are available in two kinds: one for writing and typing, the other for printing of pictures in black-and-white and in full color. Postcard papers are made in a basic size of 22½ × 28½ inches and in various basis weights. Some better grade uncoated postcard papers are called postcard bristols. Postcard papers for full-color printing are coated on one side for printing; on the other side they are treated for writing. Many museums publish postcards with reproductions of fine art subjects, sometimes on cast-coated cover papers which make excellent postcards. There are also photographic postcard papers which are coated with a silver-halide emulsion and used in the photographic mass reproduction of souvenir picture cards. Blotting papers are of decreasing importance, due to our changing writing habits. In the past when writing inks dried much less fast than they do now, when ballpoint pens were unknown, and when much more handwriting with pen and ink was done, blotters were much more widely used than now. Blotters are still used by themselves and also as a means for advertising. For this purpose a grade called enameled blotting paper is preferred. *Enameled blotting paper* consists of a coated paper laminated to blotting paper. The advertising message is, of course, printed on the coated paper side of the blotter. Blotting paper has a basic size of 19 × 24 inches and is made in basis weights ranging between 60 and 140 lb.

Label papers, blanks, and lined boards. Label papers and blanks exemplify how difficult it is to classify papers systematically and that rigid demarcation lines are not practical. Label papers are typical package papers, yet they are widely printed in shops and plants that do not specialize in package printing but are in the all around job-and-commercial class. Blanks are paper boards that are used for package printing and also for other purposes, point-of-purchase displays and car cards, to mention some. Both of these kinds of printing stocks will be discussed in the next unit, together with other stocks for package printing, but a few words on blanks belong here.

Blanks are paper boards "ranging in thickness from 0.012 to 0.078 of an inch."[102] The thickness of blanks can be a controlling factor in selecting press equipment. Most presses built for all around printing are designed for papers and relatively thin paper boards. The printing stock can be carried during the impression either by a cylinder or by a plane surface. Generally speaking, presses with impression cylinders not especially designed to handle heavy boards are not suitable for printing of blanks heavier than 0.030 inch. What thickness can be printed by a particular press must of course be individually established. All presses for gravure and lithographic printing, and all presses for relief printing, with the exception of platen presses, have impression cylinders. Lightweight boards are flexible enough to assume the curvatures of these cylinders. Heavier boards must be printed either on platen or on screen-process flatbed presses; some screen-process cylinder presses are also suitable for heavier boards.

The last item to be explained here is lined board. In lined boards paper is pasted to heavy boards with an adhesive, either on one or on both sides of the board. Lining is done by board mills, by converters, and also by finishers. Since lined boards are made to order, grade of board and paper are selected to suit individual job requirements.

Papers for Newspaper Printing

Relief printing was the only method for newspaper printing until web offset entered the lists. At present all large metropolitan newspapers are printed by relief printing; some daily and many weekly papers are printed by web offset, and some newspaper supplements are produced by rotogravure. Each of the three methods needs a somewhat different kind of paper. The paper for newspaper relief is newsprint; that for web offset can be designated as offset newsprint and that for gravure supplements as gravure newsprint.

Newsprint. The United States is consuming enormous quantities of newsprint. The raw material of newsprint is wood; some of it comes from our own forests, some from those of Scandinavia, but most comes from the forests of Canada. Newsprint must obviously be as inexpensive as possible—it represents the biggest material-cost item of newspaper production—and newsprint does not need to be permanent; unlike some book papers,

The two surfaces of newsprint, 14 times magnified. The first picture shows the wire side of newsprint, the second its felt side.

newsprint is made for the day and not for the ages. Another important characteristic of newsprint is its high absorbency. The inks used for newspaper relief printing, called *news inks*, do not form a dry film on the paper, as do other inks, but dry by absorption in the newsprint.

Newsprint has a basic size of 24 × 36 inches and a basis weight between 30 and 35 lb., "the great preponderance being 32 pounds."[103] This basis weight has proved to be the most satisfactory for newsprint, representing a practical compromise between cost and print quality. "If the newsprint is produced at significantly higher basis weight than 32 lb., it means in effect that the publisher is paying more for producing his product than if the basis weight had been 32 lb. Conversely, if the newsprint were significantly less than 32 lb. while his costs might be less for producing his product, the newsprint itself will likely be more transparent and the printing less acceptable. For this reason newsprint contracts usually specify the basis weight at which newsprint is to be delivered. ANPA (American Newspaper Publishers Association) testing programs show that about 95 per cent of all samples fall within a 31.8 to 32.2 lb. range."[104] From the point of view of production, runnability is a most important characteristic of newsprint. (Runnability, a relatively new term that refers to the performance of printing stocks during presswork, is discussed in Section 6.) Newspaper presses must be operated at ever increasing speeds and web breaks, which cause delays and interruptions, must be avoided as much as possible. A paper with ideal runnability should permit high-speed presswork with no web breaks at all.

Runnability has not been as thoroughly studied as other characteristics of newsprint. Even though much remains to be learned, "we know from our experience to date that there are inherent strength characteristics of newsprint which contribute to runnability, and it is known as well that homogeneity contributes its share. It is also widely recognized that a dry sheet of newsprint is more brittle than a sheet with high moisture content. Although the exact mechanism is not known, the addition of moisture appears to result in a more pliable, elastic and shock resistant web of newsprint. Moisture content of newsprint generally falls in the range of 6½ to 8½ per cent. Newsprint of higher runnability has a moisture content in the upper part of this range (7.5–8.5 per cent) while rolls containing less than 6.5 per cent moisture frequently have poor runnability."[105]

Smoothness, softness, opacity, and brightness are other important characteristics of newsprint. Smoothness is a controlling factor for halftone fineness in all direct-printing methods; softness is especially important in newsprint because the image carrier forces the ink into the pores of the paper during the impression. (The meaning of impression in newspaper relief printing is explained in Chapter VI, Section 1.) Opacity is important in all lightweight paper and particularly so in newspaper relief printing where the ink does not remain on the surface, but is forced deep into the paper. Brightness, or whiteness, counts because it contributes to good contrast between ink and paper in black-and-white printing and is of great importance in full-color, ROP, printing. Newsprint, has, of course, a lower brightness than good uncoated papers, let alone coated ones.

Finally, a few indications on the composition of newsprint: The usual furnish for newsprint is 75 to 85 per cent ground wood, and 15 to 25 per cent unbleached or partially bleached chemical pulp. Ground wood adds the desirable properties of high opacity, smooth surface, and high oil absorption. Chemical pulp adds the necessary strength

required to get the paper through the press without break. Newsprint is either unsized or slack sized and has a small percentage of filler, if any.

Offset newsprint. Papers for web-offset printing of newspapers must meet a number of requirements which are related to planographic printing and therefore characteristic of all offset papers. In relief printed newspapers the ink is forced between the fibers of the paper; in planographic printing, the ink is deposited on the paper surface. Inks for web offset are much stiffer than those for newspaper relief, and stiffer inks are more apt to pick or split the paper than softer ones. The construction of web-offset papers must meet this condition by better bonding of the paper fibers. Papers for web-offset printing must be stronger than similar papers for direct relief printing.

It must be kept in mind that the printing and non-printing areas of planographic plates are distinguished by their respective ink receptivity and moisture repellence, and vice versa. At each revolution of the press, the plate is dampened with the fountain solution, which consists either mainly of water or of a mixture of alcohol and water, and certain chemicals. Some of this solution is transferred to the blanket, together with the ink image and, as the paper is in contact with the blanket, from the blanket to the paper. To counteract the effects of excessive moisture, which impairs paper bonding and reduces paper strength, papers for sheet-fed offset printing are sized internally as well as on the surface. "The surface sizing also seals down the surface and prevents linting and fuzz."[106] Excessive linting and fuzz cannot be tolerated because they reduce printing quality. This means that the press must be washed up repeatedly, and press stoppage, for washup or other reasons, is most objectionable in high-speed web printing.

If sizing has the beneficial effect of strengthening offset papers, it may have another much less desirable side effect: reducing the absorption characteristics of the paper. This point is of greater consequence in web-offset printing of newspapers than in commercial web offset. Commercial web-offset installations usually have drying equipment whereas web-offset presses for newspaper printing do not have driers but rely on the absorption of the ink by the paper.

The higher printing speeds of web offset, if compared with the speed of sheet-fed presses, the much narrower cylinder gap of plate cylinders, and the resulting shorter contact between paper and blanket as well as smoother plates needing less dampening solution, all combine to reduce the amount of moisture transferred to the paper in web offset. For this reason it has become possible to print regular newsprint in web-offset newspaper production. But there are also those who prefer a modified offset version of newsprint to the regular newsprint.

Rotogravure newsprint. Rotogravure participates in the newspaper industry with three kinds of products. These are (1) gravure printed newspaper supplements, (2) HiFi gravure preprints, and (3) SpectaColor gravure preprints. Newspaper supplements are magazines, printed either in monochrome or in full color, included with the Sunday issues of newspapers. Preprints are advertisements printed on one side of the paper and supplied to newspapers in rolls. In the newspaper plant these rolls are printed on the other side of the web together with the rest of the paper. The difference between HiFi and SpectaColor preprints is that HiFi preprints can be cut, like wallpaper, at any point, whereas SpectaColor must be registered to coincide with the length of the printed pages. Rotogravure paper for supplements is a high-grade newsprint, made from groundwood and chemical pulp, and machine finished. The basic size of rotogravure newsprint is 24×36 inches, basis weights are from 32 to 34 lb. per 500-sheet ream. (Other gravure papers have a basic size of 25×38 inches.)

Flatness and smoothness are extremely important in papers for rotogravure. Rotogravure is a direct image transfer method. The paper is forced against the etched cylinder and must be sufficiently resilient to suck or lift the ink out of the cylinder cells. Irregularities in the paper surface "will prevent complete contact between the paper and the rim of individual cells, or several adjoining cells. The result is that little or no ink will be transferred and no printing will occur. The spots where printing does not take place are called skips or snow."[107]

Different from newspaper relief and offset printing which do not use forced drying, newspaper gravure printing is done with forced drying. On rotogravure presses each printing unit is followed by a drying unit through which the printed web must pass before the next color can be printed or before the web can be backed up. Since forced drying is used in rotogravure, absorptive qualities are less important in gravure paper than in newsprint which is not subjected to forced drying.

Rotogravure papers can, therefore, be sized. Surface sizing reduces ink absorption by the paper and thereby increases the gloss of printed images. However, it tends to harden the paper surface which is not desirable for the printing of highlights in rotogravure.

Receptivity to gravure ink, opacity, and whiteness are other properties desired in gravure papers. Papers for HiFi and SpectaColor inserts are usually made with better bleached pulps than those for gravure supplements where whiteness is less important.

Paper and Other Stocks for Package Printing

The spread of self-service stores and supermarkets is predicated upon packaging and package printing. The development of high-speed packaging machinery and of new, improved, and specialized package materials widened the scope of packaging, just as the increase in packaged products gave impetus to the development of less expensive, better, and more specialized package materials. The net result of this process is that package materials have become as technical as they are diversified. The present unit is a non-technical introduction to this vast field, written to explain some of the main requirements of package materials in their relation to printing.

Printing processes and package printing. Each of the four printing processes—relief, intaglio, planographic, and porous or screen-process printing—has its place in package printing. So diversified are package materials, so diversified are their purposes, that all printing methods, with the sole exception of newspaper relief printing, are called upon to do certain kinds of package printing. And so wide is the quantity range of package printing jobs that some of them are best produced on sheet-fed presses, whereas others require highly specialized web printing and inline equipment.

Labels, box wraps, and paper boards can be printed in letterpress, gravure, offset lithography, and screen process. These methods, with the exception of letterpress, are also widely used for metallic foils and plastic films. Steel-die engraving, though not widely used in package printing, may be preferred for the printing of high-prestige labels or box wraps, and screen process, also relatively little used in this field, is sometimes chosen for test runs or for production runs when some of the typical screen process features are wanted.

The most widely used mass production methods for package printing of plastic films and metallic foils are flexography and rotogravure. Both methods use solvent evaporating, low viscosity inks which lend themselves to the printing and fast drying of a wide gamut of materials, including foils and the almost unending variety of plastic films. Essentially, inks for package printing do not differ from inks for other purposes. But all inks that are used on package material for foods and drugs must conform to the requirements specified by federal supervisory agencies, notably FDA, the Food and Drug Administration, a division of the U. S. Department of Health, Education and Welfare.[108]

Which method is the best for package printing? Everything depends on the nature of the job in hand: the kind of stock, the length of run, inline fabricating, end-use requirement, and appearance preferences, not to forget price and delivery. As in all other branches of printing, the best printing method is that which can produce the wanted result with greatest speed and utmost economy.

The three main functions of packaging. All packages must do three things: attract, protect, and identify. Every package must attract the customer. Design and appearance are the salesmen in the colorful, silent yet fierce competition on the store shelves. Every package must protect the contents, if only from damage by customers' handling and manhandling, and every package must identify its contents by brand name and otherwise, in accordance with the law. Other points to be considered in selecting package materials are "machinability," which means suitability for processing on high-speed packaging equipment, and conformity with the rulings of FDA. In many cases several package materials that satisfy this last, compelling consideration are available; which of them is actually chosen depends on the nature of the case.

It is worth noting that two of the three main functions of all packaging, attracting and identifying, are provided by printing, and that package materials are responsible for protecting, the third essential function of packaging. With these points in mind, we can turn to a discussion of specific package materials.

Label papers. Label papers, wraps, and tag papers are classified as identifying papers. The label is only part of the package; the actual packages are boxes, cans, or bottles, to mention some receptacles. These contain and protect the packaged products; their labels and wraps are printed to attract customers and identify the contents. Label papers are coated for printing on one side; the other side is either uncoated, or coated with an adhesive. Adhesive-coated papers can present difficulties on the press because they may have a tendency to curl. Because of dampening, paper curl is more of a problem in offset lithography than in other methods; therefore non-curling offset label papers were developed. The basic size of label papers is 25 × 38, that of tag 22½ × 28½, and that of box covers is 24 × 36 inches.

Protective papers. Protective papers often combine all three functions, identifying, protecting, and attracting, "but their prime purpose is to protect a product from moisture, mold, insects, heat, cold, corrosion, tarnish, dust, grease, water, and so forth. For this purpose they may be treated with mold inhibitors or anti-corrosion materials, impregnated with wet-strength resins, laminated to plastic materials, or coated with plastic coatings. Such papers are usually available on mill orders only; basis weights range between 50 and 100 lb., basic size is 25 × 38 inch."[109] In the following paragraph you find brief characterizations of some widely used protective papers.

Greaseproof and glassine papers. These two kinds of papers belong to the same paper family. Greaseproof papers are made of chemical wood pulp which is treated to be oil and grease resistant. "During the beating process the hairlike fibers of cellulose are completely changed in physical appearance. These fibers absorb so much water that they become superficially gelatinized and sticky. This is called hydration."[110] Greaseproof is both an independent paper grade and also a preliminary stage in the making of glassine. "When greaseproof is further processed—at high moisture content, temperature and pressure, in roll form, over a special multi-roll supercalender stack it becomes glassine. Density is again increased, oil resistance is further improved, gloss is greatly enhanced, and (if it is not opaqued) the material becomes transparent."[111] The basic size of greaseproof and glassine is 24 × 36 inches; the basis weight of greaseproof is between 20 and 40, that of glassine between 12 and 90 lb.; most common glassine basis weights are in the range of 15 to 40 lb. Greaseproof and glassine papers are good printing surfaces, can be embossed with fine detail and are easily handled on packaging equipment.

Vegetable parchment. True parchment is not paper but a writing material prepared from animal skins. It was used in Europe before the introduction of paper. Vegetable parchment has a somewhat similar appearance but is a paper: the word "vegetable" distinguishes this kind of paper from true parchment, which is of animal origin.

Vegetable parchment is made by treating unsized paper with sulfuric acid. Depending on composition and treatments, the properties of vegetable parchment can be varied for different kinds of uses. As a package paper, vegetable parchment is distinguished by high wet strength, resistance to grease and to several chemicals found in foods, and by being tasteless as well as odorless. Vegetable parchment can be surface treated, printed, and embossed, capabilities that are desirable in all package materials. According to the *Paper Dictionary* vegetable parchment is used in various basis weights and in varying degrees of translucency when packaging frozen, moist, greasy or dry food products such as butter, margarine, dry pet food, meat and poultry.[112] Other uses for vegetable parchment are in persuasion printing, as carton and as pan liners for bake-and-serve goods, as diazo copymasters, and for a number of industrial purposes.

Decorative papers. Decorative papers are made in a wide range of colors, basis weights, finishes, and coatings. Cast coating can produce exceptionally high gloss, as described in Section 3, but this kind of coating is rather slow and expensive.

Traditionally, the coated surfaces of decorative papers are improved in their finishes by three different methods of polishing: (1) flint glazing, (2) friction glazing, and (3) brush enameling. In *flint glazing*, a polished stone is drawn back and forth across the surface of the coated paper. This action burnishes the surface and produces the glazed effect. *Friction-glazed papers* are made by passing the coated paper through a friction glazing calender where the paper is burnished by rolls operating at different speeds. For *brush enameling*, the coated side of the paper is passed under rotating brushes of varying stiffness and then supercalendered.[113]

Paper boards. Paper boards are so widely used that the fluctuations in their production volumes are considered by many economists as indicators for the whole economy. Practically all paper folding boxes are printed. The exceptions are folding boxes used by bakeries and other stores just like unprinted paper bags. Most heavier paper boards are made on cylinder machines and consist of several layers, or plies, which are combined when the paper is still wet. The inside layer, or filler, may not be suitable for printing, but the outside layer is. The printing surface may be coated or uncoated. Paper boards in the lower thickness range are also made on the fourdrinier machine; such

Courtesy Mead Corporation

Corrugated containers must stand up to rather rough handling. In this picture you see a paper and package expert test the strength of such a box.

boards can be coated either on the paper machine or off-machine (after the board has left the paper machine) on independent coating equipment. Lower board grades, not suitable for printing, are made for setup boxes and known as setup boards. Folding boxes are printed, die-cut, and creased on inline equipment and shipped flat. Setup boxes must be covered with separately printed wraps and cannot be shipped flat.

The properties of paper boards for folding boxes must satisfy folding, printing, and end-use requirements. *White patent coated* is a most widely used grade of utility folding boxboard; in spite of the name, it is not a coated board but has a top liner of uncoated white paper suitable for printing. Variations in the underliner, filler, and back-liner account for differences in mechanical properties. *Clay-coated boards* are coated boards that can be adapted for particular printing requirements by varying the coating formula; *cast-coated boards*, finally, are used for highest quality full-color printing.

Uncoated and coated paper boards are judged on a number of points as to their suitability for printing. Some of these points are the same for all printing processes, others are peculiar to one process only, and those that are common to several processes may be more critical in one and less in another. Moisture resistance, for example, is a typical requirement in offset printing but non-existent in letterpress and rotogravure. Compressibility is a critical property in boards for gravure and letterpress, though not in those for offset.[114] All methods by which paper can be coated are also used for paper boards, and different mills have proprietary brand names for their coated boards just as they have names for their coated papers.[115]

Foils and metallic papers. Aluminum foil is widely used in package printing. In mass-production printing by rotogravure, aluminum foil is combined with paper board directly on the press. (See Chapter VII, Section 3.) Aluminum foil is also supplied laminated to paper or to paper boards. Foils come in a thickness range from a maximum of 0.006 inches to a minimum commercial thickness of 0.00023 inches; the finish can be either bright or subdued and satin-like. Aluminum foil can be coated with transparent lacquers which may be clear or colored. Colored transparent coatings, applied to bright finish foil, produce mirror-like effects. If a white printing surface is required, aluminum foil can be printed with opaque white ink as part of inline package production. Aluminum can also be embossed and laminated with plastic films.[116]

Metallic papers can be made by several methods. One method consists in coating the paper or board either with an aqueous or with a lacquer-type coating which can be pigmented with aluminum powder or with uncolored or colored bronzes. Other methods proceed by coating the paper with an unpigmented adhesive and dusting the still wet adhesive with bronze powder. A third method, which produces so-called silver paper, consists in coating the paper "with a tin, lead, cadmium, antimony, or other metal oxide, dispersed in a suitable binder and friction calendering the sheet."[117]

Plastic films. Plastic films are typical materials for packaging and package printing. They are manufactured in an immense variety, a variety that increases from month to month, if not from week to week. The public meets plastic films as part of packaged consumer items, a situation in which the consumer is only interested in the removal of the package material and certainly not in learning something about it. All discarded packages are the same to the trash can (though not to the incinerator) and so they appear the same to the average consumer. If consumers meet a plastic film by name, this name is the advertiser's trade name and not an identifying chemical term. Most plastic films belonging in the same chemical category are made by several manufacturers; their trade names distinguish competing products. Chemical terms are of great meaning to specialists and those with a good chemical background, but for all other people such terms are just so many labels that help to keep things neat and separate.

Classification of plastic films. Technically, plastic films are classified by their chemical constitution and described by a number of different properties. The *Film Chart* of the 1966 Modern Plastics Encyclopedia lists about 30 different kinds of plastics; most of these plastics can be used for the making of films as needed in packaging.[118] The thickness of plastic films is expressed in mils. One *mil* is 0.001 inch. "Films and film coatings range from 0.2 to 50 mils in thickness and may be either flexible or rigid."[119] Thin films are sometimes designated as *free films* or as *unsupported films* to distinguish them from films formed by coating on other materials, paper for example. Thicker plastic materials are called sheets, or sheetings. Most plastic films are made by casting or extruding.

For our purposes *casting* can be equated with coating plastics in liquid form onto a highly polished metal surface and removing the dry film. *Extrusion* involves pressure and metal dies through which the plastic material is forced to reduce it to the desired thickness. *Inflated-tube extrusion* is a frequently used extrusion method for films. In this method the plastic is blown into a tube and expanded to its required thickness by air pressure.[120]

Each type of plastic base material has its own distinctive combination of properties. The *Films Chart* in the Modern Plastics Encyclopedia lists 37 points that are considered in describing and comparing plastics. Some of these points are of a more general nature and include method of processing (casting, extrusion, and others), forms available (sheets, rolls, tubes, etc.), thickness range, specific gravity, suitability for food and drug packaging, to mention some. Then there are several strength ratings, including tensile, bursting, tearing strength, and folding endurance. In this group belongs also per cent of elongation and water vapor permeability. The next group of points deals with various resistances. The behavior of a plastic when exposed to acids, alkalis, grease, oil, organic solvents, water, sunlight, steaming, and freezing, can be of great consequence in its usefulness as a package material. And so are the electric characteristics of plastics, including the heat-sealing temperature range of particular films. The American Society for Testing and Materials has developed many tests for plastics; the *Films Chart* lists the ASTM Test Number of every property for which ASTM tests exist.[121]

Reasons for the variety of plastic films. Functional specialization accounts for the demand of films that will have the most desirable properties for the packaging of specific products. Three techniques, peculiar to the plastics industry, make it possible to meet many of these demands without developing new, basically different kinds of plastic materials. These techniques account for the fact that the actually available plastic films are a multiple of the 30 odd types of plastic materials listed in the *Films Chart*. These techniques explain also that there are plastic films which combine many properties that are not available in the same combination in a single type of plastic material.

The three techniques that account for the great adaptability of the plastic films industry are (1) modification of plastics, (2) combination of plastic films, and (3) surface coating. These techniques

are summarized in the industry as "structuring," or as "tailoring" of plastic films. *Modification* includes variation in the chemical composition of plastic compounds to be used for films as well as orientation which realigns the molecules of films; *combination of films* is done by laminating films of different types thereby achieving new films having the combined properties of those selected for lamination; *surface coating* consists in applying especially designed coatings either to one or to both sides of plastic films, thereby endowing them with wanted properties. Even though not all plastics can be combined with each other and coated with any coating, the number of possible combinations is still huge. As each combination has characteristics of its own, specialization of product begets specialization of industry knowledge, and vice versa.[122]

Different groups of properties are of interest to the buyers of package materials and to converters or printers of plastic films. The buyers of package materials are primarily concerned with the suitability of films for the packaging of their products, including the suitability of these materials for "machining," meaning the processing by high-speed packaging machinery. Converters and printers of films are mainly interested in properties that influence printing and converting of films. The first mentioned group of properties is called end-use properties, and the second can be summarized as printability and runnability.

End-use properties of plastic films. The wanted end-use properties depend on the nature of the item to be packaged. Films considered for produce wrapping, for example, must be permeable to gases and water vapors. They must let the packaged item breathe and ripen. This "breathing" must be carefully regulated to prevent excessive weight loss and mold formation. Nor should breathing films absorb water and become soft in the process. Breathing also counts in package materials for products that have an attractive aroma, and in those that are scented for sales appeal.

If breathing is a requisite in plastic films for packaging lettuce and cantaloupes the same is not true in films for packing of poultry and hams. These meat products must be packaged air tight, and different films exist for this purpose. Air tight packaging needs films that shrink at elevated temperatures and are therefore called heat-shrink films. Films for packaging of spaghettis and macaronis must be dust and abrasion resistant; suitability for cooking is an end-use requirement in films for heat-and-serve products which are cooked in their plastic pouches and have become so popular. And all films used for packaging of foods and drugs must obviously be harmless and conform to the rulings of FDA. Many other end-use requirements could be added, but the preceding examples will make the point.

Printability and runnability. Printability describes properties of printing stocks related to the transfer of the ink image and to the final printed images; runnability is a parallel term to machinability—the machine being now a printing press.

The most telling difference between various films as regards runnability is their dimensional stability. This point is so important that printers often classify plastic films in two main groups: as stretchable films, or as non-stretchable films. A second feature of films important for runnability and printability is the temperature at which films soften, or melt. Stretching and melting characteristics can be combined for classification of films, a procedure followed by the Flexographic Technical Association which distinguishes three groups: (1) stretchable films, (2) non-stretch and non-melt films, and (3) non-stretch and easy-melt films.[123] The handling of stretchable films poses several problems, particularly in controlling web tension from unwind to rewind. Dimensionally stable, non-stretch films can be handled easier on the press than films that stretch. The softening, or melting properties of different films must be considered in the formulation of inks for their printing. The typical film printing methods—flexography and rotogravure—use solvent-evaporating inks which are dried by application of heat. The drying temperature must be lower than those that could soften or melt the plastic films being dried.

Printability is the subject matter of the next section; at this time it is merely mentioned that two points are of special importance in the printing of plastic films: one is ink receptivity, the other is adhesion of the dry ink to the plastic. Different types of plastic films usually require different kinds of printing inks. Many plastics do not pose great problems as regards ink solvents, but some are greatly weakened by solvents that have no damaging effect on other plastics. Some inks contain solvents in which the film to be printed is more or less soluble: such inks are said to "bite" into the film and thereby to help bond the ink to the film. Other plastics cannot tolerate ink bite; printing inks for these plastics rely on the adhesive qualities of their resin components for bonding of the ink to the plastic. Even though many plastic films have naturally good ink receptivity, some rather important ones do not. Some types of plastics must be made ink receptive by heat or electrical treatment; others require surface coating.

Section 6: Printability and Paper Testing

Printability is a complex, many-faceted subject. This may be surprising to those who consult the dictionary and find that printable means "capable of being printed from."[124] If the word printable could be used like a road sign or a number, if a paper were either printable or not, things would indeed be easy. Unfortunately, printability has neither a precise nor a generally accepted meaning as the following quotations show. According to one authority "*printability* of paper and paper boards is considered to be their ability to perform satisfactorily on the press. In other words, it is their freedom from defects that can cause time loss and substandard quality in production. *Print quality*, on the other hand, is the quality of the reproduction of which paper and board are capable."[125] The *Paper Dictionary*, per contra, defines printability as "that property of a paper which yields printed material of good quality" and adds emphatically that "printability should be distinguished from runnability, which refers to the efficiency with which the paper may be printed and handled in the press."[126]

Other authorities prefer the following definitions of print quality, printability, and runnability: "*Print Quality*, or the quality of a print, is the degree to which the appearance characteristics of print approach those of the desired result. *Printability*, or printing quality, of a surface is the degree to which its properties enhance the production of high-quality prints by a particular process. *Runnability* of a material on a printing press is the degree to which it can be printed on that press without operating difficulties."[127]

Each of these definitions lists a number of points that, singly and combined, affect runnability, printability, and print quality. If these specific points are considered rather than the definitions, it becomes clear that the divergence is more in the names selected for group properties than in the properties themselves. The territory, so to speak, remains the same; the difference is merely in the names with which different authorities call certain areas. In summary, it can be said that the terms runnability, printability, and print quality focus on three different aspects of paper (and other

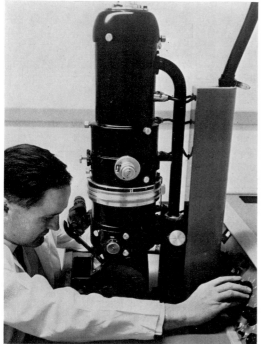

A research scientist adjusting an electron microscope capable of 80,000 times magnification. This instrument is used to study characteristics of individual fibers, the effects of calendering on paper, and the application of coatings on base stock, among other things.

printing stocks) relevant to printing. These three aspects are: (1) that all printing stocks must be suitable for processing, or, if you prefer, machining by the press equipment, (2) that all printing stocks must be suitable for making the impression, or expressed in terms of images, for transferring the ink image from the printing-image carrier to the printing stock, and (3) that the appearance of the final printed image on the stock is influenced by certain paper properties independent of image transfer. The term runnability has become widely used for summarizing paper properties relevant to machining, the term printability is most applicable to stock properties related to transfer of the ink image, and print quality is the

best actually used term for relating inherent paper qualities to the appearance of printed images.

Paper properties related to runnability. Presswork is done either on sheet-fed or roll-fed presses. For sheet-fed printing the paper is put on the press in piles of individual sheets, for web printing the paper is supplied in rolls. This difference accounts for somewhat different paper requirements in sheet-fed and in web printing. Paper for sheet-fed printing must be free of lint; it must have the required grain direction; and the sheets must be accurately trimmed, at least on guide and gripper edges. The sheets should further have a moisture content in equilibrium with the relative humidity of the pressroom, be free of curl, wavy or tight edges. Paper for web printing must, of course, also be free of the tendency to pick, lint, and dust. (Picking can take many forms; in uncoated papers it means the lifting of small clumps of fibers or of larger areas, resulting in splits or tears of the paper; in coated papers picking may result in lifting of small flakes from the surface of the coating, in separation of coating from the paper base, and in blistering, or delamination of the stock. Linting may happen in uncoated papers and means the lifting of only partly bonded fibers; dusting refers to the presence of loose paper or coating particles between sheets or in rolls of paper. Dust can be caused by slitting or guillotine cutting for example. In some mills paper is vacuumed during finishing; some printers vacuum the stock as part of feeding.[128]) Like all other papers those for web printing must have the proper moisture content and the necessary strength. Dimensional stability

A sword hygrometer. The sword hygrometer is an instrument for testing the moisture or humidity balance of skids of paper. The instrument is held by its handle and inserted with the sword into the paper pile. The dial on top of the box indicates the moisture percentage.

is another property wanted in both sheets and webs of paper. Paper rolls must have the correct width and diameter, be tightly wound, and if splices are acceptable they should be made in the desired form (either as lap or as butt splices), and the splicing should be indicated by flagging. The cores on which the paper is wound, and proper packing of rolls are other important points. This brief listing does not include such paper properties as are important for runnability in different printing methods, because these points are related to image transfer and are discussed in the next paragraph. But it must be kept in mind that modern sheet-fed presses operate at speeds of 100 impressions per minute (and possibly even faster) and that web presses print between 500 and 1,500 feet of paper per minute. At such speeds paper defects may do serious damage to the equipment.

Paper properties related to printability. Runnability can be discussed, up to a point, without regard to differences in printing methods because sheet-fed and web presses for different methods have many common mechanical features. But a discussion of printability, which is equivalent to saying of image transfer, must recognize the differences between various printing methods.

A microphotograph of supercalendered clay-starch coating on a high-grade printing paper. This picture was made through an electron microscope. The magnification is 20,000 times.

This is so because the difference between printing methods is most pronounced in the making of the impression whereby the ink image is transferred to the stock. Differences in the constitution of image carriers and of printing inks have a correlative expression in wanted and unacceptable

paper properties, depending on the printing method for which a paper will actually be used.

The meaning of these differences will become clearer as we move from the general to the particular. In lithography, technically classified as a planographic process, the distinction between the printing and the non-printing areas of the plate is made by dampening, a chemical treatment prior to the making of each impression. Papers for lithography must consequently be chemically and physically compatible with the fountain solution that is used in dampening. In printing methods that make the distinction between printing and non-printing areas of the image carrier mechanically, chemical compatibility does not even enter, but different properties become significant. Two examples will illustrate this point. Take first newspaper relief printing, the method used by our metropolitan newspapers.[129] News inks, as inks for newspaper relief printing are called, do not dry like other inks by forming a dry film. These inks become dry, if that is the right word, by absorption of the ink in the fibrous structure of the paper. Newsprint must, therefore, be quite absorbent, but it must also not be too absorbent; otherwise the printed paper will suffer from *strike-through*. Another defect in newspaper printing, *show-through*, is due to lack of paper opacity and to excessive ink absorption. Neither strike-through nor show-through is limited to newspaper printing; both can also be observed in other methods, when thin papers are printed with heavy solids, and in printing on exceptionally thin translucent papers. A final example for differences in paper properties caused by differing printing methods is paper for rotogravure. In rotogravure the paper must suck out or lift the ink from the minute intaglio cells, which are the printing areas of rotogravure cylinders. To do this the paper must be relatively smooth, soft, and resilient. Smoothness is a prerequisite for printing fine detail; good ink holdout is another property wanted in gravure papers. Ink *holdout* confers gloss or luster to the printed images. Papers that drain much of the resinous ink components off the surface down into their fibers make for lackluster printing and have poor ink holdout. Good ink holdout is equally important in other printing methods, especially when glossy inks are printed.

All printing papers must have good ink receptivity. "*Ink receptivity* is the property which causes papers to accept printing ink at the instant of contact between the paper and the ink."[130] If

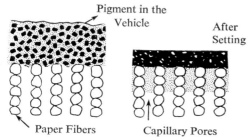

Pigment in the Vehicle

After Setting

Paper Fibers   Capillary Pores

Courtesy Graphic Arts Technical Foundation

Schematic diagram showing how an ink film sets on paper. You see that the ink vehicle has seeped into the paper during setting.

paper does not accept ink uniformly, the printed image may appear *mottled*. Other generally wanted paper characteristics include flatness and smoothness. Papers for offset must have several properties peculiar to the chemical nature of lithography. Some of them are discussed later in this unit under the head "testing papers for lithography."

Precisely which paper properties are significant for printability depends on the detail of specific printing operation. The number of variables that influence printability is considerable and their interaction makes evaluation quite complex. In reality, compromises must be made and papers having less than ideal properties must often be used, if for no other reason than cost limitations.

Inherent paper properties and print quality. You have seen that shortcomings in printability manifest themselves also as impairments of print quality. This shows that it is impossible to separate printability and the quality of printed images. But printability is not the only influence on print appearance. Equally important are some inherent paper qualities (which differ, of course, for different grades and brands) that are not modified by image transfer, but in a sense have a controlling influence on the final appearance of printed images and printed products. Among inherent paper qualities are different colors, textures, degrees of smoothness formation, brightness, gloss, freedom from dirt, and opacity. These inherent properties differ for different papers and these differences must be carefully considered in paper selection.

Reasons for the need of paper tests. Like most other industrial materials, paper must combine a variety of different properties. These properties must first be recognized and then be measured. Without recognition of different properties and

without methods for their quantitative evaluation, it is impossible to specify and describe different papers objectively. As new kinds of papers are developed, the development of new tests becomes a necessity; testing is just as much a continuous activity as manufacturing and industrial use.

In the United States two organizations, TAPPI and ASTM, develop and refine tests for paper and related materials. The tests developed by the Technical Association of the Pulp and Paper Industry are known as TAPPI tests and are identified by name and a code number. The tests developed by the American Society for Testing Materials are known as ASTM tests and are also known by name and code number. (TAPPI and ASTM test names may be the same or different ones; the code numbers are different.) TAPPI and ASTM have a joint committee on paper testing and TAPPI and ASTM test numbers are correlated in the literature.[131]

Groups of paper tests. Combined, TAPPI and ASTM tests amount to several hundreds. Many TAPPI tests pertain to the manufacturing of pulp and paper and to materials needed for manufacturing. Such tests are of no interest to those outside pulp and paper plants or research organizations. Paper tests of meaning to those interested in printing can be divided into several groups. One group is concerned with general paper characteristics. Among them are the formation of paper, its machine and cross direction, basis weight determination, and many other properties. Another group comprises end-use tests. End-use requirements depend on the actual purposes of printed products. Papers for book and publication printing may have to pass tests related to folding, whereas paper boards for packaging may be tested for bending, to give merely two examples of most common end-use tests. Then there are a number of points that influence runnability and printability of papers and paper boards. Tensile strength, flatness, and ink receptivity are illustrative of these properties. And finally, there are those paper properties that affect print quality, exemplified by the smoothness, whiteness and brightness characteristics of paper.

Paper-and-ink-compatibility tests. Tests concerned with the transfer of the ink image to the paper involve not only paper properties but also corresponding ink properties. Such tests are paper-and-ink-compatibility tests in which a pair of properties is tested. One member of this pair is a paper property, the other is the corresponding

Courtesy National Printing Ink Research Institute

A laboratory technician tests the pick resistance of paper with the IGT Printability Tester. *This tester (developed by the Institute for Graphische Techniek, Holland) uses a series of tack-graded inks or oils. These are applied to the paper at accelerating speed. The pick resistance is defined as the speed at which picking starts with a particular ink.*

ink property. If the paper is tested, the ink must have certain known characteristics; if the ink is tested the same is assumed for the paper.

Ink tack and pick resistance of papers are such a pair in which compatibility is essential; other pairs are drying properties of inks and paper properties that affect drying; ink receptivity of paper or other stocks and the adhesive qualities of printing inks; ink absorption by different papers and resistance of inks to this absorption, resulting either in good or in less satisfactory ink holdout. The more generally important ink tests which are also, in a sense, paper tests are discussed in Chapter IX, Section 4, and need not be repeated here. The point to be made is simply that ink properties and paper properties must be compatible. The same ink is not usable for all papers, and papers that perform well with one ink may not be satisfactory with another. It could be asked which of the two has a controlling position and which must follow the other. The general answer is that there is a continual process of mutual adaptation. Printing speed was increased by fast drying and by heatset inks. Application of heat and faster

printing required adaptation of the paper to these conditions, to mention one example.

Testing of papers for offset lithography. Several paper properties that are of no consequence in other printing methods are critical in lithography because in lithography the plate must be dampened at every printing cycle. The fountain solution consists mainly of water, sometimes in mixture with alcohol, and is slightly acid. Some of this solution is transferred from the plate to the blanket and further to the paper. This solution may dissolve chemical agents on the paper surface and the solutes are transferred back from the blanket to the plate and to the inking and dampening system of the press. The presence of moisture affects paper and ink in many respects. Paper properties that would cause no trouble without moisture can cause problems when fountain solution gets on the paper surface.

Here merely two typical lithographic tests will be mentioned: moisture resistance and the pH of papers for lithography. Papers defective in moisture resistance may cause so much trouble during presswork that they cannot be used for lithography. Tests of moisture resistance "are generally referred to as *wet-rub tests,* and considerable experience is needed to perform them."[132] The pH of papers indicates their acidity or alkalinity. In uncoated papers the paper itself is tested for pH; in coated papers the pH of the mineral coat on which printing takes place is of more interest than that of the base paper stock.

Three well-known strength tests. One of the

Courtesy Mead Corporation

The Mullen tester which tests the bursting strength of paper. Testing of bursting strength is described in TAPPI Method T403-m53 and in ASTM Method D774.

oldest paper tests is the *Mullen* which tests the bursting strength of papers. This test is widely used on many kinds of papers. "Since bursting strength is predominantly a measure of tensile properties, the tensile strength test has replaced the bursting test for many uses." The *Elmendorf* test is used to evaluate the tearing strength of paper. "This test has great significance in the requirements of paper and paper boards that are subjected to tearing strains in conversion or actual use." The third test to be mentioned here is the *Schopper*, a test of folding endurance. The Schopper and the MIT tester "measure the same physical property, namely, the number of double folds the paper will withstand in each of its principal directions before rupture."[133]

Formation of paper. Formation of paper influences its appearance and also its printing quality. The term refers to the degree of uniformity with which the fibers and other solids are distributed in a paper. "Paper is said to have a uniform or close formation if the texture is similar to ground glass when viewed in transmitted light. The formation is said to be poor or wild if the fibers are unevenly distributed."[134] If formation is judged by visual inspection it is expressed comparatively with reference to arbitrarily numbered standards. There are also instruments available which permit an objective, numerical expression, called formation value.

Basis weight. As explained in Section 3, paper is sold by weight but printed and consumed by area. Determination of the correct basis weight is, from the printer's point of view, less important in sheet-fed printing than in web printing. In sheet-fed printing the printer is supplied with a specified number of sheets; in web printing, for which he is supplied with rolls, variations in basis weight are more objectionable. If the basis weight is higher than needed, the delivered area is less than calculated; if it is lower than specified, the delivered area is more but the opacity of the paper and the runnability of the web may be impaired.

Determination of basis weight is in principle a simple test consisting in the weighing of properly conditioned and exactly dimensioned paper specimens on a scale of sufficient sensitivity. Such scales are often specially built basis weight scales "designed to indicate directly the weight of 1,000, 500 or 480 sheets from the weight of a single sheet of the selected size."[135]

Paper thickness or caliper. The thickness of paper and the tolerance within which this property

Courtesy Mead Corporation

A basis weight scale. The basis weight of paper is determined according to TAPPI Method T410-os on ASTM Method D646.

is kept are of great practical importance for printing performance and for paper end-uses. Since paper is compressible and affected in its thickness by changes in moisture contents, measuring of paper thickness is far from simple. The instruments for measuring paper thickness are special paper micrometers that are described in TAPPI test procedures. The pressure exerted on the sample, and the properties of the surfaces between which the sample is placed for measuring, must be strictly controlled; paper micrometers have dials that permit reading in increments of 0.0001 inches. Micrometers as used in machine shops are not suitable for accurately measuring paper thickness, but the GATF Blanket Measuring Gauge meets the TAPPI requirements and can be used for measuring the thickness of papers.

Machine direction, or paper grain. Tests for finding the machine direction, or grain, of paper are commonplace in printing and binding shops. In binding, paper grain counts because the last fold is usually in the machine direction; in sheet-fed offset printing tests for paper grain are made because presswork is usually done with paper grain long. Finding the machine direction is simple. One way is to wet a piece of paper and to observe the curl; "the axis of the curl will always be

Courtesy Testing Machines, Inc.

A paper micrometer showing the thickness of papers and paper boards in increments of 0.0001 inch. Paper micrometers must be built to conform with TAPPI Method T411-m44 and ASTM Method D645-64T.

parallel to the machine direction, or with the grain." Another simple test consists in cutting two strips of equal size from the sheet at right angles and holding them at one end; "the stiffer strip is grain long, the strip that bends is grain short."[136]

Recognizing the felt side and the wire side. The two sides of uncoated papers have different properties. In papers made on fourdrinier machines the wire side is somewhat coarser, composed of longer fibers, and more porous than the felt side. In these papers the smoother and less porous felt side is the more desirable printing surface. Paper boards made on cylinder machines differ in this respect from papers and paper boards made on fourdrinier machines. In boards made on cylinder machines the wire side is usually the printing side. In many papers the difference between the felt side and the wire side is readily noticeable when the paper is folded over and both sides are compared. If necessary, the paper can be wetted and inspected after drying; then the wire marks are usually more pronounced than in unwetted papers.

If these simple tests fail more involved ones must be made. The surface differences between the felt and the wire sides are more or less completely eliminated in well-coated papers.

Brightness. Brightness tests of papers express their relative reflectance in per cent of that of a magnesium oxide layer which is the arbitrarily selected standard. The test is highly technical; the paper is illuminated with blue light of 457 ± 0.5 millimicron wave length, and the reflectance value is defined as brightness. Testing is done with specially designed instruments, the IPC (Institute for Paper Chemistry) Automatic Color and Brightness Tester, for example. "Most printing papers fall within the range of about 60 to 90 per cent brightness."[137]

Smoothness. Smoothness, as opposed to roughness, is a tactile property; it refers to the degree of surface regularity. Smoothness can be evaluated with different instruments based on different principles. For comparison, the same method or instrument must be used. Smoothness can be judged by microscopic techniques, by using detector needles which trace the surface irregularities of paper, by measuring air flow, and also photographically. Some of these techniques can serve to show smoothness graphically, as a *paper profile.* "For practical purposes, different papers can be compared for printing smoothness by pulling spare impressions on them in black ink under identical conditions and comparing the prints for completeness of coverage.[138]

These few examples were chosen to show some of the most important paper tests; they will convince you that paper properties are extensively studied and tested. Much of this accumulated knowledge could be helpful to those who face paper problems without knowing about testing methods and available testing facilities.

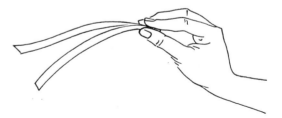

A simple test for paper grain or machine direction. Two strips of equal size are cut from the sheet at right angles. When they are held at one end, the stiffer strip (the upper one in the illustration) is grain long, the other grain short: (Adapted from GATF Publication No. 308.)

Chapter IX

Printing Inks

All printing serves one and only one final purpose: the production of the printed image. This printed image is deposited on paper, or other printing stocks, and consists of dry printing ink. Our eyes perceive the shape and color of this image, which contrasts with the stock, and our mind grasps its meaning. These are the mechanics of communication by printing.

The immense effort of image conversion and image transfer, which fills hundreds of pages in this manual, is just a transitory means to an end. This end is obviously the printed image. Physically, it consists of areas, lines, and dots of dry ink. These are the essential facts of graphic reproduction. They indicate the crucial role played by printing ink.

To itemize the main functions of printing inks, three points need mentioning. The first is that the appearance of the printed image depends to a high measure on the quality of the ink. The second refers to the suitability of the printed product for its final purpose which depends principally on the proper end-use characteristics of the ink. The third and final point in this brief summary refers to the controlling role of ink for speed, uniformity, and smoothness of presswork.

Ink is obviously a worth-while subject. It might be added that this subject can also be far from dull as this present chapter attempts to prove. One of the contributing reasons why ink is so little known and understood is the fact that it is a highly technical subject because it is based on specialized branches of chemistry and physics. The literature on ink is equally specialized and hence neither written for the layman nor easily understood by him. As this manual has the purpose of disseminating information that is not readily accessible to the non-specialist, printing ink is here given a broader treatment than might be expected.

This chapter is divided into five sections: (1) an introduction to printing inks, (2) pigments, (3) vehicles, (4) the manufacture and testing of inks, and (5) inks for different printing processes and methods. To guide and assist the reader who wants to go deeper into the subject, many references are provided.

Section 1: Introduction to Printing Ink

Few other subjects lend themselves to a demonstration of the interrelatedness of all contributing elements in contemporary printing as well as does ink. Printing ink is the final connecting link between the printing-image carrier, the paper or other printing stock, and the printing press. Unless the ink is well adjusted to these other three elements, printing cannot take place efficiently.

Even though one ink may look superficially very much like all other inks, differences between various types of printing inks must not be underestimated. Just as there is a multitude of printing equipment, of image carriers, and of papers (not to speak of other printing stocks) so printing ink, too, must be available in a corresponding variety. Even though we have no exact data on the number of different kinds of inks used in the printing industry, a well-informed guess is that this number must be surpassing at least one hundred. As each of these kinds is manufactured in a smaller or larger number of colors you can get an inkling of how many different products must be provided by the ink industry for the printing industry.

Essential information for ink specification. Printing inks are specified by considering some or all of the following nine points: (1) *printing process and method:* letterpress, offset lithography, rotogravure, screen process, and so on; (2) *kind of press:* job press, two-color flatbed cylinder press, web offset press, to mention a few; (3) *kind of paper or other stock:* coated and uncoated paper such as book, writing, bond, ledger, or index; newsprint, cellophane film, and many others; (4) *kind of drying:* air-drying, drying by heat, or baking, for example; (5) *kind of finish wanted:* matte, gloss, high gloss, etc.; (6) *end use of the printed product:* magazine, book, soap wraps, food package, and many others; (7) *color:* required hue such as blue, green, red, and others; (8) *fabricating method to which the printed stock will be subjected:* die-cutting, varnishing, laminating, hot paraffining, for instance; (9) *sequence of ink application:* the order in which multicolor and full-color inks will be used, such as dry or wet printing, first down, second down color, and so forth.

These nine points are not exhaustive; they are here listed merely as the most common ones. An ink may be simply known as black news ink, meaning that it will be used for the printing of newspapers by relief printing, or it may have a long list of specifications, for example: "full-color magenta for offset lithography, to be printed on cast-coated paper by sheet-fed single-color presses, for window displays, to be suitable for varnishing and for laminating." Each of these points is important because each influences the composition of the ink.

The Composition of Printing Inks

Inks consist primarily of two kinds of materials: pigments and vehicles. The printed images owe their color mainly to pigments. Pigments are dry powders and have neither the qualities which are required for use on various types of presses, nor the ability of adhering to the paper, nor that of assuming by themselves the well-defined and often rather minute shapes out of which the printed image must consist. These three tasks, namely, suitability for working on the press, formation of precise images, and adhesion to the printing stock,

are solved by combining pigments with the second main component of ink, the vehicle.

The vehicle is a liquid, but a liquid of a very special nature: It must remain liquid on the press and yet be completely dry on the stock. This means that it must be capable of changing from the liquid state to the dry state within the nick of time. This change is called setting or drying, depending on the type of ink. It cannot occur fast enough and must often be speeded by the use of heat, alone or together with air currents, by means of various machinery for *forced drying*. (Drying equipment is discussed in Chapter VI, Section 7.)

Pigments and vehicles are combined by dispersing. This means that pigments and vehicles are carefully mixed and milled together, as will be described in Section 4 of this chapter. Pigments and vehicles have different functions. Roughly speaking, pigments contribute not only the color of the printed image, but also many features of consequence for the end use of the printed product. Among them are light-fastness, resistance to water, organic solvents, chemical agents, and heat. The vehicle is primarily responsible for the adhesion of the printed image to the stock, as well as for kind and speed of drying. All these points will be elaborated as the discussion progresses.

But it should not be assumed that a good ink can be made simply by choosing the right materials. Their proportion is not less important than their proper selection. The working qualities of an ink—its performance on the press—will depend primarily on the proportions in which the right pigments and vehicles are combined and on the care with which they are dispersed. Other ingredients may include *driers*, though not in all types of inks, *wetting agents, anti-skinning agents, waxes,* and even *perfumes.*

Many inks consist of at least ten or more different ingredients which may be present in any proportion, say, between a half per cent and 70 per cent, depending on the specific ingredient and kind of ink. Each of these different ingredients is in turn the result of a more or less complex manufacturing process in which a considerable number of materials take part. If all of these were enumerated we could easily arrive at approximately 100 to 150 materials which are needed in order to produce a good printing ink.

The Working Properties of Inks

The working properties of inks are of greatest interest to the printer. They cannot be explained

Thixotropic inks are stiff in the can; they become fluid after mixing, stirring or having been worked on an ink stone.

without use of several indispensable terms which must now be introduced, beginning with the characteristic term "body."

Body. The word *body* refers to the consistency of inks. Inks are made in a great variety of consistencies. Some are heavy-bodied and can be compared with molasses or with honey still full of beeswax. Others have a light or thin body and resemble, in this respect, such substances as light or heavy cream. Many inks for letterpress and offset lithography are heavy-bodied, whereas flexographic and rotogravure inks are examples of thin-bodied inks. Related to the term "body" is that of *viscosity*, meaning resistance to flow. Body is a rather broad and imprecise term. Viscosity is much more exact, particularly if it is expressed in terms of some kind of measuring system, of which there are several. Speaking of body, it might be useful to mention that some inks have a rather pronounced *false body*, or that they are *thixotropic*, in technical terms. The body of thixotropic inks changes depending on their state. When such inks are at rest, they have a rather heavy pasty body, but when they are rapidly stirred, they become quite liquid.

Tack. Next comes *tack*, a most significant characteristic of inks. "An easily understood definition of tack is stickiness. This is the force required to split an ink film between two surfaces."[1] Inks for relief and planographic printing are prepared for application to the image carrier by a system of rollers. Tack is important for the transfer of ink from roller to roller, then to the image carrier and from there either directly to the stock or first to the blanket. Inks that are too tacky may *pick* the paper surface, meaning that they pluck or tear it, whereas inks that have less than the necessary tack may be incapable of producing sharp images—a defect particularly noticeable in the reproduction of the halftone images.

Tack is also of importance in ink *trapping*. The word "trapping" refers to the overprinting of successive inks which is a necessity in multicolor and full-color printing. For good overprinting in letterpress and lithography the tack of successive inks must be carefully adjusted. The first-down ink has most tack, each successive ink less. A related term might as well be explained now: *crystallization*. Crystallization, as used in the pressroom, has nothing to do with the formation of crystals. In the pressroom, crystallization means that a dry ink film is defective and does not have the needed receptivity for successive inks but rather acts in a repellent manner. The required working characteristics of a specific ink depend entirely on the printing method and on the press equipment on which this ink will be used. But one general rule might be stated at this point, namely, that the consistency of inks must decrease as the speed of the press increases. Slow-running presses can utilize much heavier inks than high-speed presses. This rule has many consequences and is worth remembering.

Doctoring of inks. As pointed out in the preceding paragraphs, the detail of a printing task may require changes in the composition of a printing ink. In pressrooms where the same inks must be used for somewhat different jobs, a condition found in all branches of custom printing, a certain amount of adjustment may be required from job to job. Such adjustments are known in the trade as the *doctoring* of inks. This task is left to highly experienced craftsmen such as pressmen, ink men, color mixers, and color matchers.

Adjusting of inks may or may not be a necessity, depending on the nature of the work and the method preferred by different concerns. How industry practices have changed is now explained by the example of lithography. As long as traditional inks made of bodied linseed oil were the only available type of lithographic inks, doctoring was a necessity. The advent of synthetics and the continual development of new inks has greatly reduced the old practice of doctoring, which is now apt to cause trouble as the old techniques may do more harm than good with differently constructed inks. At present it is generally preferred to buy inks ready for use; adjustments in the pressroom are avoided wherever possible.

But it must be added that practices are far from uniform in the many faceted printing industry. Rotogravure and flexographic inks, for example, which contain a high percentage of solvents and are consumed in huge quantities, are often purchased by large plants as concentrates to be diluted prior to use. These plants need, of course, the proper storage and mixing facilities as well as competent technical people.

Ink consumption. Ink consumption, also known as *ink mileage*, is the last point to be mentioned in this unit. Depending on the nature of a particular job or the printed product in general, ink consumption may be an important cost element or of little significance. In all mass-production printing, ink costs play an important role; in small lots of custom printing, ink costs are of much lesser consequence. Ink consumption depends on a number of points. Among them is the printing method and type of ink, its specific gravity, color, and pigment concentration; the type of stock, whether it is absorbent or not absorbent; the thickness of the deposited ink film; and of course the total area to be covered with ink. Specific data cannot be offered in a book of such general nature as this manual. Most ink manufacturers publish information pertaining to coverage or ink-mileage of their own products.

The Drying of Inks

Our next subject is the drying of inks. It is of greatest interest to all concerned with printing, as the speed and thoroughness of drying has often a controlling position in the speed of press operation. Drying in reference to printing ink means the "change from the fluid to the solid state."[2] This change takes place in two steps with certain kinds of inks. The first step is known as *setting*, the second, as *hardening* of the ink film. Setting means that the "printed sheets, though not fully dry, can be handled without smudging."[3] It should be understood that a "particular ink may set satisfactorily on a given paper for a sheet-fed operation, but not for web press. A properly set ink film, therefore, will not be rubbed off, set off, or otherwise hampered or damaged during the following operations."[4] Hardening follows setting and is characterized by the fact that a particular ink "has reached the end of its chemical or physical conversion,"[5] or to say it more generally, that the ink film has become as hard as it need be for

all practical purposes. The absolute hardness of different ink films is, of course, by no means the same and depends on the nature of each ink.

Drying of printing inks involves a number of chemical and physical actions which depend on the nature of the vehicle. It is customary to distinguish seven different kinds of drying even though it must be understood that in some types of inks several of these actions follow each other or take place simultaneously. The seven types of drying actions are: (1) oxidation of the vehicle, (2) polymerization of the vehicle, (3) penetration of the vehicle into the printing stock, (4) evaporation of the vehicle solvents, (5) gelation of the vehicle, (6) solidification of the vehicle by cooling, and (7) precipitation of vehicle solids.[6] Each of these types of action is now briefly explained.

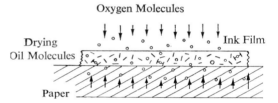

Schematic diagram of drying by oxidation of the ink vehicle. The oxygen of the air changes the vehicle from the liquid to the solid state. (This and the following six schematic diagrams of different drying actions are adapted from Herbert J. Wolfe, Pressmen's Ink Handbook, *Dorland Books, New York.)*

Drying by oxidation. This type of drying is characteristic for vehicles containing drying oils. The vehicle film absorbs oxygen from the air; the structure of the oil molecules is thereby changed and they finally become solids. Inks made with drying oils, which may be natural or synthetic, contain varying amounts of metallic driers which act as catalysts and speed the drying process. Such inks are widely used in letterpress, offset lithography, screen-process printing, and other methods. Drying by oxidation involves our next group—that of drying by polymerization—and is therefore also described as drying by *oxidative polymerization.*

Drying by polymerization. This kind of drying is related to drying by oxidation because it, too, is a chemical process rather than a physical one as are drying by evaporation or by penetration. "By polymerization is meant the combining of small molecules into larger, more complex molecules, the molecular weight of which is usually a multiple

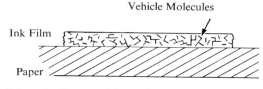

Schematic diagram of drying by polymerization of the ink vehicle. Small molecules which are liquid combine into much larger ones which are solid or dry.

of that of smaller molecules. When the simple, or small molecules comprise a fluid, polymerization generally results in a solid."[7] Inks made of China wood-oil varnishes and those made with certain synthetic resins dry by polymerization. Polymerization can take place at room temperature or it can be speeded by heat or by chemical treatments, depending on the materials involved. Drying by polymerization is the dominant drying action for most inks that are baked, and therefore of great importance in lithographic metal decorating. Certain baking enamels used in screen-process printing belong to the same group. In air-drying inks, polymerization and oxidation take place together, as already mentioned.

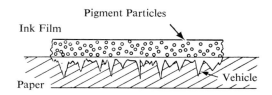

Schematic diagram of ink drying by penetration. This kind of drying action takes place by penetration of some of the ink and of most of the vehicle into the paper. The ink vehicle does not change from the liquid to the solid state.

Drying by penetration. All inks that are printed on absorbent materials also dry by penetration, even though the characteristic or dominant type of drying action may be a different one. There is, though, one type of ink which dries by penetration exclusively. This type of ink is known as news ink and is used for the printing of newspapers by relief printing. Here the vehicle consists of non-drying mineral oils in combination with inexpensive materials such as rosin oils, asphalts, and pitches. But this kind of drying, if such it can be called, is far from ideal as millions of newspaper readers will confirm who wonder why their hands sometimes get so dirty when they read and handle their daily paper.

Drying by evaporation. Inks made with vehicles consisting of solutions of resinous and similar film-forming materials in organic solvents dry by evaporation. Evaporation is, like penetration, a kind of drying which is involved in the drying ot many inks containing some volatile components.

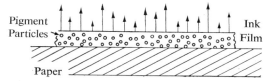

Schematic diagram of ink drying by evaporation. The volatile solvents evaporate, leaving a dry ink film on the printed stock. Evaporation is usually speeded by application of heat and air.

Among these are inks made with synthetic drying oils and oleoresinous varnishes. In this group we find fast-drying inks for letterpress, offset lithography, and screen-process printing, and, further, most rotogravure and flexographic inks. Where large quantities of such inks are printed, forced drying by heat and air exchange is often a necessity. In some large installations the solvent vapors are collected, condensed, and re-used. (A solvent recovery installation for gravure inks is described in Chapter VII, Section 3.)

Schematic diagram of drying by gelation of the ink vehicle. Inks having this drying action are wet in the can and on the rollers of the press inking system but dry when they are applied to the printing stock as thin films.

Drying by gelation. Film-forming materials which are in the state of gelation can be used for printing-ink vehicles by dispersing them in organic solvents or in drying oils. If such inks are applied to absorbent surfaces, the solvent is drained into the paper and the ink film solidifies. The transformation of the comparatively soft gel into a hardened solid usually occurs by secondary physical or chemical changes. Such inks are not generally used but are limited to special applications.

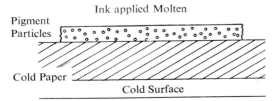

Schematic diagram of ink drying by cooling. Inks that are solid at room temperatures are applied at a temperature at which they become liquid. The thin film of printed ink solidifies on the cold paper.

Drying by cooling. In this group belong inks that are solid at room temperature but become liquid at a higher temperature and are printed by heated presses. When the ink strikes the cold paper it is cooled and therewith solidified. Inks of this nature have been used with varying success, particularly in mass-production printing.

Drying by precipitation. Steam-set inks dry by precipitation. They contain solids that cannot coexist with water. If such inks are exposed to water in one form or another, the solvents by which the film-formers are liquefied separate and are absorbed into the stock, and the solids are precipitated together with the pigments enveloped by them. Inks of this nature are used for milk containers and other package materials.

Schematic diagram of drying by precipitation. Inks drying by precipitation are steam set. The water spray precipitates the resin component of the vehicle thereby causing the formation of a dry ink film.

Section 2:   Pigments

Color is the most obvious contribution of pigments to printing inks. (Technically speaking, most printed materials are produced with inks that have no color, as black is not a color in the true sense of the word but the complete absence of reflected light.) But apart from their colors, pigments affect printing inks in several different ways. The relative opacity and transparency of inks depends primarily on the nature of the pigments. Pigments also influence the consistency of inks, their drying characteristics, and their suitability for heat treatments such as baking and curing.

Pigments are distinguished further by many characteristics that are either wanted or must not be present in different inks, considering the purpose of the final printed product. These characteristics are usually known as end-use specifications. Among them is permanence to light and to weather; resistance to chemical agents such as acids or alkalies; freedom of toxic ingredients, to mention a few.

Other points of importance are related to the process of ink manufacturing and to the working characteristics of the printing ink on the press. Examples are the particle size and structure of pigments, their specific gravity, oil absorption (meaning the relative amounts of oils or vehicles required for dispersion), color strength, mass and undertone (meaning their color in concentration and in dilution), different surface treatments, and last but not least, their effect on drying.

The making of pigments is a highly specialized branch of chemical industry and not usually included in the manufacturing program of ink makers. Some producers of pigments make related synthetic colors, others specialize in white pigments, others in black pigments, and so forth. Usually, the ink maker buys his pigments either in the form of dry or of flushed colors from these concerns. (The meaning of flushed is explained in the following unit.) He is informed by them on all points that are of consequence for the selection of pigments to be used in specific ink formulation.

Many items must be considered when selecting a pigment or a combination of pigments for inclusion in a given ink formula. Non-specialists often find it difficult to understand that certain features which are present in one kind of colored material, or even in a certain kind of ink, cannot be duplicated as a matter of course in a different kind of ink. They do not appreciate the fact that pigments have, if this expression is permitted, personalities of their own which cannot be changed at will. Practically speaking, this means that every pigment has a number of features which cannot be separated but must be taken as a whole.

A few examples will clarify this point. Often artists will use water colors in the preparation of pictures for reproduction. Many of these artists' painting media are made with pigments that cannot be used for the making of inks. Pigments that are suitable for water colors may not be usable for offset-lithographic inks, to mention one type, because they may react with the chemical fountain solution needed in lithographic printing. On the other hand, the particular hue and brilliance of such pigments may not be available at all among those that can be used for ink making. The matching of dyed fabrics by inks is another task which cannot be considered as a simple or even a necessarily possible one. Apart from other differences, dyestuffs often have hues that cannot be duplicated by the pigments which can be used in printing inks. To mention another and rather important point: price, too, is part of the personality complex of pigments. Chrome yellow, for example, is a rather inexpensive pigment, but it is considered toxic. Non-toxic pigments that can be used for food packages exist, but they are much more expensive than the inadmissible chrome yellow.

If a pigment is selected for one of its features without due regard for the others, the result can be quite disappointing and even outright disastrous. The great master Leonardo da Vinci experimented with painting techniques when he painted his "Last Supper." Unfortunately he selected the wrong pigments and this great work of art began to fade soon after it was completed. It has now practically disappeared, to the sorrow of all lovers of Renaissance art. Another example of wrong pigment selection is the tragic misuse of *Schweinfurt green*, which has an exceptionally brilliant color, for the printing of wallpaper. Several people died mysteriously of arsenic poisoning before the source of the poison was traced to the green pigments with which their wallpapers had been printed.

These examples must suffice. They should make clear that the selection of pigments is a highly technical job and that all pertinent information about use and purpose of the finished product should be collected and then transmitted to the ink manufacturer for consideration by his technical staff. We turn next to the classification of pigments and thereafter to a functional description of individual pigments.

Classification of pigments. Pigments can be grouped in many ways. For our purpose, it seems most practical to divide them into manufactured mineral pigments, technically known as inorganic, and into synthetic, or organic, pigments. (It

might be mentioned that natural inorganic and organic pigments were once of great importance; now they have lost this position completely and need not be considered by us.) Manufactured mineral pigments, which preceded synthetic pigments, are still in use even though many of them have been supplanted by synthetic pigments.

For obvious reasons it is not necessary to discuss in this manual pigments which are in our time products of complex chemical manufacturing processes in terms of their composition and chemical constitution. The study of pigments is highly specialized and predicated upon extensive knowledge of chemistry and physics, which is not assumed to be necessarily part of the reader's background. But it is nevertheless possible to explain certain effects of pigments which are of interest to all who want to appreciate how printing inks function. In this context, it is inevitable to refer from time to time to technical points and to use a few terms which belong to the vocabulary of physics and chemistry.

Manufacturing methods of inorganic pigments. To return to manufactured mineral pigments, they are made either by precipitation or by calcination, or by a combination of both. *Precipitation* means that several chemical solutions are combined, with the result that matter either previously contained in a solution, or matter formed by chemical reaction of different solutions, becomes insoluble in the mixture. The insoluble matter is, in our subject, the pigment. As it is heavier than the liquid used in the process, it drops to the bottom of the vessel, or tub, where the reaction takes place. Among pigments made by precipitation we find the chrome yellows and oranges which are compounds of lead and chromium and in some variations also of lead sulfates; molybdate orange, which contains lead molybdate and lead sulfate;

Schematic diagram of precipitation and of calcination. The picture at the left shows that mixing of two solutions can result in precipitation of a solid material, pigments for example. The picture at the right shows calcination, another method used in pigment manufacturing.

and the so-called iron blues, complex compounds of the elements of iron, carbon and nitrogen, sulfur, and potassium.[8]

The second main method for the manufacturing of mineral pigments is *calcination*, calcination means that either a single substance, or a mixture of several substances, is heated to extremely high temperatures under exclusion of air. Several pigments are made by calcination. Here we merely mention ultramarine blue which contains the elements of sodium, aluminum, sulfur, silicon, and oxygen. Both precipitation and calcination are employed successively in the making of certain kinds of cadmium pigments, which are yellow and red, and of the most important white pigment, titanium dioxide.

Main properties of mineral pigments. Most mineral pigments have several properties in common which differ widely from those of synthetic pigments. Mineral pigments contain, as you may have noticed, metals such as lead, chromium, zinc, and iron which have higher specific gravities than the synthetic pigments. A second common point is their larger particle size, and a third, their sensitivity to acids or alkalies. On the other hand, most mineral pigments dry much better in vehicles made of drying oils, which is an important point in their favor; a second asset is their insolubility in many organic solvents in which many synthetic pigments are more or less soluble.[9]

Synthetic organic pigments. Synthetic pigments, our next subject, are technically known as organic pigments. The adjective "organic" is used by chemists to indicate that a substance consists primarily of compounds of carbon in conjunction with a few other elements. These compounds account for the chemical composition of the vast majority of non-metallic matter including foods, drugs, and living beings. Synthetic colorants are classified in a highly technical system. For our purposes, it is sufficient to distinguish the two groups of pigment dyestuffs and of lakes. Pure pigment dyes, also known as *toners*, contain no mineral ingredients, whereas *lakes* do.

Synthetic organic pigments are products of the dyestuff industry. This industry derives its most important raw materials from the distillation of coal tar. Among derivatives of coal tar are certain solvents such as benzene, toluene, and xylene which are also used as ingredients for certain inks. Coal-tar derivatives must be converted into a number of different products, usually called *intermediates*, for pigment production. Solutions of such intermediates, or of intermediates of a second and third generation (meaning intermediates made from intermediates) are combined, often with other chemicals, for the production of pigments. As the resulting pigments are insoluble in their generating solutions they are, consequently, precipitated as solids.

Dry colors and flushed colors. Next, these solids must be separated from the water in which they now find themselves. This can be done in two different ways. In one method, the traditional, the water is removed by filtration and the pigment is dried until it becomes a powder. It is then known as a *dry color*. The second, and rather recent method, consists in exchanging the residual water after its largest amount has been removed for another liquid which is capable of being used as part of the future ink vehicle. These liquids are, hence, different for different types of inks.[10] In this method of dispersion the pigment is not dried but immediately dispersed in its future vehicle. Such pigments are known as *flushed* pigments. They are of steadily increasing importance in contemporary ink technology.

This brief description of the manufacturing of pigments must suffice for our purpose. We turn now to a discussion of individual pigments which are arranged by colors and grouped under seven heads: (1) black, (2) white, (3) yellow and orange, (4) red and maroon, (5) blue, (6) green pigments, and (7) miscellaneous coloring materials.

Black pigments. The printing industry consumes huge quantities of black pigments, primarily *carbon blacks*. Carbon blacks consist mainly of the element carbon. They are made by partial combustion of natural gas. Carbon black can be

Courtesy Graphic Arts Technical Foundation

A heavy duty mixer. The mixer can be tilted for emptying of the mix. Mixers of this kind may be used in the making of flushed pigments.

manufactured by different methods and in several qualities. "Different grades are produced which are useful for different purposes. The finest products are blackest in color and bluest in undertone. Carbon blacks are the blackest of black pigments, have the highest tinting strength and opacity and a tendency to adsorb driers from coating compositions. They are stable to acids, alkalies, light, heat, and atmospheric conditions."[11]

Carbon blacks are the most widely used but not the only existing kind of black pigments. We mention, next, *lamp black*, which owes its name to the fact that it was originally made in China by gathering the smoke from oil lamps. It is in our time produced by the burning of various oils rich in hydrocarbons. Other black pigments are the so-called vegetable and the animal blacks. The *vegetable blacks* are made by calcination "of grape husks, vine twigs, vine wood, old wine casks, and other similar materials."[12] The *animal blacks* are "made by charring animal bones from which the oily and fatty matter has been extracted in vertical or horizontal retorts without access of air. The charred mass is then ground to a fine powder."[13] Vegetable blacks are also known as *vine black*, *Frankfort black*, or *soft blacks*, whereas animal blacks are called *hard blacks*, *bone blacks*, and *ivory blacks*. There exist, in addition, various kinds of mineral blacks which are of very small importance at present. The development of magnetic character recognition, on the other hand, has introduced the so-called *magnetic blacks* which are mixtures of black iron oxides. These pigments are discussed in the final unit of this section under the heading of magnetic pigments.

Different kinds of black pigments have different mass tones and undertones, particle sizes, oil absorptions, specific gravities, and tinting strengths. Their blending for specific ink problems requires long experience as well as a thorough understanding of the desired ink properties.

White pigments. White pigments can be divided into two main groups: opaque white pigments and transparent white pigments. Opaque white pigments are chemically manufactured inorganic pigments. This group includes the titanium pigments, white lead, zinc oxide, lithopone, and other materials. Our discussion is limited to titanium whites because this pigment family is most important for printing inks.

Titanium pigments are made of a natural ore, ilmenite, which is of jet black color. As already mentioned, titanium white is manufactured by precipitation as well as calcination. The most concentrated titanium pigment is *titanium dioxide;* less concentrated versions include compounds of titanium with lead or with calcium sulfate and with barium sulfate, for example. Titanium dioxide is an exceptionally opaque pigment, very resistant to acids and alkalies as well as to light and the natural elements. It is insoluble in water and in organic solvents. Titanium white does not discolor if heated to the temperatures required for baking or curing, and, last but not least, it has valuable flow characteristics. This pigment is well deserving of its name as it is truly a giant among white pigments.

Transparent white pigments are often classified as *inerts* or as *extenders*. These materials are mostly mineral products of chemical manufacturing. They vary in chemical composition, specific gravity, oil absorption, and particle size, and are useful for several reasons. They serve as extenders for the highly concentrated organic color pigments and also to improve their working qualities. Among transparent white pigments are alumina hydrate, blanc fixe, precipitated calcium carbonate, gloss white, magnesium carbonate, and others. Our description is limited to the most important members of this group, namely, alumina hydrate and gloss white. *Alumina hydrate*, often simply called alumina, is very low in specific gravity, has high oil absorption, and a fluffy, flocculent texture. When ground in oil and spread on glass, the film is almost transparent."[14] It imparts good working qualities to the final product, but it reacts with certain vehicles such as lithographic varnishes, thereby increasing the body of the ink. This is an undesirable effect, technically known as *livering*. *Gloss white* is a combination of alumina hydrate and blanc fixe, arrived at by chemical manufacturing rather than by dry mixing of the two substances. It has excellent working properties, is indifferent to water and organic solvents, and can be used in all kinds of vehicles as it is much less prone to livering than alumina hydrate.

Yellow and orange pigments. A large variety of yellow and orange pigments is available for ink formulation. Among the most important ones are the chrome pigments and molybdate orange (both manufactured inorganic pigments), benzidine yellow, the Hansa yellows, and tartrazine lakes. These pigments will be briefly described, whereas a number of others will merely be mentioned. *Chrome pigments* are made in a wide range of hues from a pale primrose yellow to a deep orange.

Courtesy Graphic Arts Technical Foundation

Weighing small quantities on an analytic balance in an ink laboratory. Analytic balances are needed for the weighing of quantities that are too small for accurate weighing on less sensitive scales.

They are of varying light permanence and darken on exposure, have good hiding power, do not bleed in water and organic solvents, are heat-resistant but sensitive to acids and alkalies. As they contain substantial proportions of lead, they promote drying and are often designated as natural drying pigments. *Molybdenum orange* pigments have risen to a position of paramount importance in the printing ink industry. "They are brighter, cleaner, and stronger than the chrome oranges and possess much better working properties on the press."[15] These pigments are of high permanency in concentrated form but less so when diluted. Molybdenum orange can be used for litho inks as well as for baking, but is attacked by concentrated alkalies. Molybdate orange is often combined with synthetic organic pigments in red and orange inks.

Other mineral pigments are the *cadmium yellows* and *oranges*, *zinc yellow*, and *red lead* or *orange mineral*, to mention a few. Inorganic yellow and orange pigments of the chrome group are historically among the oldest manufactured pigments. They are increasingly replaced by synthetic organic pigments.

Benzidine yellow is a pigment dyestuff; it is a relatively new pigment that appeared approximately 20 years ago on the American market. "Since that time benzidine yellow has reached a place of major importance. In fact, this class of yellow pigment is now produced in larger tonnage than any other organic yellow."[16] Benzidine yellows do not bleed in oils, waxes, and solvents;

they have good color retention in baking enamels, and are of high color strength. Finally, it is mentioned that benzidine yellows are among the yellow pigments which can be used for full-color inks.

The Hansa yellows, our next group of pigments, are like the benzidines dyestuff pigments. They come in various hues and have much better color strength than chrome pigments, though they are in this and other respects inferior to the more recent benzidines. The light-resistance of Hansa yellows is excellent in concentration, somewhat less good in dilution; they bleed slightly in lacquer solvents and synthetic vehicles, but not in water and oil; they perform poorly in baking formulation, but have good resistance to acids and alkalies.[17]

The last pigment to be described is a lake known as *tartrazine*. It is considered by Wolfe "the most important transparent yellow lake used in the manufacture of printing inks."[18] Tartrazine lake bleeds slightly in water, not in oil and solvents, is suitable for baking, has good fastness toward acids though a poor one in alkalies. Tartrazine lake is rated of fair light-permanence if used concentrated, but of a poor one in tints. Its nonbleeding properties make tartrazine lake an important pigment for solvent evaporating inks provided that its other features are satisfactory. Of other yellow and orange organic pigments we merely mention *transparent yellow lakes* and *persian orange*.

Red and maroon pigments. This class of pigments does not contain any mineral pigments at all but consists completely of synthetic pigments, toners as well as lakes. Of the very large number of red and maroon pigments we will describe a few representative ones and merely give the names of several others.

We begin with *lithol reds* because they are among the most widely used red pigments. Lithol reds are toners and range in color from an orange to a deep bluish red. They are of excellent to fair light-permanence in concentration but less good in tints, have good resistance to acids and alkalies, do not bleed in water and most other solvents, and are of varying sensitivity to heat. *Toluidine* reds are bright red toners of excellent light-permanence, which is their outstanding asset. They are also resistant to heat, acid, and alkali and do not bleed at all in water, slightly in oils, but profusely in organic solvents. Toluidine reds retard drying and have a tendency to rub off. *Para reds* are inexpensive red toners of good light-permanence and

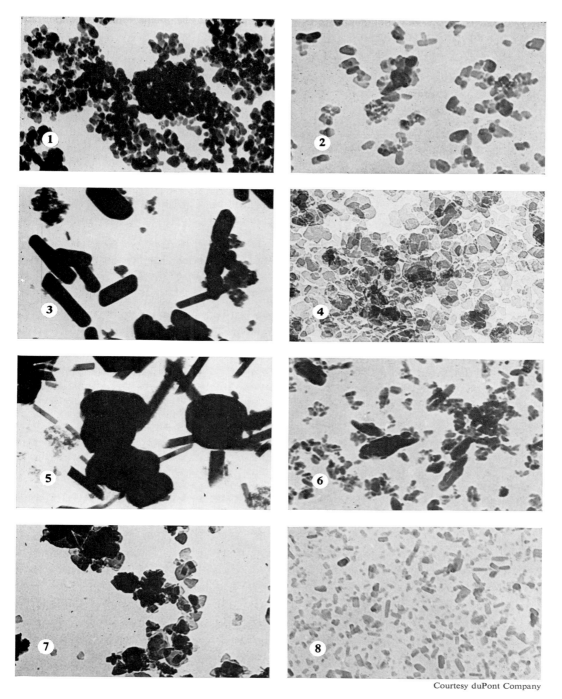

Electron micrographs of (1) *Rhodamine Y,* (2) *Monastral Blue,* (3) *Chrome Yellow,* (4) *Watchung Red,* (5) *Molybdate Orange,* (6) *Monastral Green,* (7) *Green Gold, and* (8) *Monastral Maroon.*
Magnification 40,000 times.

resistance to chemical agents but they are bleeders, though to a varying degree in water and organic solvents. They are, further, sensitive to heat; consequently, inks made with para reds should be ground with cooled rollers. As they are also poor driers, para reds are primarily used for utility inks.

Madder lake was originally a vegetable lake but is in our time a synthetic pigment belonging in the group of *alizarins* and therefore also known as alizarin madder. Alizarin pigments are extremely light-permanent; they were for this reason selected by Wolfe as the best pigments in his numerical scale of light-fastness where they have the highest number which is 20. It might be mentioned that *eosine*, a very fugitive dye, ranks lowest in this scale and has number one.[19] Madder lake is a very useful all-around pigment. It has good resistance to acids, excellent one to alkalies, and does not bleed in any of the important solvents. These pigments "are the only reds safe to use for butter wrappers and greaseproof inks."[20] But even these excellent pigments have some weak points. They tend to liver and they are of low color strength. *B.O.N. Maroon* (the three initials stand for beta-oxy-naphthoic, a reference to the organic acid with which it is made) is another pigment of excellent permanence and bleeding properties which can be used for package printing. *Tungstated rhodamines*, finally, are listed here because they include a particularly good magenta which is more suitable than other pigments for full-color printing. It has excellent permanence, good acid-resistance, and does not bleed in water or in oil. But it has its weak points, nevertheless, as it is not enough alkali-resistant and also bleeds in organic solvents to a varying degree. Other red pigments include fire-red toners, helio bordeaux reds, and watchung red, to mention some.

Blue pigments. Blue pigments are less numerous than red and maroon pigments. They comprise both manufactured mineral and synthetic organic pigments. The two inorganic families of blue pigments are the ultramarines and the iron blues. *Ultramarine blues* are made by calcination of soda ash, clay, sulfur, and other materials in varying proportions. The product is of a bright color and of good permanency, but of limited use. The *iron blues* are still quite important even though they are not nearly as dominant as they were in the past. Iron blues are complex compounds, containing principally the elements iron, carbon, and nitrogen. They are manufactured by precipitation and can be considerably varied in their hues. Iron blues have excellent light properties, do not bleed, are insensitive to diluted acid and to the customary baking temperatures, but cannot withstand alkalies. "The various shades of iron blues comprise the most important group of blue pigments used in the manufacture of printing inks. They are relatively inexpensive and may be mixed with practically all other pigments excepting those of a reducing or alkaline nature, both of which tend to destroy their color."[21] Iron blues are known by many names, as Milori blues, Prussian blues, bronze blues, among others.

Of the several available synthetic organic blue pigments we can describe but two: phthalocyanine and peacock blue. The development of phthalocyanine blue, perhaps better known under its duPont trade-mark as Monastral blue, was one of the greatest achievements in the field of pigments. Phthalocyanine blue is closer to the "ideal" pigment than any other. It is the only pigment that has a perfect rating in every respect in Pratt's table of pigment properties. Phthalocyanine blue is suitable for all kinds of printing inks. It can, fortunately, also be made in the correct hue for the cyan needed in full-color inks. Even though phthalocyanine pigments rate best in all resistance and bleed tests[22] they too have their limitation. This is last but not least the restrictive consideration of its high price. *Peacock* blue, the last pigment to be described, is a lake derived from the intermediate erioglaucine. It has a particularly attractive, clear hue but otherwise rather unsatisfactory characteristics: it is uniformly poor in light-permanence as well as in its resistance to acids, alkalies, and heat; it also bleeds slightly in water and organic solvents, though not in oils. "The principal use of peacock blue is in the manufacture of process inks, where its clear, azure color is of great value. Its unstable nature, however, is unfortunate as none of the so-called permanent peacock blues yet equal it in cleanliness of hue."[23] Other blues to be mentioned include *phosphotungstic* toners and *alkali reflex blue*.

Green pigments. The number of existing green pigments is considerable but relatively few of them are used for the pigmentation of printing inks. Our description is limited to chrome greens and to brilliant green toners. *Chrome greens* are combinations of chrome yellows and iron blues. They have the combined characteristics of these two types of manufactured mineral pigments with which you are already familiar. As the chrome yellows are less light-fast than iron blues, chrome greens do not fade but become darker and more bluish upon prolonged light exposure. *Brilliant green* toners are here mentioned because they are representatives of a group of pigments which is of general importance and includes, besides green, also blue and orange pigments. Chemically, these pigments are known as phosphotungstic and phosphomolybdic, the first indicating the elements of phosphorus and tungsten; the second a combination of phosphorus and molybdenum. Brilliant greens have good light-fastness, resist heat up to 320°F., are insensitive to acids but not to alkalies; they bleed but slightly in solvents for synthetic resins though strongly in those used for lacquer-type vehicles, but not at all in water and oils. "In general, with the other phosphotungstated colors they find wide application in glassine and cellophane inks because of their brilliance, transparency, and great tinctorial strength."[24] Other important green pigments include phthalocyanine green, permanent green toners, and various green lakes.

Miscellaneous coloring materials. Under this head we discuss four kinds of products: dyes, bronzes, daylight fluorescents, and magnetic pigments. *Dyes,* which are present in printing inks as solutions, must be distinguished from the insoluble pigment dyestuffs, or toners, and from the equally insoluble lakes. Soluble dyes were in the past the main coloring components of flexographic inks, which were then known as aniline inks because their coloring material belonged to the class of fugitive basic, or aniline, dyes. With the improvement of flexographic inks, dyes have been increasingly replaced by pigments, but as they have great color strength and brilliance, dyes are still used for inexpensive utility inks.

Next we turn to bronzes which are available in various hues of gold, as silver, and in non-metallic hues such as green or blue. *Gold bronzes* are alloys of copper and zinc; varying the proportions of the two metals results in different hues. *Silver bronzes* consist of powdered metallic aluminum; *colored bronzes* are made by precipitating various dyes on a metallic powder substratum. Bronzes can either be contained in printing inks as their pigments and then printed like other inks or they can be applied as powders by a separate operation known as *bronzing.* For the latter purpose an adhesive, known as goldsize or simply as size, is applied by the press. The still wet sheet is then dusted with bronze powder in a bronzing machine.[25] Silver is usually printed, but gold is preferably dusted or bronzed because this method produces a much higher luster.

Daylight fluorescent pigments have low color strength but unique attention-getting features. They are manufactured in a limited number of hues and differ in principle from other pigments which reflect part of the incident light but do not change the energy distribution of the material. Daylight fluorescent materials, on the other hand, have the ability of converting ultraviolet rays—which are not visible—into longer visible light waves, thereby adding to the intensity of the reflected energy. It is even questioned whether daylight fluorescents should be classified as pigments or more correctly as dyed resinous glasses.[26] Daylight fluorescent pigments are of large particle size and should be printed in heavy films for maximum effect. Originally limited to screen process printing, they are at present also available in inks for other methods, rotogravure and newspaper relief printing in particular.

Magnetic pigments are used in inks for EDP (electronic data processing) or MICR (magnetic ink character recognition), particularly for the imprinting of bank checks which will be sorted magnetically. For this purpose, the printed and coded image must be capable of magnetization. This effect is possible by using a black iron oxide powder as ink pigment. This pigment has especially low oil absorption whereby it becomes possible to achieve a high pigment concentration in the ink film. Magnetic pigments demonstrate the importance of particle size and the relation between it and the printing qualities of the ink. As the magnetically ideal particles are much too large for use in printing inks, compromises must be made between the needs of printing and those of electronic data processing.[27]

Section 3: Vehicles for Printing Inks

The subject of vehicles is even more remote for all who are not directly concerned with it than that of printing inks. This is not surprising as very few of us ever have the opportunity of meeting vehicles by themselves before they are combined with other materials into printing inks. Vehicles are consequently even for the practical printer just words but not physical substances with which he can become familiar. As long as the number of vehicles remained stationary and as long as inks did not change in their composition, there was not much need to burden one's mind with knowledge of this highly technical subject. But this situation has changed radically, and an elementary knowledge of vehicles has become indispensable for all who want to keep up with printing technology.

Few people realize that the great progress made in printing inks is predominantly progress in the field of vehicles. Speaking of lithographic inks, R. F. Reed, who observed the scene for many decades as the first research director of the Lithographic Technical Foundation, has this to say: "Thirty years ago there was only one type of offset ink. The pigments used in it were essentially the same as those used today with a few exceptions. The vehicle was mainly heat-bodied linseed varnish. Nowadays there are several types of offset inks. *These differ from each other principally in the composition of their vehicles* and the processes by which they dry. The newer inks represent both improvements in printing quality and in utility of the printed product. Some also represent special developments to meet the higher speed requirements on modern sheet-fed and roll-fed or web-offset presses."[28]

At this point a summary of the contributions made by vehicles seems to be in order. The vehicle provides the adhesion of the ink film to the paper or other stock; it is responsible for gloss, for the wearing qualities of the printed image, such as scratch or mar resistance, as well as for the speed in which an ink sets or dries, and for the manner in which this action takes place. Last, but not least, the kind of vehicle and its combination with other ingredients has also a considerable influence on the performance of the ink on the press.

The progress in vehicle chemistry is mainly due to the total or partial replacement of natural raw materials by synthetics. The chemistry and physics of synthetics is, for obvious reasons, outside the scope of this manual, but two points might be made that will help the reader to understand why synthetics are so important and why we may expect further advances from the laboratories where synthetics are developed.

Each natural raw material such as an oil, gum, resin, or solvent has its own distinct properties. Some of these properties can be influenced by subsidiary treatments, though not beyond certain limits. Synthetic materials are radically different from the natural ones because they can be de-

signed or constructed to have specifically wanted properties. This statement must, like all generalizations, be taken with a grain of salt, as a synthetic product may turn out to be rather different than the originally desired one. But it is nevertheless true that synthetics can be created to have properties which existing materials do not have. As our changing technology produces many new materials which must be used as printing stocks and for which existing inks are not always suitable, we must rely on the development of synthetics which will have properties that will result in more suitable inks for these new materials. The growth of package printing which depends so much on plastic materials affords many illustrations of this point.

The second essential difference between synthetic and natural materials is their much better uniformity. This point has a great bearing on the reliability and simplicity with which a vehicle made of synthetics can be duplicated with precision. Product uniformity can be much easier obtained with standardized synthetics than with natural raw materials.

Composition of vehicles. For our purpose it is convenient to divide the ingredients of vehicles according to their functions into three broad groups. The first group includes *film-forming* materials such as drying oils, natural and synthetic resins, cellulose esters, and synthetic rubber products, to mention some. The second group consists of *volatile* materials, also known as solvents, thinners, diluents, and retarders, such as petroleum-type solvents, aromatic solvents, alcohols, and esters, for example. The third group is here called *additives* and comprises a number of substances which serve to modify ink properties and are used in small proportions. They include metallic driers, metallic soaps, waxes, anti-skinning agents, plasticizers, retarders, dispersing agents, and even perfumes. Some of these materials are volatile; others are not.

Classification of ink vehicles. Even though many film-forming substances and solvents are used in combination, and in spite of the fact that it is impossible to draw strict lines of demarcations whereby various ink vehicles can be exactly separated, it is nevertheless expedient to divide them into the following nine groups: (1) lithographic varnishes, (2) oleo-resinous varnishes, (3) synthetic varnishes, (4) vehicles made of mineral oils, (5) lacquers, (6) spirit varnishes, (7) resin solutions, (8) aqueous vehicles, and (9) miscellaneous vehicles. Each of these nine groups is now briefly described.

Lithographic Varnishes

Lithographic varnishes were until the advent of synthetics the most important vehicles for lithographic and letterpress inks. The term "lithographic varnish" can be used either in a strict sense or rather loosely. In the strict sense, "lithographic varnish" means linseed oil bodied by heat treatments. (This material is known as *stand oil* in the English literature, a term that does not tie it as closely to lithography as does American terminology. As lithographic varnishes are also used for other inks than lithographic ones and, besides ink making, are used for paints and enamels, the more neutral English term is less confusing.) In its looser sense "lithographic varnish" may also refer to combinations of linseed oil with other natural or synthetic drying oils.

The inroads made by more modern materials into the territory of lithographic varnishes have reduced their position but by no means eliminated them. As lithographic varnishes are still widely

Courtesy Superior Varnish & Drier Company

View of a varnish cooking plant. The cooking vessels occupy two stories. In this picture you see the tops of three vessels. The first two have a capacity of 1,500 gallons each. The last holds 4,000 gallons.

used, they are described in more detail than less generally important vehicles.

Types and purposes of lithographic varnishes. Linseed oil is derived from the seeds of the flax plant either by pressing or by solvent extraction. The oil is purified before it is subjected to heat treatment whereby it changes its consistency. The extent of the change in viscosity depends primarily on the time and temperature of heating or, as is often said, *cooking*. The consistency of lithographic varnishes is indicated by a numerical scale varying from No. 00000 (five aughts) to No. 0 (one aught) and from No. 1 to No. 9. Number 00000 is least viscous whereas No. 9 is at the opposite end of the scale; "it is very heavy and stringy, and is about as heavy as it is possible to make a lithographic varnish by heat alone."[29]

Different lithographic varnishes have different functions and consequently "in the formulation of a letterpress, lithographic, or an offset ink, several varnishes of different body (viscosity) are generally employed: the *thin-bodied* varnish for shortness or softness; the *medium-bodied* varnish for wetting, flow and length; and the *heavy-* and *very heavy*-bodied varnishes for tack and for increasing the binding property of the total vehicle for the pigments."[30] Sometimes lithographic varnish is modified by other drying oils such as tung, or China wood oil, to improve certain qualities. Finally it is mentioned that burnt lithographic varnish is used for especially heavy intaglio inks and is also called *plate oil*.

Lithographic varnishes belong in the class of natural drying oils. Other natural drying oils are the already mentioned tung oil, oiticica oil, perilla oil, and soybean oil, to mention a few. These are all vegetable oils. Some fish oils which are derived from various types of fishes, menhaden in particular, also exhibit drying qualities.[31] If such materials are spread as a thin film they will change from the liquid to the solid state by a combination of oxidation and polymerization. But it may take many days and even weeks before they form a dry film if we simply let nature take its course. The drying of such oils can be substantially advanced by adding small quantities of metallic driers.

Metallic driers are catalysts, which means that they are chemicals capable of initiating and promoting chemical reactions which would either not set in at all or progress exceedingly slowly without their presence. Interestingly, catalysts themselves are not changed substantially by the chemical processes stimulated by their presence.

In the case of driers these substances are compounds of the elements cobalt, lead, and manganese, to mention the more important ones, with organic acids. If these acids are contained in resins, the driers are called *resinates*, if they are constituents of oils, the driers are known as *oleates*. These two types are usually the ingredients of the widely used *paste* driers.

The metal portion of a drier is its decisive ingredient. *Cobalt* driers are the most powerful ones and need especially careful handling. Cobalt driers are usually avoided in first-down inks in dry printing where the first-down ink is dry before the next-down ink is printed. But in wet printing of multicolor work, where all inks are applied wet-on-wet in a single press run, cobalt drier is used in all inks. The presence of cobalt driers may consequently be under certain conditions responsible for the already mentioned trouble of ink crystallization. Lead contributes to the uniformity of drying and manganese initiates the drying action. Both are much less powerful than cobalt; as lead improves its effectiveness for drying in the presence of manganese these two metals are usually combined.

It must be clearly understood that metallic driers are not an all-around nostrum for the drying of any type of ink. These driers are not effective at all with inks that do not contain drying oils and they can even act as retarders if added disproportionately to inks made with drying oil vehicles.

Limitations of lithographic varnishes. Lithographic varnishes were for many decades the exclusive vehicles for letterpress and lithographic inks. But inks made of these vehicles have several features which are often undesired. First, they are relatively slow drying; next comes the fact that their ink film is rather soft and hence prone to scratching and marring; the third limiting factor is that lithographic varnishes cannot be used alone for gloss inks.

Oleoresinous Varnishes

By a combination of drying oils and resins it is possible to make printing-ink vehicles which are in many points superior to lithographic varnishes. Oleoresinous varnishes are made by combining oils and resins at high temperatures and are therefore called "cooked" vehicles by the industry. As the cooked mixture may be at room temperature either a solid or a semi-solid mass and not fluid enough to serve as a vehicle, it is liquefied, or reduced in its viscosity, by addition of solvents.

Courtesy Superior Varnish & Drier Company

The bottom of one of the vessels shown in the preceding picture. All vessels are water jacketed; cooking is done in a carbon dioxide atmosphere, cooking time and temperature depend on the product. Temperatures are often between 500° and 600°F, cooking time is from 3 to 5 hours.

Main ingredients of oleoresinous varnishes. These are drying oils, resins, and solvents or thinners. Oleoresinous varnishes also contain metallic driers, possibly waxes and other additives.

The functions of these different ingredients are very clearly described by Mattiello as follows: "The *oils* supply the elements of drying, elasticity, toughness, adhesion, durability, and tack. The *resins* provide the elements of hardness, resistance to wear, waterproofness, acid and alkali resistance. They also impart tack, gloss, and, in some instances, may assist in drying. The *thinners* are used to reduce the viscosity or consistency and tack in order to develop easy working of the vehicle, which property is also imparted to the finished ink. Thinners will also increase penetration, and thereby aid adhesion to paper stock. As a result of these properties they have a tendency to minimize offset."[32]

We turn next to a brief discussion of these three kinds of materials. As natural drying oils have been briefly described in the preceding unit on lithographic varnishes it is here merely mentioned that each of these oils has certain properties of its own and that it can add corresponding attributes to the varnish in which it participates.

Resins. The subject of resins is vast and highly technical. The best that can be hoped for of a discussion in this manual is that the reader will become aware of their existence and usefulness. Non-technically, resins are for our purpose described as solid materials, suitable as film-forming components in printing-ink vehicles. If they are to become part of oleoresinous varnishes they are cooked together with drying oils. But not every resin is equally usable for this purpose and some are not at all.

Resins can be divided into the two main groups of natural and synthetic ones. Among natural resins there is a distinction made between resins of recent origin and fossilized resins. *Recent resins* are derived of the sap of contemporary trees, whereas *fossilized* resins come from trees that have perished long ago. Their sap was hardened in the course of time to solid substances which are now dug out of the ground. The most important domestic natural resins are gum rosin and wood rosin. *Gum rosin* is made by tapping live trees, *wood rosin* by mechanical and chemical treatments of dead trees, primarily pine stumps. Fossilized resins are found rarely in the United States and are mainly imported from overseas. The Congo, for example, used to provide us with valuable resins known as Congo copals; from Manila comes Manila copal; and the East Indies export various fossilized or semi-fossilized resins known as *copals* or *damars*.

Synthetic resins comprise a large number of different compounds. Among them are those made with rosin as their raw material, as well as other completely synthetic products. In oleoresinous varnishes we often meet products of the first group such as *ester gums* and the *phenolic* or *maleic* modified resins which improve drying, hardness, and mar resistance, and also the gloss of vehicles. There are many other synthetic resins; some of those which are widely used in other types of vehicles will be mentioned later.

The solvents, or thinners, used for oleoresinous vehicles include kerosene and other petroleum solvents of varying qualities. As solvents are main components of vehicles that dry by evaporation, lacquers in particular, the discussion of solvents is in the unit on laquers. Finally a few words on additives. Waxes and similar compounds have

the purpose of adjusting or reducing tack and anti-oxidants help prevent premature ink drying. Other additives are used for shortening of inks, still others for reduction of gloss.

Synthetic Varnishes

There is, as already mentioned, no sharp line of demarcation between several kinds of vehicles which are related to each other. Oleoresinous vehicles may contain, as mentioned in the preceding unit, a combination of oils and synthetic resins. Synthetic varnishes or synthetic oils, of which those belonging in the family of *alkyds* are particularly worth mentioning, consist of synthetic resins which are combined with natural oils. The manner of combination, though, differs considerably. But this subject, too, is beyond the scope of our elementary discussion which turns now to synthetic drying oils of the alkyd group.

Alkyds. The term "alkyd" is itself a synthetic word devised in 1927 by one of the pioneers of synthetic resins and oils, Kienle, to indicate the two types of chemical substances of which his newly invented product consisted. "It was derived from the words alcohol and acid by combining 'al' and 'cid,' and for euphony changing 'cid' to 'kyd'—al(cyd)kyd."[33] Alkyds can be modified with many substances including natural drying oils and resins.

Alkyds are available in a considerable variety and are classified either according to their constituents or their characteristic purposes. For printing inks "drying oil modified alkyds comprise the most important group. They can be thinned to a working consistency with drying oils and cheap organic solvents and have film-forming properties, since they absorb oxygen from the air and dry by air curing. The drying process is catalyzed by cobalt, lead, and manganese driers."[34] Alkyds can improve important ink features such as drying, adhesion, gloss, flexibility, and mar-resistance and are, therefore, widely used in many different types of inks. The selection of the kind of alkyd that should become part of a specific vehicle requires good familiarity with both the properties of alkyds and the purpose of the ink of which it will become part.

Vehicles Made of Mineral Oils

Mineral oils are non-drying, and so are the vehicles made with them if they are applied to non-absorbent materials. Vehicles made with mineral oils are not only very inexpensive but also non-drying on the press and are therefore widely used for "news inks," as the inks for newspaper relief printing are called. Similar inks are made for the printing of telephone directories. These types of vehicles may contain rosin oils, asphalts, pitches, and rosin for counteracting the shortness of mineral oil. Other ingredients of mineral oil vehicles are solutions of oil-soluble dyestuffs, such as Victoria blue base or methyl violet base whereby the vehicle is strongly colored. The adding of strong dyes helps to counteract the natural shortness of vehicles which is increased by carbon black. Giving the vehicle a strong color makes it possible to reduce the amount of carbon black.

Lacquers

The American Society for Testing Materials (ASTM) "defines a lacquer as a liquid composition containing cellulose esters or ethers as basic film-forming ingredients."[35]

When speaking of specific lacquers, it is customary to refer to their characteristic film-formers and to designate them accordingly as nitrocellulose, or as cellulose acetate, or as ethylcellulose, or as vinyl lacquers, and so on.

The main ingredients of lacquers. Lacquers consist of five main groups of constituents. There are: (1) the characteristic film-former or film-formers, (2) resins, (3) plasticizers, (4) solvents, and (5) diluents. Speaking of nitrocellulose lacquers, Mattiello explained the functions of these materials as follows: "*Nitrocellulose* provides the element of toughness and hardness, and causes rapid formation of dried film. The *resins* impart adhesion, gloss, and hardness, and some resins contribute plasticizing properties. The *plasticizers* impart the elements of elasticity, durability, and adhesion. The *solvents* and *diluents* have the important function of solvency and reducing viscosity or consistency to permit easy spreading (meaning good working properties) of ink films."[36]

Even a cursory discussion of film-formers, resins, and plasticizers is too technical for the purpose of this manual. It seems best to use the available space for a brief introduction to solvents and their functions. This choice was made because solvents are used in many printing plants and can present not only technical problems but also health and fire hazards.

Introduction to solvents. Solvents and the related diluents are chemically manufactured organic liquids most of which, though not all, are easy to ignite and therefore considered fire hazards. Sol-

vents are liquids of a peculiar nature. They have the faculty of entering between the smallest particles of solids and thereby to change these from the solid to the liquid state. If they are added to already existing solutions of solids, they can make these solutions even more liquid. This effect is technically expressed as a reduction of viscosity. In printing inks, solvents have several important functions and, as they differ in many ways, they must be carefully chosen by the ink formulator.

The first point to be discussed is *solvent power*. It must be understood that no solvent has unlimited ability of transforming solids into liquids, or, said in other words, that no solvent can function as a solvent for every material. A solvent that is most powerful for some kinds of solid matter is much less powerful for others and completely without power for most others. This point can be illustrated by water which is generally the most important solvent, though not for inks. Water is an excellent solvent for sugar, as everybody knows who uses sugar in his coffee. Fortunately water is no solvent for pottery and metals, otherwise our cups and spoons would not be usable.

Because of their limited solving power, various solvents are needed to put different film-formers in solution. The selection of solvents must be made with great care for several additional reasons. Some film-forming materials have either no tolerance at all or a very limited tolerance for certain solvents. This means that they react in an undesirable manner to the presence of solvents with which they are not *compatible*. They simply quit the solution, or are precipitated, to use the technical term. It may happen that shop personnel, unaware of this possibility, will add a solvent which has proved its usefulness with other inks to a new and different type of ink with which this particular solvent is not compatible. The result is then rather disappointing as the ink may be spoiled beyond repair. The same holds true for mixing various types of inks which may not be compatible with each other.

On the other hand, it should be mentioned that certain liquids which are by themselves not capable of acting as solvents for certain film-formers can be added to properly made solutions of these materials in limited proportions. They are usually designated as *diluents*. Such additions are often made either for technical reasons or to reduce the cost of a vehicle, as diluents are cheaper than the more powerful solvents.

Classification of solvents. The functional classification of solvents made by Thomas H. Durrans is most suitable for our purposes. Dr. Durrans distinguishes the following five classes: "(1) *Low boilers* of high solvent power to enable concentrated solutions of low viscosity to be prepared and to obtain quick initial drying and increase of viscosity. (2) *Medium boilers* to check the rate of evaporation and thus to reduce defects caused by excessive rates and also to impart good flowing properties. (3) *High boilers* to protract the period of drying for long periods when necessary, and to impart good brushing properties and gloss. (4) *Plasticizers* to knit all the solid constituents into a homogeneous whole, to impart flexibility, gloss and permanence, and to reduce brittleness. (5) *Diluents* to reduce cost, to control viscosity, and occasionally, to dissolve resins."[37]

This explanation must suffice; we turn next to a discussion of hazards connected with the use of solvents.

Fire hazards of solvents. Most solvents used in ink vehicles are more or less flammable. They must therefore not be exposed to open flames, burning cigars, cigarettes, and pipes or sparks of electricity. Many people understand that solvents must not be handled near open flames but too few are aware of the fact that mixtures of solvent vapor and room air can be extremely dangerous if they exceed a certain concentration and temperature. Then they can lead to powerful explosions, which may be caused by a spark or even the mere glow of a cigar. Fire hazards of solvents influence insurance and transportation rates and often necessitate installing of explosion-proof storage rooms, motors, and light fixtures.[38]

Health hazards of solvents. Certain solvents can also become health hazards if they are either inhaled or brought in direct contact with the skin. Direct contact not only may remove some of the natural oils of the skin and thereby make it dry and brittle, but may also cause certain internal diseases. Solvents can irritate and seriously disturb the human breathing apparatus and even lead to severe poisoning. Prolonged exposure to toxic solvents may also cause injuries to the reproductive organs of both sexes.

Many people believe that solvents indicate their toxicity by the unpleasantness of their odors. This is unfortunately not correct. "The possession of these injurious properties by a solvent is in no way connected with its odor, and the statement frequently made, that only strong or unpleasantly smelling solvents, or those of high volatility are injurious to health, is totally incorrect, and too much cannot be known about the desirable precautions which should be taken in the use of any particular solvent."[39]

Lacquers and lacquer-type vehicles are used for several reasons, primarily because it is possible to make exceptionally fast-drying inks with them. They may also be of sufficient adhesive quality where other types of vehicles fail, in the printing of non-absorbing materials such as plastics for example. Lacquer-type vehicles are used in flexographic, rotogravure, and in screen-process inks.

Spirit Varnishes

Spirit varnishes dry by evaporation and resemble lacquers in this respect. The most important individual film-former for spirit varnishes is still shellac, and if language were more logical, or of a simpler logic, spirit varnishes would be known as "lacquers" since this word was originally derived precisely from "shellac." But in our time the term "lacquer" excludes vehicles made of shellac which are commonly known as "spirit varnishes" by their main solvent.

Other film-formers for spirit varnishes are natural resins such as some Manila copals, Malayan and East Indian damars, gum mastic, and gum sandarac, as well as rosin. These can be supplemented with synthetic resins which add to hardness and mar-resistance of the vehicle. These film-formers are dissolved in ethyl alcohol, also known as ethanol, grain alcohol, or simply as spirit. Even though ethanol is the main solvent of spirit varnishes it can be supplemented by other alcohols and solvents of the alcohol-ether family. As spirit varnishes are rather brittle, they require the addition of plasticizers. The main use of spirit varnishes is in the field of rotogravure and flexographic inks, but they are also used for the coating of labels and other printed products.

Resin Solutions

Under the heading of resin solutions we group all vehicles drying by evaporation of organic solvents with the exception of those classified as lacquers and as spirit varnishes. It must be pointed out that this division is rather general and that a fine technical grouping needs many additional distinctions.[40] Our catch-all class contains, consequently, vehicles of very different constructions, including those for moisture-set inks, some for heat-set inks, and others that contain chemically treated rubbers or acrylic resins, to mention some.

Vehicles for moisture-set inks. Moisture-set inks are based on solvents of the glycol family because "they have the necessary water solubility, are hygroscopic, and because of their low vapor pressures, inks based on them are stable on the rollers; they are good solvents for the very polar and acidic resins used in this type of ink."[41] The resins for moisture-set vehicles "must be water insoluble yet soluble in a water-miscible solvent, such as one of the glycols. A moderately concentrated solution of the resin must have a satisfactory viscosity as a letterpress medium, and at the same time have good pigment-dispersing properties. The resin solutions must have sufficient water tolerance to be printed under various humid conditions without precipitation on the press."[42]

These are by no means all required characteristics, but they will do for our purpose. The resins that satisfy these specifications are not too numerous and belong to the families of maleic- and fumaric-rosin condensation products. Various additives, such as wetting agents and waxes, improve the rub-resistance and general performance of inks made with vehicles of this type.

Vehicles for heat-set inks drying by evaporation. Let us now discuss heat-set inks and their vehicles. One type is made with resin solutions; another type made by partial resin dispersion is discussed in the final unit of this section. The vehicles which are discussed at this point are made of resins "that belong either to the modified phenolic or maleic classes and are characterized by the rapid evaporation of solvents at elevated temperatures and by their freedom of tack at normal room tempera-

tures. The solvents are generally special petroleum fractions having boiling ranges lying between 400 degrees and 500 degrees Fahrenheit."[43] Additives for this type of vehicles include drying oils or other plasticizers and waxes which help to make the printed film slippery and to keep the ink wet on the press.

Resin solutions for flexographic inks. Our final example for vehicles that dry by solvent evaporation is taken from flexographic inks, particularly those that are used for the printing of certain plastic films which pose difficult adhesion problems. Depending on the type of material to be printed, various kinds of solvents and of resins are selected. Among such formulations we find solutions of acrylic resins in isopropyl alcohol, alone or in combination with ethyl acetate for example.[44] In formulating a vehicle for flexography only such solvents can be admitted as will not be detrimental to the image carriers. These consist either of natural or synthetic rubber and the nature of these materials limits both solvents and resins to a small number.

These three examples of resin-solution vehicles could be augmented by many others. Inks made of vehicles belonging in this group can be found in most branches of printing, in rotogravure, flexography, and screen process not less than in letterpress and lithographic printing. Among resins used for these types of vehicles are melamines, which belong to the family of urea-formaldehyde film-formers, various kinds of cyclized and chlorinated rubbers as well as certain members of the epoxy family.

Aqueous Vehicles

Aqueous vehicles contain water as a main ingredient. Printing inks made of such vehicles are commonly called *water colors* or water-color inks and can be used for letterpress, newspaper relief printing, flexography, gravure, and also for screen-process printing. Even though inks based on aqueous vehicles are not much used in general, they are of importance for certain specialties. Aqueous vehicles can be divided into three different types: (1) straight water-color vehicles, (2) emulsions of the water-in-oil type, and (3) emulsions of the oil-in-water type. Each of these will now be explained.

Straight water-color vehicles and emulsions. Straight water-color vehicles consist of solutions or dispersions of such materials as shellac, gum arabic, dextrin, and possibly starches in water, plasticized with glycerin and fortified with a pre-

Courtesy Interchemical Corporation

A high-speed propeller mixer. This mixer has three blades attached to the main shaft. These blades are in the mix and therefore not visible in this picture.

servative to prevent destruction of the organic binders. The other two types of vehicles are emulsions, which means that they are more or less stable dispersions of two immiscible liquids. Emulsions are made by careful selection of their liquids as well as of an emulsifying agent. Emulsions are of two different types. One is called oil-in-water, the other water-in-oil.

Schematic diagram of emulsions. The picture at the left shows a water-in-oil emulsion, that at the right an oil-in-water emulsion. The continuous phase of water-in-oil emulsions is oil; the continuous phase of oil-in-water emulsions is water.

The two types of emulsions. If the emulsion can be diluted with water it resembles milk which is the most common *oil-in-water* emulsion. Here the water forms the *continuous* or *outside* phase and the oil is suspended in it. If the emulsion cannot be diluted with water but requires an organic solvent, then it is called a *water-in-oil* emulsion and resembles in this case our butter which is the most common emulsion of this type. Now the oil, or resin solution, is the outside or continuous phase whereas water is dispersed in it and forms the *discontinuous* phase. (As an aid to your memory it is mentioned that the nature of the two emulsions explains why milk stains can be cleaned with soap and water and why butter stains must be removed with an organic solvent, by dry cleaning, for example.)

Emulsions of the water-in-oil type are used for the screen printing of fabrics with pigment dispersions that can be cured by heat treatments. Straight water-color vehicles and emulsions of the oil-in-water type are used for letterpress, experimentally for newspaper relief printing, rotogravure, and flexography. Among the resins for emulsions are alkyds, styrene-butadiene, vinyl compounds, and acrylics. These must of course be compounded with their appropriate solvents and emulsifying agents.

Miscellaneous Vehicles

Under the heading of miscellaneous vehicles we mention dispersed heat-set vehicles, quick-set inks, and cold-set inks which do not fit any of our specific groups.

Vehicles for heat-set inks can be made in various ways. One type you have met under the heading of resin solutions. Another type contains slightly plasticized synthetic resins which are dispersed in carefully chosen solvents.

The so-called *quick-set* inks, which dry at room temperature and dry by gelation or filtration "are based on a two-phase medium—a resin or rubbery material, and pigment in a low viscosity medium. When the ink is printed on absorbent paper, the solvent drains away and the viscous resin gels on the surface."[45] Some vehicles for high-gloss varnishes and gloss inks are based on a similar vehicle structure. Here, the resin is barely in solution; "on printing, very little of the medium filters away, and the remainder forms an even film on the surface; the final drying is often due to chemical changes as many gloss varnishes have a drying oil base."[46]

Our last item in this group is vehicles for *cold-set inks*. These vehicles consist of "plasticized waxes having melting points ranging from 150° to 200°."[47] Vehicles for cold-set inks are solids at room temperature, and inks made with them must be used on presses heated beyond their melting point.

Section 4:   The Manufacturing and Testing of Printing Inks

The manufacturing and testing of printing inks belong so closely together that both are best presented in the same section. Our discussion is therefore divided into four units: (1) the laboratory, (2) the plant, (3) testing of inks for process specifications, and (4) testing of inks for product or end-use specifications.

The Laboratory

The laboratory is the heart of every ink mill. Here, new kinds of inks are originated and their formulas developed, here the production of inks is controlled during various stages, and here the final product is tested and approved before it may be shipped to the customer. The success of an ink business depends a great deal on the quality and ingenuity of its laboratory staff.

The laboratory staff. In a well-organized and capably staffed ink laboratory we can usually meet various kinds of skilled people. Among them are chemists, chemical engineers, and physicists as well as various laboratory technicians. The graduate staff is more concerned with theoretical and development work whereas the technicians devote themselves to testing, adapting of already existing formulas for special conditions, and, last but not least, to color matching.

Equipment of an ink laboratory. A well-appointed laboratory is equipped with standard chemical apparatus and tools including analytic scales and microscopes. Where color measurements are to be made, spectrophotometers are, of course, provided. In addition, printing ink laboratories may be equipped with testing facilities, experimental machines for the mixing and dispersing of inks, and often also with small production equipment for the making of small batches of inks.

In laboratories where performance testing of inks is done, printing presses are a necessity. In many instances proof presses will answer the purpose, but one can also find production printing machines in some larger ink plants. These are operated by highly experienced pressmen.[48]

Ink-making as an assembly process. Even though this approach may be unorthodox, we can consider ink making to be essentially an assembly process. The items out of which the final product

Courtesy Interchemical Corporation

A color matcher at work in the laboratory of a printing ink plant.

is assembled are usually manufactured by the dyestuff, pigment, resin, and solvent industries but not by the ink industry itself. As the ink maker depends on these materials—and, of course, also on the skill and experience of his staff—for many of the distinctive ink properties, familiarity with available resins, solvents, pigments, and other possible ink ingredients is an absolute necessity.

Sources of information for ink ingredients. The manufacturers of raw materials publish a flood of literature in which technical information is often skilfully blended with attractive sales statements. It is the task of the technical staff to isolate the important facts and to record them in such a manner that the information can be rapidly found whenever needed by the laboratory. In some large ink-manufacturing organizations modern data processing equipment is used for this purpose. The properties of available materials are indicated on punched cards, and these are mechanically sorted to identify the materials that have the qualities thought most desirable by the ink formulator for the solution of a given problem.

Standardization of testing. It would be completely impossible to cope with the enormous number of materials used in our complex industrial society without standardization and without testing methods generally agreed upon. In the United States, the American Society for Testing Materials, known briefly as ASTM, is the central clearing house for the development of tests and the classification of materials. ASTM is a nonprofit, impartial institution which has been in

Courtesy Graphic Arts Technical Foundation

A laboratory of a printing ink plant. Ink chemists and technicians are working on formulas for new products and on special orders, including color matching.

existence more than 50 years. Its collected standards are published in many huge volumes but each standard is also individually available. Among them are several hundreds for materials which can be used in printing inks.[49] The printing-ink industry has also developed its own testing methods which are published by the National Printing Ink Research Institute, Lehigh University, Bethlehem, Pa. These are known as the NPIRI Standard Test Methods and are of particular value to ink chemists.[50]

Another widely used standard work on testing is "Physical and Chemical Examination of Paints, Varnishes, Lacquers and Colors" by Henry A. Gardner, D.Sc., and G. C. Sward, M.S., which is now in its 11th edition. This work does not deal with inks specifically, but it fully covers many of the materials used in inks as well as some important tests for inks.[51] Finally, we mention the "Color Index," a joint publication of the English Society of Dyers and Colourists and the American Association of Textile Chemists and Colorists.[52] This work consists of four volumes and is the most complete reference source on the properties of pigments and dyes.

Testing stands high on the list of routine activities performed in all ink laboratories. It can be divided into four different kinds: (1) testing of raw materials, (2) testing of manufacturing in progress, (3) testing of completed inks for process requirements, and (4) testing of inks for product requirements. The testing of raw materials and of manufacturing are too specialized to be here discussed, but the testing of inks for performance and end-use characteristics will be described immediately following the next unit which is devoted to the ink plant itself.

The Ink-Manufacturing Plant

Depending on the size and manufacturing program of various ink companies, their plants may or may not include facilities for the cooking of oils and vehicles. As this part of ink-making has not been explained, it will be briefly discussed here along with manufacturing facilities for the making of solution-type vehicles. Then we turn to the mixing of pigments and vehicles; and finally to the dispersion of the mixed components.

After a manufacturing order has been received by the plant, the materials needed for the batch must be located, weighed, or measured and assembled at the point of manufacture. All frequently used pigments and vehicles are stocked in appropriate quantities, and so are solvents and resins. Large ink plants have considerable storage room which includes tanks of different sizes for liquid staples such as basic oils and solvents.

The making of vehicles. Cooked vehicles are manufactured in varying quantities. The kettles used for cooking can be made of several metals, stainless steel and monel primarily, but there are also varnish kettles of iron, aluminum, and copper in existence. Smaller kettles are movable, the larger ones stationary. Modern oil-bodying and varnish-cooking equipment can be highly automatic and precision-instrument controlled.

Film-formers are dissolved by several techniques depending on the nature of the participating materials. If no heat is involved, the operation of dissolving is often called *cold cutting*. The equipment includes steam jacketed kettles, tumbling barrels, and others. Emulsions are usually made with high-speed mixing machines. It is often found practical to prepare highly concentrated solutions of various film-formers which are later blended and reduced as required simply by mixing.

Mixing and dispersing. The combining of pigments and vehicles can be divided into the two operations of mixing and dispersing, "By mixing is meant the initial wetting of the pigment by a liquid ink vehicle and the lowest stage of mixing is the point at which the pigment can no longer be discernible."[53] The mixed material, of tencalled "the mix," becomes a printing ink by the following operation of dispersing, more popularly known as the *grinding* or *milling* of inks.

Equipment for mixing and dispersing. The equipment for mixing of pigments and vehicles depends on the nature of the job and on the quantity to be processed. Among mixing equipment present in

Courtesy Graphic Arts Technical Foundation

Pony mixers like this one are widely used for the mixing of pigments and vehicles prior to grinding of the ink on roller mills.

many ink plants are pony mixers, high-speed mixers, and kneading mixers, to mention a few. The mixed batch can be either finished by addition of further liquids directly in the mixer or it must be put on a different type of equipment for milling or final dispersion. "Milling printing ink can be defined as dispersing pigments in vehicles to a point at which the finished product gives satisfactory results on the printing machine for which it is prepared."[54] The dispersing equipment for inks can be divided into roller mills, ball mills, and colloid mills.

Courtesy Interchemical Corporation

A three-roller mill and the ground ink running into an ink barrel. Above the three-roller mill you see the vessel in which the batch was mixed. This vessel is hoisted in position, tilted, and supplies the mill with the mixture to be ground.

Roller ink mills are made with one, two, three, four, and more rollers; in the United States three-roller mills are more common than the other types. Ball mills are large closed drums in which the material is mixed as well as milled by rotating pigments and vehicles together with a number of steel or stone balls. Paste-type colloid mills have "been developed for the purpose of grinding the softer grades of news and rotary inks. They are also of great value in dispersing pigments in volatile solvents and hence find application in the manufacture of pigmented flexographic and gravure inks and coatings."[55]

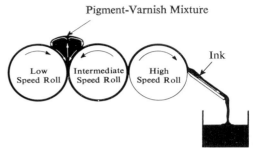

Pigment-Varnish Mixture

Low Speed Roll   Intermediate Speed Roll   High Speed Roll

Ink

Courtesy Graphic Arts Technical Foundation

Schematic diagram of a three-roller mill. The pigment-varnish mixture is prepared in a separate machine, often in a pony mixer.

As three-roller mills are among the best-known and most characteristic machinery of ink plants, a brief description seems indicated. "Three-roller mills have three cylindrical rollers of equal size: the first rotates forward, the middle roller rotates backward at faster speed, and the front roller rotates forward at a faster speed still; ink fed to the back roller passes toward the front of the mill where it is collected by a scraper knife and apron."[56] The setting of roller mills requires skill and a good familiarity with the materials to be dispersed. The most recent models of roller mills can be set completely automatically. The rollers may be equipped for cooling and for heating as either might be necessary in order to achieve the best dispersion with the materials used for specific inks.

After this rather summary description of an ink plant and its equipment, we turn to a discussion of testing, beginning with that of process specifications.

Testing the Process Characteristics of Printing Inks

The testing of process characteristics refers to the working properties of inks and must be distinguished from the testing of product characteristics or end-use specifications. In this unit we concentrate on the first kind, in the next on the second. The testing of process specifications has the object of insuring the flawless performance of inks on the press. Smoothness of operation, speed, and quality all depend on ink performance. Testing of process specifications is, hence, a most necessary insurance and protection for the efficiency of presswork.

Before we enter the subject of individual tests, a few explanatory remarks on their nature will be found helpful. Most tests used for printing inks are comparative rather than absolute. The ink to be tested is compared with the behavior of an ink which has been found suitable. This ink will be called the *comparative standard*, the ink to be examined will be designated as the *test sample*.

For our purpose it seems sufficient to select the following fifteen tests of process specifications which are of fairly general importance. These are: (1) specific gravity, (2) fineness of dispersion, (3) viscosity, (4) tack, (5) flow, (6) ink flying or misting, (7) livering, (8) adhesion, (9) drying time, (10) mass-tone, (11) undertone, (12) hiding power, (13) full-color qualities, (14) subliming, and (15) gloss.

Specific gravity. This test indicates the relation between ink weight and volume. This relation is economically important where inks are bought by the pound, as "the number of impressions that reasonably may be expected from a pound of the ink depends, to a large extent, upon the specific gravity or bulking value of the ink."[57] This test is of particular importance when the price of two inks is to be compared. Other conditions being equal, an ink 10 per cent cheaper but 15 per cent higher in specific gravity will cost more per area of printed image than the higher-priced product. The test itself is simple and can be found in Wolfe's text and many other books; it is not further described here.[58]

Grinding tests. These tests examine how finely

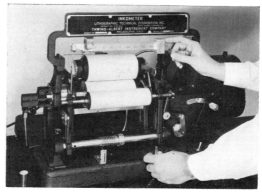

The GATF Inkometer *is used for measuring ink tack and to test inks for flying or misting at different speeds.*

inks are dispersed. All inks must for obvious reasons be free of grit and coarse particles and are examined for their absence. Grinding tests can be made in several ways by examining a comparative standard and the test sample. This can be done either by drawing a spatula through both inks, or by diluting followed by microscopic examination, or by means of an instrument developed by the National Printing Ink Research Institute, the *NPIRI Grindometer.*[59]

Viscosity, tack, and flow. These three properties are related to the body, or consistency, of inks. Different types of inks are tested in different ways. The viscosity of very fluid inks can be measured with various instruments. Heavy-bodied inks, such as those for letterpress and lithography, are often examined by various simple finger tests. If these are made by experienced people they are highly conclusive.

Another method for determining body, tack, and press stability of heavy-bodied inks is based on the *Inkometer,* an instrument developed by Robert F. Reed of the Graphic Arts Technical Foundation.[60]

Ink flying or misting. Ink flying is a considerable nuisance in high-speed relief and lithographic printing. When an ink film transfers from one roller to the other it forms many "tiny filaments or threads. These threads get longer until they are about ten times their diameter at the instant they break in two. Then they decrease in length very rapidly and merge with the main body of ink on each of the two rollers."[61] Some of these filaments may stretch quite long and break in several places. These free-floating ink particles are thrown into the air, thereby causing the flying or

The Production Grindometer *is an important aid in the grinding of printing inks. This instrument makes it possible to express the quality of the dispersion in objective terms.*

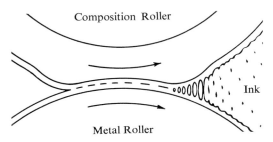

Composition Roller

Ink

Metal Roller

Diagrammatic explanation of ink flying or misting. As the two rollers separate some ink threads become longer and finally break, thereby forming ink mist.

misting of inks. The Inkometer can be used, under certain conditions, to test inks for this defect.[62]

Livering. Livering means, as you may remember, an irreparable stiffening of the ink and is therefore to be avoided. The test for livering is simple. The test sample is placed under controlled condition in a heated oven for a period varying between 24 and 72 hours. After cooling, the test sample and the comparative standard are examined for their flow characteristics.[63]

Adhesion. Adhesion is an important requirement for all inks and particularly so where non-absorbent stocks such as plastics or metal foils must be printed. Several simple tests are used. The Scotch-tape test, for example, consists in putting a strip of pressure-sensitive, adhesive-coated plastic with the adhesive side on a print and then removing it slowly. No ink should remain on the strip of Scotch tape.[64]

Drying time. The crucial role of drying has been repeatedly mentioned, and tests of this feature can be of exceptional interest. Their great importance is evidenced by the fact that three research in-

Courtesy National Printing Ink Research Institute

The NPIRI *Drying Time Recorder simulates the rubbing action of a finger on an actual print. Finger rubbing had been used for testing of drying time before this instrument was developed.*

stitutes developed machines for this purpose. Each of these has its own distinctive features[65]

Mass tone and undertone. The test whereby these two points are examined is known as a *drawdown*. It is a simple test, but requires skill in its execution. A small lump of the test sample and an equal lump of the comparative standard are placed side by side on a white surface. Then the drawdown is made with a steel blade. First both inks are spread as heavy films, then the drawdown is continued by reducing the film thickness as much as possible. "The thick film presents the mass-tone, the thin film the print-tone. Holding the drawdown up in front of a light and looking through the thin films shows us the color of the undertone."[66]

Hiding power. The term "hiding power" refers to the relative transparency and opacity of a printing ink. The test is similar to that of a drawdown and can be combined with it. The paper for this test is either printed with a black band in the center or with a checkerboard pattern. The relative hiding power of the test sample and of the comparative standard is judged by eye and depends on the ability of both inks to hide the black center band.[67]

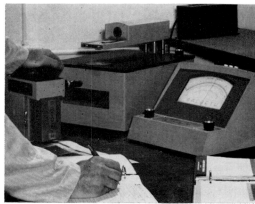

Courtesy Graphic Arts Technical Foundation

A color technician tests full-color inks with a reflection densitometer.

Evaluation for full-color printing. This series of tests has become of greatest importance with the growth of full-color printing. The GATF-Preucil Color System is based on densitometer readings and permits a fast evaluation of hue, strength, and purity of inks. The system provides a scheme for graphic recording of these features in the GATF Hue and Purity Chart.[68]

Subliming. Subliming is defined as "the change of state directly from solid to gaseous."[69] Certain pigments tend to sublimation under heat. The heat can be due to exposure to the sun or to baking, but it may also be generated in printed piles during drying. The pigment vapors deprive the printed image on the face of the sheet of color and soil its back where they condense. The subliming test prevents such mishaps.[70]

Gloss. The final item, gloss, in this group of properties to be tested can be measured with several instruments. These provide a numerical reading for both the test sample and the comparative standard. As various instruments produce different readings, tests should always be identified as to the equipment used.[71]

Testing the Product Characteristics of Printing Inks

The tests to be discussed under this head refer to the suitability of the ink for the final printed product and are therefore often called end-use tests. These tests are, like the tests for process requirements, comparative rather than absolute and should be planned to comprise all significant points of each specific situation. As end-use tests mostly examine the resistance of printing inks to chemical agents and other forces, they are often known as resistance tests.

For our purposes resistance tests can best be divided into nine different groups: (1) resistance to light, (2) to weather, (3) to water, (4) to other solvents, (5) to acids and alkalies, (6) to handling, (7) to heat, (8) to miscellaneous packaged prod-

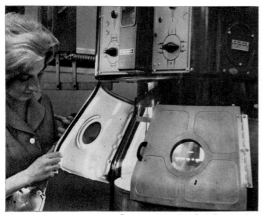

Courtesy Interchemical Corporation

A laboratory technician opening the FadeOmeter. The FadeOmeter is used to test the light fastness of printing inks.

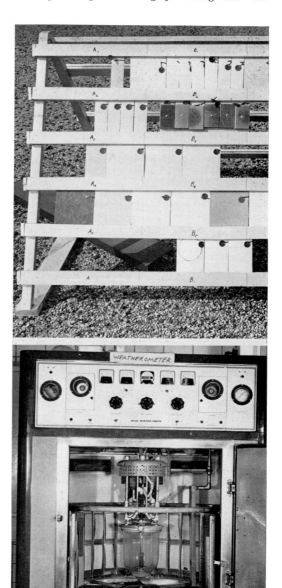

Courtesy Mead Corporation

Two methods of testing paper and ink for weather resistance. The first picture shows a testing rack on which the material is actually exposed to weather; the second illustration shows an open WeatherOmeter which is used in the laboratory for accelerated testing. The results of accelerated testing and of testing in the open air are carefully correlated.

ucts, and (9) to miscellaneous finishing and fabricating operations.

Resistance to light. Light-fastness or resistance to light deals with the relative permanence of an ink. This feature is important wherever the printed product is exposed to sunlight, outdoors or indoors. The requisite tests can be made either by actual exposure and observation or by means of a testing machine which accelerates deterioration and permits evaluation of the tested material within hours rather than months.

The testing machine for light permanence is known as the *Fade-Ometer*. Fade-Ometer tests are variously evaluated as to their correlation with actual exposures, but these tests are nevertheless of great value. Light-fastness can be tested together with resistance to weather in another machine known as the Weather-Ometer.[72]

Resistance to water and organic solvents. Resistance to water and other solvents can be tested in various ways. The tests are based on the fact that non-resistant inks when exposed to these liquids exhibit a staining effect known as *bleed*. If a print is supposed to be tested "this can be done quite simply by allowing a drop of the appropriate liquid to fall on the print in such a way that the drop includes or spreads over some unprinted paper. After the drop has dried up, the white areas, especially around the periphery of the drop, are examined for color."[73] Other tests are made with the ink itself; the principle, though, remains the same.

Resistance to chemical agents. Resistance to acids and alkalies is tested "by partly immersing a dry print of the ink in the reagent or solvent for ten minutes or longer, depending on the severity of the requirements. If the reagent is an acid or an alkali, the print is then washed in running water and allowed to dry. In case of solvents, the washing with water is omitted. The immersed area is then compared with the remainder of the print and any change noted. The back of the print should also be inspected for any stain due to bleeding."[74]

Resistance to handling. The group of tests for resistance to handling comprises a number of different tests which depend on the nature of the ink and on that of the printed product. Included are abrasion, scuffing, scratching, marring, to mention some. These tests are particularly important in the printing of package materials and in metal decorating. Rub-resistance can be tested with the *Sutherland Rub Tester* and other instruments. Sometimes these tests are made without equipment simply by rubbing two printed samples together and by comparing them with samples of approved quality.[75]

Resistance to heat. Resistance to heat must be tested in all inks and coatings which are either to be baked or cured or which will be pasteurized. All these conditions can be duplicated by laboratory equipment. After testing the samples are examined and compared with approved standards.[76]

Resistance to miscellaneous packaged goods. Printed labels and packages must be resistant to the goods for whose packaging they are made. Resistance to soap, to detergents, to vinegar, lard, butter, and other products is tested by exposing prints to these materials under controlled conditions and by comparing the test sample with a comparative standard.[77]

Resistance to finishing or fabricating. The last group of resistance tests refers to miscellaneous finishing and fabricating operations and includes such points as hot paraffining, varnishing, laminating, hot sealing, and others. The required tests are made by using representative prints for these operations and by comparing the test samples with the standards. Care must be taken that the test sample be truly representative of the manufactured product, otherwise the tests may be misleading. It has happened, for example, that a thoroughly dried printed sample was tested for varnishing, and that the result was satisfactory. The production lot, on the other hand, was not completely dry and caused trouble by bleeding of the ink in the varnish.

The preceding discussion of testing is far from exhaustive but it should serve its main purpose. This is to make the reader aware of two things: one, that there are many possible hazards in printing production; two, that there is also a substantial body of organized experience available, though by no means always used, which can prevent or minimize these risks.

Section 5:   Inks for Different Printing Processes and Methods

Different printing processes and methods have their own characteristic ink requirements. These depend on the nature of the image carrier, the stock, and the type of press for which a given ink is to be used. Every discussion of printing inks is hence related to image carriers, paper, and other stocks, presses, and the so very important press-work. All these elements are in constant inter-action which must never be forgotten.

The following presentation is divided into four major parts, one each for the process families of relief, intaglio, planographic, and porous print-ing. Printing inks for each process family are first discussed in general and then specifically for each printing method belonging to a process family.

Printing Inks for Relief Printing

All inks for relief printing must suit the main feature of relief image carriers, namely, that the printing image is raised above the bulk of the carrier material. Other points of consequence are the nature of the material used as image carrier, the fact that image transfer may require extremely high pressures, the speed of the press, and the surface characteristics of the printing stock as well as its absorbency or lack of it.

The first point worth noting is that the ink must be suitable for precise application to the image areas without being applied elsewhere on the image carrier. It must, further, be in a posi-tion of assuming the exact shapes of the image areas, no mean task indeed if we consider that halftones made with 133-line screens, which are widely used in quality reproductions, can have approximately 17,500 distinct areas per square inch. Each of these dot areas can be considered a plateau divided by a shallow gap from its neigh-bors. The ink must duplicate the exact shapes of these plateaus, neither more nor less. It must not stay shy of the edges of the many printing images nor must it spill over.

The ink must, further, be capable of taking high pressures without disfiguration. The pressures are "on the order of 1000 pounds per square inch"[78] during image transfer. The ink must also adhere uniformly to the paper, and it must dry without mark-off, or set-off, which would spoil the job. These are some general requirements; more will be mentioned under the following headings.

Inks for Letterpress Printing

Letterpress printing is asked to do a vast number of different printing tasks which require a wide range of different equipment. Without going into the many specialties, it is mentioned that generally used letterpress inks are divided according to the type of press on which they will be used. There are inks for job presses, for job automatics, for flat-bed-cylinder presses and for perfectors, as well as for sheet-fed and roll-fed rotary presses.

Printing inks for platen and flatbed cylinder presses. An outstanding difference between inks to be printed at various speeds is their difference in body. Inks for job presses which are hand fed have a very heavy body and a very buttery consistency. The body of inks for the faster job automatics is less heavy, and as the interval between individ-ual impressions is now much shorter, these inks must be faster setting than inks used on hand-fed presses. You may remember that inks must be made softer and less heavy-bodied as the speed of

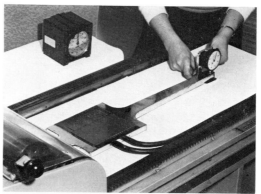

Courtesy National Printing Ink Research Institute

Research on ink transfer requires high-precision meas-urements. The plate is held by vacuum to a Huck base which provides a measurement of impression pressure. Speed is measured with a microswitch clock. The thick-ness of the ink film is determined by weighing the plate before and after each impression.

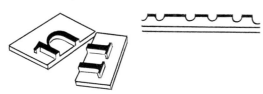

Courtesy Graphic Arts Technical Foundation

Schematic diagram of a relief printing-image carrier. Inks for relief printing, letterpress for example, are ap-plied to the raised areas of the image carrier.

printing increases. Flatbed-cylinder presses run faster than hand-fed presses but often less fast than automatic job presses, and inks for these presses vary accordingly in their body.

Inks for platen and flatbed-cylinder presses are needed in a wide range of quality; they must be available in inexpensive utility grades and also as high-quality products suitable for the printing of finest halftones. Depending on quality and price requirements, these kinds of letterpress inks are made of lithographic varnishes in combination with rosin or pitch varnishes in the less expensive groups, or with mixtures of lithographic varnishes and synthetics in the better quality grades. Various grades of carbon blacks, furnace blacks and blue toners are used as pigments for black inks. Moderate amounts of driers and non-offset compounds are some of the usual additives.

Printing inks for rotary presses. Inks for rotary presses, and particularly those for web printing, must be capable of being printed and dried at much higher speeds and are therefore less viscous than those for non-rotary presses. The vehicles of inks for rotary presses are mainly made of synthetics that can be dried much faster than lithographic varnishes. Modern magazine web printing uses primarily heat-set inks.

Some specialty inks. Letterpress printing is highly specialized and many of these special applications require their corresponding specialty inks. In the printing of milk containers, for example, inks drying by precipitation are widely used. Or, to mention another field, books and business forms printed in relief printing from rubber plates have their own ink requirements, particularly that the inks must not be injurious to the rubber or plastic duplicate plates which are here used as image carriers.

Inks for Newspaper Relief Printing

Inks for the printing of newspapers by relief methods are in a class by themselves. Several points determine their characteristics: One is the high speed (which is in excess of 1500 feet per minute) with which modern newspaper presses operate, another point is the economy factor which makes it imperative to use the least expensive kinds of materials, and a third point is the severe time pressure under which newspapers must be produced.

You may remember that news inks dry by penetration and absorption, and that newsprint is a very porous paper. You may also remember

that the vehicle of news inks is based on non-drying mineral oils to which rosin oils, pitches, and asphalts may be added. These types of vehicles do not dry at all if applied to non-absorbent stocks. Fortunately, newsprint is highly absorbent and "during drying, part of the vehicle drains off into the paper capillaries while oil-wetted carbon black is largely held in the paper's surface by mechanical entanglement with the paper fibers and to a minor extent by absorption."[79]

Inks made with true drying vehicles instead of the non-drying mineral oil types have been tried, but these have not worked out. More recently, the problem of news inks has been attacked in a different direction by the American Newspaper Publishers Association (ANPA) Research Institute. Experiments were made with inks of a water-color type which seem to be promising but have not yet reached the stage of final fruition.[80]

The drying of news inks is not completely satisfactory; but it must not be overlooked that, nevertheless, mineral oil inks have many excellent features. They are inexpensive, they can be pumped from their storage tanks to the press without clogging or drying, and the presses can be stopped and started without concern for the drying of ink on the press and on the image carrier. All these are important timesavers and highly economical features.

If the printing of black ink poses many technical problems, those attending full-color printing are still more severe. Full-color printing is called ROP (run-of-paper) printing in the newspaper industry. The high speed of printing, the cost and the nature of the paper, all add up to difficulties in obtaining fidelity of color reproductions. The newspaper industry has standardized color inks for ROP printing together with the advertising industry which is interested in this problem because most ROP printing consists of multicolor or full-color advertisements.[81]

Inks for Flexography

Flexography is a relief printing method which employs non-metallic flexible image carriers of natural or synthetic rubber. The image carrier has a limited capacity for absorbing and holding ink. This capacity makes it possible to use much more fluid inks than in other branches of relief printing where printing-image carriers are made of metals which are non-absorbing.

Flexographic inks consist of a high percentage of solvents which may amount to approximately three-quarters of the total ink volume. As solvents evaporate and do not participate in the final ink film, it is more difficult to obtain strong color effects with this type of inks than with inks that do not lose a substantial part of their volume during drying. For this reason flexographic inks were originally colored with soluble dyes of the aniline family which have very high coloring power but are rather fugitive. These aniline dyes were so characteristic for the whole printing method that it was called aniline printing.

As printing with flexible image carriers developed, the name aniline printing, which had become both undesirable and misleading, was changed into flexographic printing, a designation that refers to the characteristic feature of the image carrier. Even though flexographic inks which are dye colored are still used, pigmented flexographic inks now dominate the field.

Classification of flexographic inks. In one scheme of classifying inks, these are first grouped according to their relative hiding power and then further divided by their main solvent. Thereby nine different groups were established: (1) transparent alcohol-based inks, (2) transparent water-based inks, (3) transparent inks based on special solvents which include various alcohols and also naphthas,[82] (4) opaque alcohol-based inks, (5) opaque water-based inks, and (6) opaque inks based, like (3), on special solvents. By blending transparent and opaque inks belonging to the same solvent class, the remaining three classes are arrived at, namely (7) semi-pigmented alcohol-based inks, (8) semi-pigmented water-based inks, and finally, (9) semi-pigmented inks based on special solvents.[83]

This classification omits all reference to film-formers for the different types of inks. By way of illustration it may be said that alcohol type inks may contain for this purpose shellac, alcohol-soluble copals and damars as well as maleic and other synthetic resins. Similar materials, though treated to become soluble or dispersible in water, are used in the class of water-based inks. The film-formers for the third group that comprises miscellaneous solvents depend on the purpose of a specialty ink. It may be necessary to incorporate film-formers which are not generally used in order to obtain the required result. It should never be forgotten that toxicity and flammability of flexographic inks is an important point. Non-toxic and not too flammable solvents are of course used wherever possible.[84]

Flexographic inks are less opaque and color strong than non-evaporating inks. They can be used on papers, metal foils, and plastic materials. Depending on the purpose or end use of the printed product, the inks must pass various performance tests. Flexographically printed food package material must pass the requirements of the Food Additive Amendment, a law that has the aim of protecting the consumer from unsafe materials in the packaging of edibles.[85]

Inks for Indirect Relief Printing

The fourth and final relief printing method is indirect relief printing, more commonly known as dry offset. This method uses machine-etched relief image carriers which may be made either of metal or of light-sensitive polymers. As dry offset eliminates the dampening action of lithography, inks for this method are in principle not different from other relief printing inks. Certain adjustments may be needed because double image transfer reduces the thickness of the final ink film, and also because presses for indirect relief printing are based on the rotary principle and hence faster than platen or flatbed cylinder presses.

Inks for Intaglio Printing

All intaglio printing methods have certain functional features in common. Among these are (1) the printing image is recessed in the carrier material, (2) the printing ink must be placed into these recesses, (3) the surface of the image carrier representing the non-image areas is inevitably covered with ink in the process of inking the recessed areas and must therefore (4) be cleaned prior to image transfer, (5) and last, image transfer requires the removal of the ink from the recessed areas. But all these necessities can be satisfied in extremely different techniques. The differences are

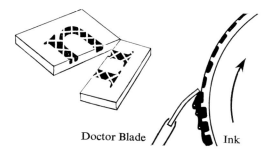

Doctor Blade   Ink

Schematic diagram of image transfer in rotogravure. The ink must be fluid in order to fill the small cells o, the printing-image carrier.

so pronounced that many people who merely look at presswork of various intaglio methods would never assume that these are based on a common principle. In accordance with these differences, we find equally unexpected differences in various types of inks for various types of intaglio methods.

For the purpose of this discussion the subject is best divided into two units: one will deal with inks for steel-die engraving and banknote printing, the other unit is devoted to the industrially most important type of intaglio printing, gravure, and to rotogravure inks.

Inks for Steel-Die Engraving and Banknote Printing

In the United States, the commercial use of intaglio, or plate printing, is at present insignificant, but intaglio printing has retained its place of eminence in the printing of the national currency, government and other bonds and stocks, and postage stamps. The United States Bureau of Engraving and Printing, which is in charge of the printing of our money, bonds, and stamps, is the biggest printer of this kind, and for security reasons also manufactures its own inks about which no information can be published.

Commercially available plate-printing ink is made of heat-bodied or burnt oils. The ink "must be short and buttery in consistency and yet greaseless so that it may be easily wiped off the plate, yet it must have sufficient cohesion and adhesion to enable it to adhere to the paper and leave the engraved lines in a clean, sharp, and unbroken manner."[86] The pigments must be soft and non-bleeding in water as the paper is usually dampened in this method as in fine-art intaglio printing.

For steel-die engraving, or die-stamping, intaglio image carriers are used in combination with embossing in order to raise the printed image over the level of the paper. Even though some die-stamping is done with non-glossy inks, most people prefer a high gloss in die-stamped printed images. "The general requirements of die-stamping inks are that they should give level prints of high gloss, should not exhibit feathering when printing, i.e., wiping should be easy so that fine minute strings of ink do not tail out from the ends of letters and lines; the printed ink should not crack on such flexing as is likely to be given to a letterhead, nor should the ink surface remain so tacky that superimposed papers will stick.[87]

The vehicles for die-stamping inks are solutions of ester gums or other resins, which are plasticized; they dry by solvent evaporation. The pigment phase of inks for die-stamping contains besides colorants also various transparent pigments such as gloss white which are needed for good working properties and for gloss retention of these inks.

Gravure Inks

Gravure is in this manual divided into the two branches of sheet-fed and rotogravure. Sheet-fed gravure is a relatively insignificant method whereas the roll-fed rotogravure is a most important industrial printing process. As inks for both kinds are in principle very similar we turn immediately to a discussion of inks for rotogravure.

As you know, image carriers for gravure (which can be plates or cylinders) contain the printing images in the form of a huge number of minute cells. These cells are flooded with ink; then the non-image areas, which form the surface of the carrier, are cleaned of the excess ink by passing the plate or cylinder under a doctor blade which performs a wiping action. During the following image transfer, or impression, the ink is sucked out of the cells by the printing stock which is forcefully pressed against the image carrier.

Main characteristics of gravure inks. In consequence of the nature of the process, rotogravure inks must have eight characteristics. These are: (1) inks must be very fluid and not only fill the cells but also flow out in the shadow areas, (2) the dispersion must be very fine, otherwise the pigment particles could not properly fill the cells, (3) rotogravure inks must not contain materials that will be repelled by the carrier metal, (4) they must be free of all abrasive materials, otherwise they would injure the image carrier and doctor blade, (5) they must not contain substances capable of reacting with the image carrier or injurious to it, (6) the cohesion of rotogravure inks must be sufficient to keep the ink in the cells between inking and image transfer in spite of the centrifugal force exerted by the fast rotation of the image carrier, (7) the ink must have low adhesion to the image carrier for proper wiping, but at the same time good adhesion to the paper, plastics, metal foil, or the printing stock in general. Finally, (8) gravure inks must harden or set without going through a sticky stage.[88]

Classification of gravure inks. Gravure printing is used for a number of different purposes and on a considerable variety of materials which include besides papers also plastics, fibers of many kinds, and metallic foils. Fortunately for their discussion, the several existing types of inks have been classified by general agreement and can therefore be presented in some order.

The different types of ink are designated by the capital letters "A," "B," "C," "D," "E," "T," "W," and "X." *Type "A" inks* are used for the printing of newspaper supplements and for magazine and catalog printing. They contain hardened rosin and asphalts as well as other natural or less expensive synthetic resins as film-formers which are dissolved in petroleum type solvents. Type "A" gravure inks are among the least expensive. *Type "B" inks* are used for coated and highly calendered stocks, have ethyl-cellulose in combination with various resins as film-formers, and contain the requisite solvents such as alcohols, ethers, and esters.

Type "C" inks serve for package printing of plastics and metallic foils. They are based on lacquer-type vehicles containing nitrocellulose. These inks have good adhesion and result in hard scratchproof ink films. *Type "E" inks* (sometimes called type "D") are based on spirit vehicles with shellac and other alcohol-soluble resins as film-forming ingredients. They are relatively free of odor, and because they can be hot paraffined, they are used for waxed bread wrappers, cartons, and labels.

Type "T" inks have excellent heat-, alcohol-, and acid-resistance and are employed where these features count, for example, in the printing of soap and detergent packages or labels for vinegar. They are made with chlorinated rubber vehicles in combination with suitable resins. Their solvents are aromatics and naphthas. *Type "W" inks* are water soluble, non-toxic, non-flammable, and practically odor-free. They can be used for wallpaper printing and for special package tasks. Their film-formers are natural and synthetic resins that can be either dissolved or dispersed in water. The final group of *type "X" inks* comprises those that cannot be classified in any of the established categories. They are specialties which are developed as gravure faces either new tasks or previously non-existent printing stocks and are therefore not further discussed.

Inks for Planographic Printing

In this manual the process group of planographic printing is divided into the methods of stone lithography, direct lithography, offset lithography, and collotype. In contemporary America,

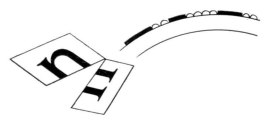

Schematic diagram of image transfer in lithographic printing. The ink-receptive areas of the plate are black, the water-receptive areas are shown with droplets.

stone lithography has become a fine-art reproduction method and inks for such methods are outside the frame of this manual. Nor do we need to discuss inks for direct lithography, as this method is of very limited importance. It might be mentioned that these two methods have direct image transfer which is accomplished with a single splitting of the ink film and that it is therefore possible to produce heavier ink lays in direct printing methods than in offset lithography where the ink film is split twice.

For our purposes the subject of planographic inks is therefore divided into that of inks for offset lithography and that of inks for collotype. In accordance with the overriding position of offset lithography, inks for this method occupy most of the following discussion.

Inks for Offset Lithography

As always, we take the nature of the printing method as point of departure. In offset lithography the printing areas of the image carrier are distinguished from the non-printing areas by means of chemical treatment and not by differences in elevation, as in relief and intaglio printing. It should also be noted that this distinction cannot be made once-and-for-all but must be kept in operating condition by repeating the chemical treatment of the image carrier as part of each printing cycle.

The chemical treatment consists in the dampening of the plate with a liquid known as the *fountain solution*. This solution contains water in the main; it is, though, chemically not neutral but slightly acid. It should be firmly kept in mind that offset lithographic inks are in continuous contact with this solution and that this fact is an important consideration in the design of offset lithographic inks. Another significant point is double image transfer. In offset lithography, the original ink image is first transferred to the blanket and then to the paper. The ink film is, therefore, split two times. Offset lithography has hence much thinner final ink films than are normally produced by direct lithographic methods. Where highly transparent effects are desired, this feature is of great advantage, but where high opacity is wanted, the thinness of the ink film can pose problems.

Relations between ink and fountain solution. First we turn to the effect of the fountain solution on printing inks. It is a mistake to assume that the mutual repellence of the fountain solution and printing ink is absolute and complete. This is not so. Lithographic ink has the tendency of accepting moisture. "It was found that a maximum of about 35 per cent of its weight of moisture can be taken up by a black ink without serious detriment to printing except grayness or loss of intensity. Mostly the amount of moisture taken up was between 5 and 15 per cent but it varied with the ink and with the coverage of the form."[89]

But it must be made clear that excessive water absorption by lithographic inks is quite harmful. It leads to losses in tack and to the flocculation of pigments. In a well-prepared ink the pigment consists of very small particles which are dispersed in the vehicle. "If something happens which causes the pigment particles to lump together to form fewer but bigger particles, we say that the pigment has *flocculated.* This happens only when the ink comes in contact with water as it is being run on the press. As a result of pigment flocculation, the ink becomes very short, that is, buttery or pasty. This may lead to stripping of the ink from the ink rollers and piling of the ink on the rollers and the plate."[90]

Tinting. The relation between printing ink and the fountain solution can become troublesome for additional reasons. If an ink emulsifies in the fountain solution, or forms an *ink-in-water*

Courtesy Graphic Arts Technical Foundation

Schematic diagram of a well-dispersed and a flocculated ink. The pigment particles of the well-dispersed ink are separated by the vehicle, as shown in picture at the left. In a flocculated ink, as shown at the right, pigment particles are bunched together. Well-dispersed inks are fluid, flocculated inks must be worked to break down the bunched structure in order to make them fluid again.

emulsion, the result is *tinting*, meaning that the non-image areas of the plate produce a slight tint of the ink color on the paper. Tinting is somewhat more related to paper coatings and to the handling of a job on the press than to the properties of inks and is therefore here not further discussed. (The relations of ink and paper are explained in Chapter VIII; the handling of jobs on the press is discussed in Chapter VII.)

Greasing or scumming. Finally we mention as a requirement of lithographic inks that they must not grease or scum. "Scumming occurs when the non-image areas of the plate lose their desensitization and begin to take ink. The scum shows on the plate and cannot be washed off with water."[91] Scumming can be due to various causes, not all related to the ink. Inks can be responsible for this condition if they have either not sufficient tack or are made with a vehicle that is too acid, or if they contain abrasive matter.[92]

Tests for lithographic inks. Among the process tests specially designed for lithographic inks are the following: (1) bleeding of inks in water, (2) tendency for water-logging, (3) tendency for tinting, and (4) test for greasing or scumming. These tests are simple to make and are described in detail in the here often-quoted book by Robert F. Reed, *What the Lithographer Should Know about Ink*, Chapter X, "Testing of Offset Inks."

As the product or end-use specifications of lithographic inks do not differ from those already explained, our discussion can be concluded by merely mentioning that lithographic inks are available in several types. The oldest type of ink is, as you know, called conventional ink and is based on lithographic varnish. More modern types include quick-set and high-gloss inks which are extensively used on sheet-fed presses. Heat-set inks are not practical with sheet-fed equipment but they are a necessity in web-offset color printing. Among specialties of lithographic inks those for metal lithography are mentioned as particularly important.

Inks for Collotype

Collotype printing is in the United States a commercially insignificant method of reproduction. It is a slow printing method and, hence, free of most of the problems with which the development of inks for fast printing methods must struggle. But collotype has some distinctive problems of its own. Inks for collotype must be extremely heavy-bodied and their pigments must not bleed in a mixture of water and glycerin which is used as a humectant, or moistener, in this printing method. The vehicles for collotype ink are either lithographic varnishes or alkyds, or combinations of these two.

Inks for Porous Printing

Porous printing is in this manual divided into the two methods of serigraphy and screen-process printing. As there is no difference between inks used for either method, and as there are no inks for serigraphy other than screen-process inks, we will discuss them under this classification.

Inks for Screen-Process Printing

Our explanation begins, as always, with a description of the relations between ink and image carrier. As you may remember, in screen-process printing the image carrier is a tautly stretched cloth (made either of natural fiber, synthetic fiber, or metal threads) with a large number of pores. The distinction between image areas and non-image areas is brought about by keeping the pores open in the image areas and by blocking them in the non-image areas. The image carrier, known as screen, serves also as ink reservoir, or fountain, in this process. The ink is distributed across the surface of the image carrier with a rubber blade, the squeegee, and forms the printed image by passing through the unblocked areas onto the stock underneath.

Ratio of open transfer area to thread area. First a rather characteristic fact which is not always understood must be pointed out. The nature of porous image carriers makes it impossible to achieve a direct 100 per cent ink transfer in the

Schematic diagram of image transfer in screen-process printing. The white letter "n" represents the open areas of the image carrier. Inks for screen process must be of proper viscosity and flow to produce uninterrupted printed images that show no pronounced mesh marks to the naked eye. (Under magnification, screen printed images usually show mesh marks.)

image areas. The emphasis is here on the word *direct*. The reason for this limitation lies in the cloth structure of the image carrier. In many types of stencil cloth the ratio of open area to area occupied by threads is approximately 30:70. In some types of cloth this ratio is even more unfavorable for the open areas, in others such as certain metal and synthetic materials, it is more favorable as these threads can be thinner than those of silk. If the printed image could only be produced by direct vertical ink transfer, it would not be possible to make solid coatings in screen process, and the result would be one of, say, 30 per cent dots in the image areas. Screen-process inks must overcome this difficulty by their flow; they resemble in this respect inks for rotogravure.

Screen-process printing is capable of depositing exceptionally heavy ink films which may attain thicknesses of approximately 50 microns. This ability is not matched by other printing methods and accounts for the fact that screen process was originally the only method capable of printing daylight-fluorescent inks. As screen process is more of a picture reproduction and decorating process than other printing methods, it needs a considerable variety of printing inks which must be usable with such materials as paper and cardboard, wood, glass, plastics, leathers, metals, fabrics, and even ceramics. In the following we present several of the more generally important screen-process inks.

Screen-process inks or paints? At this point a comment on terminology seems to be needed. Originally, when screen-process printing was in its infancy and went through the corresponding period of secrecy—a phase through which practically all printing methods had to pass—printing media were commercially unavailable and had to be concocted by the pioneers of the new process. As flat wall paints were closest to a usable ink, these served as a starting point for the making of screen-process inks. Naturally, these inks were called paints, and as they were used for the printing of displays and posters primarily, they became known as *poster paints.* Whether these materials are paints or inks has been often debated. Those who share the writer's pragmatic approach according to which the purpose of the material is decisive rather than its composition will agree with the term "poster inks"; those who like to continue traditional terms adhere to "paints."

When the ink industry began to interest itself in the making of printing media for screen process, after the end of World War II, and developed various lines of products for it, the term "ink" appeared more frequently in the screen-process business. At the time of writing, both "ink" and "paint" seem to be about equally used.

As the literature on screen-process inks is far less developed than that of inks for longer established printing methods, several types of widely used screen-process inks are now briefly described.

Poster inks or paints. These are oleoresinous printing media resulting in heavy printed films of matte appearance. Poster inks are of remarkable opacity, set fast, and can be overprinted within less than one hour if properly handled. A line of poster inks or paints includes usually an extender base and also the so-called transparent base, a metallic soap used to make the ink shorter and more transparent.

Lacquers and lacquer-type printing media. For the printing of plastics (which is an important field for screen process) various kinds of lacquers are required. Ethyl-cellulose lacquers are among them, but they are also used as fast-drying media for the printing of paper and paper boards. In this group belong various lines of inks which may be made of treated rubber and other synthetic film-formers. All dry by evaporation, pri-

marily. Most screen-process lacquers are less opaque than poster inks because they consist of a substantial proportion of volatiles which do not participate in the final ink film.

Enamels for screen process. Various objects such as glass bottles or metal novelties are often printed with enamels by screen process. Enamels are also used for the decorating of tiles and leather goods and for promotional printing when a semi-embossed effect is wanted. Screen-process enamels are available for baking or for air-drying. Air-drying enamels are widely used for decalcomanias, particularly those that are to be applied on trucks. Depending on the required characteristics, screen-process enamels are made with various vehicles, where flexibility or permanence is essential, mainly with alkyds as film-formers.

Miscellaneous printing media. These include overprint varnish, either matte or high gloss; various adhesives for flocking and beading; crystal base, a transparent ethyl-cellulose lacquer type material which can be colored with toners dispersed in an appropriate vehicle; metallic inks, and others. Water colors for poster printing and emulsions containing pigment dyes for textile printing should also be mentioned.

Chapter X

Binding and Finishing

The printed sheet as it comes off the press usually needs further work before the desired final product is achieved. There are, of course, instances where a job is ready for shipment without further processing after presswork. Simple handbills, letterheads, and calling cards—printed one-up and with no bleed—are examples of such jobs, but the overwhelming majority of printing jobs needs additional work in order to become usable for its final purpose.

The work required for turning printed sheets or webs of paper into books, magazines, catalogs, folders, and the like is classified as binding. The work necessary for making displays, labels, tags, and a variety of fancy advertising materials is classified as mounting, die-cutting, finishing, and so on. Binding and finishing, sometimes also called paper converting, comprise a highly diversified field. Many printers have their own binding

departments, and almost every printing business has either a power cutter or some other machine that serves for binding or finishing. But many of the different binding and finishing operations are performed by independent businesses which are part of the printing-service trades.

This chapter will acquaint you with the most important paper converting methods and the equipment used for their execution. The subject is so large that it requires not less than ten sections. Section 1 is a review of the main branches and phases of binding and finishing; Section 2 discusses planning for printing to be bound; Section 3. the cutting of sheets; Section 4, folding; Section 5, assembling the folded material for binding; Section 6, binding proper; Section 7, preparing the bound book for covering; Section 8, covermaking; Section 9, combining the book and cover; and Section 10, mounting and finishing.

Section 1: Review of Binding and Finishing

In this section you find first a survey of the different branches of binding and finishing, most of which consist of independent businesses. Then we present a brief characterization of the main stages of binding in order to prepare you for their detailed discussion in the following sections.

Survey of the Binding and Finishing Industry

It is convenient to distinguish the following eight branches of binding: (1) edition binding, (2) job binding and extra binding, (3) library binding, (4) pamphlet and trade binding, (5) manifold or commercial binding, (6) mechanical binding, (7) loose-leaf binding, and (8) blankbook binding and

ruling. In the finishing business things are not as clear-cut as in binding, and we discuss this industry in a more summary manner.

Edition binding. Edition binding is the business of binding identical books in quantity. It uses automatic machinery rather than handwork and produces casebound or hardbound books. The designation *casebound* indicates that "the cover of the book has two distinct characteristics. The cover is made separately from the book, and it consists of rigid or flexible boards covered with leather, leather substitutes, cloth, paper, or other material in such a manner that the covering material surrounds the outside as well as the edges of the board. In the bookbinder's language this is known as covers-turned-over-boards, and the covers always project beyond the edges of the paper."[1] As edition binding uses as much automatic machinery as possible, smaller runs than, say, 1500 copies are not ordinarily handled by edition binderies. But it should be mentioned that some of them handle shorter runs by combining handwork and automatic machines.

Job binding and extra binding. Job binding is the business of binding books in small quantities. Job binding does not use fully automatic machinery but relies on handwork, alone or in conjunction with some machine operation. It produces not only smaller lots of casebound books but also binding that cannot be done by automatic equipment such as that of Bibles and prayer books that are bound in limp leather, for example. The term *extra binding* once meant generally that a book was completely handbound. Nowadays this term is more loosely employed, and extra binding may also indicate that a book or a small lot of books is handled with special care; that it is not bound merely for utility but also with a view to the beauty and design of the binding. But some of the best binderies still hold fast to the traditional concept of extra binding and designate not completely handbound books in a different manner.

Library binding. Library binding is the business of rendering specialized binding services to public and private libraries. Library binderies rely, like job binderies, on handwork primarily, supplemented by use of some specialized machinery. The services rendered by library binders include prebinding, rebinding, and general repair work. *Prebinding* refers to the binding of new books. "The purpose of this type of binding is to provide a book rugged enough to withstand the abusive wear and tear to which library books are subjected."[2] *Rebinding* means the replacement of a worn binding or the binding of periodicals into hardbound books. Some library binders include extra binding in their services, others do not.

Pamphlet and trade binding. Pamphlet binding is the business of producing leaflets, folders, booklets, magazines, and some kinds of soft-covered books. The designation *pamphlet binding* is unfortunate. Pamphlets, originally meaning short controversial essays, are now very rarely written and published in America. In contemporary language the word "pamphlet" means a "thin booklet," disregarding its literary content. The designation *pamphlet binding* has become completely absurd if we consider that the binding of telephone directories, which have hundreds of pages and are printed and bound by the millions, is classified as pamphlet binding. The term has caused much confusion and should best be retired. Unfortunately, though, the industry has not agreed on a more significant name for this branch of binding and this misnomer will continue to vex us. Binderies who handle the above-mentioned types of work are usually trade binderies. They process not only self-covered and paper-covered books and magazines but also often do such work as perforating and drilling or punching of holes.

This is a good place to emphasize that many bindery branches overlap in their several activities and that some of the services performed by pamphlet binderies are also necessary in mechanical and loose-leaf binding. If you want to know what services a particular trade bindery is prepared to render, you cannot simply rely on its general classification but must ask the bindery in question about its specific equipment and facilities.

Manifold or commercial binding. Manifold or commercial binding is the business of binding multiple business forms such as purchase orders, sales records, or billheads. It may also include the punching of custom-made forms that are used in one of the many proprietary loose-leaf record keeping systems. Manifold binding uses power-driven but hand-operated equipment.

Mechanical binding. Mechanical binding is the business of binding individual leaves of paper in a *non-exchangeable* form by means of an independent binding device. Mechanical binding can be executed on many levels of technology. It is in most cases part of the services offered by specialty binderies. Among the products of mechanical binding are advertising and sales promotional literature, books published for sale to the public, stationery items, and packaging material.

Loose-leaf binding. Loose-leaf binding is the business of binding individual leaves of paper in an *exchangeable* form. Loose-leaf binding includes the making of the cover (though not the manufacturing of the binding mechanism which is, in general, bought by the bindery from concerns specializing in its manufacture), the punching or drilling of paper leaves as well as their assembly. Loose-leaf binding is a field of specialty binding. Its products are needed wherever records of repeatedly changing information must be kept. Such items are legion in our fast living society. Instruction manuals, catalogs, and accounting forms are often loose-leaf bound. Accounting leads us into the last branch of binding to be here discussed, namely blankbook binding.

Blankbook binding and ruling. Blankbook binding and ruling is the business of manufacturing bound books consisting either of blank or of ruled pages. Blankbooks are used for a variety of purposes most of which have to do with accounting and record keeping, even though items made for entirely different purposes such as albums and scrapbooks are also included in this category. Blankbooks are sold through stationers and manufactured on specialized automatic equipment. The ruling is done either by ruling machines or by offset lithographic printing. Blankbooks must open perfectly flat and be sturdily bound.

Finishing. Finishing is a very general term that includes a variety of businesses which defy systematic classification. Some companies specialize in mounting, die-cutting, and easeling of displays; others do varnishing or laminating. Embossing and die-stamping, pebbling, beveling, deckling, and tin-edging of printed or unprinted materials are additional examples of the many operations included in this catchall of finishing. Most of these will be briefly discussed in Section 10 which is devoted to this industry.

After this short identification of the different branches of the binding industry, we turn to a characterization of the main stages and fundamental tasks of binding. This characterization will lay the foundation for the detailed discussions to follow. It will make it easier for you to see the common thread of this diversified subject.

The Nine Main Stages of Binding

The nine main stages of binding are: (1) planning for printing to be bound, (2) cutting of sheets, (3) folding of the printed sheets, (4) assembling of the folded material for binding, (5) binding proper, or fastening the assembled material in book form, (6) trimming, (7) preparing the book for covering, (8) cover-making, and finally (9) combining of cover and bound book.

These nine stages are not an exhaustive listing of all operations that may be required in every single branch of binding. Nor does the order in which they are listed indicate their sequence in the actual production of all kinds of bound material. But knowledge of these stages should be found helpful by you, particularly if you study the accompanying diagrams.

Planning for printing to be bound. All printing jobs requiring binding must be planned with the necessities of binding in mind. Binding is done on very specialized equipment; if a job is well planned it will be fast and economically produced. If a job is planned without consideration of binding, the consequences may be rather severe. In the worst case, which is fortunately rare, it may be impossible to bind the job at all; in the best case the job will become more expensive than necessary and binding may take much more time than it should. It is therefore imperative to consider binding from the outset and to plan a job in consultation with those who will be in charge of binding.

In the planning of all printing jobs that need binding a dummy is used for checking such detail as folding and binding, best imposition, bleeds, and other items of common interest to the printer and the binder.

A major tool for co-ordination of printing and binding is the *bindery imposition layout*. Binderies and large printing plants operating their own binderies have a considerable number of such layouts all worked out on file. Whenever these standard layouts are not practical or otherwise unsatisfactory, a special imposition must be developed. This is best done in co-operation between printing and binding production people.

Cutting of sheets. As it is frequently necessary to cut unprinted sheets of paper to a size suitable for printing, sheet-cutting equipment can be found in or near pressrooms as well as in binding departments and binderies where printed sheets must be cut previous to binding. Printed sheets may also need cutting before they can be further processed, as in the die-cutting of labels. All these cutting operations are performed by machinery that is usually, though not always, power-driven. Some of this equipment is highly specialized and attached to other machinery. This is the case in newspaper and national magazine web printing where the web is cut and folded before it leaves the press. Equipment of this kind is discussed together with the presses to which it is attached, in Chapter VI. In the present context we will concentrate on the most frequently used cutting machines for sheets which are known either as *power cutters* or as *guillotine cutters.*

Folding of printed sheets. Most printing jobs that need binding are printed on large sheets that contain many pages of the final product—a booklet, magazine, or book, as the case may be. The number of pages printed on the same press sheet depends on the nature of the job, available equipment, and economy. In long runs and page sizes of approximately 6 × 9 inches, sheets having up to 128 pages are not uncommon. There are no hard-and-fast rules on the number of pages to be printed on a press sheet, but generally speaking it may be said that few jobs are produced with a much larger number of pages per sheet.

The printed sheet must be converted into book sections which are customarily called *signatures.* This operation is done by folding. Folding was originally done by hand, but hand-folding is much too slow and much too expensive for quantity production. Most contemporary folding is done on folding machines which are complex high-speed mechanisms. The two most commonly used types of folders are the *knife folder* and the *buckle folder.* These two folders are based on different principles and are used for different purposes as they are capable of folding different types of work. For specialized applications, folders utilizing other mechanical principles than do knife and buckle folders are also available.

Assembling of the folded material for binding. Most books consist of more than one section. If a book, for example, has 320 pages and if each section has 32 pages, 10 sections are needed for the complete book. The assembling of the material to be bound can be done by hand. But hand-assembling is out of the question for quantity work; high-speed machinery must be used for all production jobs.

Three kinds of assembly techniques are in use. They are designated as gathering, inserting, and collating. *Gathering* refers to the assembly of book sections in sequence, one on top of the other. *Inserting* refers to the assembly of sections within each other. Inserting is a procedure used for comparatively thin books, primarily for saddle-stitched magazines. Here every section is placed with its centerfold over the preceding section. *Collating* refers to the assembly of individual leaves. It is a rather confusing term because the traditional meaning of collating is not that of assembling but of inspecting the assembled material before binding. But collating has recently

broadened its meaning; it is now also used for the assembling of individual leaves in loose-leaf, mechanical, and manifold binding.

Binding or fastening the assembled material in book form. The next step is the fastening of the assembled material for more or less permanent use. The word "binding" has several closely related meanings and is therefore not always conducive to precision of expression. Binding can

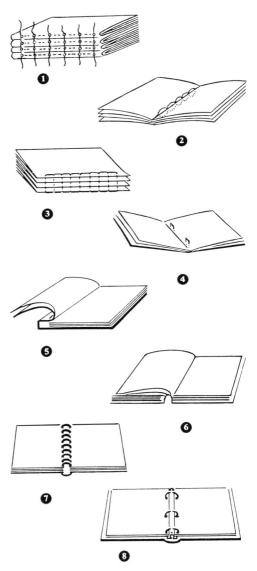

Eight kinds of binding: (1) *Smyth sewing,* (2) *saddle sewing,* (3) *side sewing,* (4) *saddle stitching,* (5) *side-wire stitching,* (6) *adhesive binding,* (7) *mechanical binding,* and (8) *loose-leaf binding.*

mean (1) the act or process whereby something is bound, (2) the state of being bound, (3) the material used in the process of binding, (4) the style in which a book is bound, and (5) binding can also have the meaning in which the word is used in this paragraph: the fastening of book sections or other material to be assembled in book form.

Here we distinguish several techniques in which the fastening of the assembled material can be achieved. They are: (1) *Smyth sewing*, where signatures are sewed through their centerfolds *and* automatically to each other; (2) *saddle sewing*, where individual signatures are sewed through their centers but not connected with each other; (3) *side sewing*, where one or several signatures are sewed along their binding edges; (4) *saddle stitching*, where individual or inserted signatures are fastened through the centerfold by means of wire staples; (5) *side-wire stitching*, where the material is fastened along its binding edge by wire staples; (6) *adhesive binding*, also known as *perfect binding*, where the material is fastened by means of adhesives; (7) *mechanical binding*, where individual leaves are fastened by means of an independent binding device in a non-exchangeable form; and (8) *loose-leaf binding*, where individual leaves are fastened by means of an independent binding device in exchangeable form.

Each of these binding techniques utilizes its own equipment and each of them can be executed on different levels of mechanization. Their differences will be discussed in some detail later on; here it is merely mentioned that these techniques not only differ in cost but also in the final result in appearance, durability, and, last but not least, the extent to which a book lies flat when it is opened.

Trimming. Trimming serves other purposes besides enhancing the appearance of a book by making it neat as the word implies. Books that consist of folded sections must be cut open before they can be read. In some countries—France in particular—this chore is customarily left to the reader, but in the United States the freeing of the pages is part of the manufacturing process and is performed by trimming. Many magazines are produced two-up or three-up, meaning that the bound unit contains two or three magazines connected with each other. In this case trimming separates the connected material and produces individual magazines.

Like most other binding operations, trimming can be done on various levels of mechanization with different equipment. As in the past, individual books can be trimmed by a *plough* and press; smaller runs may be trimmed on hand lever cutters or on power cutters. For mass production, high-speed specialized equipment is of course available. Some such trimmers can trim stacks of books. Others trim individual books, still others pairs of books. Some trimmers are equipped for trimming one side at a time, others trim all three sides in a single pass through the machine, still others make five cuts in one pass of the material through the equipment and in that way produce individually trimmed books from two-up bound units. (The word "book" means here as everywhere else in this chapter all kinds of bound material, including magazines, catalogs, and many other items.)

Preparing the book for covering. Not all bound material passes through this phase, as magazines, booklets, and similar material do not need preparation for covering. Preparing the book for covering is important in the manufacturing of edition-bound, or casebound books. There, preparing the book for covering is traditionally designated as *forwarding*, a term that is in our time meaningless and therefore not further used in this manual.

The sewed book must be prepared for covering by a series of operations which include back-gluing, smashing or nipping, trimming, edge treatments, rounding, backing, backlining, and headbanding. Some of these operations serve functional purposes, others solely enhance the appearance of the book.

The functional operations make the book uniform, shape its back or spine, and reinforce it. These operations are required if the book is bound to last. The embellishing operations are much less important; they include gilding, spraying or staining of edges, marbling, and headbanding.

Cover-making. Most books are provided with a cover. Covers are made in a wide range of style, durability, and cost. Hand-tooled deluxe covers are at one end of the scale; simple paper covers, printed in a single color, at the other end. Generally speaking, covers for blankbooks and edition binding are made in a separate manufacturing process, covers for magazines and paper-covered books are produced by printing in two or more colors just like any other color printing job, possibly with the difference that the covers are printed on a more sturdy and wear-resistant paper than the rest of the book.

Paper covers do not present manufacturing problems other than printing. Sometimes paper covers are surface-treated for enhancement or protection. Varnishing and laminating with transparent plastics increases the sales appeal of paper-covered books.

The covers of hardbound books, on the other hand, are the result of a rather complex manufacturing process involving a number of highly specialized machines. The covers used in edition binding are known as *cases;* they consist of boards over which a covering material such as cloth is applied in a manner that protects the exposed edges of the case. These covers can be made on several levels of technology, including that of very modern high-speed automatic machinery.

Assembling of cover and bound book. The manner in which book and cover are combined as well as the point where they are combined in the course of production depends first on the type of binding and then on the technological level at which binding is executed.

In saddle stitching, for example, the cover is assembled together with the book, and book and cover are bound in the same operation. In edition binding, to take another example, the operation of binding and the making of the case are completely independent of each other; book and case can be combined in a number of ways, from handwork up to automatically functioning high-speed building-in equipment.

We have arrived at the end of this bird's-eye view of binding. You have met many new terms, and it was not practical to explain all of them at this point. But when you will meet them again in the following sections you will at least have a nodding acquaintance which should help you in absorbing this new material.

Section 2:   Planning for Printing To Be Bound

It is a commonplace that all graphic-arts production must be carefully planned. It is unfortunately also correct that people sometimes tend to forget this truism when it is most necessary to remember it and to act accordingly. Graphic-arts production requires planning of many kinds. In this unit we are interested in a particular kind of planning which has the object of co-ordinating printing and binding; it is therefore named "co-ordinative planning" in this manual.

Co-ordinative planning for printing to be bound is based on the page as its unit; it deals with the position and the arrangement of pages on the printed sheet or web. In general planning for reproduction by printing we are interested in the detail to be reproduced, in reading matter and pictures; in lines, tones, and colors. All these items are essentially outside of co-ordinative planning. If we consider them in this context, then it is only inasmuch as they influence the arrangement of pages. Among the points to be so considered are *bleeds*—where the printing extends all the way to one or more of the edges of the printed page—*page spreads*, where two adjacent pages are a single unit for the reader, and several other more specialized items.

All generalizations are hazardous as there are always some cases to which they cannot be applied. But for our purpose it is expedient to keep in mind that co-ordinative planning for printing to be bound is based on the page as its unit. Whenever a printing job consists in the printing of pages, it must be remembered that these pages will be finally bound and that they must be arranged for printing in such a manner that they can be bound efficiently.

Some of the points made in this discussion may sound slightly ridiculous. Is it really necessary—the informed reader may feel—to emphasize that the printed book must have certain appearance characteristics? That the printed image must be placed exactly where it is supposed to be? We take it simply for granted that page 17 follows page 16, that every page looks alike, that the reading matter is never upside down and always lined up, that the page numbers (called *folios* by the printer) are always on the page and never cut off. It is correct that we take all of this, and quite a bit more, simply for granted.

We take most things for granted in our highly industrialized society; we never inquire how the multitude of objects that we use are made to function properly. But all of these objects, from the bread we eat to the planes in which we fly, require an enormous amount of planning and preparation as well as high-precision machinery. Printing and binding are no exception.

From the fifteenth to the nineteenth century books were printed on handmade paper with a wooden press. Handmade paper was made in small sheets rarely exceeding 18 × 24 inches and the hand press was powered by the pressman and therefore very limited in its scope, but paper and press were suited to each other.

Things have changed greatly. In our time, paper is made in continuous webs and can be supplied in practically any sheet size. Our contemporary presses are powered with electric motors and are capable of printing sheets up to any desired size, say, 52 × 76 inches. If such a press, meaning that a sheet is printed on both sides in one pass through the press, and if we assume a page size of 9 × 6 inches, this press can produce sheets with 128 pages printed on them. Not all books are, of course, printed on such huge equipment, nor do all books have a page size of 9 × 6 inches. (The order in which the two figures of a page size are given can indicate the binding direction. Unfortunately there is no general agreement on this point. In New York City, for example, edition binders assume that the first figure indicates binding edge, whereas pamphlet binders assume the opposite. The binding edge should therefore always be clearly stated.) The number of pages printed on a sheet depends on the detail of the job. Generally speaking, it can be said that few books are printed with less than 16 pages to the sheet, and that most books are produced by printing 32 or more pages on a sheet. What problem the proper arrangement of these pages entails will be seen immediately.

How is such a sheet converted into a section of a book? The answer is by folding. Let us assume a sheet with 32 pages, 16 on one side and 16 on the other. If you fold this sheet in half you have 4 areas, (2 on one side and 2 on the other) each containing 8 of the printed pages. Then you make a second fold at a right angle to the first, and now you have 8 areas, each with 4 printed pages. You fold a third time, again at a right angle to the last fold, and the result is 16 areas, each having 2 printed pages. The fourth and final fold, again made at a right angle to the preceding one, produces the desired book section of 32 folded areas or of 32 pages.

Now we suggest a little experiment for you that will teach you more about the problems attending the proper arrangement of pages than just reading. Take a piece of paper, not smaller than a letterhead, and make the described four folds. Then unfold it again and indicate where each page must be printed on the sheet so that it may be in proper position after folding. You will see that it is not so easy to figure this out.

Our example is a very simple one; most problems of planning are much more difficult. Nor is the position of the page on the sheet the only point that needs attention. As you will see in the following discussion of various phases of binding, each has its own peculiar requirements that must not be neglected. You will not be able to appreciate the full importance of planning until you have read all of these descriptions; it is therefore suggested that you read this section on planning a second time after you have assimilated the information on binding equipment and processes.

Now we want to continue our discussion of planning and turn to the main tool for co-ordinating printing and binding, the imposition.

The Imposition

The word imposition has several meanings. It

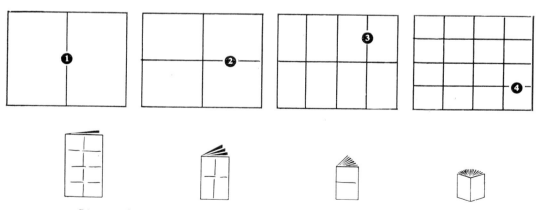

Diagram showing how a sheet is folded into a 32-page book section by four right-angle folds. The upper row shows the folds, the lower row the folded sheet as it appears after each fold. The sheet is printed with 16 pages on each side.

refers, in the context of printing, always to the general subject of arranging the printing-image carrier in accordance with a plan. But the special meanings of the term can vary enough to make an explanation desirable.

The term "imposition" originated in letterpress printing. Webster still defines it as "act or process of imposing pages of type." This definition cannot be accepted as reflecting the best use of the word in our time. The term "imposition" is experiencing a change of meaning that has so far escaped the dictionaries. In our time, other processes than letterpress are also capable of printing reading matter and these processes also use sheet-fed presses. They, too, must arrange their printing-image carrier, and they, too, use the word "imposition." Furthermore, Webster does not list the most important meaning of imposition, namely, that it is *a plan for action rather than the physical execution of this plan*. The point is important and needs to be explained.

In the past printing was executed without much formal planning. The skilled craftsman simply knew how to do the job. But as printing changes from a craft to an industry, formal planning which is functionally separated from doing the work, becomes more and more necessary. In the course of this process, separate terms for planning on the one hand and for doing on the other, become an equal necessity. In this process the noun *imposition* is increasingly used for the plan or scheme by which pages are arranged; and it is so used disregarding the printing process in which printing takes place, whether it is letterpress, lithography, gravure, or any other process.

The physical act of arranging pages for common printing is designated by a variety of terms. In letterpress printing the word *imposing* is used for the placement, or laying, of made-up pages on a flat surface; some people prefer to call this operation "press-form handling." In rotary letterpress, flexography, and newspaper printing where curved plates are needed, different expressions can be heard. Some speak of attaching plates, others of dressing the cylinder, or plating, often also of plating-up a press.

In lithography, gravure, and screen process which all use single-unit image carriers, the assembly of the material takes place prior to making the final image carrier. In lithography, these operations are known as stripping and as photocomposing, in gravure as layout, and in screen process as set-up.

After this clarification of terms we are ready for a discussion of some of the major considerations in the planning of impositions. In this discussion it must be kept in mind that planning of the correct imposition is only a part of the much more embracing all-over planning for efficient printing production in all its many phases. Our presentation is divided into four units: (1) the main kinds of impositions, (2) page layouts, (3) imposition layouts, and (4) the role of paper in the planning of impositions.

The Four Standard Types of Impositions

The following four schemes can be used in the planning of impositions: (1) sheetwise, (2) work-and-turn, (3) work-and-tumble, and finally (4) work-and-twist. The purpose of these different imposition schemes is greatest economy of printing production. Depending on the nature of the job in hand and on the equipment available in a specific plant at the time when the job must be produced, one or the other type of imposition is selected. Before we describe these different imposition schemes, which are quite technical, we want to familiarize you with the manner in which a sheet is positioned in the press, and we want to explain several terms which are needed for an understanding of the subject.

Positioning of sheets in the press. Sheets are positioned for printing by placing them with two edges at a right angle to each other against mechanical stops on the press. As most sheets used for printing are oblong, they have two longer and two shorter edges. One longer edge must be nominated the *gripper edge*, and one shorter edge must be nominated the *guide edge*. These two edges are used for positioning the sheet. The mechanical stops against which these two edges are put on the press are known as *front guides* and *side guides*, respectively. The gripper edge of the paper is positioned to the front guides, its guide edge to the side guide of the press.

Here, as so often in this manual, terminology can cause trouble because it is inconsistent. Why, you may ask, is the edge of the paper which is positioned to the front guides known as gripper edge? The gripper edge of the paper is indeed positioned to the front guides of the press. But it is also clamped during the printing cycle by a series of pincers known as grippers after the sheet is properly positioned. For clamping, a certain amount of paper is needed which cannot be printed but must of course be considered in the

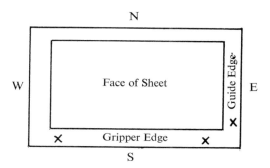

In this illustration each of the four edges of the sheet is identified by one of the letters W, N, E, and S. "S" is the gripper edge and "E" is the guide edge.

planning of a job. As you can see, the term "gripper edge" makes good sense.

In any case you must remember that the longer edge of the paper is known as the gripper edge and the shorter as the guide edge. You should also know that the position of the gripper cannot be changed on the press, whereas the side guide can usually be changed to be on either side of the press as the situation may demand. These positions will be called here, following wide usage, the *near side* and the *far side* of the press. Finally, we must name the two surfaces and the four edges of the sheet if we want to avoid confusion. The edges are identified by the directions of the compass as "S," "W," "N," and "E" on our diagram; the two surfaces are called the *face* and the *back* of the sheet respectively. The face is the first printed surface; the back is printed thereafter. Printing the back of a sheet is known as *backing up* or *perfecting* the sheet. Now we are ready for a discussion of the four imposition schemes.

Sheetwise impositions. In sheetwise impositions—also known as *work-and-back, front-and-back,* or *print-and-back* impositions—we need two image carriers for every color, one each for the face and the back of the sheet. Sheetwise impositions are selected for jobs where the number of pages to be printed on each side of the sheet is large enough to utilize the full capacity of the press. Our illustration shows placement of the sheet, guide and gripper edges, and location of guides and grippers. For backup the side guide is reset as it is customary not to change guide edges. Often the paper is not a true rectangle and then changes in guide edge result in loss of accuracy.

At this point we want to introduce you to two terms which you will meet very often if you study imposition layouts; these are *inside forms* and

outside forms. "The sheetwise form containing the low page is called the 'outside' form because when folded this low page is on the outside of the folded sheet. The sheetwise form containing the next to the low page is called the 'inside' form because this side of the sheet is folded inside the first fold."[3] All bindery impositions for sheetwise work consist of two diagrams, one the inside, the other the outside imposition.

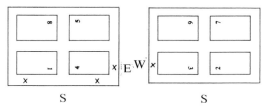

Diagram of sheetwise imposition. In sheetwise impositions the sheet is printed with a different image carrier for each side. The guide and gripper edges remain the same but the guide is moved on the press from "E" where it was for printing one side to "W" for the other side.

Work-and-turn impositions. Work-and-turn impositions, also known as *print-and-turn* impositions, are used where it is practical to print both sides of the sheet from a single image carrier per color. Work-and-turn impositions are very frequently selected. These impositions require relatively large presses as the sheet will bear two complete units, each occupying one-half of the sheet.

Let us now see to the placement of the sheet. We use again edge "S" of our paper as gripper

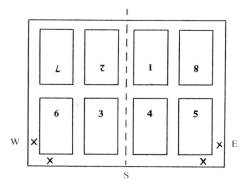

Diagram of work-and-turn imposition. In work-and-turn impositions the sheet is printed on both sides with the same image carrier. The gripper edge remains the same, the press guide is moved from "E" to "W" for the printing of the other side. The broken line indicates that the sheet is cut or slit in its short direction to separate the two printed units.

edge, and edge "W" as guide edge; the side guide is again on the far side of the press for positioning the face of our sheet. For backup the sheets are turned, the gripper edge, "S" in our example, remains the same; but "as in sheetwise printing, the side guide usually is changed to the opposite side when the sheet is turned over."[4]

As work-and-turn printing produces two complete units, the sheet must be either slit on the press during backup or cut apart after printing. Another point is worth noting: "When the sheet is slit, the inner edges of the paper will become the guide edges in the folding, and the gripper edge the second folded guide edge."[5] Work-and-turn impositions cut the number of sheets to be printed in half, but they require larger and more expensive presses than sheetwise impositions.

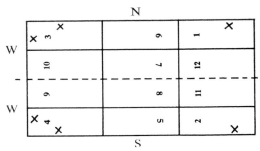

Diagram of work-and-tumble imposition. In work-and-tumble impositions the sheet is printed on both sides with the same image carrier. The guide edge and press guide are the same for both sides, the gripper edge changes for the printing of the second side. The broken line indicates that the sheet is cut in its long direction to separate the two printed units.

Work-and-tumble impositions. These impositions are also known as *print-and-tumble, work-and-roll,* or *work-and-flop* impositions. They are less frequently met than sheetwise or work-and-turn impositions. "Work-and-tumble schemes are used when a work-and-turn form cannot be used, or when two sheetwise forms would have to be run on a sheet of difficult dimensions."[6] Work-and-tumble impositions need only one printing-image carrier for the printing of both surfaces of the sheet, and are similar in this respect to work-and-turn impositions. They, too, produce two units of the job on the same sheet.

Work-and-tumble impositions are backed up by changing the gripper edge in the backup. If the face of our sheet was printed with the gripper edge "S" and the guide edge "W" for example, then it is positioned for backup with edge "N" as gripper

edge. The guide edge "W" remains the same and so does the press side-guide which does not need resetting on the press.

Changing gripper edges is hazardous; "unless the stock is very accurately squared and trimmed, a loss of register on the bottom guides is unavoidable. For this reason the work-and-tumble method should not be used unless it becomes necessary."[7]

Work-and-twist impositions. Work-and-twist impositions, also known as *work-and-twirl* impositions, differ functionally from all imposition schemes described here. These are techniques for producing sheets printed on both sides, whereas work-and-twist impositions solve problems pertaining to one-side printing. They are "sometimes used in printing blank rule and tabular forms, with cross rules in one section and vertical rules in the other."[8]

In this method "two separate sections, or divisions, of an individual form are imposed and locked up together in such a way that they may be printed side by side on a double-size sheet in one impression."[9] After completion of the run, the already printed paper is repositioned face up for the second printing from the same printing-image carrier. The change in position can best be explained by reference to our diagram. Assuming that our first printing took place with gripper edge "S" and guide edge "W," the sheet is repositioned for the second printing with "N" as gripper edge and "E" as guide edge.

Work-and-twist impositions are very rarely used; they require perfectly square stock for exe-

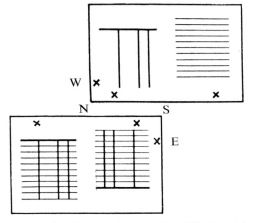

Diagram of work-and-twist imposition. This imposition serves for the printing of two units on the same side. The sheet receives two impressions; guide and gripper edges change for the second.

cution. They also produce two units of the final job which is printed on only one side of the paper. As work-and-twist impositions are not ordinarily used in the production of printing to be bound, they do not concern us any further in this chapter.

The Page and the Page Layout

The page is, as you already know, the smallest printed unit in binding. The page layout is the blueprint of the page. Before we discuss the page layout, a few words on terms are again in order. Our printing and binding vocabulary developed during the time when letterpress was the only process for the printing of books, and our binding terms consequently reflect the conditions in letterpress printing rather than those in other processes which in our own time are also used for the printing of material to be bound. These additional processes are primarily lithography and gravure. For people who do not under-

stand the relation of printing and binding terms, some of the latter do not make much sense.

If you look at our illustration of a page layout, you will notice several sizes. The largest size refers to the untrimmed paper page. This size indicates the total paper area that must be allowed for the page on the sheet. The next size inside the untrimmed paper-page size is the trimmed paper-page size. This is the final size of the page as it will appear in the bound book. Both of these sizes are given in inches and their fractions.

Inside our trimmed size you see another clearly defined area. It is designated as the *type page* and is measured in picas, the measuring unit of the American Point System in which we measure composition. All printing specifies type-page measurements in picas, paper-page measurements in inches. The use of two measuring systems complicates matters; particularly because picas and inches cannot be exactly related to each other in round figures. It is correct that 6 picas are *approximately* one inch. It is also correct that one may convert picas into inches or vice versa for *rough* correlations either by dividing picas by 6, or by multiplying inches with the same number. But most measurements cannot be exactly converted into the other system in this manner. The most practical way of dealing with inches and picas in relation to each other is the use of a printer's measuring rule that has inches along one edge and picas and points along the other.

You may think that this difficulty does not exist in jobs that are printed in other processes than letterpress. That is true provided that the printed message does not consist of type. If the printed message consists of type the term "type page" is there just as necessary as in letterpress, and you are back again at picas, as all composition of type is specified in the American Point System. Even in art books that consist of pictorial reproductions primarily, the term "type page" is often used because some pages almost always bear reading matter and are therefore set in type.

Several other terms appear on the page layout. The terms *head* and *foot* are self-explanatory. *Margins* are the unprinted paper areas surrounding the type page. They are identified as head, foot, outside, inside, and fold or bind margins, according to their position on the page. (Margins should not be confused with borders which are decorative bands or frames confining the printing area in one or several dimensions.) In most cases the page number, called *folio*, is within the type-

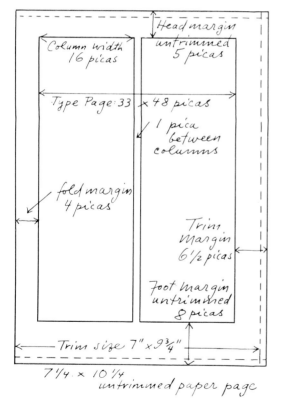

A page layout for a two-column page. All dimensions related to the type page are expressed in picas; all dimensions pertaining to the paper size and trim are expressed in inches and their fractions.

page area, in others it is not. The same holds true for the *running head*, a line on the head of the page indicating the title of a book, its chapter, or the content of a page. If folios and running heads are outside the type page this should always be clearly indicated in the page layout.

All data shown on our type-page layout pertain to the page itself. But pages are not printed by themselves, they are printed together with many others, and we need, therefore, information pertaining to the relation of several pages. Our illustration shows a page in its setting with three neighboring pages. It may strike you as peculiar

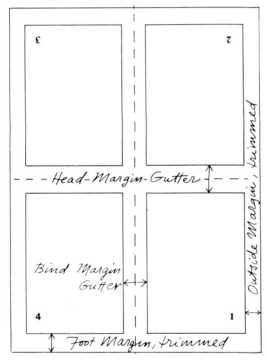

Diagram showing the position of four pages on the sheet. The broken lines indicate the folds.

that pages are arranged foot-to-foot and head-to-head; if you want to know the reasons for this topsy-turvy relation you should make a simple experiment. Take a piece of paper and draw four pages on it, indicating their head and foot; fold two times at right angles and staple them in center where they would be bound. If your pages are head-to-head they will be in proper order in your little book; if they are head-to-foot on the sheet, half of them will be upside down after folding. This is not to say that pages can never be

arranged head-to-foot; head-to-foot positioning is used in certain cases that do not concern us.

The relation of head and foot is not the only point of interest in discussing the juxtaposition of pages on a sheet. If you look at our illustration you notice a new term: *gutter*. You see four different gutters on this illustration: (1) the bind-margin gutter, (2) the head-margin gutter, (3) the outside-margin gutter, and (4) the foot-margin gutter. In letterpress printing of type forms the gutters are produced by the spacing and lock-up material that is put between individual type pages. As this material is lower than the printing matter, the word "gutter" is understandable, particularly if one knows that in olden times the type form was cleaned by scrubbing with lye that flowed off in the gutters. In other methods of printing, the word "gutter" does not make sense and is either not used at all or merely by rote.

Margin gutters indicate "the total space between any two type pages to allow for margin and trim for both pages."[10] Margin gutters are measured in picas or in inches; they are very important elements in the planning of the imposition.

This discussion of the page layout cannot be concluded without mentioning bleed pages. The term *bleed* indicates that a page is printed without one, several, or all margins. You remember that the margins are the unprinted areas of the paper outside the type page. It often happens that a

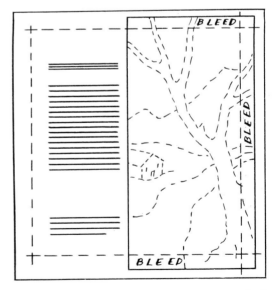

Diagram of "bleed." The picture on the right bleeds on three sides.

design calls for printing in one or several colors that extend up to the final edge of the page. This effect is obtained by printing a larger area than that of the final page and by trimming the excess off the page. The printing area must not be as large as the press sheet, otherwise ink would pile up on the impression cylinder. As it is not possible to print exactly to the edge of the page, bleeds are produced by printing beyond that line and by trimming the page through the printed areas. A page can bleed on one, two, three, or all four sides; bleeds are always indicated in a page layout.

The Imposition Layout

The imposition layout is a diagram that indicates how a given number of pages must be arranged in order to produce a specific result by folding. The imposition diagram does not indicate that every job having this particular number of pages can be so folded. The size of the sheet, the paper on which the job is printed, the page size of the job, the available folding equipment, as well as many items still to be discussed in the course of this section must all be considered before it can be decided that a given imposition layout is suitable for a job in hand. Imposition layouts cannot be interpreted and selected by inexperienced people. Their evaluation requires a thorough background of printing and binding production.

The manufacturers of folding machines publish books of impositions that show the capacity and use of their equipment. Books of impositions are also published by large binderies, book manufacturing plants, and the United States Government Printing Office (GPO). Imposition books published by trade binderies and book manufacturers, as well as those published by the GPO, show a wide variety of impositions possible on various folding machines. In some of these books the equipment on which a particular imposition can be folded is also indicated.[11]

Imposition layouts afford information on the following five points: (1) the number of pages printed on a sheet, (2) the arrangement of the pages, (3) sheet control, (4) folding, and (5) the kind of signature produced in folding. Each of these points is now briefly discussed.

Number of pages printed on a sheet. The number of pages printed on a sheet depends on the job. It is ordinarily not less than 4 and usually does not exceed 128. The GPO uses standard impositions for sheets containing 4, 6, 8, 10, 12, 16, 20, 24, 28, 30, 32, 36, 40, 48, 64, 72, 80, and 128 pages.[12] This is not to say that it is impossible to develop impositions for page numbers not listed in the GPO publication. Several additional impositions can be found in the book of impositions for Cleveland Folding Machines, for example. In many cases special impositions are worked out between binding and printing production people.

Arrangement of pages. The first point to be determined is whether an imposition shows the arrangement of pages as they appear on the printed page or as they are arranged in the printing-image carrier. In indirect printing such as offset lithography, pages appear the same way on both the printed sheet and the printing-image carrier. In direct printing this is not the case. Most imposition layouts for letterpress printing are *face up* meaning as the printing-image carrier is positioned for assembly and for printing. Such layouts are also known as *form layouts* or as *stone layouts*. (The word "stone" refers to the marble slab on which imposing of type forms used to be done; in our times, stones are much less used for imposing than heavy steel plates.) *Form, plate,* or *cylinder lays* must be distinguished from printed paper lays.

All imposition layouts for jobs to be printed sheetwise consist of two diagrams, one for the inside form and the other for the outside form. Work-and-turn and work-and-tumble impositions need only one diagram as both surfaces of the paper are printed from the same image carrier.

Sheet control. Sheets are positioned for printing and binding by placing two of their edges against mechanical stops. For this reason "provision must be made in the imposing of the pages, and in the lockup, to present the exact same edges of the sheet to the grippers and guides on both press and folder." Sheet control is particularly important in such cases where the sheet is cut or slit before it is folded. The imposition layout includes indications for guide and gripper edges as well as for cutting and scoring.

The kind and number of signatures produced by folding. The signature is one of the sections of which a book consists. As the page is the unit of the sheet, so is the signature the unit of binding. The sheet is transformed into a signature or several signatures during folding. The imposition layout indicates the kind and number of signatures produced in folding.

Various kinds of folders are capable of producing up to four signatures in one operation. These signatures may either be planned to follow each other in the book or to be inserted into each other. Some folders capable of producing four signatures are also capable of inserting two of them into two others. It is also possible to plan a book in such a manner that the units delivered by the folder consist of two or more signatures, one above the other, for common fastening or binding.

This information as well as the number of pages folded per signature is indicated in a simple and generally understood code on the imposition lay-out. The words *single*, *double*, and *quad* refer to the number of signatures produced on the folder. Double is sometimes written as "D," both double and quad are also written as figures 2 and 4. (Single means of course one signature, double two, and quad four.) Next to these designations, separated either by a dash or a fractional line, follows a figure which indicates the number of pages in each signature. If the signatures are planned for successive binding they are designated as *to follow;* if for insertion into each other, *to insert* is added. Signatures that contain several units for common binding are said to be as many *up* as they have units. These terms are not by any means all that can be used in describing signatures, but they suffice for our purpose, which is to explain some of the most commonly used expressions.

An example will help you in the understanding of these terms: An imposition layout designated as *64-page quad 16's to insert*, means that a sheet containing 64 pages is folded into four 16-page signatures; two of these are inserted into the two remaining with the result that two 32-page signatures are delivered by the folding machine. Other examples can be added by browsing through any of the many imposition books.

Paper in Its Relation to Folding

The last point to be considered in our presentation of the co-ordinative planning which is required for all printing to be bound is the role of the paper. We will understand this role better if we keep in mind that selecting the best imposition "is governed by the policy that the greatest number of pages should be folded in the least number of signatures in one operation from a full sheet of paper as the size and weight of the paper and the trim size of the book will permit."[13]

Our discussion of paper in relation to imposition is divided into the following five points: (1) stock sizes, (2) grain, (3) weight, (4) squaring, and (5) shingling.

Stock sizes. Most short and medium-length printing runs are printed on paper that is bought from paper merchants who keep a variety of papers on hand. Most papers are available in several standard sizes which do not always correspond exactly to available press size. Planning of a job includes selection of the most suitable page size for available standard size papers. In long-run printing this consideration changes. There, paper is made to order by the mill for a specific purpose.

Grain of paper. It is an elementary rule that the grain of the paper must run parallel to the spine of the book. This rule should never be neglected. Yet it is true that in some cases advertising material is planned with the grain in the opposite direction. But these cases are very rare and need very careful planning. Generally speaking, grain must run with the binding.

Weight of paper. "The weight of the paper is the controlling factor in determining the number of pages in a signature."[14] Heavy papers should be folded in 8-page signatures, whereas lighter papers are usually folded in 16-page signatures. Bible papers fold best in 32-page signatures, but are also folded in 64-page signatures. The detail of the job in hand governs specific decisions.

Squaring of paper. For all jobs of high-quality folding, and particularly in work-and-tumble impositions, the paper should be squared before printing. In other cases it is sufficient that the side guide edge and the gripper edge of the paper are at a right angle.

Diagram of shingling. Shingling is a technique to prevent "creep" or "push-out" in saddle-stitched binding of a large number of leaves or of pages printed on heavy paper.

Shingling of paper. Heavy papers are apt to cause what is known as *creep* or *push-out* in saddle-stitched binding where the number of inserted leaves can become quite large. In such jobs the page size must be selected with a view to allowing sufficient material for variations in bind margins and outside margins whereby creep is counteracted. In some instances gutter adjustment is necessary in order to properly align the folios (page numbers) for folding and trimming.

Section 3: Cutting of Sheets

Sheet cutting, like many other operations in printing and binding, can be done on a variety of materials, for a variety of purposes, and with a variety of equipment. Even though printing can be done on plastics, foils, metal, wood, glass, and many other materials, paper is nevertheless the most important material for printing. Yet the word "paper" comprises a great variety of essentially similar but actually different materials that require different cutting techniques.

The purposes of sheet cutting can be conveniently divided into four: (1) cutting of blank sheets previous to printing, (2) cutting of printed sheets previous to further processing such as folding or die-cutting, (3) cutting of sheets into individual leaves previous to their assembly in binding, and (4) dividing of sheets containing several units that must be shipped individually, such as letterheads or handbills.

The equipment on which sheets are cut is the *guillotine cutter*, also known as *paper cutter*, *power cutter*, or *flat cutter*. (In paper mills this equipment is usually called a *trimmer*.) The word "guillotine" commemorates the name of the French physician, Dr. J. I. Guillotin, who devised and advocated the use of a heavy blade, sliding in two vertical guides for the efficient and humane beheading of people during the French Revolution. Our guillotine cutters serve less "humane" but more peaceful purposes; yet they too can be dangerous. Our discussion of sheet cutting is divided into the following six units: (1) general description of guillotine cutters, (2) various types of guillotine cutters, (3) the knife, (4) safety in guillotine cutting, (5) the main steps in sheet cutting, and (6) trimming on the guillotine cutter.

General Description of Guillotine Cutters

Guillotine cutters are machines that have a single cutting knife and are equipped for the cutting of higher or lower stacks of sheets. The stack of sheets, known as *lift*, is placed on a flat metal surface, the *bed* or *table* of the cutter, for the cutting operation. Paper cutters are manufactured in a variety of sizes and models. The size of the cutter is specified in inches, usually indicating the longest cut that can be made on a specific machine. All guillotine cutters built for the printing and paper industry (as distinguished from small models designed for office purposes) permit the squaring of a sheet, provided that none of its dimensions exceeds the cutting length of the machine.

Generally speaking, on standard models the size of a sheet to be placed on a cutter must not exceed its cutting length in either direction. But there are also guillotine cutters, in larger sizes particularly, that can be supplied with longer back tables as optional equipment. Such cutters permit the trimming of the shorter dimensions (which serve often as guide edges of the press sheet) or the splitting of a sheet.

The squaring of blank sheets and the cutting of printed ones is precision work. You remember that we control the position of a sheet in the press by means of two adjoining edges, its guide and its gripper edge. Positioning of the sheet is achieved by using mechanical stops that are set with care on the press itself. The same principles of sheet control prevail on guillotine cutters. On printing presses we use a side guide and several front guides. Guillotine cutters have side frames (also known as side guides) and a *back guide*, usually called *back gauge*, overseas *back fence*. The back guide of guillotine cutters is movable; the side frames—one on each side of the bed—are not moveable but stationary.

Another important feature of guillotine cutters is known as the clamp. The *clamp* is a metal bar that runs parallel to the knife and like the knife at a 90° angle to the table. The clamp serves two functions. One is to press the air out of the pile of sheets prior to cutting, the other is to hold the pile of sheets firmly in its correct position during cutting.

This general description has acquainted you with the four essential components of guillotine cutters: (1) the knife, (2) the bed, (3) the side frames and back guide, and (4) the clamp. Now we can turn to the manner in which they operate. It takes considerable force to cut through a pile of paper. The necessary power can be supplied in several ways. The most primitive equipment is powered by the operator, but the length of the cut and the height of the pile must be relatively small. Clamp and back guide, too, can be manually operated, but with the same limitations. Nor should it be forgotten that manual operation is time-consuming as well as physically exacting. Cutters for continuous production are, therefore power driven. Power can be applied either to

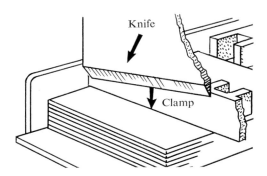

Knife

Clamp

Diagram of guillotine cutting. You see the lift of stock to be cut on the bed or table of the cutter. On the left the lift is lined up with one edge, in the rear it is lined up with another edge at the back gauge. The clamp has already moved down and the knife is descending to make the cut.

all moving members—knife, clamp, and back guide—or to only some of them. The back guide, finally, can automatically be positioned by preset signals in addition to being moved by power. All these and many other points are presented in the course of the following unit.

Safety is a very important consideration in the construction and use of guillotine cutters. You remember the head-chopping origin of this machine; if it is not operated with the necessary precaution it can injure the workman in a very serious manner. Modern technology has not only increased the scope and efficiency of power cutters, but it has also made them much more safe for the operator.

Various Types of Guillotine Cutters

The variety of guillotine cutters in existence defies rigid typifications. But if we keep in mind that our groupings are made for the purpose of explanation primarily, we can divide guillotine cutters into the following three major types: (1) guillotine cutters that are powered by the operator, (2) power-driven guillotine cutters, and (3) guillotine cutters capable of automatic spacing. Each of these three types is now briefly discussed.

Operator-powered guillotine cutters. These are the smallest and least complex sheet-cutting machines. They are known as *lever cutters* and are bench or floor models. The operator depresses the lever to which the knife is linked when he wants to make the cut. The lever pulls the knife through the pile, and multiplies the force exerted by the operator. Clamp and back guide are set by hand on lever cutters. The distance of the back guide

from the knife may or may not be indicated on the hand wheel by which the gauge is moved.

Lever cutters exist in a variety of sizes up to 36 inches; the height of the pile is relatively low and can rarely exceed 2 inches. Lever cutters are the least expensive but also the least efficient of all cutting machines; they are mainly used by small printing or binding shops.

Power cutters. Most sheet-cutting machines are power cutters. All power cutters use electrical energy for the driving of the knife. (On certain modern designs the knife is actually moved by a hydraulic mechanism which in turn is electrically powered.) On some models both clamp and back guide must be manually operated; somewhat more advanced models have automatic clamps but their back guide must still be moved by the operator; still more advanced models incorporate power drives for all three moving members, the knife, the clamp, and the back guide.

Power cutters are complex precision machines. Every motion must be very exact, and it must also be performed at great speed. The number of possible cutting cycles within a given time varies of course for different sizes and makes of machines. But it may be said, by way of general information, that many models of modern power cutters with automatic clamping action achieve a cutting cycle (comprising descent and return of clamp and knife) in a time varying between one and two seconds. In this time the clamp is brought down on the pile of paper, the knife pulled through it, and both knife and clamp are returned to their original position. Nor should the precision demanded of power cutters be underestimated. The knife must cut through the whole pile in absolute uniformity; it must stop cutting and reverse its action with equal accuracy.

The back guide controls, as you know, the position of the cut. It is therefore most important that the back guide itself be very accurately set. The tolerance required does not exceed two thousandths of an inch (plus or minus) on some of the modern automatic power cutters. This tolerance may be as small as half a thousandth on some equipment. Last, but not least, the clamp must be adjustable for the pressure that it puts on the stock; pressure adjustment too, is possible to a surprising degree.

It would, of course, go way beyond the plan of this manual to discuss the engineering of modern power cutters even in the most general terms. Here we may merely mention that a flywheel is used for storing of energy between cuts, that clamp and back gauge can be driven in many ways, for example, hydraulically by means of oil pressure; that the extent of the travel of the back gauge can also be controlled electrically, with magnetic clutches, for example.

Automatic spacing. Automatic spacing is one of the most revolutionary developments in sheet cutting; it reduces cost and increases productivity of cutting substantially. Automatic spacing means that the back gauge is automatically moved a predetermined distance after every cut. The purpose of automatic spacing and the reasons why it increases cutting efficiency are now discussed.

Automatic spacing is most effective in long-run large-size sheet cutting requiring many cuts. Assume, for example, a sheet size of 44 × 64 inches, 70-lb. paper, 25,000 sheets, 8 cuts to the sheet. Assume further that this paper is 0.005 inch thick and that we can cut it in 5-inch piles, or 1000 sheets at a time. As our job consists of 25,000 sheets, we must cut it in 25 different piles. Without automatic spacing the operator must change the setting of the back gauge 8 times for the cutting of each of the 25 required lifts. With automatic

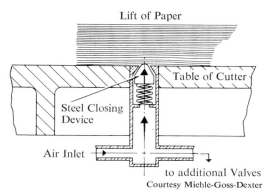

Lift of Paper

Table of Cutter

Steel Closing Device

Air Inlet

to additional Valves
Courtesy Miehle-Goss-Dexter

Schematic diagram of an air-film table. The cutting load is supported by air pressure from many valves in the cutting table. Each valve has a spring-loaded steel closing device which projects somewhat beyond the surface of the table. In this position the valve is sealed. The weight of the paper lift depresses the closing device and breaks the seal of the valve: Now the air can exert its pressure upwards on the lift to be cut.

spacing he sets the spacer bar which controls the back guide of the machine only once; from there on, it performs automatically.

Automatic spacing guillotine cutters are often equipped with air film tables that reduce the weight to be moved by the operator when he handles the sheets on the cutter. Even though such tables can be used on other models, too, they are most beneficial on automatic spacing equipment where every fraction of a minute counts. Weight-reducing tables add air pressure to the strength of the operator who is less in danger of injuring himself and will be much less fatigued. The cutting load is supported by compressed air that escapes from many valves in the table as soon as the load is applied. This load can be rather heavy, if we consider that the cutting pile in our example consists of 1000 sheets 44 × 64, 70-lb. paper, weighing approximately 400 lb.

The knife. The knife is the cutting member of guillotine cutters. It must be sharpened in the proper way and it must be in perfect condition for efficient cutting. As knives get dull easily, they must be frequently sharpened. Paper-cutting machines are designed to permit easy exchanging of knives. The handling of knives is hazardous and requires proper care.

The knife is bolted to the *knife bar* on the cutting machine with its top side. The bottom side is sharpened for cutting in the shape of a bevel. The bevel "is dictated by one or more of these factors: (1) character or peculiarity of paper to be cut, (2) physical dimension of the paper, (3) kind of cutting machine used, (4) operating condition of the machine, and (5) extent of clamp pressure."[15] The length of the bevel and the angle of the bevel are important and specified by the manufacturers of guillotine cutters. Not all papers can be cut with the same bevel and angle. Some hard-to-cut materials such as glassine papers or plastics may require a knife with a double bevel.

Safety on Guillotine Cutters

Safety provisions are very important features of guillotine cutters. But safety in sheet cutting does not depend on the equipment alone. "Safety of the flat-bed guillotine is the joint consideration of the manufacturer, plant management, maintenance, and operating personnel."[16]

One of the most important safety principles for guillotine cutting is that of two-hand operation, meaning that both hands of the operator must be kept busy, away from the cutting area during the cutting cycle. Another element of danger lies in the so-called repeating of the knife, meaning that the knife comes down, either some or all the way after completion of cutting. "Real safety for operating a guillotine cutter can only be accomplished by a control which engages both hands

Courtesy Miehle-Goss-Dexter

A 57-inch Lawson power cutter equipped with automatic spacing and air-film table.

until the knife has reached the bottom of the stroke and then stops the knife at the top of the stroke without possibility of a repeat."[17]

Modern guillotine cutters are equipped with very efficient safety features that use either electrical controls alone, or combine them with mechanical, hydraulic, or pneumatic devices. But all of these safety features require the intelligent co-operation of the operator to become fully effective. Some modern cutters cast a beam of light across the front of the knife. If the operator intercepts this beam with his hand, the machine stops automatically.

The Main Steps of Sheet Cutting

Assuming that the guillotine cutter is in perfect working order and that the knife is of proper bevel and sharpness, the main steps in sheet cutting may be the following nine operations: (1) preparing the cutting layout, (2) checking in of the uncut sheets, (3) placing of sheets on the stock table, (4) setting the back gauge for the first cut, (5) winding and jogging, (6) placing of stock in the cutter, (7) cutting, (8) removing the waste, and (9) removing the cut units. Each of these is now briefly characterized.

Preparing the cutting layout. The cutting layout is usually a sheet of the job to be cut, ruled, and marked to indicate all detail necessary for proper cutting. It may contain such items as job number, name of customer, height of lift, cutting machine to be used, number, order and position of cuts, dimensions of margins, bleeds, final sizes, and generally speaking all other information necessary or useful for efficient production.

Checking in of the uncut sheets. Every job arriving at a bindery must be checked in, meaning that the sheets are identified and that noticeable defects are reported immediately.

Placing of sheets for cutting. Modern well-equipped sheet cutting uses hydraulically powered platforms that elevate and maintain the pile or skid of uncut sheets automatically at the correct working level, namely, the height of the machine cutting table. Where such equipment is not available, sheets are cut from press skids or in small lots from stock tables.

Setting the cutter. Cutters equipped with automatic spacing have spacing bars which are set for the whole job including all different cuts. In cutters not so equipped, the back guide is set for the first cut and must be reset for every following one.

Winding and jogging. Sometimes sheets stick more or less to each other after printing. In such cases they must be *winded*, or aired, prior to *jogging*. Jogging is the operation whereby piles of sheets are evened at their guide edges.

Stacking of sheets in the cutter. In some plants the number of sheets comprising a single lift for the cutting is predetermined by the production department or by the bindery foreman, in others the height of lifts is left to the choice of the operator. All sheets must be carefully placed or jogged to side and back guides.

Cutting. After several minor moves the operator either clamps and cuts manually, or he merely actuates the clamping and the cutting mechanism. After checking the first cut, the operator proceeds according to plan with the following cuts.

Removing the waste. During cutting and at the end of a job, the waste, as the useless cut-offs are called, must be removed. Waste is then baled and sometimes sold to be used by paper mills in the making of papers and boards.

Removing the cut units. In some cases the cut units are the desired final result, in other cases they need further cutting. The operator removes them from the cutter, and if they need further cutting, he places them in such a manner that they remain as lifts of proper height for the next cutting operation.

Trimming on Guillotine Cutters

Even though the trimming of books is more efficiently done on *book trimmers*, books can also be trimmed on guillotine cutters. For book work, a technique is often employed that uses a guillotine cutter as if it consisted of three units. This technique is based on the split back guide.

A split back guide consists of three sections which can each be differently positioned. Therewith it is possible to trim three books in one cutting cycle. The books are loaded on the bed in such a manner that each lot faces the knife at a different edge: one at the *head*, the other at the *foot*, and the third at the *front* or *outside*. The same technique can also be used for the trimming of other printed material.

For the trimming of larger units where the split back-guide technique is not practical, the back guide is used as a single unit. In some cases the *running* back-guide technique is selected. In this case the back guide is not locked but moved back and forth until the whole lift is trimmed. In other cases the back guide is locked, and all lifts are first trimmed on one side, then the guide is reset for the next side, and so forth, until all three sides of the books are trimmed.

Section 4:   Folding

From the general introduction to binding you know that folding is the operation whereby the printed sheet (or web) is converted into book sections, or signatures. You also know that folding is used in the production of advertising material such as folders, broadsides, and self-mailers, for example. In the preceding unit on imposition you became acquainted with signatures and also with the important role played by the paper in folding. This section is a discussion of folding.

Our presentation begins with a discussion of different folds and their purposes, then the two basic principles underlying most folding equipment are explained, next comes a brief characterization of the most common types of folding machines, and finally a discussion of their most important operational steps.

Different Folds, Their Names, and Purposes

At the outset of every discussion of folding, the terms *parallel fold* and *right-angle fold* must be explained. These terms refer to the relation of several folds made in sequence. Parallel folds are "any series of folds in sequence made in parallel fashion."[18] Right-angle folds have "at least one fold at right angles with the others."[19] The whole variety of possible folds—some of which will be discussed in this unit—is based on these two kinds of folds. "Right-angle folds are most commonly used for book work. The parallel fold is generally used for very narrow books or for those that are printed multiples. They may be cut apart after they are bound or the folding machine may cut them apart."[20] Parallel folds are also very widely used in the production of advertising and sales promotional material, as well as in maps. It should be added that parallel folds are supposed to run parallel with the grain of the paper.

Six-page folds can be made in three ways: as *three-leaf-panel folds* (also called "letter folds"), *accordion folds*, and *reverse accordion folds*. In the three-leaf-panel fold the third leaf is folded toward the center and the first leaf over both. In the accordion fold the first leaf is folded over the center leaf and this again over the third leaf. If the first leaf opens to the right instead of the customary opening to the left, the fold is called reverse accordion fold. The *over-and-over fold* is another frequently used style where the folded object has four or more final leaves.

Some very complicated folds are used on illustrations to be inserted in books and on road

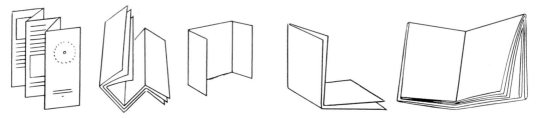

Some folds and their purposes. The first picture is a 10-page accordion fold often used for envelope stuffers; the next is a 24-page booklet to be saddle-stitched in the center; the third is a three-leaf panel or gate fold, frequently used in direct mail literature; the fourth is a landscaped French fold for prestige announcements or greeting cards; and the last is a 32-page booklet.

maps. All of them can be evolved out of parallel and right-angle folds.

Knife Folding and Buckle Folding

Hand folding is much too expensive and much too slow for all production work; it is done only on special jobs that cannot be folded by machines. All production work is machine folded. Folding machines are based on one of two principles: they are either *knife folders* or *buckle folders*. It is also possible to combine both principles in sequence on one and the same machine.

In hand folding the operator registers the edges of the sheet before he makes the fold. For folding he uses a simple hand tool known as a *bone folder* (made of bone or plastic) or *folder* for short. He repeats registering and folding until the signature is completed. Machine folding is done on high-speed equipment that runs so very fast that the uninformed person cannot recognize the way in which it operates. It may seem far fetched to connect these complex mechanisms with the slow hand folding, but closer investigation will show that there are, together with many differences, also some common points between hand and machine folding.

Let us study the *knife folder*. Here the sheet is folded by interaction of a thin blade and tapes attached to a pair of rollers rotating toward each other. At the moment of folding the sheet is accurately positioned and at rest. The knife comes down on the sheet and forces it between the two rotating *fold-rollers* where the fold is made. If you want, you can compare the knife with the bone folder; but this comparison tells you more about the differences in both ways of folding than about their similarities. In hand folding the bone folder makes the crease and therewith the fold. In knife machine folding the knife has an entirely different function, it pushes the paper between the two fold rollers; they, not the knife, make the crease and therewith the fold.

The principle of *buckle folding* is still further away from that used in hand folding. Buckle folding resembles knife folding in one respect but it differs from knife folding in several others. In buckle folding the fold is again made by two rollers that rotate against each other; here, too, the paper is forced between these two rollers where it is creased and therewith folded. The similarity between knife folding and buckle folding ends at this point. Where the two differ most is in the

Hand folding with a bone folder. Hand folding is done only on jobs that are too small to warrant machine folding or that cannot be folded by machine for some reason or other.

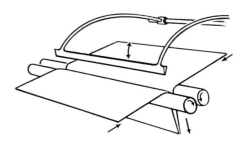

Schematic diagram of knife folding. The knife pushes the paper between the two-fold rollers which make the fold and move the folded paper away thereby making room for the next sheet.

manner in which the paper is forced between the fold rollers. This effect is achieved in a very ingenious way that is rather unexpected and needs therefore a little longer explanation that may be helped by a few simple experiments.

Take a letterhead or any similar paper—it should not be as thin as tissue and it should also not be too thick— put it on the table and push it against a stop, such as the edge of a book: The buckling of paper that is driven against a stop is the fact on which this kind of folder is based. You will also notice that paper buckles more if the grain of the paper is short than if it is long.

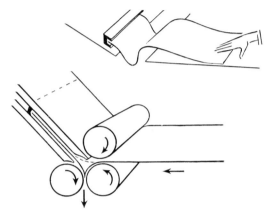

Schematic diagram of buckle folding. The upper drawing shows the buckling of paper that is forced against a stop. The lower drawing shows how the paper is folded in a buckle folder between a pair of rollers. These remove the folded sheet making room for the next, just like the fold rollers of knife folders.

In your experiment the buckle may have occurred at any point of the sheet. But the location of the buckle cannot be left to chance in a folding machine where the buckle determines the location of the crease and therewith of the fold. In the buckle folder things are arranged in a manner that permits perfect control over the location of the buckle. The elements that provide this result are the folding plates, the sheet gauges, the drive rollers, and the folding rollers.

The folding plate with the sheet gauge plays a very important role. The *folding plate* consists of two metal plates with enough space between them to permit the sheet to go in and out again but with not enough room to make it possible for the sheet to pucker or to curl up in this shallow space. The *sheet gauge* is an adjustable mechanical stop that terminates the progress of the sheet in the folding plate. The *drive roller* and the *folding rollers* work

together; the folding rollers catch the sheet at the only place where it can buckle in this arrangement, that is, at the mouth of the folding plate.

If you study our illustration you see how the first fold is made on a buckle folder. But the buckle principle leads to further and equally surprising possibilities. As you can see from our diagram the folded sheet can be immediately driven into a second and from there into a third and fourth folding plate. It is possible to make these four parallel folds in a very economical and equally speedy manner. Buckle folders have several sections at right angles to each other. In some models these sections have two, in others they have three or four folding plates.

Review of Folding Machines

In the last unit you have made the acquaintance of the two principles on which folding machines are based. Now we will summarize how these principles are basically expressed in the equipment. On knife folders the sheet runs on tapes, is positioned prior to folding and at rest—if ever so briefly—before the knife comes down on it. Knife folders

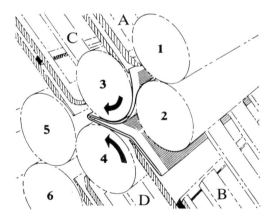

Diagram of a four-pocket section of a buckle folder. Up to four parallel folds can be made in this section. The letters A, B, C, D, indicate the four fold plates, the figures the six rollers involved. You see the sheet after it has received its second fold in "B" being guided into the third fold plate "C" by rollers 3 and 4.

are more used for right-angle folding and less for parallel work. In most buckle folders, though not all, the sheet runs on diagonal rollers; it must be in motion in order to be folded. Buckle folders are most suitable for parallel folding and less adaptable to right-angle work. But it must be kept in mind that both knife and buckle folders are capable of doing both parallel and right-angle folding. The foregoing comments discuss the basic features of folding machines but not the capabilities of specific models nor their usefulness for specific folding tasks.

After this summary we are ready for a more detailed treatment of folding. First you find a general description of knife folders, then a discussion of the most common steps taken in operating this type of equipment, thereafter a presentation of the main models in which knife folders are manufactured. The same plan is followed for buckle folders.

Description of Knife-Folding Machines

Knife-folding machines consist of two main units, the feeder and the folder. Most knife-folding machines are equipped with continuous feeders, but there are also installations in existence that use pile feeders. The folder itself consists of several knife and roller assemblies that are on different levels and are either at right angles or parallel to each other. But before we discuss the folder itself a brief description of the *Cross Feeder*, which is still widely used on knife-folding machines, is in order.

The Cross Feeder. The Cross Feeder is so named after its original manufacturer. It is a continuous feeder, meaning that it can be loaded while running without the necessity of interrupting feeding for reloading.

The Cross Feeder has two boards, one on top of the other. The top board is used for loading, the bottom board for feeding. The movement of the sheet is brought about by tapes and by other mechanical means such as rollers and comber wheels. The Cross Feeder can be distinguished from more modern continuous feeders by the fact that these use air suction and blast, whereas the Cross Feeder operates without suction, even though it may have a blower for the fanning and separating of the sheets.

A brief description of the Cross Feeder follows: "Lifts of stock are placed on the top board and fanned out, thus starting separation. Tapes automatically advance the pile of sheets around the rear drum onto the bottom feed board and to feeding position under two beaded comber wheels. These wheels comb the top sheet forward to rubber drop rollers, at which point a cut-out pendulum raises the comber wheels. The drop rollers operating on top of the sheet against the feed roller drive the sheet forward to the carrier tapes

of the folder. A tail hold-down aids in holding the sheet on the pile."[21]

The knife folder. The knife folder has in most cases three or four fold levels. Each level serves for a consecutive right-angle fold. In some models additional parallel sections are provided on one or more fold levels. In reading the customary folder diagrams it must be kept in mind that each pair of rollers on the folder is on a different level unless designated as parallel. It must also be firmly grasped that the longest rollers indicate the first fold and that every following pair of rollers becomes smaller as folding progresses. Folding knives, or tucker blades, and moving tapes are two unfailing characteristics of knife folders.

After the sheets are driven from the feeder to the tapes of the folder, they enter the first folding level. The "sheets are carried under the fold knives by tapes to the first-fold gauge, then side-registered by the sliding hammer side gripper. Drive-up wheels on top of the tapes hold the sheet against the guide. Toprods keep the sheet flat in its travel to the folder gauge. Rubber slow-downs stop the sheet as it reaches the gauge, preventing damage to the edge of sheet or crowding at the gauge.

"A saw-toothed knife descends on the sheet and tucks it into the bite of two knurled rollers, thus making the first fold. Needles in the knife blade puncture the sheet where the fold is to be made, in order to hold the register as the fold enters the roller.

"The sheet passes between the first-fold rollers onto the tapes of the second-fold level which carry it under the second-fold knife. The sheet is stopped and registered by the gauge. After the sheet is registered the folding knife descends and tucks the sheet into the second-fold rollers."[22] From there the sheet goes into the third and then into the fourth folding level. After completion of folding, the signature or signatures are delivered into the packer boxes from where they are manually removed.

Our description is restricted to the most characteristic features of folders. Perforators are one of these. Perforators are needed to prevent wrinkles in following folds and to allow escape of the air trapped by folding. Perforators can also be adjusted to cut two signatures apart if this is desired. It is finally mentioned that folders may have several parallel folding attachments and be equipped for slitting, pasting, and trimming.

The Main Steps in Operating Knife Folders

In the following you find a brief description of the seven most essential operational steps for knife folders: (1) loading the feeder, (2) adjusting the feeder, (3) maintaining the feeder, (4) adjusting the first fold level of the folder, (5) adjusting the remaining fold levels, (6) adjusting various attachments, and (7) adjusting the packer boxes. The adjustments of the feeder are discussed with the Cross Feeder in mind, because it is most commonly used with knife folders.

Loading a Cross Feeder. First the operator finds the correct position for the loader gauge on the top loading board. Then the sheets are piled on the loading board. Now he rolls a convenient lift of sheets into a cylinder and unrolls them again, thereby combing them, or separating the guide edges of sheets. Thereafter he continues loading in the same manner, always being careful of guide-edge separation.

Once the loading board is full, the sheets are cranked around the wooden drum until the guide edge of the top sheet is advanced several inches under the combing wheels on the lower feed board. The side guard on this board is of course also adjusted to suit the position of the sheets.

Adjusting a Cross Feeder. The adjustments on the feeder are rather technical. They include the setting of the tail clamp, of the comber wheels across the sheet, of the drop rollers that hold the sheet, and of the blowpipes used for winding.

Maintaining the Cross Feeder. The Cross Feeder is a continuous feeder and requires almost constant attention. New sheets must be placed in the feeder and must be correctly fanned out during the whole run.

Adjusting the first folding level on the folder. The first fold must be made with utmost precision. No subsequent fold can be precise if the first fold is off. Among the many chores are the following: The fold tapes must be adjusted to be in the right position for the size of the sheet; if the sheet is to be perforated, the perforators must be set; the fold guide, the gripper, and the knife also must be adjusted, and the same holds true for drive-up wheels, tail brushes, and the sheet slowdown. In some difficult jobs, particularly when the sheet is out of square, special adjustments and tricks of the trade are needed to see a job through.

Adjusting the remaining folding levels. The same adjustments, and some additional ones, are necessary on the subsequent folding levels. As the sheet gets folded it becomes more bulky and may need special care for this reason.

Adjusting various attachments. We know that knife folders can have parallel attachments but also others for pasting, slitting, and trimming. All of them must be properly set for the job in hand.

Adjusting the packer boxes. The signatures drop in the packer boxes resting on their back and head bolts (the term *bolt* indicates that the signature is closed) and are pushed forward by a plunger head and kept in an upright position by retaining flappers all of which need proper adjustment.

The Three Main Models of Knife Folders

Knife-type folding machines are made in a variety of sizes and in three distinct models which are known as book-and-job folders, double-sixteen folders, and quadruple folders. Each of these has its own field of application and consequently its own functional characteristics.

Book-and-job folders. Jobbing folders are considered standard utility folders because of their great economy and flexibility. They have four folding levels which permit the making of up to four right-angle folds. As they have one, and possibly two, parallel sections, their scope is further increased. Jobbing folders can also be equipped for cutting, pasting, and trimming.

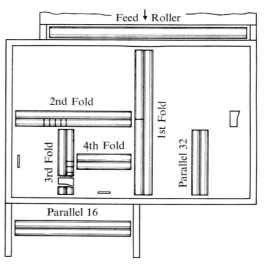

Courtesy Miehle-Goss-Dexter

Diagram of a Dexter Book and Job Folder. This folder has four sets of folding rollers, each at right angles to the preceding and following ones. The parallel 16 attachment has rollers parallel to the 2nd Fold set.

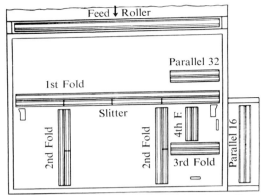

Diagram of Dexter Double Sixteen Folder. *In this folder the sheet is slit in half as it passes between the first fold rollers. Each half is folded at a right angle at the next level. The third right angle fold produces either outserts or inserts as described in the text. In the fourth right angle section each half of the sheet receives a fourth fold. The parallel 16 sections follows the second set of fold rollers and the parallel 32 section follows the third set.*

Double-sixteen folders. Double-sixteen folders are designed for publication work primarily. As you may remember, the term "double-sixteen" indicates that this folder produces two 16-page signatures. The double-sixteen folder is capable of delivering either two independent signatures or a single 32-page signature. It can also be equipped with an attachment that makes it possible to produce two 32-page signatures, though of a smaller page size. For this reason these folders are also designated as *double thirty-two folders.*

Double-sixteen folders have three folding levels and four sets of folding-rollers. The sheet is slit in half at the first folding level; each half is individually folded at right angles at the second level; at the third level there is only one pair of folding rollers. If the signatures are to be *outserts* each of the two folded sheets is here folded in succession; if the signatures are *inserts* both sheets are here combined and folded together. A fourth folding level is added for making the folder capable of delivering two 32-page signatures. This fourth set of rollers operates always two-to-one, just like the third set does. This folder can be further equipped with various attachments for special purposes.

The quadruple folder. The quadruple folder, often called *quad* folder for short, is a folder designed primarily for edition binding. It produces either four 16-page signatures or two 32-

page signatures. The quad folder has three folding levels and six sets of folding rollers. The sheet is folded in its total length in the first section; in the following section it is given a parallel fold and slit at the same time in four parts; each of these is folded at right angles in the third section. "When inserted signatures are desired, before the last

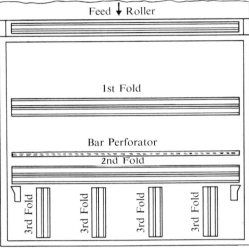

Diagram of the Dexter Quadruple Folder. *This folder is designed for edition binding. Before the sheet enters the second set of folding rollers it is perforated in its entire length. The second fold is made in line with the perforation and the sheet is divided into four parts by slitting. This fold is a parallel fold. It is followed by the right angle sections where each of the four parts receives the third fold. (The slitters are not marked in the diagram.)*

fold is made, the two center signatures are conveyed to position under the right and left outside signatures by means of hickey rolls. Here the two signatures are folded together with one operation of the right- and left-hand folding knives, and then delivered as two 32-page signatures to the two upper packer boxes."[23]

Description of Buckle-Folding Machines

Buckle-folding machines consist, like knife folders, of two main units, the feeder and the folder. Most buckle folders are equipped with continuous feeders, but they can also be used with pile feeders. The folder itself consists of several sections, each permitting several parallel folds on different levels and at right angles to each other. Before we turn to a discussion of the folder, we will describe the type of feeder most commonly used for buckle folders; it is the air-wheel continuous feeder.

The air-wheel continuous feeder. Air-wheel continuous feeders can be loaded during running without requiring stoppage. Air-wheel feeders are available in smaller sizes with a single board, but here we describe a double board machine because this type is more widely used. Like the already described Cross Feeder, the double air-wheel feeder has a top board for loading and a bottom board for feeding, as well as a rear drum connecting the two feed boards.

The sheets are placed on the top loading board "and fanned out, thus starting sheet separation. As the sheets are carried around the drum by means of feeder tapes or belts, the top loader board is emptied and new loads of stock are placed in position and fanned out. Fanning out the stock as it is loaded is a particularly valuable feature for stock that is tacky, or otherwise difficult to separate, as the fanning-out process tends to wind the sheets. The feeder tapes gradually carry the stream of fanned out sheets forward to the air wheel, which revolves continuously and feeds off the sheets from the pile in a continuous succession."[24]

The air wheel plays a decisive role in this type of feeder. It has the function of advancing the top sheet from the feeder pile after it is separated from the following sheets by blasts of air, with its leading edge onto the conveyor mechanism of the folding machine. The air wheel is a small drum with holes in part of its wall. Inside this drum is a vacuum chamber having a slot in the direction of the air-wheel wall. When the punctured area of the air wheel passes over the slot in the vacuum chamber the sheet is sucked on. It is advanced until the punctured area of the air wheel ends; then it is released because the vacuum cannot continue through the solid metal area of the air wheel. All this takes place in the nick of time, several hundred times per minute.

The buckle folder. In discussing buckle folders, two terms must be clearly understood. One is the term *fold plate*, the other is the term *section*. Buckle folders are particularly adaptable to the making of parallel folds, as you already know. The fold plate is the place where parallel folds are made. Combinations of two, three, and four successive fold plates are frequently used. These combinations are designated as sections. For right-angle folding, several such sections are combined at right angles in one folding machine. The reading of diagrams for buckle folding is difficult for the beginner. Here, as in diagrams for knife folding, it must be understood that the various sections are on different levels and that the size of fold plates decreases as folding progresses from the first plate in the top section to the last plate in the bottom section.

The first, or top, section is generally known as the *parallel section*, the following right-angle section as the *8-page section*, the next as the *16-page section*, and the fourth as the *32-page section*. These figures should not be misunderstood; they do not indicate the highest possible number of pages but exactly the contrary, namely, the lowest number of pages that will result from consecutively using each of these sections for one single fold. As each section has two or more parallel fold plates, it is possible, for example, to fold a 32-page booklet on a two-section machine with the final fold being made in the 8-page section.

The following description pertains to a most simple buckle folder having a parallel section with two fold plates and only one additional (8-page) section with three fold plates. We begin at the point where the sheet is advanced by the air wheel from the feeder "onto the diagonal roller feed table. The action of the diagonal rollers side registers the sheet against the side guide, which is equipped with a series of metal or glass balls operating on top of the diagonal rollers. The balls keep the sheet against the side guide and also hold the sheet in positive contact with the diagonal rollers, thus assuring the travel of the sheet to the folding rollers at feed-table speed.

"The sheet is carried by the feed table to the feed rollers of the parallel section. The rollers advance the sheet into the fold plate until it hits the fold gauge. It then buckles and passes between the fold rollers, thus making the fold. The folded

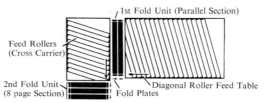

Courtesy Miehle-Goss-Dexter

Diagram of fold plates of a two-section buckle folder. The first section has two fold plates for making either one or two parallel folds. (If only a single fold is wanted here the other fold plate is bypassed.) The second section makes right-angle folds and is equipped with three fold plates for making one, two, or three parallel folds.

edge of the sheet passes into the second fold plate if desired or is deflected and delivered to the cross carrier or stacker delivery.

"Each fold plate in the machine is equipped with its own swinging deflector, for deflecting the sheet past any fold plate not used on the job being run. Fold plates are also equipped with gauges for registering the sheet as needed. The folder may be equipped with either knurled steel folding rollers or with rubber rollers. Steel rollers last longer than rubber ones and are suitable for the great majority of the work to be folded. Rubber rollers are used on such work as greeting cards that are embossed or printed by the raised printing methods to prevent marring of the work; and also for folding special hard-surfaced stocks such as vellum.

"Work receiving one or more right-angle folds is delivered from the parallel section to the cross carrier of the right angle (8-page) section. The cross carrier is equipped with diagonal rollers and adjustable ball side guide, and is similar to the diagonal roll feed table. The setting and operation of the 8-page section is very similar to that of the parallel section. The finished signature is delivered onto the stacker delivery."[25]

This description is restricted to the most essential points. It should be added that buckle folders are equipped with slitter shafts for scoring, slitting, and perforating. Jobs that are to be folded at right angles are, as a rule, scored or perforated before the right-angle fold is made. Other attachments for pasting, trimming, and special deep-scoring for greeting cards, etc., are available.

The Main Operating Steps of Buckle Folders

Our discussion of the main operational steps of buckle folders is restricted to the same essentials as those of knife folders. These are again seven: (1) loading the air-wheel feeder, (2) setting the air-wheel feeder, (3) maintaining the air-wheel feeder, (4) setting the parallel section, (5) setting the following right-angle sections, (6) setting the various attachments, and (7) setting the stacker.

Loading the air-wheel feeder. Loading an air-wheel feeder with double feed boards is similar to the loading of the Cross Feeder. The sheets are evenly fanned out on the top board, then cranked on the drum to the feed board until both boards are loaded.

Setting the air-wheel feeder. The setting of an air-wheel feeder includes the adjusting of guides, the positioning of the air wheel, the adjustment of

the front edge of the pile, the adjustment of the tail drag and air blast, and the setting of the sheet caliper (also known as sheet detector) which insures that only one sheet will pass at a time.

Maintaining the air-wheel feeder. The air-wheel feeder, like all continuous feeders, must be constantly loaded and supervised. As it is a high-speed machine, it requires repeated attention of the operator.

Setting the parallel section of buckle folders. The parallel section is the first section of a buckle folder. The preparation of this section includes setting the feed table for square and proper feeding of the sheets to the fold rollers and adjusting the fold plates.

The nature of the job determines which fold plates will be used and which not; once this is decided, the deflectors are raised on the plates to be used, and lowered on those that will be by-passed. Then the sheet gauges, often called *fold stops*, are set in the selected fold plates, and the fold rollers are adjusted for their correct pressure. If sheets are to be folded at right angles it is necessary to set the scoring or perforating members on the slitter shaft of the parallel section. If the sheet is passed on to the next section, the guide on the cross carriers must be adjusted for proper transmission of the folded sheet to the next section; and if the sheet is not further folded, the stacker must be adjusted.

Setting the following right-angle sections. The following sections are in principle not different from the first or parallel section. All adjustments necessary there must be repeated here. But it must

Courtesy Miehle-Goss-Dexter

A craftsman prepares a Cleveland buckle folder for folding a new job.

never be overlooked that these adjustments are now made for a sheet that is already folded—possibly several times—and that the setting for each successive fold must be made accordingly.

Setting various attachments. All attachments such as those for pasting, trimming, and cutting require careful setting. The detail of these operations depends, of course, on the nature of the job in hand.

Setting the stacker on buckle folders. The stacker is the receptacle for the completed job. In most though not all folders it can be moved to the section where the last fold is made. In some folders, the stacker of the last section remains there and a different stacker is used on preceding sections. The stacker must be adjusted for a smooth and even delivery of the folded signatures.

Comparison of Knife and Buckle Folders

Buckle folders are by their very nature more suitable for advertising and sales promotional work, road maps, and booklets than for book work. Buckle folders are high-speed machines and they are extremely versatile. In buckle folders the sheet is usually introduced into the folder with its shorter dimension and moved along its longer dimension. The first fold is therefore parallel to its shorter dimension which should also be parallel to the direction of the paper grain. Buckle folders are untimed machines; sheet follows sheet with as little distance between them as conditions permit. The theoretical speed of buckle folders is around 4000 running inches per minute.

Knife folders are timed machines, meaning that each cycle of the machine folds a single sheet. Knife folders are slower than buckle folders. The number of folds possible on knife folders is far smaller than the possible number of folds on comparable buckle folders. Knife folders are much more suitable for right-angle folding than for parallel work. Knife folders can be used for the folding of jobs where the first fold must be made against the grain of the paper; they can handle very thin papers, such as Bible papers, that are not practical for buckle folders, and they are available for larger sheet sizes than can be put on the largest buckle folders. Knife folders are mainly used for the folding of standard signatures of 8 pages and their multiples, whereas buckle folders can produce signatures of 12, 20, 24, 28, and 40, and more pages in addition to 8-page signatures and their multiples.

Buckle folders having facilities for the making of nine folds are common; other less common machines permit the making of sixteen folds in one pass through the machine. The number of folds depends on the paper and the kind of fold selected. The heavier the paper the fewer folds will be possible. In right-angle folding, where every folding doubles the thickness of the folded paper, fewer folds are permissible than in parallel folding of the accordion type fold where only a single paper thickness is added per fold.

Generally speaking, knife folders and buckle folders are less competitive with each other than supplementary. There is a definite need for both types. As to the quality of the work, the precision of folding in particular, opinions are divided. According to one of the leading manufacturers of both knife and buckle folders, the knife principle "is recognized as the most accurate and dependable method of making right-angle folds in both light weight and heavy weight stock, as well as in various qualities of stock used in all kinds of publication work."[26] Others consider the buckle folder superior in quality to knife folders. Their superior versatility and speed in comparison to knife folders is generally acknowledged.

Section 5: Assembling the Folded Material for Binding

The next major step after folding is assembling the folded material for binding. But before the material is ready for this operation, several preliminary steps may be required. Whether such steps are needed at all, and which of them are needed, depends on the kind of binding and the end product. Here we mention merely two such operations: *bundling* and *tipping*.

Bundling of the folded signatures "makes them much easier to stack and handle, protects them from damage and prevents them from becoming mixed."[27] Bundling also presses the air out and makes the work more compact and even. *Tipping* refers to the attaching of end papers as well as to that of illustrative material not printed together with the rest of the book.

The assembling of the material for binding can be done in one of three techniques known as *gathering*, *inserting*, and *collating*, respectively. Gathering is the assembly of book sections in

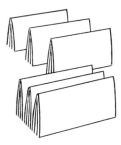

Three signatures, or book sections, are gathered for Smyth sewing, or for side sewing, or for side stitching.

sequence. Signature one is followed by signature two, this by signature three, and so on. Inserting is the assembly of signatures, or book sections, within other sections. The first signature to be assembled is at the center of the assembly and therefore also at the center of the final book. The center signature is inserted into the next signature and so on until all signatures are assembled. Collating is the assembly of individual leaves.

Binding terminology is changing at present as binding itself is changing rapidly from a handicraft to a highly automatic industry. Many traditional terms are unknown to the newcomers, and some of them have lost much of their past meaning. *Collating* is one example for this process. It was traditionally used in binding for the operation of inspecting and verifying the proper sequence of signatures after assembling and prior to binding. Now the word indicates an assembly technique as well. One can also hear and read the word "gathering" where inserting is the correct term if we want to abide by the traditional terminology. Whether the difference in meaning between the words "gathering" and "inserting" will be retained is an open question.

The following presentation is divided into five units: (1) bundling, (2) tipping, (3) gathering, (4) inserting, and (5) collating. This discussion takes you from the end of folding to the point where the material is ready for fastening either by sewing, or by stitching, or with adhesives.

Two signatures are inserted for common sewing or for saddle stitching.

Bundling

Bundling of signatures does not only serve orderliness but also affects the quality of the binding; "the signatures are made very compact since they are under pressure as long as they are in the bundles, and the completed book is more solid than it would be if they were piled loosely. Loose signatures are apt to become bent or curled which causes difficulty when they are fed to the sewing machines."[28] Bundling can be done on three kinds of presses: hand-bundling presses, power presses, and pneumatic presses. Each of them is briefly described in the following.

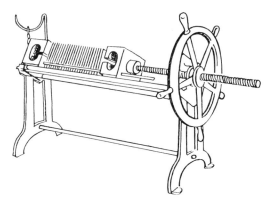

A manually operated bundling press. The operator turns the hand wheel and thereby forces the moving jaw against the signatures to be bundled. Note that the jaws have slits in the center which permit tying of the bundled signatures under pressure.

Hand-bundling signature presses. Hand-bundling signature presses consist of a floor stand on which two jaws are horizontally mounted. One of the jaws is stationary, the other is movable. The bundle of signatures with strings around it is laid between these jaws and compressed by turning a hand wheel and thereby forcing the movable jaw forward. The jaws are built so as to permit the tying of the bundles under pressure. Hand-bundling is of course neither very efficient nor capable of exerting the same pressure that can be applied with power-driven machinery.

Bundling with power presses. Power presses are either upright or horizontal machines in which a movable bed is pushed toward a stationary head. The power is supplied by an electric motor whose rotary motion is translated into a perpendicular one by gears and racks. Power presses are capable of exerting very strong pressures. For bundling, a lift of signatures several inches high is placed between wooden boards in the press, compressed, and tied after removal. Very powerful presses are designated as *smashers;* they are discussed at a later point in this chapter.

Pneumatic bundling presses. Pneumatic bundling presses are either upright or horizontal machines having a stationary and a movable jaw. The movable jaw is pushed by a piston to which power is applied by means of compressed air.

Bundling with pneumatic presses is done as follows: "A stack of signatures is placed between the jaws of the bundling press with a wooden board on the top and bottom of the stack, and pressure is applied. The jaws are slotted and the slots enlarged to holes large enough for the insertion of the operator's hands which makes it possible for him to tie the bundle with rope or chain while it is under pressure. The pressure is then released and the bundle removed from the press. The bundles are stacked to await the completion of the folding process on all signatures."[29]

Tipping

Tipping is the trade designation for the attaching of end papers or inserts to book sections. This operation consists in pasting the tips to the signatures with a thin strip of adhesive. Tipping is obviously not a complicated process. But if not properly planned, tipping can increase the cost of binding beyond all proportion in such jobs as require many inserts that must be tipped.

Depending on their position in the book section, tips are divided into *outside* and *inside tips*. Outside tipping refers to tipping at the beginning or end of a signature; inside tipping to tipping within a signature. Outside tipping can be done by machines; inside tipping is a hand operation that is very costly. Tips can cause several problems if they are not properly planned. It should be remembered that a strip of a quarter of an inch will be used for pasting the tip to the adjacent page and that this area should not be printed, otherwise the printing may be impaired. It should also be understood that not all adhesives are suitable for printed papers and that bleeds on the binding edge may necessitate special adhesives.

Machine tipping. Outside tips can be attached to signatures by tipping machines. Without entering into a discussion of specific tipping machines, it can be stated that such machines need two hoppers or pockets, one for the signature and the other for the endsheets or outside tips. If continuous operation is desired, the feed should be from

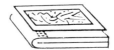 

The left-hand illustration shows an outside tip which can be tipped, or glued, without opening the signature; the right-hand illustration shows an inside tip which cannot be attached without opening the signature.

the bottom of the pile, as in automatic gathering machines. The tip is placed on a conveyor and the adhesive is applied when the tip is in motion. Then the signature is combined with the tip, put through squeeze rollers and finally delivered, sometimes staggered for easy counting, near the work bench of the operator. Production depends on the nature of the work; as a general indication it might be mentioned that it is possible to produce up to 5000 tips per hour.

Hand tipping. Hand tipping is used for inside tips. It is a very, very slow operation. "Each insert leaf is handled separately. The sheets are fanned out on the table and a thin line of paste brushed on the edges. If the inserts are to appear within the signature, the pages must be cut open by hand, using a bone folder. Even though hand tipping is tedious many bindery girls have become very adept at this work. As yet no satisfactory machine has been devised to make this handwork unnecessary."[30] Inside tips should be avoided where cost of binding counts.

Gathering

Gathering is the technique of assembling signatures in sequence, as you already know. Gathering is the most frequently used signature assembly technique of all. Practically all hard- and soft-bound as well as all side-wired and adhesive-bound books and magazines are so assembled. Disregarding mechanically bound books, we may say that gathering is used for the assembly of all books and magazines having a thickness of half an inch and more; it may or may not be used for books and magazines of lesser thickness.

Gathering can be done on various technological levels. Here we introduce you to three of them: (1) manual gathering, (2) gathering with circular gatherers, and (3) fully automatic gathering.

Manual gathering. In manual gathering all work is done by the operator without the use of any mechanical equipment whatsoever. First the individual signatures (or leaves) are piled next to each other in the proper sequence on long tables around an aisle or alley. The operator assembles the book as he walks around this *layout* of signatures by "removing from each pile one section, placing it above those previously removed. One circuit produces a complete book."[31] Gathering in this manner could be more pointedly designated as gathering by foot; the feet and legs of the workers (who may be either men or women) are as actively engaged in the work as are their hands. Manual gathering is very slow, space-consuming, and expensive; it is used on very small runs only.

Rotary collators are sometimes used for manual assembling of sheets or thin signatures in small quantities.

Gathering with circular gatherers. Circular gatherers eliminate the walking required in hand gathering and permit the operator to do his work in a sitting or standing position. Circular gatherers consist of one or more round tables of varying size, 5 to 7 feet in diameter, for example. These tables are "revolved by an electric motor in their base. The bundles of signatures are placed in order around the edge of the table and, as it revolves, the bundles pass in front of the operator who takes a signature from each pile. The speed at which the table revolves can be regulated, and the machine started and stopped by means of a foot pedal control. A number of operators can be seated around one revolving table. One disadvantage of the revolving table is that it has a tendency to make the operator dizzy."[32]

Fully automatic gathering. Fully automatic gathering is a necessity in all mass-production work. It is used in edition binding as well as in the binding of magazines that are not to be saddle stitched. All books, except inserted or saddle work, that are produced in quantity are gathered on fully automatic equipment. Fully automatic gathering is in many cases combined with other production steps such as binding with adhesives, side-wire stitching, covering, trimming, and so on. We may characterize fully automatic gathering machines as equipment that feeds and assembles individual signatures, or book sections, in sequence and that permits uninterrupted operation.

Gathering machines have feeding stations of varying number; machines with thirty-two of these stations, for example, are used in large book manufacturing plants. Each signature requires its own receptacle which is called *pocket* or *hopper* by the trade. A gathering machine assembles the book by releasing individual sections from the pockets to a conveying mechanism. Once the gathering machine is in full operation it produces at every move an assembled book. Every time the conveying mechanism advances, a signature is deposited on the conveying mechanism at every feeding station. At the first station there is a single signature, at the next there are two, at the following three, and so on until the complete book is assembled at the last station. The total number of stations depends on the number of signatures needed for the book in production.

The feeding mechanism of gathering machines deserves a few words. All gathering machines that are built for uninterrupted production have continuous feed and remove the individual signatures from the bottom of the pile. The top of the pile is thereby always accessible for adding of signatures. As to the detail of the feeding mechanism, three different systems are used. One is called the swinging gathering arm system, the other is the rotary drum system, and the third is the planetary system. Each of them is now briefly described.

In the *swinging arm gathering system*, the pile of

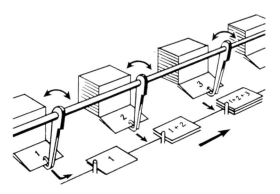

Schematic diagram of swinging arm gathering. Swinging arms take the signatures from the bottom of their pockets and put them on the conveyor.

signatures is placed in the pocket with the fold away from the operator. A sucker assembly pulls the signature down along the fold edge, away from the signature pile which is immediately supported by a lifter mechanism. The swinging arm grips the signature between the two ends of its jaw and pulls it away from the pile onto a conveying mechanism. There the signature is released and moved on by pins of the conveyor chain.

In the *rotary drum feeding system* the signatures are removed by grippers that are built into the surface of a rotating drum. Such a drum can have two grippers and can therefore remove two signatures with each revolution. The rest of the mechanism employs the same principles as the swinging arm system. The signature is again withdrawn from the bottom of the pile by means of suction nipples, the pile is supported at the signature fold edge by a mechanical device, the signature itself is clamped between the jaws of the gripper mechanism, and it is finally deposited on the conveying system.

The third and newest method is the *planetary gathering system.* Here, as in the other two gathering systems, the signatures are stacked in pockets, or hoppers, but hoppers of a different construction. The bottom of these hoppers is not stationary as in the other two systems but a moving part, a big drum. This drum is equipped with four rotary vacuum suckers, the planets, and a number of

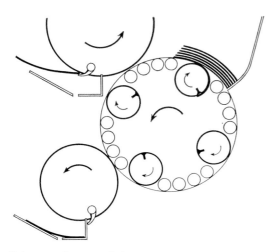

Schematic diagram of planetary gathering. The bottom of each pocket is a big, continuously rotating drum which supports the pile of signatures. For separation this drum has four rotary vacuum suckers. The separated signatures are fed to transfer drums that deposit the signatures on a raceway for assembling.

idlers, usually four, between each of the planets. The drum rotates in one direction, the planets in the opposite direction, and the pile of signatures rests on the surface of the transfer drum where it is always supported by a number of idlers.

Each sucker planet rolls a signature away from the bottom of the pile and transfers it to the grippers of a transfer cylinder which, in turn, deposits the signature on a raceway. As the drum carries four sucker planets, it removes four signatures in every revolution. High-speed installations have two transfer drums and two raceways in order to take full advantage of the high speeds at which this gatherer can be operated.

As it would be impossible to detect mistakes in the number of signatures assembled on such fast running machines, mechanical devices, called *calipers,* stop the gatherer if a signature is omitted, or if two signatures are fed instead of one, or if the signature is incomplete. Fully automatic gathering machines are complex mechanisms that perform also such minor but nevertheless very important operations as the exact lining up of all signatures which is called *jogging.*

Inserting

Inserting is the assembling of book sections or signatures by placing them within other sections. A section which is placed within another section is known either as an *insert,* or *inside signature,* and if it is in the center, as a *center signature.* A section which is placed over and outside another section is known either as *outsert* or as *outside signature.* The assembly technique of inserting can be used for books and magazines having a thickness of less than one-half inch folded, or less than one-quarter inch open. Inserted books are either bound by saddle-wire stitching or by Singer center sewing. The end products are more often booklets and magazines, but they can also be hardbound.

Soft-covered items such as booklets and magazines can be completely assembled by inserting. Some of these have independent covers, others are *self-covered.* In a self-covered book the cover is printed together with the book, whereas *covered* booklets or magazines have separately printed covers that may or may not be printed on a heavier paper than the book itself. The cover is the last unit in the assembly of a covered book or magazine. The majority of inserted work consists of soft-covered magazines or booklets. But inserting can also be used as an assembly technique for hardbound books.

The SHERIDAN
"Arm" Gatherer

This gatherer can be described as a series of identical feeder stations, spaced on uniform centers, corresponding to chain pin centers of a carrier chain running in a raceway. Signatures are delivered from each of the feeder units simultaneously to the carrier (collector) chain. As each chain pin section passes the series of feeder stations, it collects a different signature at each station, thus making a complete book, or magazine, when it completes the run.

Signatures are hand fed in lifts to the top of a horizontal type (flat) hopper. They are removed individually from the bottom of the hopper by means of a series of vacuum suckers, which impart the initial motion. A gripper arm then takes over to pull the signature clear of the hopper, transporting it to the raceway and releasing it there. The gripper arm is equipped with a caliper mechanism to detect missing signatures or double signatures, setting up a signal to stop the entire machine or notify the operator.

Speeds range from 100 to 200 cycles per minute, depending upon the type of signature, number of pages, paper, dimensions, condition of the stock, size of machine, as well as operator's technique and efficiency. Nominal signature sizes range from 17″ along fold x 12″ maximum, to 7″ x 5″ minimum.

Variations in the arm gatherer include collating of greeting cards, calendars, and a wide variety of suitable flat materials.

Although the Sheridan "Arm" Gatherer is often found in long run, high production applications, it is just as often used in short run job shops requiring rapid setup.

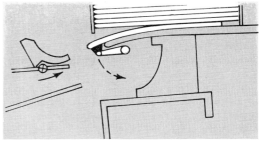

1 *Vacuum suckers impart the initial motion out of the hopper.*

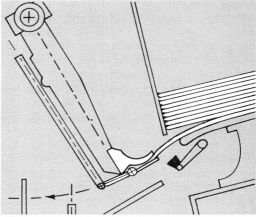

2 *Gripper arm takes over to pull the signature clear and transport it.*

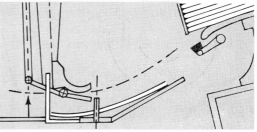

3 *Signature is released onto carrier chain.*

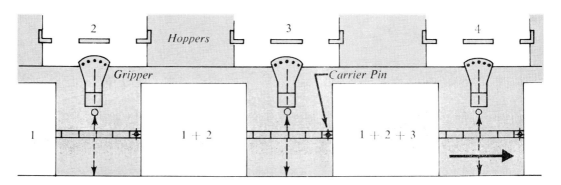

The SHERIDAN
"Rotary" Gatherer

This gatherer consists of a line of identical feeder stations feeding into a raceway equipped with a carrier chain to collect and transport the signatures to subsequent operations. Signatures are fed simultaneously to the raceway by means of gripper drums from the bottom of horizontal (flat) hoppers which are mounted over the raceway. The principal feature of this gatherer lies in the fact that signatures are delivered in-line with the direction of travel in the raceway, at raceway speed. Like Sheridan Arm Gatherers, the rotary gatherer incorporates a caliper to detect misses and doubles.

Speeds range from 125 cycles per minute up to 200 cycles per minute, again depending upon conditions. This machine favors particular types of signatures and primarily is used in long run applications.

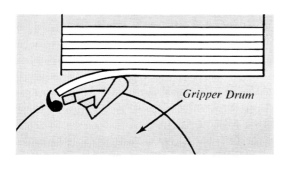

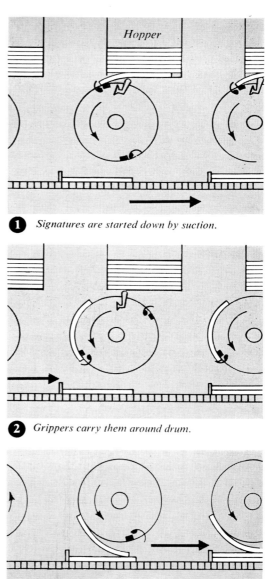

1 *Signatures are started down by suction.*

2 *Grippers carry them around drum.*

3 *Signatures drop in path of carrier pin.*

The diagram below shows the sheets on the raceway mostly hidden by the gripper drums and hoppers above them.

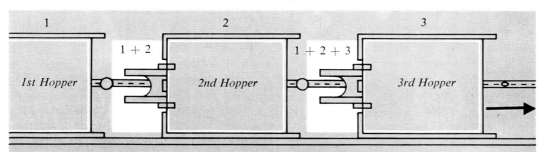

Inserting can be done on three technological levels: (1) as hand-inserting, (2) semi-automatic inserting, and (3) fully automatic inserting. Each of these is now briefly described.

Hand-inserting. Hand-inserting does not differ in principle from hand-gathering. Here, too, the individual signatures are piled in the correct sequence on tables, and here, too, the operator picks them up without the help of mechanical equipment. The signatures are opened at the center during assembly. But as inserted units consist of a comparatively small number of signatures, hand-inserting does not require very long walks. Like all other handwork, hand-inserting is not used on mass-production jobs unless these are so poorly planned that the signatures cannot be inserted by more efficient methods.

Semi-automatic inserting. In semi-automatic inserting the operator acts as a feeder; the assembling itself is done by the machine. All inserting machines used for the assembly of book sections are based on the saddle principle. You know that book sections must be opened at their center for inserting and that they are assembled in this opened position; a saddle-shaped support is very suitable for this purpose.

Semi-automatic inserting machines have several feeding stations and a conveyor chain. The feeding stations are either called "bayonets" or "saddle-bars," the conveyor chain, too, is saddle-shaped. Each signature requires its own feeding station; most machines are therefore equipped with four or more such stations. The operator opens the signature at its center and places it on the saddle-bar of the feeding stations. The conveyor chain runs right under the feeding stations and is equipped with adjustable pins. These pins push the open signatures off their feeding stations and down on the moving chain. The cover is fed just like any other signature at the last station. The assembled material can either be transferred immediately to the binding station or it can be removed from the chain and stacked for later binding. Semi-automatic inserting is much faster than hand-inserting, but it is still much too slow and costly when it comes to mass-production jobs. These must be done on fully automatic equipment.

Fully automatic inserting machines. Assembly of signatures by inserting is used for several national magazines with a circulation of hundreds of thousands of copies. The span of time in which such magazines must be produced is very short, and the cost of production must be kept as low as possible. Both of these demands can be met only by fully automatic equipment. Fully automatic inserting machines are, as a rule, used in combination with equally automatic binding, trimming, and packing machinery.

The main difference between semi-automatic and fully automatic inserting machinery is, functionally speaking, that in fully automatic inserting machines manual feeding is replaced by mechanical feeding. Mechanical feeding of signatures poses many problems. Here we merely remind you that the signatures must be opened at the center for inserting, that only one signature must be fed at a time, and that feeding must be continuous to insure uninterrupted mass production.

Not all signatures are suitable for feeding by

Courtesy Miehle-Goss-Dexter

A four-pocket McCain Saddlematic installation.

fully automatic inserting machinery. Signatures must have either closed heads or a *lip*. (A lip, often also called a *lap*, means that one-half of the signature is slightly larger than the other.) If signatures have neither closed heads nor a lip they cannot be automatically inserted. You can see how important planning is!

Without wanting to discuss the features of specific machines, we can nevertheless note that the feeding mechanism of signature-inserting equipment is based on two things: suction and gripping. Signatures having closed heads can be opened at the center by applying suction to their outside leaves. Assume for a moment that the signatures did not have closed heads but that they consisted of individual unconnected leaves. The result of applying suction to its outside would not be the opening of the whole signature but only the removal of the outside leaves from the rest of the signature. Signatures with closed heads can be opened by applying suction to them.

If signatures are open on three sides, they must have a lip in order to be suitable for automatic opening. A lip is an overlap of approximately three-eighths of an inch on the back half of a signature. In one type of machine "the grippers take hold of this lap, and, assisted by a blast of air, the signature is opened."[33] The opened signature is dropped on a stationary saddle and from there removed as described under the heading of semi-automatic inserting. In another type of equipment the signature is either opened by means of vacuum or by a pin which pierces the lip. This pin is mounted on a rotating drum. It peels the signature open and causes it to drop on the stationary saddle or bayonet.[34]

Fully automatic machines operate at a very high speed; they may have as many as fifteen feeding stations, and even more. It is absolutely impossible for the operator to notice whether a unit has the correct number of signatures or not. Control of proper assembly, at least as to the number of signatures, is, therefore, built into these machines. Caliper devices stop the machines if either no signature or more than one signature is inserted.

Finally, it should be mentioned that automatic signature inserting machines are so constructed as to permit continuous feeding. The signatures are placed in the pockets or hoppers in such a manner that the operating personnel can add additional material without stopping the machine. Fully automatic inserting machines are, as a rule, part

A rack for manual collating. Collating racks are used for relatively short runs of jobs consisting of individual leaves.

of a fully automatic production line that includes wire-stitching, trimming, and possibly other subsidiary operations.

Collating

Collating is the last assembly method on our list. It is widely used in various binding tasks, for manifold, loose-leaf, and mechanical binding in the main. Collating has the object of assembling individual leaves. As individual leaves cannot be inserted into each other, collating assembles the material in sequence. Like gathering, collating can be executed on three technological levels. These are: (1) manual collating, (2) semi-automatic collating, and (3) fully automatic collating.

Manual collating. Manual collating can be done in several ways. One is the same as described under "Manual Gathering." The work is laid out on long tables, each unit in a separate pile. The operator assembles the material by moving from pile to pile, taking a leaf from each as she progresses. The disadvantages of this method are that it is very space-consuming and fatiguing. The operators are usually women, and sitting is preferred by them to walking.

Collating in a standing or sitting position is done with collating racks. These are usually collapsible, lightweight structures having a varying number of sections, from, say, six to eighteen. Each section can hold several hundred leaves of the size of a letterhead. For standing, horizontal collating racks are used; for sitting, vertical ones are preferred. The operator sits at a table between two such racks and works with both hands. After collating, the assembled sheets must be lined up, either in a corner box or in a jogger. Then the collated material is stacked criss-cross for further assembling or for binding.

Semi-automatic collating. Semi-automatic collating can be done with several kinds of equipment including machines that are essentially circular gatherers. As the material to be assembled consists of individual leaves, such gatherers can be equipped with staggered trays that make it possible to place more piles on the rotary table. Otherwise these machines function very much like the circular gatherers which are already described. In other, more efficient machines, a set of leaves is assembled in every cycle and put within reach of the operator by the collator. The operator merely removes the set and stacks it for further processing.

Fully automatic collating. Fully automatic collating is the only method in which the mass-production assembly of individual leaves can be economically and speedily accomplished. Fully automatic collating machines resemble fully automatic gathering machines in several points. Both have individual feeding stations and a conveying mechanism. And in both methods the material is individually removed from the feeding station and deposited in sequence on the conveyor.

But there is one important difference between gathering and collating machines. Gathering machines must feed the signatures from the bottom of the pile in order to be efficient, whereas collating machines can feed the leaves from the top and still be efficient. The reason for this difference is easy to see. Gathering machines feed signatures that have ordinarily either 16 or 32, sometimes as many as 64 pages, whereas collating machines feed individual leaves having not more than 2 pages. A feeding station of the same depth can hold from eight to more than thirty-two times as many units on a collating machine as on a gathering machine. Collating machines may hold as many as 3000 leaves in their pockets or feeding stations; they can be efficiently operated even if they must be stopped

Courtesy Harris Intertype

The delivery end of a Macey flat sheet collator.

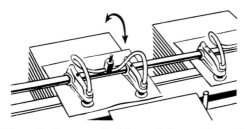

Schematic diagram of a Macey Collator. *The pickup suckers of all stations move back or forth at the same time. Here you see the picked up sheets on their way to the conveyor. The sheets are released above the conveyor and the pickup suckers return to the pile for the next sheets.*

for reloading. Gathering machines must be continuously loaded, and continuous loading requires feeding of signatures from the bottom of the pile.

If we want to describe a collating machine in a very broad way, we can say that it consists of a number of feeding stations, a conveying and a delivery mechanism. The feeding stations may be as few as four and as many as thirty-two, for example. They are arranged parallel with the conveying mechanism. The feeding stations themselves can perhaps be best described as pile feeders such as are commonly used on sheet-fed presses. The leaves are separated from the pile by air blasts and suction; the pickup suckers lift the sheet and bring it over the conveying mechanism. There it is dropped and assembled, one on top of the other. As in all pile feeders, the pile is raised as the sheets are removed from it. The collating machine assembles one complete unit with every cycle. It may deliver the material for easy separation in an offset, or criss-crossed fashion, and it may be directly connected to other processing units such as side stitchers. As all other assembly equipment, fully automatic collators have detector devices which stop the machines automatically in case of faulty assembly.

Section 6: Binding Proper—or Fastening the Assembled Material in Its Final Form

The title of this section is long and cumbersome. The writer hopes that this is due less to his own lack of skill than to the vagueness of the word "binding." You know already that binding has many meanings, and that some of them telescope into each other. Our whole chapter is on binding, and now we come to a group of operations for which the word "binding" is also used, but in a highly restricted sense. Later, when we will study the making of covers and the combining of the cover and the material to be bound, we will meet the word "binding" again; but then it has a third and rather different meaning. Words are conservative; they change very slowly, much less fast than methods of production change in our highly developed technology. This is true for all branches of the graphic arts, including binding. It is also true that the new takes its language very often from the old and thereby broadens and diversifies its meaning. As long as the word "binding" referred only to books, and as long as books were only that, and not also magazines for example, things were easy. Binding, as an activity, meant in a historical past plainly the hand binding of books.

In our times, binding comprises a vast multitude of different processes and products. Now the word can mean many and very different things. And yet it cannot be simply ignored and replaced with a more precise term. Even if we assume that such a term could easily be found (and that means assuming a great deal) the traditional words are part of our language and are dear to many people in our industry. To most of them these words are also rather clear. We must not forget that words are not the only means of communication in everyday life. The conditions under which words are used in concrete situations eliminate much of the vagueness that troubles us when we must use them in writing.

In this section we are concerned with one of the most essential functions of binding, the fastening of the assembled material in its final form. This result can be achieved by a number of procedures. Which of them is selected for a concrete case depends on many considerations. Among these are cost, time, appearance, durability, and exchangeability. Other items which may influence the choice of the binding method are the thickness of the material and the manner in which the material either must be printed or in which it simply happened to be printed. In addition to these very common considerations, specific jobs may have their own peculiar problems.

If we want to discuss the methods in which the material can be fastened we meet again a great variety. Fastening can be achieved by means of thread, wire staples, adhesives, preformed coils of wire or plastic, individual rings of metal or plastic, and a number of mechanical devices, made of both metals and plastics. To make things more complicated, it must be added that binding with thread and binding with wire staples can be done either through the folds of the assembled material or along one of its edges, and furthermore that in some of these methods the cover is fastened together with the rest of the material, whereas in others it is not.

This introduction has given you an idea of the many points that need discussion. For the purpose of systematic presentation, the subject is divided into six major units: (1) center-fold sewing, (2) side sewing, (3) saddle-wire stitching, (4) side-wire stitching, (5) adhesive binding, and (6) mechanical and loose-leaf binding.

Center-Fold Sewing

Center-fold sewing produces strong books that open perfectly flat. The term "center fold" was selected to distinguish this kind of sewing from the second kind of sewing which is known as side sewing. Side sewing can result in stronger books than center-fold sewing, but a side-sewed book does not open completely flat. Center-fold sewing comprises essentially three kinds of sewing: loom sewing, the original method of binding books; modern machine sewing as used for edition binding and known by the name of the inventor of the book sewing machine as Smyth sewing; and, finally, Singer saddle sewing.

In center-fold sewing we can distinguish two different but connected tasks. The first is the fastening of the folded leaves of which a signature consists. The second task of center-fold sewing is the fastening into a single compact unit of the several signatures which are needed for a book. There are, of course, also books consisting of a single section only; for these, the task of fastening sections to sections does not exist. Such books are sewed on different machines known as Singer saddle-sewing machines. Most books consist of several sections

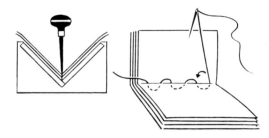

Two steps in center-fold sewing by hand. At the left you see how the folded book is punched with a hand tool prior to sewing. At the right you see how the book is sewn.

and are, therefore, sewed on equipment that is as much designed for fastening several sections to each other as it is for fastening the leaves within each section.

Center-fold sewing can be done on various technological levels. Our presentation of the subject is divided into six points: (1) hand saddle sewing, (2) machine saddle sewing, (3) loom sewing, (4) sewing with the swinging arm sewer, (5) sewing with the stationary saddle book sewer, and (6) fully automatic book sewing.

Hand saddle sewing. Hand saddle sewing is the most primitive technique of book sewing. It is mainly used for library work or small editions and consists in the sewing of a single signature. The book is punched with a hand tool where it is to be stitched and is then sewed with needle and thread through its center fold.

Machine saddle sewing. In machine saddle sewing, books consisting of a single signature are sewed through their center fold by means of a sewing machine. As these machines are manufactured by the Singer Sewing Machine Company, though not exclusively any more, this type of sewing has become known as Singer saddle sewing.

Loom sewing. Loom sewing is the traditional form of hand sewing. It is a method that has completely disappeared in industrial book production, and is now used exclusively for the very best kind of extra binding. The work is done on a *sewing frame* or sewing bench that resembles a weaving loom. The sewing loom "consists of a base, two upright spindles threaded a considerable distance down from the top, on which threads are suspended, two wooden nuts (supporting cross bar), and a cross bar which holds the upper end of cords or bands upon which the book is to be sewn. The base board also has a slot through

which the lower end of cords or bands pass to be fastened underneath the baseboard."[35]

The principle of loom sewing is easy to understand if we keep the two functions of center-fold sewing in mind. The cords and tapes serve for making a compact unit out of each sewed signature. The signatures themselves are sewed together at the same time as they are attached to the cords. For sewing, the cords and tapes are placed in position and the book is produced by sewing signature after signature through its center fold and around the cords at the same time. The position of the cords or tapes is carefully marked on the back of the signatures before sewing. "After the book has been sewed, the ends of the cords should be cut off, about two inches on each side of the book being left. These ends are called *slips*, and they must be frayed out soft enough so that they can be laced flat through the boards."[36]

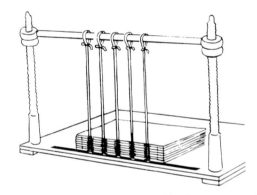

A sewing frame for hand-sewing of books consisting of several or many sections. The cords or tapes connect the different signatures and make a book of them. The leaves of each signature are sewn together and at the same time around the cords.

The foregoing description of loom sewing is very sketchy. Hand sewing has a variety of interesting techniques that are too specialized for our interest.[37] Here we merely mention that sewing on cords or tapes has not completely disappeared from industrial binding and is still done, with special machinery, on heavy blankbooks and on catalogs requiring very rugged bindings.

Sewing with the swinging arm book sewer. The swinging arm book sewing machine is the machine which originally revolutionized book sewing in the eighties of the past century. As this type of machine is still in use, it is here briefly described.

The swinging arm sewer is equipped with four saddle-shaped arms that are arranged like a cross,

Courtesy Smyth Manufacturing Co.

The swinging arm book sewing machine. This machine has four saddle-shaped arms that carry the signature through the sewing cycle. The swinging arm book sewer is hand fed.

90 degrees apart from each other. The operator places a book section that must be open at its center fold on one of these arms. The arm moves away from the operator and carries its signature under a bank of needles. The signature is punched from the bottom and sewed with a curved needle which produces a one-inch stitch. This stitch fulfills two functions: it fastens the leaves of the signature and it also fastens the signature to the preceding one. As many as six such needles operate in a row at the same time. The book section is automatically removed from its saddle arm. At this point the signature rests with its fore edge on a ledge and is also supported by sharp knives which pierce the untrimmed edges of its head and tail. In the meantime the next saddle arm has come into feeding position, the operator has placed the next signature on its saddle, and the cycle continues in the already described manner.

Swinging arm sewers can sew over cords or tapes and are particularly well suited for the sewing of thin papers. The operator must perform several other operations besides feeding on this kind of book sewer. He must paste the first and second, as well as the last and next-to-last signature, and he must cut the thread which connects book with book. If a book is sewed on cords or tapes, these too must be cut by hand.

Sewing with the stationary saddle book sewer. The stationary saddle book sewer is a semi-automatic machine capable of a much higher production and a wider range of work than the swinging arm book sewing machine. It is a most commonly used book sewer in the United States and therefore described in more detail.

The stationary saddle-sewing machine resembles the swinging arm book sewer in several

points, but it also differs from it in many respects. In both machines the sewing of the signature itself, and the sewing of the signatures to each other, take place at the same time. Both machines need as many needles as they make stitches, but the ways in which the stitches are made differ very considerably. Other differences are in the pasting of the first signature to the next and of the penultimate to the last signature, as well as in the cutting of the thread between books. These three operations must be done by hand on the swinging arm machine whereas on the stationary saddle book sewer they are done by the machine itself. Methods of feeding, too, are very different on these machines. The stationary saddle machine permits continuous feeding; in the swinging arm machine, feeding must be timed to the motion of the swinging saddle arms. Other differences are the adjustability of stitch length and range of work. Swinging arm book sewers can sew signatures up to 12 inches long; stationary saddle machines are built in various sizes, the larger models being able to handle signatures up to 18 inches. This feature makes it possible to sew books that were printed and folded two-up, having both books on the same signature.

First we turn to the making of the stitch on the stationary saddle machine as the most characteristic feature of the book sewer. You know from the preceding discussion of book sewing that it must do two things: sew the leaves contained in a single signature and also sew the required number of signatures together. In loom sewing this result is obtained by sewing each signature lengthwise through its center fold and at the same time to the cords, or tapes, which are strung at right angles to the center folds of signatures. Needle and thread traverse the whole distance between the head and foot of signatures, reversing their direction as the work progresses. The cords or tapes to which the signatures are sewed serve as structural members for fastening the sewed book sections into a single compact unit. In many cases five cords or tapes are needed, though the actual number of cords depends on the job in hand.

Mechanical center-fold sewing differs from loom sewing in several points. One is the absence of cords, the other is the number of needles used for sewing. Loom sewing is done with a single needle. But in mechanical sewing many needles are used, one for every stitch, five for example. If this figure reminds you of the cords used in hand looming you are on the right track. In mechanical

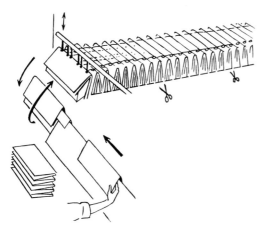

Diagram of Smyth sewing with the stationary saddle sewer. On most models the book is sewn beginning with its last signature. Feeding is continuous; the signature rides on a saddle to the sewing station. There it is punched and then sewn through its center as well as to the following signature. After all signatures are sewn the thread is cut mechanically, thereby separating the sewn book from the next signature.

center-fold sewing, each needle makes only one stitch. But these stitches fasten not only the leaves of the signature through which they are made, they also fasten signature to signature by making, so to speak, their own cords as the work progresses. A center-fold sewed book does not have its continuous sewing along the binding edge but consists of continuous upright columns of individual stitches.

For making the stitch, the signature is placed with its center fold on a saddle which positions it for sewing. The stitch is made by the interaction of two punches, a needle, a hook, a looper, thread, and the signatures involved. The two punches pierce the signature from the bottom, or inside the center fold, to make the passage of the needle and hook possible. The needle puts the thread through one of the holes made by the punch, and the looper carries the thread from the needle within the center fold under the hole punched for the hook. The hook, which has revolved 180 degrees, receives the thread from the looper and pulls it through the signature. Just after it passes out of the signature it also passes through the loop of thread from the previous signature which serves to attach it to the rest of the book. After the hook pulls the new loop through the previous loop, it revolves 180 degrees in order to carry the new loop over to the next signature.

The saddle arm moves away from the next signature. The sewed signature closes and is pushed back just enough to make room for the next one. The saddle with the next signature is placed in sewing position and the cycle begins anew.

Now to the fastening of signatures to each other. You remember that the hook carried the loop through the signature on its way up. "Now when the hook comes down again into the second signature it carries the thread loop along with it, thus binding the two signatures together. When it gets into the second signature it makes a half turn releasing the loop from the signature, turns back again, hooks the thread from the looper below and carries it up through the second signature."[38] If you study our diagrams you can see that things are not nearly as complicated as they may appear. You can also see that there is a difference between the thread connections made by the needle and those made by the looper and hook.

Stationary saddle-sewing machines are capable of a variety of sewing; they can also be used for sewing on various reinforcing material such as tapes and crash. This ability is of great importance for books that must be bound to last such as Bibles, encyclopedias, and blankbooks.

Concerning the detail of operation, it might be mentioned that "the book will be sewed backward, that is, the first section to be sewed on the machine will be the last section of the book after it is sewed."[39] The signature next to the last and

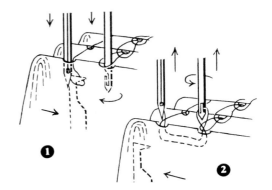

Diagram of Smyth sewing. After the signature is punched from the inside, the needle (1) pulls the thread down through one of the holes, where the looper carries it to the hook. After accepting the thread, the hook pulls the thread up through the hole in the signature (2). Simultaneously the hook turns 90° to face the next signature, and the looper returns to its original position. There it remains until it passes under the needle and hook of the next signature.

A Smyth No. 18 Fully Automatic Book Sewer with gripper feed mechanism.

the last, as well as the first signature and the second signature, are pasted together at the binding edge; the threads are automatically severed between books which can then be separated.

These two operations as well as sewing itself are actuated by stepping on various foot pedals. The operation of these machines "requires a very close coordination of hand and foot. The signatures are fed by hand one at a time; stepping on the operation pedal causes sewing of the first signature; stepping on the paste pedal causes application of a strip of paste; the operator feeds the second signature and presses the pedal for the sewing of the second, third, fourth, and fifth signatures, etc.; he steps on the paste pedal between the last two signatures, and then the final signature is sewed."[40] Finally, the operator depresses the automatic cutoff treadle to sever the thread. Such machines can produce from 70 to 85 signatures per minute, or 12 to 14 books consisting of six signatures each.

Fully automatic center-fold sewing. Fully automatic center-fold sewing machines are very similar to stationary saddle sewers. They are equipped with a feeding station where the gathered books are inserted. These machines perform all operations from here on automatically.

Each signature is opened at the center and dropped on a saddle from where it is automatically brought to the sewing station. Pasting and thread cut-off are automatic too. For feeding, signatures must either have closed heads or lips. The feeding mechanism operates from the bottom of the pile. Signatures are opened by suction or by mechanical grippers. An indexing mechanism directs pasting and cut-off; electrical devices serve for control of correct assembly. Fully automatic sewing machines are used for very long production runs. The operator merely places the signatures in the feeder and removes the sewed books.

Side Sewing

When a book is said to be side sewed, it is implied that this book does not consist of individual sections which are first fastened by themselves and then to each other, but that the whole book is sewed together along the binding edge without any sewing of individual sections at all. It is also possible to bind books by sewing individual book sections along their binding edge, but this method is known as *oversewing*. Side sewing produces extremely strong bindings and is therefore used on books which will experience rather rough handling. Another advantage of side sewing is the fact that inserts can be bound without tipping as they are simply sewed together with the rest of the material. This feature and the strength of side sewing explain why catalogs are often side sewed. But side-sewed books have one drawback which limits their acceptability in the eyes of many people: they do not open completely flat but bulge more or less at the binding edge.

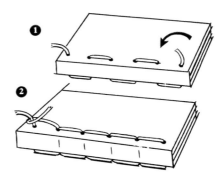

Two stages in up-and-down stitching, a form of side sewing that produces a sturdy binding though not a completely flat opening book.

Like everything else, side sewing can be done in many ways. For our purposes it is sufficient to discuss the most important side-sewing methods. This is done under the following five headings: (1) manual side sewing, (2) single-thread machine side sewing, (3) double-thread machine side sewing, (4) overcast sewing, and (5) oversewing.

Manual side sewing. Manual side sewing is mainly done in repair work. The material is lined up at the binding edge, then it is drilled or stabbed to make passage of the needle easier, and finally sewed. Manual side sewing "is sometimes called the up-and-down kind of sewing. It is a type of sewing which would be produced by a sewing machine if it were run along the back edge of the book."[41] The book is first sewed in one direction, whereby the thread is pulled through the book and alternatingly along the binding edge of its top and bottom; then it is again sewed through the same holes in the opposite direction; the thread is tied at the end of the return sewing. Manual side sewing fastens the whole material without previous sewing of sections. It is obviously much too slow for anything but for very small quantities or for repair work.

Single-thread machine side sewing. Single-thread side-sewing machines—perhaps better known as McCain sewers—are very efficient production machines; they are specifically designed for book binding and are widely used on long-run jobs. Single-thread side-sewing machines produce a result which is very similar to that of manual side sewing; but they do not require double sewing of the book. They, too, fasten the whole book in one operation without previous fastening of individual sections.

The book is sewed along its whole binding edge. Depending on the machine model, books are either automatically fed through a hopper or manually fed and guided during sewing by the operator who sits in front of the machine during his work. The book is drilled from the bottom and from the top for each stitch: first, halfway by the

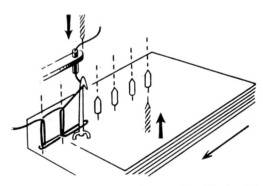

Simplified diagram of McCain sewing. The book is drilled for each stitch. Here you see the needle after it has come up through the hole and catches the thread for the next stitch.

bottom drill, then the other half by the top drill. The thread is fed through a looper tube, pulled through by the needle, cast off the bottom, pulled over to the next hole; the needle comes up through the hole and catches the thread again for the next stitch. This type of sewing machine can handle books up to two inches thick. It sews the endsheets and reinforcements into the rest of the book and glues the bottom row of stitches.

Double-thread machine side sewing. Double-thread side-sewing machines are generally known as Singer side-sewing machines; they are adaptations of the household and garment sewing machines for bookbinding. Such a machine can sew books up to a half inch thick, and is equipped with a punch that makes the hole for the needle. "It sews with two threads, one through the needle and the other from the bobbin below. The stitch is locked on the underside by passing the bobbin thread through a loop made in the needle thread," an arrangement very similar to that in household machines.[42]

Double-thread sewing machines are used more for repair work than for production runs. There, single-thread machines dominate because of their capacity and speed.

Overcast sewing. Overcast sewing, also called *whip stitching*, is a hand-sewing technique. The book is bound by sewing various sections over their binding fold. Each section is sewed diagonally in two directions, and each section is sewed at the same time to the next. The sections may consist of folded or of individual leaves. "The overcast method of sewing is one of the strongest types. The book on which it is used will not open as flat as books on which other types of sewing have been used, but this method is a strong way of fastening sections together."[43] Overcast sewing is used for library work primarily.

Oversewing. Oversewing is a machine-sewing technique used for library binding. Very few books are originally fastened by oversewing; most oversewing is resewing of old or new books. New books are oversewed when they are prebound for library use; old books are oversewed if their binding must be renewed. The oversewing machine is patterned on hand overcasting. It produces a very strong binding. It should be mentioned that an oversewed book does not open as flat as a center-fold sewed book, but more so than a side-sewed one.

Oversewing uses individual leaves; the book is trimmed at the binding fold and divided into

Diagram of oversewing. Books to be oversewn are divided into sections consisting of individual leaves in small numbers. Oversewing fastens the leaves belonging to each section and also each section to the following one. If, for example, a book consists of 10 sections, section 1 is fastened to section 2, section 2 is fastened to section 3, and so on. Oversewing produces books that open more flat than side-sewed ones.

equal sections by means of a simple gauge. The oversewing machine has a series of individual needles which move diagonally through several sections at the same time. Each section is glued on the binding edge before it is inserted into the machine for sewing. Oversewing machines are manually operated production equipment that is specifically designed for the library binding field.

As oversewed books are sewed in small lots of individual leaves, they open more flat than side-sewed books. Oversewing is practically limited to library work; it is not generally used for the binding of other books. Both oversewing and side sewing produce stronger but less flat-opening books than center sewing. One can therefore often see the same schoolbook side sewed for use by the students and center sewed for their teacher.

Saddle Wire Stitching

Saddle wire stitching is the least expensive of all binding methods. Here the material to be bound and the cover are fastened together through the center of the whole book. Saddle wire stitching produces a completely flat-opening book. The cover of saddle-stitched books is usually, but not necessarily, of paper. Sometimes the cover is made of heavier paper, sometimes of the same paper as the rest of the material. Traditionally the assembly technique for saddle-stitched books is inserting. More recently equipment has become available that can flat stitch collated material and then fold it where it was stitched.

The assembly technique for saddle-stitched books is inserting as you already know. You also know that saddle wire stitching is limited in the thickness of the book that it can produce. It is not often considered practical to use this binding method for edition binding, nor even for booklets and magazines which are thicker than half an inch.

(Opinions on the permissible thickness vary. Some people think that a half inch is too thick; others do not.) If the material becomes too thick, the wire staples tend to tear through it. Inserting sections into sections can lead to very bulky assemblies in thicker books.

There is another reason why saddle stitching may not be used for the binding of magazines

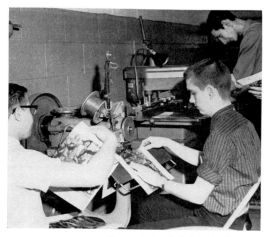

Courtesy New York School of Printing

Two students cooperate in the saddle-wire stitching of a booklet. The student at the right operates the stitcher. This machine makes its own staples from a coil of wire.

which are otherwise suitable for this method. Saddle wire stitching is not practical where inserts must be bound together with signatures. Many trade magazines carry a considerable amount of advertising in this form and therefore do not use saddle wire stitching. Inserts can, of course, be incorporated into saddle-stitched books by tipping; but tipping may be too expensive. Another reason why side stitching is often preferred is aesthetic. Some people prefer the appearance of the *square back*, characteristic for side stitching, to the *razor edge* of saddle-stitched material.

You know from our discussion of inserting, the assembly method for saddle-stitched binding, that the assembly can be done on different levels of mechanization. The same holds true for saddle stitching. Assembly and binding are properly mated only if they are both done at the same technological level. In many cases the assembly equipment and the stitching equipment are part of a production line which may end with stitching, or may include such operations as trimming and banding of magazines.

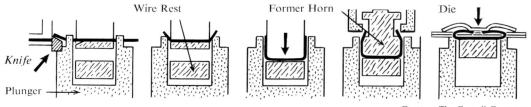

Wire Rest   Former Horn   Die

Knife

Plunger

Several stages in the making of wire staples and wire stitching. The wire for making staples is stored on the equipment in coils. In the first illustration the wire is cut to size; in the second illustration the legs of the staple are formed by bending; the next two illustrations show completion of bending and preparing the ends of the staple for stapling, and the last illustration shows the clinched staple in the wire stitched material.

Wire stitching consists in driving a wire staple through the material to be bound, and in closing the legs of the staple inside the center fold. Closing the legs of staples is called *clinching* and can be done in various ways. Even though it is possible to use preformed staples in some machines, most wire-stitching production machines form their own staples.

Saddle wire stitching can be done on a wide variety of equipment. Here we will discuss the following five kinds: (1) hand-operated wire stitchers, (2) foot-operated wire stitchers, (3) power-operated single-head wire stitchers, (4) multiple-head wire stitchers, and (5) machines combining flat stitching and folding.

Hand-operated wire stitchers. Hand-operated wire stitchers are table-top machines, somewhat larger than a good-sized office stapling machine. They are used more for making samples than for actual production of jobs. Hand-operated wire stitchers can be equipped to do both saddle and flat or side stitching; they use ready-made staples and are operated by depressing a lever arm. The assembled material is placed on the saddle and stapled as often as necessary for the specific job. In most cases three staples are sufficient.

Foot-operated wire stitchers. Foot-operated wire stitchers are floor models. They are used for short runs or for jobs that cannot be handled on more automatic machinery. Like hand-operated wire stitchers they, too, use ready-made staples and they, too, can be equipped for saddle and for flat or side stitching. The operator can use both hands for feeding; he actuates stitching by stepping on a treadle.

Power-operated single-head wire stitchers. Power-operated single-head wire stitchers are used for short-run work. In most cases they

can be adapted for both saddle and flat, or side stitching. These machines are equipped to make their own staples from a roll of wire. The operator feeds the material by hand; the staples are driven into the material as the operator steps on a foot pedal. Saddle wire stitching with power-operated stitchers is faster and cheaper than with foot-operated machines. But for real mass production, this method is still much too slow. Mass production requires multiple-head equipment with automatic operating features.

Multiple-head saddle wire stitchers. Multiple-head wire stitchers are used for production work. In very long runs they are always combined with automatic inserting machines; in medium-length runs they can also be used together with hand-fed inserting, or even be hand fed themselves.

Multiple-head saddle-stitching machines can have two, three, and also many more stitching heads in one production line. They staple the material automatically. If more staples are needed on a job than the number of heads available, the material can be automatically repositioned and stapled again by the equipment. In some machines the stapling mechanism can operate at such a speed that repositioning and stapling again can keep up with the assembly of the material. This method is designated by some as *two-to-one stitching*, by others as *double-stroke stitching*.

Multiple-head stitching machines deliver the stitched book either onto a stacker or to book trimmers. Some machines pass the book through steel rollers where it is pressed before delivery. Another feature is staggered stitching which makes the trimming of the stitched material easier. Fully automatic multiple-head stitching can produce up to approximately 12,000 units per hour. This number may be equivalent to two or

The SHERIDAN
Side Stitcher

In Sheridan side wire stitchers, gathered signatures are transported on their folds or on their back by means of a pin chain. As the signatures enter the stitcher, a reciprocating assembly clamps the signatures, accelerates the signatures ahead of the carrier pin, cuts off the wire, forms it to shape and stitches the book. Then the clamp releases and the carrier pin again contacts the book to remove it from the stitcher.

Depending upon the type of paper, thickness of book, number of staples required, operating speed, and length of book, a number of variations can be offered. Some stitchers running in pairs stitch two books simultaneously. Other pairs stitch the same book twice, offsetting the staples, in order to reduce staple centers.

Some stitchers have fixed heads, while other models have adjustable heads to locate staples as required. Each of these stitcher heads is fed from individual wire spools or reels, which are supplied in a wide variety of wire quality, hardness, etc., to meet specific conditions. Sizes range from 17″ maximum length to 7″ minimum. Thickness is limited by speed, type of stitcher, and number of staples per book, but some work up to 1⅛″ can be stapled.

Special variations include "nailing" stitchers, wherein heavy, thick books are stapled from both sides. Neither staple penetrates the entire book and no clinch is required.

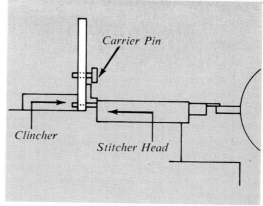

1 *Signature is clamped and accelerated to stapling position leaving its carrier pin behind.*

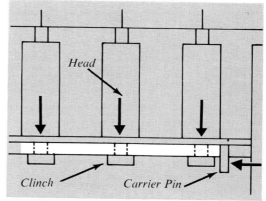

2 *Stitcher assembly cuts off the wire, forms it to shape, drives it through the book, and clinches the staples on the backside of the book.*

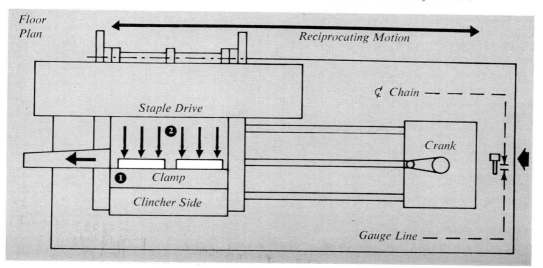

The SHERIDAN PACESETTER-*Inserter-Stitcher-Trimmer*

This "combination", as it is called, consists of an inserter, master caliper, saddle stitcher and trimmer.

Inserter

Signatures are placed in feed hoppers, fold down, and fed from the bottom at the fold. The open ends of the signature are gripped by a small transfer drum at the same time the fold edge is released at the signature stop. The transfer drum brings the open end of the signature in contact with a second drum called the opener. At this point, either mechanical grippers or vacuum is used to open the signatures before release to the saddle chain.

The stations themselves are independent units mounted on a common lower frame; they can be individually timed to take advantage of the shortest possible chain pin centers. The chain pins are adjustable.

Master Caliper

From the inserter, the books are carried through the caliper station, where they are measured for missing or extra signatures (often called doubles). The caliper is a simple memory device to set up a signal for later rejection of these imperfect books; such books bypass the stitching and trimming operations.

Saddle Stitcher

Books leave the saddle chain as they enter the stitcher, are transported by means of a reciprocating multiple gripper bar to the fixed stitcher heads, where they are stitched along the fold. The gripper bar again transports the book, bringing it to the delivery. At this point the imperfect books are rejected to a shelf, while good books are delivered to the trimmer. Books are removed from the stitcher saddle by means of a tucker blade and pinch wheels.

Trimmer

Books, upon arrival at the trimmer infeed, pass through squeeze rollers to remove trapped air and to tighten the folds. Alternate books then traverse a collector drum which serves to stack books in piles of two. From here they are carried to the trimmer, fold first, by continuously running carrier chains. When entering the first cut position (front knife), pushers overtake the carrier pins to register the books against book stops. Here the trim edge is clamped and the knife makes its cut. After the clamp releases, an intermittent chain system transports the books to the head and tail knife position, where the trim cycle is repeated. Books can be split and retrimmed in what is called a 4th and 5th knife attachment. Two-on books are trimmed and cut in half in this manner.

Trim sizes range from 19½ x 11¼" down to 7 x 4¼", with a maximum total thickness of ¾".

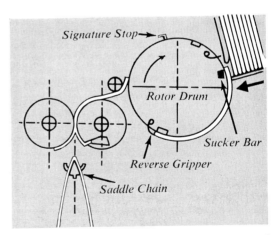

❶   *Sucker bar, air and reverse grippers remove and open signature, and release it to the saddle chain.*

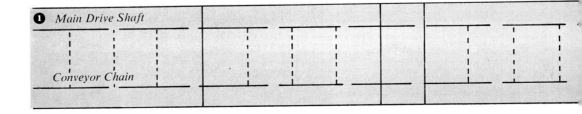

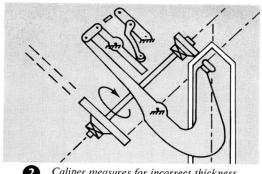

2 *Caliper measures for incorrect thickness.*

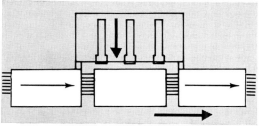

3 *Books enter reciprocating gripper bar.*

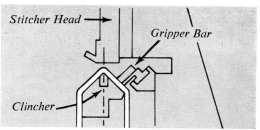

Stitcher Head

Gripper Bar

Clincher

3 *Books are stitched along the folds and transported to the delivery.*

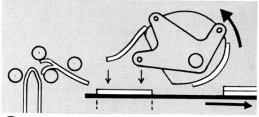

4 *At trimmer infeed alternate books go up the collector drum, which stacks them in piles of two.*

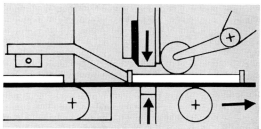

5 *For the first cut pushers overtake carrier pins, register books against stops.*

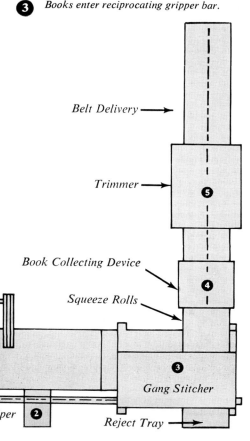

Belt Delivery

Trimmer

Book Collecting Device

Squeeze Rolls

Gang Stitcher

Reject Tray

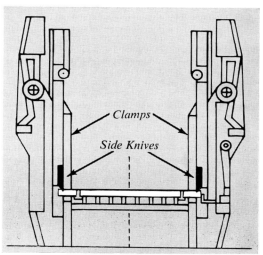

Clamps

Side Knives

6 *The trim cycle is repeated at head and tail knife positions.*

The SHERIDAN
Hi-Speed Stitcher

With the introduction of high speed (200 books per minute) gathering and covering machines, side-stitchers of a matching capacity were needed. The Sheridan Hi-Speed Stitcher can handle a full range of book sizes, up to $\frac{9}{16}''$ thick, utilizing standard removable stitcher heads.

Gathered signatures are carried on their backs in the conventional manner to the stitcher. Here they are transferred to the reciprocating stitcher clamp which carries the signatures to the stitching position. Books are stationary during stitching.

While the book is negotiating the stitcher, a delay is introduced into the carrier chain. This delay allows sufficient time to stitch the book before the carrier chain again contacts the book to remove it from the stitcher.

Book sizes are 16″ maximum length and 7″ minimum, with a maximum thickness of $\frac{9}{16}''$.

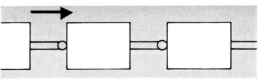

❶ *A pin chain carries signatures on their backs to the stitcher.*

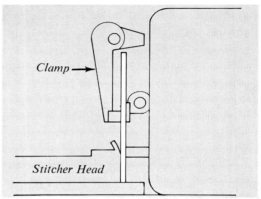

❷ *Reciprocating stitcher clamp keeps signature stationary and the chain is delayed while books are being stitched.*

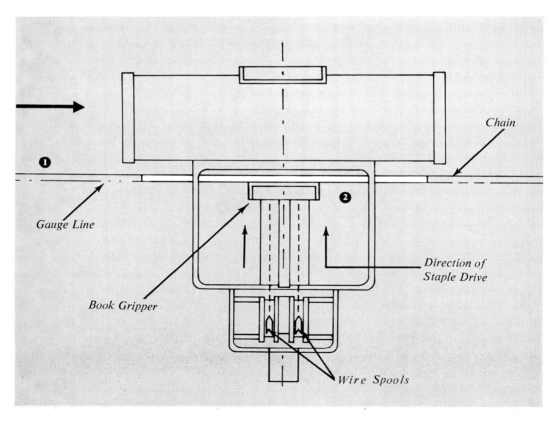

three times as many finished magazines if they are bound two- or three-up.

Machines combining flat stitching and folding. These recent additions to binding techniques make it possible to produce lightweight booklets in line with folding or with collating. One model is designed for collated sheets needing but a single fold, a second model has the purpose of converting single signatures into booklets by stitching. These are usually self-covered.

Both machines are based on the same design principle. They first stitch an assembly of sheets, either a folded signature or a number of collated papers, and then make a buckle fold where the material was stitched. The material is thereby usually folded in half. Each model is movable; one can be connected with both a collating machine or a folder. The other model is for use with a folder only. As it is not mechanically connected to the folding machine but merely positioned next to it, this model can be repositioned as production needs require. Head and foot of the stitched booklet can be trimmed with slitters.

Side Wire Stitching

Side wire stitching resembles saddle wire stitching because both methods use metal staples for fastening. But side wire stitching differs from saddle wiring in many points. For one, side-wired books do not open nearly as flat as saddle-stitched ones. Side stitching can be used for binding of much thicker assemblies than saddle stitching and is therefore suitable for the binding of school and college workbooks and similar products. Individual leaves, such as advertising inserts, can be very effectively bound together with regular signatures in side stitching. For this reason many trade magazines prefer it to saddle wiring.

The assembly method for side stitching is gathering, as already explained. Whereas the cover is usually bound together with the book in saddle stitching, side-stitched books can be covered in many different ways. In some kinds of work, in reports of governmental committees, for example, the first signature is self-covered and the material is stitched without a separate cover. Self-covered books are least expensive but also least attractive and least durable; side-wired books can, of course, be covered attractively.

Trade magazines are usually covered with paper covers which are attached to the body of the magazine after it was side wired. How this is done will be explained in Section 9: "Assembling Book and Cover." Here we are concerned with fastening only. But before we turn to the various fastening techniques it must be added that side-wired books are considered exceptionally sturdy and rugged. Some people are willing to overlook the fact that side-wired books do not open flat, others object very strongly to this kind of binding, particularly if it is used on study books or books destined for serious and sustained reading.

In side wire stitching the staples are driven through the book parallel to its binding edge, or backbone, approximately one-quarter of an inch inside. The whole assembly is bound in one operation, without previous fastening of signatures. The number of staples depends on the nature of the job, two or three are sufficient in most cases. Staples can be made from flat or from round wire.

Like saddle stitching, side wiring can be done on various levels of mechanization. Here, too, the stitching operation must be suited to several other phases of production. In the discussion of saddle stitching it is mentioned that many kinds of saddle-stitching machines can also be used for flat or side stitching, as their saddle can be made into a flat table. The feeding of the material and the operation of the stitchers are the same in both cases. For this reason they are not further described in this unit. Here we describe merely one type of side wire stitching frequently used in fully automatic magazine and catalog binding.

Automatic side wire stitching. In automatic installations the stitching mechanism is directly connected with a fully automatic gathering machine. Most automatic side wire stitching equipment is built along similar lines but various machines differ, of course, in their detail of construction and operation. Our description covers two different kinds of machines. In both types the book must be lined up for stitching. In one machine the book lies flat on the conveying mechanism during gathering. For stitching it must change its position. Now it is stood up on its back with its signature folds down. Next it is lined up (or jogged, as this operation is called by the trade), at its head and back for stitching.

After stitching, the book is put through squeeze rollers to reduce its bulk and to flatten the stitches. From there it may be automatically covered, trimmed, and even banded. A fully automatic production line may produce between 6,000 and 10,000 finished units per hour. If the books are printed two up, the final number of books can be correspondingly higher.

In a second type of machine, gathering is done in a tray which is 60 degrees inclined. Pusher fingers move the gathered material (often called simply the "gather") forward and position it for stitching. Stitching itself takes place at the same angle as gathering which obviates the need for repositioning of the gather prior to stitching.

Adhesive Binding

In adhesive binding the material is fastened by application of an adhesive. Adhesive binding, also known as "perfect" binding, is in recent times increasingly used in the binding industry because it offers many advantages in comparison with other kinds of binding. Adhesive binding produces flat-opening books of any desired thickness. Adhesive-bound books can be either paper-covered or cased-in. But the greatest attraction of adhesive binding is the fact that it lends itself to uninterrupted mass production of books.[44]

Like every other process, adhesive binding has its limitations. It is doubted by some that adhesive binding can produce a book equal in durability to a sewed one; valuable books and works of reference are therefore not adhesive bound at this time. In the edition-binding field, adhesive binding is mainly used for paper-covered or cased-in books (written for entertainment rather than for study) that must be produced at a very low price and in enormous quantities. In the trade magazine field, adhesive binding is handicapped by the fact that it becomes impractical if a great variety of papers must be used in one and the same job. Both of these limitations affect trade magazines in particular because these bring many inserts which are produced by their advertisers on a variety of coated and uncoated papers. Magazines consisting of coated papers are also successfully processed in some of the many variations that exist in adhesive binding. There are no generally valid rules; every case must be decided for itself.

The field of adhesive binding is in flux. Many new techniques are tried out; much new equipment—some of it imported from Europe—has been introduced in the last few years. Before we enter into a description of some of these methods and machines, a short exposition of the basic steps taken in adhesive binding is in order.

Outline of adhesive binding. In adhesive binding, the folding edge of signatures is trimmed off and the whole material thereby converted into individual leaves. If you want to do so, you might describe adhesive binding as a process of fastening loose leaves into a bound book. In some variations of adhesive binding the leaves are roughed in order to increase their surface for gluing, as a smooth cut presents a much smaller binding surface than a roughed one. Another method of preparing the back of the book for the application of the adhesive employs high-speed rotary cutters which produce a pattern that changes the texture of the spine and amounts to a substantial increase in the binding surface of the book. After these operations one or two films of adhesive are applied to the back of the book; reinforcing materials such as *crash*—a coarsely woven fabric—may or may not be used. In some methods of adhesive binding the material is bound together with the cover, in others the cover is separately attached.

These are the broad outlines of adhesive binding. Now we can enter into a somewhat detailed presentation of various techniques in which adhesive binding is executed. These can be divided into four: (1) padding, (2) manual adhesive binding, (3) semi-automatic adhesive binding, and (4) fully automatic adhesive binding.

Padding. Padding is the simplest form of adhesive binding. The pads of paper are stacked on a work bench and glued with hot or cold glue which is applied by brush to their backs. If it is desired to reinforce the binding, crash can be used for this purpose. After the glue is dry, the pile of pads is sliced into individual units.

Manual adhesive binding. Padding is one way of manual adhesive binding, but some binders prefer a different technique for the adhesive binding of books. This technique consists in fanning the material to be bound and applying the adhesive to it in this position. Often the material is fanned and glued in both directions. The adhesive is thereby applied in a narrow strip on every side of every leaf as well as on the binding edge.

Manual adhesive binding can be done with a variety of jigs or fixtures; some are bought from manufacturers, others may be made for the specific problems in a binding shop. Essentially these jigs are clamping mechanisms; some of them have provisions for mechanical fanning. The first step in manual adhesive binding consists in trimming the back of the book and converting the material into loose leaves. This is usually done on a guillotine cutter.

For adhesive binding, the book must be perfectly aligned. Books to be bound with straight backs are jogged straight at their binding edge and at head or tail. Then they are clamped from head

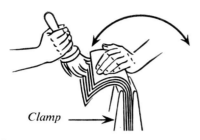

Manual adhesive binding. Small quantities are sometimes adhesive bound by clamping the material and applying adhesive to the fanned out binding edges. This technique is found useful in library binding.

Clamp

to tail near the front edge in such a manner that they can easily be fanned. Now the adhesive is applied to the fanned binding edge with a brush by the operator; first he fans the book in one direction by bending its edge over the clamp with one hand, then he brushes the adhesive on; and repeats the same in the other direction.

Books that must be bound with round backs are either jogged in a concave form, clamped in this position and then fanned and glued like straight-back books, or they are glued with straight backs and later rounded. If the book will be paper-covered, the cover can be attached immediately after gluing; crash or super can also be put on for books that will be later cased-in when the adhesive is still wet.

Semi-automatic adhesive binding. The equipment used for semi-automatic adhesive binding applies the adhesive automatically and fans the material mechanically. The operator feeds the trimmed material and actuates the equipment for its performance; he also removes the bound book.

Fully automatic adhesive binding. Fully automatic adhesive binding can be done on a variety of equipment differing in several points, most of all in its speed and production capacity. Such equipment automatically jogs the material, cuts the binding edges, roughens it, applies one or more coats of adhesive, puts crash on where desired, and also attaches paper covers which it forms at the same time. European equipment for adhesive binding is designed for production of smaller runs than domestic machinery.

Fully automatic adhesive-binding equipment can be used for the production of paper-covered or casebound books. Paper covers are attached as part of the binding operation; for case binding additional equipment is required.

Several plants use adhesive binding in the production of hardbound books. There, adhesive binding is often part of a complete manufacturing line from the folded signature to the completely bound book. Such production lines are used for books manufactured in quantities of hundreds of thousands for distribution by national book clubs. As an example for huge quantity production we mention the selections of the Readers' Digest book club, where "the books are composed of press-folded signatures, perfect bound, rounded and backed and cased-in, in a virtually continuous operation."[45]

Fully automatic adhesive binding is not only suitable for long runs but also for relatively short ones. Runs as small as 1000 copies are economically produced in this country on European slow-speed adhesive-binding machinery.[46] It is evident that adhesive binding will play a very important role in the future of the binding industry.

Mechanical and Loose-leaf Binding

Mechanical and loose-leaf binding are here discussed together because they have many similarities and use the same equipment for some operations. But it should not be forgotten that mechanical binding fastens the material to be bound in an *unchangeable* form, whereas loose-leaf binding produces bindings that make it possible to *exchange* the fastened material. For both purposes it is necessary to punch holes into the leaves to be bound, and both purposes must have independent binding devices that supply the spine of the book and permit the fastening of the punched material.

The first striking difference between loose-leaf and mechanical binding on the one hand, and all other binding methods on the other hand, is that holes are punched into the material to be bound. This point is easy to remember; the second distinguishing point, namely, the prefabricated spine, is equally characteristic, but its importance is not so obvious. It will become clear after we go a little deeper into the mechanics of binding.

Few binding terms are as apt as the words "spine" and "backbone." The spine or backbone of a book has a function very similar to the spine in the human body. It, too, is needed to keep a body, that of the book, straight and upright. Up to now we have not discussed this function of binding because we concentrated on fastening. But it must be understood that the strengthening and straightening of the book back is an essential of good binding. Different binding methods ob-

The SHERIDAN
Perfect Binder

This unit can be described as a continuous, running system of book clamps, traveling in an oval path, transporting books, backbone down, over the various processing stations.

Gathered signatures enter the clamp system by means of an inclined pin conveyor, depositing them on a level shelf, to assure register. At this point, the clamp closes, starting the books through the binding sequence.

The first station is a rotary cutoff knife to cut off the signature folds, exposing the page ends. Next, we come to the roughers, which serve a twofold purpose. The first is to square up the cutoff book. The second is used to achieve the proper texture at the backbone or to slit or notch the backbone, as required. A rotary brush is used to remove the paper chips and dust from the exposed fibres of the prepared backbone before gluing.

Adhesive pots are furnished to serve many purposes, depending upon the nature and size of the book and paper. Cold emulsion adhesive can be applied with a simple wheel, dipping in a shallow reservoir. Animal glues, hot melts and combination systems (hot and cold adhesives) require heated reservoirs, with accurate temperature and film control and, in some cases, in-process drying. Crash feeders are available to apply a crash or mull to the book back. Paper can also be applied in this manner.

Most binders are equipped with a cover feeder for feeding of paper covers, cover conveyors and appliers to apply and register a cover to the back of a book. Before opening the clamp and releasing the book at the delivery, bottom and side forming bars contact the book, under pressure, to give the book and cover rigidity and squareness. This unit is called a *cover breaker*. From here books are delivered to any number of subsequent automatic and semi-automatic operations, such as trimming, splitting, wrapping, counting, mailing, spraying, rounding and backing, etc.

Book sizes range from 7 x 4½″ minimum to 16 x 12″ maximum or 17½ x 7″ maximum, ¼″ to 2¾″ thickness. Top operating speed is approximately 200 books per minute. This machine and variations of it can be used for high speed covering.

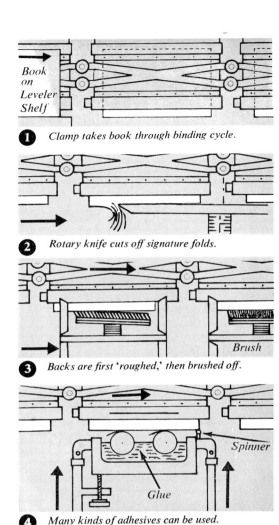

Book on Leveler Shelf

1 *Clamp takes book through binding cycle.*

2 *Rotary knife cuts off signature folds.*

Brush

3 *Backs are first 'roughed,' then brushed off.*

Spinner

Glue

4 *Many kinds of adhesives can be used.*

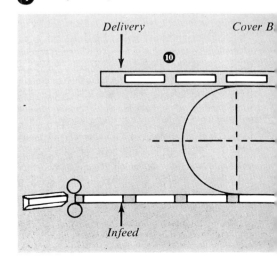

Delivery   *Cover B.*

10

Infeed

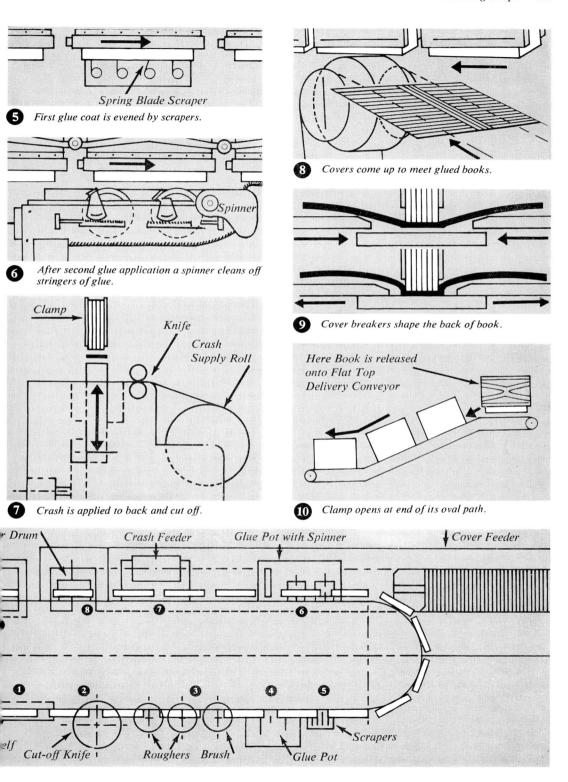

5 First glue coat is evened by scrapers.

Spring Blade Scraper

6 After second glue application a spinner cleans off stringers of glue.

Spinner

7 Crash is applied to back and cut off.

Clamp

Knife

Crash Supply Roll

8 Covers come up to meet glued books.

9 Cover breakers shape the back of book.

10 Clamp opens at end of its oval path.

Here Book is released onto Flat Top Delivery Conveyor

Drum *Crash Feeder* *Glue Pot with Spinner* *Cover Feeder*

elf *Cut-off Knife* *Roughers* *Brush* *Glue Pot* *Scrapers*

tain this effect in different ways. The subject is discussed at greater length, in Section 9: "Assembling Book and Cover." In mechanical and loose-leaf binding, the binding device may be either a completely preformed spine, or the spine may be formed by combining various binding

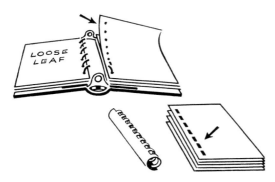

In loose-leaf binding the bound material can be removed or added to as required. The binding device is usually of metal. In mechanical binding the assembly of the bound material is final; the binding device is either plastic or metal wire.

elements with the material to be bound and with the cover.

The difference between binding devices for loose-leaf binding and those for mechanical binding is the following. Loose-leaf devices provide for a more or less simple and fast addition and removal of the material after it was bound, whereas mechanical binding devices offer no such provisions. Mechanical binding is used for material which is not intended for preservation; loose-leaf binding is widely used for accounting which requires preservation for several years.

Our presentation of mechanical and loose-leaf binding is divided into three units: (1) making of holes, (2) binding devices, (3) combining of the material to be bound with its binding device. In this section we are concerned only with the fastening of the material or binding in its narrower sense; covers and cover-making are not discussed at this point but in Section 8. Some of the binding devices to be discussed in the following are so strongly related to the covers with which they are used that repeated reference to covers and cover-making becomes inevitable.

The making of holes for binding. To be suitable for mechanical and loose-leaf binding, the material must be provided with holes. Almost all binding devices require that these holes are made

in a specific manner. There are two kinds of holes, slotted holes and closed holes. Slotted holes make it possible to exchange the material in certain bindings without necessitating the removal of the cover. They are needed in some kinds of loose-leaf binding which are mainly used for accounting and for large catalogs. Closed holes are used in the majority of mechanical bindings as well as in many kinds of loose-leaf binding.

Holes can be made either by drilling or by punching. Closed and slotted round holes are often drilled. All square and oblong holes must of course be punched. Our discussion of the subject is divided into the following four points: (1) drilling of holes, (2) hand- and foot-powered punching machines, and (3) power-operated punch presses.

Drilling of holes. For this purpose specially designed machinery is available. Paper-drilling machines are similar to other drill presses; paper drills, however, are hollow and designed to enable the waste to escape. Lifts of sheets, varying in thickness from 1 to 2 inches, are put on a table and drilled from above. Paper drilling machines may have two or more drill heads as well as attachments for slotting, slitting, round cornering, and tab cutting. Slotted or slitted holes can be made either in one or in several steps.

Hand- and foot-powered punching machines. The three-hole office punch is the most widely used hand-operated loose-leaf punch. Similar punches producing two, three, or four oblong holes are available for individual mechanical binding with plastic rings. These punches are not production equipment but serve mainly for the making of dummies by printers and binders.

In the binding business, hand- or foot-operated punching machines are needed not only for sample work but also for the production of short-run jobs. These machines permit exchange of dies, but they are limited as to size of sheets, height of individual lifts, and total output. Hand-operated punching machines are table models; foot-operated ones come as floor models.

Power-operated punch presses. All production work is done on power presses. The material is placed on the bed of the press and there positioned to a back gauge and a side gauge. The back gauge is set to obtain the proper distance of the holes from the binding edge of the paper, the side gauge to insure correct lengthwise placement. The shape of holes as well as their distance from each other is determined by the punching dies and their setting. The height of the lift to be punched depends on the job and the capacity of the press.

Binding devices for loose-leaf and mechanical binding. The number of existing binding devices is much too vast and their purposes much too specialized for a detailed discussion in this manual. As we are concerned only with a general review of the subject, we divide our discussion of binding devices into the following five groups: (1) binding coils, (2) preformed backbones for mechanical binding, (3) rings for mechanical binding, (4) preformed backbones for loose-leaf binding, and (5) posts for loose-leaf binding.

Binding coils. Binding coils are neither preformed backbones, nor are they individual elements used in multiples for binding the material. Small users of spiral binding—as binding with coils is generally called—purchase the material in spiral form. Larger users have equipment that makes the coils by forcing the wire through a coiling die; plastic wire is made by extruding.

Preformed backbones for mechanical binding. Many binding devices consist of a combination of backbone and rings. The material out of which these devices are made is either metal or plastic. Some of them need crimping, that is, mechanical

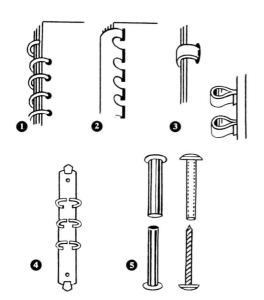

Some binding devices: Illustration (1) *shows a metal or plastic wire binding,* (2) *a plastic comb binding, and* (3) *Cercla, a binding consisting of connected plastic rings. These three are used in mechanical binding. Illustration* (4) *shows a metal spine for one kind of three ring binder and* (5) *two different kinds of screw posts. These three are used in loose-leaf binding.*

closing, after the leaves are inserted, others snap back into final position or are closed by bending or turning. It is also possible to combine loose-leaf features with mechanical binding devices.

Rings for mechanical binding. It is possible to produce mechanical bindings by a variety of rings. Most of them are plastic; some are made of round material that is coiled, others are bands of varying width. They are used in multiples from two or three up, depending on the job in hand. Individual rings save material but they must be closed manually and are not practical on production jobs.

Preformed backbones for loose-leaf binding. Loose-leaf binding must be fit for permanent wear and is therefore of much heavier construction than mechanical binding. The binding devices for loose-leaf binding are as a rule made of metal; they are called by the trade *the hardware.* This hardware is incorporated into the cover during cover-making. Hardware for loose-leaf accounting or catalog binding is very sturdy and well built. All hardware must have provisions for exchanging the bound material. In some cases this result is obtained by metal rings which open at the center, in other cases thongs are used, either staggered or opening at the center. Various kinds of loose-leaf hardware differ in their construction, the number of elements that are attached to the backbone, the manner of opening and closing. The hardware is not made by the average bindery but purchased from manufacturers specializing in these items.

Posts for loose-leaf binding. Post binders are very widely used for loose-leaf binding in the accounting field. "Originally designed to serve as a transfer book for the ledger bindery, the post binder has become an even more popular current binder than the ledger binder."[47] Screw posts are made either as solid or as sectional posts. Solid posts are used on storage binders, sectional posts are preferred for current account books. As the volume of the book increases, half inch or inch sections are added to the posts.

The usual account book has two posts. They may be self-locking or locked by caps or knurled thumb screws. In the so-called flexible or chain post binder the book is compressed by a link mechanism which is operated by a key or a crank. It is also possible to construct post binders in such a way that the content of the binder cannot be tampered with by unauthorized people. A lock that must be opened with its own key is provided for this purpose in the back of the binder. Finally, it should be mentioned that post binders use punched and slotted sheets. The slot permits exchange without removal of the binding, as already mentioned.

Combining of the binding device and the material to be bound. Mechanical binding and loose-leaf binding both combine the material with the binding device by inserting. But in mechanical binding the device is inserted into the material, whereas in loose-leaf binding the leaves are inserted into the binder. This kind of inserting is done by hand and does not need further discussion.

The inserting of the binding device into the material is an essential step in mechanical binding. We distinguish three kinds of inserting: (1) inserting of binding coils, (2) inserting of preformed backbone binding devices, and (3) inserting of individual rings.

Inserting of binding coils. It is possible to insert a binding coil by hand into the punched material without any mechanical aid. But hand inserting is much too slow for production work. The following "two methods are used: (1) The coiled wire is inserted by hand into the book for a distance of two or three inches. Then the book is held against a rapidly revolving rubber roller and the balance of the wire is thereby automatically pulled through. Thereafter the excess wire is trimmed off and the ends of the coil are turned inward. (2) The operator starts a long length of wire into the inserting machine, places a punched book with its covers into position in the machine, and the machine automatically threads the wire and trims it and turns in the ends without waste. The machine is automatic and merely guided by the operator."[48]

Inserting of preformed backbone binding devices. Some of these devices are hand inserted, others can be mechanically inserted by placing both the book and the binding device in a machine which spreads the binding rings apart and inserts them into the punched assembly.

Inserting of individual rings. These are manually inserted into the punched material. In some cases they also require hooking together or a closing of another kind.

Section 7:   Preparing the Book for Covering

This section discusses the preparatory steps required in the manufacturing of casebound books prior to combining the book with its cover. Other types of books such as side- or saddle-stitched ones, not to speak of books that are mechanically or loose-leaf bound, do not need particular preparatory steps. But casebound books are subjected to a number of operations before they are fit for covering. In the binding industry this group of operations is traditionally known as *forwarding.* Unfortunately this term is intrinsically meaningless (though, of course, not to those who are used to it) as every production process can be designated as forwarding the material toward its final shape, if one so desires. Binding is full of confusing terms; we will therefore not use the word "forwarding" in our description of industrial binding methods, but reserve it for the field of extra binding which continues the traditions of fine handbinding.

Here we discuss the processing of the book from the point when it leaves the sewing machines or wire stitchers to the point when it is ready for combining with its covers. This phase of book manufacturing has several objects and divisions. When a Smyth-sewed book leaves the sewing machines it is a rather weak assembly of folded signatures, held together by thread and by two strips of glue with which the two first and the two last signatures are pasted together. The signature folds at the head contribute to its strength, but we know that these must be cut away before long.

Sewing has another consequence of its own which must also be considered. Thin as the sewing thread is, it nevertheless swells the back of the book, which thereby becomes uneven in thickness and therewith not suitable for further processing in certain kinds of equipment. The next steps after sewing deal with these conditions. First the book is nipped or smashed and thereby brought to uniform thickness, then the back of the book is glued or coated with an adhesive, and therewith reinforced. Trimming, too, is part of these operations; it can be done before gluing or after gluing of the backs, depending on procedures adopted in a plant. The books "usually are glued before they are trimmed when trouble would be experienced in jogging them if they were trimmed first. If they are glued first, the signatures cannot slip when they are trimmed."[49]

After trimming, the edges of the book may be treated in various ways for functional improve-

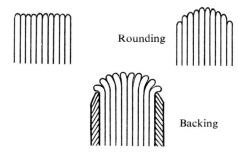

Rounding

Backing

To be hardbound, most books must be prepared for binding or casing-in by rounding and backing. You see the book before rounding, after rounding and during backing. Rounding protects the fore edge of the book, backing provides the book joints.

ment or for embellishment. These treatments can consist in staining, gilding, speckling, marbling, and even fore-edge painting. Fore-edge painting, speckling, and marbling are very rarely done, partly because they are too expensive, partly because these techniques have lost their aesthetic attractiveness. But staining and gilding are still widely used, staining on trade books, gilding on Bibles primarily. It should be added that the sequence of gluing, trimming, and edge treating is not necessarily the same as here mentioned; the order of operations varies in different plants.

Next, the book must be structurally prepared for proper functioning and durability. The first of these operations is *rounding*. The purpose of rounding is to make sure that the fore edge of the book will remain within its cover. In books that are not properly rounded the fore edge is pushed out and it may in time protrude over the edges of the cover and therewith lose the protection afforded by the cover to the book. A book with pushed-out fore edge is known in the trade as *caved-in*. The fore edges of caved-in books, particularly if they are heavy tomes, can be easily mutilated. Rounding the back prevents this defect by drawing the book inward in a neat arc. With the exception of thinner books, which may be square-backed, center-sewed books that will be covered by cases are rounded. Adhesive-bound books that are to be covered by cases are also rounded, but not so side-sewed books. Side-sewed books do not need rounding as a protective measure against the pushing out of their fore edge; if side-sewed books are rounded, rounding makes them look like "regular" books.

After rounding, the book is *backed*, as the binder says. This designation is much less de-

scriptive and explanatory than rounding. The book has, of course, already a back. Backing does not give the book a new back but provides the *joints* of the back, insures the permanency of the rounded back, and gives the book flexibility.

You can best appreciate the structural changes produced by rounding and backing if you look at our illustration where you see cross sections of a book in three successive stages. The first drawing shows a book after gluing yet before rounding. Next to it you see the rounded book, and the backed book is last. We can compare the last picture with a mushroom. The final back of the book is the top of the mushroom; during backing this top is flattened by spreading it over the body of the book with the result that it protrudes on both sides over it. Backing produces the *joints* of the book. The joints provide the cover boards with the room needed for moving. But backing does not only provide joints of the book, it also creases the leaves at their binding edge, though to a varying degree. The outermost leaves are bent, approximately to a 90-degree angle; this angle decreases toward the center to practically nothing.

The next preparatory step is *lining up*. It consists in attaching one or more strips of fabric, known as *crash*—called *mull* in Canada—and *super*, as well as a strip of strong paper to the back of the book. These strips of crash, super, and paper project at varying staggered widths beyond the back and are attached to the cover when book and cover are combined.

If a book is to be decorated with headbands these are supplied as part of lining up. In case-bound books, headbands serve merely for decoration, but in handbound books where they originated, they served a useful purpose because they protected the edge of the leather binding.

As you see, a book passes through many steps

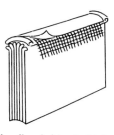

A lined-up and headbanded book. Lining up consists in attaching crash, super, and paper to the book; head banding provides decorations at the head and foot of the spine.

between sewing and combining with its cover These are divided by us into four units: (1) making the book uniform, (2) trimming, (3) edge treatments, and (4) shaping the backbone of the book.

Making the Book Uniform

Making the book uniform requires several operations which are here divided into five: (1) hand pressing, (2) nipping, (3) smashing, (4) manual back gluing, and (5) mechanical back gluing.

Hand pressing. Hand pressing can be done in several ways; one is by beating the book with a hammer on a stone, heavy iron plate, or table, embedded in sand; but this method is much less used than pressing the book in so-called standing presses. These are heavy screw presses where the books are left under pressure for some time. Hand pressing is not used in large-scale production but is common in library and extra binding.

Nipping. Nipping is done on machines known as *nippers*. Nippers are automatic presses with two jaws between which the binding edge of the book is forcibly reduced in its thickness. The jaws open and close automatically; the operator inserts the books with their binding edges down and removes them immediately after the jaws have closed and opened again. Books printed on hard papers are usually nipped, whereas those printed on soft, bulky papers are smashed.

Smashing. Smashing is done in vertical presses, known as *smashers*. Smashers apply pressures up to 250 tons on the material to be pressed. Smashers are often provided with automatic conveyor belts. The books are piled at one end of the press on the belt in equal numbers in several piles next to each other and automatically conveyed under the smasher head. There they are smashed either once or twice, as desired, and then moved out of the press by the same conveyor. The smasher remains for some time in its compressed position, or has a dwell during pressing, to use the technical term. At the other end of the press the smashed books are manually removed. Smashing is particularly important in large-scale book production where books are often rounded and backed two-up, that is, in pairs. For this purpose they must be of uniform thickness which adds importance to good smashing.

Manual back gluing. Manual back gluing is a very simple operation which can be executed either before or after trimming. The operator applies the glue by hand with a brush. First he jogs the books and stacks them carefully in a neat pile, with their backs toward himself; then he coats the whole stack of backs with glue; thereafter he separates the books and stacks them again, but this time backs and fronts alternate.

Mechanical back gluing. For quantity production, backs are glued mechanically. The back-gluing machine is often placed in line with a nipper or smasher. In such an arrangement, the operator who removes the books from the smashing conveyor puts them immediately in the back-gluing machine. In one kind of back gluer "the books are fed to a conveyor in handfuls and carried along with their backs down. As they move along, they pass an automatic jogger which jogs the books to the back. When this machine is used, the books must be jogged well before they are trimmed. If they are not, the jogging they receive in the gluer will leave the fore edges uneven. From the jogger they are carried past the gluing station where a coat of glue is applied to the backs. As they leave the machine, the operator stacks them with the backs alternating."[50] After the glue on the back is dry, the books are ready for trimming.

Trimming

Trimming designates the operations whereby bound books and other printed items are cut to their final size. Trimming should be distinguished from sheet cutting which, as a rule, precedes presswork. Trimming makes the book neat, removes the folds of signatures and therewith frees the pages, and divides two- or three-up bound books into individual units. The last operation is usually called *splitting* or *cutting apart* even though it may be performed as part of trimming.

Like most binding operations, trimming comprises a variety of work. In the production of casebound books, trimming comes after sewing and smashing or nipping. In the production of flush-cut books (where the edges of the cover do not protrude over the edges of the bound material) book and cover are trimmed together after combining. As most paper-covered books and trade magazines are flush-cut, trimming is, in that case, the final step in binding.

Trimming can be done in a number of ways. You know from our discussion of guillotine cutters that it is possible to use them for trimming. But guillotine cutters are designed for the cutting of sheets prior to printing where much longer cuts must be made than in the trimming of books. The trimming of books is most economically done on specially designed machinery known as *book trimmers*. In display and poster work, on the other hand, where the printed products are sheets of large size, guillotine cutters are the proper equipment for trimming. But guillotine cutters have been already discussed, and we can, therefore, concentrate now on trimmers.

Trimmers are high-speed machines that are designed with specific purposes in mind. They are available in several types and models that differ considerably in several points. Our presentation of trimmers covers the following six types: (1) tumbler trimmers, (2) single-knife trimmers, (3) three-knife job trimmers, (4) straight-line three-knife trimmers, (5) three-knife magazine trimmers, (6) four-and-five-knife trimmers.

Tumbler trimmers. Tumbler trimmers which are at present often superseded by various makes of three-knife trimmers are powerful and very heavy mass-production machines for the trimming of magazines in piles up to 6 inches high. Magazines printed two- or three-up must be cut apart either prior to, or after, trimming on tumblers, as tumbler trimmers can only make three cuts.

Tumbler trimmers are intermittently operating machines which perform four operations at the same time. They are equipped with a heavy tumbling block whose four planes act as beds for trimming. The tumbling block makes a quarter turn for every trimming cycle. At each turn one plane of the block serves for clamping of untrimmed material, another for trimming at the front, a third for trimming at head and foot, and a fourth for delivery of the trimmed pile.

The tumbler trimmer has its characteristic feed and delivery; it is laid out in "U" shape. One leg of the "U" is for feeding, and the other for delivery. The books are piled in the feeding trough with their backs down; the pile moves toward the tumbler and is changed in its direction (for clamping) by a transfer basket. After trimming, the pile is unclamped and delivered on the second leg of the "U," parallel with the in-feed conveyor.

Single-knife trimmers. Single-knife trimmers are flatbed machines suitable for the trimming of stacks or lifts up to 6 inches high, depending on the specific model. On one of them, for example, the knife operates at the rate of one stroke per second. This "trimmer consists of a feed table with guide and automatic mechanisms for indexing the lift forward, a cutter, and a discharge conveyor. The lift is placed on the feed table in position for the first cut and the operator pulls the starting lever with his right hand; the cut is made

and the lift advances automatically for the next cut. This is repeated until the lift is completed. A mechanical hold-down is provided for convenient handling of small-sized stock and saddle-stitched work. Its pressure reduces the swell caused by the stitches, resulting in uniform trimming."[51]

Single-knife trimmers require successive trimming and repositioning of the material for each cut. They are used for job work and can be found in many trade binderies and label printing plants for relatively short runs that do not warrant the use of more expensive equipment.

Three-knife job trimmers. Three-knife trimmers are capable of trimming front, head, and tail of books in one combined operation requiring only one feeding through the machine. These trimmers are equipped to trim lifts of books up to almost 5 inches having a wide latitude in size. They are efficient and fast, and as they do not require long setup times they are more suitable for job work than machines designed for very long runs. Three-knife job trimmers have automatic in-feeds. The lift of books is automatically clamped, trimmed in one step at its head and foot, in another step at the front, and finally automatically delivered on a conveyor belt.

Straight-line three-knife trimmers. Straight-line three-knife trimmers are mass-production machines. They take longer for setup and are therefore only used in production runs. The books are put in piles up to 6 inches high; these are placed with the back of the books down in a "V"-shaped conveyor. The books are moved with their backs against a guiding wall and are jogged head and foot with jogging fingers which are attached to separate rails moving in opposite directions. The piles are clamped at the top and first trimmed at the front, then at head and foot. The knives have a rocking shear cut. All three cuts are made at the same time though in two different places and on two different piles. The waste is pneumatically removed.

Some models of straight-line trimmers are suitable for two-up work. These have not only front, head, and tail knives, but also a fourth, called the *split* knife, which is placed between the head and tail knife in two-up cutting. In some cases the books are retrimmed at the edge where they were split to improve their appearance. Retrimming is done on single-knife cutters.

Three-knife magazine trimmers. Three-knife magazine trimmers are equipment that is used in

The SHERIDAN
CT *Trimmer*

This trimmer was designed primarily for direct trimming applications: books delivered from covering machines or binders are automatically fed into the trimmer.

The basic machine consists of a hopper feed, capable of feeding piles of books up to a total of 2″ high; an infeed table to convey single books or piles of books flat, with backbone leading into the trim area; a transport with upper and lower grippers to carry the books from the front cut to the side cut stations. The books remain clamped to assure register; they are delivered by a flat belt delivery. The top knife has a shear action working against a fixed bottom knife. A 4th and 5th knife unit is also available.

Although primarily used in the magazine field, the Sheridan CT Trimmer is often used for edition binding. The size range of books is from 6″ x 4″ up to 17½″ x 11½″ for three knife work, with a maximum total thickness of 2″. Speed is to 100 cuts per minute for single books and 80 cuts per minute in multiples.

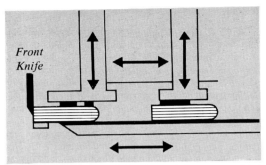

2 *The book is tightly clamped between padded grippers for safe alignment.*

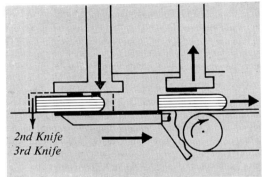

3 *The transport assembly has moved the book to the side knife station.*

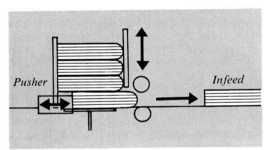

1 *Hopper has movable pile support, stripper gate and pull-out rolls.*

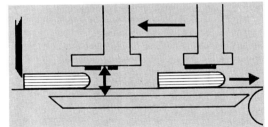

4 *Grip is loosened to allow return stroke of the transport assembly.*

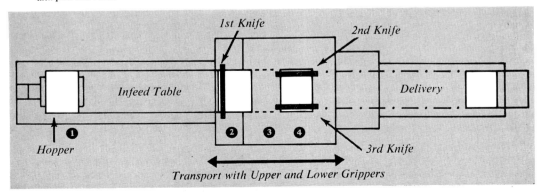

The SHERIDAN
Straight Line Trimmer

This heavy duty inline machine trims books in piles up to 6″ high at speeds up to 42 piles per minute, covering a size range of 7″ x 5″ up to 16″ x 12″.

Piles can be hand fed, but more often feeding is done automatically to an inclined "V" trough pin conveyor infeed which, in turn, feeds the material into a reciprocating transport unit. The transport unit serves to carry the pile to the knife stations and to register them prior to the trimming operations; joggers assist registering.

The heavy duty clamps at each knife are fitted with blocks to distribute the clamp pressure as required for the particular books being trimmed. The rocking shear knife cuts into a cutting stick. A 4th and 5th knife can be added for 2-on work.

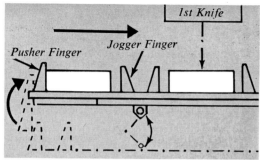

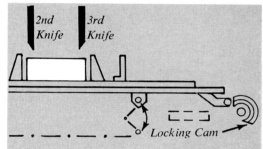

2   *A reciprocating transport unit.*

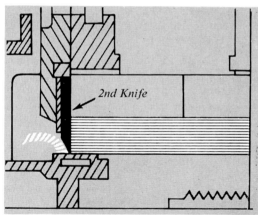

3   *Joggers also assist the register.*

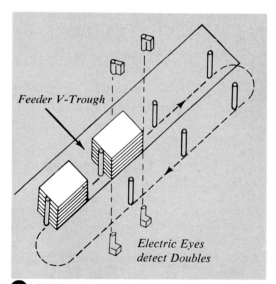

1   *Inclined 'V' trough pin conveyor infeed.*

4   *Rocking shear knife, cutting stick.*

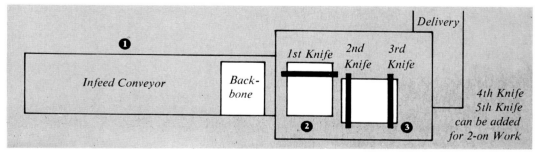

line with gathering, inserting, stitching, or adhesive binding, and covering machinery. Such equipment is designed for harmonious operation of the whole production line; its capacity must of course be in tune with that of the rest of the line. Magazine trimmers can operate as fast as the magazines can be bound; they are built for the trimming of individual magazines, or pairs, but not for trimming of magazines in high lifts. Some such trimmers are equipped for two-up work; these are discussed under the following heading of four- and five-knife trimmers.

One type of a three-knife trimmer, which is designed to work in line with equipment used for the saddle-stitched binding of tabloids, can produce up to 200 units per minute. This machine is obviously fully automatic. The stitched books are carried individually by a chain conveyor into the first cutting station where their front edge is trimmed; from there the books are moved to the second cutting station where their heads and tails are trimmed; thereafter, the trimmed magazines are delivered in fanned-out form on a conveyor belt. This type of magazine trimmer has a maximum cutting thickness of seven-eighths of an inch. It uses shear action and has two cutting blades, one moves and the other remains stationary. Other machines, using knives similar to those described for guillotine cutters, are also available.

Four- and five-knife trimmers. Four- and five-knife trimmers are used in the trimming of magazines which are bound two-up. Magazine trimmers can also be equipped with a split knife. A fifth knife is used for two-up jobs that must have an inside trim which is cleaner than the outside trim produced by the bevel of the split knife. In bleed jobs, retrimming is a necessity unless the trimmer has a fifth knife. In some cases this fifth knife is part of the trimmer, in other cases a different arrangement combining a three-knife trimmer with single-knife trimmers may be preferred.

Edge Treatments

The appearance of a book can be enhanced by a variety of edge treatments. Most edge treatments are much too time-consuming and therewith too expensive for quantity book production. Marbling and fore-edge painting are two examples of edge treatments used exclusively in extra binding, but never in mass production. But staining or spraying is suitable for industrial binding; and gilding, though mainly done by extra binders, is also performed by industrial plants specializing in

Bible work. Our discussion of edge treatments is divided into six points: (1) staining or spraying, (2) speckling, (3) gilding, (4) marbling, (5) fore-edge painting, and (6) goffering.

Staining or spraying. The terms "staining" or "spraying" are used interchangeably for the coloring of book edges. The coloring material consists of water-soluble dyes; these may be applied either by brushing, sponging, or spraying. The trimmed books are carefully stacked and then colored. They must be firmly held together during coloring to prevent seepage of the colorant into the pages. Staining has not only the purpose of enhancing the book, but it also makes a book look cleaner because the pores of the paper are more or less sealed by staining; the edges of a stained book are more resistant to dust and finger marks than those of unstained books. Books to be stained are always treated on the upper edge where most of the dust settles; sometimes, though rarely, all three edges are colored.

Speckling. Many books are letterpress printed on book paper for the text and coated paper for halftone illustrations. If such a book is stained, it might show streaks because different papers absorb the staining material in different ways. This undesired effect can be avoided by speckling, either by airbrush or by brushing across a coarse wire mesh.

Gilding. Gilding is a much more difficult and also much more expensive edge decoration than staining, not the least because real gold is used for this purpose. Gilding is used more on expensive handbound books than in edition binding. Gilding techniques vary; most craftsmen have their own preferred methods. In extra binding, some authorities say that gilding may either precede or follow sewing, depending on the desired effect. Rough-gilt books are gilded before sewing, smooth-gilt books after sewing.

In edition binding, gilding is always done on sewed books. These are smashed, trimmed, and according to some, glued in the back prior to gilding, whereas others prefer to do back gluing after gilding. Some books are gilt at their heads only, others only at their fore edge, still others at all three edges. Sometimes the edges of a book are colored, usually in red, prior to gilding. The undercolor gives tone to the gilding. It also makes minute defects in the gold less conspicuous.

The gold used for gilding comes in extremely thin leaves of varying size, usually in squares of $3\frac{3}{8}$ inches, put up in books of 25 leaves, interleaved with paper. The gold is adhered to the book edges with an albumen or egg size, also known as *glair*. "The books are first trimmed, then jogged up carefully and placed in rows in horizontal screw tension presses; the edges are scraped, a filling made of paste and color, rubbed in, allowed to dry and after sizing with an albumen size, the leaves of gold are laid on the surface thus prepared."[52] The laid-on leaves must be dry before the edge can be burnished. Burnishing is done with an agate or flint stone. After burnishing the gilded book is fanned out whereby its leaves are separated.

Marbling. At present marbling is an almost completely forgotten art, but for some centuries marbling was a decorating technique peculiarly the binder's own. Marbling can be used for edge treatments as well as for the decoration of endsheets. The results of marbling are multicolored patterns that are freely created by the marbling craftsman.

The equipment for marbling consists of a trough, approximately 4 inches deep, with an open surface of 18 × 36 inches, for example. This trough has a straight edge and may be provided with two compartments, a narrow one for the chemical used in marbling, oxgall solution, and a second compartment for the waste. The trough is charged with the *gum bath*, a size consisting of various vegetable gums prepared by cooking with water. The design is obtained by adding mixtures of mineral pigments which are not soluble in water and have been dispersed in an alcoholic solution of oxgall in water. These pigments float on the surface of the gum bath and can be formed into patterns with simple hand tools such as brushes, whisk brooms, styli, and combs.

The marbler develops his pattern according to his own taste. He transfers the pattern by dipping the book or the paper (if he marbles paper for endsheets) into the trough. "It is to be noted that an alum salt is used in treating the book edges or other paper prior to marbling. When the pigment, enveloped with oxgall, is transferred to the paper, a chemical reaction occurs" whereby the pigment together with the product of this reaction is bound "permanently to the paper fibers."[53] The remaining pigment is removed from the size and the process begins anew for every item to be marbled. It is not surprising that the art of marbling is considered out of step with the speed requirements of our own times.

Fore-edge painting. Fore-edge painting is an extremely rare and also very expensive form of edge treatment. In fore-edge painting this edge of the book is fanned out and decorated by an artist with a watercolor design. The book must be rounded first for fore-edge painting. After the picture is painted the book may or may not be gilded at the fore edge.

Goffering. Goffering is another very rarely used technique of edge decoration. Here the gilded surface is further enhanced by scribing or chasing various designs into it. Goffering can be done with or without colored embellishment. The tools used for goffering include binders' finishing tools as well as stencils and brushes for painting. Like fore-edge painting, goffering is done only where cost is less important than beauty.

Shaping the Backbone of the Book

The last unit on edge treatments discussed some of the artistic aspects of binding. The present unit has the rather technical subject of producing a book with the right structure, or *backbone*. From the introduction in the beginning of this section you know that the book must be rounded, that it must then be backed and thereby provided with a joint for the cover, and that the rounded and backed book must finally be reinforced by *backlining* which is usually combined with headbanding.

Now we will enter into a somewhat detailed description of these operations which like most others can be done on various levels of mechanization. For this purpose the subject is divided into the following seven points: (1) manual rounding and backing, (2) the main elements of mechanical rounding and backing, (3) semi-automatic rounding and backing, (4) automatic rounding and backing, (5) manual backlining and headbanding, (6) automatic backlining and headbanding, and (7) inline production of the backbone.

Manual rounding and backing. For manual rounding, the binder needs a work bench and a

Manual rounding of a book. Manual rounding is not an industrial method but still practiced in extra binding

cobbler's hammer. He places the book front edge toward himself on the bench, holds it with his left hand which draws the top edge toward himself and pushes the middle sections away at the same time. He has the hammer in his right hand and hits the book repeatedly along its back edge; then he turns the book upside down and does the same with the bottom of the book. If necessary, he repeats this operation several times until the book has its proper *round*.

Manual backing can be done either in a combination backer-and-press with a hammer, or in a roller backer. The combination backer-and-press is a table tool, the roller backer a floor-type machine. The combination backer-and-press consists of two backing boards and a bookbinder's screw press. The backing boards are heavy, tapered boards with a bevel at the top. They are best lined with steel on the inside. The book is put with its back upward between the backing boards which are tightened in the binder's press. Our illustration shows the position of the book between the backing boards before backing. The steel lining is on the inside, pressing against the book. The bevels slant toward the outside on both boards. The binder stands the press with the backer on the bench and pounds the back of the book outward over the boards on both sides. The joint of the book is formed, as you can see, at the edge of the boards and down its bevel.

The backing press is the most primitive backing equipment. A floor-type backer with two vertical backing jaws is more practical, but the backing itself is again done by hand with a hammer. The roller backer is a very widely used machine for the backing of library books. Here, too, the book is inserted between two movable vertical jaws, but backing is now done by a heavy roller which is attached to the machine in such a manner that it can move in an arc over the back of the book. The movement of the roller forces the back outward and forms its joint.

The main elements of mechanical backing. Before we begin our discussion of various rounding and backing machines, the two characteristic elements used for mechanical backing should be well understood. These are a pair of rounding rollers and the backing iron. We will explain their functioning by a comparison with manual rounding and backing.

You know that the binder rounds the book by a combination of changing the position of various signatures in the book and of hammering the

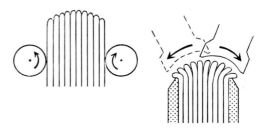

Diagram of semiautomatic rounding and backing. The first illustration shows the book between the rounding rollers, the second illustration shows the clamped book and the action of the jointing iron.

back of the book in this new position. Thereby the back becomes rounded and the front edge must follow the curvature of the back. The same result can be obtained if the book is passed, with its back first, through a pair of rollers. These rollers rotate in opposing directions with the book between them. The pull exerted by the rollers forces the book into a rounded shape; the extent to which the rollers turn, controls the round of the book. The more they turn the rounder becomes the back of the book.

Manual backing is done, as explained above, by pressing the book between two beveled boards and by pounding the backbone with a hammer. In mechanical backing the book is also between two metal surfaces, called the *jaws* of the backer; hammering is replaced in mechanical backing by hitting the book with a backing iron. The backing iron is also, and more descriptively, known as the *jointing iron*. It is a solid bar of steel differing in width for books of different thickness. The hitting surface of the jointing iron is an arc, shaped with a straight shoulder on each side. The motion of the jointing iron is oscillating, meaning that it swings in an arc back and forth over the back of the book.

After this introduction we are ready for a presentation of different rounding-and-backing equipment.

Semi-automatic rounding and backing. Semi-automatic rounding and backing is done on a machine that has provisions for both operations. The book is individually fed by the operator on a table to a pair of rounding rollers. The rounded book is clamped between two jaws which swing with the book toward the backing station in the rear of the machine. A backing iron forms the book joint by hitting each edge of the back twice; then the jaws return and open. The operator

The
SMYTH #38
Rounding and Backing Machine

Glued and trimmed books are placed fore edge down on the belts of the infeed hopper. Each book is stripped from the stack and carried to the rounding roll station. Here it is first positioned by the downward movement of the levelers, then it is clamped between the knurled rounding rolls which rotate while clamping the book, causing its center signatures to be displaced, there by forming the round.

The book is then carried, still in its rounded form, into the clamp jaws for the backing operation. Here a concave-shaped backing iron is lowered into contact with the back of the book where it oscillates over each portion twice. The book is then unclamped and carried out of the machine ready for the next operation.

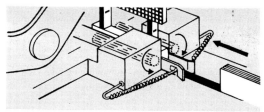

2 *The rounding rolls rotate like two meshed gears clamping the book as they rotate, causing its center signatures to be displaced forming a rounded book.*

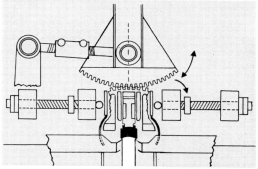

3 *The oscillating backing iron bends the signatures to form the joint.*

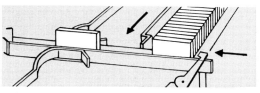

1 *Books are fed automatically from the Hopper Feeder making cyclic feeding by hand unnecessary.*

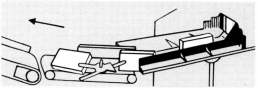

4 *Books discharged from the Rounder and Backer are tipped 90° as they enter the conveyor feeder, which transports them into the Smyth Liner.*

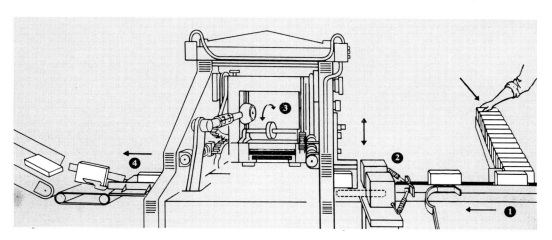

removes the backed book from the machine and inspects it before stacking.

The semi-automatic rounding-and-backing machine requires a skilled operator who must time his work with the cycle of the equipment. This is particularly true for the removal of the backed book, where a small delay may have unpleasant consequences for the workman. The output of this machine is approximately 600 books per hour. This figure is here given by way of indication only; it must be understood that the actual production of this machine, as of every other, depends on the nature of the job.

Automatic rounding and backing. Automatic rounding and backing is done in the United States on several kinds of machines. One, an independent rounder and backer, is presented at this point of our discussion. A different kind of machinery which is part of integrated equipment is presented last in this unit under the heading "Inline Production of the Backbone." In the independent rounder and backer the trimmed and back-glued books are inserted at the front of the machine; there they are automatically rounded and backed in a straight-line arrangement that delivers them at the other end ready for backlining and headbanding.

The machine is equipped with a book carrier mechanism and several pairs of book clamping jaws. The books are inserted into the machine with their backs up and moved by the carrying mechanism from station to station. After the book is properly positioned and leveled, it is rounded in the customary way between a pair of knurled steel rollers which drive it up at the same time. The rollers are adjustable for the amount of turn required. "The degree of round given the back of the book is directly proportionate to the amount of turn given the rounding rolls."[54]

After rounding, the book is released by the rounding rolls and moved by the carrying mechanism to the backing station. There it is clamped again by the two jaws of the backing or jointing mechanism and provided with its joint by the action of a jointing iron which is first lowered until it meets the book; then it swings two times over its backbone. The jointing iron is selected to fit the job in hand; it is "approximately one-quarter inch wider than the thickness of the book."[55] The jointed book is released from the jointing jaws and carried out of the machine by the book carrier. The rounded and backed book may be either stacked or conveyed automatically by a conveyor feeder to a backlining and headbanding machine. The capacity of this equipment is rated by its manufacturer as up to 36 books per minute.

Manual backlining and headbanding. The material used for backlining is, as already mentioned, super or crash and strong paper. In manual backlining, one or two strips of this material are glued to the backbone, leaving an overhang on either of its sides. This overhang is later pasted between each board of the case and its endsheet, thereby anchoring the book firmly to its case. The spine is usually covered, in addition, with a strip of backlining paper. If headbands are required, these are pasted to the backlining paper before it is glued to the spine of the book. All this can be done without any other equipment than a brush. How the same effect is obtained by automatic machinery will be seen in the next paragraph.

Automatic backlining and headbanding. Machines for automatic backlining and headbanding differ in their construction but have nevertheless many general features in common. You know already that backlining has the purpose of reinforcing the back of the book and of providing the means for a firm connection between the bound book and its cover. Automatic backlining machines have provisions for applying several coats of adhesive to the back of books. The lining material, crash or super as well as paper, is put into the machine in the form of rolls. The width of the rolls corresponds to the required width of the backlining and may change from job to job. The machine automatically coats the backs for each application of lining material, cuts the lining material to the proper length, applies it to the glued back, and presses or rolls it for firm adhesion to the back of the book. If a book is headbanded, the headbands, which are supplied in rolls, are first attached to the backlining paper and then the whole assembly is applied to the glued book.

Inline production of the backbone. The term "inline" is not customary in the binding industry but is borrowed from the packaging field where it is used to indicate a continuous manufacturing process combining many different operations. You know from the preceding discussions that rounding and backing can be done on one machine, that reinforcing and headbanding are done on a different machine, and that both can be connected to each other by a specially constructed

The SMYTH #32
Triple Lining and Headbanding
Machine

Rounded and backed books from the Smyth #38 Rounder and Backer are turned and conveyed to the Smyth #32 Liner where they are controlled by an escapement mechanism so that they enter the machine automatically at the proper instant.

These books, which are back or spine down, are then lifted into spring loaded pockets by a formed lifter bar corresponding to the shape of the back of the book being processed. When the book is properly oriented in the pocket the spring clamps it in position for the rest of its journey through the machine.

First an even coat of animal glue is applied to the back of the book, then in the next station a piece of crash or mull, approximately 2″ wider than the book, is adhered and tucked firmly around the back of the book. The process may be repeated if two pieces of crash are required. Then a third application of glue is made prior to the Lining station, where a decorative head and tail band are adhered to the back lining paper which is then attached to the book. The backlining is then thoroughly rubbed down to insure its adhesion to the book.

The spring loaded pocket is then opened while a formed set of fingers lowers the book and rotates it 90° to a discharge conveyor which carries it from the Liner and deposits it fore edge down on a conveyor feeder which moves it to the Casing-In Machine.

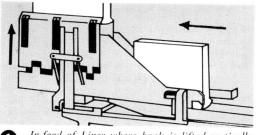

❶ *In-feed of Liner where book is lifted vertically into clamp jaws which will then carry it through the machine.*

❷ *Concave rubber roll picks up coating of animal glue and distributes it to back of book.*

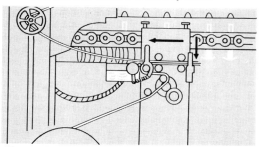

❸ *Lining station cuts paper or paper with headbands to proper width. No paper is fed if there is no book in position to receive it.*

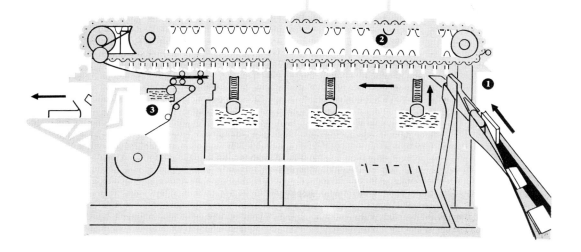

linking conveyor. Such an arrangement is one example for inline or integrated processing of books, combining rounding, backing, reinforcing, and headbanding.

Here we are interested in a different kind of inline equipment which is not obtained by connecting independent machines but is rather a single completely integrated unit. This type of equipment is used for mass-production work; it is according to the manufacturer's rating capable of producing up to 35 books per minute with a maximum dimension of $8\frac{1}{2} \times 10\frac{1}{2} \times 2\frac{1}{4}$ inches; books up to $8\frac{1}{2} \times 5\frac{1}{4} \times 2\frac{1}{4}$ inches can be processed two-up which doubles the output of the machine. Such a unit weighs approximately 16 tons, is more than 30 feet long and more than 9 feet wide.

This equipment can be described as a combination of a conveying mechanism and many individual processing stations. It operates intermittently: the conveying mechanism moves a uniform predetermined distance and stops for a short interval during which the books are subjected to the action of all processing stations at the same time. As each book moves on, it is passed through all production steps selected for a specific job. The functioning of this machine is broadly indicated in the following.

The trimmed and glued-off books are placed into a hopper feed sideways with their backs down. From this moment on, they are not touched by human hands until the books are completely rounded, backed, reinforced, and headbanded. The conveying mechanism is equipped with approximately 40 pockets, meaning pairs of book clamps. Each pocket can either hold a single book or two books in tandem, depending on their size. After the book is placed in the hopper a "book lifting shelf automatically feeds one or two books up into the clamps in perfect register. The clamps then close, holding the books firmly, and carry them to the nipping station."[56] There all backs are compressed to a uniform thickness.

After nipping, the books are rounded in two steps: First an overhead pusher pushes "the books down firmly against a former at the bottom of the book; then the clamp closes and carries the books

to the main former or roll-down station."[57] Here the books are rounded. The next operation, backing, is also done in two stages. In the first a partial joint is formed which is completed in the next station. Backing is done with backing irons that oscillate over the book in a manner similar to that already described.

Rounding and backing are followed by reinforcing. "The rounded and backed books are then forwarded to an elevating shelf which raises and accurately re-registers them in the clamps preparatory to the backlining and headbanding operations."[58] Then the books are moved to a gluing station where a brass roller coats their backs with adhesive for the reinforcing fabric, crash or super. The reinforcing material is placed in rolls of proper width on the machine where it is automatically cut to its correct length and applied to the glued back in the next station. The machine may or may not be equipped with a second gluing and a second reinforcing station.

An additional gluing station prepares the back for attachment of the backlining paper and headbanding. "The machine is arranged to handle headbands made up in rolls wound left and right. Small glue transfer rollers revolving in a glue box apply narrow strips of glue to the outer edges of the lining paper, to which the headbands, feeding simultaneously with the paper, are accurately applied at the required width. The paper with the glued-on headbands is then cut to the desired length and applied to the backs of the books."[59]

The final stations serve for the pressing of the reinforced backs: first, a rubber blanket softens the paper, then a pneumatic roll presses the reinforcing material; both rubber blanket and pneumatic roll run through water and thereby moisten the material for pressing. These are followed by "a series of specially designed spools which assure the crash, paper, and headbands being firmly glued to the extreme edges"[60] of the books. Thereafter the completely processed books are delivered onto a conveyor belt. The delivery and the feed station of the machine are next to each other. The clamps release the finished books and receive their new load at the next station, where the cycle begins anew.

Section 8: Cover-Making

All bound material is classified either as self-covered or as covered. The term self-covered is ambiguous; it really means that the material has no cover whatsoever. In self-covered bindings the first and the last leaf of the printed paper must serve as its cover. Self-covering is acceptable only for the least expensive types of binding. Practically all books and many magazines are covered with specially made covers. A notable exception is the newspaper supplement which is sold as part of the Sunday paper. Newspaper supplements are mass-produced items and are usually self-covered.

In a not-so-distant past, approximately 50 years ago, covering served two purposes, to protect and to enhance the bound material. In our times a third function, sales appeal, has been added. The overwhelming majority of all binding jobs are magazines, and their covers must attract the consumer. The sales appeal generated by the cover may often swing the decision of the consumer in the silent competition taking place on the stands in front of him. Magazines are not the only products of binding that use their covers as silent salesmen. Books for grownups, such as mystery stories, and children's books, be they soft- or hardbound, also need cover design for selling. Casebound books may either bear their sales appeal directly on the cover, or this function may be shifted to the book jacket. Book jackets were originally known as dust jackets; their protective purpose has been all but completely subordinated to that of selling.

The three functions of covers—protection, enhancement, and sales appeal—are not the only points to be considered in the selection of the manufacturing processes whereby a specific job will be produced. The nature and purpose of the job, the kind of equipment available at the place and at the time where and when the job must be produced, and, finally the generally most important items, price and delivery, must be considered. The protective and wearing qualities of a cover depend on its physical construction, its sales appeal on art work and color printing, its aesthetic value on design, materials, and execution of specific binding techniques.

The Physical Construction of Covers

Before we can enter into a discussion of the subject, we must establish a clear terminology. We begin with the unbound book. For our purpose a book is described as a six-sided block. As you can see in our illustration, these sides are designated as back, front, head, tail, top, and bottom. The top of the book is the surface at its beginning; the bottom, the surface at its end; the back is the side where the book is bound, it is also known as backbone or spine; the front is the side opposite the back, it is also known as front edge or fore edge. It must be explained that this terminology differs from that used in the industry. The words head and tail are used by some where we will use top and bottom, with others head and tail have the same meaning as here but they call front what we call top, and back what we call bottom; finally it is mentioned that some use the word lead edge for our front or fore edge. In spite of the fact that the two terms top and bottom are not in general use, they are nevertheless here employed in the interest of clarity.

If you look at any casebound book at hand, you will notice that it is covered on three of six sides; spine, top, and bottom. The other three sides are uncovered. But they are in hardbound books, for example, protected by the fact that the covers extend an eighth of an inch or more beyond these three sides. These projections make it possible for such a book to be handled in a manner that will not be injurious to the bound matter. It is obvious that the pages of a book should not be touched by anything but the (supposedly clean) fingers of the reader. The book itself should always be protected by its cover.

Let us now look at our cover and describe it. We discussed an edition bound book which was

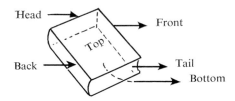

Terms used in this manual in describing a book. The book is bound at its back or spine. The head of the book is the same as the head or top of the printed pages. The front of the book is opposite its back; it is usually called the fore edge. The tail of the book is at the foot of the printed pages. The bottom signifies the cover following the printed pages. The top signifies the cover preceding the pages. The top is usually stamped or printed with the author's name and the title of the book, and so is the back or spine; the bottom is usually blank.

hardbound. (Some people use these terms synonymously, others maintain that edition binding includes the binding of paper-covered books as well as that of hardbound ones.) The cover of our book is known as a *binder's case*, or simply as a *case*. Our illustration shows a binder's case before it is combined with the book.

If you look at this illustration you notice that the case consists of four parts. Three of them are distinct and separate from each other; the fourth, namely the covering material, extends completely over one surface of the other three items and slightly over the other surface, thereby holding them together in a fixed position. You are looking at the inside of the case; what you see will cover the top, spine, and bottom of the book. The case itself consists of four elements: two boards, one for the top and one for the bottom, paper for the lining of the backbone, and the covering material which is usually cloth in edition-bound books but may also be paper, or a combination of both. Boards and paper for backlining are glued to the covering material which becomes the outside of the case and therefore of the bound book.

The cloth is *turned-in*, as the trade says, meaning that it extends approximately half an inch on the inside of the boards and the paper between them which is called the *liner*. This type of cover is also known as an *overhang cover* because it extends over the edges of the text or other assembled material. When cover and book are combined, the endsheets of the book are pasted to the inside of the cover. As they extend over the turn-in, but not over the edge of the cover, they give the inside cover its neat finished appearance.

Not all covers are cases; we selected a binder's case for this discussion because it is most suitable for a general analysis of covers and their functions. A cover must protect backbone, top and bottom of a book as well as its head, tail, and

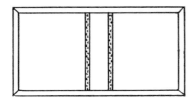

Flat view of a binder's case prior to casing-in. The two large areas are binder's board, the strip in the center is the paper for lining the spine, the shaded strips on both sides indicate the inside of the covering material, and the framing represents the turned-in outside of the covering material.

front. Books bound for continual use are stored on shelves, preferably in an upright position, and must be rigid for this purpose. Books that are sold by eye appeal usually need color printing, books that stand on library shelves must bear brief identification on their backbones.

Covers must be functionally adequate for the covered book. If it is of permanent value, the cover must be made to last, but if the material is of fleeting interest, a cover constructed for permanence would be wasted. As the cost of covers mounts with the degree of desired permanence, we divide the subject into three groups: (1) covers for permanent bindings, (2) printing and decorating of permanent covers, and (3) covers for semipermanent and impermanent bindings.

It must be understood that the permanence of a book does neither depend exclusively on its cover, nor even primarily on it. The paper on which a book is printed, the manner and quality of fastening the inside material, and certainly not least the quality of workmanship employed in preparing a book for covering, all play important roles. But, generally speaking, books that are not intended to last are very rarely covered in a manner that is used for permanent binding. In some cases better wearing qualities cannot be obtained without taking apart the impermanently bound book before it can be provided with covers suitable for permanent binding. This is often done in library binding.

It should also be explained that the words permanent, semi-permanent, and impermanent do not indicate that a cover is more or less permanently attached to the book. They indicate solely what the general purpose of the binding is. It is assumed that each kind of cover is permanently attached to the book. Finally, these distinctions are made solely with reference to the physical life expectancy of books without any concern as to their intrinsic value. Where we discuss the technical aspects of binding, great works of thought and mystery stories are put, technically, in the same class if both of them must be bound to last.

Covers for Permanent Bindings

You remember that we began our discussion of covers with a casebound book. Practically all binding for permanence is casebinding; but this was not always so. From the Middle Ages until the early decades of the nineteenth century books were bound in an entirely different technique which is described in the section on preparing the book for covering. Then covers consisted of independent units, wooden or paper boards, for the top and bottom of the book. They were individually attached to the book and so was the covering material for its backbone. This covering material was traditionally leather or parchment; it extended either over the adjacent edges of top and bottom covers, or it covered these completely on their outside.

Cases are differently constructed. They are a single unit for covering spine, top, and bottom of the book. Before we discuss the various methods of case-making we must introduce the subject of printing or decorating the outside covering material. "Broadly speaking, there are two kinds of cover printing and decorating, namely preprinted and postprinted cases. In preprinted cases, the printing and decorating precedes case-making; in postprinted cases, printing and decorating follow the case-making operation."[61] This difference is important because preprinted cases are best made with case-making machinery using sheets of the covering material, whereas postprinted cases can be made either on sheet-fed or on roll-fed case-making equipment. (It should be mentioned that the word "preprinted" is part of the trade vocabulary, whereas the word "postprinted" is not generally known; it is here used because it contributes to clarity of distinction.)

Cases consist, as you already know, of boards, paper for the backlining, and a covering material which holds the whole assembly in place and combines it into a single unit. Before case-making can begin, the boards, which are supplied as large sheets, must be cut or slitted to size, the covering material—cloth or paper—must be either slitted and rewound or cut to size. Then comes case-making itself, followed by cover decorating unless the cases were preprinted. Our presentation is consequently divided into three broad units: (1) preparation of case-making materials, (2) case-making, and (3) postprinting or stamping.

Preparation of Case-Making Materials

The preparation of case-making materials consists in various cutting and slitting operations whereby the material is converted from its delivered dimensions into those required for case-making. Our discussion covers the following five points: (1) board slitting and cutting, (2) slitting and cutting of covering materials, (3) slitting and rewinding of the backlining paper, (4) corner cutting, and (5) preprinting of covers.

Board slitting and cutting. Binder's board and other cardboard is supplied in large sheets which must be cut to the required size. Board can be cut in various ways. Here we mention three different techniques: board cutting with shears, slitting in one direction, and slitting in two directions.

Board cutting with shears is a hand operation. Cutting shears are available as table models and as floor models in various sizes. We describe a floor model because these are more frequently used than table shears. A floor model consists of a rugged stand, a table, a clamp, a table gauge, and a back gauge, not to forget the cutting blade. The board is cut into individual sheets by placing it on the table and aligning it either with the table gauge or with the back gauge which must be set accordingly. The sheet is first cut into several strips which then are cut again to their final size. The clamp which holds the board in position is foot operated, whereas the cutting blade is counterweighted and depressed by hand.

Slitting is done on power-driven machinery which may either be hand fed or equipped with automatic feeders. The sheet of board is singly driven between a series of cutting members, each consisting of a pair of rotary knives turning against each other. These slit the board as it passes between them. Slitters are equipped for the making of several parallel cuts, the sheet can therefore be completely cut in one direction in one pass through the machine. The slitted strips are again put through the slitter for their second cut.

Board cutters that slit in two directions are machines "equipped with two sets of adjustable cutter blades. The first set makes parallel cuts in one direction only, then the boards move at right angle to the original feed direction, and a second set of blades makes parallel cuts at right angles to the first. After boards are fed and cut into strips in

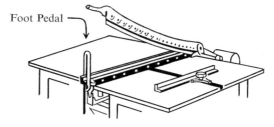

Foot Pedal

Diagram of shears for board cutting. The board is fed to the gage at the right under the clamp in the center of the shears. When the operator is ready for making the cut he depresses the foot pedal thereby clamping the stock, and then makes the cut with the blade by hand.

the first cutting section, a chain feed system gathers the strips and deposits them in a trough to be automatically fed to the cross-cutting blades for the right-angle cuts."[62]

Slitting and cutting of covering material. Depending on the type of case-making machine on which the covers will be manufactured, the covering material which is supplied in rolls must be either slitted, or slitted and cut. If the covering material will be used on roll-fed case-making equipment, the original rolls are slitted to the required width; if the material is to be used on sheet-fed equipment, the original rolls must be slitted and cut. If, finally, preprinted covers in sheet form are to be used, the material must be slitted and cut prior to printing and possibly be cut again after printing. First the covering material must be reduced to the size of the press sheet which often combines several units for common presswork. As cases must be made individually, such sheets must be cut into individual units after printing and prior to case-making.

The slitting of covering material is done on machines which slit and rewind the slitted cloth into rolls of the required width. The cutting members are pairs of rotary cutting knives, similar to those used on board cutters. The combined slitting and cutting of covering material requires machines equipped with a cutting knife which cuts the slitted material into individual sheets. The slitting knives make parallel cuts, the cutting knife operates at a right angle to the slitters. The length of material fed to the cutting knife can be set to any required measure by controlling the amount of rotation of the feed rolls. Preprinted sheets of covering material are cut to their final size on guillotine cutters, which need no further description.

Slitting and rewinding of the backlining paper. The paper for the backlining is slit into the required width and rewound at the same time. Slitting and rewinding is either done as an independent operation on equipment similar to that already described, or as part of case-making directly on the case-making machine.

Corner cutting. The corners of the covering material must be cut before the material can be used on sheet-fed case-making machines. Corners are usually cut on power-driven presses which cut piles of sheets by means of cutting dies.

Preprinting of covers. Several reasons account for the growing use of preprinted covers. The traditional manner of stamping is not suitable for the printing of fine detail such as needed for half-tone and full-color printing. Publishers can supply the desired eye appeal for their wares by means of paper jackets which are easier to print than covers. Paper jackets are customary in trade books that are cloth bound. Mass produced books for the juvenile market have often preprinted paper covers and no jackets.

Preprinting makes it possible to use many reproduction processes for cover decoration. "Offset-lithography is widely used for this purpose; letterpress, gravure, silk screen and collotype less frequently. Web printing poses severe register problems for case-making because it is difficult to exactly register the imprint on the backbone or spine of a book using a preprinted web. For this reason web printing is used mostly for random patterns; and the spine and title of the book are usually included in the web print, but are postprinted after the case is made."[63]

Case-Making

Before we enter into a detailed discussion of various case-making procedures and machines, we want to identify the operational steps of case-making. A case consists of covering material, two boards, and the backlining. The inside of the covering material must be coated with an adhesive, boards and backlining must be placed in proper position, the corners tucked if the job has round corners, the covering material must be turned over the edges of the board, and the case must be pressed. All these steps are necessary in order to produce a case; they are therefore common to all ways of case-making. You also know that cases can be made on sheet-fed or on roll-fed equipment. Roll-fed equipment requires two additional steps: corner cutting and separating of individual cases from each other. Sheet-fed case-making machines do not need these operations because they receive the covering material in the correct size for the individual case with the corners already cut.

Case-making can be done on various levels of mechanization and on a variety of equipment. Our presentation is divided into the following five points: (1) handmade cases, (2) case-making with gauges and fixtures, (3) hand-fed case-making machines, (4) machine-fed case-making machines, and (5) roll-fed case-making machines.

Handmade cases. Cases can be made completely by hand without any other aids than such simple hand tools as knives, brushes, and bone folders.

Schematic Diagram of a SMYTH *Automatic Casemaker #2*

The standard casemaker produces covers by automatically feeding one sheet of cloth from a pile feeder to the cloth cylinder on which it is carried past a glue roll where the cloth receives a thin film of hot animal glue. The cloth carrier bar with its several pairs of steel fingers then carries the cloth into position over the platform.

Simultaneously, two boards have been pushed forward from under the stack and a piece of backlining paper has been fed from under the machine through the straightener and cut off knife to a position between the two boards. A picker head with vacuum cups and support blocks picks up the boards and backlining as one unit and revolves 180°, depositing them directly over the freshly glued sheet of cloth.

The first fold in a Smyth Casemaker is always made at the head and tail of the cover by action of the picker head and supporting platform moving down through the first fold bars to form the exact size. Then the first fold bar slides move in and wrap the cloth around the edges of the board. The platform moves up slightly to create pressure between the first fold slides and the cover in order to ensure a tight fold. The process is then repeated at a lower level to form the second fold.

The discharger bar strips the case from the platform, pushing it between the press belts. Here the entire case is squeezed by a rubber platen to ensure complete adhesion between all parts of the cover.

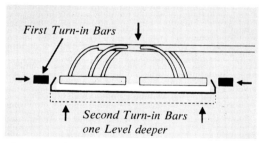

① Cover boards, backlining strip and cloth are held by the picker head to the platform while the cloth is folded over the edges of the case.

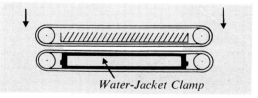

② The freshly made case is held under uniform pressure for one cycle of the machine to insure complete adhesion of the cloth to the board.

Cloth, boards, and backlining are cut to their proper sizes and then manually combined. Where many individual cases are to be made, in the rebinding of books, for example, a gluing machine and a wringer, both power-driven, are generally used. The covering material is cut to size and at the corners; it is then put through the gluing machine and covered all over its inside with glue. The bookbinder puts the boards and the backlining on the glued surface, relying on his eye and skill rather than on a jig or tool. He turns the edges of the cloth over the boards, one after the other, with his bone folder, and puts the completed case through a wringer or rotary press. Case-making by hand is, of course, much too slow for production jobs, but it is surprising to see how fast cases can be made by skilled craftsmen in a well-organized rebinding shop.

Case-making with gauges and fixtures. Case-making gauges are used for production of identical cases in small quantities. The case is still made by hand but the gauge indicates where boards and backlining are to be placed on the glued covering material. Case-making gauges are adjustable for different sizes, turn-ins, and widths of backlining. Case-making fixtures may have stationary or adjustable gauges for the various elements needed in case-making. On some fixtures the turn-in of the covering material is brought about by mechanical linkage of turning bars or rollers which are set in motion when the operator steps on a foot pedal. Other fixtures use power-driven pullers for this purpose.

The hand-fed Smyth case-maker. This machine is the most widely used hand-fed case-maker. Even though the covering material is individually fed, the boards and the backlining are stacked in the case-maker. A pusher mechanism feeds a pair of individual boards from the bottom of the feed pile onto a platform toward the center of the machine; the backlining is advanced between the boards and cut to proper size. If you stop the machine at this point of its cycle you see all parts of the case next to each other, not yet combined.

For combining, boards and backlining must be put on the covering material which is already adhesive coated. This operation is performed by a moving head, known as *picker head*, which oscillates through a 180-degree arc, and has its pivot between both kinds of materials. This picker head is equipped with suction nipples. It comes down on the board and lining paper, lifts these, and swings until it arrives over the adhesive-coated

covering material. There the arm descends and presses boards and lining down on the covering material exactly where they belong. At this point the cover is assembled but not yet turned in.

Turning in is the purpose of the next group of operations. It is done in two stages. First, head and tail of the cover are turned in by turning bars, one at the head and one at the tail, which are under the covering material, partly covered by its edges. These bars move simultaneously toward the center and thereby turn the cloth over the head and tail edges of the boards. The turning in of the remaining two edges is done by lowering the case approximately an inch to the second turning-in station. Here the front edges of the top and bottom cover are turned in. Thereafter the case is moved into a platen press of unusual design. The bed of the press is equipped with a rubber jacket filled with water. The outside of the case rests on this jacket and is very smoothly pressed because the supple surface of the jacket can apply pressure at every area of the case. The pressed case is finally delivered at the case receiver.

The Smyth automatic case-maker. The Smyth automatic case-maker is essentially the same as the Smyth hand-fed machine, but it is equipped with an automatic feeder for mechanical feeding of the covering material, paper or cloth. "The principal difference is that on the hand-fed machine the cloth is fed directly to the cloth cylinder by the operator, while on the automatic machine the cloth is fed from a pile by automatic means. The automatic machine is also equipped with electric stops which automatically stop the machine when either the cloth, board, or backlining supply fails, when cases are not correctly assembled on the platform, and when the case is not delivered to the press."[64]

The scope of this machine can be considerably increased by several special attachments. One makes it possible to use paper as a covering material for the boards and cloth for the spine of the book; another permits the making of round-cornered cases, and a third allows the use of boards instead of paper for lining the backbone of the cover. There is also an attachment for the making of album covers which have one narrow and one wide board with a hinge.

The Dexter-deFlorez case-maker. The Dexter-deFlorez case-maker is a machine that operates continuously and performs the various operations with the material in constant motion. All other case-making machines operate intermittently or in cycles; some of their operations take place with the material in motion, but most of them are performed when the material is at rest. The Dexter-deFlorez case-maker is a fully automatic sheet-fed machine. It is mainly used for preprinted covers but can also be used for covers which will be stamped. It is a complex machine and here briefly described in its general operational features.

The machine is fed on two stations, one at the end of its upper level, the other at a right angle to the first and several feet inward on a lower level. The upper level end feed is used for the boards and the backlining material; the lower level side feed for the covering material which is in the form of individual corner-cut units. Both feeders are continuous. The boards are put in hoppers from where they are removed by bottom feeding; the covering material is fed by a continuous air-wheel feeder as described in Section 4.

The covering material is put into the feeder with its preprinted side up and one of its short edges in the lead. Upon arrival in the case-maker the traveling direction of the covering material is changed by a transferring mechanism whereby the longer edge of the sheet, its head or tail edge, becomes the leading edge. The sheet is now moved with its back exposed to a gluing mechanism, and at the same time up into the top level of the case-maker, in front of the board and backlining feeding station. There it receives the two boards and the backlining. Now the case is assembled. To keep the assembly in position the case is clamped between its conveying mechanism on the bottom and two pressure chains from the top.

First the two front edges of the cover are turned up as they travel over an inclined blade; then a traveling mechanism which moves along with the cover completes the turn-in and returns in time for the next unit. The cover moves on; its lead edge, the tail of the book, is turned up by timed spring-loaded fingers. The turned-up edge is turned in as it passes through a folding roll; the remaining fold is made by a traveling mechanism, part of a flying carriage which moves faster than the case and in the same direction on its top. This fold is made before the last edge of the cover passes through the folding rolls of its leading edge. The turned-in cover is pressed between pressure rollers before it is delivered onto the delivery conveyor. This machine is high-speed production equipment. It is rated by its manufacturer as capable of producing 60 cases per minute.[65]

The Sheridan sheet-fed case-maker. At the time of writing only the first of these machines is in operation and a second is ready for shipment, according to information received by the manufacturer. As there is no descriptive literature available, this machine is less extensively described than others.

The Sheridan sheet-fed case-maker feeds the material on both ends of the machine; the boards are stacked in hoppers at the front end of the case-

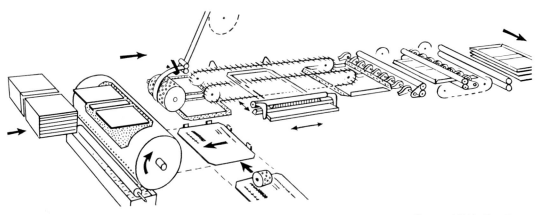

Flow-diagram of the Dexter-deFlorez case-maker. This case-maker is designed for precut covers which may or may not be preprinted. The precut covers, paper or cloth, are fed in from the side on a lower level, then transferred to the gluing mechanism at left and their glue-covered inside combined with the boards and backlining coming from the extreme left. Then the cloth is turned in in several stages by various mechanisms, all doing their work as the cases move through the equipment. This case-maker has continuous feeding and functions otherwise fully automatically.

maker, the covering material is fed at the opposite end where the finished cases are delivered. The covering material is conveyed to the front end of the machine through a glue applicator and up onto the conveying mechanism of the case-maker in front of the boards. These are deposited on the glued surface of the covering sheet by a bottom feeding mechanism. The sheet travels on a conveyor and is clamped to it with two gripper chains after it receives the boards.

The backlining paper is above the machine in a roll; it is automatically cut to size and deposited in its place. Now the case is ready for turn-in. It comes to a turn-in station where its two front edges are folded over; then the case is moved to a rotating station where it is repositioned at a 90 degree angle, with the two unturned edges parallel to the direction of travel. At the next station these two edges are turned in by the same kind of mechanism as was employed in the first turn-in station. The completed case is passed through pressure rollers before it is delivered. The Sheridan sheet-fed case-maker operates intermittently. Boards and backlining are deposited when the sheet is at rest, and the folds too are made at the same time, though of course on different units. The machine is rated by the manufacturer for a production of 60 cases per minute.

The Sheridan roll-fed case-making machine. As the designation "roll-fed" indicates, this case-maker processes rolls of covering material. In the general introduction to case-making it is mentioned that preprinted rolls of covering material requiring close register are not suitable for case-making. This statement must be qualified by adding that special electronic control devices must be employed for the purpose of making cases from preprinted material on roll-fed case-makers wherever close register is wanted. There are several such installations in operation, but their number is rather small.

The Sheridan roll-fed case-maker produces cases from rolls of covering material and slitted individual units of boards. The backlining paper is placed on the machine in roll form. The layout of roll-fed covering machines is straightforward. These machines are comparatively long, from 10 to approximately 17 feet, depending on the size of cases to be made on them. They operate intermittently, and have various stations on which the case is assembled and completed. The covering material moves from one end of the machine toward the other until it is cut, just before the final

front edge turn-in is made. The covering material serves at the same time as a conveyor belt during the assembly of the case.

The width of the roll depends on the size of the cover; it is determined in some models by the height of the final case, in others by the open size of the case. As the covering material is supplied in wide rolls, it must be slitted and rewound for use on roll-fed case-making machines. The feeding stations for the boards and the backlining can be arranged either for feed at right angles to the travel of the covering material or for feed in the same direction. The covering material passes through a gluing device before it reaches the working level of the machine. "The two boards are then positively placed on the cloth by a hopper feed. The forwarding movement is an adjustable gripper, operating in combination with the corner cutting mechanism, which cuts the corners, while the gripper, still holding the cloth and board, moves them forward to the backlining."[66]

After the boards are put on the adhesive-covered surface of the covering material, the backlining is automatically applied. The strip of paper is held by a pneumatic device when it is cut off the roll until it is safely positioned on the covering material. At the next station the case is turned in at its head and tail. A corner tuck-in device precedes the turning in which is done by turn-in bars and rolls. Then the case moves on, is turned in at one front edge, the cloth between it and the following case is cut by a guillotine knife, the second front edge is turned in by a turn-in roller, and the completed case passes through a set of pressing rollers before it is ejected from the machine.

Roll-fed case-making machines are mass production equipment, capable of producing up to 45 cases per minute. The covering material may be cloth or paper, and it can be preprinted under certain conditions. It is also possible to use board instead of paper for the backlining, but a separate attachment is required for this purpose.

Printing and Decorating of Permanent Covers

Binder's cases can be decorated either by preprinting or by postprinting. These terms indicate the sequence of printing in relation to case-making. The terms "printing" and "decorating" are less commonly used in the bookbinding industry than the traditional word *stamping*.

The most commonly used stamping techniques can be divided into three: (1) stamping with ink,

The SHERIDAN
Casemaker

Cases can be made in many ways on this machine by variations in combining webs, boards, and strips. Up to three webs are fed from below, carried over glue applier wheels, and are combined with up to 5 boards, fed from the bottom of hoppers. The next operation, if required, is the application of the paper liner. The strip feed unit used for this purpose incorporates a cutoff and applier mechanism. At this point, boards, strips and webs are lapped together, forming one continuous web. Adjustable "V" knives—called corner cutters— remove "V" sections from the web to facilitate subsequent folding operations. Side folds, followed by end folds, are used to wrap the web ends around the outer edges of the case. An ironing "case-smoothing" operation precedes the delivery.

This particular machine can make a case $4\frac{5}{8}''$ x $4\frac{5}{8}''$ up to 24" x 15", at speeds up to 45/min., depending upon the nature of the work. Electronic register control for pre-printed roll stock can be attached.

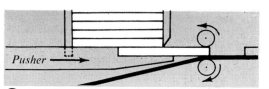

3 *Board is fed from the bottom of the hopper.*

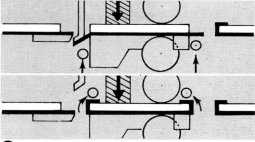

4 *Strip feed unit cuts off paper liners.*

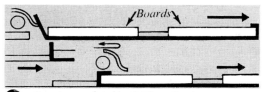

5 *Adjustable 'V' knives remove sections.*

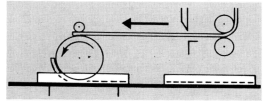

6 *Cutting and turning in of side folds.*

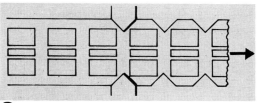

7 *Case is completed by folding of ends.*

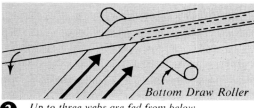

1 *Webs are carried over glue applier wheel.*

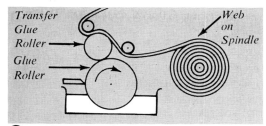

2 *Up to three webs are fed from below.*

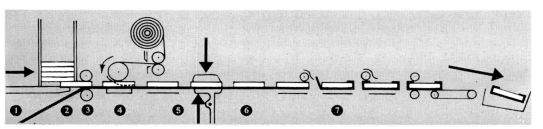

(2) stamping with foil, and (3) stamping without any coloring matter. A case can be printed and decorated in either of these techniques, which can also be combined. In ink and foil stamping the printed image is in color, in stamping without ink the image comes about by a difference in elevation between it and the surface of the case. If the image is raised, or in *relievo*, it is designated as *embossed;* if it is sunken, or in *intaglio*, it is designated as *blind stamped* or as *blanked*.

Stamping of binder's cases with ink can be done in two processes. The traditional process for ink stamping is letterpress, where the printing image is raised above the surface of the printing-image carrier. More recently screen process printing has been introduced for the decorating of binder's cases. The designation of this decorating technique is not uniform in the binding industry. Some call it stamping in silk screen, others speak of screen printing.

The printing-image carrier for stamping, be it now in relievo or in intaglio, is known as a die; stamping with ink is often designated as *cold stamping* in distinction to *hot stamping*, which term is used for stamping with foils. In stamping with foils the coloring material is supplied in rolls of many colors including gold, silver, and others of a metallic appearance. The metallic material consists of aluminum foils which are coated as required with transparent but colored coating materials. Foils used for hot stamping are known as *roll leaf*. Individual leaves of true gold or silver foils are not used any more for industrial stamping of cases, though these materials still have a place in really fine handbinding.

Roll-leaf stamping must be done at high temperatures, depending on the nature of the job. A few words on the construction of roll-leaf stamping material will explain why heat is necessary. Roll leaf can be described for our purposes as consisting of four layers of different materials. If we look at one surface of roll leaf, we see that it is colored; if we look at the opposite surface we see a carrier, paper for example. In addition, roll leaf has two other layers of material, one on top of the colored surface and one between the colored surface and the carrier material. The layer on the colored surface is a thermoplastic adhesive. It has the function of bonding the colored surface to the surface of the case, or other object, to be roll-leaf stamped. The layer between the coloring material and the carrier, or temporary support, is also thermoplastic. But it has the opposite function of

the other thermoplastic top layer; it serves to release the color layer from the support.

Hot stamping is also used for embossing and blanking or blind printing. For this purpose the covering material is often supplied with a thermoplastic surface coating. The thermoplastic coating softens under heat and hardens again when cooling, thereby making the stamped image more pronounced and more permanent.

After this general introduction we turn to a detailed discussion of cover stamping and decorating. It should be understood that our discussion pertains to postprinted covers exclusively and does not include preprinting at all. The subject of postprinting of binder's cases is here divided into nine points: (1) stamping dies, (2) ink stamping on platen presses, (3) roll-leaf stamping on platen presses, (4) ink stamping on vertical presses, (5) roll-leaf stamping on vertical presses, (6) blind stamping and embossing, (7) screen process printing of binder's cases, (8) combination of various decorating, printing, and stamping processes, and (9) hot stamping of individual names.

Stamping dies. Stamping dies are made in different techniques and from different materials. The longer the production run and the more intricate the design, the harder and better the dies must be. Steel dies are considered the best for long-run quality stamping, brass dies are equally used for this purpose and are often chromium plated for long runs. Magnesium dies, electrotypes, Ludlow, and even Linotype slugs can also be used for stamping, the last two only for very short runs, such as the stamping of individual names, for example.

In the case of brass dies for "hand lettering or other artwork a drawing is made in correct proportion, the die-maker photographs it and prints the negative on a smooth sheet of sensitized brass ¼ inch thick. The plate is then etched, much as in regular photoengraving, and routed deeply so as to prevent filling up of minute details in the stamping."[67] Dies can also be made with engraving machines based on the pantograph principle. There the engraver traces the outlines of the drawing which is engraved by a cutting head at the same time on the die stock. Such machines permit reduction or enlargement of drawings in a simple manner. Electrotypes and type slugs do not need additional discussion at this point as you are familiar with them from preceding chapters.

Ink stamping on platen presses. Platen presses used for ink stamping of binder's cases are letterpress printing machines. These are described in detail in Chapter VI, "Printing Presses." Platen presses for stamping must be very rugged; they are manufactured in different sizes and by different companies.

Platen presses produce the impression by the interaction of two parallel plane surfaces. One of them, the *bed*, is stationary and the other, the *platen*, is moving. The stamping die is attached to the bed either with an adhesive or with machine screws. The cases to be stamped are individually positioned on the platen of the press, the die is inked and the printing image is produced when the platen is pressed against the inked die.

Platen presses may be either open presses or they may be equipped with feeders. On open presses the operator takes care of feeding and delivery, whereas these operations are performed by the machine itself on automatic presses. Some platen presses are equipped for two-up printing. Here two cases can be fed at the same time to two independent stamping dies; these may be different and so may be the two ink colors if split-fountain printing is selected.

Stamping inks have their own specific requirements; they must be very viscous and they must be suited to the covering material to which they are applied. It happens often that a design calls for a dark color of the covering and a light color of the stamping. Such stamping tasks can be rather difficult. They require not only very opaque inks but also sometimes repeated printing in the same color ink, one, two, or three impressions on top of each other.

Roll-leaf stamping on platen presses. Platen presses must be equipped with roll-leaf attachments and heating plates if they are to be used for roll-leaf stamping. The heating plate is mounted on the platen, the heat is electrically generated and thermostatically controlled. The temperature can be regulated within the required limits by adjusting the heat control instrument which may be connected to a thermometer having a dial indicator and be attached to the press at a suitable place.

For roll-leaf stamping the inking rollers must be removed from the press; it is not possible to do ink stamping and hot stamping in one and the same operation. But the roll-leaf attachment itself does not interfere when the press is used for ink stamping, and can therefore be permanently installed on the press. A typical roll-leaf attachment makes it possible to put one or several rolls on the press at the same time and to use them

simultaneously. The rolls can be of different widths and they can also be fed at different lengths. Usually, there are three independent feeding devices, each adjustable in steps of one-sixteenth of an inch. The feed length can vary for each feeding device, from 7 to 12 inches, for example. The roll feed is timed with the press. It moves the band of roll leaf after every impression across the heated stamping die. The impression is taken the same way as for ink stamping; feeding of cases, too, remains the same.

Hot stamping makes it possible to apply several colors at the same time. It can be compared to split-fountain printing; everything is already provided for this purpose in the attachment itself. As roll leaf is available in a wide variety of colors, and as the image produced by hot stamping is more opaque than the image produced by ink stamping, hot stamping is a very commonly employed technique for decorating binder's cases.

Ink stamping on vertical presses. It is possible to do ink stamping on vertical presses but vertical presses are much less efficient for ink stamping than platen presses. The main reason for using vertical presses for ink stamping is that covers may be too large for platen presses but not for vertical presses which are usually available in larger sizes than platen presses.

Roll-leaf stamping on vertical presses. Vertical presses are used a great deal in the bookbinding industry. They have two flat surfaces: a platen and a bed. The bed is stationary, it is part of the head of the press; the platen is underneath the bed, it receives the material to be processed and forces it with great power toward the bed. Vertical presses for hot stamping and similar operations must be very sturdy and are capable of exerting up to 250 tons of pressure. They are manufactured in different sizes and with different feeding arrangements. Their vertical structural elements consist of four heavy corner posts which leave all four sides of the press unobstructed between bed and platen. This feature is important for roll-leaf stamping, as you will see immediately.

Vertical stamping presses can be fed in three different ways: directly in the press, with a sliding platen, and automatically. The first two kinds are manually operated. In manual feeding, one hand of the operator removes the stamped binder's case and his other hand positions an unstamped one. Without sliding platens this must be done within the press, whereas it can be done on the outside if the press is equipped with a sliding platen. After removal and feeding the operator pushes the platen into the press for stamping.

The bed of the press is equipped with a heating unit, thermostatically controlled and adjustable in its temperature. The stamping die is at-

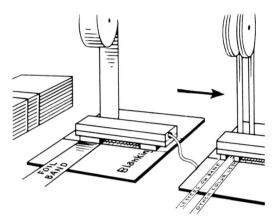

Diagram of Dexter foil and gold stamping machine. This machine is automatic and has three different working stations. It can stamp foil, emboss, and blank, meaning that it can flatten embossed material.

tached to the heatable plate, and the press is equipped with roll-leaf attachments. These may run either from front to rear, or from side to side, or criss-cross, in both directions. The open construction of the vertical press permits all these arrangements and their flexibility is often very desirable.

Recently, the Dexter Company introduced a high-speed foil and gold case stamping machine which is automatic from infeed to delivery. It is equipped with three different working stations. The first two are used for the decoration of the spine which can be embossed, debossed, stamped, and overprinted. The third station serves for the stamping of the front cover. The undecorated cases are stacked in a hopper and automatically fed to the first station, worked, and automatically moved to the second station; worked again, and then automatically transferred to the third station. After the front covers are stamped, the completely decorated case is automatically delivered to a hopper. This machine is rated for a production of 20 to 60 finished covers per minute.

Blind stamping and embossing. Blind stamping and embossing are both done on the same equip-

ment but they produce entirely different results, and require different methods for their execution. Blind stamping produces intaglio images, as we already know, whereas embossing produces relief images. Both are done without the use of coloring material. Blind stamping is often used to flatten structured covering material in such areas as will be ink or roll-leaf stamped. This operation is also known as *blanking*. Blind stamping and blanking use brass dies, and are performed just like hot stamping. If the material is very structured or if a particularly well-pronounced result is desired, the press is run slowly, which increases its dwell at the impression and the depth of the stamping.

Embossing produces relief images. It presses the material between two surfaces, a female or intaglio embossing die and a male, or relievo, counter. The embossing die is usually made of brass; it is attached just like a stamping die to the top plate of the press. The counter plate is also known as the *embossing make-ready*. The subject is further discussed in Section 10 under the heading of embossing.

Screen printing of binder's cases. Screen printing of binder's cases can be done either manually, or on semi-automatic, or on fully automatic machinery. Screen printing produces very opaque images and is therefore often used where light colors must be printed on dark covering materials. Another feature of screen printing is its ability to produce very glossy, semi-embossed effects.

Combination of various printing and stamping techniques. Many binder's cases are postprinted by combining several decorating techniques. Sometimes cases made on roll-fed equipment from preprinted material are hot stamped or silk screened on their spine. Hot stamping and ink stamping are combined in some jobs, and so are embossing and silk screen printing. Available equipment, nature of the design, and cost are the main considerations in the selection of decorating techniques for specific jobs.

Hot stamping of individual names. Presentation copies are sometimes hot stamped with the name of each recipient. Where only a single stamping is needed (or a few), slugs of type, made on linecasting machines, are satisfactory. They are, of course, much cheaper than regular stamping dies. The stamping itself can be done on a variety of equipment, mainly bench models of one make or another. One machine specifically designed for this type of work is briefly described in the following. The slugs of type are stacked on a heated feed table and thereby preheated. The book is hand fed, the operator feeds the new slug and actuates the press, which automatically ejects the last slug when the new one is brought into position. This machine illustrates that not everything is mass production, even in our times.

Covers for Semi-permanent and Impermanent Bindings

Few people will disagree with the classification of casebound books as permanent bindings, nor will many people take exception if paper-covered magazines are considered as impermanently bound. But opinions differ when bindings are classified as semi-permanent. It is therefore again explained that these groupings are arbitrary. They have only one purpose, namely, to organize the subject for discussion.

Covers for Semi-permanent Bindings

The types of binding to be discussed under this head are mainly used for mass production of juvenile books. These products are made to be sold in chain stores rather than in regular bookstores. They must, therefore, be priced in line with other merchandise sold in chain stores and they must have sufficient eye appeal to attract the browsing customer. Last, but not least, these bindings must be sufficiently sturdy for the repeated handling by sales personnel and customers neither of whom always approach books with loving care. Only mass production methods are capable of producing such books at the price for which they must be sold.

Juvenile books are not the only kind of books that are bound semi-permanently. Many college workbooks or specialized texts must also be bound in a comparatively durable and yet rather inexpensive way. Some of the techniques developed for mass production of juvenile books are evidently also applicable to other books.

You may remember that a casebound book is protected on all of its six sides; three of them are covered by the case which protrudes over the other three and thereby protects the book itself. You may also remember that books are, as a rule, cloth-covered. Book cloth can have very good wearing qualities and is often impregnated with plastic materials that make it soil-resistant and permit the cleaning of the cover with soap and water. The covers discussed in this unit do not afford the same degree of protection and durability. Most of them have paper as covering material, and the edges may be either turned in or cut flush. Our brief discussion of this very specialized subject is restricted to three points: (1) paper-covered cases, (2) connected boards, and (3) individual boards.

Paper-covered cases. It must be remembered that juvenile books need eye-catching covers which are mostly produced by preprinting of sheets. Juvenile books produced for mass distribution are very often rather thin, and thin books do not need backlinings. Paper-covered cases requiring backlinings are manufactured on the same equipment as edition-bound books. But paper-covered cases without backlining can be produced on different high-speed equipment specially designed for the actual purpose.

Connected boards. Connected boards are used for covering of thin juvenile books that must be very economically produced. Books covered with connected boards are cut flush, which means that book and cover are trimmed together to the same final dimensions. As the covers on flush-cut bindings do not protrude beyond the edges of the book, flush-cut books are not protected at the head, tail, or front of the book by their covers. In thin juvenile books this is hardly a drawback. Flush-cut books with connected boards can be very economically manufactured, much less expensively than if they are bound in cases where the edges are turned in.

This little item, the *turn-in*, can make all the difference in the cost of a book, if we assume, of course, all other conditions equal. Turned-in covers must be made individually, and book and cover must also be individually combined. Flush-cut covers can be made two, three, four, and five up. "For this reason the inside of the book can also be bound two, three, four, or five up and fastened into the cover as a unit. When completed,

Illustration of a childrens' book covered with paper over connected boards, flush cut.

the book and cover are cut in a single operation to make individual books. The saving made possible by making this multiple cover and inside, binding and trimming, is an excellent example of large scale, efficient, economical book manufacture."[68] The equipment on which this type of cover is made is often called a *combiner*.

The *combiner* is widely used in the manufacturing of displays, toys, and games as well as for cover making. It is designed to paste sheets of paper to sheets of board. Paper and board are stacked in the machine; a sheet of paper is passed through a gluing unit where it is coated with adhesive on its back; this paper meets a sheet of board which is fed in timing with the paper, and is combined with it under pressure of a roller system. The combined material is passed through additional pressing rollers and finally delivered on a table. "One, two, or three boards can be fed into the machine side by side at the same time to be glued onto a common wrapper. This makes it possible to feed front and back cover boards of a book cover."[69] The boards are connected at the binding edge by the paper to which they are glued.

Individual boards. Many books for which case binding is too expensive need a better protection than paper covers. Putting them between boards can be a good compromise solution. Individual boards are used in library binding for the rebinding of books, but also for new books as their original binding. Sometimes such boards are directly printed for identification of the book; more often the printing is done on paper which is mounted on the covering boards prior to binding. This operation can be done on the combiner in long production runs. For short runs, glue is mechanically applied to either board or paper and the two are manually combined or mounted. After mounting, the board is pressed, either in a vertical or in a rotary press. The backbone of the book may be protected in the same operation whereby boards and book are assembled, or it may follow the combining of boards and book as an independent step. All this is further discussed in the sections devoted to the subject of assembling book and cover.

Covers for Impermanent Bindings

Most printed material is printed for the day's needs, real or imagined, and therefore, if bound at all, is covered accordingly. Magazines of all kinds are ordinarily paper-covered. Sometimes the cover is printed on heavier paper, sometimes on a paper of the same characteristics as that used for the whole magazine. A wide variety of papers that are particularly suitable for covering is available under the general name of *cover stocks*. These are made in many colors besides white. Our discussion of covers for impermanent bindings is divided into three points: (1) magazine covers, (2) covers for paperbacks, and (3) covers for mechanical binding.

Magazine covers. Covers for magazines extend over the backbone to the edges of top and bottom of the magazine. They are completely made of paper and very often printed in colors. The process in which they are printed depends on many considerations. As all major printing processes can be used for production of paper covers without influencing the mechanics of covering, this point is irrelevant for the present discussion. Practically all mass-produced magazines have flush-cut covers. But certain journals or quarterlies, and some items of advertising literature are covered with *overhang* paper covers. The operations whereby paper covers are prepared for covering are discussed in the next section of this chapter. Magazines are as a rule not capable of standing by themselves on book shelves; they are therefore rebound as cased books for libraries and collectors who want to preserve them.

Covers for softbound books. Paper covers are used on softbound books which are also called paperbound books, paperbacks, or pocket books. These are often but not always less expensive reprints of books originally produced in hard-cover editions. Softbound books can be bound and covered in several ways. The cheapest variety, such as mysteries, are produced by hundreds of thousands and are usually adhesive bound. Serious books are more expensive; they are often sewed through the center of signatures, just like edition-bound books. The covers of paperbound books are as a rule printed on heavier paper than their text. Mystery novels have covers that may graphically depict the content of the book. Such covers are printed in color and either varnished or laminated with a thin plastic to improve the attractiveness of their sexy and lurid pictures. It may be added that paperbound books are ordinarily flush-cut.

Covers for mechanical binding. Covers for mechanical binding can be merely two leaves of paper, but they can also be of a very sturdy construction. It should be mentioned that mechanical binding utilizes not only impermanent but also permanent bindings. The reason for inclusion of mechanical binding under the head of impermanent binding lies in the fact that mechanical binding is mostly used for impermanent material, less for semi-permanent, and least for the permanent binding of books.

It would be possible to break down covers for mechanical binding into these three groups, but for the purposes of our discussion it seems sufficient to warn the reader of applying generalizations to specific jobs. Impermanent covers for mechanical binding do not need backbones, as the binding device takes care of protecting the back of the book. In most cases mechanical bindings have paper covers, but sometimes boards or plastic covers are used. All these are usually flush-cut together with the material to be bound between them.

Section 9:   Assembling Book and Cover

The manner in which the bound material is assembled with its cover depends on the nature of the cover and the kind of binding employed, as is so often stated in preceding sections of this chapter. You may remember that saddle-stitched material is combined with its cover before stitching, and that in mechanical binding, too, covers and the material belonging between them are assembled before the binding device is inserted. These binding methods do not need further discussion, nor does loose-leaf binding, which is designed for instant exchange of the material. There the punched leaves are hand inserted into the cover, either by the bindery that produced the job or by the consumer.

Assembling of book and cover is an important phase in the production of casebound books; it is less complex in the production of paper-covered books and magazines. We divide the subject into three units: (1) assembling the book and its case, (2) combining the book and its paper cover, and (3) jacketing, packing, and shipping.

Assembling the Book and Its Case

Assembling the book and its cover is the last major phase of book production; after it, the book has taken on its final shape and it is ready for use. In the book industry this phase is customarily designated as *casing-in* and *building-in*. Casing-in is defined as "the operation of applying paste or glue to the end papers of a book, inserting the book into the cover and building into presses between boards to dry.[70] Building-in is defined in the same work as "placing freshly cased-in books in press between either smooth or edged boards, shaping backs carefully, and applying sufficient pressure in press or by clamping devices to hold books firmly while drying."[71] The definitions are overlapping as that of casing-in includes building-in.

Lack of precision is not the only disadvantage of these terms. Building-in, as here described, is also fast becoming outmoded in mass-production binding. The operation of building cased-in books into standing presses is at this time mainly used for shorter and medium-length runs, whereas for long-run work books are processed in high-speed equipment which produces acceptable results at much less expense and in a much shorter space of time. But before we can enter into a detailed discussion of various assembly methods, a brief exposition of the problems and purposes of this phase of book production is in order.

If you look at the illustration of the two units which are now to be assembled, you see that the book is rounded, has two joints and two overhangs of crash (single or double), one on each side. The cover is flat; it consists of three connected parts. In our illustration you look at the inside of the cover; the top and the bottom show the bare boards and the turn-ins; the back is covered with backlining paper. Between the back and the top cover as well as between the back and the bottom cover, you see a narrow uncovered

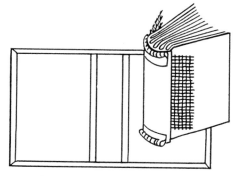

Diagram of the rounded and backed book and a binder's case prior to casing-in, or combining the book and its cover.

strip of the covering material. These strips will form the joints of the covered or cased-in book. The insides of the top and bottom cover will be attached to the endsheets of the book. The overhangs of crash, one or two on either side, will be pasted between the boards and the endsheets.

Casing-in of rounded books therefore involves several steps. The flat back of the case must be rounded; the outsides of the endsheets must be covered with adhesive; the rounded case must be placed around the book in such a manner that the top and bottom boards come to lie correctly on the two pasted endsheets and that the two uncovered strips of the covering material are correctly positioned over the joints of the book.

The cased-in book must then be pressed until the adhesive which was applied over the surface of both endsheets has dried. Pressing the books has several functions: one is to firmly adhere cover and book without wrinkling of endsheets, another to prevent warping of boards, and a third to form the joint of the cover and to make sure that its back will remain rounded.

In the following discussion you will see how casing-in and building-in, the two groups of operations of which the assembly of a book and its cover consists, are done on various levels of mechanization. Our discussion is divided into the following seven points: (1) manual casing-in, (2) semi-automatic casing-in, (3) fully automatic casing-in, (4) building-in with standing presses, (5) building-in with removable presses, (6) building-in with automatic equipment, and (7) inline equipment for combining book and cover.

Manual casing-in. Manual casing-in is done in library and extra-binding. The cover "should first be rounded by placing the book in the casing and shaping the backbone with a folder to conform to the contour of the book."[72] Then a piece of waste paper is inserted between the top endsheet and the book as a protector for the following application of adhesive. The adhesive is applied with a brush, the crash is pasted to the endsheet, the waste paper removed and the endsheet is placed with its adhesive side out, on the inside of the top cover. The same operation is repeated with the bottom endsheet and the bottom cover. This technique of casing-in is not the only one. It is also possible to apply the adhesive to the cover instead of the endsheets. Casing-in sounds simple but requires considerable skill, particularly if even squares are expected. These are "the portion of the cover that projects beyond the book."[73] Per-

fect squares are a mark of craftsmanship; their deficiencies are immediately noticed, and not always kindly, by the expert binder.

Semi-automatic casing-in. Semi-automatic casing-in is done on a machine that has great leeway in the size and thickness of the books that can be handled on it. This machine is commonly known as the *three-wing casing-in machine*, referring to rotating wings which are essential elements of this equipment. The assistant operator or feeder places, or *hangs*, the book in its center over a metal plate, the *wing*. The operator removes the cased-in book from this wing two cycles later. These two operations must be timed with the cycle of the machine. The cases are not individually placed on the machine but put in quantity in a stacker from which they are automatically removed for processing. With the exception of feeding the opened book and removing the cased-in book, this machine performs automatically.

The case is first moved to a forming station where it is given the required shape by pressing with a heated forming iron and by creasing for its joints. At the same time the book is moved past two pasting boxes where both endsheets are coated by knurled rollers with a film of adhesive. The wing carrying the book moves upward during pasting until it meets the formed cover which is ready for it. "The cover is lifted thus straddling the book. Two position stops on the wing, one for the book-inside and the other for the cover, assure the proper positioning of the cover. When the wing, with the completed book, has returned to its top position, the wing makes another one-third turn after which the operator lifts off the completed book and clears the wing for the next series of operations."[74] The operator inspects the book, forces the book tightly back at the bind, and stacks the books, which are then removed for further processing.

The three-wing casing-in machine is rated by its manufacturer for books up to 3 inches thick for covers (lying open) up to 14×22 inches; its speed is given as up to 25 books per minute.

Fully automatic casing-in. The automatic casing-in machine neither requires timed feeding and removal of books nor that the book be placed with its open center onto a wing. The operator either feeds the books into a trough, or they are automatically delivered from a conveyor feeder to the same trough. As the book moves along the trough it passes over a splitter where it is split in the middle by the conveyor blade. The conveyor blade

The SMYTH *#24*
Casing-In Machine
with Smyth Book Back Gluer

Books are fed into the Smyth #24 Casing-In Machine fore edge down on a horizontal support bar with a vertical fin or strip which splits the book in the center. If the book is Smyth sewn it is fed directly from the Smyth #32 Liner via a conveyor feeder into the Casing-In Machine where it receives a coat of quick setting adhesive over the crash and joint area. This is applied by the Joint & Side Pasting attachment while the book is moving in the horizontal direction.

It is then moved vertically on a blade between two paste boxes which apply paste to both the front and rear end sheets. At this time the case or cover, which has been pre-formed to the shape of the back of the book, is moved into position enabling the blade with the pasted book to move up under the case. The cover then hangs on the book by virtue of gravity until the book is removed from the blade by the discharger mechanism and allowed to slide spine first down the discharge chute into the conveyor feeder of the Book Forming and Pressing Machine.

For side sewn books which do not require crash or mull the process moves directly from the Rounding and Backing machine to the Book Back Gluer of the Casing-In Machine where a coat of animal glue is applied to the back of the book just prior to the casing-in operation. This enables the cover to adhere directly to the spine to produce what is called "tight-back" books.

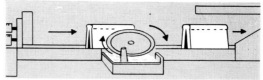

1 *Joint and Side Pasting Attachment which applies quick setting adhesive.*

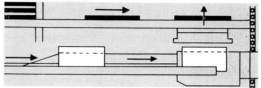

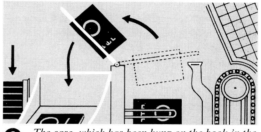

2 *Blade passes through center of book carrying it between paste boxes which apply adhesive to front and rear end sheets.*

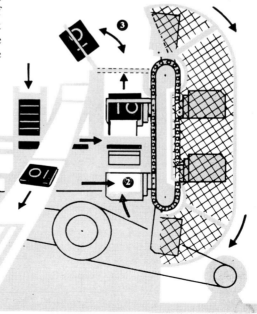

3 *The case, which has been hung on the book in the joint, and the whole assembly is removed from the blade.*

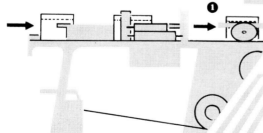

carries the book vertically through the paste boxes. While the book moves through the trough it passes between two knurled disks which apply a quick-setting adhesive to the joint line of the book. The covers are put in quantity into a stacker, and the machine does the rest automatically, including the ejection of the cased-in books with their backs down onto a chute. The cased-in books can then be either manually removed for building-in or they can be transmitted by a conveyor into a building-in machine without being touched by the operator. Fully automatic casing-in machines are necessary for combining of book and cover by inline production.

Fully automatic casing-in machines can handle books measuring from head to tail not less than 3⅜ inches and not more than 9⅜ inches, their width may vary between 2½ and 7½ inches, their thickness can be between one-quarter of an inch and 1⅝ inches. This machine is rated by its manufacturer as capable of producing up to 35 books per minute.

Building-in with standing presses. The cased-in book must be pressed until the adhesive which holds the case and the book together has dried. "Pressing is done between brass-bound boards usually made of cherry wood. The binding is a brass strip about one-sixteenth inch thick which is fastened to the edges and projects about one-sixteenth inch beyond the face of the pressing board. The books are placed around the edges of the pressing board with their backs out and the brass strip in the joint, which is a groove formed by the space between the backing ridge and the board of the cover. The press is filled with alternate layers of books and boards, pressure is applied, and the books are kept under pressure until thoroughly dry. Customary procedure is to leave the books in the press at least overnight."[75] Standing presses are traditionally simple screw presses which are manually operated. Such presses are used for library and extra binding as well as for binding of books in small job lots. Building-in for quantity book production does not use standing presses, but employs removable ones.

Building-in with removable presses. Large plants would need an enormous number of standing presses to take care of their daily production. In removable presses the application of pressure and the keeping of the books under pressure is divided between two implements. "The books are loaded on a separate base that is supported on casters instead of on the base of the press. When the

The cased-in books are stacked for building-in, or pressing, on brass-bound boards which are put in standing presses or removable presses. Building-in on boards is practiced in extra binding, library binding, and for short run editions. Longer runs are processed in building-in machines.

press is full, a special board is placed on top of the last pressing board. After the pressure is applied, threaded steel rods are used to connect the top board to the caster-mounted base. The pressure can then be released and the entire load of books rolled out of the press. With this equipment it is necessary to have only one press for each casing-in machine. There must be enough of the special bases and top boards to provide one for each press load of books that will be done in a day's work."[76] It is easy to see how serious a bottleneck building-in on boards must be for modern book production. All other phases were, indeed, already highly mechanized when building-in was still done in the traditional manner. Building-in machines, the next point in our discussion, are a comparatively recent innovation which permits much faster and more economical pressing and forming of books.

Building-in with automatic equipment. Building-in machines are the latest major step in the mechanization of book production; they make it possible to eliminate the tedious and space-consuming manual building-in of books into stationary presses. Several types of building-in machines are on the market. Each of them has its own design and operational features. All building-in machines use heat and pressure for speedy drying of the adhesive and the forming of joints.

Originally, building-in machines were designed for mass production, but they proved so successful that several different models were developed which make it possible and practical to use them for smaller runs and even for library work where individual books are handbound. The capacity of

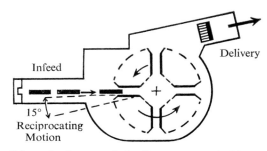

Schematic diagram of the Dexter rotary building-in machine. The cased-in books enter the building-in machine at the infeed and are clamped between metal plates that have controlled heat and pressure. Building-in is completed in several minutes and the built-in books are discharged at the delivery.

a building-in machine depends, other conditions being equal, on the number of clamps with which a machine is equipped.

For intermittent small production, a single clamp machine is available. It can process books up to 12 × 14 × 4 inches and can be operated at varying speeds up to 5 books per minute. A four-clamp machine, for example, has a capacity of up to 20 books per minute, and an eight-clamp machine can take care of 36 books per minute, or more than 2000 per hour.

The books are either manually inserted into a building-in machine or they are automatically fed into it after completion of casing-in. Each book is individually clamped between powerful pressing plates and creased in one of several ways at its joints. The heat applied during creasing melts and cures the adhesive; the joint is formed in this stage and the adhesive set thereafter. Building-in machines can keep pace with casing-in equipment. In less than a minute, the book passes through a building-in machine and is ready for use.

Inline equipment for combining books and covers. Edition binding has become highly mechanized in the more recent past. Modern equipment makes it possible to arrange all operations which are needed to combine book and cover, beginning with rounding and backing up to building-in and jacketing in a single production line which is completely mechanized. In one such system independent casing-in machines are connected to building-in machines; their product is transferred mechanically to a jacketing machine. Interlocking electrical controls can be provided for stopping one or all machines in the line if something goes wrong. These controls prevent damage to the work as well as to the equipment.

A second approach provides different equipment which is specifically designed for high-speed mass-production runs. In this type of equipment books are fed either manually or automatically from the previous operation, spine up, to a pusher conveyor which centers, splits, and transfers them to moving blades, or saddles, which move horizontally without interruption. These blades carry the books past a series of adhesive applicators which can selectively apply adhesive to the spine (for tight-back binding), the joints, the crash area, and the endsheets of each book. The cases are automatically fed, formed, and joined to the moving books in accurate register. Then, while the covers are still traveling on their blades, they are prepressed on the books. After prepressing, the books are automatically stripped from their blades and transferred to the building-in section.

The building-in section consists of a continuously moving pressure belt which presses the endsheets of the books and successive pairs of heated joint-forming irons, which engage each book as it enters the belts and travels with it as it is carried through the building-in section.[77]

Inline production saves space and time. The work is no longer piled on skids between operations but flows in a steady stream from rounding and backing to the finished product. All the many operations which were described in this unit can be performed in not more than two minutes.

Combining the Book with Its Paper Cover

Paper covers are not only used for magazines, catalogs, and advertising material, but also for the so-called paperbacks. We know already that in saddle-stitched books, cover and inside material are assembled prior to fastening. Side-stitched, sewed, and adhesive-bound books, on the other hand, are combined with their covers in separate operations. Depending upon the thickness of the paper cover and upon the equipment used for covering, scoring or creasing previous to covering may or may not be required.

Generally speaking, most magazines, catalogs, and paperbacks do not need prescored covers; the equipment used for such mass-production work is capable of handling flat cover sheets which are formed into their required shape during covering. Most paper-covered books are covered before trimming, and cut flush after covering. Even though paper-covered books are mostly flush-cut, there are also exceptions to be noted. Limited editions of deluxe books, for example, in

The SMYTH #57
Book Forming and Pressing Machine

Books from the Smyth #24 Casing-In Machine are delivered spine down to the conveyor-feeder of the #57 Book Forming and Pressing Machine, which feeds them on to the book lifter at the proper instant determined by the escapement mechanism. The book lifter positions each book individually in a spring loaded pocket which carries the book around the machine where it receives heat and pressure applied to the joint area seven times.

At the first of these stations the book is held lightly by the clamp pocket as the book body is tucked into the cover of the book while the heated creasers hold it for positioning in the joint.

The quick setting adhesive applied by the Joint and Side Pasting Attachment of the #24 Casing-In Machine holds the book in the shape formed by the heated joint creasers.

As the books complete their travel around the machine the clamp pocket is opened allowing the book to drop down the discharge chute on to a conveyor for inspection and jacketing before packing and shipping.

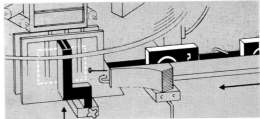

1 The infeed portion of the #57 coordinates the random timing of the book to match the cycling of the machine.

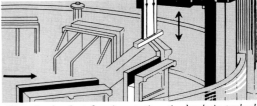

2 At the first forming station the book is tucked into the cover which is held in position by the joint creaser irons.

3 Completely formed and pressed books are released from the clamp pockets, slide down the discharge chute onto a conveyor for further processing.

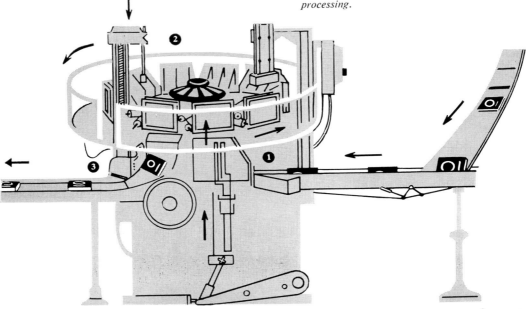

Europe are paper covered and are not trimmed at all until they receive their final binding, which is customarily individually designed for each collector. Overhang covers are used not only as temporary protectors for such books, but also for some quarterlies which may either be trimmed before covering or be sold without trimming. The latter is less customary in the United States than in Europe.

Related to paper covers and therefore presented together with them are covers made of individual units for the top and bottom of the book. The backbone may remain unprotected or it may be covered with paper or cloth. After this introduction we turn to a discussion of covering which is divided into the following five points: (1) manual covering, (2) semi-automatic covering, (3) fully automatic covering, (4) inline covering, and (5) covering with the stripping machine.

Manual covering. Manual covering is much too slow and costly to be used in long-run production work, but short runs or jobs that are not suitable for existing machinery may be manually covered in a number of ways. Side-stitched books may be stitched before covering and then glued on their backs to which the cover is thereafter applied. Both gluing and *drawing-on* of paper covers are done with such simple hand tools as brushes and bone folders. Sewed books can be handled in the same manner. If the cover is made of heavy paper it may be necessary to score or crease it before attaching it to the back of the book. In adhesive binding the cover can be folded back with its inside backbone out and coated with glue together with the material to be bound. After application of the adhesive, the cover is folded over the book and pressed onto its backbone; this operation is known as drawing-on.

Semi-automatic covering. Some systems of adhesive binding provide equipment for semi-automatic covering. The cover and the book are manually fed to equipment where they are glued; then the operator puts the cover over the book and inserts the covered book into a pressing station. Application of the adhesive to the cover, its placement over, and pressing with, the book may also be automatically performed by such a machine. The work of the operator merely consists in feeding the unbound material and in removing the covered books.

Fully automatic covering. Long-run production jobs must be done on fully automatic equipment. Such equipment may be either independent or part of a complete production line. First we discuss independent equipment for automatic covering; inline production is treated under the following heading.

One widely used covering machine is based on a rotating table with eight working stations. The table moves intermittently; when the table is at rest the work is done in all stations simultaneously. The rotating table is at working height. The operator occupies the first position in our diagram. Here he feeds the uncovered books into the machine. Each station is equipped with a pair of self-acting clamping jaws; the book is inserted between them where it remains for the whole trip through the machine. At the second station the back and both sides of the book are glued by a plunger and two angular tippers. At station three the book is permitted to rest and therewith to let the adhesive become set. The cover is applied at the fourth station. Now the book is positioned over the cover stacker in which the covers are loaded. The stacker rises and presses the top cover with its inside onto the glued backbone of the book; then the stack moves down, leaving the adhered cover on the book. A blower and mechanical devices insure the proper separation of the cover from its pile. At the next station, the fifth, book and cover are permitted to rest for drying. At the following sixth stop, the cover is pressed to the backbone of the book by a plunger and to both sides by a pair of nipping jaws. These bend the cover over and thereby form it to the shape of the book. In the seventh station the covered book is again allowed to dry; in the eighth and final position the clamps open and discharge the covered book with its backbone down onto a delivery mechanism. When the open clamps arrive at the next position, the cycle begins anew.

This machine is rated by its manufacturer at a production speed of 1400 to 1800 units per hour; it can handle books up to $1\frac{1}{8}$ inches thick in sizes up to $15 \times 10\frac{5}{8}$ inches.

Inline covering. Magazines, catalogs, and many other mass-production jobs are covered by inline equipment. Inline covering machinery may be part of a production line including either side stitching, or adhesive binding, or both. Imported inline covering equipment is used for adhesive binding; domestic equipment forms part of production lines which are often capable of side stitching as well as adhesive binding.

We briefly describe two designs of inline covering machines which are used in conjunction with adhesive binding. One kind is very similar to the automatic covering equipment presented in the preceding paragraphs. It has a rotary turntable equipped with eight pairs of clamps. By the type of its motion this machine is often described as merry-go-round equipment. The book is fed into the machine with its back down. The back is trimmed in order to remove the folds of signatures; now the book consists completely of individual leaves. Then the back is coated with adhesive and the cover is applied to the back by pressing and forming. The covered book is ejected onto a delivery conveyor.

The second, and more recent, model here described is constructed of vertical clamp conveyor units and is often likened to a Ferris wheel. In this design, too, the backs of signatures are first trimmed, then the back is coated with adhesive, and the cover is attached to the back. The speed of either type of machine is approximately the same, namely up to 200 units per minute.

Domestic inline covering equipment is connected to the conveying system used for adhesive-bound or side-stitched books. Either kind arrives at the covering station in a more or less bound form; side-stitched books pass the stitcher heads before they arrive at the covering stations; adhesive-bound books receive one coating of adhesive prior to covering. Either kind is coated at its backbone by an adhesive before the cover is attached to the book.

The covers are placed on a continuous feeder and conveyed onto the main conveyor in perfect timing with the books after their backbone is coated with adhesive. The cover-forming mechanism presses the cover at the backbone to the book as well as to its side, thereby giving the cover the proper shape. Domestic equipment is rated for upward of 150 books per minute. It is manufactured in two models. One binds books up to 1 inch, the other books up to 2½ inches thick; the largest size book that can be handled by these models is 16 × 11½ inches for the first and 16 × 12 inches for the second type; these large sizes often permit two-up production whereby the output can be doubled.

Covering with the stripping machine. The stripping machine would be better designated as a reinforcing machine. It permits the application of strips of reinforcements, paper or cloth, to two units at their joining sides. This machine is also capable, with the necessary attachment, of putting the reinforcement around the backbone of a book and over the edges of its top and bottom cover. In many instances the covers are side stitched together with the book and then reinforced at the backbone on the stripping machine.

Jacketing, Packing, and Shipping

Assembling of book and cover is the last major step in book production; it results in the final product of binding, the completely bound book. Depending on the nature of this final product and depending on the requirements of the specific job, this end product may be subjected to various subsidiary operations such as jacketing, inspecting, packing, and shipping. Jacketing is peculiar to edition binding of books to be sold through retail stores. You may remember that the book jacket has two functions; one is to protect the book, the other to attract the eye of customers.

Inspecting, packing, and shipping are not peculiar to specific branches of binding as they are necessities in all production processes. But some binding plants are also equipped to handle the individual packing and shipping of magazines or books. As this kind of packing and shipping is very important in mass production and mass distribution of bound material, it deserves to be explained. Our discussion of the subject is divided into the following five points: (1) inspecting, (2) jacketing, (3) individual packing and shipping of casebound books, (4) individual packing and shipping of magazines, and (5) packing and shipping in bulk.

Inspecting. The extent to which the end product of binding is inspected depends on the nature of the work and on the standards of a bindery. Many edition-binding plants inspect every book as a matter of course before jacketing. Magazines and mass-produced catalogs, for example, are not

Diagram of the Dexter jacketing machine. The built-in book is usually provided with a paper jacket. The book is automatically opened, the flat jacket is put on it and the two flaps of the jacket are mechanically turned in. The jacketed book is closed and discharged.

The SHERIDAN
Clam Shell Coverer

The primary purpose of the Sheridan Clam Shell Coverer is to apply a paper cover to a set of previously gathered and side stitched signatures. The machine itself consists of a hinged top, book clamp conveyor traveling in an oval path over the various processing stations. Book backbones are exposed below the clamps.

Books enter the clamp system in-line, are registered against a pin in the clamp, then transported over a gluing station. Simultaneously, a cover has been fed by a cover feeder from a fanned supply of covers by means of a sucker bar system and pinch rollers to a cover conveyor. The book and the corresponding cover arrive in register at the cover applier drum at which point the cover is rolled or pressed to the backbone of the book. The book, with cover attached, is then carried to a cover breaker, where the back and two sides along the backbone are pressed by formers, giving the book a tight, square back. From here it is carried to the discharge or delivery.

Book sizes range from 7 x 5″ minimum to 12 x 9″ maximum, up to 1⅛″ thickness, with special attachments for 2″ thickness. Operating speeds go to 160 books per minute.

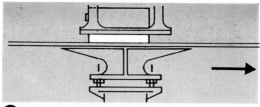

1 *Incoming books on levelling plate.*

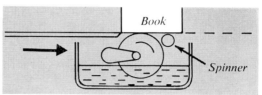

2 *Books are transported over gluing station.*

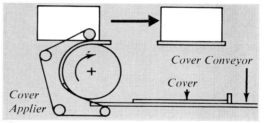

3 *Covers arrive and are pressed to backbone.*

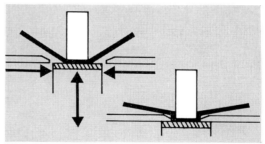

4 *The cover breaker shapes the two sides along the backbone by applying formers.*

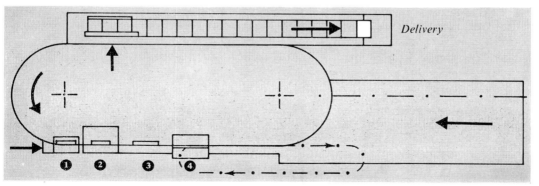

Flow Plan of a SMYTH *Automation Line*

The diagram below shows one possible automation line where books are forwarded automatically from the Hopper Feeder of the Smyth Rounder and Backer through the Triple Lining and Headbanding Machine to the Casing-In Machine and on into the Book Forming and Pressing Machine without manual handling.

This system is made possible by the use of timing or escapement fingers which stop the book from proceeding along the conveyor feeder, allowing it to enter each machine only at the proper instant. An electrical interlock stops each preceding machine should a jam or malfunction occur anywhere along the line. The four machines are individually shown and described on the opposite page.

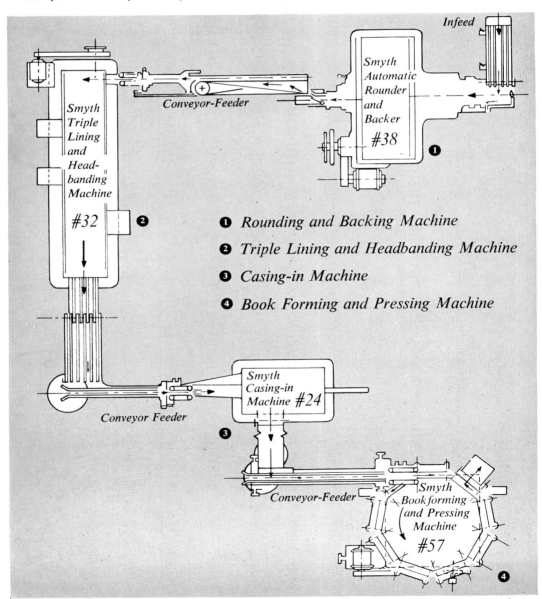

❶ *Rounding and Backing Machine*

❷ *Triple Lining and Headbanding Machine*

❸ *Casing-in Machine*

❹ *Book Forming and Pressing Machine*

❶ *Smyth Automatic
Rounder and Backer #38*

❷

*Smyth Triple Lining and
Headbanding Machine #32*

The book is processed in this machine spine down
so it can easily receive three coats of hot animal
glue, two pieces of mull or crash and one lining
paper, usually with two headbands attached.
Variations in the quantity and type of material
must be accommodated in order to provide for
differences in specifications of the book. This array of material is completely rolled four times to
insure good adhesion to the back of the book.

The first machine in the line forms a round in the
back of the book after which a joint is formed on
each side of the book by an oscillating, concave
backing iron which deforms the signatures to the
required shape. Books proceed through the rest of
the line with no manual handling.

❸

Smyth #24 Casing-In Machine

Books from the Smyth Triple Liner must be
turned over with the spine up in order to be processed on the Casing-In Machine. Here special
adhesive is usually applied to the joint and crash
area while less expensive paste is applied to both
end sheets as the book moves vertically between
two knurled paste rolls while it is carried on a conveyor blade. The case or cover is actually hung
over the freshly pasted book. Both cover and book
are lifted free of the blade as one unit and released
spine down so they may travel with no damage
along the conveyor into the Book Forming and
Pressing Machine #57.

❹

Smyth Book Forming and Pressing Machine #57

This machine applies pressure over the entire end
sheet area of the book continuously during its trip
through the machine. At the first forming station
the book is tucked firmly into the cover which is
held at the joint line by the creasers in order to
square the end sheet with the cover. At 7 stations
intermittent heat and pressure is applied by the
yielding creaser bars in order to set the adhesive
in the joint and form the cover to the book. Pneumatic rubbing rolls press the back of the cover to
the book to insure adhesion between the cloth
back of the case and the book whenever tight-
back side-sewn books are processed. The completed book is now ready for inspection and
packing.

necessarily inspected individually; inspection can also be done by a method of planned sampling. If a job has trouble spots of its own, these are particularly watched during inspection; otherwise inspecting is concerned with the general quality level of the work.

Jacketing. Jacketing can be done either by hand or by a jacketing machine. Depending on the weight of the paper on which they are printed, jackets may need prescoring before they can be put over the book covers by hand jacketing. In machine jacketing, the books are loaded in a hopper and the jackets in a continuous feeder. The machine forms the jacket into the required shape and applies it to the book. Some jacketing machines can produce up to 4000 units per hour.

In fully automatic book production "jacketing machines may be attached directly to the output of the casing-in and building-in equipment. Books traveling continuously through the machine are split and the covers opened up in such a manner that the jackets are fed in on top of the opened covers and these two elements are carried through folding belts which fold and crease the jackets around the covers, after which the covers are closed and the finished book is delivered."[78]

Individual packing and shipping of casebound books. Casebound books must be well protected for shipping. Various kinds of corrugated containers are commonly used for this purpose. It is, of course, possible to put a book into its container by hand; but manual packing is much too expensive for production runs. These are packed on semi-automatic equipment of one kind or another. In one such machine the containers are sleeves with open ends; the books are inserted into these

sleeves and the container with the inserted book is placed on the machine which closes and seals both ends, applies an identifying symbol and, where desired, a shipping label. Book manufacturing plants often render warehousing services to their customers; the packed books may be stored until the publisher orders shipment.

Individual packing and shipping of magazines. Some magazines are shipped without any packing at all; the shipping label is attached directly to their covers. This operation is done by automatic equipment on long-run jobs. Other magazines are packed by putting them into either envelopes or sleeves. The name and address of the recipient are either put on labels or directly applied to the envelope or sleeve. Individual packing and shipping of magazines require very careful planning; their numbers may go into many hundreds of thousands, and they must be addressed in accordance with post office regulations. In some very large publication printing plants, a United States Post Office is located directly in the plant for convenience.

Packing and shipping in bulk. Not all printing and binding is done on a mass-production scale. Very many jobs are comparatively small, and very many jobs are often shipped in bulk to the customer. A quantity of the material is put in cartons, which should neither be too large nor too heavy for handling, and delivered by one of the various transportation media to the customer. This kind of packing is still done by hand.

At long last, the job is out of the house, as the printer or binder says, and if the customer is pleased with it and pays his bill everybody is happy.

Section 10:   Miscellaneous Supplementary and Finishing Processes

Binding is by no means the only manufacturing process whereby a printed product receives its final form. As the scope of printing expanded and as the number of its products multiplied, many supplementary processes became necessary. In this section we will briefly review some of the more commonly used subsidiary and finishing processes. Unfortunately these cannot easily be systematized. Some subsidiary processes result in visible images and therefore resemble printing as defined in this manual. Others take the already printed sheet as their point of departure and merely convert and adapt it as needed for the

end product. For our purposes it is expedient to divide the subject into four units: (1) ruling, (2) bronzing, varnishing, and other surface treatments, (3) die-cutting, and (4) various finishing methods.

Ruling

Ruling stands almost completely by itself. As it produces visible images starting from unprinted paper, it is in this respect the equivalent of printing itself. But as these images are limited to simple lines, and to lines only, ruling is a highly specialized method of printing. Ruling is traditionally discussed in conjunction with binding and we therefore follow this procedure.

Ruling is used for the making of accountants' forms, notebooks, and similar purposes. It is also possible to print patterns of lines such as are obtained by ruling, but ruling has three distinct advantages over printing. One is the absence of glare, the other is simplicity of multicolor work, the third is that printer's ink may cause writing done with pen and ink to skip. Glare refers to the effect of more light being reflected from printed rules than from the paper on which the rules are printed. Glare is a strain on the user's eyes and therefore objectionable. The reason why ruled lines do not glare is to be found in the composition of ruling inks. These are aqueous liquids, and their color is not provided by insoluble pigments, as in printing ink, but by dyes which are absorbed into the surface of the paper. It should be added that offset lithography seems to be capable of producing less glary lines than other printing methods and that certain kinds of ruled forms are now often produced by web offset printing.

The second advantage of ruling over printing, the simplicity of ruling in various colors side by side in one operation, is also closely related to the nature of ruling inks. Essentially, ruling uses the same technique that is commonly known as *split fountain* in printing. In split-fountain printing, the ink reservoir is divided into several compartments, each holding ink of a different color. But here the analogy ends. Printing ink is a highly viscous material that must be passed through a series of rollers before it can be applied to the image carrier. Ruling ink is of low viscosity and can be fed to the ruling pens or disks by capillary action. Therefore many different colors can be ruled extremely close to each other.

Ruling can be done with two different kinds of machines. One is known as *pen-ruling* machine, the other as *disk-ruling* machine. Both will now be described.

Pen ruling. The ruling element for this type does "not resemble the ordinary writing pen. Ruling pens are made of brass and actually are tiny channels made by folding a strip of brass in a T-shape. These pens have a flat shank by means of which they are clamped into the beam, and more than one pen may be on the same shank."[79] Pen-ruling machines are equipped with a moving blanket on which the paper is firmly held by means of cords. The blanket with the paper passes under the ruling pens which are stationary and

deposit the ruling ink on the moving paper. Ingenious mechanical arrangements make it possible to raise and lower the pens according to a given ruling pattern. Lines to be made at angles to each other are known as *struck* lines in the trade. Contemporary pen-ruling machines are automatically fed and operated. They can rule sheets of paper on both sides in both directions and in many different colors during a single trip through the machine.

Disk ruling. The ruling elements of this type of equipment are thin metal disks, attached to a common shaft, or spindle. "The disks are inked by means of a rubber roller which revolves in an ink trough supplied with the proper amount of ink from automatic ink fountains."[80] Disk ruling is faster than pen ruling; the paper is fed in rolls, automatically sheeted, and completely processed by the machine.

It might be mentioned that mass-production items such as stenographers' pads can be produced on fully automatic equipment which not only rules but also prints, binds, and counts the final product.

Bronzing, Varnishing, and Other Surface Treatments

Such printed products as labels and box tops are often further enhanced by bronzing, embossing, and varnishing. Other products which are exposed to repeated handling—catalog covers or book jackets, to mention some—are varnished or laminated for protection. In this unit we present brief descriptions of these surface treatments, beginning with bronzing.

Bronzing. Bronzing has the object of embellishing printed items by application of metallic powders. "Bronzing consists of three related operations. First an adhesive known as *goldsize* is applied to the sheet, then the sheet is dusted with bronze powder, and finally the bronzed sheet is run through a burnishing machine."[81]

The first step is the application of the size or adhesive for the bronze. This adhesive is a tacky ink whose color depends on the color of the bronze to be used. For gold bronze the size may range "in color from yellow to a dark green according to the color bronze and the effect desired." Sizing for bronzing is done on a printing press either by letterpress or by lithography. The printing-image carrier used for sizing determines the shape of the bronzed image. After the sheet is printed with size of the required color, it is automatically fed in the bronzing machine while still wet. There the bronze powder is dusted "over the entire surface of the sheet; where the sheet is printed with size, the bronze adheres; dusting pads dust off the excess bronze before the sheet leaves the bronzing machine."

After the sheet has dried it is burnished. Burnishing gives the bronzed areas additional luster. "This effect is obtained by flattening and polishing the bronze particles until they form a very smooth surface. Burnishing machines have one or several pairs of cylinder units. Each of these consists of a steel and a composition roller. The steel roller runs faster than the composition roller; friction is caused whereby the bronzed sheet is polished." After burnishing the sheet can be either varnished or not, as the job may demand.

Varnishing. Varnishing, our next subject, has two different purposes. One is to protect the printed sheet, the other is to make it glossy and therefore more attractive. Varnishing can be done in several ways, either directly on the press, or by screen-process printing, or on coating machines. Another point worth mentioning is that there are various types of coatings available, each of which has its own purpose.[82]

Print varnish. Print varnish is also known as *press* varnish because it can be applied directly on a printing or lithographic press. Print varnish is often called *spot* varnish because it is possible in print varnishing to select place and shape in which the varnish will appear on the printed sheet. The shape and position of the varnished image are determined by the image carrier used for print varnishing. Spot varnishing can be done either as an independent operation after the sheet has been printed, or by use of multicolor presses in the same press run in which the sheet is printed. Print varnishing is a very economical procedure but does not result in as high a sheen as is obtainable by other methods. Consequently, print varnishing is not selected for high gloss jobs.

Varnishing by screen printing. Screen printing has, as you remember, the ability of depositing exceptionally thick ink films. The same holds true for overprint varnishes, and varnishing by screen printing can therefore be used where exceptionally high gloss is wanted. As the varnish is here also applied in the press—either manually or mechanically—by means of an image carrier, the shape and position of the varnished image can be controlled as in press varnishing. Screen printing

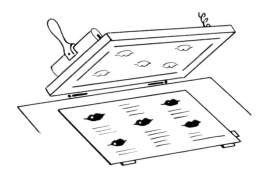

Varnishing by manual screen-process printing. Short run jobs can be efficiently spot varnished in screen process.

thereby supplements print varnishing, but it does so at a higher cost.

Varnishing with coating machines. Sheets that are to be varnished all over are processed on coating machines where the coating of varnish is applied to the sheet by means of a roller. After coating, the sheet is passed through a drier where the varnish is force-dried in a minimum of time. Heat and air exchange is usually employed for this purpose. The dried sheet is delivered in a stacker.

Laminating. Laminating is another method of protecting a printed sheet and endowing it with a very high sheen. In this method a thin film of a plastic material is bonded to the sheet, either by means of adhesives or by heat and pressure. The method of application depends on the nature of the job in hand and on the plastic material selected for it. This selection can be made to endow the sheet with certain characteristics besides gloss, depending on the kinds of plastic selected. It should be mentioned that the term *liquid laminating*, which is sometimes used, does not indicate laminating of a plastic film with paper, but refers to the coating of paper with coating materials made from plastics.

Embossing. Embossing is defined "as an industrial way of creating relief images on printed, lithographed or blank paper and similar material in order to create a beautifying effect."[83] Embossing is done in two different ways. One is called *roller embossing*, the other *plate embossing*. These two types of embossing are executed on different equipment and serve different purposes.

Roller embossing or pebbling. Roller embossing applies continuous patterns over the whole surface of the material to be embossed. The equipment is a rolling press where two rollers rotate against each other. The pattern is engraved on the embossing roller which is usually made of steel. The second roller has a soft surface, either cotton or papier-mâché (a composition material consisting of several paper layers bonded together). The stock is pressed between these two rollers which are adjustable for regulating the depth of embossing. Advertising material is often pebbled in one of the several standard patterns which are available at trade shops specializing in this field. Among these patterns are usually eggshell, moire, linen, and similar designs.

Plate or spot embossing. Plate or spot embossing is the method whereby individual designs, as distinguished from all-over patterns, are embossed. This type of embossing is used in label work as well as for many other purposes. Plate embossing is done in vertical presses as already described. The embossing plate or embossing die may be made in one of many techniques, such as hand engraving, pantograph engraving, and etching, for example. Duplicates of these dies can be made by electrotyping. Electrotypes for embossing are either nickel or chromeplated for long-run work.

The paper is embossed by placing it between the embossing die and the *counter*, or makeready, in a press and by forcing it into the intaglio areas of the die. The counter is made by pressing the embossing die into a specially prepared makeready plate which is soft at this stage but hardens thereafter for good. Forcing the embossing die into the makeready plates produces a relief, or male, counter to the intaglio, or female, embossing die. All non-embossing areas are cut away in the makeready in order to permit forcing of the paper into the recesses of the intaglio die.

Flocking and beading. Flocking and beading are other embellishing methods for printed products. They are used for so-called novelties, as well as for greeting cards and gift wrappings. Flocking, beading, and the similar application of sequins require the laying down of an adhesive in the desired shape. Then one of these materials, either flock, or beads, or sequins, are dusted onto the stock where they will stick to the wet adhesive. Beads and sequins do not need further treatments but flock, which consists of colored cotton or rayon fibers, must be made to stand up in order to achieve the velour-like effect for which it was selected. This effect can be obtained in various ways, either electrically or by exposing the flocked sheet to beater bars.

Die-cutting

Certain printed products such as displays, labels, and folding paper boxes must be cut to fancy or irregular shapes. Such cutting tasks cannot be performed by guillotine cutters, which can only make straight cuts, but are accomplished by means of cutting dies and a variety of different presses or other specialized machines. For our purposes it is convenient to divide the subject into three points: (1) steel-rule die-cutting, (2) die-cutting with high dies in vertical presses, and (3) PMC die-cutting. Each of these kinds is now briefly discussed.

Steel-rule die-cutting. Cardboard displays, advertising folders, and paper folding boxes are usually shaped by steel-rule die-cutting. Steel-rule die-cutting is distinguished in several points from other kinds of die-cutting. One of these is the fact that steel-rule die-cutting can combine cutting, scoring, and creasing in a single operation; another difference is that the material is either cut singly or in rather small quantities; the third, that the die itself is made in a distinctly different technique which is much less expensive than other die-making methods and most significantly so where dies of large sizes are needed.

Steel-rule dies consist of three different materials. One is steel, the second is plywood, and the third is either rubber or cork. Plywood is the base of the die; steel—or more precisely cutting, scoring, or creasing steel rule—does the cutting, scoring, and creasing. Rubber or cork, finally, which are both compressible, function as springs which are compressed during the act of cutting but expand again once the pressure is released and thereby push the cut material away from the die. What follows is a brief outline of the main steps taken in the making of steel-rule dies.

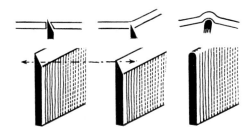

Different kinds of steel rules are used for cutting, for the making of cut scores, and for creasing. The first picture shows a cutting rule, the second a rule for making cut scores, and the third a creasing rule for crease scores.

Small portion of a steel-rule die. The steel rule is in-serted into channels jig-sawed into the die board with the cutting edge protruding. The two blocks adjacent to the rule are either rubber or cork. These blocks are compressed during the cutting action but expand when the pressure is removed; when they expand they push the cut and scored stock away from the die.

The first step is the drawing of a plan for the die. This plan is usually made directly on the printed sheet to be die-cut, known as the *die-sheet*. Next, this plan is transferred to the *die-board*, as the plywood base is usually called. Now the board shows the blueprint for the future die. As the die is made by inserting cutting and creasing rules into the die-board, the board must be jigsawed next. Jigsawing results in saw tracks into which the steel rule will be later inserted. In jigsawing, the die-maker leaves several smaller areas of the board unsawed, thereby providing the *bridges* whereby the die-board is held together. After the board is sawed, strips of rules are bent into the required shapes by means of male and female dies. In order to make it possible to insert the rule where the board is uncut, the steel rule is notched in all places which correspond to the bridges in the board. After inserting, the die is provided with its rubber or cork springs, an operation known sometimes as *corking*.

Steel-rule dies can be either single-unit or multiple-unit dies. Single-unit dies are ordinarily used in display work and in other applications where several different units are combined on a sheet. Multiple steel-rule dies are sometimes used for the making of paper folding boxes and, wherever many items of the same shape and size are present on the same sheet.[84]

Die-cutting with steel-rule dies can be done on several kinds of presses, including platen presses, flatbed-cylinder presses, and vertical presses. Such presses may or may not be equipped with auto-matic feeders, deliveries, and stripping attach-ments whereby the die-cut product is separated

from the *waste*, as the remaining areas of the sheet are called.

Cutting with high, or hollow, dies. Many label orders are cut with high, or hollow, dies on descending vertical presses. These dies are capable of cutting lifts of varying thickness, say up to about one inch, in a single operation. "For die-cutting on descending type presses, the sheet is first cut into sections of appropriate size; quarters, for example. A lift of such sections, varying with the job from 25 and up, is placed on the bed of the press which has a wooden base. The high-die is carefully registered manually on this lift by the operator. The down stroke causes the die to penetrate the stack of labels."[85] Then the operator removes the die-cut product as well as the waste and proceeds with the job.

Die-cutting on PMC machines. This kind of die-cutting is a method especially suitable for mass-production label work. It is known as PMC by the initials of the Printing Machinery Company which manufactures the machines used in this method. Dies for PMC cutting are of the high-die family. "The die is positioned in the bed of the machine, the lifts of square-cut labels, which may contain as many as 500 units, are fed into the machine, positioned by guides and automatically forwarded into cutting position. The die-cut labels come up through the hollow cutting die and are removed by the operator."[86]

Miscellaneous Finishing Methods

Depending on the purpose and nature of a printed job, it can be subjected to a number of different finishing processes, some of which are already described in the preceding units. Here we will first explain the mounting and assembling of card-board displays and then briefly identify some of the many other subsidiary operations.

Mounting of cardboard displays. Most card-board displays are printed either by lithography or by screen process. Lithographed displays are usually printed on paper, whereas screen-printed displays may be printed either on paper or on cardboard of the required final thickness in which case they do not need to be mounted after print-ing. Mounting of paper to board can be done either with a gluing machine or with a mounting machine. In both cases the paper to be mounted must be coated with an adhesive, then placed on the board and pressed thereafter. If a gluing ma-chine is used for application of the adhesive, the whole operation is manual. The sheet is manually fed in the gluing machine, removed by hand, placed in the same manner on the mounting board, and the mounted material is finally either put through a rolling press known as a wringer, or put into a standing press of one kind or another.

Mounting machines can either mount to one side of the board or to both. In the latter case, they are called duo-mounters. Here the whole operation is automatic but for the feeding. The sheet is glued, combined with the mounting board and put automatically through a rolling press before it is delivered and stacked. Mounted displays are either straight cut on a guillotine cutter or die-cut, as already described.

Display assembly. Many cardboard displays need assembly operations which entail the attaching of various parts to the body of the display. These operations often consist in pasting and are executed either by brush, or by screen printing, or by means of a margin gluing machine. Among the most frequent and also most simple of these operations is *easeling*, meaning the attaching of a collapsible cardboard stand to the display. Displays can also be equipped with light flashers and motors; the last kind is called *animated*.

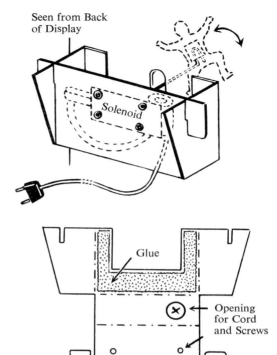

Example of a motorized or animated cardboard display. The display is shipped flat and set up where it will be used. A diecut cardboard pocket glued to the back of the display, serves as housing for the solenoid motor. The motor produces a rocking motion on the display.

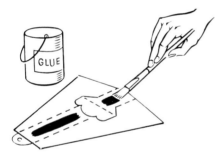

Glue is applied to the back of a cardboard easel with a brush. The unglued area in the center is the lock of the easel.

Finishing of folding paper boxes. Die-cutting and stripping are essential operations in the manufacturing of paper folding boxes. Gluing, windowing, waxing, varnishing, and laminating are some of the more generally employed optional finishing methods of folding boxes. As these products are manufactured in huge quantities, all finishing operations are done by means of high-speed specialized equipment.

Die-cutting for folding cartons is done with steel-rule dies. Two kinds of steel-rule dies are distinguished in this industry. One is known as *jigged* and is made by jigsawing the die-board as

already described. A second type is arrived at by assembling strips of cutting and creasing rules in a chase between wooden furniture. As stripping is an important production step in the making of folding cartons, this industry has developed several stripping techniques. Stripping "can be done by hand, with the aid of pneumatic or electric hammers or specially built mechanical stripping machines some of which permit inline operation with the cutting and creasing press."[87] (Cutting and creasing in line with rotogravure printing of paper folding boxes is described in Chapter VII, Section 3.)

Some types of folding boxes need gluing prior to use. This operation can be done either by the manufacturers of cartons or in the plants of their users. Gluing machines of various kinds are available for this purpose. In many cases, gluing is combined with folding of cartons and attaching of the glued flaps to the corresponding parts of the carton itself. *Windowing* has the purpose of showing the product which is inside the carton to the customer. A window is die-cut when the carton is manufactured. This window is stripped and later protected on automatic equipment with a piece of transparent plastic. *Waxing* is used to impregnate cartons; varnishing and laminating have beautifying as well as functional results.

The bound or otherwise finished product has now become ready for shipment to the printer's customer. The products that were made in so many different stages, that have been on the minds of so many craftsmen, supervisors, management people, and salesmen, finally leave the precincts of printing which are already occupied by new jobs. A thorough discussion of printed products is outside the frame of this manual. It must suffice to mention that some printed products enter the arenas of advertising and sales promotion where the contests are short, deadly, and with no end; some that serve for packaging, travel through wholesale warehouses into retail shops and supermarkets, and many terminate their existence before your dinner time; some that give us our daily news are left in subway cars, trains, planes, and buses to re-enter the field as raw material of paper and board making; some flow through our wallets, disappearing mysteriously at jet age speed; some amuse us for a short time; and a good number of them is preserved on the shelves of public and private libraries for their lasting value.

Chapter XI

Art-and-Copy Preparation

Few other phases of printing production command as broad and diversified an audience as does art-and-copy preparation. Practically everybody active in the graphic arts meets the problems of product appearance—and with that some aspect of art-and-copy preparation—at some time or another; and a vast number of people must wrestle with this subject day in and day out. Among them are advertising production men, account executives, authors, binders, buyers of printed material, camera men, commercial artists, compositors, copywriters, creative photographers, designers, editors, electrotypers, estimators, finishers, layout men, operators, paper and printing salesmen, pasteup men, planners, photoengravers, strippers, and typographers, to mention some representative occupational groups.

This chapter is divided into four sections: (1) different kinds of printed products and their art-and-copy preparation, (2) the conversion of reading matter for printing, (3) the preparation of pictures (including all kinds of illustrative material) for printing, and (4) the assembly of pictures and reading matter for reproduction.

Section 1: Different Kinds of Printed Products and Their Art-and-Copy Preparation

The purpose of the printed-product-to-be is the first and foremost concern of everybody participating in art-and-copy preparation. This purpose governs practically everything: it is decisive for format and design of the piece, and it controls not only the printing but also the binding or other finishing operations to which the printed piece must be subjected.

The number of printed products is legion; it is hence absolutely impossible to enumerate them all. Nor is this necessary for the understanding of the relations between printed products and the task of art-and-copy preparation, particularly not since the nature of a printed product alone cannot be taken as decisive, disregarding the quantity in which this product must be produced. Take, for example, a quarterly journal, of interest to a limited number of learned people and a national magazine read by the millions. Both are classified as magazines, but the first is printed in lots of a few thousands and the second may be manufactured by the hundreds of thousands or even in millions. Obviously these two kinds of magazines pose very different problems for art-and-copy preparation in spite of their common classification. The same holds true for many other printed products.

If we want to arrive at a grouping practical for our purposes, we cannot rely on the simple method of generic classification but must look into the different social tasks for which printed products are intended. Surprisingly, we can arrive at such a grouping if we ask the question: Who pays for the printed product? In answer to this question, we can divide printed products into three broad classes: (1) printed products that are completely paid for by the final customer, for example, consumer goods and packages, (2) printed products that are partially paid for by the final customer and partially by advertisers, such as newspapers and other periodicals, and (3) printed products for which the recipient does not pay at all, namely, advertising and similar material which in this manual is classified as *persuasion* printing. Each of these different groups poses its own problems for art-and-copy preparation.

Printed consumer goods. In our first group of printed products, those which are completely paid for by the final customer, are such items of commerce as books, greeting cards, maps, and pictures which are bought by the public for individual consumption. In the same category belong also several different printed products which are not bought by the public but by business, government, and similar organizations for administrative purposes. Here we have business forms of many different kinds, tickets, and stationery, to mention only some. All products of this group have the common denominator that printing—and the related binding or other finishing—is the main industrial process whereby these items are manufactured.

Package printing. Package printing, too, belongs in the class of printed products which are completely paid for by the final customer. To be sure, the final customer of packaged wares is not informed how much of their price is due to the cost of the printed package, but he, or more frequently she, must still pay for this part of the total cost whenever a box of candy, a carton of frozen food, a can of beer, or a plastic bag of vegetables is bought. Box tops, labels, heat-sealed plastics, lithographed metal cans, paper folding boxes, and many similar items belong in this group of package printing, which has experienced an unprecedented growth in recent times.

Newspapers and other periodicals. The group of printed products which are sold to the public for less than cost is enormous. It includes practically all daily and weekly newspapers and most magazines, as well as many specialized reference books for technical and business purposes. Most of these items are sold to the public; but the price paid by the public is considerably less than it would have to be without advertising. The final consumer pays a subsidized price with advertising revenue taking care of the difference.

Persuasion printing. This last of our groups is composed of printed products for which the recipient does not pay at all. In this group we place not only advertising material but also all other printed pieces that have the purpose of in-fluencing the recipient in some way or other—politically, charitably, or culturally, to mention some non-business uses of persuasion printing. Examples of persuasion printing can be found on every desk and in every mail box at any time. They include direct mail advertising, broadsides, announcements, catalogs, house organs, company magazines, as well as those called *controlled circulation*, which are given to the subscriber.

Length-of-run or quantity. Like many other schemes of classification, that of taking "who pays" as a criterion is not always completely satisfactory. But if we combine this criterion with the second of quantity, or, as the printer often says, length-of-run, we arrive at a practical method of grouping. The standard of quantity is here used to divide printing into the three groups of mass production or long-run printing, into medium-length runs, and into short runs.

National magazines, newspapers published in our larger cities, package printing for widely known consumer goods, and the very popular paper-bound mystery novels are typical products of mass-production printing. Most persuasion printing and many non-fiction paperbacks, weekly newspapers, and specialized magazines for a larger audience are printed in medium-length runs, whereas learned journals, presentations, circulars for local distribution or to highly specialized groups can exemplify short-run jobs. It is unfortunately not possible to form neat numerical brackets for each of these three classifications as everything depends on the nature of the product. Twenty-five thousand trade books is a substantial run, but twenty-five thousand trading stamps is a very small order.

Our next step is to test the usefulness of these classifications by applying them to the present subject, art-and-copy preparation. We begin with our first group, that of consumer products.

Art-and-copy preparation for consumer goods. Economically, printed consumer goods are not different from other consumer goods; all must conform to the laws of the market place where price is the most stringent qualification. As price is of paramount importance, manufacturing must be carefully planned and controlled. Each type of product has, of course, its specific design and manufacturing problems, but all printed consumer goods have, nonetheless, certain common denominators which express themselves in art-and-copy preparation methods. One of these denominators is standardization of products, the other is specialization of people in charge of art-and-copy preparation. As economy of production is an overriding consideration in this field, some measure of standardization is inevitable. It should be understood that mass-produced consumer items must be more standardized than those produced in medium-length runs, and that these are still more standardized than short-run items. How does the degree of standardization influence art-and-copy preparation? A few examples will clarify these relations.

Take the product "book," for example. Paperbacks and low-priced children's books are sold in enormous quantities by variety department stores, chain drugstores, and similar outlets. These kinds of books are highly standardized; art-and-copy preparation is, consequently, in the hands of experienced specialists who know what is possible and practical under given conditions, just as they know what cannot be done with the available equipment and facilities. If basic changes in design are intended, they are extensively discussed with the people in charge of manufacturing until the most satisfactory solution has been found.

But not all books are mass produced; some are manufactured in medium-length runs, others in very small quantities. In such cases, standardization is less noticeable but specialization of designers and layout people is still prevalent. In art-and-copy preparation for consumer goods there is, in general, less time pressure and a more fully developed co-operation between the printer and his customer than in persuasion printing. Nor is this relation of manufacturing and design staffs hampered by a lack of knowledge on the part of the latter group. The design and production of books, possibly the most important short-run consumer items produced by printing, is amply discussed in the literature, and a novice who wants to learn can find plenty of information in print.[1]

Art-and-copy preparation for package printing. The situation in this field is similar to that in the field of printed consumer goods. As the cost of the package is part of the total unit cost, manufacturers using package printing must be cost and price conscious. Specialization and standardization develop as a matter of necessity, and the co-operation between the producers and the buyers of package material is usually very close as all concerned are most interested in efficient and inexpensive production. Package design has become a highly specialized field; package de-

signers are trained to understand the requirements of package production and they have learned to adapt their designs to these requirements. Art-and-copy preparation for packaging is therefore a clearly defined activity with a well-developed literature.[2]

Art-and-copy preparation for newspapers and other periodicals. Newspapers and magazines are the two main representatives of printed products partially paid for by the buyer and partially by the advertiser. There are many differences between newspapers and other periodicals, as well as within each of these two main groups. But all of them have some points in common: one is the regularity with which they are published; the second is the constancy of their format and of the printing method by which they are produced; the third and final common feature is that they all need two kinds of art-and-copy preparation: one for editorial content, the other for advertisements. The first mentioned is customarily assigned to staff specialists who do this kind of work as a matter of course and are experts at it.

The preparation of advertisements for newspapers and other periodicals can be assigned to different occupational specialists, depending on the nature of the publication and of the advertisement. Newspapers are, as a rule, printed in the publisher's printing plant which has its own composing room and is sometimes also equipped to make photoengravings. Some large newspapers have their own photoengraving departments; more commonly, a newspaper has working arrangements with a nearby photoengraver. In the last decade, many newspapers have installed electromechanical photoengraving equipment which has been found satisfactory in this field for the conversion of photographs into relief image carriers. Local advertisers can submit their copy to the advertising department of a newspaper which will assist in and may take care of art-and-copy preparation for them.

The advertisements of large regional or national advertisers are usually prepared by advertising agencies or by the art departments of advertisers; image conversion is included in the preparation of such advertisements and these arrive at the newspaper plant most often as stereotype mats but also as duplicate plates including electrotypes, stereotypes, and plastic plates. Advertisements to be printed in gravure newspaper supplements are handled differently. In these cases the advertising agencies which develop the advertisements also procure the necessary positives from gravure trade plants which are in a position to supply this material as needed for reproduction in each of the several methods whereby gravure supplements are produced in different plants.

In the preparation of advertisements for newspapers it is kept in mind that various papers have differences in page sizes, column width, number of columns per page, different specifications as to solids and fineness, or ruling number of halftone screens, type faces and sizes, particularly if the type image is to appear in reverse, that is, white on a black background. Nor will all newspapers print spot colors and ROP colors.

Fortunately the literature on art-and-copy preparation for newspapers is well developed. Many large newspapers publish their own guides for art-and-copy preparation. In addition there are a number of reports prepared by the Joint Committee on Newspaper Printing formed by the American Newspaper Publishers Association (ANPA) and the American Association of Advertising Agencies (AAAA).[3]

Most recently, several weekly newspapers have changed to web-offset printing from the traditional newspaper relief printing method. Art-and-copy preparation follows here the procedures customary for offset lithography which is discussed in following sections of this chapter.

Art-and-copy preparation for magazines. Now we will discuss art-and-copy preparation for magazines. Here we distinguish again between art-and-copy preparation of the editorial content and that of advertisements. Editorial art-and-copy is, as already mentioned, prepared by staff specialists. These are either employed by the publisher or by the printing company where the magazine is produced. Even though some publishers of magazines operate their own printing plants most magazines are printed in specialized printing plants which are not owned by magazine publishers and are independently controlled.

Preparation of advertising art for magazines must follow certain specifications that are not uniform but differ for various magazines. Each magazine has, as a rule, its own instruction sheets where specifications for column width and length, kind of halftones, bleed and color printing are listed. The paper on which a magazine is printed and the method whereby it is produced—letterpress, rotogravure, or offset lithography—must, of course, be considered in the planning of an advertisement.

Advertisements consisting exclusively of reading matter are often set without charge to the advertiser in the magazine printing plant. Advertisements combining reading matter and pictures are either transmitted by the advertiser to the publisher as original photoengravings or as duplicate plates, electros primarily, for letterpress printing; as gravure positives where this method is used; and as original artwork, ready for the camera if the publication is printed in offset lithography.[4]

Art-and-copy preparation for persuasion printing. Persuasion printing consists primarily of advertising and sales promotional material. These kinds of printed items are needs developed under conditions that differ fundamentally from those under which printed consumer goods and periodicals are produced. All persuasion printing has the main task of attracting the attention of the often involuntary recipient and of holding it as long as possible.

If this premise is accepted, it follows logically that art-and-copy preparation for persuasion printing is first and foremost concerned with originality, and that cost and economy are subordinated to the main consideration of attractiveness. Cost and economy are, of course, hardly ever completely disregarded but they do not dominate assignments for the creation and design of persuasion printing to the same extent as they dominate other fields of printing. Generally speaking, copywriters, artists, and idea men are charged by their clients or employers with the task of aiming for the arresting and unusual rather than the least expensive. This attitude on the part of all concerned differs radically from that prevalent in the development of other kinds of printed items. It has certain unexpected consequences for art-and-copy preparation and for the final production of this material.

It is, obviously, not possible to arrive at the unusual by adhering to tried and tested techniques. The creators of persuasion printing must, on the contrary, constantly search for effects which have not been achieved before and for which the past can offer but little guidance. Understandably, it can often happen that the brainchild of an artist's imagination poses serious difficulties when it reaches the stage of production. So printers, binders and finishers, must find ways to manufacture effectively and speedily what was purposely designed without consideration for speedy and efficient production.

The preceding characterization of persuasion printing may seem a gross exaggeration to those who know that not all promotional jobs pose such exceptional difficulties. There are, to be sure, plenty of simple promotional jobs. But the purpose of the preceding discussion is to open the reader's eyes to the essential differences between various kinds of printed products, and such eye-opening is best done by describing extreme situations. In clarification, it might perhaps be better said that persuasion printing of the most effective type and for the most sophisticated circles is done along the above-mentioned lines; that less elaborate jobs and jobs for less sophisticated customer groups will be less complex, but that even there some of the described features can be found in many instances.

This situation is responsible for the many difficulties and adaptations that attend the production of persuasion printing. It is also the reason why art-and-copy preparation for this kind of product is much more difficult than for consumer goods or periodicals. Finally, the available literature is far from ample. But how could one expect a developed literature for the uncommon and unusual, for the unknown?

Just as the creators of unusual material must rely on their own ingenuity rather than on instructions, so must the producers of this material match them in unusual manufacturing know-how. It bears adding that tolerance and a truly cooperative spirit are essential in this common enterprise between customers, artists, salesmen, and manufacturing personnel.

Section 2:   The Conversion of Reading Matter for Printing

In this manual all subject matter for graphic reproduction is divided into the two main classes of reading matter and of pictures. To avoid misunderstandings it is again mentioned that the class of pictures includes not only painted and photographed material but also graphs, charts, diagrams, or, generally speaking, all kinds of illustrations. This division is made because each of these two kinds poses, as you well know, entirely different image-conversion problems. In the present section we are concerned with the conversion of reading matter into standardized letterforms, or type, whereas pictures will be the subject matter of the following section.

Originally, printing and typography were synonymous. Design, casting, and setting of type

*James Harper, the founder of the
printing and publishing firm
now known as that of Harper*

James Harper, the founder
of the printing and pub-
lishing firm now known as

James Harper, the founder of the printing and publishing firm now known as

Composition converts text into standardized letterforms. The first illustration shows handwriting, the second is a typed version, and the third is typeset.

were in past centuries most characteristic activities of the printer. Typographer meant then simply "printer," and it is still so defined in many dictionaries. But language changes faster than dictionaries, and the word "typographer" is at present used in the United States in a rather different sense. Now it means a person skilled in the art of arranging type images. Consistent with this usage we consider typography the art of arranging type and typographic copy preparation the work by which this arrangement is directed.

The Typographer and His Task

Typography and typesetting should not be confused in their present meaning. Typesetting, or composition, is the operation by which either metallic or non-metallic types are assembled; the person who does this work is not a typographer but a compositor or an operator of typesetting machinery. This distinction is not always and not everywhere made. In many small printshops the printer is still, as of yore, typographer and compositor in one person. But these cases are now the exception and they are insignificant for best contemporary printing practice.

What, then, are the functions of a typographer? And how is typographic copy prepared for image conversion? A typographer must, first, be thoroughly conversant with existing type faces and their proper usage. He must, of course, second, know the mechanics of metallic and non-metallic composition systems. Third, he must be thoroughly familiar with the customary procedures of marking of copy and proofs. Fourth, he must do copy-fitting, which means to choose and arrange type in such a manner that a given text can be composed within a given area. All in all, he must be able to present the printed message tastefully and correctly, which can be a difficult task if the many limitations imposed by reality are considered.

Like everything else, typography has become quite specialized. There is book typography, newspaper typography, and, last but not least, advertising typography, to mention the most important specializations. Each of these fields is constantly discussed in the periodical literature as well as in books devoted to various specialities.[5]

The Art of Typography

Typography has attracted some of the best minds of the graphic arts who were not only first-rate practitioners but also excellent writers on this subject. In the following you find three opinions on typography quoted from the writings of outstanding students of typography. These citations will show you how some of our best typographers conceive of their own art.

First, we quote a passage from *The Crystal Goblet* by Beatrice Warde of the London Monotype Corporation. Mrs. Warde sets forth what is common belief of many typographers, namely, that typography must be in the service of the text rather than serving itself. Speaking of good typography, Mrs. Warde writes: "The good typographer has the job of erecting a window between the reader inside the room and that landscape which is the author's words. He may put up a stained-glass window of marvelous beauty, but a failure as a window; that is, he may use some rich superb type like text gothic that is something to be looked at, not *through*. Or he may work in what I call transparent or invisible typography . . . This is that the mental eye focuses *through* type and not *upon* it. The type which through any arbitrary warping of design or excess of color gets in the way of the mental picture to be conveyed is a bad type."[6] Mrs. Warde expressed one of the fundamental typographic rules, the rule of modesty, in beautiful metaphors.

If Beatrice Warde has told us what typography must avoid, we are still uninformed on what it must do, wherein good typography actually consists. W. A. Dwiggins, an outstanding designer of type and of printing, advises us that type must

meet several conditions: "There are four prime qualities that a printing designer demands in type. In the order of their importance they are: (1) legibility, (2) vigor, (3) newness, and (4) grace."[7]

These four points seem to be clear and simple. But if you reflect about their meaning you will notice that they are far from precise. The first, *legibility*, is discussed later on in this section. At this point it is sufficient to merely state that legibility cannot be simply defined and accurately measured. The second, *vigor*, implies highly personal judgments that will vary from person to person and depend as much on temperament as on the changing taste of the times. The third quality of type demanded by Dwiggins, *newness*, is not simply ascertained by reference to the calendar, by noting the date when a type face was first made available. Newness can be quite deceptive as many so-called new types are merely variations of long-existing designs. The fourth and final point, *grace*, is essentially again a matter of individual preference that cannot be expressed in objective terms.

The question of type selection has puzzled generations of tyros and has been discussed by some of the best typographic artists. Daniel Berkely Updyke, a great student of type and one of the foremost American printers, has sound advice on this point: "How is a man to arrive at a right selection of types? The answer is by a mixture of knowledge and taste. This knowledge must come from a trained mind and experience. Where is the taste to come from? It might as well be admitted that some persons have no taste at all, but such persons would not be likely to try to produce a well-made book or know one when they saw it. Most men who go into printing have some sort of taste, and a few an almost impeccable taste—which is a gift of the gods. It seems to me that a right taste is cultivated in printing as in other forms of endeavor by knowing what has been done in the past and what has been so esteemed that it has lived. If a man examines masterpieces of printing closely, he will begin to see why they are thought masterpieces and in what the mastery lay. He will perceive that all great printing processes have certain qualities in common, that these qualities may be transferable in some slight degree to his own problems, and then he will find himself braced and stimulated into clearer, simpler views of what he can make of his task."[8]

Even this short discussion has shown that the art of typography poses many problems. Two related subjects, readability and legibility, are next briefly explained.

Readability and Legibility

Readability and legibility are used interchangeably by most people who are not concerned with the fine points of typography. But technicians of the subject distinguish between the two: readability signifies for them the ease of reading the printed page or message, whereas legibility refers to the speed with which each individual character can be perceived and recognized.

Practically speaking, legibility is a consideration of type design, whereas readability refers to the arrangement of types. As most of our contemporary types are of good legibility, this problem concerns only the designers of type faces but not typographers who are, as a rule, not designing types but simply using already existing type for copy preparation. Beatrice Warde goes again to the heart of the problem when she writes that "the legibility of a type face has an exact parallel in the audibility of the human voice. A lecturer must make every word audible and distinct. Yet within the limits of audibility lies a whole range of speaking tones from a metallic monotonous drawl to the infinitely flexible and persuasive tones of the good speaker. The printed page can be legible and dull, or legible and fascinating, according to its design and treatment. In other words, what the book lover calls readability is not the synonym for what the optician calls legibility."[9]

Even though readability has been extensively studied, we have no hard and fast rules for it. This is particularly true for the length of lines, a vital consideration of typography. Most people

There is a fundamental principle of modern design, namely that "form follows function." When we apply this to typography, it simply means consideration must first be given to the purpose or

There is a fundamental principle of modern design, namely that "form follows function." When we apply this to typography, it simply means consideration must first be given to the purpose or

There is a fundamental principle of modern design, namely that "form follows function." When we apply this to typography, it simply means consideration must first be given to the purpose or

There is a fundamental principle of modern design, namely that "form follows function." When we apply this to typography, it simply means consideration must first be given to the purpose or

The color of the background affects the readability of type. The first illustration shows the type in reverse, white on a black background. The second illustration shows type on a 60 per cent, the third on a 30 per cent tint; the last illustration shows black type on white paper.

agree that lines equivalent to one-and-one-half to two alphabets, or 40 to 50 characters, are well readable, but some prefer shorter and some longer lines. Yet length of line is only one of many points that influence readability. Others are type size, white space between lines, color of paper and ink, texture of paper in relation to type design, the use of italics, of capitals and of small capitals, mixing of various type faces, use of type in reverse (type appearing in the color of the paper against an ink background), and so forth.[10]

Selection of Type Faces

Before the typographer can choose a type face, or several type faces, for a given job, he must con-

MEDITERRANEAN

Household

Typical Printing

FATHERS

Four examples of type faces with poor legibility.

sider a number of points. They include availability, relation to paper and printing method, the historical, aesthetic and psychological implications of different type designs.

Type design, paper, and printing method must be properly matched. The first step in determining which of the available type faces will be used for a specific job consists in determining printing method and paper to be used for the job in hand. Not every type face is suitable for every paper, nor is every face in every size indicated for every printing method. As a general rule you may remember that type faces having very delicate design elements must be printed on perfectly smooth papers and should not be selected for newspaper relief printing, photogravure and rotogravure, the printing with rubber or plastic plates, and screen-process printing. Letterpress and offset lithography can use any existing type design provided the paper is correctly matched.[11]

Historical, psychological, and aesthetic implications of type designs. Different type designs have various historical, psychological, and aesthetic connotations. Some designs stem from the early times of printing and evoke feelings of past centuries; others are of more recent origin and stress contemporary taste. Certain type faces are said to be masculine, others feminine, and still others neutral. Some designs have a festive or formal character, others are quite inconspicuous, and so forth. Masculine types are preferred for the traditional masculine pursuits in industry; feminine types are desirable for cosmetics and ladies' fashions; formal types are used for announcements; and inconspicuous ones for highly technical and impersonal subjects, to mention some examples.

Classification of Type Faces

The selection of type faces would be an all but hopeless task without some kind of classification. Various authorities classify type faces in different ways; in this book we follow the system set forth in *the PIA Composition Manual* (published by the Printing Industries of America), because this system is widely accepted in the American printing industry.

The *Composition Manual* [12] establishes eight classes of type faces: (1) oldstyle types, (2) modern-face types, (3) transitional faces, (4) square-serif types, (5) sans-serif types and "Gothics," (6) cursives and scripts, (7) text letters, and (8) decorative types. Each of these eight

Oldstyle
Modern Face
Transitional
Square Serif
Sans-Serif
Script
Text-Letter
Decorative

Eight different types, each representative of one of the eight classes of type faces. Oldstyle is ATF Garamond No. 459, Modern Face is ATF Bodoni No. 22, Transitional is ATF Baskerville No. 15, Square Serif is ATF Craw Clarendon No. 710, Sans-Serif is ATF Univers No. 65, Script is ATF Typo Script No. 399, Text-Letter is ATF Engravers Old English No. 148, and Decorative is ATF Caslon Openface No. 1571.

classes will now be briefly identified and described.

Oldstyle types. Oldstyle type designs are patterned by letter forms used on classical Roman inscriptions. These types are a decided improvement on the originally used black-letter types which follow the letter forms used by the scribes. Oldstyle types originated in Italy and spread from there to other countries. As these types are rugged and unsymmetric, they were ideally suited for the primitive methods by which they themselves were manufactured in the sixteenth century and by which printing was done at this time. Small imperfections in oldstyle types are relatively insignificant and their legibility remains excellent even though the paper on which they were originally printed has a coarse and uneven surface. Contemporary oldstyle types are either revivals of types used in the past, sixteenth to eighteenth century, or types designed by contemporary designers who either took the classical types as their model or who went back to the sources that inspired the first designers of these historical types, namely, the original Roman inscriptions themselves.

In our time, oldstyle types are widely used where rugged faces of good readability are needed.

As oldstyle types can be well printed on relatively coarse papers, they play an important role in mass-production printing by all processes.

Modern-face types. Modern-face types have a much higher degree of mechanical perfection than oldstyle types and are distinguished by very delicate hairlines and serifs. This class of type faces was originated by the famous Italian type designer and printer, Giambattista Bodoni, in the last third of the eighteenth century. At that time, skills in punch cutting and type casting had greatly advanced and, most important, smooth-surfaced paper had become available. To distinguish these perfectly constructed types from the irregular, freehand designs of the past, the new types were designated modern-face and the earlier ones oldstyle. Our contemporary modern-face types are, like our oldstyle faces, either revivals of historic designs or new creations by contemporary designers. Modern-face types should be printed on smooth paper; they have a rather formal and demanding appearance and should be avoided where highest precision is unattainable.

Transitional types. Transitional types are halfway between oldstyle and modern-face designs. The classic and first transitional faces were designed by the English innovator of printing, John Baskerville, in the middle of the eighteenth century. Baskerville emphasized the relationship of all elements that must be combined in printing and insisted on perfect typography, ink, paper, and presswork. Contemporary transitional faces are again partly revivals and partly new creations. They are more sturdy than modern-face types and considerably less so than their oldstyle predecessors.

Caslon Old Style

Baskerville

Bodoni

If you want to get a good idea of the three classes of types you can do so best by comparing three representative faces. In our illustration you see a specimen of Caslon, an oldstyle type; of Baskerville, a transitional; and of Bodoni, a modern-face type. All three are revivals adapted for use with line-casting machines. If you compare these specimens you will see for yourself wherein they differ.

ABCDEFGHIJKLMNO PQRSTUVWXYZ abcdefghijklmnopqr stuvwxyz

ABCDEFGHIJKLMNOP QRSTUVWXYZ abcdefghijklmnopqr stuvwxyz

ABCDEFGHIJKLMNOP QRSTUVWXYZ abcdefghijklmnopqr stuvwxyz

Upper and lower case alphabets of three oldstyle types. The first is ATF Goudy Oldstyle No. 178, the second is ATF Garamond No. 459, and the third is ATF Caslon O.S. No. 471.

ABCDEFGHIJKLMNOP QRSTUVWXYZ abcdefghijklmnopqr stuvwxyz

ABCDEFGHIJKLMNO PQRSTUVWXYZ abcdefghijklmnopqr stuvwxyz

Upper and lower case alphabets of two transitional types. The first is ATF Baskerville No. 15, the second is ATF Whitehall No. 566.

ABCDEFGHIJKLMNO
PQRSTUVWXYZ
abcdefghijklmnopqr
stuvwxyz

ABCDEFGHIJKLMN
OPQRSTUVWXYZ
abcdefghijklmnopqrs
tuvwxyz

Upper and lower case alphabets of two modern-face types. The first is ATF Bodoni No. 22, the second is ATF Century School Book No. 454.

The preceding three classes of type faces have one thing in common: they were all developed for book composition, which dominated printing at the time when these faces were originally designed. But book composition did not retain this almost exclusive position as time went on. Growth of population, industry, and commerce—which fill the history of the nineteenth and twentieth centuries—revolutionized society and printing with it. The type classes to be discussed in the following refer to designs that were developed in response to more recent social demands brought about by the growth of the newspaper, of advertising, and of specialization in the graphic arts. Many of these newer type designs owe their existence just as much to the needs of business competition among the suppliers of type as to the craving for novelty so characteristic of our own time.

Square-serif types. Serifs are finishing strokes that play a vital part in type design. Square-serif types are mainly used for display composition,

Stymie Bold
Craw Clarendon

for headlines, and for short pieces of reading matter. They are distinguished by straight serifs and by more or less uniform strokes. Square-serif letters are also known as slab-serif letters, in England particularly.

Sans-serif types. Sans-serif letters (meaning letters without serifs) enjoy great popularity at present. They are of uniform weight, and are sometimes known as *skeleton letters* because of their great simplicity. In our time these plain and sober types are well expressive of the general mood and hence have a strong appeal for designers of graphic arts material.

Spartan
Univers

Sans-serif types exist in a surprising variety and under several group names. In England they are known as *grotesques*, in the United States they are also called *block letters* or *Gothics*. The latter name is unfortunate as it does not refer to the Gothic style of art and therefore causes confusion. Sans-serif types are widely used for display composition, for headlines, for captions and legends in books and magazines. For text composition this class of type is usually avoided in the United States because sans-serif faces are here considered less readable than serifed faces. (In Europe sans-serif faces are used for composition of body type.)

Cursive and script types. Both of these kinds of type images resemble handwriting. If such types have a rather formal or calligraphic appearance,

Typo Script

Lydian Cursive

the designation "cursive" is preferred; if they look like informal writing the word "script" is often added. Both kinds are used for special effects in advertising typography and for announcements or invitations.

Text letters or Gothic types. Text letters or Gothic types are patterned after the earliest printing types that were used by Gutenberg and other pioneer printers prior to the introduction of Roman types. These types resemble the letters used

Wedding Text

Engravers Old English

by the scribes at the time of the invention of printing. Text-letter types are rather heavy, large, angular, and often quite condensed. The word "Gothic" is here correctly used, as these types belong to the Gothic period of art and architecture. Other current names are *Old English* and *Black-Letter*. These type faces have festive and historical connotations and are selected where this kind of "feeling" is desired.

Decorative types. Decorative types are classified as "novelty faces." These types are used in

Stradivarius

Peignot Bold

advertising composition and in persuasion printing but rarely, if ever, for the text of books. The class of decorative or novelty types is a catchall for faces of pronounced individuality if not eccentricity, designed to express particular moods. The popularity of different novelty faces ebbs and crests with the waves of fashion.

The Mechanics of Converting Manuscript into Type

At this point we leave the all but endless subject of type design and turn to the steps required in the conversion of text, or manuscript, into type images. These steps are not the same in all cases and depend on the nature and purpose of a job. Here we will consider merely the most essential three points of copy-fitting, layouts for advertising composition, and book typography.

Copy-fitting. Copy-fitting refers to the space that will be occupied by a given text. In advertising composition various copy elements must occupy predetermined areas, and it is the task of the typographer to select the kind and size of type that will do the job to the best advantage. Copy-fitting of advertising typography can be very difficult; it is sometimes not possible to bring text and allotted area into agreement. If this happens, either the text, or the prescribed area, or both, must be adjusted. In book composition, copy-fitting presents a less tedious task but here, too, decisions on type face and size must be made in relation to the paper and the printing method selected for the specific instance.

Different type designs may occupy different areas in the same type size. The exact data for each

Character Count by Picas

Lower-Case Alphabet Length in Points	Character Count by Picas						
	1	10	12	14	16	18	20
106	3.15	32	38	44	50	57	63
108	3.1	31	37	43	50	56	62
110	3.05	31	37	43	49	55	61
112	3.	30	36	42	48	54	60
114	2.95	30	35	41	47	53	59
116	2.9	29	35	41	46	52	58
118	2.85	29	34	40	46	51	57
120	2.8	28		39	45	50	56
122	2.75	28	33	39	44	50	55
124	2.7	27	32	38	43	49	54

Copyfitting by lower case alphabet length. The lower case alphabet length in points is listed for each face in each point size by the manufacturers of type. This table shows a number of different alphabet lengths and their character counts for lines of increasing length. (Adapted from Copy Fitting, *booklet available from the Mergenthaler Linotype Company, Brooklyn, N. Y.)*

type face in each size are published by manufacturers of foundry type and of matrices for typesetting machines in their data sheets and catalogs. There are also various copy-fitting devices on the market which can help the typographer in the making of the right selection.[13] It should be remembered that not every type is suitable, aesthetically or technically, for every purpose, and that the best face and size are often not available for composition. These many limitations make good copy-fitting an art rather than a mere exercise in arithmetic.

Layouts for advertising composition. In advertising composition things can sometimes be rather difficult because a considerable number of people may be in a position to influence a job. As some of them are not well versed in typography, it is customary to proceed in small steps and to reach general agreement before the next step is made. Consequently, several layouts must be made in sequence, normally at least three kinds: first, the typographer or layout man makes a general layout that indicates his conception of the piece; after approval, several more detailed sketches are made, which are often called *thumbnail sketches* or *roughs;* these are followed either by still more detailed drawings, sometimes called *comprehen-*

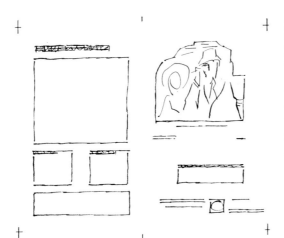

*A rough layout or thumbnail sketch
of a mailing piece.*

sives, or directly by the final layout for the composing room.

In the *final layout*, which is often in the form of a tracing—as the typographer may trace headlines from type specimens for accuracy—he indicates exactly which text element should be set in which type; which area each copy element will occupy; and how the whole job will ultimately appear in print. This layout must be done quite carefully and may require intricate copy-fitting. The final layout is turned over to the composing room where the actual job of composition is performed.

Layouts for book composition. Book composition has its own traditions and rules. The bulk of the text is in contemporary American practice set by machine composition, either by line-casting machines, or by Monotype, or by various photographic composing machines. Before actual composition can begin, so-called *style pages* are designed where the intended treatment is shown. There are various ways of handling paragraphs, notes, folios, and running heads as well as tables and illustrations, which can have captions or legends or both. The meaning of these items is self-evident and needs no explanation.

But there is much more to book typography than the proper arrangement of type for the text. A book usually has *front* and *back matter* in addition to the text, and there is always the typographically most important title page; sometimes a *half* or *bastard* title, the copyright page, a preface, an introduction, possibly a dedication page, and the table of contents. The back matter may include references or notes, a bibliography, various exhibits known as appendixes, an index of

*Detailed version of the rough layout shown before. This comprehensive shows
position of text and picture as well as type specifications.*

subjects and of names, and, more rarely, brief glossaries of technical terms or of biographies.

This concludes our section on typographic copy preparation. Unfortunately, a discussion of other specialized fields of composition, for letterheads, business forms, packages, and so forth, is beyond the frame of this manual. Those further interested in the subject should consult the PIA *Composition Manual.*

Section 3: Preparation of Pictures for Printing

The preparation of reading matter, also known as *copy preparation*, was presented in the preceding section of this chapter. In the present section the preparation of pictures, often called *art preparation* is briefly explained. The subject will be concluded in the following section where the assembly of reading matter and pictures for common reproduction will be discussed.

This division of art-and-copy preparation into three phases corresponds to our contemporary practice of relying on many different specialists for individual assignments whereby art-and-copy is developed. You know already that the preparation of reading matter is in the hands of typographers, as those specializing in this phase of art-and-copy preparation are called, and you also know that there are several specialists among typographers who concentrate in such fields as book, newspaper, or advertising typography.

In the preparation of pictures, specialization has progressed even farther. The all-around commercial artist of the past has been dying out. Now we have layout men, letterers, black-and-white illustrators, airbrush and poster artists, to mention some of those who took his place, and just as many photographic specialists. Some artists have even narrowed their field to the representation of certain product groups. They make pictures of fashions, food, or real estate, and hardly anything else but those.

As always, specialization is impossible without co-ordination, and here the art director enters the scene. After a printing project has been defined between art director, account executive, and representatives of the client, a plan for the whole job must be developed. This plan is known as a dummy or comprehensive layout and is discussed in the following section. On the basis of this plan, individual art elements are then parceled out to various specialists. Most of these are very little interested in anything but their own jobs. After they have completed their assignments another artist or reproduction technician must put to-gether the many resulting pieces by assembling art-and-copy for common reproduction.

These are the conditions under which art-and-copy preparation is done. It is not surprising if some of the many people, who normally work under great pressure, tend to overlook the fact that the preparation of pictures must be done with a view to the necessities of image conversion for printing. For this reason, we will first recapitulate briefly the various methods for image conversion; then we will present a classification of pictures for reproduction; thereafter, various techniques in which pictures can be prepared in each of our classifications will be explained.

Review of Image Conversion Methods

From our extensive discussion in several of the preceding chapters you may remember that pictures can be converted into original image carriers by three main methods. These are: (1) manual, (2) photographic, and (3) electronic. These three methods are here listed historically and not by their contemporary importance for the industry at large. In our time the overwhelming majority of printing jobs rely on photographic image conversion. Manual methods, which preceded photographic ones, are practically restricted to steel-die engraving and to screen-process printing. Electronic image conversion methods are the most recent additions to printing technology, but they are, at the time of this writing, not yet in general use even though they have established themselves firmly in the field of short-run newspaper relief printing. As electronic image conversion methods do not require special art-preparation techniques, they need no further discussion. But a few words are in order on manual image conversion before we turn to the main theme of this section, namely, the preparation of pictures for photographic image conversion.

Manual image conversion methods. Manual image conversion is, of course, limited as it cannot reproduce continuous-tone images; it is, therefore, selected where line images or bold areas are to be printed. As manual image conversion is performed by highly skilled craftsmen, the original images do not necessarily need to be finished in the same sense in which this word will be used for artwork to be converted by means of photography. In some cases it is found both expedient and practical to transmit pictures and other hand-rendered reproduction elements, such as lettering, to the printer in an unfinished sketchy state, thereby saving expense in art preparation. The skilled artist-craftsman who converts these images is usually capable of arriving at a satisfactory result by his own skills.

The three main functions of graphic arts photography. Graphic arts photography has, as you remember, the following three different tasks in the conversion of original images: (1) it provides transparencies of line and area images for photomechanics, (2) it converts continuous-tone images into halftones, and (3) it segregates full-color images into the necessary color separations. These three kinds of graphic arts photography are known as line, halftone, and color-separation photography. Each of these three kinds uses, generally speaking, different photographic materials which are of different costs; each of these three kinds uses also somewhat different equipment. For this reason line, continuous-tone, and full-color originals are normally not photographed together but separately. This is the reason why these three kinds of images must be prepared in such a manner that they can be photographed either individually or together with other pictures of their own kind.

The controlling position of graphic arts photography. The controlling position of graphic arts photography and of its division into these branches must be clearly understood. It accounts for much of the detailed procedures which must be followed in the preparation of art-and-copy *ready-for-the-camera*. Another consequence is worth noting. All but the simplest printing jobs combine line and continuous-tone images, often in several colors, and many jobs contain full-color images in combination with line and continuous-tone originals. Of course, for the lens of the camera type images are no different than other line images.

The three essential tasks of art-and-copy preparation for photographic image conversion. Art-and-copy preparation for photographic image conversion has essentially three different but closely related tasks: (1) to prepare the individual images as needed for best quality and economy, (2) to prepare various kinds of images as they are needed for the separate kinds of photography, and (3) to prepare these images in such a manner that they can be brought together into a harmonious final printed image, which is—does it need emphasizing?—the required end product.

The first two of these points, namely, the quality required for reproduction of individual images and their preparation for individual or group photography, is the theme of this section. The third point, the assembly of various kinds of images for proper relationship to each other, is reserved for the final section of this chapter.

Classification of Original Images

It is convenient to take two kinds of characteristics as the ordering principles for the classification of original images: one is the presence or absence of continuous tone, the other is the kind of color in which these images must be reproduced. Images where continuous tones are absent are called line images, those where continuous tones are present are called either continuous-tone or halftone images. Speaking of color, we distinguish single-color, multicolor, and full-color images. Single-color images are also known as black-and-white; multicolor images are those that require two or more color inks for reproduction; and full-color images are those that require three carefully chosen color inks for reproduction of a wide gamut of color. For various practical reasons black and possibly additional color inks may be used in the printing of such images, as explained in Chapter III.

Eight classes of original images. If we combine the characteristics of tone and color we arrive at the following eight classes of original images, or art-and-copy: (1) line images in single color, or black-and-white; (2) continuous-tone images in single color, or black-and-white; (3) line and continuous-tone images in combination for single color, or black-and-white, reproduction; (4) line images for multicolor reproduction; (5) continuous-tone images for multicolor reproduction; (6) line and continuous-tone images in combination for multicolor reproduction; (7) full-color images; (8) full-color images in combination with line and continuous-tone images.

You may notice that not all possible combinations are separately mentioned in this list. The reason for these omissions is simply that the

A coquille board drawing. This drawing was made with a soft pencil. The swatch shows the texture of the coquille board. This and the other three pictures on this page are line engravings and do not need halftone photography.

This illustration was made on Craftint Doubletone board. Two developers are used—the dark one first—to bring out the dark and light tints. Solid black lines and areas were added as final touches.

A Ross board drawing. The swatch shows the texture of the board. Black was added for emphasis with regular ink. The completed drawing was photographically reduced to decrease the size of the Ross board dots.

A scratchboard drawing. The scratchboard is white; black ink is applied to it in the image areas. The design comes about by scratching off the black ink with hand tools where white is wanted.

omitted combinations are implicitly treated under some of the listed headings and do not present additional problems. As classification of art-and-copy plays a considerable part in graphic arts communications; it is mentioned that black-and-white is a more common designation than the more precise expression of single color, that black-and-white is abbreviated in informal writing as b&w, and that the trade often speaks of original images such as photographs prior to their conversion into halftones as if their conversion had been already made. But in the interest of clarity the term "halftone" should be reserved for the products of halftone photography and not be used for photos and other continuous-tone images.

Next a grouping of these eight classes of original images is in order. Classes 1, 2, 4, 5, and 7 are discussed in the course of this section. Classes 3, 6, and 8 pose no new problems as to images themselves but they cause problems of assembly and are, therefore, treated in the following section of this chapter.

After this introduction we can turn to our various classes of images beginning with class 1, line images, or, as it is often said, line art.

Preparation of Single-Color Line Images

Line images can be made in many different techniques. Most of these techniques have been developed in order to obtain differences in tones, or, to say it more precisely, differences in value, without the expense of halftone photography. For the purpose of our discussion, line images are divided into four groups: (1) type images, (2) drawn, painted, or generally speaking, hand-rendered line images, (3) line images arrived at by tint-laying, and finally, (4) line images made by photographic conversion of continuous-tone images—mainly photographs.

Type images. Type images are technically line images and must be incorporated in the finished artwork for printing methods that need photo-mechanical printing-image carriers, notably offset lithography, rotogravure and wrap-around printing. (Metallic and non-metallic composition are extensively discussed in Chapter II, and so is proofing.) If the type images were produced by metallic composition, reproduction proofs are most common though proofs pulled on transparent plastics are also used. If the type images were produced by photographic composition, photographic prints on paper or transparencies are available.

A free-hand drawing in pen-and-ink.

Hand-rendered line images. The group of drawn and painted images, which we call generically *hand-rendered*, comprises a substantial proportion of all pictures prepared for graphic reproduction. It is perhaps equaled in number and popularity only by black-and-white photographs.

Hand-rendered line images can be made in numerous techniques, among them pen-and-ink drawing, painting with poster paints or with India ink. In addition, line images can also be created by means of several commercially available art boards, some of which are now briefly described. There is, first, *scratch board*, an artist's illustration board coated on its surface with a white material that has the ability of accepting black India ink and of permitting its removal without any traces. The artist can create images resembling white-line wood engravings with this material. He first applies India ink in small or large blotches, and then removes it by scratching with pointed tools wherever he wants the white of the underlying coating to appear.

Next we mention *ross boards* and *coquille boards*, two similar proprietary materials suitable for hand-rendered line images of a different kind. These materials are coated on their surface and embossed in a number of different patterns. The artist uses soft and hard crayons which deposit their coloring matter on the peaks of the embossed hills and leave the valleys white. The result is a hand-rendered image with several color values. This image can be converted into a printing-image carrier without halftone photography.

Another technique of obtaining images with value variations without halftone photography is based on two kinds of proprietary artist's boards; these are *Craftint single-tone* and *Craftint double-tone* drawing sheets, available in 60 different patterns. Craftint single-tone boards come in various patterns resulting in a single additional color value, whereas the double-tones can add two color values to a drawing. These patterns are latent and must be developed with chemical solutions which are applied by artist's brushes. The Craftint double-tone sheets bear two such latent images, one crisscrossed by the other. As each of them must be developed with a different chemical solution, the artist can combine various values in the same piece and thereby enjoys considerable latitude in the creation of his designs.

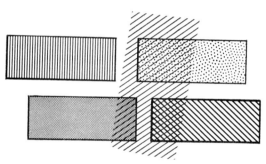

Tint sheets are available in a wide variety of patterns. This illustration shows a few and also that it is possible to combine different patterns for additional effects.

Tint-laying. Tint-laying, sometimes known as bendaying, is another technique for distinguishing various areas in a drawing by endowing them with different patterns. Tint-laying can be done either as part of art-and-copy preparation or as part of image conversion in a graphic arts plant. In the context of this chapter we are primarily interested in tint-laying as part of art-and-copy preparation and will therefore concentrate on techniques used by commercial artists.

Tint-laying as part of art preparation is based on proprietary materials manufactured by several companies and known as *shading sheets* or by their brand names. Most of them are printed in various patterns on a transparent paper or plastic sheet; in some brands this sheet is coated on its back with a wax adhesive which makes it easy to adhere the tint to the illustration board on which the artist prepares his pictures. Techniques vary in detail. Some shading sheets must be cut to the

required shape and then applied to the drawing; other brands of shading sheets have their patterns printed in such a manner that these can be transferred by rubbing or burnishing; the shading sheet can then be applied to the drawing without cutting it to the required shape.

If tint-laying is part of image conversion, the original material must be differently prepared. In such instances the areas where tints are to be laid are not left white but prepared as solid black blotches. Negative photography converts these black blotches into clear areas into which the graphic arts craftsman then inserts his tint-laying material which is exposed together with the negative of the original image for platemaking.

Line images obtained by photographic conversion of continuous-tone images. This last group of line images does not play a conspicuous role in art-and-copy preparation. It is worth mentioning primarily as an example of the almost unlimited contribution made by photography to the graphic arts. Not only does photography enable us to reproduce continuous-tone pictures by means of the halftone process, but it also makes it possible to convert photographs from continuous-tone to line images by selecting certain values and areas of these pictures. The techniques are highly specialized; their detail is, obviously, much too complex for our discussion. The results have a distinct character of their own and are often used to replace halftone images in reproduction tasks where these special effects are wanted.

Preparation of Continuous-Tone Pictures for Single-Color Reproduction

Continuous-tone images for single-color reproduction can be divided into the two main groups of rendered images and of photographs. The reproduction of continuous-tone pictures in relief, planographic, porous printing, and some intaglio methods is based on halftone photography. Conventional gravure and collotype are the two outstanding exceptions where other image-conversion techniques can be used. The necessities of halftone photography as well as other conditions attending the reproduction of continuous-tone images pose several problems which must be well understood in order to prepare this class of images for printing. Our discussion of the subject begins, therefore, with an exposition of these problems; it is followed by brief presentations of rendered and of photographic continuous-tone pictures for single-color reproduction.

A continuous-tone photograph can be converted by special photographic techniques to a line picture. Such conversions are also known as posterizations.

Courtesy Martin J. Weber Studios

Some reproduction problems of continuous-tone images. Many reproduction problems of continuous-tone pictures are related to halftone photography as well as to the nature of papers and inks commonly used for printing. The paramount position of halftone photography in the reproduction of continuous-tone pictures becomes clear if we list some of the printing methods which require halftones for the reproduction of continuous-tone images. These include letterpress, newspaper relief printing, flexography, offset-lithography, many rotogravure methods, and screen-process printing. (Halftone photography is extensively discussed in Chapter IV which should be consulted by readers who wish to refresh their memory.)

You will remember that halftones can evoke the appearance of continuous-tone images because the resolving power of the human eye is limited. This limitation accounts for the optical illusion whereby individual small dots of varying sizes, if viewed at the proper distance, cannot be recognized as such but appear as continuous-tone images. Halftone photography is capable of excellent results but these can never exceed the intrinsic limitations of various reproduction methods.

Among these limitations we have foremost those of image contrast. Photography can produce pictures with a much greater contrast than printing can obtain. The reason for this difference lies in the differences between photographic and printing coloring media and papers. In a photographic print metallic silver is the coloring medium; in a printed image this function is assumed by printing ink. Unfortunately, the blackest printing ink cannot match in blackness or light-absorbent quality the deposit of metallic silver in the shadows of a photograph. Nor can the paper which must be used for quantity printing where price is a controlling factor ever be as white and otherwise of a quality equivalent to that of photographic papers. It stands to reason that the contrast of printed images must be less than that of photographs if printing paper is less white than photographic paper and printing ink less black than metallic silver. This elementary truth cannot be repeated too often.

The interrelationship of paper, printing ink, method of reproduction, and image quality must be thoroughly understood by everybody who prepares art-and-copy for printing. In mass-production printing, paper is the highest individual cost element. The price of paper is, hence, more decisive in this kind of printing than its quality. As the fineness of halftone images depends on the surface quality of paper, in relief printing more than in other methods, decisions on the kind of paper to be used are implicitly also decisions on the detail of halftone images to be reproduced with the selected paper.

Expert commercial artists and photographers understand these relations and prepare their continuous-tone pictures in such a manner that they will print to good advantage under the specific conditions that govern their reproduction.

Rendered continuous-tone pictures. Rendered continuous-tone pictures can be painted, drawn, crayoned, water colored, airbrushed; or they can be the result of combinations of some of these techniques. Among the tools used by the commercial artist are pens, pencils, brushes, and air brushes; the color media can be India ink, oil and water colors, crayons, chalks, and so on. The artist works freely and creates his pictures on the kind of paper or other surface best suited for his technique, whichever this may be. As the manner in which continuous-tone pictures are prepared has a telling effect on the quality of the printed image, the artist must be well aware of the conditions under which his work is reproduced.

Photographic continuous-tone images. Photographic continuous-tone images are either individual black-and-white prints or combinations of several such prints, known as *photomontages.* Photography for reproduction by printing has become an important field in which we find many high-skilled specialists. Among them are those for interiors, for machinery, for food, and for fashions, to mention only a few. If photographic pictures are retouched and airbrushed before they are turned over to the printer, they represent a combination of manual and photographic methods. In all cases it is most desirable that the photographic specialist be familiar with the requirements for reproduction and that he keep another point in mind: the quality of his work cannot be judged by the photographic print provided by him, but depends on the final printed image. The product of his own effort, namely the photographic picture, is merely an intermediate element on the way to the printed image.

Line Images for Multicolor Printing

The preparation of line images for multicolor printing follows the procedures described under the head of line images for single-color printing. But the fact that this class of originals must be reproduced by more than one printing-image carrier, and often also in more than one press run, adds several additional considerations. One of these is the spatial relation of different color images, known in the printer's vernacular as *register;* color effects obtainable by combination of several color inks is the second point to be explained; a third and rather complex subject consists in tech-

niques of art preparation arriving at a satisfactory compromise between the desire to show finished art in color on the one hand, and the necessities of image conversion on the other. Last but not least, there are several special techniques which must also be briefly described.

Register. Printers distinguish several kinds of register, depending on the intricacy of a job. *No-register* means that the several color areas are

Three different kinds of color register. The first picture shows a no-register job, the second a loose register job, and the third a close or tight register job.

completely independent of each other, *loose register* that minor variations in their relations are inconsequential; *tight*, *close*, or *hairline* register indicates that these relations must be quite exact. Unfortunately, terminology is here, as so often, far from uniform throughout the industry, and some printers have four and even more classes of register distinguishing between close and hairline register, for example.

Among typical examples for no-register multicolor jobs we might mention books in which chapter headings, initials, or marginalia are printed in one color and the text in another. Other examples are charts or sales literature where the illustrations appear in one color and the reading matter in another. In some cases the number of colors used may be considerable but each of them may nevertheless stand completely by itself, as is the case in color cards for paints or cosmetics, to mention a few examples. Loose register indicates that color areas are contiguous or interlocked but without requiring exact relative positioning. A colored background or blotches of color for emphasis belong in this classification of register. Close or tight register is essential wherever the effect of the printed image depends on precision placement of each color element.

The technical means by which register is achieved are register marks, indicating the exact relative position of different but related images. The subject of register is further discussed in the following section on assembling art-and-copy for common reproduction.

Overprinting. Overprinting is a technique whereby additional colors and color values can be achieved by judicious combination of two or more color inks which may include black. You know already that full-color printing is capable of obtaining a wide gamut of colors by means of three carefully selected color inks which are in actual practice often supplemented by black ink. In multicolor printing, our present subject, the dominant colors of the artwork must be matched by corresponding color inks. These inks can then be further utilized by overprinting. It must be kept in mind that overprinting of other than full-color inks is not capable of producing a wide color gamut but that it is quite limited in its results. These limits are perhaps best expressed by stating that *in multicolor overprinting we can specify the dominant colors but cannot accurately predict without a color chart what colors will result by their combination.*

This point will be best made clear by an example. Let us assume that the two dominant colors are black and red, and let us assume that they are to be overprinted. Is it, then, possible to arrange things in such a way that an orange will be the result of overprinting? The answer is no. Black and red can never produce orange by overprinting, but they can be combined to provide shades of brown and gray, for example. If an artist intends to use overprinting and if he wants to predict which colors can be obtained by overprinting, he can select his dominant colors from color charts that also show how these colors can be combined by overprinting.

Overprinting can be done in solid areas but also by using tints having specified percentage values. In these cases the solids equal 100 per cent of the area in question, whereas the tints occupy such area percentages as are designated by their percentage figures. A 20 per cent tint, for example, consists of dots that cover 20 per cent of the total area in which they appear. It is quite impressive to see what diversification in colors and values can be created by skilful use of overprinting, and it might be added that tint-laying for multicolor work can be rather involved and that it can require considerable skill. Several charts are commercially available for this purpose.

Appearance of finished artwork for multicolor reproduction. The appearance of finished artwork for multicolor reproduction can pose difficult problems of communication. Here difficulty in communication is not between printer and commercial artist, but between the artist who prepares art-and-copy and the people for whom he does this work, his employers or customers.

This problem in communication is due to the fact that finished art for photomechanical multicolor reproduction is best and most economically prepared in black-and-white and not in color. It should perhaps be repeated that multicolor art can be prepared in color for certain non-photomechanical reproduction methods, among them screen-process printing with knife-cut stencils and for handmade, or tusched, lithographic plates. There, the mentioned problems of communications are avoided, but other more severe limitations may make these methods ineligible.

Such problems in communication can be particularly troublesome if the finished artwork must be approved by several business executives. These are very important people and generally speaking both uninformed and uninterested concerning the technical difficulties of the situation. A way must be found to communicate to them the final appearance of the printed product-to-be, though without adding greatly to the cost of image conversion.

Before we discuss various techniques for this purpose it should be perfectly clear in the mind of the reader why it is most economical to prepare multicolor artwork in black-and-white. Here again we must refer to the controlling position of photography. If original images are prepared in black-and-white, they can be converted into the required intermediate transparencies by line photography, which is, as you are well aware, the least expensive kind of graphic arts photography. If original images are prepared in many colors they must be either manually converted into black-and-white images, or, if this division is to be done photographically, treated as full-color images. The first of these alternatives adds unnecessary expenses, the second is completely out of the question for many reasons.

The problem of communicating the final appearance of multicolor images without undue expenses can be solved in two ways. One is to prepare finished art in black-and-white as needed for photography and to supplement it with detailed colored dummies or sketches. This technique is generally used whenever the subject matter is not too complex, where overprinting is either inter-

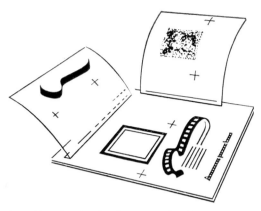

Assembly of multicolor line artwork. The key-color is on the board; the art for the other colors is on flaps registered with crosses to the mechanical on the board.

preted by competent people or not used too extensively. The second kind of solution lies in such proprietary methods as those developed by Bourges and others. There, line art is prepared in color but in such a way that it can, nevertheless, be photographed by black-and-white photography, as you will see presently.

Multicolor line images prepared as overlays. It must be kept in mind that each of the several color inks needs a separate printing-image carrier, disregarding special techniques of limited use, such as split-fountain printing. Therefore all individual multicolor images must be segregated accordingly, and those to be printed in the same color ink must be later assembled together. This result can be obtained by making opaque black overlays either on illustration board or on a transparent plastic. These overlays must be properly related to each other and also to various copy elements with which they may be printed in combination. The task is one of controlling spatial relations of various images, a subject discussed in the following section on assembly.

Multicolor images for tint-laying. Color comics and many other kinds of images requiring extensive tint-laying are usually prepared as *keyline* drawings. The artist draws the outlines of different color areas on illustration board and indicates the final colors on a paper tissue attached to his illustration board. The tissue guides the graphic arts craftsman in tint-laying, a rather intricate operation.

The Bourges method of preparing finished multicolor artwork in color. The Bourges method is based on a number of transparent plastic sheets

Black and white keyline art with colored crayon overlay and color swatches.

coated with different transparent colors. The artist segregates the different color images during art preparation and selects for this purpose sheets that match the final ink color. He can remove the color coating of Bourges sheets in various ways and he can also add color if he so desires. After individual color separations have been made, they are vertically assembled in the proper order, and the result is a fair likeness of the future printed image.[14]

For image conversion, these colored sheets are photographed through complementary filters supplied by Bourges. Thereby it becomes possible to photograph them as black-and-white images, just like other black-and-white art.

Sometimes black-and-white images arrived at by other than Bourges techniques are to be evaluated for their appearance in color. This can be done by making photographic transparencies, negatives and positives, and by contact printing of these transparencies on color foils. These foils are either of the diazo family or made by applying pigmented photomechanical coatings to them. Diazo foils come already light sensitive; other materials need as a rule sensitizing prior to contact printing. After processing, these foils are superimposed and the resulting image is a fair likeness of the final multicolor print. These techniques are also extensively used as part of image conversion, to permit evaluation of full-color separations prior to color correcting.

Continuous-Tone Pictures for Multicolor Reproduction

The class of continuous-tone pictures for multicolor reproduction is small. The only items of consequence are duotones and possibly reproductions of black-and-white photographs in several colors. Duotones are reproductions of black-and-white photographs for which two closely related color inks, or even two black inks, are used. Here, the original picture is photographed twice; one negative emphasizes the highlights, the other the shadows of the picture. Two image carriers are made, one from each of the two negatives, and the picture is printed with two different inks either of the same hue or of two carefully chosen related hues, one lighter and the other darker. If black-and-white photographs are to be printed in several colors, the artist supplies a color tissue and the photograph is processed in a manner similar to fake color printing which is described in Chapter III.

Images for Full-Color Printing

Images for full-color reproduction are divided into the two broad classes of reflection copy on the one hand and transmission copy on the other. Reflection copy is a collective name for all images that are on an opaque surface be it painters' canvas, paper, or drawing board, to mention some of the most generally used materials. This class of images is photographed in the light which is reflected from their surface through the lens of the camera. Transmission copy, on the contrary, is the designation for all full-color images that are on a transparent surface which is illuminated in such a manner that the light passes through the

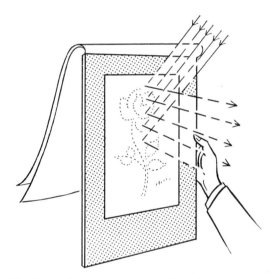

Paintings, photos, and other original images on an opaque surface are classified as reflection copy.

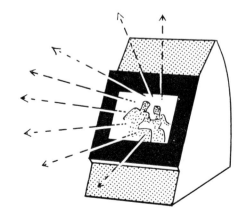

Color transparencies and other original images on a transparent surface are classified as transmission copy.

transparent original image into the camera during color-separation photography.

Rendered reflection copy for full-color printing. Reflection copy is most conveniently divided into rendered, or painted, and into photographed images. In the first group, we can distinguish between painted images created for their own sake and without any thought to reproduction by printing, and between painted images which were produced with the main purpose of multiplication by printing in mind. Fine-art pictures belong in the first group, paintings for commercial purposes including advertising, in the second.

From the printer's point-of-view the differences between fine-art subjects and commercial art are several. In the reproduction of fine-art originals, the printer must aim for utmost fidelity. He cannot expect help or concessions by the creator of the painting, even if the painter is still alive. In commercial subjects where the printing is not an end in itself but merely a means to the end of selling merchandise, cost of reproduction counts with all concerned. The advertiser and the artist will more or less co-operate, make changes and compromises if thereby expenses can be reduced. Another point, made already in this chapter, is the tendency of advertisers to request changes and modifications of the original images at the time of their production.

Photographic reflection copy for full-color printing. We now turn to photographic reflection copy for full-color printing. Every color print can serve as original image for reproduction by printing if it has the desired image quality. Here we mention three kinds of color prints which are more frequently used than others. These are *carbros*, *dye-transfers*, and *Kodak Ektacolor* prints. Carbros are high-quality color prints made by specialists for the purpose of full-color reproduction. The prints consist of three layers of differently pigmented carbon tissue, a material which we have met before in conjunction with photo-

mechanical methods of gravure and screen process image carriers. Dye-transfer prints are another specialty; there the color image is the result of three different dyes which are transferred from photographic matrices to the final support. Both of these methods are rather involved, require high skills, and are consequently quite costly. The last kind, Kodak Ektacolor prints (originally known as "Type C" prints), is less expensive to produce and enjoys considerable popularity. Such prints can be made either from Kodachromes or from Ektachromes, both color transparencies, and are widely used for catalogs and many other purposes.

Transmission copy for full-color printing. By definition all colorful images borne by a transparent support belong in this class of copy. But in actual practice, transmission copy consists almost exclusively of color transparencies. These can be made with a variety of photographic materials, but as Kodachromes and Ektachromes dominate the field in the United States, these two Kodak products are here selected for a brief discussion.

The first of these materials, *Kodachrome*, is designed and used for amateur photography primarily. It is only available in a single small size (35 mm.) and must be developed by a licensed laboratory. Kodachromes can serve as original images for reproduction by printing, particularly on short-run jobs. If the image needs strong enlargement, Kodachromes may pose several technical problems.

Many of these difficulties can be avoided by the use of *Ektachromes*, the Kodak material developed for professional photographers. Ektachrome is available in several sizes and can be developed either by processing laboratories or under the control of the properly equipped photographer. As Ektachromes are usually made by specialists, they are suitable for full-color reproduction and therefore are widely used in long-run printing jobs.

Section 4:   Assembly of Reading Matter and Pictures for Reproduction

The assembly of art-and-copy for printing can be a very simple job or a very difficult one, depending entirely on the job in hand and its complexity. Often the task entails the assembly of some elements requiring changes in size; or omission of certain areas; possibly, addition of others; and perhaps adaptations in several respects.

Printing of advertising and sales promotional material is usually distinguished by a high degree of complexity in the assembling of art-and-copy.

One of the reasons for this complexity is the custom to use as many already existing art-and-copy elements for as many jobs as possible. This practice helps to save money on new artwork;

it is not less in the service of repetition, which is a main tenet of contemporary advertising. As generally agreed, certain images cannot be too often brought to the attention of the public. Among these are, of course, trade-marks and logotypes but also other images that are essential parts of a campaign and may be needed in newspaper and magazine advertisements, as well as in folders and brochures and point-of-purchase advertising. As each different use of these art elements takes place under new and more or less different conditions, the required adaptations can be rather extensive.

Another point worth noting is that different printing methods may need not only different assembly techniques but also adaptations of already existing images. For this reason we will begin our discussion of assembling with a brief summary of the main printing methods and the techniques by which art-and-copy is assembled for them. The next unit will present layouts and dummies which guide artists in the assembling and printers in the production of the assembled material. The final unit is concerned with the handling of images and the assembly techniques for all eight classes of art-and-copy.

Assembling of Art-and-Copy for Different Printing Methods

Assembling of art-and-copy for relief printing. Traditionally, relief printing is based on metallic type for reading matter and on photoengravings for pictures. The assembly of type and photoengravings is not done by an artist but by skilled craftsmen. These are guided by a layout supplied to them by artists, editors, or production men, which consists of type proofs and those of engravings, usually pasted together and known as pasteup. A skilled craftsman, called the makeup man, then assembles the material into pages, either for use in a type form or for duplicate platemaking.

The advent of photopolymer and wrap-around plates introduced different techniques into the relief printing industry. These new kinds of plates are made by means of photomechanics. It is, therefore, necessary to assemble the requisite images prior to photomechanics. Essentially, the assembly techniques for these new types of relief image carriers are the same as used in other photomechanical image conversion methods, offset lithography in particular.

Assembling of art-and-copy for intaglio printing. Photogravure and rotogravure are two related intaglio methods that need extensive assembly of art-and-copy. The other methods of this process group, steel-die engraving and banknote printing, do not require much of an assembly operation and can, therefore, be omitted here. Image carriers for both methods of gravure are of the single-unit or integral type, and they are made by means of photomechanics. It should be remembered that as a rule type images are not exposed to the gravure tissue together with continuous-tone images. This necessity must be considered in the planning of the assembly method.

Assembling of art-and-copy for planographic printing. Offset lithography, the dominant planographic method, is based on photomechanical single-unit image carriers. Art-and-copy is prepared *ready-for-the-camera*. The main techniques for this kind of art preparation are explained in the course of this section. Collotype, the second planographic method of general interest, follows offset lithography in art-and-copy preparation.

Assembling of art-and-copy for porous printing. Screen-process printing, the industrial method of porous printing, uses single-unit image carriers. Copy can be prepared either for manual image conversion by the knife-cut film method, or for photomechanical image conversion, or for a combination of these two methods. Art-and-copy preparation for photomechanical image conversion does not differ from that used for image conversion by means of photomechanics for other printing methods. Assembly of images for manual conversion is usually in final size and in color, either as finished or as unfinished artwork.[15]

Layouts and Dummies

Art-and-copy preparation passes through three distinct stages. The first extends from the inception of the future printed piece to a decision on its final form; the second stage is occupied with the development of individual art-and-copy elements; the third and final stage is devoted to the assembly of individual images for common reproduction. Each of these stages results in certain products which have their own distinctive purposes and their own names. These are, alas, not as precisely defined as one might desire. The term "layout" is one of them and the term "dummy" another. Both are used with different meanings which will be discussed presently.

Rough, visual, finished, and comprehensive layouts. The first and most sketchy graphic ex-

First rough for black-and-white advertisements. Such roughs show idea, general format, and size.

zines can be evaluated on the basis of layouts, but other printed items need in addition to their layouts also dummies whereby certain physical qualities can be previewed. This is the case with booklets, folders, broadsides, packages, point-of-purchase displays, books, toys, games, etc.

The dummy is made of the material to be used in actual production and is shaped to the final form of the printed product. Usually, blank dummies are supplied to the customer or his printer by those who will either sell material, such as paper, or render certain required services, such as binding or finishing, for the project in hand. Most paper merchants are prepared to make dummies for booklets and similar items; trade binders will assist in the planning of folders; package printers will develop dummies of folding cartons; finishers will submit construction dummies of cardboard displays; and edition binders or book manufacturers will do the same for hard- and for softbound books.

Dummies are submitted blank. If the physical properties and the shape of the dummy are more or less acceptable, it is turned into a representative sample of the final product by indicating the future printed images on its blank surfaces. This can be done in several ways; by drawing, sketching, coloring, pasting of type proofs or of a layout. A dummy bearing the final images is often needed for the assembly of pictures and type images for printing.

pression of a printing project is often called a rough layout or simply a *rough;* one can also hear the terms *pencil layout* and *visual.* (Some people think that the word visual is preferred where color or third dimensions must be indicated, for example, in package design or in point-of-sale material.) With the progress of a project, additional layouts may be needed; these are sometimes also called *finished layouts.* But this term is misleading and means in reality a *more* finished layout than a rough. The final layout is usually called *comprehensive layout* or simply a *comprehensive.* This final layout serves as a basis of reference for all concerned. It must either be accurately drawn or accurately marked to serve its purpose and to be usable as a reliable guide for art-and-copy assembly.[16]

Various kinds of dummies. Advertisements scheduled for publication in newspapers or maga-

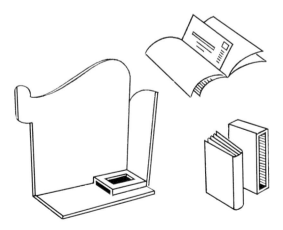

Dummies are made for several purposes. The point-of-purchase display shows construction; the dummy of the booklet, top right, shows enclosure of an order card; the book and its slip case were dummied to test fit of book in slip case.

General Considerations for the Assembly of Art-and-Copy

With layout and dummy to guide him, the artist charged with the final assembly gathers all individual images, makes sure that he has all needed material, inspects the individual art elements for defects, adjusts these if necessary, adapts what needs adapting, and finally combines the material as it must be prepared for printing. In the following, all these points are individually explained. The emphasis is here, as always in this manual, on reasons and purposes rather than on the details of execution.

Inspection of individual art-and-copy elements. It seems almost unnecessary to explain the reason for inspecting each and every element before it is passed for assembly. Inspecting is an indispensable feature of quality control, and quality control is one of the pillars on which modern manufacturing rests. Depending on the standards customary in a particular organization, inspection may be anything from the superficial to the extremely rigorous. In some cases minor defects, such as broken serifs in type images or little streaks in photos, are passed; in others they must be eliminated before these images are accepted for assembly.

Scaling and cropping. Later, at the discussion of assembly methods, you will read that only such images as can be photographed at the same ratio of reduction or enlargement can be assembled for common photography. Every change in this ratio requires a different setting of the camera; elements which must be photographed individually cannot be assembled together with others; individual handling can be more expensive than combined handling and is avoided as much as possible.

As it is customary to use certain art-and-copy elements for many different pieces, a certain amount of individual handling may be inevitable, but individual handling should be kept down to a minimum, and always is, if experts are at work. Assemblies must have the same proportion of reduction or enlargement, or *focus*, to use technical language. If some images, photographs in particular, vary but slightly in these proportions, refocusing can be eliminated by a compromise ratio, applicable to all of them.

Sometimes the desired uniformity of ratio can be achieved by cropping with a view to this effect. Cropping is a technical term meaning the selection of certain areas from a picture. Scaling and cropping are operations that can save much money by a relatively small effort.

Scaling and cropping of a photograph. The lines for scaling and cropping were made on a plastic overlay. At the right you see the reduced picture.

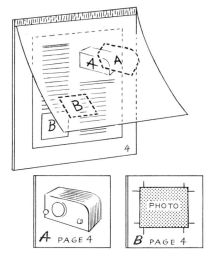

An example of cross referencing different art elements with the mechanical by letters.

All images must be carefully protected and, where necessary, related to other copy elements by cross-referencing or keying, a technique which will be explained in the following. The notations referring to keying, as well as the ratios of reductions and crop marks, are put in the margins outside the image areas.

Separate assembly of line and continuous-tone images. The next consideration prior to assembly of material for photographic image conversion is already known to you: it is the controlling position of graphic arts photography and its requirements. You have read more than once in this manual that line images, including type images, are photographically in one group, that continuous-tone images belong into a second group, and that images for full-color reproduction form a third group. Images belonging to one group must not be assembled with images belonging to another group. As images for full-color printing are usually not assembled with other images, this means practically that separate assemblies must be made for line and for continuous-tone images.

Problems of spatial relationship. The next and third group of considerations for assembling art-and-copy is the correct spatial relation of all images. Spatial relation is of two kinds: horizontal and vertical. Horizontal spatial relations refer to the positioning of images assembled in the same plane and printed by the same printing image carrier. Vertical spatial relations constitute those between (1) images in different planes which are

printed by different image carriers as well as (2) spatial relations between printed images and the paper or other stock on which the printed images will appear.

Many people use the word "register" when they refer to spatial relations of images, whatever these relations may be. It was recently suggested to revise the existing terminology. "Technically there should be a distinction between register and fit, or external and internal register. If every sheet goes through the press and is printed in the same position relative to the gripper edge and the guide-side, the press is printing in register. If the plate has been made incorrectly, or if the paper distorts and some of the images are out of place in relation to others on a sheet that is printed in register, then the term should be 'misfit' or internal register."[17]

Cross-referencing of various art-and-copy elements. The fourth group of considerations deals with cross-referencing of images. Images that are not assembled together must be cross-referenced for image conversion. Frequently it is not feasible or practical to assemble all elements in a single unit, and the job must be divided into a number of subassemblies which must, of course, also be properly related to each other. This operation is called keying; it is rather technical and we are restricted to a general description of the methods employed. One of them consists in making an outline drawing of the image to be added and of identifying the image with a letter or number. The image in question is keyed to the mechanical by the same symbol. Another method identifies various images by means of photostats—inexpensive photographic paper prints—which are pasted in the areas of the mechanical where the key images will appear. If images are to be keyed for color, this can be done by attaching a paper tissue to the mechanical and by indicating different color areas with colored pencils or crayons. These few examples are merely hinting at some of the many existing techniques, but they are sufficient for our purposes.

Subsidiary manufacturing steps. The fifth and final group of considerations is related to production steps following presswork. Practically all printing projects entail some subsidiary manufacturing operations, of which binding is perhaps the most common, but by no means the only example. These considerations find their expression in several ways. One of them is the arrangement of pages according to a folding imposition; an-

New!

osophers themselves have come to final terms with desparo-
has eliminated catharsis, comedy has turned its back on joy, and pornog-

*A mechanical, or pasteup, combining line art
with different copy elements.*

other is the presence of guide marks on the main
assembly unit, the next topic of our discussion.

Pasteup and mechanical. The final assembly of
art-and-copy is usually known as *pasteup* or as
mechanical. It does not comprise images for
full-color reproduction which are always handled
separately and turned over individually to the
printer. But pasteups or mechanicals do comprise
both line and continuous-tone images even though
some of either kind may be transmitted to the
printer individually.

As these remarks indicate, the pasteup is not
necessarily a complete assembly of all art-and-
copy elements. Actually, the pasteup has another
and most important function. It is the blueprint
for image conversion and printing production. As
the word "mechanical" expresses this connotation
much better than the word "pasteup," we will use
mechanical for the assembly of images to be
reproduced by photomechanics. The word
"pasteup" is better reserved for letterpress, where
it was originally used, and where it signifies the
pasting of galley proofs and those of engravings
to the dummy of a book or periodical in order
to indicate the arrangement of individual pages.

To return to our mechanical, it may happen in
extreme cases that a mechanical does not bear a
single original image at all if each of them must
be handled individually. Such a mechanical

would, nevertheless, retain the function of being
the blueprint for the job. But such extreme cases
are rare, and a mechanical is normally an assembly of various copy elements. At its simplest, the
mechanical is a piece of artists' illustration board,
somewhat larger than the final size of the printed
piece. To this board are attached, by cementing
or pasting (hence the word "pasteup"), a number
of line images, all in the same focus and, of course,
of inspected quality. This board bears, furthermore, all notations that will enable it to serve as
the blueprint of the job. The nature of these notations depends on the job.

Things are relatively simple if art-and-copy is
to be reproduced in single color and if it consists
of line images exclusively. As soon as line images
must be combined with continuous-tone images,
and particularly if they must be reproduced in
more than one color, the assembly of art-and-
copy becomes more complex.

Overlays. As already explained, line and continuous-tone images must be assembled separately, even if they will be printed with the same
image carrier. As these two kinds of images must
be in proper spatial relation to each other, it is
customary to assemble one kind on illustration
board and the other on a transparent plastic sheet
which is hinged to the illustration board. The
board itself also functions normally as the mechanical. These additional assemblies are known
as *overlays* or, colloquially, as *flaps*.

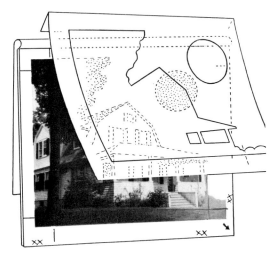

*A die sheet that shows the exact cut lines is hinged in
register to the printed sheet. This die sheet will serve as a
guide for making the steel-rule die and for diecutting.*

Register and other marks. As mentioned before, the mechanical must bear a number of indications that are of importance for printing and subsidiary converting operations. Among them are marks for determining exact spatial relations, known as register marks, and those for trimming and for folding. If a job is die-cut, as happens in label printing or the production of advertising material, the desired outline may be either marked on the mechanical or drawn on a separate die-sheet, depending on the customs of the printer and finisher handling the job.

Now you are informed on the general points of assembling art-and-copy and we can proceed to a discussion of assembly methods for each of our eight classes of art-and-copy.

Assembly Techniques for Different Classes of Art-and-Copy

In the preceding section, devoted to the preparation of pictures, art-and-copy is divided into eight different classes. In the present unit we will discuss the procedures by which each of these classes is assembled for image conversion.

Assembling of single-color line art. Single-color line art normally consists of type images and line drawings, sometimes in combination with tints. The assembly of this material takes place along the lines set forth above for the simplest kind of mechanical. If some of the line pictures to be included do not exist in the proper size, they are usually photographed or possibly photostated to such dimensions as are required for their common reproduction with type images. Tints can be laid either by an artist or by a graphic arts craftsman. In the latter case, the respective areas are either outlined or made to appear in solid black on the mechanical.

Assembling of single-color continuous-tone art. This class is not often met in actual experience as continuous-tone images usually require some explanatory text. But if continuous-tone pictures are to be assembled entirely by themselves, the assembly is made in the same manner as that of single-color line art.

If all pictures are scaled for a common focus and if their image quality permits common photography, they can be assembled in one mechanical. If they are too numerous for one, then they are assembled on several mechanicals. If some of the images need individual photography, the area allotted to them is indicated on the mechanical which must, of course, be cross-referenced with such pictures. Changes within the images such as vignetting, silhouetting, or outlining, are indicated on tissue overlays, and the respective pictures are best transmitted individually as subassemblies to the printer.

Assembling of line and continuous-tone images in combination for single-color reproduction. This class of art-and-copy preparation is extremely frequent and therefore quite important. As line images must not be assembled on the same plane with continuous-tone images, the assembly must be made by means of at least two units, sometimes even more.

The material is, as always, inspected and where necessary corrected, then scaled and cropped before it is passed for assembly. In certain cases the main assembly must be supplemented by subassemblies, particularly when the number of images is large; when material originally prepared

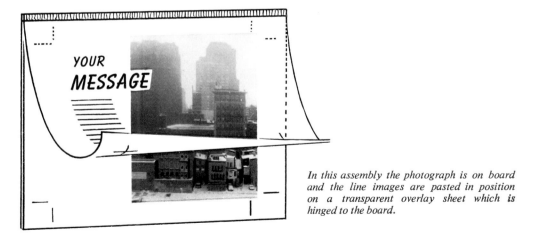

In this assembly the photograph is on board and the line images are pasted in position on a transparent overlay sheet which is hinged to the board.

for different purposes is to be included; or when image changes, such as the ones already mentioned, are needed; and also when tints are to be laid and reading matter is to be combined with continuous-tone images.

It bears mentioning that continuous-tone images are not the only kind of material that may need to be individually transmitted. The same can be said of line pictures and of some kinds of type images. If type images are present in the form of reproduction proofs, they can be attached to the base on which the assembly is made, but if type images are prepared on a photographic film or on transparent material by proofing on glassine paper or plastic, they cannot be pasted down together with other images and must be handled individually.

All these qualifications are far from exceptional; they are run-of-the-mill items and do not exhaust the list of possible complications. You can see that art-and-copy preparation becomes quite complex as our discussion progresses.

Perhaps the most important two decisions to be made before the work of assembling can begin are on the relative placement of line and continuous-tone images and on the method to be used for keying. A few words on each of these points are in order. As you know, line images must be assembled in one plane and continuous-tone pictures in another plane. Some people prefer to paste all line images to the board, which will also serve as the mechanical, and to assemble continuous-tone images on a plastic overlay. Others prefer the opposite procedure. Nor are opinions undivided on various methods of cross-

referencing. Some prefer outlines, others windowing, photostating or the use of special proprietary material.

In utility printing and where the quality of halftones is not critical, a different technique is sometimes used to good advantage. Continuous-tone images are in these instances converted into halftones before the assembly of art-and-copy. A black-and-white print of the halftone image, known as a *Velox*, is made and used for the final assembly. Such a print is technically more or less equivalent to other line images and can therefore be assembled together with them. This method is only one of several possible techniques.

Assembling of line art for multicolor printing. The assembly methods of line art for multicolor printing are essentially the same as already explained. The mechanical is made on illustration board, where also type images and those of the most extensive color, known also as key color, are attached. Images to be printed in other colors are assembled in different planes as overlays. If a job uses a second color in various areas that are not contiguous, all images may be pasted on a single piece of illustration board and be identified as to their different colors by a single tissue overlay. In such cases it may be possible to get by with a single photographic negative which will be adapted by the craftsman during photomechanical exposure in such a manner that two image carriers can be produced with it.

Multicolor printing has several specific problems, one of which is the spatial relation of several colors which are supposed to appear as contiguous images, or *butted*, to use the printer's terms. It is not always possible to achieve this result, particularly not in mass-production printing and with dimensionally unstable papers. Art-and-copy preparation must allow for these conditions by permitting a slight amount of overprinting or overlapping. The areas provided for this purpose are sometimes known as underlays. If an image is to be printed in one color, but not in another color contiguous to it, the image must be removed from this color area, usually by means of photographic techniques. This operation is often called *knocking out* of a color, or making *thicks* and *thins*, meaning that the proper underlays will be established.

The complexity of multicolor printing can be quite considerable, particularly where extensive tint-laying is requested. But the methods of assembly do not differ essentially from those de-

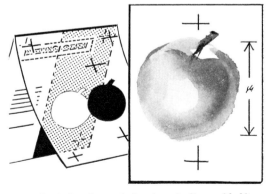

A mechanical and a wash drawing of a line and halftone combination job. The line art and type images are on the board; the flap is registered with the board and has a solid black area where the halftone will appear.

An assembly for a complex full-color job. The mechanical at the left indicates positions of all pictures, and carries black line art and type. The color transparency is in an envelope behind the assembly at the right. This assembly shows in a rough which area of the transparency will print, and has an overlay for line copy.

scribed in the preceding unit. If preseparated color foils are used, these elements are, of course, handled individually and they are transmitted to the printer as subassemblies, carefully cross-referenced to the mechanical.

Assembling of multicolor continuous-tone art. This class of images for reproduction is rather rare as you may remember from the preceding discussion of its preparation. As multicolor continuous-tone images are practically always assembled together with line images, we can turn immediately to this subject.

Assembly of line and continuous-tone art in combination for multicolor printing. This class of images represents a substantial portion of contemporary printing tasks. The assembly operation for this kind of art-and-copy is governed by a combined application of the considerations which were explained for the assembling of line and continuous-tone images in black-and-white as well as those expressed at the description of assembly methods for multicolor line art. A mechanical is, of course, needed under all conditions; subassemblies tend to increase in number, because the complexity of the job can now become much greater, and cross-referencing must include image qualities as well as color relations. Here, as in multicolor line art, a colored dummy showing the final ar-

rangement of all individual elements is a necessity; it is always included in well-prepared jobs.

Assembling of full-color images. If full-color images are to be printed completely by themselves, all that is needed is a mechanical indicating their correct position on the sheet. The images themselves are, as already stated, usually turned over to the printer individually. This class of art-and-copy is rather infrequent, as most full-color images are reproduced in combination with line and continuous-tone images, our last and final subject of this chapter.

Assembling of full-color art-and-copy in combination with line and continuous-tone art. This last class of art-and-copy makes the highest demands on image conversion and on printing production in general. Depending on the nature of the job, it can be incredibly complex, as now all the hazards of multicolor line and continuous-tone reproduction are compounded with the hazards of full-color printing

In art-and-copy preparation of this class colored dummies and mechanicals are a matter of course; the number of subassemblies increases again, as full-color images are now added to multicolor and single-color line and continuous-tone pictures. Even though the essential preparation methods remain the same, now a much higher degree of precision enters the battlefield of image conversion. In this class of art-and-copy, experience and critical judgment are vital for those in charge of preparation. Every seemingly minor decision here can affect a number of other unforeseen items and can therefore be of greatest consequence.

This may be the right moment to explain why art-and-copy preparation, which is in point of time at the beginning of every printing project, became the last chapter of this manual. A real understanding of the subject presupposes thorough familiarity with printing production, in particular with composition, graphic arts photography, full-color printing but also with presses, binding and finishing.

Art-and-copy preparation can simplify production and save time and money; but art-and-copy preparation can also have the opposite effect. Nowhere is the French proverb *C'est le premier pas qui coûte* (it's the first step that costs) more apropos than here.

Introduction to Notes and References

Each Item (book, magazine, article, or paper) is fully identified when it first appears in the notes to a chapter. In following notes the same item is listed either by the author's name or by a shortened title, followed by [see No.] referring the reader to its first entry in a particular chapter. The titles of books, articles, or papers are in italics, the names of magazines or of books consisting of a number of articles are in small caps. Latin bibliographical abbreviations, such as *op. cit.*, *loc. cit.*, or *ibid.* are avoided, and undated or unpaginated material is not so indicated. After the name of many magazines the word "magazine" is added to distinguish books from magazines. A list of abbreviations follows:

AAAA	Association of American Advertising Agencies	NPIRI	National Printing Ink Research Institute
ANPA	American Newspaper Publishers Association	PIA	Printing Industries of America
FTA	Flexographic Technical Association	R&E COUNCIL	Research and Engineering Council of the Graphic Arts Industry
GATF	Graphic Arts Technical Foundation	TAGA	Technical Association of the Graphic Arts
GPO	U.S. Government Printing Office	TAPPI	Technical Association of the Pulp and Paper Industry
GTA	Gravure Technical Association		

Notes to Chapter I: *Printing Processes and Methods*

1. In November, 1965, Printing Industries of America published a circular containing the following statistical data: Of the 20 major manufacturing groups in the U.S. covered in the U.S. Government's 1963 Census of Manufactures, printing and publishing ranks: *Third in Number of Establishments:* 35,580 in the latest official census preliminary report of 1963, showing steady growth from 35,350 in 1958, 28,986 in 1947, and 24,878 in 1939. Its size is exceeded only by food and kindred products, and apparel and related products. *Third in Average Hourly Earnings:* $2.97 (1964 BLS report). This is about 53¢ an hour above the average for *all* manufacturing. *Eighth in Total Dollar Payroll:* About $5,542,000,000 (1963 Preliminary Survey of Manufactures—U.S. Bureau of Census). *Eighth in Value Added by Manufacturing:* $10,494,-000,000 (1963 Preliminary Survey of Manufactures). *Eighth in Number of Employees:* 919,000 (1963 Preliminary Survey of Manufactures). *Tenth in Dollars Re-invested in Capital Expenditures:* $437,000,000 in (1963 Census of Manufactures). *Eleventh in Value of Shipments:* $16,-097,000,000 (1963 Preliminary Survey of Manufactures). Despite its high ranking among manufacturing industries, printing is still primarily an industry composed of thousands of small establishments giving employment to skilled workers all over the United States. About 81 per cent (nearly 29,000 plants) have fewer than 20 employees.

2. The most popular historical book on papermaking is by Dard Hunter, *Papermaking—The History and Technique of an Ancient Craft.* Revised and enlarged (New York, 1947).

3 The only relatively modern book on the history of printing ink is by Frank B. Wiborg, *Printing Ink, A History* (New York and London, 1926).

4. *Private Presses and Their Books*, originally published 1929, and *Selective Check Lists of Private Books*, originally published between 1945 and 1950, both by Will Ransom, are bibliographies widely used by collectors of private press books.

5. The history of the Kelmscott Press is described by H. Halliday Sparling, Secretary to the Press, *The Kelmscott Press and William Morris* (London, 1924).

6. The colophon of books published by the Limited Editions Club, New York, lists the designer or

12. Joseph Moxon, *Mechanick Exercises on the Whole Art of Printing* (1683–84), edited by Herbert Davis and Harry Carter (London, 1958), page 173.

13. The *Manuel Typographique* by [Simon Pierre] Fournier le jeune, 2 volumes (Paris, 1764–76) is translated into English and annotated by Harry Carter as *Fournier on Typefounding* (London, 1930). The quoted passage is on page 104.

14. Bohadti [see No. 7], page 201.

15. Carter [see No. 13] has a short bibliography on hand casting, pages XI and XII; DeVinne [see No. 1] sketches the development of mechanical type casting on pages 24–28; Bohadti [see No. 7] describes contemporary fully automatic manufacturing methods of foundry types.

16. *Webster's New International Dictionary*, Second Edition, Unabridged (Springfield, Mass., 1950).

17. *A Monotype Composing Machine Described for Prospective Users, Overseers and Students* (London and Salfords, 1953), page 11.

18. *Monotype Book of Information* (London and Salfords, 1959), pages 50 and 51, for example. On pages 54–57 are tables expressing units of different sets in thousandths of inches.

19. Same reference as No. 17, page 13.

20. The *Composition Manual* [see No. 4] contains an introductory description of the Monotype System, suitable for management personnel, on pages 221–44. Operating and supervisory personnel use two books published by the English National Committee of Monotype Users' Associations and the Monotype Corporation Ltd. One is *The Monotype Keyboard Operator's Manual* (London, 1950), the other is *The Monotype Casting Machine Manual* (London, 1952).

21. *Composition Manual* [see No. 4], page 221.

22. *Mathematics in Type*, published by the William Byrd Press (Richmond, Va., 1954); for authors and publishers' production people rather than for operating personnel.

23. The number of smaller newspapers using web offset is substantial. "There are approximately 10,130 weekly and semi-weekly papers. An estimated 2,000 have converted to offset. There are about 1,030 dailies with less than 15,000 circulation. Between 175 and 200 of these have converted to offset. These figures represent about a 20 per cent conversion to offset out of the total small-newspaper population (weeklies, semi-weeklies, and dailies of under 15,000 circulation). It should be remembered that this included sheet-fed offset. When the conversion to offset first began, about 1958–60, sheet-fed offset was encountered quite frequently but has become relatively less important in recent years." Letter of December 24, 1965, from Mr. George M. Petrasko, The Cottrell Company, a Division of Harris Intertype Corporation, to the writer.

24. *The Official Manual—Linotype Machine Principles* (Brooklyn, N.Y., 1940), page 3.

25. *Composition Manual* [see No. 4], page 188.

26. Same reference as before.

27. Same reference as No. 25.

28. Same reference as No. 25.

29. For a more detailed description of matrices, the literature published by manufacturers should be consulted.

30. *Linotype Machine* [see No. 24], page 39.

31. Hugo Jahn, *The Dictionary of Graphic Arts Terms* (Chicago, 1928), page 156.

32. *Composition Manual* [see No. 4], page 190.

33. Adapted from *Composition Manual* [see No. 4], page 190.

34. Same reference as before.

35. *Linotype Machine* [see No. 24], page 4.

36. Five different Linotype spacebands are listed in the *Linotype Machine* [see No. 24], page 85. These range between 0.028 inches minimum and 0.0146 maximum expansion. The expansion range of different Linotype spacebands varies between 0.066 and 0.100 inches. *The Intertype—A Book of Instruction for Its Operation and General Maintenance* (Brooklyn, 1943), lists six kinds of Intertype spacebands on page 37. Intertype spaces have somewhat different minimum and maximum dimensions and expansion ranges compared with Linotype spacebands.

37. *Composition Manual* [see No. 4], page 210.

38. The *Composition Manual* [see No. 4] contains an introductory discussion, suitable for management personnel, on pages 187 to 220. Operating and supervising personnel can use the Linotype and the Intertype manuals [see No. 24 and No. 36]; the *Linotype Maintenance Manual* (Brooklyn, 1951); Oscar R. Abel and Windsor L. Straw, *Mechanism of the Linotype and Intertype* (Brookings, S.D., 1961); and an English work by J. Ashworth, *Operation and Mechanism of the Linotype and Intertype*, 2 volumes (London, 1955).

39. Adapted from Frank B. Foster, *Perforated Tape—Robot of the Composing Room*, PRINTING PRODUCTION magazine, June, 1962.

40. Same reference as before.

41. *The Linotype Handbook for Teletypesetter Operation* (New York, 1951), pages 6 and 7.

42. Same reference as before, condensed from pages 8 and 9.

43. *Linotype Handbook* [see No. 41], page 27.

44. *Composition Manual* [see No. 4], page 273.

45. J. Ashworth [see No. 38], condensed from Volume II, page 289.

46. *Linotype Handbook* [see No. 41], condensed from pages 10 and 11.

47. Wm. Hagan, *Proceedings of Meeting Tape Operation Slug-Casting Machines*, R&E COUNCIL, Chicago, 1959, page 6.

48. The description of the Friden LCC perforator is culled from *Technical Manual for Friden LCC-VF*.

49. Descriptive literature on the Linasec.

50. Hyphenation procedure on the Linasec 1 is described in Report of Proceeding, *Computer Typesetting Conference, London University, July, 1964*, page 26.

51. The description of the Di-An Computer Keyboard is based on literature published by Di-An Controls, Inc., Boston, and on article *Computer Doubles Tape Production* in the August 1965 issue of NEW ENGLAND PRINTER & LITHOGRAPHER.

52. *R. & E., Tape Operation* [see No. 47] adapted from Cy MacKinnon, page 11.

53. *Composition Manual* [see No. 4], page 255.

54. *Composition Manual* [see No. 4], pages 254–67.

55. *Composition Manual* [see No. 4], page 263.

56. *Composition Manual* [see No. 4], pages 268–82.

57. *Composition Manual* [see No. 4], page 269.

58. *Composition Manual* [see No. 4], condensed from pages 277 and 278.

59. Condensed from *Film and Cold Typesetting Today*, PRINTING MAGAZINE, December, 1962.

60. Same reference as before.

61. Same reference as No. 59.

62. *The Lithographers Manual*, 20th Anniversary Edition, edited by Victor Strauss (New York, 1958), Vol. I, page 4:106.

63. Same reference as before, Vol. I, page 4:100.

64. E. A. Kilheffer, *The Monophoto*, in the AMERICAN PRESSMAN magazine, April, 1957.

65. For a discussion of quality control with the Monophoto see article by Frank H. Smith, F.R.P.S., and R. E. Snell, *Control of Photo-Composition Quality*, in MODERN LITHOGRAPHY, December, 1958.

66. ATF data sheet on Press Wire Tape Convertor.

67. The Photon Textmaster 713 is described on the basis of a Photon sales brochure and on 713 Textmaster specifications, dated Nov. 2, 1964, revised April 12, 1965.

68. MEDLARS and GRACE is described in a paper by Charles J. Austin, printed in AUTOMATION AND ELECTRONICS IN PUBLISHING, edited by Lowell H. Hattery and George P. Bush (Washington and New York, 1965), pages 61–70. The electronic controls of the GRACE are described by Michael M. Stern, *Control System for High-Speed Photocomposition*, in COMPUTER DESIGN magazine, October, 1965.

69. Description of the Photon Zip is based on *Product Report Number Two—Photon Zip Series 900*, published by Photon, Inc.

70. The description of the Linofilm Quick is based on descriptive company literature and on information received from Mr. John L. Peterson, Product Manager, Linofilm Quick.

71. *Intertype Presents New Horizons for the Modern Printer* (New York, 1950), adapted from page 9.

72. *Lithographers Manual* [see No. 62], Vol. I, page 4:102.

73. The summary descriptions of the Photon 513, 540, and 560 follow company literature.

74. *Lithographers Manual* [see No. 62], Vol. I, page 4:93.

75. Same reference as before.

76. Descriptive booklet on Linofilm Converter, published by Mergenthaler Linotype Company.

77. All data on the Fototronic system are taken from Intertype literature.

78. All quotations pertaining to the Linotron are from Victor M. Corrado, *Experience in Development of an Electronic Photocomposer* in Hattery and Bush [see No. 68], pages 83–87.

79. Same reference as No. 59.

80. Same reference as No. 59.

81. An excellent survey of all phases of photocomposition, with the Monophoto, including correction methods, is *Filmsetting in Focus*, in the summer, 1965, issue of THE MONOTYPE RECORDER magazine, published by the Monotype Corporation, Ltd., in the United Kingdom.

82. *Transparent Proofs from Type Forms—Government Printing Office Process*, GPO Research and Engineering Council of the Graphic Arts Industry, Inc., Composition Series No. 3.

83. Sales literature on Scotchprint by the 3M Company.

84. *Lithographers Manual* [see No. 62], Vol. I, page 4:38.

85. Adapted from descriptive booklet, *The Cronapress Conversion System*, published by the duPont Photo Products Department.

86. A good survey of American approaches to computerized composition is in *Proceedings of International Conference on Computerized Typesetting, March 2 and 3, 1965*, published by the R&E COUNCIL (Washington, D.C., 1965), and in Hattery and Bush [see No. 68]. This book has an annotated bibliography of 211 items, published after January 1, 1963. European approaches are described in the papers presented at the First International Technical Information Congress, published in French, English, and German by the French magazine Caractère (Paris, 1965) and Proceedings, London University [see No. 50].

87. Paul Siegel, *Understanding Digital Computers* (New York and London, 1961), page 6.

88. O. H. Davie, M.I.E.E., *The Elements of Pulse Techniques* (London and New York, 1954), page 1.

89. Siegel [see No. 87], page 8.

90. George Kozmetsky and Paul Kircher, *Electronic Computers and Management Control* (New York, 1956), page 10.

91. Same reference as before.

92. Readers who have a more than fleeting interest in computerized composition will want to have the *CIS Glossary of Automated Typesetting and Related Computer Terms*, as well as the *CIS Newsletter* published by Composition Information Services, 1605 Cahuenga Blvd., Los Angeles, Calif. 90028.

93. C. C. Gottlieb and J. N. P. Hume, *High-Speed Data Processing* (New York, 1948), page 14.

94. Herman Blum, *The Loom Has a Brain* (Philadelphia, 1958), page 77.

95. Product Report Two [see No. 69].

96. Several systems of optical character recognition are described in *Optical Character Recognition* edited by George L. Fisher, Jr., Donald K. Pollock, Bernard Raddack, Mary Elizabeth Stevens (Washington, D.C., 1962).

97. *Computers for the Graphic Arts* by J. Homer Winkler, talk at the 15th Annual Conference of the R&E COUNCIL, May 17, 1965.

98. Adapted from *CIS Glossary* [see No. 92], page 26.

99. Same reference as before, adapted from page 35.

100. Rocappi, Inc., *Report to Stockholders*, 1965, page 2.

101. Descriptions of rack-type, type-wheel and spinning-disk printout devices can be found in Siegel [see No. 87], pages 112–14; chain printers are described in the IBM literature.

102. Sales literature on Linofilm Computer-Option Photo Unit.

103. Condensed from PRINTING PRODUCTION magazine, June, 1965, page 78.

104. Stuart, E. Arnett, *Computer Composition—Present and Future*, speech at 46th convention, Printing House Craftsmen (San Francisco, 1965).

105. Paper presented at the Fall Joint Computer Conference, 1965, by M. V. Mathews and Joan Miller, *Computer Editing, Typesetting and Image Generation*, page 17.

106. Release from the *Denver Post*, Dec. 13, 1963. In March, 1965, the writer was informed by the *Denver Post* that the same system was in operation and that it will be continued; the paper has a considerable gain in circulation since the new system was put in force.

107. Bergen Evans and Cornelia Evans, *A Dictionary of American Usage* (New York, 1957), page 139, article *Division of words*.

108. Webster [see No. 16], pages lix–lxxviii.

109. H. W. Fowler, *A Dictionary of Modern English Usage*, Second Edition, revised by Sir Ernest Gower (New York, 1965), article *Syllabize*.

110. Frank H. Smith, *Computers and Composition*, in MODERN LITHOGRAPHY magazine, January, 1964, page 41.

111. Webster [see No. 16], pages lviii and lix.

112. *Thorndike Century Senior Dictionary*, by E. L. Thorndike (Chicago, 1941), page xii.

113. Thomas T. Seelye, Jr., *How Computer Logic Works in Hyphenation*, in PRINTING PRODUCTION magazine, December, 1965.

114. John Markus, *Computers in Commercial Publishing*, March 15, 1965, a paper written not for publication but for use within the McGraw-Hill organization.

115. Special Report: *The Revolution in Book Composition*, Part II, BOOK PRODUCTION magazine, page 13.

116. Same reference as before, page 11.

117. C. J. Duncan, *Look! No Hands!*, PENROSE ANNUAL, 1964, page 124.

118. Hard-Copy Proofs—A New Dimension for Authors and Publishers, article in BOOK PRODUCTION INDUSTRY magazine, June, 1965, page 53.

119. Daniel Melcher, *Notes on Authors' Alterations and the New Technology*, in PUBLISHERS WEEKLY, May 3, 1965, page 36.

120. John G. Kelly, *What Authors Should Know To Work with Hard-Copy*, in BOOK PRODUCTION INDUSTRY magazine, June, 1965.

121. Arnett [see No. 104].

122. Lee Ohringer, *Progress in Computerized Typesetting*, TAGA PROCEEDINGS, 1965.

123. Product Report Two [see No. 69].

124. Same reference as before.

125. Article by Leonard Karel, Charles J. Austin, Martin M. Cummings, *Computerized Bibliographical Services for Biomedicine*, in SCIENCE magazine, May 7, 1965.

126. Article by Charles J. Austin, *The Medlars System*, in DATAMATION the Magazine of Automatic Information Handling, December, 1964.

127. George Z. Kunkel, *Computerized Composition without Hyphens*, R. & E. Proceedings, 1965 [see No. 86].

128. Same reference as before.

129. George Z. Kunkel and Tilmon H. Marcum, *Now: Hyphenless Justification*, PRINTING PRODUCTION magazine, April, 1965, page 45.

130. Kunkel, same reference as No. 127.

131. Letter to the writer from Mr. George Z. Kunkel, CIA, dated September 28, 1965.

132. Same reference as before.

133. ANPA *Research Institute, Bulletin 852*, May 3, 1965, page 49.

134. Adapted from *Electronics Solves Spaceband Problems; You Throw 'Em Away*, by Marion Marsh in SOUTHBEND TRIBUNE, June 15, 1965, special issue describing this newspaper's computer operation.

135. Descriptive literature on *Auto-Controlled Elektrons* by Mergenthaler, May 21, 1965.

136. Allan Woods, *House of Tape*, PRINTING PRODUCTION magazine, June, 1965, page 57.

137. Same reference as before, page 130.

138. In a letter to the writer, dated November 22, 1965, Mr. John H. Perry, Jr., made the following comment: "My opinion is that most of these executives have not looked into the matter sufficiently. We certainly have as much pressure on our operation as most big city papers. In fact, our annual production is well over twice that of many metropolitan newspapers. In a recent test, we have set our stock market page with two high-speed photographic composing machines faster than we previously did with six or eight tape-operated line-casting machines."

139. Ernest Schmattola, *The Fundamentals of Digital Computers for Graphic Arts Personnel* (Long Island City), 1965, pages 30–32.

140. John Markus, *Directory Production*, in Hattery and Bush [see No. 68], pages 47–60.

141. PUBLISHERS' WEEKLY, April 5, 1965, page 51.

142. FORTUNE magazine, July, 1965, page 2.

143. Same reference as before, page 97.

144. Gilbert Burck and the editors of Fortune, *The Computer Age and Its Potential for Management* (New York, 1965), condensed from pages 52–55.

145. Donald D. Dissly, *Keyboard Study*, made at the Courier-Journal and Louisville Times (November, 1962).

146. P. L. Anderson, *Compatibility of Input and Output Devices* in Hattery and Bush [see No. 68], pages 91–101.

Notes and References to Chapter III: *The Theory and Practice of Full-Color Printing*

1. *Thorndike Century Senior Dictionary* by E. L. Thorndike (Chicago, 1941).
2. Committee on Colorimetry, Optical Society of America, *The Science of Color* (New York, 1953), page 366.
3. Same reference as before, page 220.
4. *Colour in Theory and Practice*, edited by H. D. Murray, new and revised edition (London, 1952), page 95.
5. OSA [see No. 2], page 84.
6. OSA [see No. 2], page 86.
7. OSA [see No. 2], page 91.
8. Ralph M. Evans, *An Introduction to Color* (New York, 1948), page 111.
9. OSA [see No. 2], page 39.
10. Murray [see No. 4], page 6.
11. The division of the spectrum preferred by the Optical Society of America is in OSA [see No. 2], page 41. There it is stated "that visible radiant energy is confined to wavelengths between about 380 and 760 millionth of a millimeter (milli-micron, abbreviated mμ) and that the following range of wave lengths correspond to the indicated colors:

380 mμ to 450 mμ	violet
450 mμ to 490 mμ	blue
490 mμ to 560 mμ	green
560 mμ to 590 mμ	yellow
590 mμ to 630 mμ	orange
630 mμ to 760 mμ	red."

12. OSA [see No. 2], page 379.
13. The Kelvin degree of carbon arc lamps is taken from OSA [see No. 2], page 294; all other Kelvin degrees are from Matthew Luckiesh and Frank P. Moss, *The Science of Seeing* (New York, 1948), page 410.
14. *Lighting for Color Appraisal in Graphic Arts*, R&E COUNCIL (Washington, 1957), page 3.
15. The Time, Inc., viewing system is described in TAGA *Proceedings of the 9th Annual Meeting, 1957, Part A;* a discussion of this system is in *Part B.*
16. Evans [see No. 8], page 118.
17. Same reference as before.
18. Matthew Luckiesh, *Color and Colors* (New York, 1938), page 40.
19. For a comprehensive discussion of various color standards consult Deane B. Judd, *Color in Business, Science, and Industry* (New York, 1952).
20. The CIE System is extensively described in OSA [see No. 2].

21. See the *Munsell Book of Color*, Munsell Color Co. (Baltimore, Md., Vol. I, 1929; Vol. II, 1943).
22. A. H. Munsell, *A Color Notation* (Baltimore, Md., 1941), pages 15 and 16.
23. Same reference as before, page 19.
24. The Ostwald-Container Corporation Color System is described in *Color Harmony Manual*, Color Standards Department, Container Corporation of America, Third Edition (Chicago, Ill., 1948).
25. A discussion of the relative merits of the Munsell and the Ostwald-Container Corporation color systems is outside the frame of this manual. A comparison of ten different color systems can be found in Judd [see No. 19], page 199.
26. The GATF-Preucil Color System is described in GATF Publication No. 320 (New York, 1957).
27. Robert Ridgway, *Color Standards and Color Nomenclature* (Baltimore, Md., 1912).
28. OSA [see No. 2], page 337.
29. See *A Dictionary of Color* by A. Maerz and M. Rea Paul (New York, 1950).
30. Judd [see No. 19], pages 184 and 186.
31. For a discussion of eight-color printing see *The Reproduction of Color* by Arthur C. Hardy and F. L. Wurzburg, Jr., INTERCHEMICAL REVIEW, Vol. IX, No. 3.
32. GATF Publication No. 509, Erwin Jaffe, Edward Brody, Frank Preucil, and Jack W. White, *Color Separation Photography* (New York, 1959), page 96.
33. Judson A. V. Hyatt in SHARE YOUR KNOWLEDGE REVIEW, January, 1961, page 14.
34. Samuel Tankel in GRAPHIC ARTS MONTHLY, November, 1960, page 24.
35. Hyatt [see No. 33].
36. Herbert P. Paschel in MODERN LITHOGRAPHY magazine, August, 1960, page 50.
37. F. L. Wurzburg, Jr., *Process Printing and Inks* in PROCEEDING OF THE TECHNICAL CONFERENCE ON COLOR PHOTOGRAPHY AND COLOR PRINTING, R&E COUNCIL, 1954, page 80.
38. GATF RESEARCH PROGRESS No. 70, *The New Color Survey of 1963–64* by Frank Preucil, Figure 16.
39. The Kodak Three-Color System is described by J. A. C. Yule in THE LITHOGRAPHERS MANUAL, 20th Anniversary Edition, Vol. I (New York, 1958), page 7:21.
40. *PIA Standard Photoengraving Specifications Manual*, Revised Edition (Washington, D.C., 1962), page 10.

Notes and References to Chapter IV: *Graphic Arts Photography*

1. A good elementary introduction to graphic arts cameras is by Herbert P. Paschel, *The Process Camera*, in the LITHOGRAPHERS MANUAL, 20th Anniversary Edition, edited by Victor Strauss, Vol. I (New York, 1958), pages 5:45–5:56.

2. Accessories used in the camera department are described and illustrated in the same reference as before, pages 5:112–5:125. Catalogs of manufacturers should be consulted for currently available accessories.

3. Photography is explained in a large number of books and articles, often highly technical. A brief discussion of photographic fundamentals, written as a college text, is by Lewis Larmore, Ph.D., *Introduction to Photographic Principles* (Englewood Cliffs, N.J., 1958).

4. Paul J. Hartsuch, Ph.D., *The Chemistry of Lithography*, GATF Publication No. 401 (New York, 1960) discusses the chemistry of photography in Chapter 10.

5. The specification sheets of photographic material, supplied by their manufacturers, should be consulted on the properties of these materials.

6. Readers interested in densitometry will want to consult the following three GATF publications: *Optical Density as a Measure of Tone Values in Lithography*, Technical Bulletin No. 4 (New York, 1960); *The Relations between Dot Area, Dot Density and Tone Value in Lithography*, Technical Bulletin No. 5; and Paul W. Dorst, *Reproduction of Tones by Offset Lithography* (New York, 1960).

7. Erwin Jaffe, Edward Brody, Frank Preucil, and Jack W. White, *Color Separation Photography for Offset Lithography with an Introduction to Masking*, GATF Publication No. 509 (New York, 1959), page 128.

8. H. David McKinney, *Handling and Scaling of Art*, in the LITHOGRAPHERS MANUAL [see No. 1], Vol. I, pages 4:62–4:69.

9. The resolving power of the human eye is discussed in Ralph M. Evans, W. T. Hanson, Jr., and W. Lyle Brewer, *Principles of Color Photography* (New York, 1953), pages 25 and 26.

10. The making of crossline screens is described in Louis Flader and J. F. Mertle, *Modern Photoengraving* (Chicago, 1948), pages 48–51.

11. An operational description of halftone photography is by Erwin Jaffe, *Halftone Photography for Offset Lithography*, GATF Publication No. 508, Third Edition (Pittsburgh, 1964). Readers interested in the development of halftone theories can find an extensive listing of the literature in Bruce E. Tory, *Photolithography* (Sidney and Chicago, 1953), page 79.

12. Diaphragms are discussed in many books on photography, for example, in L. P. Clerc, *Ilford Manual of Process Work* (London, 1953).

13. The Eastman Kodak publication, *Kodak Wratten Filters for Scientific and Technical Use* (Rochester, 1951) is a monograph on filters.

14. Letter, dated January 2, 1966, from Mr. Frank Preucil to the writer.

15. A comprehensive discussion of color correcting by photographic masking is in the LITHOGRAPHERS MANUAL [see No. 1], Chapter VII.

16. The booklet *Color Correction with Kodak Tri-Mask Film* (Rochester, 1965) and the booklet *Masking with Multimask Film*, published by the Gevaert Company of America, explain masking with these materials.

17. A detailed description of dot-etching is in Bernard R. Halpern, *Tone and Color Correcting for Offset Lithography*, GATF Publication No. 510/11 (New York, 1956).

18. Fake color process for letterpress is discussed by Louis Cheskin, *Color Guide for Marketing Media* (New York, 1954); fake color process for lithography is discussed by Halpern, same reference as before.

Notes and References to Chapter V: *Printing-Image Carriers*

1. Helmut Gernsheim in collaboration with Allison Gernsheim, *The History of Photography* (London, 1955), page 357.

2. George W. Jorgensen and Michael H. Bruno, *The Sensitivity of Lithographic Coatings*, GATF Research Bulletin No. 218 (New York, 1954), page 1.

3. Paul H. Smith in the ELECTROTYPERS AND STEREOTYPERS MAGAZINE, March, 1959, page 14.

4. For a discussion of presensitized plates see Paul J. Hartsuch, Ph.D. *Chemistry of Lithography*, GATF Publication No. 401 (New York, 1961), page 186; for wipe-on coatings, page 197.

5. Jorgensen and Bruno [see No. 2] discuss insolubilization of bichromated coatings, Chapter IX.

6. Many contemporary books explain woodcutting and wood engraving, for example, Jules Heller *Printmaking Today* (New York, 1958).

7. Linoleum engraving is explained in Heller, same reference as before; rubber engraving for flexography is discussed in *Flexography—Principles and Practices* published by the Flexographic Technical Association (New York, 1962).

8. The *Standard Scale for Photoengravings* and the *Standard Scale for Color Process Engravings*, as well as an explanatory book, *The Standard Scale in Theory and Practice*, are published and from time to time revised by the American Photoengravers Association, Chicago.

9. *PIA Standard Photoengraving Specification Manual for Letterpress Printing from Electrotypes*

for Magazine, Catalog and Commercial Work, Revised Edition (Washington, D.C., 1962).

10. *Kodak Graphic Arts Films and Plates—A Kodak Graphic Arts Data Book*, Second Edition (Rochester, 1955), page 25.

11. Traditional stripping for photoengraving is explained in Louis Flader and J. S. Mertle, *Modern Photoengraving* (Chicago, 1948), Chapter VIII.

12. The Cold-Enamel process, the Bichromated-Albumin process, and the Glue-Enamel process are operationally discussed in Flader and Mertle, same reference as before, pages 156–64.

13. Polyvinyl alcohol resists are operationally discussed in J. S. Mertle and Gordon L. Monsen, *Photomechanics and Printing* (Chicago, 1957), page 162.

14. The making of KPR plates is explained in *Kodak Photo Resist for Making Photoengraved Plates*.

15. Meyer L. Sugerman, *Electrofax—A New Tool for the Graphic Arts*, paper in TAGA PROCEEDINGS, 1955, page 59.

16. Adapted from Harold G. Greig, *The Electrofax Photoresist Makes Exposure by Projection Printing a Possibility*, PHOTOENGRAVERS BULLETIN, November, 1956, pages 135–36.

17. At the 1961 Convention of the American Photoengravers Association Mr. Stuart E. Arnett, then Manager, Graphic Arts Products, Radio Corporation of America, announced that work on Electrofax had progressed to the point that production shipments of Electrofax-coated engravers metal were being made. (See PHOTOENGRAVERS BULLETIN, November, 1961, page 164.) At the time of writing, this material had been discontinued by RCA, and development work of Electrofax-coated metal had been transferred to the Dow Chemical Company, Midland, Mich.

18. Flader and Mertle [see No. 11], page 151.

19. Magnesium plates are discussed in the GPO-PIA Joint Research Bulletin, Plates Series No. 1, *Magnesium Plates* (Washington, D.C., 1949).

20. *PIA Photoengraving Specification Manual* [see No. 9], page 8.

21. For a discussion of etching powders, see *Mallinckrodt Etching Powder Handbook* (St. Louis, Mo., 1948).

22. An operational description of four-way powdering is in Flader and Mertle [see No. 11], pages 174–75.

23. J. Homer Winkler, *Significant Developments Affecting Photoengraving* in the PHOTOENGRAVERS BULLETIN, November, 1947, pages 96–97.

24. A detailed discussion of conventional etching is given in Flader and Mertle [see No. 11] Chapters XI and XII; electrolytic etching of copper is discussed by J. Homer Winkler in the PHOTOENGRAVERS BULLETIN, October, 1949, pages 55–61.

25. John A. Easley, *A New Chemical Method for Etching Magnesium Printing Plates* in TAGA PROCEEDINGS, 1954, page 77.

26. Same reference as before.

27. Adapted from Easley [see No. 25], italics added.

28. Paul F. Borth and Marvin C. Rogers, *Powderless Etching of Copper* in TAGA PROCEEDINGS, 1961, page 4.

29. Same reference as before.

30. Borth and Rogers [see No. 28], page 5.

31. Robert Downie, *Proceedings of Seminar Rotary Relief Printing with Wrap-Around Plates*, New York, September 10, 1959, R&E COUNCIL, page 11.

32. *Background Memorandum on Dycril*, duPont Public Relations Department.

33. *The Lithographers Manual*, 20th Anniversary Edition, edited by Victor Strauss (New York, 1958), Vol. I, page 2:2.

34. Description of the Kodak Relief Plate is based on a paper by Henry C. Staehle, NAPL convention, September 9, 1964, and on information received from Kodak. The TI-Plate is described by George P. Howland, *TI-Plate, Clad Metal Printing Plate* in PRINTING PLATES MAGAZINE, July, 1965.

35. G. A. Harrison, *Mechanization Comes to Photoengraving* in PHOTOENGRAVERS BULLETIN, November, 1950, page 76.

36. Adapted from S. W. Levine, R. N. Hotchkiss, F. P. Willcox, *Fairchild Variable Response Unit* in TAGA PROCEEDINGS, 1955, page 48.

37. Otto Isenschmid, *Electronic Masking and Engraving Equipment*, PHOTOENGRAVERS BULLETIN, November, 1960, page 195.

38. Descriptive booklet on I181 Vario-Klischograph.

39. Adapted from Heinz Tandt, *The Vario Klischograph*, in KLISCHOGRAPH, No. 3, U.S. Edition, 1957.

40. For a survey of electromechanical engraving equipment, see Dr. Marvin Rogers, *The Electronic Engraving Machine—A Tool for the Photoengraver* published by Photoengravers Research, Inc., 1961.

41. *Electrotype and Stereotype Handbook*, Second Edition, page 32, published by the International Association of Electrotypers and Stereotypers, Inc., Cleveland.

42. Hugo Jahn, *The Dictionary of Graphic Arts Terms* (Chicago, 1928), page 270.

43. Mac D. Sinclair in PRINTING PRODUCTION magazine, January, 1960, page 35.

44. *Manual of Stereotype Operations*, published by the American Newspaper Publishers Association Research Institute (New York, 1958), page 89.

45. William Blum and George B. Hogabom, *Principles of Electroplating and Electroforming* (New York, 1949), page 234.

46. Same reference as before.

47. Blum and Hogabom [see No. 45], page 232.

48. J. Homer Winkler, *Duplicate Printing Plates* in the ELECTROTYPERS AND STEREOTYPERS MAGAZINE, December, 1959, page 3.

49. *Electrotyping in the Government Printing Office*, GPO-PIA Joint Research Bulletin, page 11.

50. Same reference as before, page 12.

51. Winkler [see No. 48], page 8.

52. Electrotyping [see No. 49], page 9.

53. Ben R. Preston, *The Bista Plate* in the ELECTROTYPERS AND STEREOTYPERS MAGAZINE, March, 1960, page 38.

54. Winkler [see No. 48], page 9.

55. This and the following quotations on the molding of rubber plates are from *Flexography* [see No. 7], pages 45–48.

56. Condensed from *Rubber and Plastics Used in the Printing Industry*, R&E COUNCIL (Washington, D.C., 1953), pages 11 and 12.

57. Same reference as before, page 9.

58. Condensed from *Flexography* [see No. 7], page 48.

59. Condensed from *Flexography* [see No. 7], pages 51–52.

60. *Rubber and Plastics* [see No. 56], page 14.

61. *Rubber and Plastics* [see No. 56], page 15.

62. Winkler [see No. 48], page 12.

63. Fine art intaglio methods are described in many books; Joseph Pennel, *The Graphic Arts* (Chicago, 1921) is an excellent introduction; John Buckland Wright, *Etching and Engraving* (London, 1953) emphasizes relations between techniques and aesthetic results; Heller [see No. 6] contains descriptions of contemporary American equipment and lists suppliers.

64. Robert N. Steffens, *Engraved Stationery Handbook* (New York, 1950), page 109.

65. Same reference as before, condensed from page 76.

66. H. Mills Cartwright, FRPS, *Photogravure* (Boston, 1939), page 64.

67. See Harvey F. George, *Flow Chart of Gravure Advertising Production* in GTA BULLETIN, Vol. IV, No. 2, December, 1953, page 15.

68. Condensed from Russ B. Leech, *Base Cylinders and Ballard Shells for Plating* in GTA BULLETIN, Vol. IV, No. 2, December, 1953, page 15.

69. Same reference as before.

70. H. M. Cartwright and Robert Mackay, *Rotogravure* (Lyndon, Kentucky, 1956), page 121.

71. Leech [see No. 68], page 16.

72. Cartwright and Mackay [see No. 70], page 130.

73. Cartwright and Mackay [see No. 70], page 131.

74. Leech [see No. 68], page 18.

75. Cartwright and Mackay [see No. 70], condensed from pages 137–40.

76. David A. Cutler, *The GTA Cylinder Gauge* in GTA BULLETIN, Vol. VIII, No. 2, January, 1958, page 16.

77. Gravure processes are from time to time summarized in GRAVURE magazine; reprints of such articles may be available.

78. Elmer G. Stacy, *The Henderson Cylinder Engraving Process* in the GTA BULLETIN, Vol. IV, No. 2, December, 1953, page 139.

79. Oscar Smiel, *Gravure* article in ADVERTISING REQUIREMENTS, November, 1955, page 106.

80. Oscar Smiel, *News-Dultgen Halftone Process*, GTA BULLETIN, Vol. IV, No. 2, December, 1953, pages 37 and 38.

81. Condensed from George H. Carl, *Review of All Gravure Halftone Processes* in GTA BULLETIN, Vol. IX, No. 2, June, 1960, page 157. See also Edward Behringer, *Dultgen Hard Dot* in GTA BULLETIN, Vol. III, No. 1, May, 1956.

82. Condensed from Cartwright and Mackay [see No. 70], page 117.

83. Condensed from *Technical Guide for the Gravure Industry* (New York, 1955), Part IV, pages 7 and 8.

84. Cartwright [see No. 66] discusses the general principles of gravure etching in Chapter XVIII; a more modern study is by James A. Dugan, *Fundamentals of Single Solution Etching in Gravure*, TAGA PROCEEDINGS, 1960.

85. Cartwright and Mackay [see No. 70] mention storage of sensitized tissue for a few days; William Doerrfeld, *Handling of Tissue at Kable* in GTA BULLETIN, Vol. IX, No. 2, June, 1960, reports that sensitized tissue is stored up to six weeks.

86. Condensed from Dr. William H. Vinton, *New Developments in Rotofilm* article in GRAVURE magazine, December, 1951, page 20.

87. *Technical Guide* [see No. 83], Part IV, page 4.

88. Jerry J. Mayer, *Screens for Gravure Engraving*, article in GRAVURE magazine, October, 1955, page 31.

89. *Technical Guide* [see No. 83], Part V, page 13.

90. Same reference as before.

91. GRAVURE magazine, August, 1959, page 21.

92. Robert Hazzard, *Detroit Gravure's Automatic Etching Procedure* in the GTA BULLETIN, Vol. IX, No. 2, pages 172 and 173.

93. D. R. Lowe, *What Black Light Is* in the GTA BULLETIN, Vol. XII, No. 1, February, 1961, page 15.

94. Ernest Wattier, *Black Light and One-Bath Etching* in the GTA BULLETIN, Vol. IX, No. 2, June, 1960.

95. Matthew J. Romano, *Black Light and One-Acid Etch at Triangle* in the GTA BULLETIN, Vol. XII, No. 1, February, 1961, page 12.

96. Cartwright and Mackay [see No. 70], page 200.

97. Cartwright and Mackay [see No. 70], page 201.

98. Cartwright and Mackay [see No. 70], page 206.

99. Condensed from Silas Coulson, *Chromium Plating of Rotogravure Cylinders* in the GTA BULLETIN, Vol. VI, No. 1, May, 1955, page 94.

100. Cartwright and Mackay [see No. 70], page 201.

101. Bernard R. Halpern, *Color Stripping for Offset Lithography* (New York, 1955), pages 12 and 13.

102. Michael H. Bruno, *The Platemaking Department* in LITHOGRAPHERS MANUAL [see No. 33], Vol. I, page 10:2.

103. Hartsuch [see No. 4], page 186.

104. Chemists interested in presensitized plates will want to consult Jaromir Kosar, *Light Sensitive Systems* (New York, 1965). Chapter VII is devoted to presensitized plates; the list of references comprises 147 items, patents in the main. A less detailed chemical discussion of diazos is in Hartsuch [see No. 4], pages 186–90.

105. Condensed from Hartsuch [see No. 4], pages 189 and 190.

106. Letter, dated December 31, 1965, from Mr. Frank Preucil. Another letter from Mr. Harry

H. Lerner (vice-president, Triton Press, Inc.—collotype printers in New York City—and a consultant to Union Carbide) dated February 21, 1966, comments on screenless printing and the Union Carbide plate: "It is interesting that only the positive-working plates of various manufacturers seem usable for screenless printing while their negative-working plates do not work at all for this purpose. Evidently, the non-exposed areas on positive plates have sufficient residual sensitivity to bring in a few more steps on the scale. If the exposure is very high or if there is initial over exposure, the continuous-tone characteristics of these plates are almost non-existent.

"Union Carbide (Plastics Division at Bound Brook, N.J.) is experimenting with a new plastic lithographic plate which will print in continuous-tone under standard offset conditions. The basis of the plate is a newly developed photo-responsive resin which is used as a thin coating on a suitable backing. The printing surface is composed entirely of this new resin material which initially is strongly water absorbing but at the same time is insoluble and wear resistant. Exposure causes the resin to become oleophilic in proportion to the degree of exposure. The image areas still consist of a resin surface differing from the original mainly in their degree of hydrophilicity. Printing is thus from a resin/resin surface, and neither ink nor water carrying ability depend upon the composition of the supporting substrate.

"The Union Carbide plate is negative working and presensitized. Results from multicolor work are reported to be excellent with very good tone control in both highlight and shadow areas. Run life is moderately good with no loss of image. Exposure conditions and press operation is normal, using standard commercial equipment. One of the more interesting aspects of this plate is that no processing steps are required between exposure and presswork."

107. Robert F. Reed, *Offset Platemaking—Deep-Etch* (New York, 1955), page 6.
108. Adapted from same reference as before, page 129.
109. Adapted from Michael H. Bruno, LITHOGRAPHERS MANUAL [see No. 33], Vol. I, page 10:36.
110. LITHOGRAPHERS MANUAL [see No. 33], Vol. I, pages 11:3 and 11:4.
111. Same reference as before.
112. Adapted from LITHOGRAPHERS MANUAL [see No. 33], Vol. I, pages 11:3 and 11:4.
113. LITHOGRAPHERS MANUAL [see No. 33], Vol. I, page 11:6.
114. On the origin of collotype see Joseph Maria Eder, *History of Photography* (New York, 1945), Chapter XCII.
115. The only English book on collotype is by Thomas A. Wilson, *The Practice of Collotype* (New York, 1935). In 1961 Faustino Ledesma submitted a paper *The Collotype Process* in partial fulfillment of the requirements of the degree of M.A. at Long Beach State College, California. A copy of this paper is in the library of GATF; GATF has also a bibliography of articles on collotype.
116. Harry H. Lerner, *Results of a Study on Offset Collotype* in TAGA PROCEEDINGS, 1954, page 26.
117. Harry L. Hiett, *Hiett's Manual on Screen Process Work* (Indianapolis, 1926), page 24.
118. Harry Steinberg, *Silk Screen Color Printing* (New York, 1942), page VII.

Notes and References to Chapter VI: *Printing Presses*

1. The Western invention of printing, letterpress or typography, is credited to Johannes Gutenberg, Mainz, *ca.* 1440. Printing was practiced in many European towns by the end of the fifteenth century; William Caxton introduced letterpress into England in 1476. Printing began in America in the 1530's in Mexico City; the first printing press was established in the American Colonies in Cambridge, Mass., by Stephen Day, in 1638. Alois Senefelder invented lithography in Munich, Bavaria, in 1798. Offset lithography was used during the later part of the nineteenth century for tin printing; for the printing of paper it was possibly independently invented by Ira Rubel, in Nutley, N.J., assumedly between 1904 and 1905. Rotogravure was secretly practiced in England in the 1890's; in 1904 the "American Photogravure Company" was founded in Philadelphia, using a rotogravure press built in England and imported into the United States.
2. PRINTING PRODUCTION magazine publishes each year in its December issue a list of *Printing Press Specifications*.
3. The monograph *Printing Pressures*, published by the Research and Engineering Council of the Graphic Arts Industries, Inc. (Washington, D.C., 1959), is an introduction to printing pressure in relief printing.
4. A comprehensive listing of European flatbed-cylinder presses can be found in the *Specification Manual of Printing Machinery*, published since 1962 from time to time by the BRITISH PRINTER, London.
5. All data for single-color flatbed-cylinder presses built in 1962 are taken from the *29th Annual Where To Buy Guide*, PRINTING PRODUCTION magazine, December, 1962, page 252.
6. Same reference as before.
7. The data for flatbed-cylinder presses are from a catalog sheet of the Miehle Printing Press and Manufacturing Company, Chicago, coded 11-11-27.
8. The data of sheet-fed rotaries were taken either from the *Buyers Guide* [see No. 5], page 256, or from manufacturers' catalogs.
9. For a discussion of newspaper page length see

William Braasch, *Newspaper Presses* (Chicago, 1958), page 21.

10. All descriptive quotations are from Braasch, same reference as before, pages 15 and 16.
11. Braasch [see No. 9], page 119.
12. *Flexography: Principles and Practices* (New York, 1962), page 20.
13. Same reference as before, page 21.
14. E. F. Boughton, *Flexographic Printing* (Chicago, 1958), page 9.
15. *Flexography* [see No. 12], page 21.
16. FLEXOGRAPHY magazine publishes a *Flexography Buyers' Guide* in the November issue of even numbered years; this buyers' guide carries about 6,000 listings of sources of equipment, supplies and services. A parallel buyers' guide is published by GRAVURE magazine in the November issue of odd numbered years.
17. *Flexography* [see No. 12], page 293.
18. *Dry Offset Techniques at Washington Plant*, unsigned article in PRINTING MAGAZINE—NATIONAL LITHOGRAPHER, October, 1963, page 60.
19. Tours through the plant of the Bureau of Engraving and Printing are arranged by the Bureau and are quite popular.
20. *The Bureau of Engraving and Printing* (Washington, D.C., 1959), page 19.
21. The *Specification Manual* [see No. 4] contains information on many European sheet-fed gravure presses.
22. Adapted from Elmer G. Stacy, *Gravure Sheet Fed vs. Roto!*, article in the GRAPHIC ARTS MONTHLY, December, 1959, page 24.
23. Same reference as before.
24. *Giant Presses Now Rolling at Standard Gravure Plant*, article in GRAVURE magazine, May, 1960.
25. Adapted from *15 Million Catalog Pages per Hour*, article in GRAVURE magazine, October, 1959.
26. *Gardner Opens New $3 Million Roto Plant*, article in GRAVURE magazine, December, 1958.
27. Same reference as before.
28. The LITHOGRAPHERS MANUAL, 20th Anniversary Edition, edited by Victor Strauss (New York, 1958), Vol. I, page 12:58.
29. The trade press reports consistently about various kinds of specialty printing and brings, from time to time, surveys of equipment for such important fields as rotary business forms, for example. See also *Lithographic Abstracts*, published by GATF, and *Graphic Arts Progress*, published by Graphic Arts Information Service, Rochester Institute of Technology, Rochester, N.Y.
30. George J. Mills, *Platen Press Operation* (Pittsburgh, 1959) adapted from page 8.
31. Same reference as before, page 7.
32. Mills [see No. 30], adapted from page 8.
33. *Theory and Practice of Press Work*, United States Government Printing Office, Apprentice Training Series (Washington, D.C., 1948), page 165.
34. Same reference as before, page 163.
35. The width of the impression nip is discussed in

Craig R. Spicher, *The Practice of Presswork*, Second Edition (Chicago, 1929), pages 157–60.
36. Adapted from same reference as before, page 71.
37. There is no book on the history of the printing press in English. The closest thing to it is by Fred Roblin, *Printing Press Development, 1450–1965* in the 75th anniversary issue of the AMERICAN PRESSMAN, November, 1965. This monograph covers presses for all printing processes and methods and is profusely illustrated.
38. *Theory and Practice, 1948* [see No. 33], condensed from page 188.
39. Some prefer headline to deadline, for example Spicher [see No. 35], page 161.
40. *Theory and Practice, 1948* [see No. 33], adapted from page 86.
41. Technical Trade School Correspondence Course, *Printing Presses and Sheet Feeders* (Pressmens Home, Tenn., 1941), page 1.
42. The best source of information on a specific press for operating personnel is the manufacturer's manual which is furnished together with the press.
43. Ralph W. Polk and Harry L. Gage, *A Composition Manual* (Washington, D.C., 1953), page 23.
44. Paul J. Thoma, *Roller Setting and Plate Breathing Affect Print Quality*, article in the AMERICAN PRESSMAN, November, 1961, adapted from pages 14 and 15.
45. Same reference as before, page 16.
46. *Rotary Letterpress Operation Is Improved and Speeded by the Spiral Tension System*, article in PRINTING PRODUCTION magazine, February, 1960, page 31.
47. S. C. Saunders, *High-Speed Letterpress Developments*, article in the AMERICAN PRESSMAN, September, 1957, page 56.
48. *Basic Data—Principal Mechanism of Cox-O-Type Explained*, Vol. 3, No. 1 of the GOSS-DUPLEX SERVICE GUIDE, January, 1955, adapted from page 6.
49. Adapted from Braasch [see No. 9], page 474.
50. Braasch [see No. 9], page 15.
51. See descriptive literature for the Goss Unitube press, no date, Circular No. 134.
52. Braasch [see No. 9], page 128.
53. Braasch [see No. 9], page 128.
54. Braasch [see No. 9], page 128.
55. Braasch [see No. 9], page 132.
56. Braasch [see No. 9], page 132.
57. Braasch [see No. 9], condensed from pages 119–21.
58. Braasch [see No. 9], adapted from page 125.
59. Braasch [see No. 9], page 123.
60. *Report of the Proceedings Third Annual Meeting and Technical Forum*, Flexographic Technical Association (FTA), February 6–7, 1961, New York, pages 2 and 3.
61. Alexander A. Bradie, *The Role of Plate Cylinders in Flexographic Printing* in the AMERICAN PRESSMAN, July, 1956, page 12.
62. Same reference as before, condensed from pages 12 and 14.
63. *Flexography* [see No. 12], page 52.

64. *Flexography* [see No. 12], page 50.
65. *Flexography* [see No. 12], page 282.
66. *Flexography* [see No. 12], page 282.
67. Robert N. Steffens, *Engraved Stationery Handbook* (New York, 1950), page 237.
68. Charles W. Latham, *Lithographic Offset Press Operating*, GATF Publication No. 505–6, Revised Edition (New York, 1956), page 14.
69. Latham, same reference as before, condensed from pages 17 and 18.
70. Latham [see No. 68], page 16.
71. Latham [see No. 68], page 18.
72. Latham [see No. 68], adapted from page 19.
73. Latham [see No. 68], pages 19 and 20.
74. Latham [see No. 68], adapted from page 21.
75. LITHOGRAPHERS MANUAL [see No. 28], Vol. II, Chapter XII (New York, 1958), adapted from pages 12:19 and 12:20.
76. Dr. K. Fox, *Blankets and Rollers in Lithography*, undated information sheet, by the National Association of Photo Lithographers.
77. Same reference as before.
78. Michael H. Bruno in MODERN LITHOGRAPHY, August, 1960.
79. Victor Strauss, *Silk Screen Mechanization*, in TAGA, PROCEEDINGS, FIFTH ANNUAL MEETING, 1953, pages 54–59.
80. *High Speed Letterpress Developments*, Part II in the AMERICAN PRESSMAN, October, 1957, page 45.
81. H. C. Cook, *Ideas on Flexographic Press Design* in the PAPER FILM AND FOIL CONVERTER, February, 1959, page 34.
82. Latham [see No. 68], page 29.
83. Latham, same reference as before.
84. Louis M. Larsen, Ph.D., *Industrial Printin Inks* (New York, 1962), page 162.
85. Andries Voet, *Ink and Paper in the Printing Process* (New York and London, 1952), pages 50 and 51.
86. Larsen [see No. 84], page 5.
87. *Care and Use of Printers' Rollers*, R. & E. Council, Pressroom Series No. 1 (Washington, D.C., 1953), page 9.
88. Same reference as before, adapted from page 9.
89. Voet [see No. 85], page 51.
90. *Printing Ink Manual*, Commissioned by the Technical Training Board of the Society of British Printing Ink Manufacturers (Cambridge, England, 1961), page 47. Printers' Rollers are discussed in Chapter 3.
91. James K. Brown, *Printing Rollers* in the AMERICAN PRESSMAN, January, 1959, adapted from page 39.
92. *Printers' Rollers* [see No. 87], page 9.
93. *Printing Ink Manual* [see No. 90], page 50.
94. A detailed description, and pictures, of roller casting is in Jack Deller, *Printers' Rollers, Their Manufacture and Use* (London, 1959).
95. Sidney Rosenblatt, *Roller Information* in the AMERICAN PRESSMAN, October, 1957, page 24.
96. Brown [see No. 91], page 41.
97. *Printers' Rollers* [see No. 87], adapted from page 10.
98. Brown [see No. 91].
99. *Printing Ink Manual* [see No. 90], adapted from page 57.
100. Brown [see No. 91].
101. *Printers' Rollers* [see No. 87], page 9.
102. This paragraph is based on the *Printing Ink Manual* [see No. 90], pages 61 to 63.
103. Brown [see No. 91], condensed from page 44.
104. *Printing Ink Manual* [see No. 90], page 60.
105. Comment by D. W. Hubbard, Vice President, Ideal Roller and Manufacturing Company, Chicago, made in his letter of February 3, 1965.
106. Deller [see No. 94], page 98.
107. Brown [see No. 91], page 44.
108. Brown [see No. 91].
109. Comment by K. Fox, Chief Chemist, Rapid Roller Company, made in his letter of March 25, 1965.
110. Mills [see No. 30], page 13.
111. *Theory and Practice, 1948* [see No. 33], pages 27 and 28.
112. Braasch [see No. 9], page 87.
113. Braasch [see No. 9], pages 88 and 89.
114. Braasch [see No. 9], page 90.
115. *Operation, Care and Adjustment of the Goss Headliner Newspaper Press*, Reprint from the AMERICAN PRESSMAN, no date, no page numbers.
116. *Specifications Manual for Hoe Colormatic Unit* by R. Hoe & Co., Inc., New York City, condensed from pages 8–11.
117. A description of an ink tank with double bottom can be found in *Press Mechanics*, *Sound Application for Better Printing* by Kenneth W. Huffman in FLEXOGRAPHY magazine, October, 1961, pages 26 and 63.
118. *Flexography* [see No. 12], page 19.
119. Huffman [see No. 117], page 63.
120. William D. Donohue, *Cylinder Accuracy—the Heart of a Flexographic Press* in FLEXOGRAPHY magazine, January, 1961, condensed from pages 25 and 26.
121. *Flexographic Printing and the Anilox Distribution System*, adapted from page 8.
122. Joseph W. Dragonetti, *Sheet Fed Gravure*, in GRAVURE magazine, August, 1961, page 51.
123. *Specifications Covering Hoe Super Production Monotone and Color Gravure Presses*, page 3.
124. *Commercial Rotogravure Printing with Champlain Rotogravure Equipment* (Bloomfield, N.J., 1954), page 8.
125. Paul J. Hartsuch, Ph.D., *The Chemistry oj Lithography*, GATF Publication No. 401 (New York, 1961), page 316.
126. Same reference as before. Chemical copperizing of steel rollers is described in GATF, *Research Progress No. 27*, December, 1953.
127. Latham [see No. 68], page 46.
128. A survey of selected dampening systems, from 1868 to 1954, is by W. H. Wood, *A Review of Dampening Systems*, printed in the 1955 TAGA PROCEEDINGS OF THE SEVENTH ANNUAL MEETING, pages 177–86.
129. Latham [see No. 68] condensed from pages 47 and 48.
130. Victor J. Shaw, *How To Use Paper Dampeners*, in NATIONAL LITHOGRAPHER, April, 1963.

131. Culled from sales literature on *3M Dampening Sleeves*.
132. Quoted from sales literature, *The Mullen Air Doctoring System*, composed on Photon and printed by the Mullen Printing Corporation, Woburn, Mass.
133. Michael H. Bruno, *The Dampening Problem in Offset Printing*, article in the AMERICAN PRESSMAN, November, 1962, page 29.
134. John D. Payne, *Some Comments on the Dahlgren Dampening System for Offset Presses*, in the AMERICAN PRESSMAN, April, 1960, page 46.
135. Unsigned article *The Dahlgren System* in the AMERICAN PRESSMAN, January, 1965, page 13.
136. Bruno [see No. 133], condensed from pages 29 and 30.
137. Bruno [see No. 133].
138. Bruno [see No. 133].
139. The description of the Dampen-Orr system is based on sales literature by Roberts & Porter, Inc., who distribute this system.
140. Latham [see No. 68], adapted from page 61.
141. Mills [see No. 30], page 53.
142. Mills [see No. 30], page 65.
143. Mills [see No. 30], page 74.
144. For special-purpose attachments to platen presses, the literature of press manufacturers should be consulted.
145. Latham [see No. 68], adapted from page 55.
146. Latham [see No. 68], page 70.
147. *Lithographers Manual* [see No. 28], Vol. II, adapted from pages 12:10 and 12:11.
148. Latham [see No. 68], page 75.
149. A detailed description of tumbler grippers is in Latham [see No. 68], pages 70 and 71.
150. *Lithographers Manual* [see No. 28], Vol. II, page 12:11, condensed.
151. Latham [see No. 68], adapted from pages 72 and 73.
152. Roy P. Tyler and Roy Barnes, *Operating Large Harris Presses*, page 7.
153. *Lithographers Manual* [see No. 28], Vol. II, page 12:11.
154. Charles W. Latham, *Advanced Pressmanship (Sheet-Fed Presses)*, GATF Publication No. 513 (New York, 1963), page 102.
155. Same reference as before.
156. *Advanced Pressmanship* [see No. 154], condensed from page 111.
157. This description refers to the Web/Sheet Feeder for Miehle 38 presses. It is from a letter, dated January 15, 1965, by Mr. Owen L. Gore, Vice-President, The Dexter Company.
158. Braasch [see No. 9], page 161.
159. Braasch [see No. 9], adapted from page 162.
160. *Webster's New International Dictionary*, Unabridged, Second Edition (Springfield, Mass., 1950). Webster does not mention reels for printing, nor do two other dictionaries used by the writer.
161. Braasch [see No. 9], page 177.
162. Braasch [see No. 9], adapted from page 165.
163. *Commercial Rotogravure* [see No. 124], page 11.
164. Technical Trade School Correspondence Course, *Reels, Tension, Pasters* (Pressmens Home, Tenn.), page 26.
165. Same reference as before, adapted from page 30.
166. *Reels, Tension, Pasters* [see No. 164], adapted from pages 31 and 32.
167. *Reels, Tension, Pasters* [see No. 164], adapted from pages 32–34.
168. Readers interested in automatic pasters should consult Braasch [see No. 9], pages 183–89, where various pasters are described.
169. *Hoe Develops Fully Automatic Reel, Tension and Paster* in the AMERICAN PRESSMAN, September, 1958, adapted from page 21.
170. Harvey F. George, *Instrumentation and Quality Controls for Press Register and Quality, Part 3* in GRAVURE magazine, January, 1960, pages 20 and 54.
171. Braasch [see No. 9], page 158.
172. *Commercial Rotogravure* [see No. 124], page 12.
173. *Reels, Tension, Pasters* [see No. 164], page 3.
174. *Reels, Tension, Pasters* [see No. 164], page 18.
175. A detailed description of the Jones Automatic Tension Governor is in *Reels, Tension, Pasters* [see No. 164], pages 18–22.
176. Braasch [see No. 9], page 175.
177. *Commercial Rotogravure* [see No. 124], page 13.
178. *Commercial Rotogravure* [see No. 124], page 14.
179. Braasch [see No. 9], page 175.
180. Edwin C. Koriath and Henry F. Thiele, Jr., *Some Comments on Web Break Detectors* in the AMERICAN PRESSMAN, June, 1959, condensed from page 22.
181. *Ultrasonics Put To Work at Meredith* in the GRAPHIC ARTS MONTHLY, January, 1962, condensed from page 41.
182. Braasch [see No. 9], page 46.
183. Braasch [see No. 9], page 46.
184. Braasch [see No. 9], page 46.
185. R. T. Otepka, *Devices for Better Web Control* in the NATIONAL LITHOGRAPHER magazine, January, 1963, page 68.
186. Harvey F. George, *Instrumentation and Automatic Controls for Press Register and Quality*, Part two of three parts, published in GRAVURE magazine, December, 1959, page 28.
187. Condensed from the same reference as before.
188. *Crosfield Electronics for the Graphic Arts*, equipment catalog of Crosfield Electronics, Inc. (Westbury, N.Y.), page 6.
189. Herbert L. Weiss, *Offset Web Control Systems Analyzed*, First Part, PRINTING PRODUCTION magazine, October, 1961, page 64.
190. Kenneth W. Huffman, *Web Guiding*, article in FLEXOGRAPHY magazine, February, 1962, page 15.
191. Same reference as before.
192. Herbert L. Weiss, *Electronics Perform Press Production Miracles*, PRINTING PRODUCTION magazine, March, 1963, page 79.
193. Same reference as before.
194. Weiss [see No. 192].
195. Crosfield Catalog [see No. 188], page 14.
196. Crosfield Catalog [see No. 188], page 15.
197. Crosfield Catalog [see No. 188], page 17.

198. *A Review of Web Viewers*, Part One, GRAVURE magazine, May, 1963, page 51.
199. Same reference as before.
200. For a description of several web viewers see GRAVURE magazine of May, June, and July, 1963.
201. Otto Jahn, *The Dictionary of Graphic Arts Terms* (Chicago, 1928), page 100.
202. Adapted from Jahn, same reference as before.
203. Latham [see No. 68], page 81.
204. *Advanced Pressmanship* [see No. 154], page 115.
205. *Advanced Pressmanship* [see No. 154], page 114.
206. *Commercial Rotogravure* [see No. 124], page 35.
207. *Commercial Rotogravure* [see No. 124], adapted from page 35.
208. Same reference as before.
209. Same reference as before, page 37.
210. *New York Times*, January 10, 1965.
211. Braasch [see No. 9], adapted from page 208.
212. Braasch [see No. 9], page 213.
213. Braasch [see No. 9], page 220.
214. Braasch [see No. 9], condensed from pages 220 and 221.
215. An illustrated description of two-to-one and three-to-two folding for both straight and collect runs is in Braasch [see No. 9], pages 218–33.
216. Braasch [see No. 9], page 222.
217. Reginald Wardley, *How To Buy a Web Offset Press* in PRINTING MAGAZINE AND THE OFFSET PRINTER, April, 1963, adapted from page 81.
218. *Operation of a Blanket-to-Blanket Perfecting Web Offset Press* booklet published by the Miehle Company, Division of Miehle-Goss-Dexter, Inc. (Chicago), page 29.
219. Same reference as before, page 28.
220. Wardley [see No. 217].
221. Miehle booklet [see No. 218], page 30.
222. The relative advantages of inline and separate carton production are discussed in *Gravure Printing and Die Cutting, Inline vs. Separate*, published in GRAVURE magazine, May, 1959.
223. *Commercial Rotogravure* [see No. 124], page 45.
224. Same reference as before, adapted from page 47.
225. Joseph Moxon, *Mechanick Exercises on the Whole Art of Printing (1683–84)*, edited by Herbert Davis & Harry Carter (London, 1958), pages 311–14.
226. *Printing Ink Manual* [see No. 90], page 392.
227. B. Offen, *Proper Drying on Presses* in the GRAPHIC ARTS MONTHLY, November, 1960, page 11.
228. B. Offen, *Dryers for Web-Offset Presses* in the GRAPHIC ARTS MONTHLY, March, 1961, page 88.
229. *IES Lighting Handbook*, Second Edition, published by the Illuminating Engineering Society (New York, 1954), pages 18–25.
230. Same reference as before.
231. *IES Handbook* [see No. 229].
232. B. Offen [see No. 227], page 12.
233. Eugene Gaspardo, *Effective Flexo Drying* in FLEXOGRAPHY magazine, July, 1963, adapted from page 17.
234. Paper by Werner F. Gerlach, given at Annual Meeting of the PIA Web Offset Section, Pittsburgh, May 15 to 17, 1963 printed in BOOK PRODUCTION magazine, June, 1963, page 72. Those interested in the theoretical aspects of high velocity drying will want to read T. A. Gardner, *A Theory of Drying with Air* published in TAPPI, Vol. 43, No. 9, September, 1960, pages 796–800.
235. A. K. Chatterjee and F. R. Gross, *Heat Transfer in Single and Double Shell Cooling Rolls* in I&EC PROCESS DESIGN AND DEVELOPMENT, Vol. I, January, 1962, pages 41–45.
236. The Kodak drier is described in SCREEN PROCESS MAGAZINE, October, 1954.
237. A discussion of several different drying systems can be found in Section E of *Ideas Now for the Industry with a Future*, containing papers and speeches presented at the Fifth World Convention, Screen Process Printing Association, International (Chicago, 1954).
238. B. Offen [see No. 228], adapted from page 18.
239. Same reference as before.
240. Same reference [see No. 238].
241. Condensed from a paper by Vincent Stafford, given at Annual Meeting of the PIA Web Offset Section in Pittsburgh, May 15–17, 1963, printed in BOOK PRODUCTION magazine, June, 1963, page 70.
242. Paper given by Thomas A. Gardner at the Annual Meeting of the PIA Web Offset Section in Pittsburgh, May 15–17, 1963, printed in BOOK PRODUCTION magazine, June, 1963, pages 71 and 72.
243. T. A. Gardner, *High Velocity Air Drying o, Offset and Letterpress Inks* in TAGA, 1963 PROCEEDINGS, pages 131 and 132.
244. Eugene Gaspardo, *Effective Flexographic Drying* in FLEXOGRAPHY magazine, July, 1963, adapted from page 53.
245. Larsen [see No. 84], adapted from page 53.
246. Jay Waters, *Drying with Multi-Frequency Thermal Radiation* in FLEXOGRAPHY magazine, September, 1960, condensed from pages 38 and 76.
247. An extensive discussion of proofing for offset lithography is in the *Lithographers Manual* [see No. 28], Vol. I, Chapter Eleven.
248. The following definition of proofing—part of the comments made by Mr. J. Homer Winkler—will be of interest to many readers: "Proofing is the operation of obtaining single or multi-color ink impressions, usually on paper, from printing-image carriers. The presses used are generally designed for the purpose. The conditions for proofing, such as ink, paper (or the substrate), pressure and speed, are matched as closely as possible to those to be used on production equipment. Proofs may be used for reproduction, or in comparison with the original copy for customer approval, and production planning. Factors such as color match, color register, position, resolution, tonal density, ink film thickness, printing pressure, and the presence of errors and imperfections may be observed and measured on proofs."
249. The PIA *Standard Photoengraving Specifications Manual*, Revised Edition (Washington, D.C.,

1962) is published by Printing Industries of America, 20 Chevy Chase Circle, N.W., Washington 15, D.C.

250. *Challenge Proof Presses, 1963 Edition*, page 7, published by the Challenge Machinery Company, Grand Haven, Mich.

251. Catalog of Vandercook & Sons, Inc. (Chicago, September, 1963) descriptive sheet of SP13 Galley Proof Press.

252. For more detail on power-operated galley proof presses see the catalog sheet of *Vandercook 13-28 Safe Electric Galley Proof Presses*, available from Vandercook & Sons, Chicago.

253. *Proofing in the Typographic Industry*, published by the INTERNATIONAL TYPOGRAPHIC COMPOSITION ASSOCIATION, INC. (Washington, D.C., 1962), page 8.

254. *The Vandercook Story*, unsigned article in the PHOTOENGRAVERS BULLETIN, January, 1964, page 9.

255. For information on stationary-bed proof presses, the catalog of Vandercook & Sons, Chicago, should be consulted. The Challenge Machinery Company, Grand Haven, Mich., has literature on its line of reciprocating-bed proof presses.

256. *Vandercook Story* [see No. 254], adapted from page 11.

257. Catalog sheet of Vandercook & Sons, Inc.

258. For a detailed description of proof presses for full-color engraving sets, the catalog or specification sheets of Vandercook & Sons, Chicago, should be consulted. The correct proofing procedures are set forth in the PIA *Photoengraving Manual* [see No. 249].

259. *Electrotyper Designs Own Proof Press*, unsigned article in PRINTING PRODUCTION magazine, October, 1962, page 100.

260. The detail of the Flower Multi Diameter Proof Press is culled from descriptive sales leaflet published by the Flower Steel Electrotype Co., New York City.

261. The description of the Mosstype Mounter-Proofer is based on descriptive literature by Mosstype, Waldwick, N.J.

262. Burch F. Seaman, *Rotogravure Cylinder Proving* in GRAVURE magazine, October, 1955, page 17.

263. Oscar Smiel, *Proofing Methods in Gravure* in PRODUCTIONWISE magazine, January, 1957, adapted from page 43.

264. Same reference as before, adapted from page 44.

265. Elmer Stacy, *Rotogravure: Rotary Cylinder Proof Presses* in the GRAPHIC ARTS MONTHLY, August, 1958, adapted from page 28.

266. Same reference as before.

267. Seaman [see No. 262], adapted from page 14.

268. Same reference as before.

269. *Kable Acquires New Variable Size Proof Press* in GRAVURE magazine, March, 1961, condensed from pages 25 and 96.

270. Same reference as before, page 24.

271. Joseph Mazzaferri, *Proofing on Proof Presses*, in the LITHOGRAPHERS MANUAL [see No. 28], Vol. I, adapted from page 11:9.

272. Same reference as before.

273. Mazzaferri [see No. 271].

274. Descriptive literature of Rutherford Machinery Company, a Division of Sun Chemical Corporation.

275. *Vandercook Graphic Equipment*, catalog, page 6.

Notes and References to Chapter VII: *Presswork*

1. Robert H. Roy in *Proceedings of the First Technical Conference on Makeready and Premakeready*, December 4–5, 1952, R. & E. Council, page 7.

2. A list of undercuts on flatbed cylinder presses used in the GPO at the present time can be found in *Theory and Practice of Presswork*, GPO Training Series (Washington, D.C., 1962), page 126.

3. *Theory and Practice of Presswork* GPO, Apprentice Training Series (Washington, D.C., 1948), pages 133 and 134.

4. Sales literature on *Spherkote* by 3M Company.

5. Same reference as before.

6. Fred W. Hoch in *Proceedings of First Makeready Conference* [see No. 1], page 91.

7. Technical Trade School, Correspondence Course, *Underlaying, Interlaying and Overlaying* (Pressmens Home, Tenn., 1938), page 1.

8. Same reference as before.

9. Same reference as No. 7.

10. Craig R. Spicher, *The Practice of Presswork*, Second Edition, Revised (Chicago, 1929), page 202.

11. Technical Trade School, Correspondence Course, *Makeready Procedure* (Pressmens Home, Tenn., 1938), page 9.

12. *Theory and Practice, 1948* [see No. 3], adapted from page 147.

13. *Makeready Procedure* [see No. 11], condensed from page 10.

14. *Makeready Procedure* [see No. 11], condensed from page 11.

15. *Proceedings of the Second Technical Conference on Makeready and Premakeready*, October 1–2, 1953, R. & E. Council, page 155.

16. The AMERICAN PRESSMAN magazine, March, 1963, page 36.

17. The Perfex Top Sheet is briefly described by Alan S. Holliday, *A Factual Report on the 3M Makeready Process* in the AMERICAN PRESSMAN magazine, February, 1957, page 64.

18. Adapted from *Pressmen's Guide for Using 3M Brand Makeready* (1959); see also article by E. A. Kilheffer, *3M Makeready* in the AMERICAN PRESSMAN magazine, June, 1957.

19. *Drawing Maps and Cutting Paper Dolls*, unsigned

article in the AMERICAN PRESSMAN magazine, May, 1959, page 24.

20. *First Makeready Conference* [see No. 1], page 119.

21. W. H. Ticehurst, *Level Impression Printing*, at the 42nd Annual Convention of International Association of Printing House Craftsmen, Chicago, 1961, in PRINTING MAGAZINE, September, 1961, page 125.

22. Report of the *Letterpress Forum on Minimum Makeready* sponsored by Letterpress Division, New York Employing Printers Assn., November 12, 1959, in the ELECTROTYPERS AND STEREOTYPERS MAGAZINE, January, 1950, page 13.

23. PRINTING MAGAZINE, September, 1961, page 125.

24. The development work which resulted in high-speed level impression printing at Curtis is described by Nelson B. Coleman, *Level Impression Printing Can Revolutionize Letterpress*, in the March and April, 1959, issues of the GRAPHIC ARTS MONTHLY.

25. *Theory and Practice, 1948* [see No. 3], page 140.

26. Those interested in letterpress makeready will find the proceedings of the first and second makeready conference [see No. 1 and No. 15] indispensable. The paper by B. L. Sites, *An Improvement in the Method of Makeready for Letterpress Presses* [see No. 1], page 94, and that of Victor Letouzey, *Makeready Origins and Prevention* [see No. 1], page 162, are particularly interesting.

27. *The Vandercook Minimum Makeready System*, published by Vandercook & Sons, Chicago, page 17.

28. George J. Mills, *Platen Press Operation* (Pittsburgh, 1959), page 17.

29. A recent textbook is *General Printing* by Glen U. Cleeton and Charles W. Pitkin, revised by Raymond L. Cornwell (Bloomington, Ill., 1963); the book by Mills [see No. 28] is the most comprehensive monograph on the subject. Another good monograph is *Elementary Platen Presswork* by Ralph W. Polk (Peoria, Ill., 1955).

30. Mills [see No. 28], condensed from page 24.

31. Mills [see No. 28], adapted from page 37.

32. Mills [see No. 28], page 43.

33. *Theory and Practice, 1948* [see No. 3], adapted from page 176.

34. *Theory and Practice, 1948* [see No. 3], page 178.

35. Formal planning methods for flatbed-cylinder printing are discussed by Howard P. Wampler in *Second Makeready Conference* [see No. 15], pages 109–32.

36. The description of press preparation and running of flatbed-cylinder presses follows the article by E. A. Kilheffer, *Presswork*, in the AMERICAN PRESSMAN magazine, January, 1957. Material in quotation marks is taken from this article.

37. Fred W. Hoch, *Handbook for Pressmen* (New York, 1950), page 72.

38. Same reference as before, condensed from page 91.

39. Hoch [see No. 37], page 77.

40. Hoch [see No. 37], page 83.

41. A detailed discussion of troubles encountered

in the running of flatbed-cylinder presses, written for operating personnel, is in the unit *Wrinkles, Slurs, and Offsetting* of the Correspondence Course, published by the Technical Trade School (Pressmens Home, Tenn., 1939).

42. Spicher [see No. 10], page 131.

43. Spicher [see No. 10], page 133.

44. Spicher [see No. 10], page 71.

45. Spicher [see No. 10], pages 74 and 75.

46. Spicher [see No. 10], page 73.

47. R. G. Radford, *Letterpress Machine Work*, Vol. One (London, 1951), page 251.

48. *Operation and Maintenance of the V-50 Miehle Vertical*, Technical Trade School Correspondence Course (Pressmens Home, Tenn., 1947), page 8.

49. Same reference as before, page 7.

50. *Miehle Vertical* [see No. 48], adapted from pages 7 and 8.

51. *Miehle Vertical* [see No. 48], page 13.

52. Same reference as No. 51.

53. Same reference as No. 51.

54. *Operation Manual for the Original Heidelberg Cylinder Press*, page 15.

55. *The Reasons for My Success*, booklet published by Heidelberg-Eastern, page 8.

56. *Operation Manual for Heidelberg Two-Color Presses*, page 20.

57. Same reference as before, page 22.

58. *Proceedings Seminar on Direct and Indirect Wrap-Around Printing, Chicago, March 5 and 6, 1963*, R&E COUNCIL, adapted from paper by Kenneth DeSoto, page 37.

59. *Heidelberg Manual* [see No. 56], adapted from pages 63 and 64.

60. Heidelberg literature [see No. 55], adapted from page 9.

61. The unit on rotary sheet-fed printing was written based on information received primarily from Mr. Edward Blank, Printing Industries of Metropolitan New York; the described practices are common in the New York City area.

62. Adapted from descriptive literature on the Rotary Registerscope by the Taylor Machine Company, Baltimore, Md.

63. *Wrap-Around Printing Seminar* [see No. 58], adapted from paper by Robert H. Downie, page 89.

64. *Wrap-Around Printing Seminar* [see No. 58], adapted from paper by Charles C. Harris, page 34.

65. The comment on Harris wrap-around presses is by the U.S. Government Printing Office in a letter dated February 8, 1965. In this letter the GPO points out that it has been operating two 25×38 Harris wrap-around presses for nearly two years.

66. The ability of Harris wrap-around presses to produce heavy solids with glossy inks was emphasized by several participants in the *Wrap-Around Printing Seminar* [see No. 58].

67. *Flexography: Principles and Practices* (New York, 1962), page 36.

68. The grouping of plastic films for package printing follows the tables printed in *Flexography*

[see No. 67], pages 142 and 143; a listing correlating trade names, chemical designations and manufacturers of plastic films can be found in the same book on pages 146 and 147.

69. Readers interested in the relations between ink solvents and plate molding materials should consult the Solvent Compatibility Chart in *Flexography* [see No. 67], page 64.

70. *Proceedings Third Annual Meeting and Technical Forum*, Flexographic Technical Association, New York, 1961, page 15.

71. Several simple end-use tests of flexographic inks are described in *Flexography* [see No. 67] Chapter X, "Ink Test Methods," beginning on page 92.

72. *Flexography* [see No. 67], page 270.

73. FTA *Proceedings* [see No. 70], page 7.

74. FTA *Proceedings* [see No. 70], adapted from page 41.

75. Frank Davis, *The Mechanics of Good Makeready* in FLEXOGRAPHY magazine, June, 1964, adapted from page 15.

76. An extensive discussion of ink viscosity and of methods for its control is in *Proceedings, First Annual Meeting and Technical Forum*, Flexographic Technical Association, New York, 1959.

77. Frank Davis [see No. 75], page 61.

78. *Flexography* [see No. 67], page 26.

79. The data for polyethylene are from *Flexography* [see No. 67], page 130.

80. A more technical definition of blocking can be found in the Glossary of Flexographic Terms in *Flexography* [see No. 67], page 261.

81. FTA *Proceedings* [see No. 70], page 54.

82. The repeatedly quoted FTA *Proceedings* [see No. 70] contain valuable detailed information on running and should be consulted by interested readers.

83. *Champlain Web-Fed Printing and Converting Equipment*, catalog published by Champlain, Inc., Roseland, N.J., pages 189 and 190.

84. Same reference as before, adapted from page 211. Another method of register control consists in moving the gravure cylinder rather than the compensating roller.

85. Ira Rubel died on September 4, 1908, in Bury, Lancashire. A brief biographical sketch of Rubel by Fredrick Sears, *Alzinography— Lithography of the Future* is in PENROSE'S PICTORIAL ANNUAL, Vol. 14 (1908–09), pages 20–24.

86. Robert F. Reed, *Offset Press Troubles* (Sheet-Fed Presses), GATF Publication No. 501 (New York, 1962) discusses ink troubles in Section 3 and dampening troubles in Section 4.

87. Charles W. Latham, *Advanced Pressmanship* (Sheet-Fed Presses), GATF Publication No. 513 (New York, 1963), page 133.

88. Same reference as before.

89. *Advanced Pressmanship* [see No. 87], page 136.

90. Charles W. Latham, *Offset Press Operating*, Revised Edition, GATF Publication No. 505–6 (New York, 1956) adapted from page 96.

91. Same reference as before, page 32.

92. A detailed description of the Picture Test including several instructive photographs can be

found in the *Lithographers Manual*, 20th Anniversary Edition, edited by Victor Strauss, Vol. II (New York, 1958), pages 12:34–12:36.

93. Latham [see No. 90], condensed from page 23.

94. Descriptions of the thumbprint test for bearer contact can be found in Latham [see No. 90], pages 23–25, and in the *Lithographers Manual*, Vol. II [see No. 92], pages 12:26 and 12:27.

95. *Advanced Pressmanship* [see No. 87], condensed from page 139.

96. *Lithographers Manual*, Vol. II [see No. 92], condensed from page 12:24.

97. Robert F. Reed, *Instruments for Quality Control in Lithography*, GATF publication No. 321 (New York, 1963), adapted from page 92.

98. *Instruments for Quality Control* [see No. 97], pages 89 and 90.

99. Paul J. Hartsuch, Ph.D., *Chemistry of Lithography*, GATF Publication No. 401 (New York, 1961) discusses the fountain solution on pages 299 to 305.

100. *Instruments for Quality Control* [see No. 97] contains descriptions of various pH meters, pages 87–89.

101. Formal quality control as practiced in the Printing Division, Aeronautical Chart and Information Center, U.S. Air Force, is described by Otto C. Stoessel in the following articles: *Quality Control of Litho Inks* in the NATIONAL LITHOGRAPHER magazine, December, 1959; *Quality Measurement of Printed Material*, NATIONAL LITHOGRAPHER magazine, June, 1950; *Quality Measurement of Printed Material Part II*, NATIONAL LITHOGRAPHER, July, 1960; see also the paper by Otto C. Stoessel, *Color and Print Quality—Densitometry Calibration* in the AMERICAN INK MAKER magazine, March, 1961.

102. Latham [see No. 90], page 115.

103. Technical Trade School, Correspondence Course, *Offset Printing*, adapted from Booklet No. 5 "Offset Presses and Presswork Procedure."

104. A number of additional targets, developed by GATF, is described in *Research Department, Report of Progress during 1964* in the section by David B. Crouse, pages 11–15.

105. A discussion of color patches is in *The GATF Color Chart*, GATF Publication No. 302 (New York, 1957).

106. *Advanced Pressmanship* [see No. 87], page 261.

107. George W. Jorgenson, *The LTF Star Target for Ink Spread and Resolution Measurements* in the AMERICAN PRESSMAN magazine, September, 1961, page 26.

108. Quoted from sales literature of Lithos, Inc., 1964.

109. *Advanced Pressmanship* [see No. 87], page 189. The full reference for the mentioned paper is *Cleaning Lithograph Rolls* by John A. Hinckley, TAGA PROCEEDINGS, 1952, pages 47 to 50.

110. Hartsuch [see No. 99], page 317.

111. A detailed discussion of three-solution washup can be found in Latham's *Advanced Pressmanship* [see No. 87], pages 188–92 and in GATF *Re-*

search Progress No. 27, From Black to Yellow in One Washup, September, 1951.

112. *Harris-Cottrell Model 1000 Web-Offset Press,* descriptive literature published by Harris Intertype, pages 6 and 11.

113. Same reference as before, page 13.
114. Quoted from descriptive literature on the Harris-Cottrell Key Register System, patent pending, for web-offset presses.

Notes and References to Chapter VIII: *Paper and Other Printing Stocks*

1. Hanns F. Arledter in SYNTHETIC FIBERS IN PAPERMAKING, edited by O. A. Battista (New York, 1964), pages 7 and 8.
2. James P. Casey, *Pulp and Paper, Chemistry and Chemical Technology,* Second Edition, Revised and Enlarged (New York, 1960), Vol. I, page 1.
3. Casey, same reference as before, Vol. I, page 85.
4. ASTM Special Technical Publication No. 60-B, *Paper and Paperboard, Characteristics, Nomenclature and Significance of Tests,* Third Edition (Philadelphia, 1963), page 2.
5. All figures are based on Casey [see No. 2], Vol. I; the first three are on page 67, the per cent extractives are on page 85, that of mineral matter on page 79.
6. Casey [see No. 2], Vol. I, page 101.
7. Compare *The Dictionary of Paper,* Third Edition (New York, 1965), pages 357–58 and Casey [see No. 2], Vol. II, page 586.
8. George D. Bearce, *Mechanical Pulping* in PULP AND PAPER SCIENCE AND TECHNOLOGY, edited by C. Earl Libby (New York, 1962), Vol. I, page 142.
9. Same reference as before, page 152.
10. Casey [see No. 2], Vol. I, page 288.
11. E. O. Ericsson, J. L. McCarthy, and D. A. Pearson, *Sulfite Pulping* in PULP AND PAPER [see No. 8], Vol. I, page 254.
12. J. N. Swartz and R. C. MacDonald, *Alkaline Pulping* in PULP AND PAPER [see No. 8], Vol. I, pages 160–62.
13. Edwin Sutermeister, S.B., D.Sc., *The Story o Papermaking* (Boston, 1954), page 89.
14. Casey [see No. 2], Vol. I, page 214.
15. On the history of chemical pulping, consult C. E. Libby in PULP AND PAPER [see No. 8], Vol. I, pages 11–13.
16. H. Hardman and E. J. Cole, *Paper-Making Practice* (Toronto, 1960), page 30.
17. Robert Henderson Clapperton, *Modern Paper-Making* (Oxford, MCMLII), condensed from page 69.
18. Casey [see No. 2], Vol. I, page 288.
19. Condensed from Sutermeister [see No. 13], page 88.
20. John N. McGovern, *Semichemical and Chemimechanical Pulping* in PULP AND PAPER [see No. 8], Vol. I, page 282.
21. Hardman and Cole [see No. 16], page 10.
22. Casey [see No. 2], Vol. I, page 335.
23. Sutermeister [see No. 13], condensed from page 187.
24. Casey [see No. 2], Vol. I, page 341.
25. Hardman and Cole [see No. 16], page 11, condensed.
26. Casey [see No. 2], Vol. I, page 343.

27. Readers interested in the yields of different pulping processes will want to consult Table II-1 of PULP AND PAPER [see No. 8], Vol. I, page 282; Figure 11-2 of the same work shows the removal of hardwood chemical constituents in semichemical and chemimechanical pulping; chemigroundwood is discussed in Chapter 12 of this book.
28. Casey [see No. 2], Vol. I, page 380.
29. Dard Hunter, *Papermaking, The History and Technique of an Ancient Craft,* Second Edition, Revised and Enlarged (New York, 1947), page 382.
30. Permanence is discussed in Kenneth W. Britt, Editor, HANDBOOK OF PULP AND PAPER TECHNOLOGY (New York and London, 1964), pages 474–76. See also literature cited at end of Chapter 14, pages 478–79. W. J. Barrow, *Deterioration of Book Stocks—Causes and Remedies* (Richmond, Va., 1959) and W. J. Barrow, *The Manufacture and Testing of Durable Book Papers* (Richmond, Va., 1960) are two publications based on the work done at Virginia State Library under a grant from the Council on Library Resources, Inc.
31. Those interested in the detail of handling of rags can find an extensive discussion, representing English practice, in Clapperton [see No. 17], Chapter III.
32. Sutermeister [see No. 13], condensed from pages 22 and 24; on pulping of rags including cotton linters, consult Casey [see No. 2], Vol. I, pages 392–98; pulping of flax is discussed in the same work on pages 416–17.
33. Hardman and Cole [see No. 16], page 64.
34. Letter to the writer from Mr. Morris S. Kantrowitz, Technical Director, U.S. Government Printing Office, dated August 12, 1966.
35. Casey [see No. 2], Vol. I, page 457.
36. Sutermeister [see No. 13], page 114.
37. Same reference as before, page 117.
38. Edward M. Root, *Stock Preparation* in PULP AND PAPER [see No. 8], Vol. II, page 4.
39. Same reference as before.
40. Hunter [see No. 29], page 162.
41. Reg. F. Bowles, Editor-in-Chief, *Printing Ink Manual* (Cambridge, 1961), page 92.
42. Same reference as before, page 92.
43. ASTM No. 60-B [see No. 4], page 4.
44. Root [see No. 38], page 4.
45. Sutermeister [see No. 13], condensed from pages 135 and 136.
46. Casey [see No. 2], Vol. II, page 591.
47. Edward M. Engel, *The Internal Sizing of Papers* in PULP AND PAPER [see No. 8], Vol. II, page 44.

48. H. C. Schwalbe, *Fillers and Loading* in PULP AND PAPER [see No. 8], Vol. II, page 60.

49. Sutermeister [see No. 13], page 142.

50. Schwalbe [see No. 48], condensed from pages 74–75.

51. The figures for offset paper are from the U.S. Government Printing Office, letter to the writer, dated August 12, 1966; those for Bible papers are from Casey [see No. 2], page 990, Table I.

52. Sutermeister [see No. 13], page 147.

53. John W. Swanson, *Special Additives* in PULP AND PAPER [see No. 8], Vol. II, page 113, condensed.

54. Casey [see No. 2], Vol. II, page 948.

55. Paper Dictionary [see No. 7], page 475.

56. Various classes of paper needing wet strength are listed in PULP AND PAPER [see No. 8], Vol. II, page 124.

57. Casey [see No. 2], Vol. II, pages 1155–56.

58. Hunter [see No. 29], Chapter IV.

59. Dr. Walter W. Roehr, *Paper and the Graphic Arts* (Neenah, Wis., 1960), page 11.

60. Sutermeister [see No. 13], page 152.

61. W. H. Kennedy and P. E. Wrist, *The Fourdrinier Paper Machine* in PULP AND PAPER [see No. 8], Vol. I, page 166.

62. H. D. Cook, *Cylinder Machine Wet-End* in PULP AND PAPER [see No. 8], Vol. II, page 209.

63. Clapperton [see No. 17], adapted from page 364.

64. Casey [see No. 2], Vol. II, page 759.

65. The detail of the cylinder machine wet end is concisely discussed in Cook [see No. 62].

66. The relative advantages of cylinder and fourdrinier machines are discussed in Casey [see No. 2], Vol. II, page 762; the advantages and shortcomings of cylinder machines are analyzed in PULP AND PAPER [see No. 8], Vol. II, pages 220–21.

67. *How Paper Serves America*, gravure supplement of the NEW YORK TIMES, October 17, 1965, page 19.

68. H. G. Rappolt, *Drying and Ventilation* in PULP AND PAPER [see No. 8], Vol. II, page 238.

69. Same reference as before, condensed from pages 240–41.

70. All data on the Consolidated Coater are from the paper by Frank Kaulakis, *The Consolidated Coating Process* in PIGMENTED COATING PROCESSES FOR PAPER AND BOARD, TAPPI Monograph Series No. 28 (New York, 1965), pages 3–8.

71. W. H. Welliver, Jr., *Gravure Coater* in TAPPI Monograph No. 28 [see No. 70], condensed from pages 33–39.

72. Dexter L. Wolfe, *Recent Coated Paper Developments for Improved Graphics Reproduction*, TAPPI JOURNAL, October, 1965, page 88A.

73. Adapted from C. G. Whelpton, *The Champion Machine Coating Process* in TAPPI Monograph No. 28 [see No. 70], pages 40–45.

74. Adapted from G. A. Richardson, *Trailing Blade Coating of Publication Grades* in TAPPI Monograph No. 28 [see No. 70], pages 52–62.

75. Casey [see No. 2], Vol. III, page 1553.

76. *Facts and Views of Papermaking at S. D. Warren Company* (Boston, 1965), page 19.

77. J. C. Stinchfield and W. K. Thorndike, *Air Doctor Coater* in TAPPI Monograph No. 28 [see No. 70], condensed from pages 46–50.

78. J. P. Casey, *Ultrahigh Finish Coated Papers— Cast Coating and Other Processes* in TAPPI Monograph No. 28 [see No. 70], page 75.

79. Facts and Views [see No. 76], page 20.

80. Casey [see No. 2], Vol. III, page 1651.

81. Same reference as before.

82. All figures of coat weights are from TAPPI Monograph No. 28 [see No. 70]. Those for the Consolidated process are on page 3; those for Champion machine coating on page 43; those for air doctor coaters on page 49; and those for cast coating on page 79.

83. Casey [see No. 2], Vol. III, page 1713.

84. Casey [see No. 2], Vol. III, page 1714.

85. Casey [see No. 2], Vol. III, page 1403.

86. Robert F. Reed, *What the Lithographer Should Know about Paper*, GATF Publication No. 8 (Pittsburgh, 1961), pages 13 and 14.

87. In the United States mold-made papers are usually made in webs with two deckle edges; mold-made sheets with four deckle edges are not usually on the market. How mold-made sheets with four deckle edges can be made on a cylinder machine is described by Clapperton [see No. 17], on pages 370–371.

88. Reed [see No. 86], page 13.

89. Charles V. Morris, *Don't Take Paper Qualities for Granted* in the INLAND PRINTER/AMERICAN LITHOGRAPHER, March, 1964, page 50.

90. Reed [see No. 86], condensed from pages 20 and 21.

91. For a discussion of relative humidity as it affects paper properties consult Britt [see No. 30], pages 445–48.

92. Paper Dictionary [see No. 7], pages 61–62.

93. Edward Blank, *How the MM Plan Operates* in the INLAND PRINTER/AMERICAN LITHOGRAPHER, March, 1965, page 50, condensed.

94. *A Common Standard for Basic Paper Weights* in PRINTING MAGAZINE, November, 1960. This article reviews the efforts made after World War II in behalf of basic size and basis weight reforms; it contains two tables correlating traditional and MM data. A brief history of paper standardization in Europe is in the French trade magazine CARACTÈRE, *La Normalisation des Formats de Papier*, October, 1965.

95. Henry A. Paulsen, *A Course in Estimating*, PIA Tools of Industry Series (Washington, D.C., 1953), page 38.

96. A good and fair summary is in the article "MM" *Pros & Cons—Advantages and Disadvantages of the MM Proposals as Seen by the Mills*, PRINTING MAGAZINE, March, 1961.

97. See TAPPI Method T 410 os and ASTM Method D 646-63T. The conversion factors to the gm² system are also in ASTM No. 62-B [see No. 4], page 65.

98. *Standards Adopted by Members of National Paperboard Association*, Effective July 1, 1934 (New York and Chicago, 1937), page 13.

99. Same reference as before, page 6.

100. Punched Card paper is extensively discussed in ASTM No. 60-B [see No. 4], pages 48–50. The *Paper Dictionary* [see No. 7] has no entry under punched card paper, but one on *tabulating board*, the term preferred by paper people.

101. ASTM No. 60-B [see No. 4], page 22.

102. Paper Dictionary [see No. 7], page 69.

103. Same reference as before, page 309.

104. Burnett M. Thall, *Understanding Newsprint*, article in PRINTING PRODUCTION magazine, December, 1963, page 127.

105. Same reference as before, condensed from page 128.

106. William N. Bureau, *Newsprint for Web Offset*, GRAPHIC ARTS MONTHLY, June, 1965, page 92.

107. William H. Bureau, *Papers for Gravure Printing*, GRAPHIC ARTS MONTHLY, July, 1965, page 92.

108. On inks for food and drug package printing see Louis M. Larsen, Ph.D., *Industrial Printing Inks* (New York, 1962), pages 246–53.

109. R. I. Drake, *Label and Box Wrap Papers* in AMA MANAGEMENT REPORT NUMBER 5, KNOW YOUR PACKAGING MATERIALS, A Revised Edition (New York, 1958), condensed from page 29.

110. William P. Hintz, *Glassine, What It Is and How To Print It*, FLEXOGRAPHY magazine, January, 1963, page 15.

111. M. L. Downs, *Glassine and Greaseproof Papers* in AMA REPORT No. 5 [see No. 108], page 20.

112. Paper Dictionary [see No. 7], page 459.

113. Robert H. Mosher, *Specialty Papers* (New York, 1950), pages 125–26.

114. Robert Nitz, *Requirements for Good Printing Qualities of Cylinder Boxboards*, TAPPI JOURNAL, January, 1966, pages 85A–86A.

115. A discussion of boxboard properties as related to end use is in AMA REPORT No. 5 [see No. 109], pages 40–48.

116. A detailed discussion of aluminum foil is in AMA REPORT No. 5 [see No. 109], pages 7–18.

117. Mosher [see No. 113], page 166.

118. The *Modern Plastics Encyclopedia* is published annually as the September issue of MODERN PLASTICS MAGAZINE.

119. Charles C. Winding and Gordon D. Hiatt, *Polymeric Materials* (New York, 1961), page 99.

120. Precise definitions of film, sheet, sheeting, cast film, and extrusion can be found in *Tentative Nomenclature Relating to Plastics*, ASTM Designation: D883–65a T issued 1946, last revised 1965. Inflated-tube extrusion is described in Winding and Hiatt, same reference as before, pages 110–12.

121. The ASTM BOOK OF STANDARDS, 1966, consists of 32 volumes. Parts 26 and 27 contain tests for plastics.

122. A good example of "structuring" is the discussion of polypropylene films in the 1966 Plastics Encyclopedia [see No. 118], pages 549–52, including a chart of "Tailored Polypropylene Films."

123. *Flexography: Principles and Practices* (New York, 1962), pages 142–43.

124. *Webster's New International Dictionary*, Second Edition, Unabridged (Springfield, Mass., 1950). Webster also lists a second meaning of printable, "worthy of being published," which does not apply to the technical side of printing.

125. Reed [see No. 86], pages 101–2.

126. Paper Dictionary [see No. 7], pages 353–54.

127. William C. Walker and Robert F. Carmack, *The Printing Smoothness of Paper* in HALFTONE PRINTING, Proceedings of the Seventh International Conference of Printing Research Institutes, held in London, 1963, edited by W. H. Banks (New York and London, 1964), page 203.

128. Not all writers on paper prefer the same definitions for picking, linting, and dusting. This manual follows the terminology as developed by the Graphic Arts Technical Foundation and set forth in Reed [see No. 86], pages 29–33.

129. "In the Larocque Printability Test the newspaper industry has a test that has been found to be quite accurate in predicting the general printing quality of newsprint." Letter by Mr. Lloyd E. Foss, Supervisor, Newsprint Quality Program, ANPA Research Institute, to the writer, dated September 7, 1966. ANPA publishes *Procedures for Printability Test*, and also *Procedure for Show-thru Test in the Newsprint Quality Program*. See also L. E. Foss and G. R. Cashan, *The Correlation between a Modified Larocque Printability Test and the Newspaper Letterpress*, TAPPI JOURNAL, Vol. 46, No. H, November, 1963.

130. Casey [see No. 2], Vol. III, page 1788.

131. The complete set of TAPPI *Standard Testing Procedures* fills two binders; ASTM paper tests are in Vol. 15 of the *1966 Book of* ASTM *Standards;* individual tests are also available from either organization. Corresponding ASTM and TAPPI paper tests are identified in the ASTM No. 60-B [see No. 4], pages VII to X.

132. Reed [see No. 86], page 143.

133. All quotations are from ASTM No. 60-B [see No. 4], pages 69, 115, and 80–81, respectively.

134. Casey [see No. 2], Vol. III, page 1277.

135. ASTM No. 60-B [see No. 4], page 66.

136. Reed [see No. 86], pages 115–16.

137. Reed [see No. 86], page 151.

138. Reed [see No. 86], page 148.

Notes and References to Chapter IX: *Printing Inks*

1. Robert F. Reed, *What the Lithographer Should Know about Ink*, GATF Publication No. 310 (New York, 1960), page 44.

2. Herbert J. Wolfe, *Pressmen's Ink Handbook* (New York, 1952), page 113.

3. *Printing Ink Handbook*, published by the National Association of Printing Ink Makers (New York, 1958), page 54.

4. Andries Voet, *Ink and Paper in the Printing Process* (New York, 1952), page 159.

5. Same reference as before.
6. *Pressmen's Ink Handbook* [see No. 2], pages 113 to 119.
7. *Pressmen's Ink Handbook* [see No. 2], page 117.
8. A brief exposition of inorganic pigments is in John Stewart Remington and D. Wilfred Francis, *Pigments, Their Manufacture, Properties and Use* (London, 1954).
9. *Raw Materials Used in Printing Ink*, A Volume of Lectures, sponsored by Printing Ink Makers' Association of Philadelphia (Philadelphia, 1942), pages 7–19.
10. A non-technical discussion of organic pigments can be found in the same reference as before, pages 20–29.
11. *Protective and Decorative Coatings*, Prepared by a Staff of Specialists under the Editorship of Joseph J. Mattiello, Ph.D., Vol. II (New York and London, 1942), page 42.
12. Herbert Jay Wolfe, *Printing and Litho Inks*, Fifth and Completely Revised Edition (New York, 1957), page 196.
13. Mattiello [see No. 11], page 45.
14. Wolfe [see No. 12], page 98.
15. Wolfe [see No. 12], page 112.
16. Wolfe [see No. 12], page 141.
17. The properties of benzidine yellow and of other organic pigments are taken from Lyde T. Pratt, Ph.D., *The Chemistry and Physics of Organic Pigments* (New York and London, 1947), pages 312 and 313.
18. Wolfe [see No. 12], page 172.
19. Wolfe [see No. 12], page 140.
20. Same reference as before.
21. Wolfe [see No. 12], page 108.
22. For a discussion of phthalocyanine troubles see Aaron Permut in the AMERICAN INK MAKER magazine, October, 1961, page 43.
23. Wolfe [see No. 12], page 160.
24. Wolfe [see No. 12], page 180.
25. For a description of bronzing see Chapter X, Section 10.
26. Aaron Permut in the AMERICAN INK MAKER magazine, August, 1958, page 39.
27. For general information on magnetic check imprinting, see *Common Machine Language for Mechanized Check Handling*, Publication No. 147 by the American Banking Association, New York, 1959; a survey of the whole subject is by C. H. Love, *Magnetizing, Magnetic Recording and Magnetic Inks* in the AMERICAN INK MAKER magazine, May, 1961; a discussion of printing inks and quality control by G. L. Erikson, *Magnetic Ink—Magnetic Printing* is in the AMERICAN PRESSMAN magazine, May, 1960.
28. Reed [see No. 1], page 1, italics added.
29. Wolfe [see No. 12], page 43.
30. *Raw Materials* [see No. 9], page 95, italics added.
31. An extensive treatment of drying oils is in Mattiello, Vol. I [see No. 11].
32. *Raw Materials* [see No. 9], page 80, italics added.
33. Matiello, Vol. I [see No. 11], page 339.
34. E. A. Apps, B.S., *Printing Ink Technology* (London, 1958), page 62.
35. Jeffrey R. Stewart, *The National Paint Dic-*

tionary, Third Edition (Washington, D.C., 1948), page 341.
36. *Raw Materials* [see No. 9], condensed from pages 101 and 102; italics added.
37. Thomas H. Durrans, D.Sc., *Solvents* (New York and London, 1950), page 35.
38. Lillian Stemp, *Safety Manual for the Graphic Arts Industry*, A joint publication of the Education Council of the Graphic Arts Industry, Inc., and the National Safety Council (Washington, D.C. and New York, 1953), Chapter 3.
39. Otto Jordan, *The Technology of Solvents* (London, 1938), page 126.
40. Charles C. Winding and Gordon D. Hiatt, *Polymeric Materials* (New York, 1961) present a detailed and extensive classification of vehicles for industrial coatings on pages 90–94. Even though printing inks are not mentioned, this table is worth studying because many of the discussed resins are also used in the making of vehicles for printing inks.
41. Apps [see No. 34], page 378.
42. Apps [see No. 34], page 379.
43. Wolfe [see No. 12], page 326.
44. Apps [see No. 34], page 397.
45. Apps [see No. 34], page 291.
46. Same reference as before.
47. Wolfe [see No. 12], page 337.
48. An extensive discussion of the ink laboratory and its equipment is in Apps [see No. 34], Chapter 14.
49. The American Society for Testing Materials (ASTM), Philadelphia, Pa., offers a free catalog of their publications.
50. The NPIRI *Standard Test Methods* are divided into a number of groups; among them are tests for the identification of pigments, tests for quantitative determination of characteristics; performance and resistance tests, and tests for related materials, including paper.
51. Henry A. Gardner, D.Sc., and G. C. Sward, M.S., *Physical and Chemical Examination of Paints, Varnishes, Lacquers and Colors* (Washington, D.C., 1946).
52. Consult the NPIRI Tests [see No. 50] and those by the New York Printing Ink Production Club.
53. *Printing Ink Manual*, commissioned by the Technical Training Board of the Society of British Ink Manufacturers, Reg. F. Bowles, Editor-in-Chief (Cambridge, 1961), pages 595 and 596.
54. Same reference as before, page 601.
55. Wolfe [see No. 12], pages 395 and 396.
56. Apps [see No. 34], page 483.
57. Wolfe [see No. 12], page 461.
58. Various methods to determine specific gravity of fluids are described in Wolfe [see No. 12], pages 439 to 441.
59. Wolfe [see No. 12], page 455.
60. Reed [see No. 1], page 177.
61. Paul J. Hartsuch, Ph.D., *Chemistry of Lithography*, GATF Publication No. 401 (New York, 1961), page 258.
62. Reed [see No. 1], page 185.
63. Reed [see No. 1], page 193.

64. For this and other tests see R. E. Boughton, *Flexographic Printing* (Chicago, 1958), Chapter X, and *Flexography: Principles and Practices* (New York, 1962), pages 92–129.

65. Reed [see No. 1], page 187, and *Printing Ink Manual* [see No. 53], pages 656 and 657.

66. Dr. L. M. Larsen in the *Lithographers Manual*, 20th Anniversary Edition, edited by Victor Strauss, Vol. II (New York, 1958), page 13:12.

67. Hiding power and its testing is extensively discussed in Gardner and Sward [see No. 51], Chapter 1.

68. A description of the GATF-Preucil Color System is available in Reed [see No. 1], Chapter VIII.

69. Stewart [see No. 35], page 548.

70. Reed [see No. 1], describes the subliming test on pages 192 and 193.

71. Reed [see No. 1], page 177. A detailed discussion of gloss and its measurement is in Gardner and Sward [see No. 51], Chapter 6.

72. A brief discussion of the Fade-Ometer and the Weather-Ometer is in Reed [see No. 1], pages 195–97; an extensive treatment can be found in Gardner and Sward [see No. 51], Chapters 12 and 13.

73. *Printing Ink Manual* [see No. 53], page 671.

74. Reed [see No. 1], page 198.

75. Reed [see No. 1], pages 194 and 195.

76. Reed [see No. 1], page 201.

77. Dr. L. M. Larsen in the *Lithographers Manual* [see No. 66], Vol. II, pages 13:12–13:17.

78. *Printing Ink Manual* [see No. 53], page 360.

79. Andries Voet and William H. Whitten, Jr., *Ruboff of Printed News Stock* in the AMERICAN INK MAKER magazine, March, 1960, page 34.

80. AMERICAN PRESSMAN, June, 1960, page 29.

81. See the reports prepared by ANPA and AAAA Joint Committee on Newspaper Printing. Report No. 7 is *Recommended Standards for Run-of-Paper Printing;* Report No. 11 is *Preparation of Run-of-Paper Color Advertising.*

82. VM & P Naphtha is a co-solvent for certain flexographic inks; co-solvent type flexographic inks are discussed in *Flexography: Principles and Practices* (New York, 1962), pages 72 and 73.

83. Jean M. Fisher, *Understanding Flexographic Inks* in AMERICAN INK MAKER magazine, February, March, and April, 1959.

84. Dr. Dominic J. Bernardi, *Facts on Toxicity of Flexo Ink Solvents* in the PAPER, FILM AND FOIL CONVERTER MAGAZINE, October, 1958.

85. Einar T. Wulfsberg, *Printing Inks under the Food Additives Amendment* in the AMERICAN PRESSMAN magazine, October, 1960.

86. Wolfe [see No. 12], page 309.

87. *Printing Ink Manual* [see No. 53], page 530.

88. These points were adapted from *Gravure Inks* by Frank V. Johnson, reprinted from the Bulletin of the GTA by the Interchemical Corporation, Printing Ink Division, under the title *Gravure*, page 16.

89. Reed [see No. 1], pages 67 and 68.

90. Hartsuch [see No. 61], page 246.

91. Reed [see No. 1], page 161.

92. Same reference as before.

Notes and References to Chapter X: *Binding and Finishing*

1. Edward J. Triebe, *Case Binding* in the LITHOGRAPHERS MANUAL, 20th Anniversary Edition, edited by Victor Strauss, Vol. II (New York, 1958), page 14:13.

2. Melvin B. Summerfield, A.B., *Bound To Stay Bound* (Jacksonville, Ill., 1956), page 7.

3. Albert E. Kilheffer, *Position and Arrangement* in the AMERICAN PRESSMAN magazine, October, 1957, page 40.

4. Ralph W. Polk and Harry L. Gage, *A Composition Manual*, PIA Tools of Industry Series (Washington, D.C., 1953), page 103.

5. Same reference as before, page 104.

6. Kilheffer [see No. 3], page 41.

7. *Composition Manual* [see No. 4], page 109.

8. *Composition Manual* [see No. 4], page 109.

9. *Composition Manual* [see No. 4], page 140.

10. Albert E. Kilheffer in the AMERICAN PRESSMAN magazine, September, 1957, page 39.

11. There are many books on imposition, among them is *Layouts for Flat-Bed, Rotary, and Web Press Impositions*, GPO (Washington, D.C., 1948); H. Wayne Warner, *Planning for Better Imposition* (Washington, D.C., 1958); *Helpful Aids in Book Production*, Book Manufacturers' Institute, Inc. (New York, 1953) discusses impositions and shows a number of diagrams on pages 161 to 178; and many book manufacturers publish their own imposition charts.

12. *Layouts* GPO, same reference as before, pages VI–XI.

13. *Tapley Book of Impositions*, Fourth Edition (Long Island City, N.Y., 1955), page 7.

14. Same reference as before.

15. Lindemeyr Library, Booklet No. 1 (New York, 1953), page 5.

16. Lillian Stemp, *Safety Manual for the Graphic Arts Industry*, A Joint Publication of the Education Council of the Graphic Arts Industries, Inc., and of the National Safety Council (Washington, D.C. and New York, 1953), page 63.

17. Frank N. Burt in the SPECIALTY WORKER magazine, January, 1957, page 8.

18. Kingsport Press *Glossary of Technical Terms* (Kingsport, Tenn., 1931), page 245.

19. *Theory and Practice of Bookbinding* GPO, Apprentice Training Series (Washington, D.C., 1950), page 69.

20. Same reference as before.

21. *Manual for Salesmen*, Dexter Folder Company (Pearl River, N.Y., 1946), page 14.

22. Same reference as before.
23. *Dexter Manual* [see No. 21], page 23.
24. *Dexter Manual* [see No. 21], page 37.
25. *Dexter Manual* [see No. 21], pages 30 and 31.
26. *Dexter Products* (Pearl River, N.Y., 1946), page 22.
27. *Bookbinding* [see No. 19], page 79.
28. Same reference as before.
29. *Bookbinding* [see No. 19], pages 79 and 80.
30. Frank B. Myrick, *A Primer in Book Production* (New York, 1950), page 70.
31. *Glossary* [see No. 18], page 211.
32. *Bookbinding* [see No. 19], page 80.
33. *Dexter Products* [see No. 26], page 37.
34. See descriptive literature on the *Macey Saddle Gatherer and Single-Book Trimmer* by Harris Seybold, A Division of Harris Intertype Corporation, Cleveland, Ohio.
35. E. W. Palmer, *A Course in Bookbinding for Vocational Training*, Part One (New York, 1927), page 273.
36. Edith Diehl, *Bookbinding, Its Background and Technique*, Vol. II (New York, 1946), page 130.
37. An excellent description of hand sewing is in Diehl, same reference as before, Vol. II, Chapter IX, "Sewing."
38. The Racine Lithographic Institute, *Course of Related Training for the Printing Trades*, Fourth Unit.
39. Smyth instruction manual for No. 4 Book Sewing Machine, page 14.
40. Racine Institute [see No. 38].
41. Kenneth F. Perry and Clarence T. Baab, *The Binding of Books* (Peoria, 1940), page 111.
42. Racine Institute [see No. 38].
43. Perry and Baab [see No. 41], page 11.
44. Even though adhesive binding was known, and used to some extent, in the 19th century, it was not widely practiced before the end of World War II. Improved adhesives and special equipment made its application to mass production possible.
45. BOOK PRODUCTION magazine, June, 1957, page 46.
46. James Milliken and Winthrop H. Lee, *The Riverside Press* in BOOK PRODUCTION magazine, August, 1957, page 38.
47. *How To Sell Loose Leaf*, Manual No. 3, National Stationers Association (Washington, D.C., 1949), page 38.
48. Jack Sloves, *Mechanical and Looseleaf Binding* in the LITHOGRAPHERS MANUAL [see No. 1], Vol. II, page 14:12.
49. *Bookbinding* [see No. 19], page 103.
50. *Bookbinding* [see No. 19], page 104.
51. Description of the Brackett Safety Trimmer in the LITHOGRAPHERS MANUAL [see No. 1], Vol. II, page 14:28.
52. Kingsport *Glossary* [see No. 18], page 211. See also the monograph by Richard H. Barnes, *Gilding and the Making of Gold Leaf* (Philadelphia, 1962).
53. *The Process of Marbling Paper* GPO-PIA Joint

Research Bulletin (Washington, D.C., 1948), page 6. This publication contains a reprint of the *Bibliography of Marbled Paper* by Dard Hunter, originally published in the PAPER TRADE JOURNAL, April 28, 1921.
54. Smyth instruction manual for rounding and backing machine, page 6.
55. Same reference as before, page 5.
56. Sheridan Rounder, Backer, Backliner; descriptive company booklet.
57. Same reference as before.
58. Same reference as No. 56.
59. Same reference as No. 56.
60. Same reference as No. 56.
61. Triebe [see No. 1], page 14:17.
62. Western Technical Institute, *Course of Related Training in the Printing Trades* Fourth Unit (Racine, Wis.)
63. Triebe [see No. 1], page 14:18.
64. Smyth instruction manual for No. 1 Casemaker, page 4.
65. Descriptive literature on the Dexter-deFlorez Casemaker.
66. *Sheridan Casemakers for Making Cloth and Paper Cases*, page 2.
67. Myrick [see No. 30], pages 38 and 39.
68. Western [see No. 62].
69. Western [see No. 62].
70. *Glossary* [see No. 18], page 187.
71. Glossary [see No. 18], page 185.
72. Diehl [see No. 36], Vol. II, page 261.
73. *Bookbinding* [see No. 19], page 111.
74. Western [see No. 62].
75. *Bookbinding* [see No. 19], page 112.
76. Same reference as before.
77. Building-in machines are manufactured by all companies supplying equipment for mass-production binding.
78. Information received from Mr. Peter deFlorez describing the Dexter-deFlorez Book Jacketing Machine.
79. *Bookbinding* [see No. 19], page 197.
80. *Bookbinding* [see No. 19], page 199.
81. Sidney S. Levine, *Bronzing and Varnishing* in the LITHOGRAPHERS MANUAL [see No. 1], Vol. II, pages 15:1 and 15:2.
82. Dr. Leo Cahn, *Varnishing and Coating of Lithographed Papers* in the LITHOGRAPHERS MANUAL [see No. 1], identifies 14 different kinds of coating, Vol. II, pages 15:4 and 15:5.
83. Levine [see No. 81], page 15:2.
84. Steel-rule dies for folding boxes are described in *Orientation Lectures on the Manufacture of Folding Boxes*, Folding Paper Box Association of America (Chicago, 1956) and in the literature published by some manufacturers of steel-rule dies.
85. LITHOGRAPHERS MANUAL [see No. 1], Vol. II, page 15:6.
86. Same reference as before.
87. LITHOGRAPHERS MANUAL [see No. 1], Vol. II, page 15:18.

Notes and References to Chapter XI: *Art-and-Copy Preparation*

1. The most modern book on the subject is by Marshall Lee, *Bookmaking—The Illustrated Guide to Design and Production* (New York, 1965). *Book Publishers Guide*—A manual on the selection of paper and the design and production of bound books, published by Oxford Paper Company (New York, 1960) and *Helpful Aids in Book Production*, published by the Book Manufacturers Institute (New York, 1953) are two other valuable sources of information.

2. Robert P. Long, *Package Printing* (New York, 1964) discusses art-and-copy preparation for package printing in Chapter 12.

3. Art-and-copy preparation for newspaper printing is the subject of several reports prepared by the AAAA-ANPA Joint Committee on Newspaper Printing. These reports are periodically revised and can be obtained, free of charge, from the American Association of Advertising Agencies, New York City, or from the American Newspaper Publishers Association, New York City.

4. *Recommended Standard Specifications for Advertising Material in Magazine Letterpress Wet Printing* published by AAAA-MPA Joint Committee on Magazine Advertising Production (New York, 1961) available, free of charge, from the American Association of Advertising Agencies, New York City, or the Magazine Publishers Association, New York City.

5. Three branches of typography are treated in the following books: *ATA Advertising Production Handbook* published by the Advertising Typographers Association, New York City; Edmund C. Arnold, *Functional Newspaper Design* (New York, 1956) and book typography in Lee [see No. 1], Chapter 6.

6. Beatrice Warde, *The Crystal Goblet* (London, 1955), pages 15 and 16.

7. W. A. Dwiggins, *Layout in Advertising*, Revised Edition (New York, 1948), page 17.

8. Daniel Berkeley Updike, *Some Aspects of Printing—Old and New* (New Haven, 1941), page 29.

9. Warde [see No. 6], page 137.

10. Donald G. Patterson and Miles A. Tinker, *How To Make Type Readable* (New York, 1940) and Miles A. Tinker, *Legibility of Print* (Ames, Iowa, 1963); pages 267–332 of the 1963 book contain a most valuable annotated bibliography, listing 238 items.

11. The role of smoothness of paper is explained in Chapter VIII.

12. Ralph W. Polk and Harry A. Gage, *A Composition Manual*, PIA Tools of Industry Series (Washington, D.C., 1953), pages 151–59.

13. All copy fitting of reading matter in bulk is based on the lower case alphabet length of specific type faces in specific type sizes. Lower case alphabet length is expressed in points and varies for the same face in different point sizes and of course also for different faces in the same point size. The manufacturers of type, metallic and non-metallic matrices, and photographic type grids or strips publish the lower case alphabet length of their type faces and sizes. Most companies also indicate the number of characters per pica of each of their type faces and sizes, and some companies publish tables that can be used to find the number of characters for a specific line length and even for type pages consisting of varying numbers of lines.

The advent of computerized composition has made precision in copyfitting more important than ever, and the following information may be of interest.

As the number of characters per pica is central to copyfitting, two methods of determining this figure will be described. When the Mergenthaler Linotype Company developed their copyfitting tables (available as a booklet, *Copy Fitting—A Simple Method Complete with Tables, for Linotype Composition*) they considered "the variations that are inevitable in setting type in varying line lengths, in variations in spacing that cannot be standardized, plus variations in copy and style. These variables caused a lot of debate when we were preparing the Copyfitting Tables. The alphabet lengths were predetermined—but how the type was set and how the breaks of hyphens and punctuation might vary brought conditions that inevitably were subject to some bits of compromise.

"Thus, to establish a fairly true factor for *character count per pica* we found that the setting of that face in a typical body size and appropriate line length became a formula for X picas of line width, into which Y number of characters has been normally composed. Each word space counted as 1 character, and the variable there is obvious. But the use of typical body size and best-adapted line measure seemed sound. Then Y divided by X equals number of characters per pica." [Letter from Mr. Harry L. Gage, March 31, 1966; Mr. Gage was Vice-President of Mergenthaler Linotype and is the co-author of the PIA Composition Manual.]

A different approach was taken by the Monotype Corporation, Ltd., in the United Kingdom. (The Monotype uses a unit system which is discussed in Chapter III of this manual.) Copyfitting is based "on the average letter width in a 1,000 character *lower-case font*, the figures against the characters shown below being the number of times each character will appear in normal *English* text for every 1,000 characters and spaces. These figures have been based on counts covering hundreds of thousands of words in a very wide range of printed matter." The relative frequency of letters in a 1,000 character lower-case font follows:

a	64	g	14	n	56	u	31
b	14	h	42	o	56	v	10
c	27	i	63	p	17	w	18
d	35	j	3	q	4	x	3
e	100	k	6	r	49	y	18
f	20	l	35	s	56	z	2
		m	20	t	71	spaces and punctuations: 166	

All of these characters are multiplied by their unit values, and the products of multiplications are totaled. The sum is the length of a 1,000 lower case alphabet sample including spaces and marks of punctuation in Monotype units. The user of the Monotype copyfitting system does not need to make these and the following calculations whereby Monotype units are expressed in terms of the point system. The Monotype provides a factor for each face and size and also tables which show the number of characters per line, from 5 to 30 picas, for each factor. (See *Scientific Copyfitting* published by the Monotype Corporation Limited.) American typographers who prefer to work with characters per pica rather than Monotype factors might like to know that the reciprocal of these factors is the equivalent to characters per pica.

14. Jean Mayfield Bourges, *The Bourges Process* in the LITHOGRAPHERS MANUAL, 20th Anniversary Edition (New York, 1958), Vol. I, pages 4:83 to 4:86.
15. Edith Pilpel, *How To Prepare Art for Silk Screen Printing* (Chicago, 1959).
16. For a discussion of layouts from the advertising man's point-of-view, see Irving Graham, *Encyclopedia of Advertising* (New York, 1952).
17. Charles W. Latham, *Lithographic Press Operating*, GATF Publication No. 505/6 (New York, 1956), page 67.

Selective Bibliography

In keeping with the introductory character of this manual its bibliography is a selective guide to the literature, prepared to stimulate the reader and to make him aware of the wealth of available information. The bibliography is limited to books and similar publications that are in print, available either from publishers or booksellers at the time of writing. Books out of print are not listed here. The books and articles used by the writer are printed in the "Notes and References," pages 751 to 776; some of them are included in this bibliography, all can probably be found in most large reference libraries.

The sources for this bibliography were of five kinds: (1) the *Subject Guide to Books in Print*, 1966, where all books currently offered by book publishers are listed; (2) trade and professional graphic arts organizations that are not in the publishing business but publish books for the benefit of their industries; (3) manufacturers of products used in the graphic arts industry who publish literature related to the use of their wares, (4) occasional publishers that have no sustained publishing program, and (5) the U.S. Government Printing Office and the Department of Commerce including the Bureau of the Census. The first group consists of book publishers, the next three groups might be called incidental publishers to set them apart, and the last group is of course in a class by itself.

If all titles including those of our incidental publishers were listed in the same reference book, a literature search would indeed be fast and easy. Unfortunately few incidental publishers have their books in the Subject Guide; Printing Industries of America (PIA) and the Technical Association of the Pulp and Paper Industry (TAPPI) are the most important exceptions. Yet the books developed by organizations other than book publishers are indispensable because in the printing industry they are often the only ones, or the best ones, on certain subjects. This is not surprising: the reason why graphic arts organizations expend considerable efforts in the development of books is simply that the wants of their industries cannot be satisfied on the market. Such books as those published by the Graphic Arts Technical Foundation must obviously be known to every serious student of graphic arts technology. They should, consequently, be listed in all important bibliographical books of reference, particularly in the *Subject Guide* which can be found in practically all libraries and in many larger book stores.

The *Subject Guide to Books in Print* is published every year in October by the R. R. Bowker Company, New York City. The 1966 edition lists 165,000 titles published by 1,600 publishers. It has 250,000 entries under 30,000 subject headings with 39,000 cross references. All listed books are available in this country, most are published here though some are imported from Europe. These are either co-published or distributed by American companies.

The following bibliography contains a listing of more than 350 titles under 30 subject headings. In certain subjects this listing is only part of that collected in the *Subject Guide* which should therefore be consulted by readers who want a more comprehensive bibliography. In subjects dominated by incidental publishers and in those where the U.S. Government is the main publisher the present listing is more extensive. For reasons of space each book is listed only once with no cross references and annotations. Related subject headings should therefore be checked by interested readers. If the same publisher appears less than three times, each entry contains full name and address; publishers appearing more often are listed by key words. These together with the full name and address are printed immediately after this introduction.

Book Publishers and Other Organizations Listed by Key Words

AAAA. American Association of Advertising Agencies, 420 Lexington Ave., New York, N.Y. 10017

ABP. Associated Business Publications, 205 E. 42 St., New York, N.Y. 10017

ALA. American Library Association (Publishing Department), 50 E. Huron St., Chicago, Ill. 60611

AMA. American Management Association, 135 W. 50 St., New York, N.Y. 10020

AMER. TECHNICAL. American Technical Society, 848 E. 58 St., Chicago, Ill. 60637

ANPA. American Newspaper Publishers Association, 370 Lexington Ave., New York, N.Y. 10017

ATA. Advertising Typographers Association of America, Inc., 461 Eighth Ave., New York, N.Y. 10001

BMI. Book Manufacturers Institute, Inc., 25 W. 43 St., New York, N.Y. 10036

CAMBRIDGE. Cambridge University Press, 32 E. 57 St., New York, N.Y. 10022

CHILTON. Chilton Books, 401 Walnut St., Philadelphia, Pa. 19106

DOVER. Dover Publications, Inc., 180 Varick St., New York, N.Y. 10014

GATF. Graphic Arts Technical Foundation, 4615 Forbes Ave., Pittsburgh, Pa. 15213

GEVAERT. Agfa-Gevaert, Inc., Photo Products, 275 North St., Teterboro, N.J. 07608

GPO. United States Government Printing Office, Division of Public Documents, Washington, D.C. 20402

GRAPHIC MAGAZINES. Graphic Magazines, Inc., 61 Hilton Ave., Garden City, N.Y. 11534

GTA. Gravure Technical Association, Inc., 60 E. 42nd. St., New York, N. Y. 10017

HARPER. Harper & Row Publishers, 2500 Crawford Ave., Evanston, Ill. 60201

HARVARD. Harvard University Press, Kittridge Hall, 79 Garden St., Cambridge, Mass. 02138

HASTINGS. Hastings House Publishers, Inc., 151 E. 50 St., New York, N.Y. 10022

HOLT. Holt, Rinehart & Winston, Inc., 383 Madison Ave., New York, N.Y. 10017

INTERTYPE. Intertype Company, 360 Furman St., Brooklyn, N.Y. 11201

KENNIKAT. Kennikat Press, Box 270, Port Washington, N.Y 11050

KODAK. Eastman Kodak Company, 343 State Street, Rochester 4, N.Y. Kodak literature is available through all Kodak dealers.

LANSTON. Lanston Monotype Company, 360 G Street, Philadelphia, Pa. 19134

LITHOGRAPHIC TEXTBOOK. Lithographic Textbook Publishing Company, 30 W. Washington St., Chicago, Ill. 60602

McGRAW-HILL. McGraw-Hill Book Company, 330 W. 42 St., New York, N.Y. 10036

MERGENTHALER. Mergenthaler Linotype Company, 29 Ryerson St., Brooklyn, N.Y. 11205

NBP. National Business Publications, 1913 Eye Street, N.W., Washington 6, D.C.

NORTH AMERICAN. North American Publishing Company, 134 N. 13 St., Philadelphia, Pa. 19107

OXFORD. Oxford University Press, Inc., 417 Fifth Avenue, New York, N.Y. 10016

OXFORD PAPER. Oxford Paper Company, 277 Park Avenue, New York, N.Y. 10017

PENGUIN. Penguin Books, Inc., 330 Clipped Mill Road, Baltimore, Md. 21211; 39 W. 55 St., New York, N.Y. 10019

PERGAMON. Pergamon Press, Inc., 44-01 21 St., Long Island City, N.Y. 11101

PHOTOENGRAVERS. American Photoengravers Association, 166 West Van Buren St., Chicago, Ill. 60604

PITMAN. Pitman Publishing Corp., 20 E. 46 St., New York, N.Y. 10017

PIA. Printing Industries of America, Inc., 20 Chevy Chase Circle, N.W., Washington, D.C. 20015

PM/NL. Printing Magazine/National Lithographer, 466 Kinderkammack Rd., Oradell, N.J. 07649

REINHOLD. Reinhold Publishing Corp., 430 Park Ave., New York, N.Y. 10022

RONALD. Ronald Press Company, 15 E. 26 St., New York, N.Y. 10010

TAPLINGER. Taplinger Publishing Co., Inc., 29 E. 10 St., New York, N.Y. 10003

TAPPI. Technical Association of the Pulp & Paper Industry, 360 Lexington Ave., New York, N.Y. 10017

TUDOR. Tudor Publishing Company, 221 Park Ave. South, New York, N.Y. 10003

VAN NOSTRAND. D. Van Nostrand Co., Inc., 120 Alexander St., Princeton, N.J. 08540

WARREN. S. D. Warren Company, 225 Franklin St., Boston, Mass. 02101

WATSON. Watson-Guptill Publications, Inc., 165 W. 46 St., New York, N.Y. 10036

WILEY. John Wiley & Sons, Inc., 605 Third Ave., New York, N.Y 10016

Advanced Printing Technology and Applied Science

Adams, J. M. *Optical Measurements in the Printing Industry.* PERGAMON. Paperback, $3.95.

Banks, W. H., Editor. *Printing Inks and Color.* Proceedings of the Fifth International Conference of Printing Research Institutes held at National Printing Ink Research Institute, Lehigh University, Bethlehem, Pa., 1959. PERGAMON.

Banks, W. H., Editor. *Problems in High Speed Printing: The Influence of Printing Speed and Pressure on Print Quality.* Proceedings of the Sixth International Conference of Printing Research Institutes held at Elsinore, Denmark, 1961. PERGAMON.

Banks, W. H., Editor. *Halftone Printing.* Proceedings of the Seventh International Conference of Printing Research Institutes held in London, 1963. PERGAMON.

FTA Proceedings. Published annually by the Flexographic Technical Association, Inc., 157 W. 57 St., New York, N.Y.

Hartsuch, Paul J., Ph.D. *The Chemistry of Lithography.* 1961.

GATF. Paperback, members $3.60, non-members $12.00.

Jaffe, Erwin and Robert F. Reed. *The Science of Physics in Lithography.* 1964. GATF. Paperback, members $1.80, non-members $6.00.

Proceedings of Conferences organized by the R & E Council, available from Research and Engineering Council of the Graphic Arts Industry, 1411 K Street, N.W., Washington, D.C.

TAGA Proceedings. Published annually by the Technical Association of the Graphic Arts, P.O. Box 3064, Federal Station, Rochester, N.Y. 14614.

Advertising Design and Production

Bahr, Leonard F. *ATA Advertising Production Handbook*. Third edition. 1963. ATA. $5.50, special student rate $3.50.

Cardamone, Tom. *Advertising Agency and Studio Skills*. 1959. WATSON. $5.50.

DeLopatecki, Eugene. *Advertising Layout and Typography*. Revised edition. RONALD. $4.25.

Hymes, David. *Production in Advertising and the Graphic Arts*. 1958. HOLT. $9.95.

Latimer, H. C. *Advertising Production Planning and Copy Preparation for Offset Printing*. The Five Mile River Press, P.O. Box 68, Rowayton Station, Norwalk, Conn. Paperback $4.95.

Longyear, William L. *Advertising Layout*. 1954. RONALD. $6.50.

Schlemmer, Richard M. *Handbook of Advertising Art Production*. 1966. PRENTICE-HALL. $5.25.

Stanley, Thomas R. *Technique of Advertising Production*. Second edition. 1954. PRENTICE-HALL. $11.00.

Bibliographical Services and Book Lists

Book List for Convenient Reference. Catalog of graphic arts books sold by the Graphic Arts Monthly, 7373 North Lincoln Ave., Chicago, Ill. 60646. Free.

Books of Interest to Lithographers. Bibliography available from GATF.

Catalog of Graphic Arts Books. Available from Inland Printer/American Lithographer, 300 West Adams St., Chicago, Ill. 60606. Free.

GATF Publications and Services 1967. Catalog describing the many services rendered by GATF and listing all available GATF publications. GATF. Free.

Graphic Arts Abstracts. The GATF Research Department regularly abstracts papers and articles from nearly 300 technical and scientific journals. Published monthly. GATF Members, free; non-members $20.00 per year.

Information about Information Services. 1967. Graphic Arts Information Service, Rochester Institute of Technology, Box PF-1, Rochester, N.Y. 14608. Free.

Printing and the Graphic Arts. A Bibliography. 1961. Available from Business and Technology Department, Cleveland Public Library, 325 Superior Ave., Cleveland, Ohio. 44114. Price 25¢.

Binding

Cockerell, Douglas. *Bookbinding and the Care of Books*. Fifth edition. 1953. PITMAN. $6.50.

Development of Performance Standards for Library Binding, Phase I. 1961. ALA. Paperback, $3.00.

Development of Performance Standards for Binding Used in Libraries, Phase II. 1966. ALA. Paperback, $3.00.

Diehl, Edith. *Bookbinding: Its Theory and Practice*. 2 vols. KENNIKAT. $27.50.

Feipel, Louis and E. Browning. *Library Binding Manual*. 1951. ALA. Paperback $1.50.

Groneman, Chris. *General Bookbinding*. 1958. TAPLINGER. Paperback, $2.00.

How to Sell Loose Leaf. 1949. Manual No. 3, published by the National Stationers Association, 740 Investment Bldg., Washington, D.C. Paperback $1.00.

Perry, Kenneth F. and Clarence C. Baab. *The Binding of Books*. 1940. TAPLINGER. $3.60.

The Theory and Practice of Bookbinding. GPO. Cat. No. GP 1.26:B 64/962. $1.75.

Book Design and Production

Book Publishers Guide. A Manual on the Selection of Paper and the Design and Production of Bound Books. Third edition in preparation. OXFORD PAPER.

Goodhue, Bertram G. *Book Decorations*. 1931. Grolier Club, 47 E. 60 St., New York, N.Y. 10022. $15.00.

Helpful Aids in Book Production. 1953. BMI. $8.50.

Lee, Marshall. *Bookmaking*. 1965. BOWKER. $12.75.

Loring, Rosamont Bowditch. *Decorated Book Papers*. Second edition by Philip Hofer. 1952. HARVARD. $3.75.

McLean, Ruari. *Modern Book Design from William Morris to the Present Day*. 1959. OXFORD. $4.75.

Official Manufacturing Standards and Specifications for Textbooks, as revised effective July 19, 1965. Published by the Joint Committee on Textbook Specifications, American Textbook Publishers Institute, National Association of State Textbook Directors, and Book Manufacturers Institute. Available from BMI. $2.00.

Trade Customs—Book Manufacturing Industry. In the Absence of Written Contracts to the Contrary. Revised, May, 1963. Distributed by BMI. $1.50.

Williamson, Hugh. *Methods o Book Design*. Second edition. 1967. OXFORD. $10.00.

Wilson, Adrian. *The Design of Books*. 1967. REINHOLD. $15.00.

Color Theory and Full-Color Printing

A Closer Look at How to Use the DuPont Explographic Color Chart. The DuPont Color Council, 2243 Nemours Building, Wilmington, Del. 19898. Free.

Basic Color for the Graphic Arts. 1964. Kodak Graphic Arts Data Book Q-7. KODAK. Paperback $1.00.

Billmeyer, Fred W., Jr. and Max Saltzman. *Principles of Color Technology*. 1967. WILEY. $11.95.

Birren, Faber. *Color: A Survey in Words and Pictures from Ancient Mysticism to Modern Science*. 1963. University Books, Inc., 1615 Hillside Ave., New Hyde Park, N.Y. 11041. $15.00.

Burnham. W. R., R. M. Hanes, and James Bartleson. *Color: A Guide to Basic Facts and Concepts*. 1967. WILEY. $9.25.

DuPont Ink Wedge Palette System Production Handbook. Photo Products Department, E. I. duPont de Nemours & Co., Inc., Wilmington, Del. 19898. Free.

Engdahl, David A. *Color Printing, Material Processes, Color Control*. 1967. CHILTON. $6.95.

Evans, Ralph M. *Eye, Film and Camera in Color Photography*. 1959. WILEY. $9.50.

Evans, Ralph M. *Introduction to Color*. 1948. WILEY. $16.00.

Judd, Deane B. and Guenter Wyszecki. *Color in Business, Science and Industry*. Second edition, 1963. WILEY. $16.00.

John E. Kaufman, Editor. *IES Lighting Handbook*. Fourth

edition. 1966. Illuminating Engineering Society, 345 E. 17 St., New York, N.Y. 10017. $15.00.

Munsell, H. A. *A Color Notation.* 11th edition. Munsell Color Co., Inc., 2441 N. Calvert St., Baltimore, Md. 21218.

White, Jack W. *GATF Color Chart Bulletin.* 1957. GATF. Paperback, $4.00.

Yule, John A. C. *Principles of Color Reproduction—Applied to Photomechanical Reproduction, Color Photography, and the Ink, Paper and Other Related Industries.* 1967. WILEY. $15.00.

Composition: Methods and Machines

Abel, Oscar R. and Windsor A. Straw. *Mechanism of the Linotype and Intertype.* 14th edition. Lebawarts Press, Box 458, Brookings, South Dakota. $5.00.

CIS Newsletter. Published by Composition Information Services, 1605 N. Cahuenga Blvd., Los Angeles, Calif. 90028.

Dowding, G. *Finer Points in the Spacing and Arrangement of Type.* 1957. Museum Books, Inc., 48 E. 43 St., New York, N.Y. 10017. $3.00.

Gordon, Max M. *Making Type Behave.* 1961. General Composition Company, 281 Summer St., Boston, Mass. 02210. Paperback $1.50.

Instruction Manuals for Monotype Equipment, the Type and Rule Caster, The Giant Caster, The Monophoto, and others are available from LANSTON.

Intertype Engineering Department. *Engineering Bulletin,* supplementing the Intertype Book of Instructions. 1965. INTERTYPE. $2.50.

Linotype Machine Principles. The Official Manual. MERGENTHALER.

The Monotype Recorder. Published periodically by the Monotype Corporation, Ltd., England. Distributed in U.S.A. by LANSTON.

Picture Book of Monotype Machines. Distributed in U.S.A. by LANSTON.

Plaut, Harold B. *The Intertype—Book of Instruction.* 1943. INTERTYPE. $5.00.

Polk, Ralph W. and Harry L. Gage. *A Composition Manual.* 1953. PIA. $35.00.

Soblick, Herman, M. A. *Photocomposition Methods and Equipment.* Quad Publishing Company, Box 68, Bellmore, New York. Paperback $12.50.

Theory and Practice of Composition. GPO. Cat. No. GP 1.26:C 73/962. $1.75.

Computers and Computerized Composition

Adler, Irving. *Thinking Machines.* 1961. New American Library, Inc., 1301 Avenue of the Americas, New York, N.Y. 10019. Paperback 60¢.

Barnett, Michael P. *Computer Typesetting: Experiments and Prospects.* 1966. M.I.T. Press, 50 Ames St., Cambridge, Mass. 02142. $10.00.

Brooks, Frederick P. and Kenneth E. Iverson. *Automatic Data Processing.* 1963. WILEY. $10.75.

Electronic Composing System: A Guide for Its Utilization. GPO. Cat. No. GP 1.23/4: El 2. Price 25¢.

Gottlieb, C. C. and J. N. P. Hume, *High-Speed Data Processing.* 1958. McGRAW-HILL. $11.00.

Guidelines for Planning Computer Printout for Printing Press Production. GPO. Cat. No. GP 1.23/4:B 96/no. 1. Price 10¢.

Hattery, Lowell H. and George P. Bush, Editors. *Automation and Electronics in Publishing.* 1965. Spartan Books, 1250 Connecticut Ave., N.W., Washington, D.C. 20036.

Kozmetsky, George and Paul Kircher. *Electronic Computers and Management Control.* McGRAW-HILL. Paperback $2.95.

Kubilius, Walter. *Basic Guide to Computers.* Reprinted from PM/-NL. Available from PM/NL. 50¢.

Moore, L. Lee, III and W. T. Johnson. *Automation of Newspaper Composition.* Management Reports, 38 Cunnington St., Boston, Mass. 02215. $17.00.

Siegel, Paul. *Understanding Digital Computers.* 1961. WILEY. $7.95.

Copyfitting

Chaundy, Theodore W. and others. *Printing of Mathematics.* 1954. OXFORD. $4.00.

Copyfitting. A Simple Method Complete with Tables for Linotype Composition. MERGENTHALER. Free.

Intertype Ready Reckoner. 1963. INTERTYPE. Free.

Lee Streamlined Copyfitting Manual and Handbook. 1966. Arthur B. Lee & Associates, 22 W. 45 St., New York, N.Y. 10036. $10.50.

Scientific Copyfitting. Published by the Monotype Corporation, Ltd., London. Distributed in the U.S.A. by LANSTON. Free.

Dictionaries

CIS Glossary of Automated Typesetting and Related Computer Terms. Second edition. 1966. Composition Information Services, 1605 N. Cahuenga Blvd., Los Angeles, Calif. 90028. $15.00.

Collins, F. H. *Authors' and Printers' Dictionary.* Tenth edition. 1956. OXFORD. $2.00.

The Dictionary of Paper, Including Pulp, Paperboard, Paper Properties and Related Papermaking Terms. Third edition. 1965. American Paper & Pulp Assn., 220 E. 42 St., New York, N.Y. 10017. $8.40.

Dictionary of Printing Terms. Porte Publishing Company, Salt Lake City, Utah. $3.50.

Hostettler, Rudolf. *Technical Terms of the Printing Industry.* Third revised edition. 1959. (English, French, German, Italian, and Spanish) George Wittenborn, Inc., 1018 Madison Ave., New York, N.Y. 10021. $4.00.

Martin, J. H. and W. N. Morgans. *Glossary of Pigments, Varnish and Lacquer Constituents.* 1959. TUDOR. $3.50.

Melcher, Daniel and Nancy Larrick. *Printing and Promotion Handbook: How to Plan, Produce and Use Printing Advertising and Direct Mail.* Third edition. 1966. McGRAW-HILL. $15.00.

Pepper, William M. *Dictionary o- Newspaper and Printing Terms. English—Spanish, Spanish—En₁ glish.* 1959. COLUMBIA: $10.00.

Sams, Howard W., and Company. *Pocket Dictionary of Computer Terms.* 1962. Bobbs-Merrill

Company, Inc., 4300 W. 62 St., Indianapolis, Ind. 46206. Paperback, $1.50.

Stevenson, George A. *Graphic Arts Handbook and Products Manual*. 1960. Penn and Press Publications, Inc., 22419 Halldale Ave., Torrance, Calif.

Turner, Mary, Editor. *Bookman's Glossary*. Fourth edition. 1961. BOWKER. $5.00.

Wordingham, J. A. and P. Reboul. *Dictionary of Plastics*. 1964. Philosophical Library, Inc., 15 E. 40 St., New York, N.Y. 10016. $15.00.

Estimating and Printing Production

Hoch, Fred W. *Estimating Standards for Printers*. Fred Hoch Associates, New York, N.Y. $6.00.

Layouts for Impositions. (Contains layouts for flatbed, rotary and web presses.) Cat. No. GP 1.2:L 45/2/957. GPO. $4.00.

Offset Techniques. Reprints of 43 articles. PM/NL. $2.50.

Ouderkirk, John C. *An Introduction to Printing Plant Layout*. 1967. Printing Industry of Illinois Association, 12 E. Grand Ave., Chicago, Ill. 60611. $10.00.

Paulsen, Henry A. *A Course in Estimating*. 1953. PIA. $35.00.

PIA Production Par. 1960. PIA. Looseleaf, $30.00 a year.

PIA SimPar. PIA. $25.00 annually.

Reed, Robert F., Editor. *Instruments for Quality Control*. 1963. GATF. Paperback, members $1.50, non-members $5.00.

Roy, Robert H. *Management of Printing Production*. 1953. PIA. $35.00.

Warner, Wayne H. *Planning for Better Imposition*. Judd & Detweiler, Washington, D.C. $10.00.

Fine-Art Printing and Printmaking

Arnold, Grant. *Creative Lithography and How To Do It*. 1965. DOVER. Paperback $1.65.

Biegeleisen, J. I. and M. A. Cohn. *Silk Screen Technique*. 1959. DOVER. Paperback $1.85.

Biggs, John R. *The Craft of Woodcuts*. 1963. Sterling Publishing Co., Inc., 419 Park Ave., S., New York, N.Y. 10016. $2.95.

Heller, Jules. *Printmaking Today*. 1958. HOLT. $7.25.

Kafka, Francis J. *Linoleum Block Printing*. 1958. TAPLINGER. Paperback $2.00.

Kent, Cyril and Mary Cooper. *Simple Printmaking*. 1967. WATSON. Paperback $1.95.

Rasmusen, Henry N. *Printmaking With Monotype*. 1960. CHILTON. $7.50.

Zigrosser, Carl. *The Book of Fine Prints*. Crown Publishers, Inc., 419 Park Ave. South, New York, N.Y. 10016. $4.95.

Graphic Arts Photography

Basic Photography for the Graphic Arts. 1965. Kodak Graphic Arts Data Book Q-1. KODAK. Paperback 75¢.

Biggs, Dorsey and K. W. Beattie. *How to Print and Publish Photomechanically*. 1967. NORTH AMERICAN. Philadelphia, Pa. 19103.

Boucher, Paul E. *Fundamentals of Photography*. Fourth edition. 1963. VAN NOSTRAND. $7.95.

Brody, E., Frank M. Preucil and J. W. White. *Photography—Color Separation*. 1959. GATF. Paperback, members $2.40, non-members $8.00.

Color Correction with Kodak Tri-Mask Film. 1965. Kodak Graphic Arts Data Book Q-6A. KODAK. Paperback $1.50.

Elementary Principles and Terminology of Densitometry. GEVAERT. Paperback, free.

Focal Encyclopedia of Photography. Revised edition. 2 Vols. 1965. PITMAN. $39.00 the set.

Fossett, R. O. *Techniques in Photography for the Screen Process Printer*. 1963. Signs of the Times Publishing Co., 407 Gilbert Ave., Cincinnati, Ohio. 45202. Paperback $3.00.

Graphic Material—Continuous-Tone Photography. GEVAERT. Paperback, free.

Graphic Material—Screen Photography. GEVAERT. Paperback, free.

Jaffe, Erwin. *Halftone Photography for Offset Lithography*. 1960. GATF. Paperback, members $1.80, non-members $6.00.

Jaffe, Erwin. *Contact Printing*. 1964. GATF. Paperback, members $1.50, non-members $5.00.

Jardine, Don. *Better Line Photography for Reproduction Plants*. Revised edition, 1966. Scott Blueprint and Lithograph Co., 8479 Higuera St., Culver City, Calif. 90231. $4.90.

Kodak Direct-Screen Color-Separation Dial. 1964. KODAK. $2.00.

Kodak Contact Screens—Types and Applications. Kodak Graphic Arts Data Book Q-21. KODAK. Free.

Kosar, Jaromir. *Light Sensitive Systems*. 1965. WILEY. $15.00.

Kosloff, Albert. *Photographic Screen Process Printing*. Revised edition, 1962. Signs of the Times Publishing Co., 407 Gilbert Ave., Cincinnati, Ohio. 45202. $7.00.

Larmore, Lewis. *Introduction to Photographic Principles*. Second edition. Peter Smith, 6 Lexington Ave., Gloucester, Mass. 01930. $3.50.

Masking with Multimask Film. GEVAERT. Paperback, $1.00.

Mees, C. E. K. and T. H. James. *Theory of the Photographic Process*. Third edition. 1966. MACMILLAN. $25.00.

Neblette, D. B. *Photography: Its Materials and Processes*. Sixth edition. 1962. VAN NOSTRAND. $15.00.

Noemer, Ewald F. *The Handbook of Modern Halftone Photography*. 1966. Perfect Graphic Arts Supply Co., P.O. Box 62, Demares, N.J. 07627. $11.80.

Robinson, Karl Davis. *Line Photography for the Lithographic Process*. 1948. GATF. Paperback, members $1.20, non-members $4.00.

Sayre, Irene. *Choosing an Enlarger for the Graphic Arts*, LITHOGRAPHIC TEXTBOOK. Paperback, $3.00.

Sayre, I. H. *Photography and Platemaking for Photolithography*. 1965. LITHOGRAPHIC TEXTBOOK. $10.50.

History

The Bookbinder in Eighteenth Century Williamsburg. Craft House, Williamsburg, Va. Paperback 50¢ and 15¢ for postage.

Butler, Pierce. *Origin of Printing in Europe*. 1940. UNIV. OF CHICAGO. $6.00.

Carter, Thomas F. and L. C. Goodrich. *The Invention of Printing in*

China and its Spread Westward. Second edition. 1955. RONALD. $10.00.

Dürer, Albrecht. *Of the Just Shaping of Letters*. Transl. from the Latin text of 1535 by R. T. Nichol. 1965. DOVER. Paperback $1.25.

Eckman, Dr. James. *The Heritage of the Printer*. 1965. NORTH AMERICAN. $15.00.

Ettlinger, John R. *Historical Specimens of Book Printing*. 1966. DOVER. Paperback $2.00.

Fontana, John M. *We Thank Gutenberg for Shakespeare and Ben Franklin*. 1964. John M. Fontana, Publisher, 829 E. 45 St., Brooklyn, N.Y. 11203. $1.25.

Fontana, John M. *Mankind's Greatest Invention*. 1964. John M. Fontana, Publisher, 829 E. 45 St., Brooklyn, N.Y. 11203. $4.95.

100 GPO Years, 1861–1961. A History of the United States Public Printing. GPO. Cat. No. GP 1.2:G 74/7/861–961. $1.00.

Hargrave, Catherine Perry. *A History of Playing Cards and a Bibliography of Cards and Gaming*. 1966. DOVER. Paperback $3.00.

Hind, Arthur M. *History of Engraving and Etching*. 1923. Third edition. DOVER. Paperback $3.00.

Jennett, Sean. *Pioneers in Printing*. 1958. OXFORD. $4.50.

Lawson, Alexander S. *A Printer's Almanac*. 1967. Volume 2 in the "Heritage of the Printer" series. NORTH AMERICAN. $15.00.

Lehmann-Haupt, Hellmut. *Gutenberg and the Master of the Playing Cards*. 1966. Yale University Press, 92a Yale Station, New Haven, Conn. 06520. $15.00.

Lehmann-Haupt, Hellmut, Hannah Dustin French, and Joseph W. Rogers. *Bookbinding in America*. 1967. BOWKER. U.S. and Canada $10.00, elsewhere $11.00.

Lehmann-Haupt, Hellmut, and others. *The Book in America*. Second edition. 1964. Bowker. $12.50.

McMurtrie, D. C. *The Book: The Story of Printing and Bookmaking*. Third revised edition, 1943. OXFORD. $12.50.

Morison, Stanley. *On Type Designs, Past and Present*. Revised edition, 1962. John DeGraff, Inc., 34 Oak Ave., Tuckahoe, N.Y. 10707. $3.00.

Morison, Stanley and Kenneth Day. *The Typographical Book, 1450–1935*. CHICAGO. $30.00.

Moxon, Joseph. *Mechanick Exercises on the Whole Art of Printing. 1683–4*. Edited by Herbert Davis and Harry Carter. Second edition. 1962. OXFORD. $16.80.

Oswald, John C. *Printing in the Americas*. 2 vols. KENNIKAT. $19.50.

The Printer in Eighteenth Century Williamsburg. Craft House, Williamsburg, Va. Paperback 50¢ and 15¢ for postage.

Roblin, Fred. *A Keepsake of the IPP & AU*. 1964. International Printing Pressmen and Assistants' Union, Pressmen's Home, Tenn. 37850. $5.00.

Roblin, Fred. *Development of the Printing Press*. 1965. The American Pressman. Pressmen's Home, Tenn. 37850. Paperback $2.00, hardbound $4.00.

Silver, Rollo G. *Typefounding in America, 1787–1825*. 1965. University Press of Virginia, Charlottesville, Va. 22903. $7.50.

Sipley, Louis W. *The Photomechanical Halftone*. American Museum of Photography, 338 S. 15 St., Philadelphia, Pa. 19102. $7.50.

Sipley, Louis W. *A Half Century of Color*. 1951. American Museum of Photography, 338 S. 15 St. Philadelphia, Pa. 19102. $10.00.

Steinberg, Sigfrid H. *Five Hundred Years of Printing*. Revised edition. 1962. PENGUIN. Paperback $1.95.

Thomas, Isaiah. *The History of Printing in America*. 2 vols. Second edition. Burt Franklin, 235 E. 44 St., New York, N.Y. 10017. $47.50.

Updike, Daniel B. *Printing Types: Their History, Forms and Use*. Third edition. 2 vols. 1951. HARVARD. $15.00.

Wroth, Lawrence C. *The Colonial Printer*. 1964. University Press of Virginia, Charlottesville, Va. 22903. $5.00, paperback $2.75.

Illustration and Art Preparation

Cutler, Merritt D. *How to Cut Drawings on Scratchboard*. WATSON. $4.95.

Fabri, Ralph. *Color: A Complete Guide for Artists*. 1967. WATSON. $12.50.

How to Prepare Artwork for Letterpress and Lithography. Booklet published by Kimberly-Clark Corp., Neenah, Wis. 54957.

Lamb, Lynton. *Drawing for Illustration*. 1962. OXFORD. $8.00.

Maurello, S. R. *How to Do Pasteups and Mechanicals*. 1960. TUDOR. $7.95.

Mayer, Ralph. *Artist's Handbook of Materials and Techniques*. Revised edition, 1956. VIKING. $6.95.

Preparation of Illustrations for Reports of U.S. Geological Survey with Brief Descriptions of Process of Reproduction. GPO. Cat. No. 1 1912: I1 6. Price 70¢.

Silver, Gerard A. *Modern Graphic Arts Paste-Up: The Workshop Approach to the Graphic Arts*. 1966. AMERICAN TECHNICAL. Paperback $3.75.

Stone, Bernard and Arthur Eckstein. *Preparing Art for Printing*. 1965. REINHOLD. $15.00.

Thomas, T. A. *Technical Illustration*. 1960. McGRAW-HILL. $6.50.

Willis, F. H. *Layout*. 1965. Sterling Publishing Co., Inc., 419 Park Avenue South, New York, N.Y. 10016. $5.95.

Lettering and Letter Design

Biegeleisen, J. I. *The ABC of Lettering*. Third edition. 1965. HARPER. $9.50.

Goudy, Frederic W. *The Alphabet and Elements of Lettering*. DOVER. Paperback $2.00.

Holub, Rand. *Lettering Simplified: A Manual for Beginners*. WATSON. $3.75.

Longyear, William L. *Type and Lettering*. Fourth revised and enlarged edition. 1966. WATSON. $6.95.

Thompson, Tommy. *The Script Letter: Its Form, Construction and Application*. 1965. DOVER. Paperback $1.00.

Manuscript Preparation and Proofreading

Burbidge, P. G. *Notes and References*. 1952. CAMBRIDGE. 75¢.

Carey, Gordon V. *Mind the Stop*. Second edition. 1958. CAMBRIDGE. Paperback, 95¢.

Crutchley, Brooke. *Preparation of Manuscripts and Correction of Proofs.* Second edition. CAMBRIDGE. 75¢.

Evans, Nell Womack. *Scripteasers.* 1958. Golden Bell Press, 1400 Curtis St., Denver, Colorado. 80205. $3.50.

Harper & Row Author's Manual. 1966. HARPER. $3.50.

Lasky, Joseph. *Proofreading and Copy-Preparation.* 1954. Mentor Press, 360 W. 23 St., New York, N.Y. 10011. $7.50.

Mann's Speller—Divider. Third edition. 1966. Lomanco Publishers, 3602 Carrison Rd., Toledo, Ohio 43613. $1.49.

New York Times. *Style Book for Writers and Editors.* 1962. McGRAW-HILL. $3.75.

Skillin, Marjorie E., and Robert M. Gay. *Words Into Type.* Revised edition. Appleton-Century-Crofts, 440 Park Ave. South, New York, N.Y. 10016. $7.50.

Thomas, Payne E. L. *Guide for Authors: Manuscript, Proof and Illustration.* 1958. Thomas Printing & Publishing Co., Ltd., 724 Desnoyer St., Kaukauna, Wis. 54130. Paperback $2.50.

Trelease, Sam F. *How to Write Scientific and Technical Papers.* Third edition. 1958. Williams & Wilkins Company, 428 E. Preston St., Baltimore, Md. 21202. $3.25.

The University of Chicago Press. *Manual of Style.* 11th edition. 1949. CHICAGO. $6.00.

United States Government Printing Office. *Style Manual.* GPO. In preparation.

Word Division: Supplement to Government Printing Office Style Manual. Sixth edition. 1962. GPO. Cat. No. GP 1.2:W 89/3/962. Price 50¢.

Miscellaneous

Boden, J., Editor. *Annual of Advertising & Editorial Art & Design.* 44th edition. Sponsored by the Art Directors Club of New York. REINHOLD. $16.50.

Herdegg, Walter, Editor. *Graphis Annual* 65/66. HASTINGS, $16.00.

Journalist 1 and C. GPO. Cat. No. D 208.11:J 82.2 Price $1.25.

Pilpel, Harriet F. and Morton D. Goldberg. *Copyright Guide.*

Third edition. 1967. BOWKER. Paperback $3.00.

Printing Purchasing Manual 1966/ 67. PM/NL. Paperback $2.50.

Printing Trades Blue Books. Three different regional editions: (1) Metropolitan New York-New Jersey, (2) Northeastern States, (3) Southeastern States. Published annually. A. F. Lewis & Company, 853 Broadway, New York, N.Y. 10003. Each edition $25.00 plus 65¢ for postage.

Spencer, Herbert, Editor. *The Penrose Annual.* Vol. 60, 1967. HASTINGS. $16.50.

Newspaper Design and Production

Arnold, Edmund C. *Functional Newspaper Design.* 1956. HARPER. $9.95.

Astel, George B. *Manual of Newspaper Style.* 1959. University of Washington Press, Seattle, Wash. 98105. Paperback $1.95.

Color Comics, Recommendation for Improving the Quality of Reproduction. Prepared by A.N.P.A.—A.A.A.A. Joint Committee on Newspaper Printing. Available from either organization.

Hutt, Allen. *Newspaper Design.* 1960. OXFORD. $8.00.

Preparation of Artwork, Engravings and Duplicate Printing Materials for Black-and-White Newspaper Production. Report No. 10, prepared by A.N.P.A.—A.A.A.A. Joint Committee on Newspaper Printing. Available from either organization.

Preparation of Run-of-Paper Color Advertising. Report No. 11, prepared by A.N.P.A.—A.A.A.A. Joint Committee on Newspaper Printing. Available from either organization.

Woods, Allan. *Modern Newspaper Production.* 1963. HARPER. $5.75.

Package Design and Printing

Gravure Packaging Guide— Copy Preparation Section. 1966. GTA.

Look at Packaging Trends. 1964. AMA. Paperback $1.50.

Long, Robert P. *Package Printing.* 1964. GRAPHIC MAGAZINES. $12.00.

McGuire, Patrick E. *Packaging and Paper Converting.* Palmerton Publishing Company, New York, N.Y. $8.00.

Paine, F. A. *Fundamentals of Packaging.* 1962. Gordon & Breach, Science Publishers, Inc. 150 Fifth Ave., New York, N.Y. 10011. $12.50.

Sutnar, Ladislav. *Package Design. The Force of Visual Selling.* Arts, Inc., 667 Madison Ave., New York, N.Y. 10021. $9.75.

Paper and Other Printing Stocks

Book of ASTM Standards, Part 15: Paper; Packaging; Cellulose; Casein; Flexible Barrier Materials; Leather. Issued Annually in April. Published by American Society for Testing and Materials, 1916 Race St., Philadelphia, Pa. 19103. $13.00, members $9.10. Tests are also available individually.

Britt, Kenneth W., Editor. *Handbook of Pulp and Paper Technology.* 1964. REINHOLD. $22.00.

Casey, James P. *Pulp and Paper.* Second edition. 3 vols. Vol. 1, 1960, $21.00; vol. 2, 1960, $25.00; vol. 3, 1961, $29.50. WILEY.

Deterioration of Book Stock: Causes and Remedies. 1959. Virginia State Library, Richmond, Va. Free.

Government Paper Specification Standards No. 5. 1966. Subscription service includes supplementary material for an indefinite period. Loose leaf, punched for 3-ring binder. Issued by Joint Committee on Printing, Congress of the U.S. GPO. Cat. No. Y4.P 93/1:7/5. Subscription $2.00, foreign $2.50.

Hardman, H. and E. J. Cole. *Paper-Making Practice.* 1961. University of Toronto Press, Toronto 5, Ont., Canada. $7.50.

Herman, Ezra D. *Job Lot Paper.* 1964. M. C. Luce Paper Company, Inc., 218 Seventh Ave., New York, N.Y. 10011. Single copies free.

A History of Paper. Booklet available from Advertising Dept., Fraser Paper Limited, 330 Madison Ave., New York, N.Y. 10017.

History of Paper Making. OXFORD PAPER. Free.

Libby, C. Earl, Editor. *Pulp and Paper Science and Technology.* 2 Vols. Vol. 1, Pulp; Vol. 2, Paper, 1962. McGRAW-HILL. $9.00 each.

Manufacture and Testing of Durable Book Papers. 1960. Virginia State Library, Richmond, Va. Free.

Mosher, Robert H., Editor. *Technology of Coated and Processed Papers.* 1952. TUDOR. $15.00.

The Paper Catalog. Published semi-annually in six sectional editions by Walden, Sons & Mott, Inc., 466 Kinderkamack Rd., Oradell, N.J. 07649. $5.00 for two copies a year.

Paper Coating Additives. TAPPI Monograph No. 25, 1963. TAPPI. $5.00.

Paper and the Graphic Arts. Booklet published by Kimberly-Clark Corp., Neenah, Wis. 54957.

Paper and Paperboard—Characteristics Nomenclature, and Significance of Tests. Third edition. ASTM Special Technical Publication No. 60-B. 1963. Available from American Society for Testing and Materials, 1916 Race St., Philadelphia, Pa. 19103. Members $2.80, non-members $4.00.

Paper and Web Offset Printing. 1960. OXFORD PAPER. Free.

The Paper Yearbook. Published annually by Davidson Publishing Company, 405 E. Superior St., Duluth, Minn. and 250 Fifth Ave., New York City.

Permanent Durable Book Paper. 1960. Virginia State Library, Richmond, Va. Free.

Pigmented Coating Processes for Paper and Paperboard. TAPPI Monograph No. 28. 1965. TAPPI. $5.00.

Reed, Robert F. *Paper Addenda.* 1966. GATF.

Reed, Robert F. and Gordon C. Wheeler. *The GATF Pick Tester for Offset Papers.* 1953. GATF. Paperback, members $1.20, non-members $4.00.

Reed, Robert F. *What the Lithographer Should Know About Paper.* 1957. GATF. Paperback, members $1.50, non-members $5.00.

Simonds, Herbert R., and J. M. Church. *Concise Guide to Plastics.* Second edition. 1963. REINHOLD. $12.00.

Society of the Plastics Industries. *Plastics Engineering Handbook.* Third edition. 1960. REINHOLD. $15.00.

Sutermeister, Edwin. *The Story of Papermaking.* 1954. BOWKER. $6.00.

Synthetic and Protein Adhesives for Paper Coating. TAPPI Monograph No. 22. 1952. TAPPI. $5.00.

TAPPI Annual Bibliography of Papermaking and U.S. Patents. 1963 to 1965. TAPPI. $7.50 each.

TAPPI Standard Testing Procedures. 2 Vols. Published continually by the Technical Association of the Pulp and Paper Industry, 360 Lexington Ave., New York, N.Y. 10017. Individual tests are also available.

Type and Its Relation to Paper. Booklet published by Kimberly-Clark Corp., Neenah, Wis. 54957.

Web Offset Round Table. 1964. OXFORD PAPER.

Presses and Presswork

Braasch, William. *Newspaper Presses. The General Principles Common to Newspaper Press Design and Operation.* Second edition. 1958. ANPA Research Institute. ANPA.

Flexographic Press Specifications. Revised in all even-numbered years. GRAPHIC MAGAZINES. $2.00.

Gravure Packaging Guide—Doctor Blade Section. 1964. GTA.

Gravure Packaging Guide—Impression Roll Section. 1965. GTA.

Gravure Packaging Press Specifications. Revised in all odd-numbered years. GRAPHIC MAGAZINES. $2.00.

Latham, Charles W. *Advanced Pressmanship—Sheetfed Presses.* 1963. GATF. Paperback, members $1.80, non-members $6.00.

Latham, Charles W. *Press Operating—Sheetfed Presses.* 1956. GATF. Paperback, members $1.80, non-members $6.00.

Makarius, Theodore F. *Operation of the Offset Press.* American Graphic, Inc., Irvington, N.J. $15.00.

Mills, George J. *Platen Press Operation.* 1959. Carnegie Institute of Technology, Pittsburgh, Pa.

Paper Merchant's Guide to Web Printing. National Paper Trade Association, 220 E. 42 St., New York, N.Y. 10017. Members $50.00, non-members $100.00.

Polk, Ralph W. *Elementary Platen Presswork.* 1965. BENNETT. $4.20.

Reed, Robert F. *Offset Press Troubles—Sheetfed Presses.* 1962. GATF. Paperback, members $1.50, non-members $5.00.

Reed, Robert F. *Web Offset Press Troubles.* 1965. GATF. Paperback, members $3.00, non-members $10.00.

Sayre, Irene. *The Single Color Offset Press.* LITHOGRAPHIC TEXTBOOK. $7.70.

Standard Color Control Bars for the American Photoengravers Assn. Recommended by A.A.A.A., M.P.A. and P.I.A., approved by American Photoengravers Assn. Available from A.A.A.A.

Theory and Practice of Presswork. GPO. Cat. No. GP 1.26:p 92/962. $1.75.

Printing as a Business

Becker, Peter Jr. *Managing Your Business.* 1959. PIA. $37.50.

Becker, Peter Jr. *Simplified Cost System.* 1949. PIA. $4.75.

How To Do Business with the GPO. A Guide for Contractors. GPO. Cat. No. GP 1.23/4:B 96. Price 15¢.

Jayne, John J. *Small Printing Plant Management.* 1965. Graphic Arts Publishing Company, 7373 North Lincoln Ave., Chicago, Ill. 60646. $5.00.

PIA Ratios for Better Printing Management. Revised annually. PIA. $15.00.

Preparing Contractors Reports for NASA. Data Presentation. Cat. No. NAS 1.21:7025. *Repro. Typing and Layout.* Cat. No. NAS 1.21:7007. *Technical Illustrating.* Cat. No. NAS 1.21:7008. GPO. Price each 15¢.

Tucker, Spencer A. *Pricing for Higher Profits: Criteria, Methods, Applications.* 1966. McGRAW-HILL. $12.50.

Printing as a Career

Bedell, Earl L. *Careers in Graphic Reproduction.* 1966. VAN NOSTRAND. $6.96.

Karch, R. Randolph. *Printing and the Allied Trades.* Fifth edition. 1962. PITMAN. $5.25.

Lithographer 1 and C. GPO. Cat. No. D 208.11:L 71/2966. Price $1.75.

Lithographer 3 and 2. GPO. Cat. No. D 208.11:L 71/963. Price $2.75.

Mueller, L. W. *Exploring Printing.* Revised edition. 1963. Harlo Printing Company, 16721 Hamilton Ave., Detroit, Mich. 48203.

Pollack, Philip. *Printing: Careers and Opportunities for You.* 1959. CHILTON. Paperback $2.50.

Reinfeld, George, Jr. *Your Future in Printing.* Richard Rosen Press, Inc., 29 E. 21 St., New York, N.Y. 10010. $2.95.

Simon, Irving B. *The Story of Printing.* Harvey House, Inc., Publishers, Irvington-on-Hudson, N.Y. $3.50.

Your Career Opportunities in Printing. 1962. Littlefield, Adams & Company, 81 Adams Drive, Totowa, N.J. 07512. Paperback $10.00.

Printing-Image Carriers

Blum, William and George B. Hogabom. *Principles of Electroplating and Electroforming (Electrotyping).* Third edition. 1949. McGRAW-HILL. $10.00.

Deckter, G. *Practical Photo-Offset Stripping.* LITHOGRAPHIC TEXTBOOK. $7.50.

The Electrotype and Stereotype Handbook. Duplicate Plates . . . How They Are Made and Used by the Letterpress Industry. Second edition. Published by the International Association of Electrotypers & Stereotypers, Inc., 758 Leader Building, Cleveland 14, Ohio.

The Fundamentals of Photoengraving. 1966. PHOTOENGRAVERS. Paperback, $1.25.

Gravure Packaging Guide—Base Cylinder Section. 1965. GTA.

Gravure Processes. Illustrated descriptions of eight different gravure processes, reprinted from Gravure Magazine. GRAPHIC MAGAZINES. $1.50.

Halpern, Bernard R. *Color Stripping.* 1955. GATF. Paperback, members $1.50, non-members $5.00.

Halpern, Bernard R. *Offset Stripping—Black and White.* 1958. GATF. Paperback, members $3.00, non-members $10.00.

Halpern, Bernard R. *Tone and Color Correcting.* 1965. GATF. Paperback, members $1.80, non-members $6.00.

Latham, Charles W. and Jack W. White. *Photo-Composing (Including Pin-Register Systems).* 1964. GATF. Paperback, members $1.50, non-members $5.00.

Manual of Stereotype Operations. Standard Operations Based on Present Day Materials and Equipment. 1958. ANPA Research Institute. ANPA.

Mertle, J. A. and Gordon L. Monsen. *Photomechanics and Printing.* 1957. Mertle Publishing Company, Oshkosh, Wis. $15.00.

PIA Standard Photoengraving Specifications Manual for Letterpress Printing from Electrotypes for Magazine, Catalog and Commercial Work. Revised edition. 1962. PIA. $20.00.

Recommended Standard Second Colors for Business Publications. Revised 1966. Developed by A.A.A.A. in cooperation with A.B.P. and N.B.P. Available at no cost from either organization.

Recommended Standard Specifications for Advertising Reproduction Material in Magazine Letterpress Wet Printing. Report No. 4. 1961. Published by A.A.A.A. and M.P.A. Available from either organization.

Reed, Robert F. *Offset Platemaking—Deep-Etch.* 1957. GATF. Paperback, members $1.50, non-members $5.00.

Reed, Robert F. *Offset Platemaking—Surface.* 1959. GATF. Paperback, members $1.50, non-members $5.00.

Standard Scale for Photoengravings. Form K. Different scales are published and revised as needed, for black-and-white photoengravings and for four-color process engravings of different sizes. PHOTOENGRAVERS.

The Standard Scale in Theory and Praxis. Third edition. 1966. PHOTOENGRAVERS.

Printing Inks

Apps, E. A. *Ink Technology for Printers and Students.* 3 vols. 1964. TUDOR. Each vol. $10.00.

Apps, E. A. *Printing Ink Technology.* 1959. TUDOR. $19.50.

Gravure Packaging Guide—Ink Section. 1963. GTA.

Larsen, Louis M., Ph.D. *Industrial Printing Inks.* 1962. REINHOLD. $10.00.

NPIRI Standard Test Methods—Methods for the Examination of Printing Inks, Raw Materials, and Related Substances. Published by the National Printing Ink Research Institute, Lehigh University, Bethlehem, Pa.

Printing Ink Handbook. Prepared by the Technical and Educational Committees of the National Association of Printing Ink Manufacturers. Third edition in preparation. Available from the National Association of Printing Ink Manufacturers, 39 W. 59 St., New York, N.Y. 10019. Free.

Printing Ink Manual. Commissioned by the Technical Training Board of the Society of British Printing Ink Manufacturers. 1961. Cambridge, England. Available from MacNair-Dorland, 254 W. 31 St., New York, N.Y. 10001. $13.00 in the U.S., other countries $13.50.

Reed, Robert F. *What the Lithographer Should Know About Ink.* 1960. GATF. Paperback, members $1.50, non-members $5.00.

Voet, Andries. *Ink and Paper in the Printing Process.* 1952. WILEY. $8.50.

Wolfe, Herbert J. *Printing and Litho Inks.* Sixth edition in preparation. MacNair-Dorland, 254 W. 31 St., New York, N.Y. 10001.

Printing Processes and Methods

Arnold, Emund C. *Ink on Paper.* 1963. HARPER. $8.95.

Biegeleisen, J. I. *Complete Book of Silk Screen Printing Production.* 1963. DOVER. Paperback $2.00.

Boughton, Frank E. *Flexographic Printing.* 1958. Available from Frank E. Boughton, 5040 W. Windsor, Chicago, Ill. $5.00.

Bragdon, Charles R. *Metal Decorating from Start to Finish.* 1961. The Bond Wheelwright Company, Freeport, Maine.

Cartwright, H. M. and Robert Mackay. *Rotogravure—A Survey of European and American Methods.* 1956. Mackay Publishing Co., Inc., Lyndon, Kentucky.

Cleeton, Glen U. and Charles W. Pitkin. *General Printing*. Revised edition. 1958. TAPLINGER. $5.20.

Curwen, Harold. *Processes of Graphic Reproduction in Printing*. Third revised edition by Charles Mayo. 1958. DOVER. $6.00.

Flexography: *Principles and Practices*. 1962. Flexographic Technical Association, Inc., 157 W. 57 St., New York, N.Y.

Karch, R. Randolph. *Graphic Arts Procedures*. Third edition. 1966. AMER. TECHNICAL. $5.25.

Kosloff, Albert. *Screen Process Printing*. Revised edition. 1964. Signs of the Times Publishing Co., 407 Gilbert Ave., Cincinnati, Ohio. 45202.

Latimer, Henry C. *Survey of Lithography*. 1954. GATF. Paperback, members $1.20, non-members $4.00.

Odhams Practical Printing and Binding. Third edition. Transatlantic Arts, Inc., 565 Fifth Ave., New York, N.Y. 10017. $9.75.

Pocket Pal: A Graphic Arts Digest for Printers and Advertising Production Managers. Ninth edition. 1966. International Paper Company, 220 E. 42 St., New York, N.Y. 10017. 50¢.

Polk, Ralph W. *The Practice of Printing*. Revised edition. 1964. BENNETT. $6.00.

Shapiro, Charles, Editor. *The Lithographers Manual*. 1965. GATF. Members, reg. ed. $5.00, deluxe ed. $7.00; non-members, reg. ed. $10.00, deluxe ed. $14.50.

Steffen, Robert N. *Engraved Stationery Handbook*. 1950. The Cronite Company, Inc., 8707 Kennedy Blvd., North Bergen, N.J.

Theory and Practice of Lithography. GPO. Cat. No. GP 1:26L 71. $1.75.

Selling of Printing

The Annual Report. What it is . . . Why it is issued. Booklet No. 1 of a series—Managing a Business with the Help of Printing. WARREN. Free.

Birren, Faber. *Selling Color to People*. 1956. University Books, Inc., 1615 Hillside Ave., New Hyde Park, N.Y. 11041. $7.50.

Brantley, Owen C. *How to Sell Printing by Mail*. PM/NL. $5.95.

The Employee Manual. Booklet No. 2 of the series—Managing a Business with the Help of Printing. WARREN. Free.

Knox, Frank M. *The Knox Standard Guide to Design and Control of Business Forms*. 1966. McGRAW-HILL. $12.95.

McGiffin, Vida B. and Orissa Frost Kingsbury. *Creative Yearbook Journalism Workbook*. HASTINGS. Paperback $1.42.

More Business Through House Organs. Revised edition. 1955. WARREN. Free.

PIA Sales Development Program. PIA. $50.00.

PIA Course in Selling Printing. PIA. $35.00.

Printing Salesman's Herald. Issued bi-monthly by Champion Papers, Inc. One East Wacker Dr., Chicago, Ill. 60601. Available free from Marketing Services.

The Sales Catalog. Check List and Index for Catalog Planning. Booklet No. 4 of a series—Managing a Business with the Help of Printing. WARREN. Free.

Segal, Mendel. *How to Sell Printing Creatively*. 1956. Segal Services, Inc., Box 13426, Atlanta, Ga. 30324. $25.00.

Talucci, Don A. Editor. *Ideas How to Prepare Better Annual Reports*. Research Bureaus, Inc., Box 335, Southfield, Mich. $20.00.

Statistics and Industry Surveys

1965 Annual Survey of Manufacturers. Expenditures for New Plant and New Equipment. Publ. 1967. M65 (AS)-5. Price 10¢. *General Statistics for Industry Groups and Industries*. Publ. 1966. M65 (AS)-1. Price 25¢. *Value of Shipments by Classes of Products*. Publ. 1967. M65 (AS)-2. Price 50¢. These publications are issued annually. For sale by the Bureau of the Census, Washington, D.C. 20233, and U.S. Dept. of Commerce Field offices.

1963 Census of Manufacturers. Industry Statistics: Newspaper, Periodicals, Books and Miscellaneous Publishing. Publ. 1966. GPO. MC63 (2)-27A. Price 35¢. *Industry Statistics: Commercial Printing and Manifold Business Forms*. Publ. 1966. GPO. MC63(2)-27B. Price 30¢. *Industry Statistics: Greeting Cards, Bookbinding and Service Industries*. Publ. 1966. GPO. MC63(2)-27C. Price 30¢. These publications are issued approximately every five years.

Containers and Packaging. Quarterly Industry Report. GPO. Annual subscription, 75¢.

Employment Outlook in Printing Occupations. GPO. Cat. No. L 2.3:1450–61. Price 15¢.

Printing and Publishing. Quarterly Industry Report. GPO. Annual subscription $1.00.

Pulp, Paper and Board. Quarterly Industry Report. GPO. Annual subscription 75¢.

Small Business Administration. Free Management Assistance Publications. Lists issued periodically; available from any Small Business Administration Field Office or U.S. Dept. of Commerce Field Office. *For-Sale S.B.A. Publications*. Lists issued periodically. Available from GPO or any U.S. Dept. of Commerce Field Office.

Union Wages and Hours: Printing Industry, July 1, 1965 and Trend 1907–65. GPO. Cat. No. L 2.3:1489. Price 40¢.

U.S. Industrial Outlook. Issued annually. GPO. $1.25.

Type Faces

Alphabets and Character Showings of 197 Intertype Faces, 1965. INTERTYPE. Free.

Berry, William T. and others. *Encyclopedia of Type Faces*. Third edition. 1962. PITMAN. $18.50.

Biegeleisen, J. I. *Art Directors' Work Book of Type Faces*. Arco Publishing Company, Inc., 219 Park Ave. South, New York, N.Y. 10003. $9.95.

Graphic Arts Typebook, 2 vols. 1965. REINHOLD. $5.95 each.

Hutchings, R. S. *A Manual of Decorated Type Faces*. 1965. HASTINGS. $6.95.

Hutchings, R. S. *The Western Heritage of Type Design*. 1965. HASTINGS. $7.50.

Hutchings, R. S. *A Manual of Script Type Faces*. 1966. HASTINGS. $6.95.

Hutchings, R. S. *A Manual of Sans-Serif Typefaces*. 1967. HASTINGS. $6.95.

Karch, R. Randolph. *How to Recognize Type Faces*. 1958. TAPLINGER. $7.95.

Merriman, Frank. *ATA Type Comparison Book*. 1965. ATA. $10.00, special student rate $5.00.

Nesbitt, Alexander. *Decorative Initials and Alphabets*. 1959. DOVER. Paperback $2.25.

Specimens of Type Faces in Government Office Printing. GPO. Cat. No. GP 1.2:T 98/11/959. $1.25.

Typographic Design

Blumenthal, Walter Hart. *Eccentric Typography and Other Diversions in the Graphic Arts*. 1963. Achille J. St.Onge, 7 Arden Road, Worcester, Mass. $5.00.

Burns, Aaron. *Typography*. 1961. REINHOLD. $12.50.

Lieberman, J. Benjamin. *Printing as a Hobby*. Revised edition 1965. Sterling Publishing Co., Inc., 419 Park Ave. South, New York, N.Y. 10016. $3.95.

Morison, Stanley. *First Principles of Typography*. 1936. CAMBRIDGE. Paperback 75¢.

Ruder, Emil. *Typography: A Manual of Design*. 1967. HASTING. $19.50.

Simon, Oliver. *Introduction to Typography*. Transatlantic Arts, Inc., 565 Fifth Ave., New York, N.Y. 10017. $7.50.

Tinker, Miles A. *Legibility of Print*. 1963. Iowa State University Press, Ames, Iowa. 50010. $4.50.

Tinker, Miles A. *Bases for Effective Reading*. 1966. University of Minnesota Press, 2037 University Ave., S.E., Minneapolis, Minn. 55414. $7.50.

Tschichold, Jan. *Assymetric Typography*. 1967. REINHOLD. $7.50.

Typography and Design. GPO. Cat. No. GP 1.26:T 98/962. $1.50.

Subject Index

A

B

Back gauge of guillotine cutters 631

back lining of hard-bound books 682

back lining paper, slitting and rewinding of 688

back matter, in book composition 728

back stops, in rotary letterpress 442

backing of flat electrotypes 230

backing-up, in sheet-fed printing 625

backer roller, in rotogravure 482

back-up register, in web printing, ill. 371

back-up roll, in rotogravure 325

bagasse as paper fiber 528

Baldwin Automix, photo 498

  Circulation Water Levels, photo 350

  Gravity Feed Water Levels, photo 505

  Ink Agitators, photo 504

  Press Washer, photo 507

Ballard cylinders, in gravure 241

balloon formers, in web printing 382

banking, meaning in photoengraving 217

banknote printing presses for 290

U.S. currency, photo 291

baseboard for screen-process set-ups 520

basic area and size, meaning in paper industry 561

basis weight, meaning in paper industry 561

basis weight scale, photo 579

basso, meaning of term 239

bastard title, in book typography 728

bath technique of adding photographic densities 196

bayonets of saddle gatherers 650

beading, in finishing of printed products 713

beaters, in papermaking, photo 539

beating of paper fibers 539

bed of flatbed-cylinder presses 313

  of guillotine cutters 631

  of platen presses 310

  of stamping presses 695

benday, meaning of term 186

bendaying, in lithographic stripping 258

bending jigs for offset plates 330

Bible papers identified 565

Bible printing, technical problems of 471

Bierbauer Mechanical Overlay 422

bichromated albumin process, in photo-engraving 212

billing weight, meaning in paper industry 563

bimetallic offset plates, diagr. 264

bimetallic wrap-around plates for letterpress 222

binary notation, in digital computers 125

binder's case, diagr. 686

bindery imposition layout 619

binding, eight kinds of, ill. 620

  coils 671

  devices for mechanical binding, ill. 671

Bista Electrotype Plate 231

bit, meaning of term 129

bite as applied to printing inks 574

  meaning in etching of metal plates 237

black-body radiator 155

black letters, a class of type faces 727

black-light one iron etch, in gravure 249

black-line engraving 208

black newspapers as opposed to gray ones 342

black-printer, meaning of term in color-separation photography 191

blanket care, in offset printing 499

blanket cylinders, of offset presses 328

blanket selection 499

blanket-to-blanket presses 300

blankets, construction of for offset printing 329

  in indirect relief printing 27

blankbook binding characterized 619

blanking, in the sense of blind stamping 694

  in the sense of debossing 557

blanks, meaning in paper industry 566

bleached esparto fiber, microphoto 629

bleached sulfite pulp 534

bleaching of paper pulps 538

bleed, meaning in page layouts 628

bleeding of printing inks 608

blind stamping, in binding 696

blind tape punching equipment, in composition 79

blinding as applied to lithographic plates 266

block dies, for cutting and creasing 486

block letters, a kind of type faces 726

blocking medium, for hand-tusched screens 274

  of photoengravings 210

  of rewound printed webs 469

blower nozzles of sheet feeders 433

blowing the digester, meaning in chemical pulping 532

blue-grass stripping, in lithographic platemaking 258

blue-line stripping, in lithographic platemaking 258

blueprint paper, in photomechanical proofing 267

board slitting and cutting, in binding 687

body, meaning in ink industry 583

  size, meaning in type specification 59

  type, as opposed to display type 59

bolts, meaning in folding 639

bone folder, in hand folding 636

book and job folders, ill. 639

book composition characterized 728

  covering with stripping machine 706

  flush cut, ill. 697

  papers, discussion of 548

  terms used in describing of, diagr. 685

  trimmers 675

bottom guides on platen presses 425

boundary layers, in high-velocity drying 392

Bourges method of art preparation 737

brake shoe margin control, in web printing 367

brass-back plates, in flexography 234

brayer, meaning of term 402

break pages, in newspaper industry 455

breast roll of paper machine 546

breathing of plates, in rotary letterpress 316

bridges, in steel-rule dies 714

  in gravure image carriers 245

brightness of paper 580

  numbers of papers 538

  improvements, in papermaking 542

Brightype method of image conversion 122

brilliant green toner ink pigment 593

bringing up a collotype plate 516

bristol papers identified 565

bronzes for printing and bronzing 593

brohnzing echaracterized 593

  macin 711

I

Acknowledgments

As mentioned in the preface, drafts of each chapter of the manuscript were submitted to a number of specialists for review and comments. These reviewers were selected to represent a cross section of the whole graphic arts industry and included people active in printing companies, staff of research institutes, executives of equipment and material manufacturers, professional educators, heads of training departments, designers and buyers of printing. Some reviewers read only those sections that are related to their particular fields, others reviewed one or more chapters. Actually most chapters were completely reviewed by at least a dozen experts and several by a multiple of this figure. Each comment was entered opposite the page of the manuscript to which it belonged. This arrangement made it possible to study all comments in their proper context and to evaluate them together. After the writer had studied the comments, he revised the original draft and made the final decisions on the text. The responsibility for the book therefore rests exclusively with the writer.

Another point may be of interest: not a single reviewer suggested shortening of the text but many wanted additions. How much the volume and the scope of the book grew can be seen from the fact that the original plan called for a 100,000 word book, whereas the volume in your hand is approximately 500,000 words long.

Thanks for reviewing of the whole manuscript are due to four outstanding graphic arts organizations, the R. R. Donnelley & Sons Company, Chicago; the Graphic Arts Technical Foundation, Pittsburgh; the School of Printing, Rochester Institute of Technology, Rochester; and the United States Government Printing Office, Washington, D.C. Mr. *Loren Carter*, Manager of Training Services, reviewed some chapters himself and co-ordinated the reviewing by Donnelley specialists; Mr. *William H. Webber*, Executive Director, made the resources of the Graphic Arts Technical Foundation available; Mr. *Byron G. Culver*, Director Emeritus, School of Printing, Rochester Institute of Technology, reviewed the whole manuscript himself. The Honorable *James L. Harrison*, the Public Printer, authorized co-operation by the United States Government Printing Office; Mr. *Morris S. Kantrowitz*, Technical Director, reviewed two chapters himself and co-ordinated the reviewing of other chapters by GPO specialists.

Particular interest in this project was taken by Mr. *Harry L. Gage*, past Vice-President of, and Consultant to, Mergenthaler Linotype Company, Gloucester, Mass.; by Mr. *Walter M. Sackett*, Sales Department, R. R. Donnelley & Sons, Chicago; and by Mr. *J. Homer Winkler*, Consultant, Battelle Memorial Institute, Columbus, Ohio. Their unflagging, generous co-operation is here gratefully acknowledged by the writer.

The following listing comprises experts who have reviewed manuscript and persons who assisted otherwise in this project. Their efforts contributed greatly to the authenticity of the book.

A

Emanuel M. Abrams, President, The Lawson Company, Division of MGD, Chicago • *Leonard S. Alexander*, Director of Marketing Services, Miehle-Goss-Dexter, Inc., Chicago • *Mary D. Alexander*, Production Editor, University of Chicago Press, Chicago • *Howard W. Amos*, Superintendent of Letterpress Division, United States Government Printing Office, Washington, D.C. • *J. E. Anderlik*, Director, Sales Development, Consolidated Papers, Inc., Chicago • *Stuart E. Arnett*, General Manager Computer Typesetter Division, Photon, Inc., Wilmington, Mass. • *Joseph C. Ashmead*, President, Capital Electrotype Company, Albany, N.Y.

B

Warren W. Ball, Supervisor—Sales and Service, Smyth Manufacturing Company, Bloomfield, Conn. • *Gilbert W. Basset*, President, The Miehle Company, Division of MGD, Chicago • *William Baumrucker*, Director, Chas. T. Main, Inc., Boston • *George D. Beck*, Chairman, The Beck Engraving Company, Philadelphia • *Michael Benedetto*, Printing Foreman, M & M Displays, Inc., Philadelphia • *Carl N. Becker*, President, Badger-Becker, Inc., Milwaukee • *Richard Bethel*, President, William Marley Company, Philadelphia • *Amos Bethke*, Manager—Central Printing Department, Time Incorporated, New York City • *Edward Blank*, Director of Production Management and New Developments, Printing Industries of Metropolitan New York • *Martin Blumberg*, Vice-President, Manufacturing, American Book-Stratford Press, Inc., New York City • *John J. Boyle*, Special Assistant to Production Manager for Electronic Printing, United States Government Printing Office, Washington, D.C. • *Dr. William F. Braasch, Jr.*, Dean of Students, Allegheny Community College, Pittsburgh • *William J. Bradley*, Director, Research and Development, American Photoengraving Company, Philadelphia • *Lawrence Brehm*, Training Director, Western Printing and Lithographing Company, Racine, Wis. • *Ralph P. Brighton*, Industrial Relations and Personnel Director, J. W. Clement Company, Depew, N.Y. • *Kenneth W. Britt*, Associate Director, Research Division, Scott Paper Company, Philadelphia • *Thomas E. Brookover*, General Manager, Paperboard Division, Downingtown Paper Co., Downingtown, Pa. • *Michael H. Bruno*, Manager, Graphic Arts Research, International Paper Company, New York City.

C

Robert E. Canfield, Vice-President—Paper, American Paper Institute, New York City • *John M. Centa*, Manager—Printing Markets, Photo Products Department, E. I. duPont de Nemours & Co., Wilmington, Del. • *M. B. E. Clarkson*, President, Graphic Controls Corporation, Buffalo, N.Y. • *S. W. Cochran*, Division Vice-President and General Manager Graphic Systems Division, Radio Corporation of America, Princeton, N.J. • *Charles W. Cook*, Vice-President and Technical Director, Lithographic Division, Fawcett Haynes Printing Corporation, Rockville, Md. • *Richard S. Coyne*, Editor and Publisher, C A Magazine, Palo Alto • *A. L. E. Crouter*, Assistant Vice-President, New York Life Insurance Company, New York City • *David Cutler*, Director of Research and Engineering, Triangle Publications, Inc., Philadelphia.

D

Ray Danzeisen, Production Manager, Offset Division, The Beck Engraving Company, Philadelphia • *Glenn G. Davidson*, Director of Research, Robert Hart Printing Company, Rochester • *Donald Davis*, Premium Division Manager, Kaumagraph Company, Wilmington, Del. • *Frank A. Davis*, Vice-President of Manufacturing, Paramount Packaging Corporation, Chalfont, Pa. • *Peter de Florez*, President, MGD Research and Development Corporation, Fair Lawn, N.J. • *Donald G. DeGraw*, Superintendent of Platemaking, United States Government Printing Office, Washington, D.C. • *Frank A. DeWitt*, Graphic Arts Product Planning Specialist, Friden, Inc., Rochester • *Donald D. Dissly*, Director of Graphics and Research, Sedgwick Printout Systems, Inc., New York City • *Theodore B. Dolmatsch*, President, Pitman Publishing Corporation, New York City • *Dick Drum*, Vice-President, The Beck Engraving Company, Philadelphia • *Harold F. Drury*, Director, Printing and Publishing Industries Division, Business and Defense Services Administration, U.S. Department of Commerce, Washington, D.C. • *Ben Duby*, Technical Director, H. Wolff Book Manufacturing Company, New York City • *James M. Dugan*, Vice-President, Research and Development, Springfield Gravure Corporation, A Subsidiary of American Cyanamid, Springfield, Ohio • *C. J. Duncan, M.A., F.R.P.S., F.R.M.S.*, Director, Department of Photography, The Medical School, The University Newcastle, Upon Tyne, England • *Charles O. Dyker*, President, Progressive Color Corporation, Rockville, Md.

E

Joseph G. Elliott, Assistant Business Manager, Evening and Sunday Bulletin, Philadelphia • *John Ensign*, Ensign Art Service, New York City • *G. L. Erikson*, Executive Vice-President, Braden Sutphin Ink Company, Cleveland • *P. C. Evanoff*, Director—Customer Services Department, The Mead Corporation, Chillicothe, Ohio • *E. W. Evans*, Marketing Manager, Miller Printing Machinery Co., Pittsburgh.

F

Jacqueline Fetsko, Assistant Research Director, National Printing Ink Research Institute, Lehigh University, Bethlehem, Pa. • *Frank Fortney*, President, Russel Rutter, Inc., New York City • *Lloyd E. Foss*, Member of Staff, ANPA Research Institute, Inc., Easton, Pa. • *Dr. K. Fox*, Chief Chemist, Rapid Roller Company, Chicago.

G

Arthur E. Gardner, Director, Composition Information Services, Los Angeles • *Eugene J. Garrity*, Vice-President, Security Columbian Banknote, Division of United States Banknote Corporation, Philadelphia • *William W. Garth, Jr.*, President, Compugraphic Corporation, Reading, Mass. • *William J. Gaul*, Assistant Advertising Manager, Harris-Intertype Corporation, Cleveland • *Harvey F. George*, Research Director, Gravure Research Institute, Port Washington, N.Y. • *Walter R. Gesell*, Manager—Communications, The Goss Company, Division of MGD, Chicago • *William E. Ginsburg*, President, Practical Bookbinding Co., Inc., Long Island City, N.Y. • *Alex Glassman*, Manager—Product Control, Oxford Paper Company, New York City • *Arthur F. Goat*, President, Bobst Champlain, Inc., Roseland, N.J. • *Lester E. Goda, Jr.*, Director of Sales Development—Graphic Arts, Eastman Kodak Company, Rochester • *Clare W. Goodsell*, General Sales and Marketing Manager, Printing Products Division, 3M Company, St. Paul, Minn. • *Edward Gottschall*, Senior Editor, Popular Merchandise Company, Passaic, N.J. • *Joseph J. Green*, Vice-President—Sales, Mack Printing Company, Easton, Pa. • *J. Roderick Greig*, Advertising Coordinator, Riegel Paper Corporation, New York City • *Joseph J. Grossman*, President, Masta Displays, Inc., New York City.

H

K. Lewis Hackley, Associate Director—Machine Coating, Champion Papers Inc., Hamilton, Ohio • *William D. Hall*, Assistant Professor, Dept. of Printing and Photography, Southern Illinois University, Carbondale, Ill. • *Bernard R. Halpern*, In Charge of Training—Photo Products Department, E. I. duPont de Nemours & Co., Philadelphia • *Horace Hart*, President, Lanston Monotype Company, Division of United States Banknote Corporation, New York City • *Carlton C. Herrick*, Consultant-Designer in Graphic Arts, New York City • *George E. Hess*, Assistant to the President, Franklin Printing Company, Primos, Pa. • *Theodore Hommel*, Graphic Arts Specialist, Poughkeepsie, N.Y. • *John F. Howe*, Director of Advertising, S. D. Warren Company, Bos-

ton • *Dennis F. Hoynes*, Treasurer, The Central Electrotype Company, Cleveland • *Bruce W. Hubbard*, Research Director, Ideal Roller—W. R. Grace and Company, Chicago • *Charles A. Hunter*, Executive Vice-President, The Beck Engraving Company, Philadelphia.

I—J

Sam A. Inzinger, Senior Design Engineer, George Hantscho Company, Mt. Vernon, N.Y. • *Erwin Jaffe*, Director of Research and Development, Mack Printing Company, Easton, Pa. • *Dr. T. H. James*, Senior Research Associate, Eastman Kodak Company, Rochester • *Emil A. Jeisi*, Technical Manager, Griffin, Campbell, Hayes, Walsh, Inc., New York City • *Russell K. Johnson*, Printing Technologist, E. I. duPont de Nemours & Co., Wilmington, Del. • *Stephen W. Johnson, Jr.*, President, Printing Plates Company, San Francisco • *Willis C. Johnston*, Vice-President of Sales, American Type Founders Company, Elizabeth, N.J. • *George W. Jorgensen*, Supervisor—Physics Division, Graphic Arts Technical Foundation, Pittsburgh.

K

Yale Karmell, Technical Service Manager, Samuel Bingham Company, Franklin Park, Ill. • *Viola D. Kershner*, Administrative Assistant, Robert Hart Printing Company of Philadelphia • *E. A. Kilheffer*, Associate Editor, The American Pressman, Pressmen's Home, Tenn. • *Albert Kosloff*, Assistant Principal, Roosevelt High School, Chicago • *William O. Krenkler*, Executive Vice-President, National Publishing Company, Philadelphia • *John L. Kronenberg*, Vice-President and Director, S. D. Warren Company, Boston • *Walter Kubilius*, Editor, Printing Impressions, Philadelphia • *George Z. Kunkel*, Printing Production Specialist, Central Intelligence Agency, Washington, D.C.

L

Earl Landis, Manager, Installation and Service, Harris-Seybold Company, Division of Harris Intertype Corporation, Cleveland • *Floyd C. Larson*, Executive Secretary-Treasurer, International Association of Electrotypers and Stereotypers, Cleveland • *Harry H. Lerner*, Vice-President, Triton Press, Inc., New York City • *Dr. Robert L. Leslie*, President, The Composing Room, Inc., New York City • *George W. Little*, Director, Monotype School, Lanston Monotype Company, Division of United States Banknote Corporation, Philadelphia • *Robert P. Long*, Co-publisher and Editorial Director, Graphic Magazines, Inc., Garden City, N.Y. • *Frank H. Longenecker*, Manufacturing Manager, Downingtown Paper Company, Packaging Division-Lancaster, Lancaster, Pa. *McKinley M. Luther*, Director of Special Programs Department, Graphic Arts Technical Foundation, Pittsburgh.

Mc

Walter F. McArdle, President, The McArdle Printing Co., Inc., Washington, D.C. • *J. J. McCall*, Advertising Manager, Heidelberg Eastern, Inc., New York City • *J. Gibson McIlvain, Jr.*, Vice-President, Downingtown Paper Company, Downingtown, Pa. • *Joseph A. McSweeney*, Vice-President, Progressive Color Corporation, Rockville, Md. • *James H. McWilliams*, Chairman Typographic Workshop, Philadelphia College of Art, Philadelphia.

M

Vincent Mace, President, M & M Displays, Inc., Philadelphia • *David Madoff*, Pressroom Superintendent—Gravure Division, Triangle Publications, Philadelphia • *Harry A. Mallon*, President, Peter F. Mallon, Inc., Long Island City, N.Y. • *John Markus*, Manager—Information Research, McGraw-Hill, Inc., New York City • *M. V. Mathews*, Director—Behavioral Research Laboratory, Bell Telephone Laboratories, Inc., Murray Hill, N.J. • *George A. Mattson*, Managing Director—Web Offset Section, Printing Industries of America, Inc., Washington, D.C. • *Joseph W. Mazzaferri*, Colorcraft Company, Philadelphia • *Daniel Melcher*, President, R. R. Bowker Company, New York City • *Carleton Mellick*, Vice-President, Miehle-Goss-Dexter, Inc., Chicago • *Joseph E. Meyer*, Senior Vice-President—Engineering, The Cottrell Company, Westerly, R.I. • *Dr. R. Hunter Middleton*, Director—Department of Typeface Design and Vice-President, Ludlow Typograph Company, Chicago • *Ernst L. Midgette*, Engineering Consultant, Intertype Company, Division of Harris-Intertype Corporation, Brooklyn, N.J. • *Robert A. Miller*, Printing and Industrial Advertising, E. I. duPont de Nemours & Co., Wilmington, Del. • *J. Tom Morgan*, President, Litho-Krome Company, Columbus, Ga. • *Henry Morris*, President, City Wide Press, Inc., Philadelphia • *Frank H. Mortimer*, Director of Typography and Design, United States Government Printing Office, Washington, D.C. • *Richard P. Moses*, Sales Representative, Edward Stern Majestic Press, Philadelphia • *Edward F. Mullin*, Digital Computer Systems Analyst, United States Government Printing Office, Washington, D.C. • *Frank B. Myrick*, Director of Research and Development, Sendor Bindery, New York City.

N—O

Robert J. Niederhauser, Director of Merchandising, Harris-Seybold Company, Division of Harris-Intertype Corporation, Cleveland • *Theodore Niggli*, Harris-Intertype Corporation, Paris • *Hilda R. Olesnanik*, Editorial Assistant, Mack Printing Company, Easton, Pa. • *George Olmsted*, District Sales Manager, S. D. Warren Co., St. Louis, Mo.

P

Ralph E. Painter, Jr., Manager—Printing Department, The Beck Engraving Company, Philadelphia • *Kyle Panovec*, Reader, Mack Printing Company, Easton, Pa. • *Briant W. Patterson*, Manager—Domestic Sales Administration, Mergenthaler Linotype Company, Brooklyn, N.Y. • *Hunter H. Payne*, Principal Technical Assistant, United States Government Printing Office, Washington, D.C. • *Charles J. Peck*, Vice-President—Manufacturing, Excelsior Process and Engraving, Inc., North Adams, Mass. • *John H. Perry, Jr.*, Chairman of The Board and President, Perry Publications, Inc., West Palm Beach, Fla. • *George M. Peters*, Management Consultant, Booz, Allen, Hamilton, Inc., Cleveland • *John L. Peterson*, Product Manager, Mergenthaler Linotype Company, Brooklyn, N.Y. • *Rehn C. Peterson*, Director of Engineering, The Sheridan Company, Division of Harris-Intertype Corporation, New York City • *Leonard S. Pinover*, President and Chairman of the Board, Intaglio Service Corporation, New York City • *Harold B. Plaut*, Advertising Manager, Intertype Company, Division of Harris-Intertype Corporation, Brooklyn, N.Y. • *Austin Pomerantz*, Treasurer, A. Pomerantz & Company, Philadelphia • *Richard Powers*, Assistant Production Manager, Philadelphia Bulletin • *Frank M. Preucil*, Supervisor—Photo and Color Division, Graphic Arts Technical Foundation, Pittsburgh • *Malcolm L. Pritzker*, Industrial Relations Director, Graphic Arts Association of the Delaware Valley, Inc., Philadelphia.

R

Morris H. Reaves, Superintendent of Composition, United States Government Printing Office, Washington, D.C. • *Robert F. Reed*, Consultant, Graphic Arts Technical Foundation, Inc., Pittsburgh • *Jerome L. Reinitz*, President, Royal Zenith Corporation, New York City • *A. P. Reynolds*, Director—Graphic Arts Research, S. D. Warren Company, Westbrook, Me. • *John G. Ries*, President, American Photoengraving Company, Philadelphia • *Andrew J. Rimol*, Director of Advertising and Sales Promotion, Bobst Champlain, Inc., Roseland, N.J. • *E. W. Roberson*, Typographic Department, Mack Printing Company, Easton, Pa. • *Fred Roblin*, Editor, The American Press-man, Pressmen's Home, Tenn. • *Joseph Rockoff*, Consultant, The Richardson Company, Melrose Park, Ill. • *Charles H. Rodd*, President, Rodd Electrotype Company, Cambridge, Mass. • Dr. *Walter W. Roehr*, Senior Research Associate, Kimberly-Clark Corporation, Neenah, Wis. • *Marvin C. Rogers, Ph.D.*, Executive Director, Photoengravers Research Institute, Park Forest, Ill. • *Jack L. Roser*, Vice-President and Director of Printing Technology, Milprint, Inc., Milwaukee • *Julian Ross*, Executive Secretary, Flexographic Technical Association, New York City • *Leonard Rubin*, Vice-President, Gilliams & Rubin, Inc., New York City.

S

Mitchell M. Sackson, P.E., Consulting Engineer, Brooklyn, N.Y. • *Carl W. Saunders*, Manager—General Sales Office, The Cottrell Company, Westerly, R.I. • *Clifford R. J. Schaible*, Director of Advertising, The Mead Corporation, Dayton, Ohio • *Kenneth G. Scheid*, President, Kenneth G. Scheid and Associates, Pittsburgh • *Ernest Schmattola*, Vice-President, Publishers Printing—Admiral Press, Division of Printing Corporation of America, Long Island City, N.Y. • *C. William Schneidereith*, Chairman of The Board, Schneidereith & Sons, Inc., Baltimore • *Frank J. Schreiber*, Editor of The Photoengravers Bulletin and Executive Secretary, American Photoengravers Association, Chicago • *Miriam Schwartz*, President, Westcott & Thomson, Inc., Philadelphia • *W. E. Seaman, Jr.*, General Sales Manager, The Sheridan Company, Division of Harris-Intertype Corporation, New York City • *Mortimer S. Sendor*, Executive Vice-President, Sendor Bindery, Inc., New York City • *John W. Seybold*, President, Rocappi, Inc., Swarthmore, Pa. • *Hy Shannon*, Vice-President—Production, Chicago Sunday Times and Chicago Daily News • *Charles Shapiro*, Manager of Manufacturing, Peter F. Mallon, Inc., Long Island City, N.Y. • *Stanley E. Sims*, Eastern Manager, Lanston Monotype Company, Division of United States Banknote Corporation, Philadelphia • *Evelyn M. Sloyer*, Manager of Special Services, Mack Printing Company, Easton, Pa. • *William H. Smith*, Assistant Education Director, Graphic Arts Technical Foundation, Pittsburgh • *Walter E. Soderstrom*, Brooklyn, N.Y. • *Donald E. Sommer*, Secretary, Master Printers Section, Printing Industries of America, Inc., Washington, D.C. • *Carl C. Sorensen*, Consultant, Huntingdon Valley, Pa. • *Willard F. Spengeman*, Laboratory Director, Pigments Department, E. I. duPont de Nemours & Co., Wilmington, Del. • *Frank Sportelli*, Vice-President, Research, Intaglio Service Corporation, New York City • *Otto C. Stoessel*, Chief—Printing and Distribution Division, Aeronautical Chart and Information Center (USAF), St. Louis, Mo. • *Earl Sundeen*, Senior Technical Editor—Graphic Arts, Eastman Kodak Company, Rochester.

T—U

Ferdy J. Tagle, Principal, The New York School of Printing, New York City • *Clyde H. Throckmorton*, Director of Advertising and Public Relations, R. Hoe & Co., Inc., New York City • *C. Howard Thomas*, President and Treasurer, National Publishing Company, Philadelphia • *Michael Tikson*, Associate Manager, Systems and Electronics Department, Battelle Memorial Institute, Columbus, Ohio • *Charles M. Todaro*, Typographer, Mack Printing Company, Easton, Pa. • *Richard B. Tullis*, President, Harris-Intertype Corporation, Cleveland • *Joseph Ulano*, President Ulano Companies, Brooklyn, New York.

V

E. O. Vandercook, President, Vandercook & Sons, Inc., Chicago • *H. Leslie Varley*, Director of Composition, Mack Printing Company, Easton, Pa. • *William S. Vogel*, Chief Engineer, Miller Printing Machinery Company, Pittsburgh • *John Vollmuth*, Editor, The American Ink Maker, New York City.

W

Dr. *William C. Walker*, Technical Assistant to Corporate Research Director, West Virginia Pulp and Paper Company, New York City • *Reginald F. Wardley*, Vice-President, Edgar Steiner & Company, Packaging Consultants, New York City • *Betty Whitfield*, Administrative Assistant—Education Department, Printing Industries of America, Inc., Washington, D.C. • *Robert M. Wilson*, Public Information Officer—National Library of Medicine, Department of Health, Education and Welfare, Bethesda, Md. • *George Wolfer*, Superintendent of Gravure and Engineering, Packaging Division, Downingtown Paper Company, Downingtown, Pa. • *F. L. Wurzburg, Jr.*, Director of Sales Training, Interchem Printing Inks, Division of Interchemical Corporation, New York City.

Y—Z

J. A. C. Yule, Research Associate, Eastman Kodak Company, Rochester • *Henry P. Zahn*, Production Assistant, Kingsport Press, Inc., New York City • *Walter E. Zerweck*, Executive Director, Graphic Arts Association of the Delaware Valley, Inc., Philadelphia • Dr. *Albert C. Zettlemoyer*, Vice-President—Research, Lehigh University, Bethlehem, Pa.

This book was printed by the Mack Printing
Company in Easton, Pennsylvania,
from Monotype and photoengravings.

The type face is Times New Roman
cut by the Lanston Monotype Company, Philadelphia.

The paper is Mead Superb Enamel,
Dual Purpose, 70 lbs.

The photoengravings were made by the
American Photoengraving Company, Philadelphia.

The full-color insert was printed by the
DuPont Printing Plant, Philadelphia.

The book was bound by the
National Publishing Company, Philadelphia.

The Progressive Color Corporation, Rockville, Maryland,
produced the jacket of the book.